W9-CLR-265

GREAT BOOKS OF THE WESTERN WORLD

GREAT BOOKS
OF THE WESTERN WORLD

ROBERT MAYNARD HUTCHINS, *EDITOR IN CHIEF*

45.

LAVOISIER

FOURIER

FARADAY

MORTIMER J. ADLER, *Associate Editor*

Members of the Advisory Board: STRINGFELLOW BARR, SCOTT BUCHANAN, JOHN ERSKINE, CLARENCE H. FAUST, ALEXANDER MEIKLEJOHN, JOSEPH J. SCHWAB, MARK VAN DOREN.

Editorial Consultants: A. F. B. CLARK, F. L. LUCAS, WALTER MURDOCH.

WALLACE BROCKWAY, *Executive Editor*

ELEMENTS OF CHEMISTRY

BY ANTOINE LAURENT LAVOISIER

ANALYTICAL THEORY OF HEAT

BY JEAN BAPTISTE JOSEPH FOURIER

EXPERIMENTAL RESEARCHES IN ELECTRICITY

BY MICHAEL FARADAY

WILLIAM BENTON, *Publisher*

ENCYCLOPÆDIA BRITANNICA, INC.

CHICAGO · LONDON · TORONTO · GENEVA · SYDNEY · TOKYO · MANILA

FERNALD LIBRARY
COLBY-SAWYER COLLEGE
NEW LONDON, N. H. 03257

AC
1
.G72
vol.45
copy 2

68610

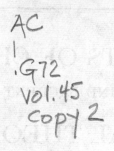

THE UNIVERSITY OF CHICAGO

The Great Books
is published with the editorial advice of the faculties
of The University of Chicago

No part of this work may be reproduced or utilized in any form or by any means, electronic or mechanical, including photocopying, recording, or by any information storage and retrieval system, without permission in writing from the publisher.

1952
BY ENCYCLOPÆDIA BRITANNICA, INC.

COPYRIGHT UNDER INTERNATIONAL COPYRIGHT UNION

ALL RIGHTS RESERVED UNDER PAN AMERICAN AND UNIVERSAL COPYRIGHT CONVENTIONS BY ENCYCLOPÆDIA BRITANNICA, INC.

Library of Congress Catalog Card Number: 55–10351

GENERAL CONTENTS

ELEMENTS OF CHEMISTRY

BIOGRAPHICAL NOTE
Antoine Lavoisier, 1743-1794

Lavoisier was born in Paris, August 26, 1743. His father was attorney to the Parliament of Paris. His mother was the daughter of the secretary to the Vice-Admiral of France and heiress to a considerable fortune.

After completing his elementary education Lavoisier was sent to the *College Mazarin*. His early ambitions were literary rather than scientific, and in 1760 he won second prize in a rhetorical contest. Although on leaving the college he went on to prepare for law, and received his Licentiate in 1764, he devoted himself to science, studying, with well-known teachers of the time, mathematics, astronomy, botany, mineralogy, geology, and chemistry. He also began to conduct experiments and observations of his own. One of the earliest was in meteorology; he made barometrical observations several times daily and engaged others in the same pursuit with the aim of discovering the laws governing the weather. His zeal for investigation was so great that at the age of nineteen he decided to cut himself off from all social activity; he gave ill-health as an excuse and for several months lived in retirement on a diet of milk.

His formal career as a scientist began in 1763 when he was invited by Guettard, his teacher in geology, to collaborate in preparing the first mineralogical atlas of France. Lavoisier's part of the project consisted largely of collecting data; he kept elaborate notebooks which indicate that he was not only amassing material but analysing and developing ideas for later research. While engaged in this work, he entered the contest held by the French Academy of Science for the best essay on methods for lighting the streets of a large city at night. The essays were divided into two groups, practical and scientific, and while the prize was given to entries in the first group, Lavoisier alone was singled out from the second for special mention and a gold medal from the King. The work with Guettard also yielded material which Lavoisier worked up in the form of *mémoires* to be presented to the Academy of Science. In 1768, after he had presented four such papers, two on hydrometry and two on gypsum, he was elected a member of the Academy. His youth excited comment, and, as a friend of the family remarked, at the age of twenty-five he had obtained "a position which is usually won, with great difficulty, by men past their fiftieth year."

Desirous of securing a larger income for research, Lavoisier, shortly after his nomination to the Academy, bought an interest in the *Ferme*, an association of financiers who had the privilege of collecting the national taxes in return for a fixed annual sum paid in advance to the Government. His friends at the Academy did not entirely approve of this association, but it did provide him with the money he sought, and it also made him acquainted with Farmer-General Paulze, whose daughter he married in 1771.

Lavoisier entered further into public life when the Government took over the manufacture of gunpowder. Upon his suggestion, Turgot, Minister of the Treasury, canceled the private production of gunpowder and established the *Régie des poudres*, a four-man administrative committee headed by Lavoisier. With this appointment he was assigned a house at the Arsenal, where with his own funds he established a fully-equipped laboratory, which he made available to all scientists interested in his work. As his scientific fame increased, the laboratory became a meeting place for prominent scientists, and among his guests he numbered Priestley, Franklin, Watt, Tennant, and Arthur Young. Lavoisier always retained an interest in younger scientists, providing financial assistance for many and making laboratory assistants of others, among whom was the Dupont who later went to America and founded the munitions firm.

Although occupied with many practical concerns in connection with the *Ferme* and the *Régie des poudres*, Lavoisier reserved six hours a day, from six to nine in the morning and from seven to ten at night, for his scientific work, and one full day each week for experiments.

His wife, who was fourteen at the time of her marriage, became an active partner in his research. She assisted in the laboratory, learned English so as to translate the technical works of Priestley and Cavendish, and drew the illustrations for the *Traité Elémentaire de Chimie* (1789). He also engaged in many works of philanthropic nature, starting a model farm to demonstrate the advantages of scientific agriculture, and planning the establishment of savings banks, insurance societies, canals, and work houses for improving the conditions of the community.

When the Revolution occurred, Lavoisier had long been a national figure. He was Director of the Academy of Sciences, deputy to the States-General of 1789, and a prominent member of the club founded to promote the cause of constitutional monarchy. For some years after 1789 Lavoisier continued to work as secretary and treasurer of the commission to secure uniformity of weights and measures. In 1791 he was made a member of the commission on arts and professions; his report for this commission, *Réflexions sur l'instruction publique* (1793), presented a detailed scheme for public free education. But almost from the beginning of the Revolution, Lavoisier had been under suspicion because of his association with the *Ferme* and *Régie des poudres,* and from early 1791 he was subjected to vitriolic attack from Marat. In 1794 he and the other farmers-general were placed on trial by the Revolutionary Tribunal and condemned to death. Lavoisier and his father-in-law were guillotined May 8, 1794, at the Place de la Révolution and their bodies thrown into nameless graves in the cemetery of La Madeleine.

CONTENTS

PREFACE

WHEN I began the following work, my only object was to extend and explain more fully the memoir which I read at the public meeting of the Academy of Sciences in the month of April, 1787, on the necessity of reforming and completing the nomenclature of chemistry. While engaged in this employment, I perceived, better than I had ever done before, the justice of the following maxims of the Abbé de Condillac, in his *Logic*, and some other of his works.

"We think only through the medium of words.—Languages are true analytical methods.—Algebra, which is adapted to its purpose in every species of expression, in the most simple, most exact, and best manner possible, is at the same time a language and an analytical method.—The art of reasoning is nothing more than a language well arranged."

Thus, while I thought myself employed only in forming a nomenclature, and while I proposed to myself nothing more than to improve the chemical language, my work transformed itself by degrees, without my being able to prevent it, into a treatise upon the elements of chemistry.

The impossibility of separating the nomenclature of a science from the science itself is owing to this, that every branch of physical science must consist of three things: the series of facts which are the objects of the science, the ideas which represent these facts, and the words by which these ideas are expressed. Like three impressions of the same seal, the word ought to produce the idea, and the idea to be a picture of the fact. And, as ideas are preserved and communicated by means of words, it necessarily follows that we cannot improve the language of any science without at the same time improving the science itself; neither can we, on the other hand, improve a science without improving the language or nomenclature which belongs to it. However certain the facts of any science may be and however just the ideas we may have formed of these facts, we can only communicate false impressions to others while we want words by which these may be properly expressed.

To those who will consider it with attention, the first part of this treatise will afford frequent proofs of the truth of the above observations. But as, in the conduct of my work, I have been obliged to observe an order of arrangement essentially differing from what has been adopted in any other chemical work yet published, it is proper that I should explain the motives which have led me to do so.

It is a maxim universally admitted in geometry, and indeed in every branch of knowledge, that, in the progress of investigation, we should proceed from known facts to what is unknown. In early infancy, our ideas spring from our wants; the sensation of want excites the idea of the object by which it is to be gratified. In this manner, from a series of sensations, observations, and analyses, a successive train of ideas arises, so linked together that an attentive observer may trace back to a certain point the order and connection of the whole sum of human knowledge.

When we begin the study of any science, we are in a situation, respecting that science, similar to that of children; and the course by which we have to advance is precisely the same which nature follows in the formation of their ideas. In a child, the idea is merely an effect produced by a sensation; and, in the same manner, in commencing the study of a physical science, we ought to form no idea but what is a necessary consequence, and immediate effect, of an experiment or observation. Besides, he that enters upon the career of science is in a less advantageous situation than a child who is acquiring his first ideas. To the child, nature gives various means of rectifying any mistakes he may commit respecting the salutary or hurtful qualities of the objects which surround him. On every occasion his judgments are corrected

1

by experience; want and pain are the necessary consequences arising from false judgment; gratification and pleasure are produced by judging aright. Under such masters, we cannot fail to become well informed; and we soon learn to reason justly, when want and pain are the necessary consequences of a contrary conduct.

In the study and practice of the sciences it is quite different; the false judgments we form neither affect our existence nor our welfare; and we are not forced by any physical necessity to correct them. Imagination, on the contrary, which is ever wandering beyond the bounds of truth, joined to self-love and that self-confidence we are so apt to indulge, prompts us to draw conclusions which are not immediately derived from facts; so that we become in some measure interested in deceiving ourselves. Hence, it is by no means to be wondered that, in the science of physics in general, men have often made suppositions instead of forming conclusions. These suppositions, handed down from one age to another, acquire additional weight from the authorities by which they are supported, till at last they are received, even by men of genius, as fundamental truths.

The only method of preventing such errors from taking place, and of correcting them when formed, is to restrain and simplify our reasoning as much as possible. This depends entirely upon ourselves, and the neglect of it is the only source of our mistakes. We must trust to nothing but facts: these are presented to us by nature and cannot deceive. We ought, in every instance, to submit our reasoning to the test of experiment and never to search for truth but by the natural road of experiment and observation. Thus mathematicians obtain the solution of a problem by the mere arrangement of data and by reducing their reasoning to such simple steps, to conclusions so very obvious, as never to lose sight of the evidence which guides them.

Thoroughly convinced of these truths, I have imposed upon myself, as a law, never to advance but from what is known to what is unknown; never to form any conclusion which is not an immediate consequence necessarily flowing from observation and experiment; and always to arrange the facts, and the conclusions which are drawn from them, in such an order as shall render it most easy for beginners

in the study of chemistry thoroughly to understand them. Hence, I have been obliged to depart from the usual order of courses of lectures and of treatises upon chemistry, which always assume the first principles of the science as known, when the pupil or the reader should never be supposed to know them till they have been explained in subsequent lessons. In almost every instance, these begin by treating of the elements of matter and by explaining the table of affinities, without considering that, in so doing, they must bring the principal phenomena of chemistry into view at the very outset: they make use of terms which have not been defined and suppose the science to be understood by the very persons they are only beginning to teach. It ought likewise to be considered that very little of chemistry can be learned in a first course, which is hardly sufficient to make the language of the science familiar to the ears or the apparatus familiar to the eyes. It is almost impossible to become a chemist in less than three or four years of constant application.

These inconveniences are occasioned not so much by the nature of the subject as by the method of teaching it; and, to avoid them, I was chiefly induced to adopt a new arrangement of chemistry, which appeared to me more consonant to the order of nature. I acknowledge, however, that in thus endeavouring to avoid difficulties of one kind I have found myself involved in others of a different species, some of which I have not been able to remove; but I am persuaded that such as remain do not arise from the nature of the order I have adopted, but are rather consequences of the imperfection under which chemistry still labours. This science still has many chasms, which interrupt the series of facts and often render it extremely difficult to reconcile them with each other: it has not, like the elements of geometry, the advantage of being a complete science, the parts of which are all closely connected together: its actual progress, however, is so rapid, and the facts, under the modern doctrine, have assumed so happy an arrangement that we have ground to hope, even in our own times, to see it approach near to the highest state of perfection of which it is susceptible.

The rigorous law from which I have never deviated, of forming no conclusions which are not fully warranted by experiment, and of never supplying the absence of facts, has prevented me from comprehending in this work the branch of chemistry which treats of affinities, although it is perhaps the best calculated of any part of chemistry for being reduced into a completely systematic body. MM. Geoffroy, Gellert, Bergman, Scheele, de Morveau, Kirwan, and many others, have collected a number of particular facts upon this subject, which only wait for a proper arrangement; but the principal data are still wanting, or, at least, those we have are either not sufficiently defined or not sufficiently proved to become the foundation upon which to build so very important a branch of chemistry. This science of affinities, or elective attractions, holds the same place with regard to the other branches of chemistry as the higher or transcendental geometry does with respect to the simpler and elementary part; and I thought it improper to involve those simple and plain elements, which I flatter myself the greatest part of my readers will easily understand, in the obscurities and difficulties which still attend that other very useful and necessary branch of chemical science.

Perhaps a sentiment of self-love may, without my perceiving it, have given additional force to these reflections. Mr. de Morveau is at present engaged in publishing the article *Affinity* in the *Methodical Encyclopædia* and I had more reasons than one to decline entering upon a work in which he is employed.

It will, no doubt, be a matter of surprise, that in a treatise upon the elements of chemistry there should be no chapter on the constituent and elementary parts of matter; but I shall take occasion, in this place, to remark that the fondness for reducing all the bodies in nature to three or four elements proceeds from a prejudice which has descended to us from the Greek philosophers. The notion of four elements, which, by the variety of their proportions, compose all the known substances in nature, is a mere hypothesis, assumed long before the first principles of experimental philosophy or of chemistry had any existence. In those days, without possessing facts, they framed systems; while we, who have collected facts, seem determined to reject them when they do not agree with our prejudices. The authority of these fathers of human philosophy still carry great weight, and there is reason to fear that it will even bear hard upon generations yet to come.

It is very remarkable that, notwithstanding the number of philosophical chemists who have supported the doctrine of the four elements, there is not one who has not been led by the evidence of facts to admit a greater number of elements into their theory. The first chemists that wrote after the revival of letters considered sulphur and salt elementary substances entering into the composition of a great number of substances; hence, instead of four, they admitted the existence of six elements. Beccher assumes the existence of three kinds of earth, from the combination of which, in different proportions, he supposed all the varieties of metallic substances to be produced. Stahl gave a new modification to this system; and succeeding chemists have taken the liberty to make or to imagine changes and additions of a similar nature. All these chemists were carried along by the influence of the genius of the age in which they lived, which contented itself with assertions without proofs; or, at least, often admitted as proofs the slightest degrees of probability, unsupported by that strictly rigorous analysis required by modern philosophy.

All that can be said upon the number and nature of elements is, in my opinion, confined to discussions entirely of a metaphysical nature. The subject only furnishes us with indefinite problems, which may be solved in a thousand different ways, not one of which, in all probability, is consistent with nature. I shall therefore only add upon this subject that if by the term *elements* we mean to express those simple and indivisible atoms of which matter is composed, it is extremely probable we know nothing at all about them; but, if we apply the term *elements*, or *principles of bodies*, to express our idea of the last point which analysis is capable of reaching, we must admit, as elements, all the substances into which we are capable, by any means, to reduce bodies by decomposition. Not that we are entitled to affirm that these substances we consider as simple may not be compounded of two, or even of a greater number of principles; but, since these principles cannot be separated, or rather since we have not hitherto discovered the means of separating them, they act with regard to us as simple substances, and we ought never to suppose them compounded until experiment and observation has proved them to be so.

The foregoing reflections upon the progress of chemical ideas naturally apply to the words by which these ideas are to be expressed. Guided by the work which, in the year 1787, Messrs. de Morveau, Berthollet, de Fourcroy, and I composed upon the nomenclature of chemistry, I have endeavoured, as much as possible, to denominate simple bodies by simple terms, and I was naturally led to name these first. It will be recollected that we were obliged to retain that name of any substance by which it had been long known in the world, and that in two cases only we took the liberty of making alterations; first, in the case of those which were but newly discovered and had not yet obtained names, or at least which had been known but for a short time and the names of which had not yet received the sanction of the public; and, secondly, when the names which had been adopted, whether by the ancients or the moderns, appeared to us to express evidently false ideas, when they confounded the substances to which they were applied with others possessed of different or perhaps opposite qualities. We made no scruple, in this case, of substituting other names in their room, and the greatest number of these were borrowed from the Greek language. We endeavoured to frame them in such a manner as to express the most general and the most characteristic quality of the substances; and this was attended with the additional advantage both of assisting the memory of beginners, who find it difficult to remember a new word which has no meaning, and of accustoming them early to admit no word without connecting with it some determinate idea.

To those bodies which are formed by the union of several simple substances we gave new names, compounded in such a manner as the nature of the substances directed; but, as the number of double combinations is already very considerable, the only method by which we could avoid confusion was to divide them into classes. In the natural order of ideas, the name of the class or genus is that which expresses a quality common to a great number of individuals: the name of the species, on the contrary, expresses a quality peculiar to certain individuals only.

These distinctions are not, as some may imagine, merely metaphysical, but are established by nature. "A child," says the Abbé de Condillac, " is taught to give the name *tree* to the first one which is pointed out to him. The next one he sees presents the same idea, and he gives it the same name. This he does likewise to a third and a fourth, till at last the word *tree*, which he first applied to an individual, comes to be employed by him as the name of a class or a genus, an abstract idea, which comprehends all trees in general. But, when he learns that all trees serve not the same purpose, that they do not all produce the same kind of fruit, he will soon learn to distinguish them by specific and particular names." This is the logic of all the sciences and is naturally applied to chemistry.

The acids, for example, are compounded of two substances, of the order of those which we consider as simple; the one constitutes acidity, and is common to all acids, and, from this substance, the name of the class or the genus ought to be taken; the other is peculiar to each acid, and distinguishes it from the rest, and from this substance is to be taken the name of the species. But, in the greatest number of acids, the two constituent elements, the acidifying principle and that which it acidifies, may exist in different proportions, constituting all the possible points of equilibrium or of saturation. This is the case in the sulphuric and the sulphurous acids; and these two states of the same acid we have marked by varying the termination of the specific name.

Metallic substances which have been exposed to the joint action of the air and of fire lose their metallic lustre, increase in weight, and assume an earthy appearance. In this state, like the acids, they are compounded of a principle which is common to all and one which is peculiar to each. In the same way, therefore, we have thought proper to class them under a generic name, derived from the common principle; for which purpose, we adopted the term *ox-*

ide; and we distinguish them from each other by the particular name of the metal to which each belongs.

Combustible substances, which in acids and metallic oxides are a specific and particular principle, are capable of becoming, in their turn common principles of a great number of substances. The sulphurous combinations have been long the only known ones in this kind. Now, however, we know, from the experiments of Messrs. Vandermonde, Monge, and Berthollet, that charcoal may be combined with iron, and perhaps with several other metals, and that, from this combination, according to the proportions, may be produced steel, plumbago, &c. We know likewise, from the experiments of M. Pelletier, that phosphorus may be combined with a great number of metallic substances. These different combinations we have classed under generic names taken from the common substance, with a termination which marks this analogy, specifying them by another name taken from that substance which is proper to each.

The nomenclature of bodies compounded of three simple substances was attended with still greater difficulty, not only on account of their number, but, particularly, because we cannot express the nature of their constituent principles without employing more compound names. In the bodies which form this class, such as the neutral salts for instance, we had to consider, 1st, the acidifying principle, which is common to them all; 2nd, the acidifiable principle which constitutes their peculiar acid; 3rd, the saline, earthy, or metallic basis, which determines the particular species of salt. Here we derived the name of each class of salts from the name of the acidifiable principle common to all the individuals of that class and distinguished each species by the name of the saline, earthy, or metallic basis, which is peculiar to it.

A salt, though compounded of the same three principles, may, nevertheless, by the mere difference of their proportion, be in three different states. The nomenclature we have adopted would have been defective had it not expressed these different states; and this we attained chiefly by changes of termination uniformly applied to the same state of the different salts.

In short, we have advanced so far that from the name alone may be instantly found what the combustible substance is which enters into any combination; whether that combustible substance be combined with the acidifying principle, and in what proportion; what is the state of the acid; with what basis it is united; whether the saturation be exact, or whether the acid or the basis be in excess.

It may be easily supposed that it was not possible to attain all these different objects without departing, in some instances, from established custom and adopting terms which at first sight will appear uncouth and barbarous. But we considered that the ear is soon habituated to new words, especially when they are connected with a general and rational system. The names, besides, which were formerly employed, such as *powder of algaroth, salt of alembroth, pompholix, phagadenic water, turbith mineral, colcothar,* and many others, were neither less barbarous nor less uncommon. It required a great deal of practice, and no small degree of memory, to recollect the substances to which they were applied, much more to recollect the genus of combination to which they belonged. The names of *oil of tartar per deliquium, oil of vitriol, butter of arsenic and of antimony, flowers of zinc,* &c. were still more improper, because they suggested false ideas: for, in the whole mineral kingdom, and particularly in the metallic class, there exist no such things as butters, oils, or flowers; and, in short, the substances to which they give these fallacious names are nothing less than rank poisons.

When we published our essay on the nomenclature of chemistry, we were reproached for having changed the language which was spoken by our masters, which they distinguished by their authority and handed down to us. But those who reproach us on this account have forgotten that it was Bergman and Macquer themselves who urged us to make this reformation. In a letter which the learned Professor of Uppsala, M. Bergman, wrote, a short time before he died, to M. de Morveau, he bids him *spare no improper names; those who are learned will always be learned, and those who are ignorant will thus learn sooner.*

There is an objection to the work which I am going to present to the public, which is perhaps better founded, that I have given no account of the opinion of those who have gone before me; that I have stated only my own opinion, without examining that of others. By this I have been prevented from doing that justice to my associates, and more especially to foreign chemists, which I wished to render them. But I beseech the reader to consider that, if I had filled an elementary work with a multitude of quotations, if I had allowed myself to enter into long dissertations on the history of the science and the works of those who have studied it, I must have lost sight of the true object I had in view and produced a work the reading of which must have been extremely tiresome to beginners. It is not to the history of the science, or of the human mind, that we are to attend in an elementary treatise: our only aim ought to be ease and perspicuity and with the utmost care to keep everything out of view which might draw aside the attention of the student; it is a road which we should be continually rendering more smooth, and from which we should endeavour to remove every obstacle which can occasion delay. The sciences, from their own nature, present a sufficient number of difficulties, though we add not those which are foreign to them. But, besides this, chemists will easily perceive that, in the first part of my work, I make very little use of any experiments but those which were made by myself: if at any time I have adopted, without acknowledgment, the experiments or the opinions of M. Berthollet, M. Fourcroy, M. de la Place, M. Monge, or, in general, of any of those whose principles are the same as my own, it is owing to this circumstance, that frequent intercourse, and the habit of communicating our ideas, our observations, and our way of thinking to each other, has established between us a sort of community of opinions in which it is often difficult for every one to know his own.

The remarks I have made on the order which I thought myself obliged to follow in the arrangement of proofs and ideas are to be applied only to the first part of this work. It is the only one which contains the general sum of the doctrine I have adopted and to which I wished to give a form completely elementary.

The second part is composed chiefly of tables of the nomenclature of the neutral salts. To these I have only added general explanations,

the object of which was to point out the most simple processes for obtaining the different kinds of known acids. This part contains nothing which I can call my own and presents only a very short abridgment of the results of these processes, extracted from the works of different authors.

In the third part, I have given a description, in detail, of all the operations connected with modern chemistry. I have long thought that a work of this kind was much wanted, and I am convinced it will not be without use. The method of performing experiments, and particularly those of modern chemistry, is not so generally known as it ought to be; and had I, in the different *Mémoires* which I have presented to the Academy, been more particular in the detail of the manipulations of my experiments, it is probable I should have made myself better understood, and the science might have made a more rapid progress. The order of the different matters contained in this third part appeared to me to be almost arbitrary; and the only one I have observed was to class together, in each of the chapters of which it is composed, those operations which are most connected with one another. I need hardly mention that this part could not be borrowed from any other work, and that, in the principal articles it contains, I could not derive assistance from anything but the experiments which I have made myself.

I shall conclude this preface by transcribing, literally, some observations of the Abbé de Condillac, which I think describe, with a good deal of truth, the state of chemistry at a period not far distant from our own. These observations were made on a different subject; but they will not, on this account, have less force, if the application of them be thought just.

"Instead of applying observation to the things we wished to know, we have chosen rather to imagine them. Advancing from one ill-founded supposition to another, we have at last bewildered ourselves amidst a multitude of errors. These errors becoming prejudices, are, of course, adopted as principles, and we thus bewilder ourselves more and more. The method, too, by which we conduct our reasonings is as absurd; we abuse words which we do not understand, and call this the art of reasoning.

When matters have been brought this length, when errors have been thus accumulated, there is but one remedy by which order can be restored to the faculty of thinking; this is to forget all that we have learned, to trace back our ideas to their source, to follow the train in which they rise, and, as Bacon says, to frame the human understanding anew.

"This remedy becomes the more difficult in proportion as we think ourselves more learned. Might it not be thought that works which treated of the sciences with the utmost perspicuity, with great precision and order, must be understood by everybody? The fact is, those who have never studied anything will understand them better than those who have studied a great deal, and especially than those who have written a great deal."

At the end of the fifth chapter, the Abbé de Condillac adds: "But, after all, the sciences have made progress, because philosophers have applied themselves with more attention to observe and have communicated to their language that precision and accuracy which they have employed in their observations. In correcting their language they reason better."

FIRST PART

Of the Formation and Decomposition of Aeriform Fluids—of the Combustion of Simple Bodies, and the Formation of Acids

CHAPTER I

Of the Combinations of Caloric, and the Formation of Elastic Aeriform Fluids or gases

THAT every body, whether solid or fluid, is augmented in all its dimensions by any increase of its sensible heat was long ago fully established as a physical axiom, or universal proposition, by the celebrated Boerhaave. Such facts as have been adduced for controverting the generality of this principle offer only fallacious results, or, at least, such as are so complicated with foreign circumstances as to mislead the judgment: but, when we separately consider the effects, so as to deduce each from the cause to which they separately belong, it is easy to perceive that the separation of particles by heat is a constant and general law of nature.

When we have heated a solid body to a certain degree and have thereby caused its particles to separate from each other, if we allow the body to cool, its particles again approach each other in the same proportion in which they were separated by the increased temperature; the body returns through the same degrees of expansion which it before extended through; and, if it be brought back to the same temperature from which we set out at the commencement of the experiment, it recovers exactly the same dimensions which it formerly occupied. But, as we are still very far from being able to arrive at the degree of absolute cold, or deprivation of all heat, being unacquainted with any degree of coldness which we cannot suppose capable of still further augmentation, it follows that we are still incapable of causing the ultimate particles of bodies to approach each other as near as is possible and, consequently, that the particles of all bodies do not touch each other in any state hitherto known, which, tho' a very singular conclusion, is yet impossible to be denied.

It is supposed that, since the particles of bodies are thus continually impelled by heat to separate from each other, they would have no connection between themselves and, of consequence, that there could be no solidity in nature, unless they were held together by some other power which tends to unite them, and, so to speak, to chain them together; which power, whatever be its cause or manner of operation, we name *attraction*.

Thus the particles of all bodies may be considered as subjected to the action of two opposite powers, the one repulsive, the other attractive, between which they remain *in equilibrio*. So long as the attractive force remains stronger, the body must continue in a state of solidity; but if, on the contrary, heat has so far removed these particles from each other as to place them beyond the sphere of attraction, they lose the adhesion they before had with each other, and the body ceases to be solid.

Water gives us a regular and constant example of these facts; whilst below zero[1] of the French thermometer, or 32° of Fahrenheit, it remains solid, and is called ice. Above that degree of temperature, its particles being no longer held together by reciprocal attraction, it becomes liquid; and, when we raise its temperature above 80° (212°), its particles, giving way to the repulsion caused by the heat, assume the state of vapour or gas, and the water is changed into an aeriform fluid.

The same may be affirmed of all bodies in nature: they are either solid or liquid, or in the state of elastic aeriform vapour, according to the proportion which takes place between the attractive force inherent in their particles, and the repulsive power of the heat acting upon these; or, which amounts to the same thing, in proportion to the degree of heat to which they are exposed.

It is difficult to comprehend these phenom-

[1] Whenever the degree of heat occurs in this work, it is stated by the author according to Reaumur's scale. The degrees within parentheses are the correspondent degrees of Fahrenheit's scale, added by the translator.—TRANSLATOR.

ena, without admitting them as the effects of a real and material substance, or very subtile fluid, which, insinuating itself between the particles of bodies, separates them from each other; and, even allowing the existence of this fluid to be hypothetical, we shall see in the sequel that it explains the phenomena of nature in a very satisfactory manner.

This substance, whatever it is, being the cause of heat, or, in other words, the sensation which we call *warmth* being caused by the accumulation of this substance, we cannot, in strict language, distinguish it by the term *heat;* because the same name would then very improperly express both cause and effect. For this reason, in the *Memoir* which I published in 1777[1], I gave it the names of *igneous fluid* and *matter of heat:* And, since that time, in the work[2] published by M. de Morveau, M. Berthollet, M. de Fourcroy, and myself, upon the reformation of chemical nomenclature, we thought it necessary to banish all periphrastic expressions, which both lengthen physical language and render it more tedious and less distinct, and which even frequently does not convey sufficiently just ideas of the subject intended. Wherefore, we have distinguished the cause of heat, or that exquisitely elastic fluid which produces it, by the term of *caloric.* Besides that this expression fulfils our object in the system which we have adopted, it possesses this further advantage, that it accords with every species of opinion, since, strictly speaking, we are not obliged to suppose this to be a real substance; it being sufficient, as will more clearly appear in the sequel of this work, that it be considered as the repulsive cause, whatever that may be, which separates the particles of matter from each other, so that we are still at liberty to investigate its effects in an abstract and mathematical manner.

In the present state of our knowledge, we are unable to determine whether light be a modification of caloric, or if caloric be, on the contrary, a modification of light. This, however, is indisputable, that, in a system where only decided facts are admissible, and where we avoid, as far as possible, to suppose any thing to be that is not really known to exist, we ought provisionally to distinguish, by distinct terms, such things as are known to produce different effects. We therefore distinguish light from caloric; though we do not there-

fore deny that these have certain qualities in common, and that, in certain circumstances, they combine with other bodies almost in the same manner, and produce, in part, the same effects.

What I have already said may suffice to determine the idea affixed to the word *caloric;* but there remains a more difficult attempt, which is to give a just conception of the manner in which caloric acts upon other bodies. Since this subtile matter penetrates through the pores of all known substances; since there are no vessels through which it cannot escape, and, consequently, as there are none which are capable of retaining it, we can only come at the knowledge of its properties by effects which are fleeting and with difficulty ascertainable. It is in these things which we neither see nor feel that it is especially necessary to guard against the extravagance of our imagination, which forever inclines to step beyond the bounds of truth and is with great difficulty restrained within the narrow line of facts.

We have already seen that the same body becomes solid, or fluid, or aeriform, according to the quantity of caloric by which it is penetrated; or, to speak more strictly, according as the repulsive force exerted by the caloric is equal to, stronger, or weaker, than the attraction of the particles of the body it acts upon.

But, if these two powers only existed, bodies would become liquid at an indivisible degree of the thermometer and would almost instantaneously pass from the solid state of aggregation to that of aeriform elasticity. Thus water, for instance, at the very moment when it ceases to be ice, would begin to boil, and would be transformed into an aeriform fluid, having its particles scattered indefinitely through the surrounding space. That this does not happen must depend upon the action of some third power. The pressure of the atmosphere prevents this separation, and causes the water to remain in the liquid state till it be raised to 80° of temperature (212°) above zero of the French thermometer, the quantity of caloric which it receives in the lowest temperature being insufficient to overcome the pressure of the atmosphere.

Whence it appears that, without this atmospheric pressure, we should not have any permanent liquid and should only be able to see bodies in that state of existence in the very instant of melting, as the smallest additional caloric would instantly separate their particles and dissipate them through the surrounding

[1] Collections of the French Academy of Sciences for that year, p. 420.
[2] *Chemical Nomenclature.*

medium. Besides, without this atmospheric pressure we should not even have any aeriform fluids, strictly speaking, because the moment the force of attraction is overcome by the repulsive power of the caloric the particles would separate themselves indefinitely, having nothing to give limits to their expansion, unless their own gravity might collect them together, so as to form an atmosphere.

Simple reflection upon the most common experiments is sufficient to evince the truth of these positions. They are more particularly proved by the following experiment, which I published in the *Recueil de l' Académie* for 1777, p. 426.

Having filled with sulphuric ether[1] a small narrow glass vessel A (Plate VII, *Fig. 17*), standing upon its stalk P, the vessel, which is from twelve to fifteen lines[2] diameter, is to be covered by a wet bladder, tied round its neck with several turns of strong thread; for greater security, fix a second bladder over the first. The vessel should be filled in such a manner with the ether as not to leave the smallest portion of air between the liquor and the bladder. It is now to be placed under the recipient BCD of an air-pump, of which the upper part B ought to be fitted with a leathern lid, through which passes a wire EF, having its point F very sharp; and in the same receiver there ought to be placed the barometer GH. The whole being thus disposed, let the recipient be exhausted, and then, by pushing down the wire EF, we make a hole in the bladder. Immediately the ether begins to boil with great violence and is changed into an elastic aeriform fluid which fills the receiver. If the quantity of ether be sufficient to leave a few drops in the phial after the evaporation is finished, the elastic fluid produced will sustain the mercury in the barometer attached to the airpump, at eight or ten inches in winter, and from twenty to twenty-five in summer. To render this experiment more complete, we may introduce a small thermometer into the phial A, containing the ether, which will descend considerably during the evaporation.

The only effect produced in this experiment is the taking away the weight of the atmosphere, which, in its ordinary state, presses on

the surface of the ether; and the effects resulting from this removal evidently prove that, in the ordinary temperature of the earth, ether would always exist in an aeriform state, but for the pressure of the atmosphere, and that the passing of the ether from the liquid to the aeriform state is accompanied by a considerable lessening of heat; because, during the evaporation, a part of the caloric, which was before in a free state, or at least *in equilibrio* in the surrounding bodies, combines with the ether and causes it to assume the aeriform state.

The same experiment succeeds with all evaporable fluids, such as alcohol, water, and even mercury with this difference, that the atmosphere formed in the receiver by alcohol only supports the attached barometer about one inch in winter, and about four or five inches in summer; that formed by water, in the same situation, raises the mercury only a few lines, and that by quicksilver but a few fractions of a line. There is therefore less fluid evaporated from alcohol than from ether, less from water than from alcohol, and still less from mercury than from either; consequently there is less caloric employed, and less cold produced, which quadrates exactly with the results of these experiments.

Another species of experiment proves very evidently that the aeriform state is a modification of bodies dependent on the degree of temperature and on the pressure which these bodies undergo. In a *Memoire* read by M. de Laplace and me to the Academy in 1777, which has not been printed, we have shown that, when ether is subjected to a pressure equal to twenty-eight inches of the barometer or about the medium pressure of the atmosphere, it boils at the temperature of about 32° (104°), or 33° (106.25°), of the thermometer. M. de Luc, who has made similar experiments with spirit of wine, finds it boils at 67° (182.75°). And all the world knows that water boils at 80° (212°). Now, boiling being only the evaporation of a liquid, or the moment of its passing from the fluid to the aeriform state, it is evident that, if we keep ether continually at the temperature of 33° (106.25°), and under the common pressure of the atmosphere, we shall have it always in an elastic aeriform state; and that the same thing will happen with alcohol when above 67° (182.75°), and with water when above 80° (212°); all which are perfectly conformable to the following experiment.[3]

[1] As I shall afterwards give a definition, and explain the properties of the liquor called *ether*, I shall only premise here, that it is a very volatile inflammable liquor, having a considerably smaller specific gravity than water, or even spirit of wine.— AUTHOR.
[2] Line (from the French *ligne*) equals one-twelfth of an inch.—EDITOR.

[3] *Vide Recueil de l' Académie*, 1780, p. 335.

I filled a large vessel ABCD (Plate VII, *Fig. 15*) with water at 35° (110.75°), or 36° (113°); I suppose the vessel transparent, that we may see what takes place in the experiment; and we can easily hold the hands in water at that temperature without inconvenience. Into it I plunged some narrow necked bottles F, G, which were filled with the water, after which they were turned up, so as to rest on their mouths on the bottom of the vessel. Having next put some ether into a very small matrass, with its neck *a b c*, twice bent as in the Plate, I plunged this matrass into the water so as to have its neck inserted into the mouth of one of the bottles F. Immediately upon feeling the effects of the heat communicated to it by the water in the vessel ABCD it began to boil; and the caloric, entering into combination with it, changed it into elastic aeriform fluid, with which I filled several bottles successively, F, G, &c.

This is not the place to enter upon the examination of the nature and properties of this aeriform fluid, which is extremely inflammable; but, confining myself to the object at present in view, without anticipating circumstances which I am not to suppose the reader to know, I shall only observe that the ether, from this experiment, is almost only capable of existing in the aeriform state in our world; for, if the weight of our atmosphere was only equal to between 20 and 24 inches of the barometer, instead of 28 inches, we should never be able to obtain ether in the liquid state, at least in summer; and the formation of ether would consequently be impossible upon mountains of a moderate degree of elevation, as it would be converted into gas immediately upon being produced, unless we employed recipients of extraordinary strength, together with refrigeration and compression. And, lastly, the temperature of the blood being nearly that at which ether passes from the liquid to the aeriform state, it must evaporate in the *primae viae*, and consequently it is very probable the medical properties of this fluid depend chiefly upon its mechanical effect.

These experiments succeed better with nitrous ether, because it evaporates in a lower temperature than sulphuric ether. It is more difficult to obtain alcohol in the aeriform state because, as it requires 67° (182.75°) to reduce it to vapour, the water of the bath must be almost boiling, and consequently it is impossible to plunge the hands into it at that temperature.

It is evident that, if water were used in the foregoing experiment, it would be changed into gas when exposed to a temperature superior to that at which it boils. Although thoroughly convinced of this, M. de Laplace and myself judged it necessary to confirm it by the following direct experiment. We filled a glass jar A (Plate VII, *Fig. 5.*) with mercury, and placed it with its mouth downwards in a dish B, likewise filled with mercury, and having introduced about two gross of water into the jar, which rose to the top of the mercury at CD, we then plunged the whole apparatus into an iron boiler, EFGH, full of boiling sea-water of the temperature of 85° (223.25°), placed upon the furnace GHIK. Immediately upon the water over the mercury attaining the temperature of 80° (212°), it began to boil; and, instead of only filling the small space ACD, it was converted into an aeriform fluid which filled the whole jar; the mercury even descended below the surface of that in the dish B; and the jar must have been overturned if it had not been very thick and heavy and fixed to the dish by means of iron wire. Immediately after withdrawing the apparatus from the boiler, the vapour in the jar began to condense, and the mercury rose to its former station; but it returned again to the aeriform state a few seconds after replacing the apparatus in the boiler.

We have thus a certain number of substances, which are convertible into elastic aeriform fluids by degrees of temperature not much superior to that of our atmosphere. We shall afterwards find that there are several others which undergo the same change in similar circumstances, such as muriatic or marine acid, ammonia or volatile alkali, carbonic acid or fixed air, sulphurous acid, &c. All of these are permanently elastic in or about the mean temperature of the atmosphere and under its common pressure.

All these facts, which could be easily multiplied if necessary, give me full right to assume, as a general principle, that almost every body in nature is susceptible of three several states of existence, solid, liquid, and aeriform, and that these three states of existence depend upon the quantity of caloric combined with the body. Henceforwards I shall express these elastic aeriform fluids by the generic term *gas;* and in each species of gas I shall distinguish between the caloric, which in some measure serves the purpose of a solvent, and the substance, which in combination with the caloric, forms the base of the gas.

To these bases of the different gases, which are but little known, we have been obliged to assign names; these I shall point out in Chapter IV of this work, when I have previously given an account of the phenomena attendant upon the heating and cooling of bodies, and when I have established precise ideas concerning the composition of our atmosphere.

We have already shown, that the particles of every substance in nature exist in a certain state of equilibrium, between that attraction which tends to unite and keep the particles together and the effects of the caloric which tends to separate them. Hence the caloric not only surrounds the particles of all bodies on every side but fills up every interval which the particles of bodies leave between each other. We may form an idea of this by supposing a vessel filled with small spherical leaden bullets, into which a quantity of fine sand is poured, which, insinuating into the intervals between the bullets, will fill up every void. The balls, in this comparison, are to the sand which surrounds them exactly in the same situation as the particles of bodies are with respect to the caloric; with this difference only, that the balls are supposed to touch each other, whereas the particles of bodies are not in contact, being retained at a small distance from each other by the caloric.

If, instead of spherical balls, we substitute solid bodies of a hexahedral, octahedral, or any other regular figure, the capacity of the intervals between them will be lessened and consequently will no longer contain the same quantity of sand. The same thing takes place, with respect to natural bodies; the intervals left between their particles are not of equal capacity but vary in consequence of the different figures and magnitude of their particles, and of the distance at which these particles are maintained, according to the existing proportion between their inherent attraction and the repulsive force exerted upon them by the caloric.

In this manner we must understand the following expression, introduced by the English philosophers, who have given us the first precise ideas upon this subject: *the capacity of bodies for containing the matter of heat.* As comparisons with sensible objects are of great use in assisting us to form distinct notions of abstract ideas, we shall endeavour to illustrate this by instancing the phenomena which take place between water and bodies which are wetted and penetrated by it, with a few reflections.

If we immerge equal pieces of different kinds of wood, suppose cubes of one foot each, into water, the fluid gradually insinuates itself into their pores and the pieces of wood are augmented both in weight and magnitude: but each species of wood will imbibe a different quantity of water; the lighter and more porous woods will admit a larger, the compact and closer grained will admit of a lesser quantity; for the proportional quantities of water imbibed by the pieces will depend upon the nature of the constituent particles of the wood and upon the greater or lesser affinity subsisting between them and water. Very resinous wood, for instance, though it may be at the same time very porous, will admit but little water. We may therefore say that the different kinds of wood possess different capacities for receiving water; we may even determine, by means of the augmentation of their weights, what quantity of water they have actually absorbed; but, as we are ignorant how much water they contained previous to immersion, we cannot determine the absolute quantity they contain after being taken out of the water.

The same circumstances undoubtedly take place with bodies that are immersed in caloric; taking into consideration, however, that water is an incompressible fluid, whereas caloric is, on the contrary, endowed with very great elasticity; or, in other words, the particles of caloric have a great tendency to separate from each other, when forced by any other power to approach; this difference must of necessity occasion very considerable diversities in the results of experiments made upon these two substances.

Having established these clear and simple propositions, it will be very easy to explain the ideas which ought to be affixed to the following expressions, which are by no means synonimous, but possess each a strict and determinate meaning, as in the following definitions:

Free caloric is that which is not combined in any manner with any other body. But, as we live in a system to which caloric has a very strong adhesion, it follows that we are never able to obtain it in the state of absolute freedom.

Combined caloric is that which is fixed in bodies by affinity or elective attraction, so as to form part of the substance of the body, even part of its solidity.

By the expression *specific caloric* of bodies we understand the respective quantities of caloric requisite for raising a number of bodies of the same weight to an equal degree of temperature. This proportional quantity of caloric depends upon the distance between the constituent particles of bodies and their greater or lesser degrees of cohesion; and this distance, or rather the space or void resulting from it, is, as I have already observed, called the *capacity of bodies for containing caloric.*

Heat, considered as a sensation, or, in other words, sensible heat, is only the effect produced upon our sentient organs by the motion or passage of caloric, disengaged from the surrounding bodies. In general, we receive impressions only in consequence of motion, and we might establish it as an axiom *that,* WITHOUT MOTION, THERE IS NO SENSATION. This general principle applies very accurately to the sensations of heat and cold: when we touch a cold body, the caloric which always tends to become *in equilibrio* in all bodies, passes from our hand into the body we touch, which gives us the feeling or sensation of cold. The direct contrary happens, when we touch a warm body, the caloric then passing from the body into our hand produces the sensation of heat. If the hand and the body touched be of the same temperature, or very nearly so, we receive no impression, either of heat or cold, because there is no motion or passage of caloric; and thus no sensation can take place without some correspondent motion to occasion it.

When the thermometer rises, it shows that free caloric is entering into the surrounding bodies: the thermometer, which is one of these, receives its share in proportion to its mass and to the capacity which it possesses for containing caloric. The change therefore which takes place upon the thermometer only announces a change of place of the caloric in those bodies of which the thermometer forms one part; it only indicates the portion of caloric received, without being a measure of the whole quantity disengaged, displaced, or absorbed.

The most simple and most exact method for determining this latter point is that described by M. de Laplace, in the *Recueil de l'Académie* 1780, p. 364, a summary explanation of which will be found towards the conclusion of this work. This method consists in placing a body, or a combination of bodies, from which caloric is disengaging, in the midst of a hollow sphere of ice; and the quantity of ice melted becomes an exact measure of the quantity of caloric disengaged. It is possible, by means of the apparatus which we have caused to be constructed upon this plan, to determine not, as has been pretended, the capacity of bodies for

containing heat, but the ratio of the increase or diminution of capacity produced by determinate degrees of temperature. It is easy with the same apparatus, by means of divers combinations of experiments, to determine the quantity of caloric requisite for converting solid substances into liquids, and liquids into elastic aeriform fluids; and, *vice versa,* what quantity of caloric escapes from elastic vapours in changing to liquids, and what quantity escapes from liquids during their conversion into solids. Perhaps, when experiments have been made with sufficient accuracy, we may one day be able to determine the proportional quantity of caloric necessary for producing the several species of gases. I shall hereafter, in a separate chapter, give an account of the principal results of such experiments as have been made upon this head.

It remains, before finishing this article, to say a few words relative to the cause of the elasticity of gases and of fluids in the state of vapour. It is by no means difficult to perceive that this elasticity depends upon that of caloric, which seems to be the most eminently elastic body in nature. Nothing is more readily conceived than that one body should become elastic by entering into combination with another body possessed of that quality. We must allow that this is only an explanation of elasticity, by an assumption of elasticity, and that we thus only remove the difficulty one step further, and that the nature of elasticity, and tne reason for caloric being elastic, remains still unexplained. Elasticity in the abstract is nothing more than that quality of the particles of bodies by which they recede from each other when forced together. This tendency in the particles of caloric to separate, takes place even at considerable distances. We shall be satisfied of this, when we consider that air is susceptible of undergoing great compression, which supposes that its particles were previously very distant from each other; for the power of approaching together certainly supposes a previous distance, at least equal to the degree of approach. Consequently, those particles of the air, which are already considerably distant from each other, tend to separate still farther. In fact, if we produce Boyle's vacuum in a large receiver, the very last portion of air which remains spreads itself uniformly through the whole capacity of the vessel, however large, fills it completely throughout, and presses everywhere against its sides. We cannot, however, explain this effect without supposing that the particles make an effort to separate themselves on every side, and we are quite ignorant at what distance, or what degree of rarefaction, this effort ceases to act.

Here, therefore, exists a true repulsion between the particles of elastic fluids; at least, circumstances take place exactly as if such a repulsion actually existed; and we have very good right to conclude that the particles of caloric mutually repel each other. When we are once permitted to suppose this repelling force, the *rationale* of the formation of gases, or aeriform fluids becomes perfectly simple; tho' we must, at the same time, allow that it is extremely difficult to form an accurate conception of this repulsive force acting upon very minute particles placed at great distances from each other.

It is, perhaps, more natural to suppose that the particles of caloric have a stronger mutual attraction than those of any other substance and that these latter particles are forced asunder in consequence of this superior attraction between the particles of the caloric, which forces them between the particles of other bodies that they may be able to reunite with each other. We have somewhat analogous to this idea in the phenomena which occur when a dry sponge is dipped into water: the sponge swells; its particles separate from each other; and all its intervals are filled up by the water. It is evident that the sponge in the act of swelling, has acquired a greater capacity for containing water than it had when dry. But we cannot certainly maintain that the introduction of water between the particles of the sponge has endowed them with a repulsive power, which tends to separate them from each other; on the contrary, the whole phenomena are produced by means of attractive powers; and these are, 1st, the gravity of the water, and the power which it exerts on every side, in common with all other fluids; 2nd, the force of attraction which takes place between the particles of the water, causing them to unite together; 3rd, the mutual attraction of the particles of the sponge with each other; and, *lastly*, the reciprocal attraction which exists between the particles of the sponge and those of the water. It is easy to understand that the explanation of this fact depends upon properly appreciating the intensity of, and connection between, these several powers. It is probable that the separation of the particles of bodies, occasioned by caloric, depends in a similar manner upon a certain combination of differ-

ent attractive powers, which, in conformity with the imperfection of our knowledge, we endeavour to express by saying that caloric communicates a power of repulsion to the particles of bodies.

CHAPTER II

General Views Relative to the Formation and Composition of our Atmosphere

THESE views which I have taken of the formation of elastic aeriform fluids or gases throw great light upon the original formation of the atmospheres of the planets and particularly that of our earth. We readily conceive that it must necessarily consist of a mixture of the following substances: 1st, of all bodies that are susceptible of evaporation, or, more strictly speaking, which are capable of retaining the state of aeriform elasticity in the temperature of our atmosphere, and under a pressure equal to that of a column of twenty-eight inches of quicksilver in the barometer; and, 2nd, of all substances, whether liquid or solid, which are capable of being dissolved by this mixture of different gases.

The better to determine our ideas relating to this subject, which has not hitherto been sufficiently considered, let us, for a moment, conceive what change would take place in the various substances which compose our earth, if its temperature were suddenly altered. If, for instance, we were suddenly transported into the region of the planet Mercury, where probably the common temperature is much superior to that of boiling water, the water of the earth and all the other fluids which are susceptible of the gaseous state at a temperature near to that of boiling water, even quicksilver itself, would become rarified; and all these substances would be changed into permanent aeriform fluids or gases, which would become part of the new atmosphere. These new species of airs or gases would mix with those already existing, and certain reciprocal decompositions and new combinations would take place, until such time as all the elective attractions or affinities subsisting amongst all these new and old gaseous substances had operated fully; after which, the elementary principles composing these gases, being saturated, would remain at rest. We must attend to this, however, that, even in the above hypothetical situation, certain bounds would occur to the evaporation of these substances, produced by that very evaporation itself; for as, in proportion to the increase of elastic fluids, the pressure of the atmosphere would be augmented, as every degree of pressure tends, in some measure, to prevent evaporation, and as even the most evaporable fluids can resist the operation of a very high temperature without evaporating, if prevented by a proportionally stronger compression, water and all other liquids being able to sustain a red heat in Papin's digester; we must admit that the new atmosphere would at last arrive at such a degree of weight that the water which had not hitherto evaporated would cease to boil and, of consequence, would remain liquid; so that, even upon this supposition as in all others of the same nature, the increasing gravity of the atmosphere would find certain limits which it could not exceed. We might even extend these reflections greatly further, and examine what change might be produced in such situations upon stones, salts, and the greater part of the fusible substances which compose the mass of our earth. These would be softened, fused, and changed into fluids, &c.: but these speculations carry me from my object, to which I hasten to return.

By a contrary supposition to the one we have been forming, if the earth were suddenly transported into a very cold region, the water which at present composes our seas, rivers, and springs, and probably the greater number of the fluids we are acquainted with, would be converted into solid mountains and hard rocks, at first diaphanous and homogeneous, like rock crystal, but which, in time, becoming mixed with foreign and heterogeneous substances, would become opaque stones of various colours. In this case, the air, or at least some part of the aeriform fluids which now compose the mass of our atmosphere, would doubtless lose its elasticity for want of a sufficient temperature to retain it in that state: it would return to the liquid state of existence, and new liquids would be formed, of whose properties we cannot, at present, form the most distant idea.

These two opposite suppositions give a distinct proof of the following corollaries: 1st that *solidity*, *liquidity*, and *aeriform elasticity*, are only three different states of existence of the same matter, or three particular modifications which almost all substances are susceptible of assuming successively, and which solely depend upon the degree of temperature to which they are exposed; or, in other words, upon the quantity of caloric with which they are penetrated. 2nd, that it is extremely probable that air is a fluid naturally existing in a state of vapour;

or, as we may better express it, that our atmosphere is a compound of all the fluids which are susceptible of the vaporous or permanently elastic state, in the usual temperature and under the common pressure. 3rd, that it is not impossible we may discover, in our atmosphere, certain substances naturally very compact, even metals themselves; as a metallic substance, for instance, only a little more volatile than mercury, might exist in that situation.

Amongst the fluids with which we are acquainted, some, as water and alcohol, are susceptible of mixing with each other in all proportions; whereas others, on the contrary, as quicksilver, water, and oil, can only form a momentary union; and, after being mixed together, separate and arrange themselves according to their specific gravities. The same thing ought to, or at least may, take place in the atmosphere. It is possible, and even extremely probable, that, both at the first creation and every day, gases are formed, which are with difficulty miscible with atmospheric air and are continually separating from it. If these gases be specifically lighter than the general atmospheric mass, they must, of course, gather in the higher regions and form strata that float upon the common air. The phenomena which accompany igneous meteors induce me to believe that there exists in the upper parts of our atmosphere a stratum of inflammable fluid in contact with those strata of air which produce the phenomena of the aurora borealis and other fiery meteors.—I mean hereafter to pursue this subject in a separate treatise.

CHAPTER III

Analysis of Atmospheric Air, and its Division into Two Elastic Fluids; the One Fit for Respiration, the Other Incapable of Being Respired.

FROM what has been premised, it follows that our atmosphere is composed of a mixture of every substance capable of retaining the gaseous or aeriform state in the common temperature, and under the usual pressure which it experiences. These fluids constitute a mass, in some measure homogeneous, extending from the surface of the earth to the greatest height hitherto attained, of which the density continually decreases in the inverse ratio of the superincumbent weight. But, as I have before observed, it is possible that this first stratum is surmounted by several others consisting of very different fluids.

Our business, in this place, is to endeavour to determine, by experiments, the nature of the elastic fluids which compose the inferior stratum of air which we inhabit. Modern chemistry has made great advances in this research; and it will appear by the following details that the analysis of atmospherical air has been more rigorously determined than that of any other substance of the class. Chemistry affords two general methods of determining the constituent principles of bodies, the method of analysis, and that of synthesis. When, for instance, by combining water with alcohol we form the species of liquor called, in commercial language, brandy or spirit of wine, we certainly have a right to conclude that brandy, or spirit of wine, is composed of alcohol combined with water. We can produce the same result by the analytical method; and in general it ought to be considered as a principle in chemical science never to rest satisfied without both these species of proofs.

We have this advantage in the analysis of atmospherical air, being able both to decompound it, and to form it anew in the most satisfactory manner. I shall, however, at present confine myself to recount such experiments as are most conclusive upon this head; and I may consider most of these as my own, having either first invented them or having repeated those of others, with the intention of analysing atmospherical air, in perfectly new points of view.

I took a matrass A (Plate II, *Fig. 14*) of about 30 cubic inches capacity, having a long neck BCDE of six or seven lines internal diameter, and having bent the neck as in Plate IV, *Fig. 2*, so as to allow of its being placed in the furnace MMNN, in such a manner that the extremity of its neck E might be inserted under a bell-glass FG, placed in a trough of quicksilver RRSS; I introduced four ounces of pure mercury into the matrass and, by means of a siphon, exhausted the air in the receiver FG, so as to raise the quicksilver to LL, and I carefully marked the height at which it stood by pasting on a slip of paper. Having accurately noted the height of the thermometer and barometer, I lighted a fire in the furnace MMNN, which I kept up almost continually during twelve days, so as to keep the quicksilver always almost at its boiling point. Nothing remarkable took place during the first day: the mercury, though not boiling, was continually evaporating and covered the interior surface of the vessels with small drops, at first very minute, which, gradually augmenting to a sufficient size, fell back into the mass at the bottom of the vessel. On the second day, small red particles began to appear on the surface of the mercury, which, during the four or five following days, gradually increased in size and number, after which they ceased to increase in either respect. At the end of twelve days, seeing that the calcination of the mercury did not at all increase, I extinguished the fire, and allowed the vessels to cool. The bulk of air in the body and neck of the matrass, and in the bell-glass, reduced to a medium of 28 inches of the barometer and 10° (54.5°) of the thermometer, at the commencement of the experiment was about 50 cubic inches. At the end of the experiment the remaining air, reduced to the same medium pressure and temperature, was only between 42 and 43 cubic inches; consequently it had lost about ⅙ of its bulk. Afterwards, having collected all the red particles formed during the experiment from the running mercury in which they floated, I found these to amount to 45 grains.

I was obliged to repeat this experiment several times, as it is difficult in one experiment both to preserve the whole air upon which we operate and to collect the whole of the red particles, or calx of mercury, which is formed during the calcination. It will often happen in the sequel that I shall, in this manner, give in one detail the results of two or three experiments of the same nature.

The air which remained after the calcination of the mercury in this experiment, and which was reduced to ⅚ of its former bulk, was no longer fit either for respiration or for combustion; animals being introduced into it were suffocated in a few seconds, and when a taper was plunged into it, it was extinguished as if it had been immersed into water.

In the next place, I took the 45 grains of red matter formed during this experiment, which I put into a small glass retort, having a proper apparatus for receiving such liquid, or gaseous product, as might be extracted: having applied a fire to the retort in a furnace, I observed that, in proportion as the red matter became heated, the intensity of its colour augmented. When the retort was almost red hot, the red matter began gradually to decrease in bulk, and a few minutes afterwards, it disappeared altogether; at the same time 41½ grains of running mercury were collected in the recipient, and 7 or 8 cubic inches of elastic fluid, greatly more capable of supporting both respiration and combustion than atmospherical air, were collected in the bell-glass.

A part of this air being put into a glass tube of about an inch diameter showed the following properties: a taper burned in it with a dazzling splendour and charcoal, instead of consuming quietly as it does in common air, burnt with a flame, attended with a decrepitating noise, like phosphorus, and threw out such a brilliant light that the eyes could hardly endure it. This species of air was discovered almost at the same time by M. Priestley, M. Scheele, and myself. M. Priestley gave it the name of *dephlogisticated air*, M. Scheele called it *empyreal air*. At first I named it *highly respirable air*, to which has since been substituted the term of *vital air*. We shall presently see what we ought to think of these denominations.

In reflecting upon the circumstances of this experiment, we readily perceive that the mercury, during its calcination, absorbs the salubrious and respirable part of the air, or, to speak more strictly, the base of this respirable part; that the remaining air is a species of mephitis, incapable of supporting combustion or respiration; and consequently that atmospheric air is composed of two elastic fluids of different and opposite qualities. As a proof of this important truth, if we recombine these two elastic fluids, which we have separately obtained in the above experiment, viz., the 42 cubic inches of mephitis, with the 8 cubic inches of respirable air, we reproduce an air precisely similar to that of the atmosphere and possessing nearly the same power of supporting combustion and respiration, and of contributing to the calcination of metals.

Although this experiment furnishes us with a very simple means of obtaining the two principal elastic fluids which compose our atmosphere separate from each other, yet it does not give us an exact idea of the proportion in which these two enter into its composition: for the attraction of mercury to the respirable part of the air, or rather to its base, is not sufficiently strong to overcome all the circumstances which oppose this union. These obstacles are the mutual adhesion of the two constituent parts of the atmosphere for each other and the elective attraction which unites the base of vital air with caloric; in consequence of these, when the calcination ends, or is at least carried as far as is possible in a determinate quantity of atmospheric air, there still remains a portion of respirable air united to the mephitis, which

the mercury cannot separate. I shall afterwards show that, at least in our climate, the atmospheric air is composed of respirable, and mephitic airs, in the proportion of 27 and 73; and I shall then discuss the causes of the uncertainty which still exists with respect to the exactness of that proportion.

Since, during the calcination of mercury, air is decomposed, and the base of its respirable part is fixed and combined with the mercury, it follows, from the principles already established, that caloric and light must be disengaged during the process: but the two following causes prevent us from being sensible of this taking place: as the calcination lasts during several days, the disengagement of caloric and light, spread out in a considerable space of time, becomes extremely small for each particular moment of that time, so as not to be perceptible; and, in the next place, the operation being carried on by means of fire in a furnace, the heat produced by the calcination itself becomes confounded with that proceeding from the furnace. I might add the respirable part of the air, or rather its base, in entering into combination with the mercury, does not part with all the caloric which it contained but still retains a part of it after forming the new compound; but the discussion of this point, and its proofs from experiment, do not belong to this part of our subject.

It is, however, easy to render this disengagement of caloric and light evident to the senses, by causing the decomposition of air to take place in a more rapid manner. And for this purpose, iron is excellently adapted, as it possesses a much stronger affinity for the base of respirable air than mercury. The elegant experiment of M. Ingenhouz, upon the combustion of iron, is well known. Take a piece of fine iron wire twisted into a spiral BC (Plate IV, *Fig. 17*), fix one of its extremities B into the cork A, adapted to the neck of the bottle DEFG, and fix to the other extremity of the wire C a small morsel of tinder. Matters being thus prepared, fill the bottle DEFG with air deprived of its mephitic part; then light the tinder and introduce it quickly, with the wire upon which it is fixed, into the bottle which you stop up with the cork A, as is shown in the figure (17, Plate IV). The instant the tinder comes into contact with the vital air it begins to burn with great intensity; and, communicating the inflammation to the iron-wire, it too takes fire and burns rapidly, throwing out brilliant sparks, which fall to the bottom of the vessel in rounded globules, which become black in cooling but retain a degree of metallic splendour. The iron thus burnt is more brittle even than glass and is easily reduced into powder, and is still attractable by the magnet, though not so powerfully as it was before combustion. As M. Ingenhouz has neither examined the change produced on iron nor upon the air by this operation, I have repeated the experiment under different circumstances, in an apparatus adapted to answer my particular views, as follows.

Having filled a bell-glass A (Plate IV, *Fig. 3*) of about six pints measure with pure air, or the highly respirable part of air, I transported this jar by means of a very flat vessel, into a quicksilver bath in the basin BC, and I took care to render the surface of the mercury perfectly dry both within and without the jar with blotting paper. I then provided a small capsule of chinaware D, very flat and open, in which I placed some small pieces of iron, turned spirally and arranged in such a way as seemed most favourable for the combustion being communicated to every part. To the end of one of these pieces of iron was fixed a small morsel of tinder, to which was added about the sixteenth part of a grain of phosphorus, and, by raising the bellglass a little, the china capsule, with its contents, were introduced into the pure air. I know that, by this means, some common air must mix with the pure air in the glass; but this, when it is done dexterously, is so very trifling as not to injure the success of the experiment. This being done, a part of the air is sucked out from the bell-glass, by means of a siphon GHI, so as to raise the mercury within the glass to EF; and, to prevent the mercury from getting into the siphon, a small piece of paper is twisted round its extremity. In sucking out the air, if the motion of the lungs only be used, we cannot make the mercury rise above an inch or an inch and a half; but, by properly using the muscles of the mouth, we can, without difficulty, cause it to rise six or seven inches.

I next took an iron wire, (MN, Plate IV, *Fig. 16*) properly bent for the purpose, and making it red hot in the fire passed it through the mercury into the receiver and brought it in contact with the small piece of phosphorus attached to the tinder. The phosphorus instantly takes fire, which communicates to the tinder, and from that to the iron. When the pieces have been properly arranged, the whole iron burns,

even to the last particle, throwing out a white brilliant light similar to that of Chinese fireworks. The great heat produced by this combustion melts the iron into round globules of different sizes, most of which fall into the china cup; but some are thrown out of it and swim upon the surface of the mercury. At the beginning of the combustion, there is a slight augmentation in the volume of the air in the bellglass, from the dilatation caused by the heat; but, presently afterwards, a rapid diminution of the air takes place and the mercury rises in the glass; insomuch that, when the quantity of iron is sufficient, and the air operated upon is very pure, almost the whole air employed is absorbed.

It is proper to remark in this place that, unless in making experiments for the purpose of discovery, it is better to be contented with burning a moderate quantity of iron; for, when this experiment is pushed too far, so as to absorb much of the air, the cup D, which floats upon the quicksilver, approaches too near the bottom of the bell-glass; and the great heat produced, which is followed by a very sudden cooling, occasioned by the contact of the cold mercury, is apt to break the glass. In which case, the sudden fall of the column of mercury, which happens the moment the least flaw is produced in the glass, causes such a wave as throws a great part of the quicksilver from the basin. To avoid this inconvenience, and to ensure success to the experiment, one gross and a half of iron is sufficient to burn in a bell-glass, which holds about eight pints of air. The glass ought likewise to be strong, that it may be able to bear the weight of the column of mercury which it has to support.

By this experiment, it is not possible to determine, at one time, both the additional weight acquired by the iron, and the changes which have taken place in the air. If it is wished to ascertain what additional weight has been gained by the iron, and the proportion between that and the air absorbed, we must carefully mark upon the bell-glass, with a diamond, the height of the mercury, both before and after the experiment. After this, the siphon GH (Plate IV, *Fig. 3*) guarded, as before, with a bit of paper, to prevent its filling with mercury, is to be introduced under the bellglass, having the thumb placed upon the extremity, G, of the siphon, to regulate the passage of the air; and by this means the air is gradually admitted, so as to let the mercury fall to its level. This being done, the bell-glass is to be carefully removed, the globules of melted iron contained in the cup, and those which have been scattered about, and swim upon the mercury are to be accurately collected, and the whole is to be weighed. The iron will be found in that state called *martial ethiops* by the old chemists, possessing a degree of metallic brilliancy, very friable, and readily reducible into powder under the hammer or with a pestle and mortar. If the experiment has succeeded well, from 100 grains of iron will be obtained 135 or 136 grains of *ethiops*, which is an augmentation of 35 per cent.

If all the attention has been paid to this experiment which it deserves, the air will be found diminished in weight exactly equal to what the iron has gained. Having therefore burnt 100 grains of iron, which has acquired an additional weight of 35 grains, the diminution of air will be found exactly 70 cubic inches; and it will be found, in the sequel, that the weight of vital air is pretty nearly half a grain for each cubic inch; so that, in effect, the augmentation of weight in the one exactly coincides with the loss of it in the other.

I shall observe here, once for all, that, in every experiment of this kind, the pressure and temperature of the air, both before and after the experiment, must be reduced, by calculation, to a common standard of 10° (54.5°) of the thermometer and 28 inches of the barometer. Towards the end of this work, the manner of performing this very necessary reduction will be found accurately detailed.

If it be required to examine the nature of the air which remains after this experiment, we must operate in a somewhat different manner. After the combustion is finished, and the vessels have cooled, we first take out the cup, and the burnt iron, by introducing the hand through the quicksilver under the bell-glass; we next introduce some solution of potash, or caustic alkali, or of the sulphuret of potash, or such other substance as is judged proper for examining their action upon the residuum of air. I shall, in the sequel, give an account of these methods of analysing air, when I have explained the nature of these different substances, which are only here in a manner accidentally mentioned. After this examination, so much water must be let into the glass as will displace the quicksilver, and then, by means of a shallow dish placed below the bell-glass, it is to be removed into the common water pneumato-chemical apparatus, where the air remaining may be examined at large and with great facility.

When very soft and very pure iron has been employed in this experiment, and, if the combustion has been performed in the purest respirable or vital air, free from all admixture of the noxious or mephitic part, the air which remains after the combustion will be found as pure as it was before; but it is difficult to find iron entirely free from a small portion of charry matter, which is chiefly abundant in steel. It is likewise exceedingly difficult to procure the pure air perfectly free from some admixture of mephitis, with which it is almost always contaminated; but this species of noxious air does not in the smallest degree disturb the result of the experiment, as it is always found at the end exactly in the same proportion as at the beginning.

I mentioned before that we have two ways of determining the constituent parts of atmospheric air, the method of analysis, and that by synthesis. The calcination of mercury has furnished us with an example of each of these methods, since, after having robbed the respirable part of its base, by means of the mercury, we have restored it, so as to recompose an air precisely similar to that of the atmosphere. But we can equally accomplish this synthetic composition of atmospheric air by borrowing the materials of which it is composed from different kingdoms of nature. We shall see hereafter that when animal substances are dissolved in the nitric acid a great quantity of gas is disengaged, which extinguishes light and is unfit for animal respiration, being exactly similar to the noxious or mephitic part of atmospheric air. And, if we take 73 parts, by weight, of this elastic fluid, and mix it with 27 parts of highly respirable air, procured from calcined mercury, we will form an elastic fluid precisely similar to atmospheric air in all its properties.

There are many other methods of separating the respirable from the noxious part of the atmospheric air, which cannot be taken notice of in this part without anticipating information which properly belongs to the subsequent chapters. The experiments already adduced may suffice for an elementary treatise; and, in matters of this nature, the choice of our evidences is of far greater consequence than their number.

I shall close this article by pointing out the property which atmospheric air, and all the known gases, possess of dissolving water, which is of great consequence to be attended to in all experiments of this nature. M. Saussure found, by experiment, that a cubic foot of atmospheric air is capable of holding 12 grains of water in solution: other gases, as carbonic acid, appear capable of dissolving a greater quantity; but experiments are still wanting by which to determine their several proportions. This water, held in solution by gases, gives rise to particular phenomena in many experiments which require great attention and which has frequently proved the source of great errors to chemists in determining the results of their experiments.

CHAPTER IV

Nomenclature of the Several Constituent Parts of Atmospheric Air

HITHERTO I have been obliged to make use of circumlocution to express the nature of the several substances which constitute our atmosphere, having provisionally used the terms of *respirable* and *noxious*, or *non-respirable parts of the air*. But the investigations I mean to undertake require a more direct mode of expression; and, having now endeavoured to give simple and distinct ideas of the different substances which enter into the composition of the atmosphere, I shall henceforth express these ideas by words equally simple.

The temperature of our earth being very near to that at which water becomes solid and reciprocally changes from solid to fluid, and as this phenomenon takes place frequently under our observation, it has very naturally followed that, in the languages of at least every climate subjected to any degree of winter, a term has been used for signifying water in the state of solidity when deprived of its caloric. The same, however, has not been found necessary with respect to water reduced to the state of vapour by an additional dose of caloric; since those persons who do not make a particular study of objects of this kind are still ignorant that water, when in a temperature only a little above the boiling heat, is changed into an elastic aeriform fluid, susceptible, like all other gases, of being received and contained in vessels and preserving its gaseous form so long as it remains at the temperature of 80° (212°) and under a pressure not exceeding 28 inches of the mercurial barometer. As this phenomenon has not been generally observed, no language has used a particular term for expressing water in this state; and the same thing occurs with all fluids and all substances which do not evaporate in the common temperature and under the usual pressure of our atmosphere.

For similar reasons, names have not been given to the liquid or concrete states of most of the aeriform fluids: these were not known to arise from the combination of caloric with certain bases; and, as they had not been seen either in the liquid or solid states, their existence, under these forms, was even unknown to natural philosophers.

We have not pretended to make any alteration upon such terms as are sanctified by ancient custom and, therefore, continue to use the words *water* and *ice* in their common acceptation. We likewise retain the word *air* to express that collection of elastic fluids which composes our atmosphere; but we have not thought it necessary to preserve the same respect for modern terms, adopted by latter philosophers, having considered ourselves as at liberty to reject such as appeared liable to occasion erroneous ideas of the substances they are meant to express, and either to substitute new terms, or to employ the old ones after modifying them in such a manner as to convey more determinate ideas. New words have been drawn, chiefly from the Greek language, in such a manner as to make their etymology convey some idea of what was meant to be represented; and these we have always endeavoured to make short and of such a nature as to be changeable into adjectives and verbs.

Following these principles, we have, after M. Macquer's example, retained the term *gas* employed by van Helmont, having arranged the numerous classes of elastic aeriform fluids under that name, excepting only atmospheric air. *Gas*, therefore, in our nomenclature becomes a generic term, expressing the fullest degree of saturation in any body with caloric; being, in fact, a term expressive of a mode of existence. To distinguish each species of gas, we employ a second term from the name of the base, which, saturated with caloric, forms each particular gas. Thus, we name water combined to saturation with caloric, so as to form an elastic fluid, *aqueous gas;* ether, combined in the same manner, *etherial gas;* the combination of alcohol with caloric becomes *alcoholic gas;* and, following the same principles, we have *muriatic acid gas, ammoniacal gas,* and so on of every substance susceptible of being combined with caloric, in such a manner as to assume the gaseous or elastic aeriform state.

We have already seen that the atmospheric air is composed of two gases, or aeriform fluids, one of which is capable, by respiration, of contributing to animal life, and in which metals are calcinable and combustible bodies may burn; the other, on the contrary, is endowed with directly opposite qualities; it cannot be breathed by animals, neither will it admit of the combustion of inflammable bodies, nor of the calcination of metals. We have given to the base of the former, or respirable portion of the air, the name of *oxygen*, from οξυς, *acidum*, and γείνομαι, *gignor;* because, in reality, one of the most general properties of this base is to form acids by combining with many different substances. The union of this base with caloric we term *oxygen gas*, which is the same with what was formerly called *pure* or *vital air*. The weight of this gas, at the temperature of 10° (54.50°), and under a pressure equal to 28 inches of the barometer, is half a grain for each cubic inch, or an ounce and a half to each cubic foot.

The chemical properties of the noxious portion of atmospheric air being hitherto but little known, we have been satisfied to derive the name of its base from its known quality of killing such animals as are forced to breathe it, giving it the name of *azote*, from the Greek privative particle α and ζωή, *vita;* hence the name of the noxious part of atmospheric air is *azotic gas;* the weight of which, in the same temperature and under the same pressure, is 1 *oz.* 2 *gros*[1] and 48 *grs.* to the cubic foot, or 0.4444 of a grain to the cubic inch. We cannot deny that this name appears somewhat extraordinary; but this must be the case with all new terms, which cannot be expected to become familiar until they have been some time in use. We long endeavoured to find a more proper designation without success; it was at first proposed to call it *alkaligen gas*, as, from the experiments of M. Berthollet, it appears to enter into the composition of ammonia, or volatile alkali; but then, we have as yet no proof of its making one of the constituent elements of the other alkalies; beside, it is proved to compose a part of the nitric acid, which gives as good reason to have called it *nitrogen*. For these reasons, finding it necessary to reject any name upon systematic principles, we have considered that we run no risk of mistake in adopting the terms of *azote* and *azotic gas*, which only express a matter of fact, or that property which it possesses, of depriving such

[1] *Gros* equals one-eighth of an ounce.—EDITOR.

animals as breathe it of their lives.

I should anticipate subjects more properly reserved for the subsequent chapters were I in this place to enter upon the nomenclature of the several species of gases: it is sufficient, in this part of the work, to establish the principles upon which their denominations are founded. The principal merit of the nomenclature we have adopted is that, when once the simple elementary substance is distinguished by an appropriate term, the names of all its compounds derive readily, and necessarily, from this first denomination.

CHAPTER V

Of the Decomposition of Oxygen Gas by Sulphur, Phosphorus, and Charcoal, and of the Formation of Acids in General

IN performing experiments, it is a necessary principle, which ought never to be deviated from, that they be simplified as much as possible, and that every circumstance capable of rendering their results complicated be carefully removed. Wherefore, in the experiments which form the object of this chapter, we have never employed atmospheric air, which is not a simple substance. It is true that the azotic gas, which forms a part of its mixture, appears to be merely passive during combustion and calcination; but, besides that it retards these operations very considerably, we are not certain but it may even alter their results in some circumstances; for which reason I have thought it necessary to remove even this possible cause of doubt, by only making use of pure oxygen gas in the following experiments which show the effects produced by combustion in that gas; and I shall advert to such differences as take place in the results of these, when the oxygen gas, or pure vital air, is mixed, in different proportions, with azotic gas.

Having filled a bell-glass A (Plate IV, *Fig. 3*), of between five and six pints measure, with oxygen gas, I removed it from the water trough, where it was filled, into the quicksilver bath by means of a shallow glass dish slipped underneath, and having dried the mercury I introduced 61¼ grains of Kunkel's phosphorus in two little china cups, like that represented at D (*Fig. 3*), under the glass A; and that I might set fire to each of the portions of phosphorus separately, and to prevent the one from catching fire from the other, one of the dishes was covered with a piece of flat glass I next raised the quicksilver in the bell-glass up to EF, by sucking out a sufficient portion of the gas by means of the siphon G HI. After this, by means of the crooked iron wire (*Fig. 16*), made red hot, I set fire to the two portions of phosphorus successively, first burning that portion which was not covered with the piece of glass. The combustion was extremely rapid, attended with a very brilliant flame and considerable disengagement of light and heat. In consequence of the great heat induced, the gas was at first much dilated, but soon after the mercury returned to its level and a considerable absorption of gas took place; at the same time, the whole inside of the glass became covered with white light flakes of concrete phosphoric acid.

At the beginning of the experiment, the quantity of oxygen gas, reduced, as above directed, to a common standard, amounted to 162 cubic inches; and, after the combustion was finished, only $23\frac{1}{4}$ cubic inches, likewise reduced to the standard, remained; so that the quantity of oxygen gas absorbed during the combustion was $138\frac{3}{4}$ cubic inches, equal to 69.375 grains.

A part of the phosphorus remained unconsumed in the bottom of the cups, which being washed on purpose to separate the acid weighed about $16\frac{1}{4}$ grains; so that about 45 grains of phosphorus had been burned: but, as it is hardly possible to avoid an error of one or two grains, I leave the quantity so far qualified. Hence, as nearly 45 grains of phosphorus had, in this experiment, united with 69.375 grains of oxygen, and as no gravitating matter could have escaped through the glass, we have a right to conclude that the weight of the substance resulting from the combustion in form of white flakes must equal that of the phosphorus and oxygen employed, which amounts to 114.375 grains. And we shall presently find that these flakes consisted entirely of a solid or concrete acid. When we reduce these weights to hundredth parts, it will be found that 100 parts of phosphorus require 154 parts of oxygen for saturation and that this combination will produce 254 parts of concrete phosphoric acid, in form of white fleecy flakes.

This experiment proves, in the most convincing manner, that, at a certain degree of temperature, oxygen possesses a stronger elective attraction, or affinity, for phosphorus than for caloric; that, in consequence of this, the phosphorus attracts the base of oxygen gas from the caloric, which, being set free, spreads itself over the surrounding bodies. But, though this experiment be so far perfectly conclusive, it is not sufficiently rigorous, as, in the apparatus described, it is impossible to ascertain the weight of the flakes of concrete acid which are formed; we can therefore only determine this by calculating the weights of oxygen and phosphorus employed; but as, in physics and in chemistry, it is not allowable to suppose what is capable of being ascertained by direct experiment, I thought it necessary to repeat this experiment as follows, upon a larger scale and by means of a different apparatus.

I took a large glass balloon A (Plate IV, *Fig. 4*) with an opening three inches diameter, to which was fitted a crystal stopper ground with emery, and pierced with two holes for the tubes *yyy, xxx*. Before shutting the balloon with its stopper, I introduced the support BC, surmounted by the china cup D, containing 150 *grs.* of phosphorus; the stopper was then fitted to the opening of the balloon, luted with fat lute, and covered with slips of linen spread with quicklime and white of eggs: when the lute was perfectly dry, the weight of the whole apparatus was determined to within a grain or a grain and a half. I next exhausted the balloon, by means of an air pump applied to the tube *xxx*, and then introduced oxygen gas by means of the tube *yyy*, having a stop-cock adapted to it. This kind of experiment is most readily and most exactly performed by means of the hydro-pneumatic machine described by M. Meusnier and me in the *Recueil de l'Académie* for 1782, page 466, and explained in the latter part of this work, with several important additions and corrections since made to it by M. Meusnier. With this instrument we can readily ascertain, in the most exact manner, both the quantity of oxygen gas introduced into the balloon and the quantity consumed during the course of the experiment.

When all things were properly disposed, I set fire to the phosphorus with a burning glass. The combustion was extremely rapid, accompanied with a bright flame and much heat; as the operation went on, large quantities of white flakes attached themselves to the inner surface of the balloon, so that at last it was rendered quite opaque. The quantity of these flakes at last became so abundant that although fresh oxygen gas was continually supplied, which ought to have supported the combustion, yet the phosphorus was soon extinguished. Having allowed the apparatus to cool completely, I first ascertained the quantity of oxygen gas employed, and weighed the balloon accurately, before it was opened. I next washed, dried, and weighed the small quantity of phosphorus remaining in the cup, on purpose to determine the whole quantity of phosphorus consumed in the experiment; this residuum of the phosphorus was of a yellow ochre colour. It is evident that by these several precautions I could easily determine, 1st, the weight of the phosphorus consumed; 2nd, the weight of the flakes produced by the combustion; and, 3rd, the weight of the oxygen which had combined with the phosphorus. This experiment gave very nearly the same results with the former, as it proved that the phosphorus, during its combustion, had absorbed a little more than one and a half its weight of oxygen; and I learned with more certainty that the weight of the new substance produced in the experiment exactly equalled the sum of the weights of the phosphorus consumed and oxygen absorbed, which indeed was easily determinable *a priori*. If the oxygen gas employed be pure, the residuum after combustion is as pure as the gas employed; this proves that nothing escapes from the phosphorus capable of altering the purity of the oxygen gas, and that the only action of the phosphorous is to separate the oxygen from the caloric with which it was before united.

I mentioned above, that when any combustible body is burnt in a hollow sphere of ice, or in an apparatus properly constructed upon that principle, the quantity of ice melted during the combustion is an exact measure of the quantity of caloric disengaged. Upon this head, the *Mémoire* given by M. de Laplace and me, 1780, p. 355, may be consulted. Having submitted the combustion of phosphorus to this trial, we found that one pound of phosphorus melted a little more than 100 pounds of ice during its combustion.

The combustion of phosphorus succeeds equally well in atmospheric air as in oxygen gas, with this difference, that the combustion is vastly slower, being retarded by the large proportion of azotic gas mixed with the oxygen gas, and that only about one-fifth part of the air employed is absorbed, because as the oxygen gas only is absorbed the proportion of the azotic gas becomes so great toward the close of the experiment as to put an end to the combustion.

I have already shown that phosphorus is changed by combustion into an extremely light,

white, flaky matter; and its properties are entirely altered by this transformation: from being insoluble in water, it becomes not only soluble, but so greedy of moisture as to attract the humidity of the air with astonishing rapidity; by this means it is converted into a liquid considerably more dense and of more specific gravity than water. In the state of phosphorus before combustion, it had scarcely any sensible taste; by its union with oxygen it acquires an extremely sharp and sour taste: in a word, from one of the class of combustible bodies it is changed into an incombustible substance and becomes one of those bodies called acids.

This property of a combustible substance to be converted into an acid, by the addition of oxygen, we shall presently find belongs to a great number of bodies: wherefore, strict logic requires that we should adopt a common term for indicating all these operations which produce analogous results; this is the true way to simplify the study of science, as it would be quite impossible to bear all its specific details in the memory if they were not classically arranged. For this reason, we shall distinguish this conversion of phosphorus into an acid by its union with oxygen, and in general every combination of oxygen with a combustible substance, by the term of *oxygenation:* from which I shall adopt the verb to *oxygenate*, and of consequence shall say, that in *oxygenating* phosphorus we convert it into an acid.

Sulphur is likewise a combustible body or, in other words, it is a body which possesses the power of decomposing oxygen gas by attracting the oxygen from the caloric with which it was combined. This can very easily be proved by means of experiments quite similar to those we have given with phosphorus; but it is necessary to premise that in these operations with sulphur the same accuracy of result is not to be expected as with phosphorus; because the acid which is formed by the combustion of sulphur is difficultly condensible, and because sulphur burns with more difficulty, and is soluble in the different gases. But I can safely assert, from my own experiments, that sulphur in burning absorbs oxygen gas; that the resulting acid is considerably heavier than the sulphur burnt; that its weight is equal to the sum of the weights of the sulphur which has been burnt and of the oxygen absorbed; and, lastly, that this acid is weighty, incombustible, and miscible with water in all proportions: the only uncertainty remaining upon this head is with regard to the proportions of sulphur and of oxygen which enter into the composition of the acid.

Charcoal, which, from all our present knowledge regarding it, must be considered as a simple combustible body, has likewise the property of decomposing oxygen gas by absorbing its base from the caloric: but the acid resulting from this combustion does not condense in the common temperature; under the pressure of our atmosphere, it remains in the state of gas, and requires a large proportion of water to combine with or be dissolved in. This acid has, however, all the known properties of other acids, though in a weaker degree, and combines, like them, with all the bases which are susceptible of forming neutral salts.

The combustion of charcoal in oxygen gas may be effected like that of phosphorus in the bell-glass A (Plate IV, *Fig. 3*) placed over mercury: but, as the heat of red hot iron is not sufficient to set fire to the charcoal, we must add a small morsel of tinder with a minute particle of phosphorus, in the same manner as directed in the experiment for the combustion of iron. A detailed account of this experiment will be found in the *Recueil de l'Académie* for 1781, p. 448. By that experiment it appears that 28 parts by weight of charcoal require 72 parts of oxygen for saturation and that the aeriform acid produced is precisely equal in weight to the sum of the weights of the charcoal and oxygen gas employed. This aeriform acid was called *fixed* or *fixable air* by the chemists who first discovered it; they did not then know whether it was air resembling that of the atmosphere or some other elastic fluid, vitiated and corrupted by combustion; but since it is now ascertained to be an acid, formed like all others by the oxygenation of its peculiar base, it is obvious that the name of *fixed air* is quite ineligible.

By burning charcoal in the apparatus mentioned, p. 24, M. de Laplace and I found that one *lb.* of charcoal melted 96 *lbs.* 6 *oz.* of ice; that, during the combustion, 2 *lbs.* 9 *oz.* 1 *gros* 10 *grs.* of oxygen were absorbed, and that 3 *lbs.* 9 *oz.* 1 *gros* 10 *grs.* of acid gas were formed. This gas weighs 0.695 parts of a grain for each cubic inch, in the common standard temperature and pressure mentioned above, so that 34,242 cubic inches of acid gas are produced by the combustion of one pound of charcoal.

I might multiply these experiments and show by a numerous succession of facts that all acids are formed by the combustion of certain substances; but I am prevented from doing so in this place by the plan which I have laid down of proceeding only from facts already ascertained to such as are unknown and of drawing my examples only from circumstances already explained. In the mean time, however, the three examples above cited may suffice for giving a clear and accurate conception of the manner in which acids are formed. By these it may be clearly seen that oxygen is an element common to them all which constitutes their acidity, and that they differ from each other according to the nature of the oxygenated or acidified substance. We must therefore, in every acid, carefully distinguish between the acidifiable base, which M. de Morveau calls the *radical*, and the acidifying principle or oxygen.

CHAPTER VI

Of the Nomenclature of Acids in General, and Particularly of Those Drawn from Nitre and Sea-Salt

It becomes extremely easy, from the principles laid down in the preceding chapter, to establish a systematic nomenclature for the acids: the word *acid* being used as a generic term, each acid falls to be distinguished in language, as in nature, by the name of its base or radical. Thus, we give the generic name of acids to the products of the combustion or oxygenation of phosphorus, of sulphur, and of charcoal; and these products are respectively named the *phosphoric acid*, the *sulphuric acid*, and the *carbonic acid*.

There is, however, a remarkable circumstance in the oxygenation of combustible bodies, and of a part of such bodies as are convertible into acids, that they are susceptible of different degrees of saturation with oxygen, and that the resulting acids, though formed by the union of the same elements, are possessed of different properties, depending upon that difference of proportion. Of this, the phosphoric acid, and more especially the sulphuric, furnishes us with examples. When sulphur is combined with a small proportion of oxygen, it forms, in this first or lower degree of oxygenation, a volatile acid, having a penetrating odour and possessed of very particular qualities. By a larger proportion of oxygen, it is changed into a fixed, heavy acid, without any odour, and which, by combination with other bodies, gives products quite different from those furnished by the former. In this instance, the principles of our nomenclature seem to fail; and it seems difficult to derive such terms from the name of the acidifiable base as shall distinctly express these two degrees of saturation, or oxygenation, without circumlocution. By reflection, however, upon the subject, or perhaps rather from the necessity of the case, we have thought it allowable to express these varieties in the oxygenation of the acids by simply varying the termination of their specific names. The volatile acid produced from sulphur was anciently known to Stahl under the name of *sulphurous* acid. We have preserved that term for this acid from sulphur under-saturated with oxygen; and distinguish the other, or completely saturated or oxygenated acid, by the name of *sulphuric* acid. We shall therefore say, in this new chemical language, that sulphur, in combining with oxygen, is susceptible of two degrees of saturation: that the first or lesser degree constitutes sulphurous acid, which is volatile and penetrating; whilst the second or higher degree of saturation produces sulphuric acid, which is fixed and inodorous. We shall adopt this difference of termination for all the acids which assume several degrees of saturation. Hence we have a phosphorous and a phosphoric acid, an acetous and an acetic acid; and so on, for others in similar circumstances.

This part of chemical science would have been extremely simple, and the nomenclature of the acids would not have been at all perplexed as it is now in the old nomenclature, if the base or radical of each acid had been known when the acid itself was discovered. Thus, for instance, phosphorus being a known substance before the discovery of its acid, this latter was rightly distinguished by a term drawn from the name of its acidifiable base. But when, on the contrary, an acid happened to be discovered before its base, or rather when the acidifiable base from which it was formed remained unknown, names were adopted for the two, which have not the smallest connection; and thus, not only the memory became burdened with useless appellations, but even the minds of students, nay even of experienced chemists, became filled with false ideas, which time and reflection alone are capable of eradicating. We may give an instance of this confusion with respect to the acid sulphur: the former chemists having procured this acid from the vitriol of iron gave it the name of the vitriolic acid

from the name of the substance which produced it; and they were then ignorant that the acid procured from sulphur by combustion was exactly the same.

The same thing happened with the aeriform acid formerly called *fixed air;* it not being known that this acid was the result of combining charcoal with oxygen, a variety of denominations have been given to it, not one of which conveys just ideas of its nature or origin. We have found it extremely easy to correct and modify the ancient language with respect to these acids proceeding from known bases, having converted the name of *vitriolic acid* into that of *sulphuric*, and the name of *fixed air* into that of *carbonic acid;* but it is impossible to follow this plan with the acids whose bases are still unknown; with these we have been obliged to use a contrary plan and, instead of forming the name of the acid from that of its base, have been forced to denominate the unknown base from the name of the known acid, as happens in the case of the acid which is procured from sea-salt.

To disengage this acid from the alkaline base with which it is combined, we have only to pour sulphuric acid upon sea-salt; immediately a brisk effervescence takes place, white vapours arise, of a very penetrating odour, and, by only gently heating the mixture, all the acid is driven off. As in the common temperature and pressure of our atmosphere this acid is naturally in the state of gas, we must use particular precautions for retaining it in proper vessels. For small experiments, the most simple and most commodious apparatus consists of a small retort G (Plate v, *Fig. 5*), into which the sea-salt is introduced, well dried; we then pour on some concentrated sulphuric acid, and immediately introduce the beak of the retort under little jars or bell-glasses A (same Plate and *Fig.*), previously filled with quicksilver. In proportion as the acid gas is disengaged, it passes into the jar and gets to the top of the quicksilver, which it displaces. When the disengagement of the gas slackens, a gentle heat is applied to the retort and gradually increased till nothing more passes over. This acid gas has a very strong affinity with water, which absorbs an enormous quantity of it, as is proved by introducing a very thin layer of water into the glass which contains the gas; for, in an instant, the whole acid gas disappears and combines with the water.

This latter circumstance is taken advantage of in laboratories and manufactures on purpose to obtain the acid of sea-salt in a liquid form; and for this purpose the apparatus (Plate IV, *Fig. 1*) is employed. It consists, 1st, of a tabulated retort A, into which the sea-salt, and after it the sulphuric acid, are introduced through the opening H; 2nd, of the balloon or recipient *c, b*, intended for containing the small quantity of liquid which passes over during the process; and, 3rd, of a set of bottles, with two mouths, L, L, L, L, half filled with water, intended for absorbing the gas disengaged by the distillation. This apparatus will be more amply described in the latter part of this work.

Although we have not yet been able, either to compose or to decompound this acid of sea-salt, we cannot have the smallest doubt that it, like all other acids, is composed by the union of oxygen with an acidifiable base. We have therefore called this unknown substance the *muriatic base*, or *muriatic radical*, deriving this name, after the example of M. Bergman and M. de Morveau, from the Latin word *muria*, which was anciently used to signify sea-salt. Thus, without being able exactly to determine the component parts of *muriatic acid*, we design by that term a volatile acid, which retains the form of gas in the common temperature and pressure of our atmosphere, which combines with great facility, and in great quantity, with water, and whose acidifiable base adheres so very intimately with oxygen that no method has hitherto been devised for separating them. If ever this acidifiable base of the muriatic acid is discovered to be a known substance, though now unknown in that capacity, it will be requisite to change its present denomination for one analogous with that of its base.

In common with sulphuric acid, and several other acids, the muriatic is capable of different degrees of oxygenation; but the excess of oxygen produces quite contrary effects upon it from what the same circumstance produces upon the acid of sulphur. The lower degree of oxygenation converts sulphur into a volatile gaseous acid, which only mixes in small proportions with water, whilst a higher oxygenation forms an acid possessing much stronger acid properties, which is very fixed and cannot remain in the state of gas but in a very high temperature, which has no smell, and which mixes in large proportion with water. With muriatic acid, the direct reverse takes place;

an additional saturation with oxygen renders it more volatile, of a more penetrating odour, less miscible with water, and diminishes its acid properties. We were at first inclined to have denominated these two degrees of saturation in the same manner as we had done with the acid of sulphur, calling the less oxygenated *muriatous acid*, and that which is more saturated with oxygen *muriatic acid:* but, as this latter gives very particular results in its combinations, and as nothing analogous to it is yet known in chemistry, we have left the name of muriatic acid to the less saturated and given the latter the more compounded appellation of *oxygenated muriatic acid.*

Although the base or radical of the acid which is extracted from nitre or saltpetre be better known, we have judged proper only to modify its name in the same manner with that of the muriatic acid. It is drawn from nitre by the intervention of sulphuric acid, by a process similar to that described for extracting the muriatic acid, and by means of the same apparatus (Plate IV, *Fig. 1*). In proportion as the acid passes over, it is in part condensed in the balloon or recipient and the rest is absorbed by the water contained in the bottles L, L, L, L; the water becomes first green, then blue, and at last yellow, in proportion to the concentration of the acid. During this operation, a large quantity of oxygen gas, mixed with a small proportion of azotic gas, is disengaged.

This acid, like all others, is composed of oxygen, united to an acidifiable base, and is even the first acid in which the existence of oxygen was well ascertained. Its two constituent elements are but weakly united and are easily separated by presenting any substance with which oxygen has a stronger affinity than with the acidifiable base peculiar to this acid. By some experiments of this kind, it was first discovered that azote, or the base of mephitis or azotic gas, constituted its acidifiable base or radical, and consequently that the acid of nitre was really an azotic acid, having azote for its base, combined with oxygen. For these reasons, that we might be consistent with our principles, it appeared necessary either to call the acid by the name of *azotic* or to name the base *nitric radical;* but from either of these we were dissuaded by the following considerations. In the first place, it seemed difficult to change the name of nitre or saltpetre, which has been universally adopted in society, in manufactures, and in chemistry; and, on the other hand, azote having been discovered by M. Berthollet to be the base of volatile alkali, or ammonia, as well as of this acid, we thought it improper to call it nitric radical. We have therefore continued the term of azote to the base of that part of atmospheric air which is likewise the nitric and ammoniacal radical; and we have named the acid of nitre, in its lower and higher degrees of oxygenation, *nitrous acid* in the former and *nitric acid* in the latter state; thus preserving its former appellation properly modified.

Several very respectable chemists have disapproved of this deference for the old terms and wished us to have persevered in perfecting a new chemical language, without paying any respect for ancient usage; so that, by thus steering a kind of middle course, we have exposed ourselves to the censures of one sect of chemists, and to the expostulations of the opposite party.

The acid of nitre is susceptible of assuming a great number of separate states, depending upon its degree of oxygenation or upon the proportions in which azote and oxygen enter into its composition. By a first or lowest degree of oxygenation it forms a particular species of gas, which we shall continue to name *nitrous gas;* this is composed nearly of two parts, by weight, of oxygen combined with one part of azote; and in this state it is not miscible with water. In this gas, the azote is by no means saturated with oxygen, but, on the contrary, has still a very great affinity for that element and even attracts it from atmospheric air, immediately upon getting into contact with it. This combination of nitrous gas with atmospheric air has even become one of the methods for determining the quantity of oxygen contained in air and consequently for ascertaining its degree of salubrity.

This addition of oxygen converts the nitrous gas into a powerful acid, which has a strong affinity with water and which is itself susceptible of various additional degrees of oxygenation. When the proportions of oxygen and azote is below three parts, by weight, of the former to one of the latter, the acid is red coloured and emits copious fumes. In this state, by the application of a gentle heat, it gives out nitrous gas, and we term it, in this degree of oxygenation, *nitrous acid*. When four parts, by weight, of oxygen are combined with one part

of azote, the acid is clear and colourless, more fixed in the fire than the nitrous acid, has less odour, and its constituent elements are more firmly united. This species of acid, in conformity with our principles of nomenclature, is called *nitric acid*.

Thus, nitric acid is the acid of nitre, surcharged with oxygen; nitrous acid is the acid of nitre surcharged with azote or, what is the same thing, with nitrous gas; and this latter is azote not sufficiently saturated with oxygen to possess the properties of an acid. To this degree of oxygenation, we have afterwards, in the course of this work, given the generical name of *oxide*.

CHAPTER VII

Of the Decomposition of Oxygen Gas by Means of Metals and the Formation of Metallic Oxides

OXYGEN has a stronger affinity with metals heated to a certain degree than with caloric; in consequence of which, all metallic bodies, excepting gold, silver, and platinum, have the property of decomposing oxygen gas, by attracting its base from the caloric with which it was combined. We have already shown in what manner this decomposition takes place, by means of mercury and iron; having observed, that, in the case of the first, it must be considered as a kind of gradual combustion, whilst, in the latter, the combustion is extremely rapid and attended with a brilliant flame. The use of the heat employed in these operations is to separate the particles of the metal from each other and to diminish their attraction of cohesion or aggregation or, which is the same thing, their mutual attraction for each other.

The absolute weight of metallic substances is augmented in proportion to the quantity of oxygen they absorb; they, at the same time, lose their metallic splendour, and are reduced into an earthy pulverulent matter. In this state metals must not be considered as entirely saturated with oxygen, because their action upon this element is counterbalanced by the power of affinity between it and caloric. During the calcination of metals the oxygen is, therefore, acted upon by two separate and opposite powers, that of its attraction for caloric and that exerted by the metal, and only tends to unite with the latter in consequence of the excess of the latter over the former, which is, in general, very inconsiderable. Wherefore, when metallic substances are oxygenated in atmospheric air or in oxygen gas, they are not converted into acids like sulphur, phosphorus, and charcoal, but are only changed into intermediate substances, which, though approaching to the nature of salts, have not acquired all the saline properties. The old chemists have affixed the name of *calx* not only to metals in this state but to every body which has been long exposed to the action of fire without being melted. They have converted this word *calx* into a generical term, under which they confound calcareous earth, which, from a neutral salt, which it really was before calcination, has been changed by fire into an earthy alkali, by *losing* half of its weight, with metals which, by the same means, have joined themselves to a new substance, whose quantity often *exceeds* half their weight, and by which they have been changed almost into the nature of acids. This mode of classifying substances of so very opposite natures under the same generic name would have been quite contrary to our principles of nomenclature, especially as, by retaining the above term for this state of metallic substances, we must have conveyed very false ideas of its nature. We have, therefore, laid aside the expression *metallic calx* altogether and have substituted in its place the term *oxide*, from the Greek word οξυς.

By this may be seen that the language we have adopted is both copious and expressive. The first, or lowest, degree of oxygenation in bodies converts them into *oxides;* a second degree of additional oxygenation constitutes the class of acids, of which the specific names, drawn from their particular bases, terminate in *ous*, as the *nitrous* and *sulphurous* acids; the third degree of oxygenation changes these into the species of acids distinguished by the termination in *ic*, as the *nitric* and *sulphuric* acids; and, lastly, we can express a fourth, or highest degree of oxygenation, by adding the word *oxygenated* to the name of the acid, as has been already done with the *oxygenated muriatic* acid.

We have not confined the term *oxide* to expressing the combinations of metals with oxygen, but have extended it to signify that first degree of oxygenation in all bodies, which, without converting them into acids, causes them to approach to the nature of salts. Thus, we give the name of *oxide of sulphur* to that soft substance into which sulphur is converted

by incipient combustion; and we call the yellow matter left by phosphorus, after combustion, by the name of *oxide of phosphorus*. In the same manner, nitrous gas, which is azote in its first degree of oxygenation, is the *oxide of azote*. We have likewise oxides in great numbers from the vegetable and animal kingdoms; and I shall show, in the sequel, that this new language throws great light upon all the operations of art and nature.

We have already observed that almost all the metallic oxides have peculiar and permanent colours. These vary not only in the different species of metals, but even according to the various degrees of oxygenation in the same metal. Hence we are under the necessity of adding two epithets to each oxide, one of which indicates the metal *oxidated*, while the other indicates the peculiar colour of the oxide. Thus, we have the black oxide of iron, the red oxide of iron, and the yellow oxide of iron; which expressions respectively answer to the old unmeaning terms of martial ethiops, colcothar, and rust of iron, or ochre. We have likewise the gray, yellow, and red oxides of lead, which answer to the equally false or insignificant terms, ashes of lead, massicot, and minium.

These denominations sometimes become rather long, especially when we mean to indicate whether the metal has been oxidated in the air, by detonation with nitre, or by means of acids; but then they always convey just and accurate ideas of the corresponding object which we wish to express by their use. All this will be rendered perfectly clear and distinct by means of the tables which are added to this work.

CHAPTER VIII

Of the Radical Principle of Water and of its Decomposition by Charcoal and Iron

UNTIL very lately, water has always been thought a simple substance, insomuch that the older chemists considered it as an element. Such it undoubtedly was to them, as they were unable to decompose it; or, at least, since the decomposition which took place daily before their eyes was entirely unnoticed. But we mean to prove that water is by no means a simple or elementary substance. I shall not here pretend to give the history of this recent and hitherto contested discovery, which is detailed in the *Recueil de l'Académie* for 1781, but shall only bring forwards the principal proofs of the decomposition and composition of water; and I may venture to say that these will be convincing to such as consider them impartially.

First Experiment

Having fixed the glass tube EF (Plate VII, *Fig. 11*) of from 8 to 12 lines diameter across a furnace, with a small inclination from E to F, lute the superior extremity E to the glass retort A, containing a determinate quantity of distilled water, and to the inferior extremity F the worm SS fixed into the neck of the doubly tubulated bottle H, which has the bent tube KK adapted to one of its openings, in such a manner as to convey such aeriform fluids or gases as may be disengaged, during the experiment, into a proper apparatus for determining their quantity and nature.

To render the success of this experiment certain, it is necessary that the tube EF be made of well annealed and difficultly fusible glass, and that it be coated with a lute composed of clay mixed with powdered stone-ware; besides which, it must be supported about its middle by means of an iron bar passed through the furnace, lest it should soften and bend during the experiment. A tube of chinaware, or porcelain, would answer better than one of glass for this experiment, were it not difficult to procure one so entirely free from pores as to prevent the passage of air or of vapours.

When things are thus arranged, a fire is lighted in the furnace EFCD, which is supported of such a strength as to keep the tube EF red hot but not to make it melt; and, at the same time, such a fire is kept up in the furnace VVXX as to keep the water in the retort A continually boiling.

In proportion as the water in the retort A is evaporated it fills the tube EF, and drives out the air it contained by the tube KK; the aqueous gas formed by evaporation is condensed by cooling in the worm SS and falls, drop by drop, into the tubulated bottle H. Having continued this operation until all the water be evaporated from the retort, and having carefully emptied all the vessels employed, we find that a quantity of water has passed over into the bottle H exactly equal to what was before contained in the retort A, without any disengagement of gas whatsoever: so that this experiment turns out to be a simple distillation, and the result would have been exactly the same, if the water had been run from one vessel into the other,

through the tube EF, without having undergone the intermediate incandescence.

Second Experiment

The apparatus being disposed, as in the former experiment, 28 *grs.* of charcoal, broken into moderately small parts and which have previously been exposed for a long time to a red heat in close vessels, are introduced into the tube EF. Everything else is managed as in the preceding experiment.

The water contained in the retort A is distilled, as in the former experiment, and, being condensed in the worm, falls into the bottle H; but, at the same time, a considerable quantity of gas is disengaged, which, escaping by the tube KK, is received in a convenient apparatus for that purpose. After the operation is finished, we find nothing but a few atoms of ashes remaining in the tube EF, the 28 *grs.* of charcoal having entirely disappeared.

When the disengaged gases are carefully examined, they are found to weigh 113.7 *grs.*;[1] these are of two kinds, viz., 144 cubic inches of carbonic acid gas weighing 100 *grs.* and 380 cubic inches of a very light gas weighing only 13.7 *grs.*, which takes fire when in contact with air, by the approach of a lighted body; and, when the water which has passed over into the bottle H is carefully examined, it is found to have lost 85.7 *grs.* of its weight. Thus, in this experiment, 85.7 *grs.* of water, joined to 28 *grs.* of charcoal, have combined in such a way as to form 100 *grs.* of carbonic acid, and 13.7 *grs.* of a particular gas capable of being burnt.

I have already shown, that 100 *grs.* of carbonic acid gas consists of 72 *grs.* of oxygen combined with 28 *grs.* of charcoal; hence the 28 *grs.* of charcoal placed in the glass tube have acquired 72 *grs.* of oxygen from the water; and it follows that 85.7 *grs.* of water are composed of 72 *grs.* of oxygen combined with 13.7 *grs.* of a gas susceptible of combustion. We shall see presently that this gas cannot possibly have been disengaged from the charcoal and must, consequently, have been produced from the water.

I have suppressed some circumstances in the above account of this experiment, which would only have complicated and obscured its results in the minds of the reader. For instance, the inflammable gas dissolves a very small part of

---

[1] In the latter part of this work will be found a particular account of the processes necessary for separating the different kinds of gases, and for determining their quantities.—AUTHOR.

the charcoal, by which means its weight is somewhat augmented and that of the carbonic gas proportionally diminished. Altho' the alteration produced by this circumstance is very inconsiderable, yet I have thought it necessary to determine its effects by rigid calculation, and to report, as above, the results of the experiment in its simplified state, as if this circumstance had not happened. At any rate, should any doubts remain respecting the consequences I have drawn from this experiment, they will be fully dissipated by the following experiments, which I am going to adduce in support of my opinion.

Third Experiment

The apparatus being disposed exactly as in the former experiment, with this difference, that instead of the 28 grs. of charcoal the tube EF is filled with 274 grs. of soft iron in thin plates, rolled up spirally. The tube is made red hot by means of its furnace, and the water in the retort A is kept constantly boiling till it be all evaporated, and has passed through the tube EF so as to be condensed in the bottle H.

No carbonic acid gas is disengaged in this experiment, instead of which we obtain 416 cubic inches, or 15 grs. of inflammable gas, thirteen times lighter than atmospheric air. By examining the water which has been distilled, it is found to have lost 100 grs. and the 274 grs. of iron confined in the tube are found to have acquired 85 grs. additional weight and its magnitude is considerably augmented. The iron is now hardly at all attractable by the magnet; it dissolves in acids without effervescence; and, in short, it is converted into a black oxide, precisely similar to that which has been burnt in oxygen gas.

In this experiment we have a true *oxidation* of iron, by means of water, exactly similar to that produced in air by the assistance of heat. One hundred grains of water having been decomposed, 85 grs. of oxygen have combined with the iron, so as to convert it into the state of black oxide, and 15 grs. of a peculiar inflammable gas are disengaged: from all this it clearly follows that water is composed of oxygen combined with the base of an inflammable gas, in the respective proportions of 85 parts, by weight of the former, to 15 parts of the latter.

Thus water, besides the oxygen which is one of its elements in common with many other substances, contains another element as its constituent base or radical and for which we

must find an appropriate term. None that we could think of seemed better adapted than the word *hydrogen*, which signifies the *generative principle of water*, from νδορ *aqua*, and γεινομαι *gignor*.[1] We call the combination of this element with caloric *hydrogen gas;* and the term hydrogen expresses the base of that gas, or the radical of water.

This experiment furnishes us with a new combustible body, or, in other words, a body which has so much affinity with oxygen as to draw it from its connection with caloric and to decompose air or oxygen gas. This combustible body has itself so great affinity with caloric that, unless when engaged in a combination with some other body, it always subsists in the aeriform or gaseous state, in the usual temperature and pressure of our atmosphere. In this state of gas it is about $\frac{1}{13}$ of the weight of an equal bulk of atmospheric air; it is not absorbed by water, though it is capable of holding a small quantity of that fluid in solution, and it is incapable of being used for respiration.

As the property this gas possesses, in common with all other combustible bodies, is nothing more than the power of decomposing air and carrying off its oxygen from the caloric with which it was combined, it is easily understood that it cannot burn unless in contact with air or oxygen gas. Hence, when we set fire to a bottle full of this gas, it burns gently, first at the neck of the bottle, and then in the inside of it, in proportion as the external air gets in. This combustion is slow and successive and only takes place at the surface of contact between the two gases. It is quite different when the two gases are mixed before they are set on fire: if, for instance, after having introduced one part of oxygen gas into a narrow mouthed bottle, we fill it up with two parts of hydrogen gas and bring a lighted taper or other burning body to the mouth of the bottle, the combustion of the two gases takes place instantaneously with a violent explosion. This experiment ought only to be made in a bottle of very strong green glass, holding not more than a pint, and wrapped round with twine, otherwise the operator will be exposed to great danger from the

[1] This expression *hydrogen* has been very severely criticised by some, who pretend that it signifies engendered by water and not that which engenders water. The experiments related in this chapter prove that when water is decomposed hydrogen is produced, and that when hydrogen is combined with oxygen water is produced: so that we may say, with equal truth, that water is produced from hydrogen, or hydrogen is produced from water.—AUTHOR.

rupture of the bottle, of which the fragments will be thrown about with great force.

If all that has been related above, concerning the decomposition of water, be exactly conformable to truth;—if, as I have endeavoured to prove, that substance be really composed of hydrogen, as its proper constituent element, combined with oxygen, it ought to follow that, by reuniting these two elements together, we should recompose water; and that this actually happens may be judged of by the following experiment.

Fourth Experiment

I took a large crystal balloon A (Plate IV, *Fig. 5*) holding about 30 pints, having a large opening, to which was cemented the plate of copper BC pierced with four holes in which four tubes terminate. The first tube, H*h*, is intended to be adapted to an air pump, by which the balloon is to be exhausted of its air. The second ture *gg*, communicates, by its extremity MM, with a reservoir of oxygen gas, with which the balloon is to be filled. The third tube *d*D*d'* communicates, by its extremity *d*NN, with a reservoir of hydrogen gas. The extremity *d'* of this tube terminates in a capillary opening, through which the hydrogen gas contained in the reservoir is forced, with a moderate degree of quickness, by the pressure of one or two inches of water. The fourth tube contains a metallic wire GL, having a knob at its extremity L, intended for giving an electrical spark from L to *d'*, on purpose to set fire to the hydrogen gas: this wire is moveable in the tube, that we may be able to separate the knob L from the extremity *d'* of the tube D*d'*. The three tubes *d*D*d'*, *gg*, and H*h*, are all provided with stop-cocks.

That the hydrogen gas and oxygen gas may be as much as possible deprived of water, they are made to pass, in their way to the baloon A, through the tubes MM, NN, of about an inch diameter, and filled with salts, which, from their deliquescent nature, greedily attract the moisture of the air: such are the acetite of potash, and the muriate or nitrate of lime.[1] These salts must only be reduced to a coarse powder, lest they run into lumps, and prevent the gases from getting through their interstices.

We must be provided beforehand with a sufficient quantity of oxygen gas, carefully purified from all admixture of carbonic acid by long contact with a solution of potash.[2]

We must likewise have a double quantity of hydrogen gas, carefully purified in the same manner by long contact with a solution of potash in water. The best way of obtaining this gas free from mixture is by decomposing water with very pure soft iron, as directed in Exp. 3 of this chapter.

Having adjusted everything properly, as above directed, the tube H*h* is adapted to an air-pump, and the balloon A is exhausted of its air. We next admit the oxygen gas so as to fill the balloon and then, by means of pressure as is before mentioned, force a small stream of hydrogen gas through its tube D*d'*, which we immediately set on fire by an electric spark. By means of the above described apparatus, we can continue the mutual combustion of these two gases for a long time, as we have the power of supplying them to the balloon from their reservoirs, in proportion as they are consumed. I have in another place[3] given a description of the apparatus used in this experiment and have explained the manner of ascertaining the quantities of the gases consumed with the most scrupulous exactitude.

In proportion to the advancement of the combustion, there is a deposition of water upon the inner surface of the balloon or matrass A: the water gradually increases in quantity and, gathering into large drops, runs down to the bottom of the vessel. It is easy to ascertain the quantity of water collected, by weighing the balloon both before and after the experiment. Thus we have a twofold verification of our experiment, by ascertaining both the quantities of the gases employed and of the water formed by their combustion: these two quantities must be equal to each other. By an operation of this kind, M. Meusnier and I ascertained that it required 85 parts, by weight, of oxygen, united to 15 parts of hydrogen, to compose 100 parts of water. This experiment, which has not hitherto been published, was made in presence of a numerous committee from the Royal Academy. We exerted the most scrupulous attention to its accuracy and have reason to believe that the above propositions cannot vary a two-hundredth part from absolute truth.

From these experiments, both analytical and synthetic, we may now affirm that we have ascertained, with as much certainty as is pos-

---

[1] See the nature of these salts in the second part of this book.—AUTHOR.

[2] The method of obtaining this pure alkali of potash will be given in the sequel.—AUTHOR.
[3] See the third part of this work.—AUTHOR.

sible in physical or chemical subjects, that water is not a simple elementary substance but is composed of two elements, oxygen and hydrogen; which elements, when existing separately, have so strong affinity for caloric as only to subsist under the form of gas in the common temperature and pressure of our atmosphere.

This decomposition and recomposition of water is perpetually operating before our eyes, in the temperature of the atmosphere, by means of compound elective attraction. We shall presently see that the phenomena attendant upon vinous fermentation, putrefaction, and even vegetation, are produced, at least in a certain degree, by decomposition of water. It is very extraordinary that this fact should have hitherto been overlooked by natural philosophers and chemists: indeed, it strongly proves that, in chemistry as in moral philosophy, it is extremely difficult to overcome prejudices imbibed in early education and to search for truth in any other road than the one we have been accustomed to follow.

I shall finish this chapter by an experiment much less demonstrative than those already related, but which has appeared to make more impression than any other upon the minds of many people. When 16 ounces of alcohol are burnt in an apparatus[1] properly adapted for collecting all the water disengaged during the combustion, we obtain from 17 to 18 ounces of water. As no substance can furnish a product larger than its original bulk, it follows that something else has united with the alcohol during its combustion; and I have already shown that this must be oxygen, or the base of air. Thus alcohol contains hydrogen, which is one of the elements of water; and the atmospheric air contains oxygen, which is the other element necessary to the composition of water. This experiment is a new proof that water is a compound substance.

CHAPTER IX

Of the Quantities of Caloric Disengaged from Different Species of Combustion

We have already mentioned that, when any body is burnt in the center of a hollow sphere of ice and supplied with air at the temperature of zero (32°), the quantity of ice melted from the inside of the sphere becomes a measure of

[1] See an account of this apparatus in the third part of this work.—AUTHOR.

the relative quantities of caloric disengaged. M. de Laplace and I gave a description of the apparatus employed for this kind of experiment in the *Recueil de l'Académie* for 1780, p. 355; and a description and plate of the same apparatus will be found in the third part of this work. With this apparatus, phosphorus, charcoal, and hydrogen gas, gave the following results:

one pound of phosphorus melted 100 *lbs.* of ice;

one pound of charcoal melted 96 *lbs.* 8 *oz;*

one pound of hydrogen gas melted 295 *lbs.* 9 *oz.* 3½ *gros.*

As a concrete acid is formed by the combustion of phosphorus, it is probable that very little caloric remains in the acid and, consequently, that the above experiment gives us very nearly the whole quantity of caloric contained in the oxygen gas. Even if we suppose the phosphoric acid to contain a good deal of caloric, yet, as the phosphorus must have contained nearly an equal quantity before combustion, the error must be very small, as it will only consist of the difference between what was contained in the phosphorus before, and in the phosphoric acid after combustion.

I have already shown in Chapter V that one pound of phosphorus absorbs one pound eight ounces of oxygen during combustion; and since, by the same operation, 100 *lbs.* of ice are melted, it follows that the quantity of caloric contained in one pound of oxygen gas is capable of melting 66 *lbs.* 10 *oz.* 5 *gros* 24 *grs.* of ice.

One pound of charcoal during combustion melts only 96 *lbs.* 8 *oz.* of ice, whilst it absorbs 2 *lbs.* 9 *oz.* 1 *gros* 10 *grs.* of oxygen. By the experiment with phosphorus, this quantity of oxygen gas ought to disengage a quantity of caloric sufficient to melt 171 *lbs.* 6 *oz.* 5 *gros* of ice; consequently, during this experiment, a quantity of caloric sufficient to melt 74 *lbs.* 14 *oz.* 5 *gros* of ice disappears. Carbonic acid is not, like phosphoric acid, in a concrete state after combustion but in the state of gas and requires to be united with caloric to enable it to subsist in that state; the quantity of caloric missing in the last experiment is evidently employed for that purpose. When we divide that quantity by the weight of carbonic acid formed by the combustion of one pound of charcoal, we find that the quantity of caloric necessary for changing one pound of carbonic acid from the concrete to the gaseous state would be capable of melting 20 *lbs.* 15 *oz.* 5 *gros* of ice.

We may make a similar calculation with the combustion of hydrogen gas and the conse-

68610

FERNALD LIBRARY,
COLBY-SAWYER COLLEGE
NEW LONDON, N. H. 03257

quent formation of water. During the combustion of one pound of hydrogen gas, 5 *lbs*. 10 *oz*. 5 *gros* 24 *grs*. of oxygen gas are absorbed, and 295 *lbs*. 9 *oz*. 3½ *gros* of ice are melted. But 5 *lbs*. 10 *oz*. 5 *gros* 24 *grs*. of oxygen gas, in changing from the aeriform to the solid state, loses, according to the experiment with phosphorus, enough of caloric to have melted 377 *lbs*. 12 *oz*. 3 *gros* of ice. There is only disengaged from the same quantity of oxygen, during its combustion with hydrogen gas, as much caloric as melts 295 *lbs*. 2 *oz*. 3½ *gros;* wherefore there remains in the water at zero (32°), formed, during this experiment, as much caloric as would melt 82 *lbs*. 9 *oz*. 7½ *gros* of ice.

Hence, as 6 *lbs*. 10 *oz*. 5 *gros* 24 *grs*. of water are formed from the combustion of one pound of hydrogen gas with 5 *lbs*. 10 *oz*. 5 *gros* 24 *grs*. of oxygen, it follows that in each pound of water, at the temperature of zero (32°), there exists as much caloric as would melt 12 *lbs*. 5 *oz*. 2 *gros* 48 *grs*. of ice, without taking into account the quantity originally contained in the hydrogen gas, which we have been obliged to omit for want of data to calculate its quantity. From this it appears that water, even in the state of ice, contains a considerable quantity of caloric, and that oxygen, in entering into that combination, retains likewise a good proportion.

From these experiments, we may assume the following results as sufficiently established.

Combustion of phosphorus

From the combustion of phosphorus, as related in the foregoing experiments, it appears that one pound of phosphorus requires 1 *lb*. 8 *oz*. of oxygen gas for its combustion and that 2 *lbs*. 8 *oz*. of concrete phosphoric acid are produced.

The quantity of caloric disengaged by the combustion of one pound of phosphorus, expressed by the number of pounds of ice melted during that operation, is   100.00000
The quantity disengaged from each pound of oxygen during the combustion of phosphorus, expressed in the same manner, is   66.66667
The quantity disengaged during the formation of one pound of phosphoric acid   40.00000
The quantity remaining in each pound of phosphoric acid   0.00000[1]

[1] We here suppose the phosphoric acid not to contain any caloric, which is not strictly true; but, as I have before observed, the quantity it really contains is probably very small, and we have not given it a value, for want of sufficient data to go upon.— AUTHOR.

Combustion of charcoal

In the combustion of one pound of charcoal, 2 *lbs*. 9 *oz*. 1 *gros* 10 *grs*. of oxygen gas are absorbed, and 3 *lbs*. 9 *oz*. 1 *gros* 10 *grs*. of carbonic acid gas are formed.

Caloric disengaged during the combustion of one pound of charcoal   96.50000
Caloric disengaged during the combustion of charcoal, from each pound of oxygen gas absorbed   37.52823
Caloric disengaged during the formation of one pound of carbonic acid gas   27.02024
Caloric retained by each pound of oxygen after the combustion   29.13844
Caloric necessary for supporting one pound of carbonic acid in the state of gas   20.97960

Combustion of hydrogen gas

In the combustion of one pound of hydrogen gas, 5 *lbs*. 10 *oz*. 5 *gros* 24 *grs*. of oxygen gas are absorbed and 6 *lbs*. 10 *oz*. 5 *gros* 24 *grs*. of water are formed.

Caloric from each *lb*. of hydrogen gas   295.58950
Caloric from each *lb*. of oxygen gas   52.16280
Caloric disengaged during the formation of each pound of water   44.33840
Caloric retained by each *lb*. of oxygen after combustion with hydrogen   14.50386
Caloric retained by each *lb*. of water at the temperature of zero (32°)   12.32823

Formation of nitric acid

When we combine nitrous gas with oxygen gas so as to form nitric or nitrous acid a degree of heat is produced which is much less considerable than what is evolved during the other combinations of oxygen; whence it follows that oxygen, when it becomes fixed in nitric acid, retains a great part of the heat which it possessed in the state of gas. It is certainly possible to determine the quantity of caloric which is disengaged during the combination of these two gases and consequently to determine what quantity remains after the combination takes place. The first of these quantities might be ascertained by making the combination of the two gases in an apparatus surrounded by ice; but, as the quantity of caloric disengaged is very inconsiderable, it would be necessary to operate upon a large quantity of the two gases in a very troublesome and complicated apparatus. By this consideration, M. de Laplace and I have hitherto been prevented from making the attempt. In the meantime, the place of such an experiment may be supplied by calculations, the results of which cannot be very far from truth.

M. de Laplace and I deflagrated a convenient quantity of nitre and charcoal in an ice apparatus and found that twelve pounds of ice were melted by the deflagration of one pound of nitre. We shall see, in the sequel, that one pound of nitre is composed, as below, of

potash   7 oz. 6 gros 51.84 grs. = 4515.84 grs.
dry acid   8   1   21.16   = 4700.16

The above quantity of dry acid is composed of

oxygen 6 oz. 3 gros 66.34 grs. = 3738.34 grs·
azote   1   5   25.82   = 961.82

By this we find that during the above deflagration 2 gros 1¼ gr. of charcoal have suffered combustion, alongst with 3738.34 grs. or 6 oz. 3 gros 66.34 grs. of oxygen. Hence, since 12 lbs. of ice were melted during the combustion, it follows that one pound of oxygen burnt in the same manner would have melted 29.58320 lbs. of ice. To which the quantity of caloric, retained by a pound of oxygen after combining with charcoal to form carbonic acid gas, being added which was already ascertained to be capable of melting 29.13844 lbs. of ice, we have for the total quantity of caloric remaining in a pound of oxygen, when combined with nitrous gas in the nitric acid 58.72164; which is the number of pounds of ice the caloric remaining in the oxygen in that state is capable of melting.

We have before seen that, in the state of oxygen gas, it contained at least 66.66667; wherefore it follows that, in combining with azote to form nitric acid, it only loses 7.94502. Further experiments upon this subject are necessary to ascertain how far the results of this calculation may agree with direct fact. This enormous quantity of caloric retained by oxygen in its combination into nitric acid explains the cause of the great disengagement of caloric during the deflagrations of nitre; or, more strictly speaking, upon all occasions of the decomposition of nitric acid.

Combustion of wax

Having examined several cases of simple combustion, I mean now to give a few examples of a more complex nature. One pound of wax-taper being allowed to burn slowly in an ice apparatus melted 133 lbs. 2 oz. 5⅓ gros of ice.

According to my experiments in the Recueil de l'Académie for 1784, p. 606, one pound of wax-taper consists of 13 oz. 1 gros 23 grs. of charcoal and 2 oz. 6 gros 49 grs. of hydrogen.

By the foregoing experiments, the above quantity
of charcoal ought to melt   79.39390 lbs. of ice
The hydrogen should melt   52.37605
                             ——————
                    Total   131.76995 lbs.

Thus, we see the quantity of caloric disengaged from a burning taper is pretty exactly conformable to what was obtained by burning separately a quantity of charcoal and hydrogen equal to what enters into its composition. These experiments with the taper were several times repeated, so that I have reason to believe them accurate.

Combustion of Olive Oil

We included a burning lamp, containing a determinate quantity of olive oil, in the ordinary apparatus and, when the experiment was finished, we ascertained exactly the quantities of oil consumed and of ice melted; the result was that during the combustion of one pound of olive oil, 148 lbs. 14 oz. 1 gros of ice were melted. By my experiments in the Recueil de l'Académie for 1784, and of which the following chapter contains an abstract, it appears that one pound of olive oil consists of 12 oz. 5 gros 5 grs. of charcoal and 3 oz. 2 gros 67 grs. of hydrogen. By the foregoing experiments, that quantity of charcoal should melt 76.18723 lbs. of ice, and the quantity of hydrogen in a pound of the oil should melt 62.15053 lbs. The sum of these two gives 138.33776 lbs. of ice, which the two constituent elements of the oil would have melted had they separately suffered combustion, whereas the oil really melted 148.88330 lbs. which gives an excess of 10.54554 in the result of the experiment above the calculated result, from data furnished by former experiments.

This difference, which is by no means very considerable, may arise from errors which are unavoidable in experiments of this nature, or it may be owing to the composition of oil not being as yet exactly ascertained. It proves, however, that there is a great agreement between the results of our experiments, respecting the combination of caloric and those which regard its disengagement.

The following desiderata still remain to be determined, viz: what quantity of caloric is retained by oxygen, after combining with metals, so as to convert them into oxides; what quantity is contained by hydrogen, in its different states of existence; and to ascertain, with more precision than is as yet attained, how much caloric is disengaged during the formation of water, as there still remain considerable doubts with respect to our present determination of this point, which can only be removed by further experiments. We are at present occupied with this inquiry and when once these several points are well ascertained, which we hope they will soon be, we shall probably be under the necessity of making considerable corrections upon most of the results of the experiments and calculations in this chapter. I did not, however, consider this as a sufficient reason for withholding so much as is already known from such as may be inclined to labour upon the same subject. It is difficult in our endeavours to discover the principles of a new science, to avoid beginning by guess-work; and it is rarely possible to arrive at perfection from the first setting out.

CHAPTER X

Of the Combination of Combustible Substances with Each Other

As combustible substances in general have a great affinity for oxygen, they ought likewise to attract or tend to combine with each other; *quae sunt eadem uni tertio, sunt eadem inter se;* and the axiom is found to be true. Almost all the metals, for instance, are capable of uniting with each other and forming what are called *alloys*,[1] in common language. Most of these, like all combinations, are susceptible of several degrees of saturation; the greater number of these alloys are more brittle than the pure metals of which they are composed, especially when the metals alloyed together are considerably different in their degrees of fusibility. To this difference in fusibility part of the phenomena attendant upon *alloyage* are owing, particularly the property of iron called by workmen *hotshort*. This kind of iron must be considered as an alloy, or mixture of pure iron, which is almost infusible, with a small portion of some other metal which fuses in a much lower degree of heat. So long as this alloy remains cold, and both metals are in the solid state, the

[1] This term *alloy*, which we have from the language of the arts, serves exceedingly well for distinguishing all the combinations or intimate unions of metals with each other, and is adopted in our new nomenclature for that purpose.—AUTHOR.

mixture is malleable; but, if heated to a sufficient degree to liquefy the more fusible metal, the particles of the liquid metal, which are interposed between the particles of the metal remaining solid, must destroy their continuity and occasion the alloy to become brittle. The alloys of mercury, with the other metals, have usually been called *amalgams*, and we see no inconvenience from continuing the use of that term.

Sulphur, phosphorus, and charcoal readily unite with metals. Combinations of sulphur with metals are usually named *pyrites*. Their combinations with phosphorus and charcoal are either not yet named or have received new names only of late; so that we have not scrupled to change them according to our principles. The combinations of metal and sulphur we call *sulphurets*, those with phosphorus *phosphurets*, and those formed with charcoal *carburets*. These denominations are extended to all the combinations into which the above three substances enter, without being previously oxygenated. Thus, the combination of sulphur with potash, or fixed vegetable alkali, is called *sulphuret of potash;* that which it forms with ammonia, or volatile alkali, is termed *sulphuret of ammonia*.

Hydrogen is likewise capable of combining with many combustible substances. In the state of gas it dissolves charcoal, sulphur, phosphorus, and several metals; we distinguish these combinations by the terms, *carbonated hydrogen gas, sulphurated hydrogen gas,* and *phosphorated hydrogen gas*. The sulphurated hydrogen gas was called *hepatic air* by former chemists, or *foetid air from sulphur*, by M. Scheele. The virtues of several mineral waters, and the foetid smell of animal excrements, chiefly arise from the presence of this gas. The phosphorated hydrogen gas is remarkable for the property, discovered by M. Gengembre, of taking fire spontaneously upon getting into contact with atmospheric air, or, what is better, with oxygen gas. This gas has a strong flavour, resembling that of putrid fish, and it is very probable that the phosphorescent quality of fish in the state of putrefaction arises from the escape of this species of gas. When hydrogen and charcoal are combined together, without the intervention of caloric to bring the hydrogen into the state of gas, they form oil, which is either fixed or volatile according to the proportions of hydrogen and charcoal in its composition. The chief difference between fixed or fat oils drawn from vegetables by expression, and volatile or essential oils, is that the former contains an excess of charcoal, which is separated when the oils are heated above the degree of boiling water; whereas the volatile oils, containing a just proportion of these two constituent ingredients, are not liable to be decomposed by that heat, but, uniting with caloric into the gaseous state, pass over in distillation unchanged.

In the *Recueil de l'Académie* for 1784, p. 593, I gave an account of my experiments upon the composition of oil and alcohol, by the union of hydrogen with charcoal, and of their combination with oxygen. By these experiments, it appears that fixed oils combine with oxygen during combustion and are thereby converted into water and carbonic acid. By means of calculation applied to the products of these experiments, we find that fixed oil is composed of 21 parts, by weight, of hydrogen combined with 79 parts of charcoal. Perhaps the solid substances of an oily nature, such as wax, contain a proportion of oxygen to which they owe their state of solidity. I am at present engaged in a series of experiments, which I hope will throw great light upon this subject.

It is worthy of being examined whether hydrogen in its concrete state, uncombined with caloric, be susceptible of combination with sulphur, phosphorus, and the metals. There is nothing that we know of which, *a priori*, should render these combinations impossible; for combustible bodies being in general susceptible of combination with each other, there is no evident reason for hydrogen being an exception to the rule: however, no direct experiment as yet establishes either the possibility or impossibility of this union. Iron and zinc are the most likely, of all the metals, for entering into combination with hydrogen; but, as these have the property of decomposing water, and as it is very difficult to get entirely free from moisture in chemical experiments, it is hardly possible to determine whether the small portions of hydrogen gas obtained in certain experiments with these metals were previously combined with the metal in the state of solid hydrogen, or if they were produced by the decomposition of a minute quantity of water. The more care we take to prevent the presence of water in these experiments, the less is the quantity of hydrogen gas procured; and, when very accurate precautions are employed, even that quantity becomes hardly sensible.

However this inquiry may turn out respecting the power of combustible bodies, as sulphur, phosphorus, and metals, to absorb hydrogen, we are certain that they only absorb a very small portion; and that this combination, instead of being essential to their constitution, can only be considered as a foreign substance which contaminates their purity. It is the province of the advocates for this system to prove, by decisive experiments, the real existence of this combined hydrogen, which they have hitherto only done by conjectures founded upon suppositions.

CHAPTER XI

Observations upon Oxides and Acids with Several Bases, and upon the Composition of Animal and Vegetable Substances

WE have in Chapters V and VIII examined the products resulting from the combustion of the four simple combustible substances, sulphur, phosphorus, charcoal, and hydrogen: we have shown in Chapter X that the simple combustible substances are capable of combining with each other into compound combustible substances and have observed that oils in general, and particularly the fixed vegetable oils, belong to this class, being composed of hydrogen and charcoal. It remains, in this chapter, to treat of the oxygenation of these compound combustible substances and to show that there exist acids and oxides having double and triple bases. Nature furnishes us with numerous examples of this kind of combination, by means of which, chiefly, she is enabled to produce a vast variety of compounds from a very limited number of elements or simple substances.

It was long ago well known that when muriatic and nitric acids were mixed together a compound acid was formed, having properties quite distinct from those of either of the acids taken separately. This acid was called *aqua regia*, from its most celebrated property of dissolving gold, called *king of metals* by the alchemists. M. Berthollet has distinctly proved that the peculiar properties of this acid arise from the combined action of its two acidifiable bases; and for this reason we have judged it necessary to distinguish it by an appropriate name: that of *nitro-muriatic* acid appears extremely applicable, from its expressing the nature of the two substances which enter into its composition. plicable, from its expressing the nature of the two substances which enter into its composition.

This phenomenon of a double base in one

acid, which had formerly been observed only
in the nitro-muriatic acid, occurs continually
in the vegetable kingdom, in which a simple
acid, or one possessed of a single acidifiable
base, is very rarely found. Almost all the acids
procurable from this kingdom have bases composed of charcoal and hydrogen, or of charcoal,
hydrogen, and phosphorus, combined with
more or less oxygen. All these bases, whether
double or triple, are likewise formed into oxides, having less oxygen than is necessary to
give them the properties of acids. The acids
and oxides from the animal kingdom are still
more compound, as their bases generally consist of a combination of charcoal, phosphorus,
hydrogen, and azote.

As it is but of late that I have acquired any
clear and distinct notions of these substances,
I shall not, in this place, enlarge much upon
the subject, which I mean to treat of very fully
in some *Mémoires* I am preparing to lay before
the Academy. Most of my experiments are already performed; but, to be able to give exact
reports of the resulting quantities, it is necessary that they be carefully repeated and increased in number: wherefore, I shall only give
a short enumeration of the vegetable and animal acids and oxides and terminate this article
by a few reflections upon the composition of
vegetable and animal bodies.

Sugar, mucus, under which term we include
the different kinds of gums, and starch, are
vegetable oxides, having hydrogen and charcoal combined, in different proportions, as their
radicals or bases, and united with oxygen so as
to bring them to the state of oxides. From the
state of oxides they are capable of being changed
into acids by the addition of a fresh quantity
of oxygen; and, according to the degrees of
oxygenation, and the proportion of hydrogen
and charcoal, in their bases, they form the several kinds of vegetable acids.

It would be easy to apply the principles of
our nomenclature to give names to these vegetable acids and oxides by using the names of
the two substances which compose their bases:
they would thus become hydro-carbonous acids
and oxides. In this method we might indicate
which of their elements existed in excess, without circumlocution, after the manner used by
M. Rouelle for naming vegetable extracts: he
calls these *extracto-resinous* when the extractive
matter prevails in their composition, and *resi-
no-extractive* when they contain a larger proportion of resinous matter. Upon that plan,
and by varying the terminations according to

the formerly established rules of our nomenclature, we have the following denominations:
*hydro-carbonous, hydro-carbonic; carbono-hyd-
rous*, and *carbono-hydric* oxides. And for the
acids: *hydro-carbonous, hydro carbonic, oxygenated hydro-carbonic; carbono-hydrous, carbono-
hydric*, and *oxygenated carbono-hydric*. It is
probable that the above terms would suffice
for indicating all the varieties in nature, and
that, in proportion as the vegetable acids become well understood, they will naturally arrange themselves under these denominations.
But, though we know the elements of which
these are composed, we are as yet ignorant of
the proportions of these ingredients and are
still far from being able to class them in the
above methodical manner; wherefore, we have
determined to retain the ancient names provisionally. I am somewhat further advanced in
this inquiry than at the time of publishing our
conjunct essay upon chemical nomenclature,
yet it would be improper to draw decided consequences from experiments not yet sufficiently
precise. Though I acknowledge that this part
of chemistry still remains in some degree obscure, I must express my expectations of its
being very soon elucidated.

I am still more forcibly necessitated to follow the same plan in naming the acids which
have three or four elements combined in their
bases; of these we have a considerable number
from the animal kingdom, and some even from
vegetable substances. Azote, for instance, joined
to hydrogen and charcoal forms the base or
radical of prussic acid; we have reason to believe that the same happens with the base of
gallic acid; and almost all the animal acids
have their bases composed of azote, phosphorus, hydrogen, and charcoal. Were we to endeavour to express at once all these four component parts of the bases, our nomenclature
would undoubtedly be methodical; it would
have the property of being clear and determinate; but this assemblage of Greek and Latin
substantives and adjectives, which are not yet
universally admitted by chemists, would have
the appearance of a barbarous language, difficult both to pronounce and to be remembered.
Besides, this part of chemistry being still far
from that accuracy it must arrive to, the perfection of the science ought certainly to precede that of its language; and we must still,
for some time, retain the old names for the
animal oxides and acids. We have only ventured to make a few slight modifications of
these names, by changing the termination into

ous when we have reason to suppose the base to be in excess, and into *ic* when we suspect the oxygen predominates.

The following are all the vegetable acids hitherto known:

1. Acetous acid	8. Pyro-mucous acid
2. Acetic acid	9. Pyro-lignous acid
3. Oxalic acid	10. Gallic acid
4. Tartarous acid	11. Benzoic acid
5. Pyro-tartarous acid	12. Camphoric acid
6. Citric acid	13. Succinic acid
7. Malic acid	

Though all these acids, as has been already said, are chiefly, and almost entirely, composed of hydrogen, charcoal, and oxygen, yet, properly speaking, they contain neither water, carbonic acid, nor oil but only the elements necessary for forming these substances. The power of affinity reciprocally exerted by the hydrogen, charcoal, and oxygen, in these acids is in a state of equilibrium only capable of existing in the ordinary temperature of the atmosphere; for, when they are heated but a very little above the temperature of boiling water, this equilibrium is destroyed, part of the oxygen and hydrogen unite and form water; part of the charcoal and hydrogen combine into oil; part of the charcoal and oxygen unite to form carbonic acid; and, lastly, there generally remains a small portion of charcoal, which, being in excess with respect to the other ingredients, is left free. I mean to explain this subject somewhat farther in the succeeding chapter.

The oxides of the animal kingdom are less known than those from the vegetable kingdom, and their number is as yet not at all determined. The red part of the blood, lymph, and most of the secretions, are true oxides, under which point of view it is very important to consider them. We are only acquainted with six animal acids, several of which, it is probable, approach very near each other in their nature, or, at least, differ only in a scarcely sensible degree. I do not include the phosphoric acid amongst these, because it is found in all the kingdoms of nature. They are:

1. Lactic acid	4. Formic acid
2. Saccho-lactic acid	5. Sebacic acid
3. Bombic acid	6. Prussic acid

The connection between the constituent elements of the animal oxides and acids is not more permanent than in those from the vegetable kingdom, as a small increase of temperature is sufficient to overturn it. I hope to render this subject more distinct in the following chapter than has been done hitherto.

CHAPTER XII

Of the Decomposition of Vegetable and Animal Substances by the Action of Fire

BEFORE we can thoroughly comprehend what takes place during the decomposition of vegetable substances by fire, we must take into consideration the nature of the elements which enter into their composition, the different affinities which the particles of these elements exert upon each other, and the affinity which caloric possesses with them. The true constituent elements of vegetables are hydrogen, oxygen, and charcoal: these are common to all vegetables, and no vegetable can exist without them. Such other substances as exist in particular vegetables are only essential to the composition of those in which they are found and do not belong to vegetables in general.

Of these elements, hydrogen and oxygen have a strong tendency to unite with caloric and be converted into gas, whilst charcoal is a fixed element having but little affinity with caloric. On the other hand, oxygen, which, in the usual temperature, tends nearly equally to unite with hydrogen and with charcoal, has a much stronger affinity with charcoal when at red heat[1] and then unites with it to form carbonic acid.

Although we are far from being able to appreciate all these powers of affinity, or to express their proportional energy by numbers, we are certain that, however variable they may be when considered in relation to the quantity of caloric with which they are combined, they are all nearly in equilibrium in the usual temperature of the atmosphere; hence vegetables neither contain oil,[2] water, nor carbonic acid, tho' they contain all the elements of these substances. The hydrogen is neither combined with the oxygen nor with the charcoal, and reciprocally; the particles of these three substances form a triple combination which remains in equilibrium whilst undisturbed by caloric, but a very slight increase of temperature is suf-

[1] Though this term, *red heat*, does not indicate any absolutely determinate degree of temperature, I shall use it sometimes to express a temperature considerably above that of boiling water.—AUTHOR.

[2] I must be understood here to speak of vegetables reduced to a perfectly dry state; and, with respect to oil, I do not mean that which is procured by expression either in the cold, or in a temperature not exceeding that of boiling water; I only allude to the empyreumatic oil procured by distillation with a naked fire, in a heat superior to the temperature of boiling water; which is the only oil declared to be produced by the operation of fire. What I have published upon this subject in the *Recueil de l'Académie* for 1786 may be consulted.—AUTHOR.

ficient to overturn this structure of combination.

If the increased temperature to which the vegetable is exposed does not exceed the heat of boiling water, one part of the hydrogen combines with the oxygen and forms water, the rest of the hydrogen combines with a part of the charcoal and forms volatile oil, whilst the remainder of the charcoal, being set free from its combination with the other elements, remains fixed in the bottom of the distilling vessel.

When, on the contrary, we employ red heat, no water is formed, or, at least, any that may have been produced by the first application of the heat is decomposed, the oxygen having a greater affinity with the charcoal at this degree of heat combines with it to form carbonic acid, and the hydrogen being left free from combination with the other elements unites with caloric and escapes in the state of hydrogen gas. In this high temperature, either no oil is formed, or, if any was produced during the lower temperature at the beginning of the experiment, it is decomposed by the action of the red heat. Thus the decomposition of vegetable matter, under a high temperature, is produced by the action of double and triple affinities; while the charcoal attracts the oxygen on purpose to form carbonic acid, the caloric attracts the hydrogen and converts it into hydrogen gas.

The distillation of every species of vegetable substance confirms the truth of this theory, if we can give that name to a simple relation of facts. When sugar is submitted to distillation, so long as we only employ a heat but a little below that of boiling water, it only loses its water of crystallization, it still remains sugar and retains all its properties; but, immediately upon raising the heat only a little above that degree, it becomes blackened, a part of the charcoal separates from the combination, water slightly acidulated passes over accompanied by a little oil, and the charcoal which remains in the retort is nearly a third part of the original weight of the sugar.

The operation of affinities which take place during the decomposition, by fire, of vegetables which contain azote, such as the cruciferous plants, and of those containing phosphorus, is more complicated; but, as these substances only enter into the composition of vegetables in very small quantities, they only, apparently, produce slight changes upon the products of distillation; the phosphorus seems to combine with the charcoal and, acquiring fixity from that union, remains behind in the retort,

while the azote, combining with a part of the hydrogen, forms ammonia or volatile alkali.

Animal substances, being composed nearly of the same elements with cruciferous plants, give the same products in distillation, with this difference that, as they contain a greater quantity of hydrogen and azote, they produce more oil and more ammonia. I shall only produce one fact as a proof of the exactness with which this theory explains all the phenomena which occur during the distillation of animal substances, which is the rectification and total decomposition of volatile animal oil, commonly known by the name of Dippel's oil. When these oils are procured by a first distillation in a naked fire they are brown, from containing a little charcoal almost in a free state; but they become quite colourless by rectification. Even in this state the charcoal in their composition has so slight a connection with the other elements as to separate by mere exposure to the air. If we put a quantity of this animal oil, well rectified, and consequently clear, limpid, and transparent, into a bell-glass filled with oxygen gas over mercury, in a short time the gas is much diminished, being absorbed by the oil, the oxygen combining with the hydrogen of the oil forms water which sinks to the bottom, at the same time the charcoal which was combined with the hydrogen, being set free, manifests itself by rendering the oil black. Hence the only way of preserving these oils colourless and transparent, is by keeping them in bottles perfectly full and accurately corked, to hinder the contact of air, which always discolours them.

Successive rectifications of this oil furnish another phenomenon confirming our theory. In each distillation a small quantity of charcoal remains in the retort, and a little water is formed by the union of the oxygen contained in the air of the distilling vessels with the hydrogen of the oil. As this takes place in each successive distillation, if we make use of large vessels and a considerable degree of heat, we at last decompose the whole of the oil and change it entirely into water and charcoal. When we use small vessels, and especially when we employ a slow fire or degree of heat little above that of boiling water, the total decomposition of these oils, by repeated distillation, is greatly more tedious, and more difficult to accomplish. I shall give a particular detail to the Academy, in a separate *Mémoire*, of all my experiments upon the decomposition of oil; but what I have related above may suffice to give just ideas of the composition of animal and vegetable substances and of their decomposition by the action of fire.

CHAPTER XIII

Of the Decomposition of Vegetable Oxides by the Vinous Fermentation

THE manner in which wine, cider, mead, and all the liquors formed by the spiritous fermentation, are produced is well known to everyone. The juice of grapes or of apples being expressed, and the latter being diluted with water, they are put into large vats which are kept in a temperature of at least 10° (54.5°) of the thermometer. A rapid intestine motion, or fermentation, very soon takes place; numerous globules of gas form in the liquid and burst at the surface; when the fermentation is at its height, the quantity of gas disengaged is so great as to make the liquor appear as if boiling violently over a fire. When this gas is carefully gathered, it is found to be carbonic acid perfectly pure and free from admixture with any other species of air or gas whatever.

When the fermentation is completed, the juice of grapes is changed from being sweet and full of sugar into a vinous liquor which no longer contains any sugar, and from which we procure, by distillation, an inflammable liquor, known in commerce under the name of *spirit of wine*. As this liquor is produced by the fermentation of any saccharine matter whatever diluted with water, it must have been contrary to the principles of our nomenclature to call it spirit of wine rather than spirit of cider or of fermented sugar; wherefore, we have adopted a more general term, and the Arabic word *alcohol* seems extremely proper for the purpose.

This operation is one of the most extraordinary in chemistry. We must examine whence proceed the disengaged carbonic acid and the inflammable liquor produced and in what manner a sweet vegetable oxide becomes thus converted into two such opposite substances, whereof one is combustible and the other eminently the contrary. To solve these two questions, it is necessary to be previously acquainted with the analysis of the fermentable substance and of the products of the fermentation. We may lay it down as an incontestible axiom that, in all the operations of art and nature, nothing is created; an equal quantity of matter exists both before and after the experiment; the quality and quantity of the elements remain precisely the same and nothing takes place beyond changes and modifications in the combination of these elements. Upon this principle the whole art of performing chemical experiments depends. We must always suppose an exact equality between the elements of the body examined and those of the products of its analysis.

Hence, since from must of grapes we procure alcohol and carbonic acid, I have an undoubted right to suppose that must consists of carbonic acid and alcohol. From these premises, we have two methods of ascertaining what passes during vinous fermentation, by determining the nature of, and the elements which compose, the fermentable substances, or by accurately examining the products resulting from fermentation; and it is evident that the knowledge of either of these must lead to accurate conclusions concerning the nature and composition of the other. From these considerations, it became necessary accurately to determine the constituent elements of the fermentable substances; and, for this purpose, I did not make use of the compound juices of fruits, the rigorous analysis of which is perhaps impossible, but made choice of sugar, which is easily analyzed and the nature of which I have already explained. This substance is a true vegetable oxide with two bases, composed of hydrogen and charcoal brought to the state of an oxide by a certain proportion of oxygen; and these three elements are combined in such a way that a very slight force is sufficient to destroy the equilibrium of their connection. By a long train of experiments, made in various ways, and often repeated, I ascertained that the proportion in which these ingredients exist in sugar are nearly eight parts of hydrogen, 64 parts of oxygen, and 28 parts of charcoal, all by weight, forming 100 parts of sugar.

Sugar must be mixed with about four times its weight of water to render it susceptible of fermentation; and even then the equilibrium of its elements would remain undisturbed, without the assistance of some substance to give a commencement to the fermentation. This is accomplished by means of a little yeast from beer; and, when the fermentation is once excited, it continues of itself until completed. I shall, in another place, give an account of the effects of yeast, and other ferments, upon fermentable substances. I have usually employed 10 *lbs.* of yeast, in the state of paste, for each 100 *lbs.* of sugar, with as much water as is four times the weight of the sugar. I shall give the results of my experiments exactly as they were obtained, preserving even the fractions produced by calculation.

TABLE I. *Materials of Fermentation*

		lbs.	oz.	gros	grs.
Water		400	0	0	0
Sugar		100	0	0	0
Yeast in paste, 10 *lbs.* composed of	Water	7	3	6	44
	Dry yeast	2	12	1	28
	Total	510	0	0	0

TABLE II. *Constituent Elements of the Materials of Fermentation*

		lbs.	oz.	gros	grs.
407 *lbs.* 3 *oz.* 6 *gros* 44 *grs.* of water, composed of	Hydrogen	61	1	2	71.40
	Oxygen	346	2	3	44.60
100 *lbs.* sugar, composed of	Hydrogen	8	0	0	0
	Oxygen	64	0	0	0
	Charcoal	28	0	0	0
2 *lbs.* 12 *oz.* 1 *gros* 28 *grs.* of dry yeast, composed of	Hydrogen	0	4	5	9.30
	Oxygen	1	10	2	28.76
	Charcoal	0	12	4	59
	Azote	0	0	5	2.94
	Total	510	0	0	0

TABLE III. *Recapitulation of these Elements*

		lbs.	oz.	gros	grs.	lbs.	oz.	gros	grs.
Oxygen	of water	340	0	0	0				
	of water in yeast	6	2	3	44.60	411	12	6	1.36
	of sugar	64	0	0	0				
	of dry yeast	1	10	2	28.76				
Hydrogen	of water	60	0	0	0				
	of water in yeast	1	1	2	71.40	69	6	0	8.70
	of sugar	8	0	0	0				
	of dry yeast	0	4	5	9.30				
Charcoal	of sugar	28	0	0	0	28	12	4	59.00
	of yeast	0	12	4	59.00				
Azote of yeast						0	0	5	2.94
	Total	510	0	0	0				

Having thus accurately determined the nature and quantity of the constituent elements of the materials submitted to fermentation, we have next to examine the products resulting from that process. For this purpose, I placed the above 510 *lbs.* of fermentable liquor in a proper[1] apparatus, by means of which I could accurately determine the quantity and quality of gas disengaged during the fermentation, and could even weigh every one of the products separately, at any period of the process I judged proper. An hour or two after the substances are mixed together, especially if they are kept in a temperature of from 15° (65.75°) to 18°

[1] The above apparatus is described in the Third Part.—AUTHOR.

(72.5°) of the thermometer, the first marks of fermentation commence; the liquor turns thick and frothy, little globules of air are disengaged which rise and burst at the surface; the quantity of these globules quickly increases, and there is a rapid and abundant production of very pure carbonic acid, accompanied with a scum which is the yeast separating from the mixture. After some days, less or more according to the degree of heat, the intestine motion and disengagement of gas diminish; but these do not cease entirely, nor is the fermentation completed for a considerable time. During the process, 35 *lbs.* 5 *oz.* 4 *gros* 19 *grs.* of dry carbonic acid are disengaged, which carry alongst with them 13 *lbs.* 14 *oz.* 5 *gros* of water. There remains in the vessel 460 *lbs.* 11 *oz.* 6 *gros* 53 *grs.* of vinous liquor, slightly acidulous. This is at first muddy, but clears of itself, and deposits a portion of yeast. When we separately analyse all these substances, which is effected by very troublesome processes, we have the results as given in the following tables. This process, with all the subordinate calculations and analyses, will be detailed at large in the *Recueil de l'Académie.*

TABLE IV. *Products of Fermentation*

		lbs.	oz.	gros	grs.
35 *lbs.* 5 *oz.* 4 *gros* 19 *grs.* of carbonic acid, composed of	Oxygen	25	7	1	34
	Charcoal	9	14	2	57
408 *lbs.* 15 *oz.* 5 *gros* 14 *grs.* of water, composed of	Oxygen	347	10	0	59
	Hydrogen	61	5	4	27
57 *lbs.* 11 *oz.* 1 *gros* 58 *grs.* of dry alcohol, composed of	Oxygen, combined with hydrogen	31	6	1	64
	Hydrogen, combined with oxygen	5	8	5	3
	Hydrogen, combined with charcoal	4	0	5	0
	Charcoal, combined with hydrogen	16	11	5	63
2 *lbs.* 8 *oz.* of dry acetous acid, composed of	Hydrogen	0	2	4	0
	Oxygen	1	11	4	0
	Charcoal	0	10	0	0
4 *lbs.* 1 *oz.* 4 *gros* 3 *grs.* of residuum of sugar, composed of	Hydrogen	0	5	1	67
	Oxygen	2	9	7	27
	Charcoal	1	2	2	53
1 *lb.* 6 *oz.* 0 *gros* 5 *grs.* of dry yeast, composed of	Hydrogen	0	2	2	41
	Oxygen	0	13	1	14
	Charcoal	0	6	2	30
	Azote	0	0	2	37
510 *lbs.*	Total	510	0	0	0

TABLE V. *Recapitulation of the Products*

		lbs.	oz.	gros	grs.
409 *lbs.* 10 *oz.* 0 *gros* 54 *grs.* of oxygen contained in the	Water	347	10	0	59
	Carbonic acid	25	7	1	34
	Alcohol	31	6	1	64
	Acetous acid	1	11	4	0
	Residuum of sugar	2	9	7	27
	Yeast	0	13	1	14
28 *lbs.* 12 *oz.* 5 *gros* 59 *grs.* of charcoal contained in the	Carbonic acid	9	14	2	57
	Alcohol	16	11	5	63
	Acetous acid	0	10	0	0
	Residuum of sugar	1	2	2	53
	Yeast	0	6	2	30
71 *lbs.* 8 *oz.* 6 *gros* 66 *grs.* of hydrogen, contained in the	Water	61	5	4	27
	Water of the alcohol	5	8	5	3
	Combined with the charcoal of the alcohol	4	0	5	0
	Acetous acid	0	2	4	0
	Residuum of sugar	0	5	1	67
	Yeast	0	2	2	41
2 *gros* 37 *grs.* of azote in the yeast		0	0	2	37
510 *lbs.*	Total	510	0	0	0

In these results I have been exact, even to grains; not that it is possible, in experiments of this nature, to carry our accuracy so far, but as the experiments were made only with a few pounds of sugar, and as, for the sake of comparison, I reduced the results of the actual experiments to the quintal or imaginary hundred pounds, I thought it necessary to leave the fractional parts precisely as produced by calculation.

When we consider the results presented by these tables with attention, it is easy to discover exactly what occurs during fermentation. In the first place, out of the 100 *lbs.* of sugar employed, 4 *lbs.* 1 *oz.* 4 *gros* 3 *grs.* remain, without having suffered decomposition; so that, in reality, we have only operated upon 95 *lbs.* 14 *oz.* 3 *gros* 69 *grs.* of sugar; that is to say, upon 61 *lbs.* 6 *oz.* 45 *grs.* of oxygen, 7 *lbs.* 10 *oz.* 6 *gros* 6 *grs.* of hydrogen, and 26 *lbs.* 13 *oz.* 5 *gros* 19 *grs.* of charcoal. By comparing these quantities, we find that they are fully sufficient for forming the whole of the alcohol, carbonic acid and acetous acid produced by the fermentation. It is not, therefore, necessary to suppose that any water has been decomposed during the experiment, unless it be pretended that the oxygen and hydrogen exist in the sugar in that state. On the contrary, I have already made it evident that hydrogen, oxygen and charcoal, the three constituent elements of vegetables, remain in a state of equilibrium or mutual union with each other which subsists so long as this union remains undisturbed by increased temperature, or by some new compound attraction; and that then only these elements combine, two and two together, to form water and carbonic acid.

The effects of the vinous fermentation upon sugar is thus reduced to the mere separation of its elements into two portions; one part is oxygenated at the expense of the other so as to form carbonic acid, whilst the other part, being disoxygenated in favour of the former, is converted into the combustible substance alcohol; therefore, if it were possible to reunite alcohol and carbonic acid together, we ought to form sugar. It is evident that the charcoal and hydrogen in the alcohol do not exist in the state of oil. They are combined with a portion of oxygen, which renders them miscible with water; wherefore these three substances, oxygen, hydrogen, and charcoal, exist here likewise in a species of equilibrium or reciprocal combination; and in fact, when they are made to pass through a red hot tube of glass or porcelain, this union or equilibrium is destroyed, the elements become combined, two and two, and water and carbonic acid are formed.

I had formally advanced, in my first *Mémoires* upon the formation of water, that it was decomposed in a great number of chemical experiments and particularly during the vinous fermentation. I then supposed that water existed ready formed in sugar, though I am now convinced that sugar only contains the elements proper for composing it. It may be readily conceived that it must have cost me a good deal to abandon my first notions, but by several years reflection, and after a great number of experiments and observations upon vegetable substances, I have fixed my ideas as above.

I shall finish what I have to say upon vinous fermentation by observing that it furnishes us with the means of analysing sugar and every vegetable fermentable matter. We may consider the substances submitted to fermentation, and the products resulting from that operation, as forming an algebraic equation; and, by successively supposing each of the elements in this equation unknown, we can calculate their values in succession, and thus verify our experiments by calculation, and our calculation by experiment reciprocally. I have often successfully employed this method for correcting the first results of my experiments and to direct me in the proper road for repeating them to advantage. I have explained myself at large upon this subject, in a *Mémoire* upon vinous fermentation already presented to the Academy which will speedily be published.

CHAPTER XIV

Of the Putrefactive Fermentation

THE phenomena of putrefaction are caused, like those of vinous fermentation, by the operation of very complicated affinities. The constituent elements of the bodies submitted to this process cease to continue in equilibrium in the threefold combination and form themselves anew into binary combinations, or compounds, consisting of two elements only; but these are entirely different from the results produced by the vinous fermentation. Instead of one part of the hydrogen remaining united with part of the water and charcoal to form alcohol, as in the vinous fermentation, the whole of the hydrogen is dissipated, during putrefaction, in the form of hydrogen gas, whilst, at the same time, the oxygen and charcoal, uniting with caloric, escape in the form of carbonic acid gas; so that, when the whole process is finished, especially if the materials have been mixed with a sufficient quantity of water, nothing remains but the earth of the vegetable mixed with a small portion of charcoal and iron. Thus putrefaction is nothing more than a complete analysis of vegetable substance, during which the whole of the constituent elements is disengaged in form of gas, except the earth which remains in the state of mould.[1]

Such is the result of putrefaction when the substances submitted to it contain only oxygen, hydrogen, charcoal and a little earth. But this case is rare, and these substances putrify imperfectly and with difficulty, and require a considerable time to complete their putrefaction. It is otherwise with substances containing azote, which indeed exists in all animal matters and even in a considerable number of vegetable substances. This additional element is remarkably favourable to putrefaction; and for this reason animal matter is mixed with vegetable when the putrefaction of these is wished to be hastened. The whole art of forming composts and dunghills, for the purposes of agriculture, consists in the proper application of this admixture.

The addition of azote to the materials of putrefaction not only accelerates the process; that element likewise combines with part of the hydrogen and forms a new substance called *volatile alkali* or *ammonia*. The results obtained by analysing animal matters, by different processes, leave no room for doubt with regard to the constituent elements of ammonia; whenever the azote has been previously separated from these substances, no ammonia is produced; and in all cases they furnish ammonia only in proportion to the azote they contain. This composition of ammonia is likewise fully proved by M. Berthollet, in the *Recueil de l'Académie* for 1785, p. 316, where he gives a variety of analytical processes by which ammonia is decomposed and its two elements, azote and hydrogen, procured separately.

I mentioned in Chapter X that almost all combustible bodies were capable of combining with each other. Hydrogen gas possesses this quality in an eminent degree; it dissolves charcoal, sulphur, and phosphorus, producing the compounds named *carbonated hydrogen gas*,

sulphurated hydrogen gas, and *phosphorated hydrogen gas*. The two latter of these gases have a peculiarly disagreeable flavour; the sulphurated hydrogen gas has a strong resemblance to the smell of rotten eggs, and the phosphorated smells exactly like putrid fish. Ammonia has likewise a peculiar odour, not less penetrating or less disagreeable than these other gases. From the mixture of these different flavours proceeds the fetor which accompanies the putrefaction of animal substances. Sometimes ammonia predominates, which is easily perceived by its sharpness upon the eyes; sometimes, as in feculent matters, the sulphurated gas is most prevalent; and sometimes, as in putrid herrings, the phosphorated hydrogen gas is most abundant.

I long supposed that nothing could derange or interrupt the course of putrefaction; but M. Fourcroy and M. Thouret have observed some peculiar phenomena in dead bodies, buried at a certain depth and preserved to a certain degree from contact with air, having found the muscular flesh frequently converted into true animal fat. This must have arisen from the disengagement of the azote, naturally contained in the animal substance, by some unknown cause, leaving only the hydrogen and charcoal remaining, which are the elements proper for producing fat or oil. This observation upon the possibility of converting animal substances into fat may some time or other lead to discoveries of great importance to society. The faeces of animals, and other excrementitious matters, are chiefly composed of charcoal and hydrogen and approach considerably to the nature of oil, of which they furnish a considerable quantity by distillation with a naked fire; but the intolerable fetor which accompanies all the products of these substances prevents our expecting that, at least for a long time, they can be rendered useful in any other way than as manures.

I have only given conjectural approximations in this chapter upon the composition of animal substances, which is hitherto but imperfectly understood. We know that they are composed of hydrogen, charcoal, azote, phosphorus, and sulphur, all of which, in a state of quintuple combination, are brought to the state of oxides by a larger or smaller quantity of oxygen. We are, however, still unacquainted with the proportions in which these substances are combined, and must leave it to time to complete this part of chemical analysis, as it has already done with several others.

[1] In the Third Part will be given the description of an apparatus proper for being used in experiments of this kind.—AUTHOR.

CHAPTER XV

Of the Acetous Fermentation

THE acetous fermentation is nothing more than the acidification or oxygenation of wine, produced in the open air by means of the absorption of oxygen. The resulting acid is the acetous acid, commonly called *vinegar*, which is composed of hydrogen and charcoal united together in proportions not yet ascertained and changed into the acid state by oxygen. As vinegar is an acid, we might conclude from analogy that it contains oxygen, but this is put beyond doubt by direct experiments: in the first place, we cannot change wine into vinegar without the contact of air containing oxygen; secondly, this process is accompanied by a diminution of the volume of the air in which it is carried on from the absorption of its oxygen; and, thirdly, wine may be changed into vinegar by any other means of oxygenation.

Independent of the proofs which these facts furnish of the acetous acid being produced by the oxygenation of wine, an experiment made by M. Chaptal, Professor of Chemistry at Montpellier, gives us a distinct view of what takes place in this process. He impregnated water with about its own bulk of carbonic acid from fermenting beer and placed this water in a cellar in vessels communicating with the air, and in a short time the whole was converted into acetous acid. The carbonic acid gas procured from beer vats in fermentation is not perfectly pure but contains a small quantity of alcohol in solution, wherefore water impregnated with it contains all the materials necessary for forming the acetous acid. The alcohol furnishes hydrogen and one portion of charcoal, the carbonic acid furnishes oxygen and the rest of the charcoal, and the air of the atmosphere furnishes the rest of the oxygen necessary for changing the mixture into acetous acid. From this observation it follows that nothing but hydrogen is wanting to convert carbonic acid into acetous acid; or more generally that, by means of hydrogen and according to the degree of oxygenation, carbonic acid may be changed into all the vegetable acids; and, on the contrary, that, by depriving any of the vegetable acids of their hydrogen, they may be converted into carbonic acid.

Although the principal facts relating to the acetous acid are well known, yet numerical exactitude is still wanting, till furnished by more exact experiments than any hitherto performed; wherefore I shall not enlarge any farther upon the subject. It is sufficiently shown by what has been said that the constitution of all the vegetable acids and oxides is exactly conformable to the formation of vinegar; but further experiments are necessary to teach us the proportion of the constituent elements in all these acids and oxides. We may easily perceive, however, that this part of chemistry, like all the rest of its divisions, makes rapid progress towards perfection, and that it is already rendered greatly more simple than was formerly believed.

CHAPTER XVI

Of the Formation of Neutral Salts and of their Different Bases

WE have just seen that all the oxides and acids from the animal and vegetable kingdoms are formed by means of a small number of simple elements, or at least of such as have not hitherto been susceptible of decomposition, by means of combination with oxygen; these are azote, sulphur, phosphorus, charcoal, hydrogen, and the muriatic radical. We may justly admire the simplicity of the means employed by nature to multiply qualities and forms, whether by combining three or four acidifiable bases in different proportions or by altering the dose of oxygen employed for oxidating or acidifying them. We shall find the means no less simple and diversified, and as abundantly productive of forms and qualities, in the order of bodies we are now about to treat of.

Acidifiable substances, by combining with oxygen and their consequent conversion into acids, acquire great susceptibility of further combination; they become capable of uniting with earthy and metallic bodies, by which means neutral salts are formed. Acids may therefore be considered as true *salifying* principles, and the substances with which they unite to form neutral salts may be called *salifiable* bases. The nature of the union which these two principles form with each other is meant as the subject of the present chapter.

This view of the acids prevents me from considering them as salts, though they are possessed of many of the principal properties of saline bodies, as solubility in water, &c. I have already observed that they are the result of a first order of combination, being composed of two simple elements, or at least of elements which act as if they were simple, and we may therefore rank them, to use the language of Stahl, in the order of *mixts*. The neutral salts, on the contrary, are of a secondary order of combination, being formed by the union of two *mixts* with each other, and may therefore be termed *compounds*. Hence I shall not arrange the alkalies[1] or earths in the class of salts, to which I allot only such as are composed of an oxygenated substance united to a base.

I have already enlarged sufficiently upon the formation of acids in the preceding chapter and shall not add anything further upon that subject; but having as yet given no account of the salifiable bases which are capable of uniting with them to form neutral salts, I mean in this chapter to give an account of the nature and origin of each of these bases. These are potash, soda, ammonia, lime, magnesia, barytes, argill, and all the metallic bodies.

Of Potash

We have already shown that, when a vegetable substance is submitted to the action of fire in distilling vessels, its component elements, oxygen, hydrogen, and charcoal, which formed a threefold combination in a state of equilibrium, unite, two and two, in obedience to affinities which act conformably to the degree of heat employed. Thus, at the first application of the fire, whenever the heat produced exceeds the temperature of boiling water, part of the oxygen and hydrogen unite to form water; soon after, the rest of the hydrogen, and part of the charcoal, combine into oil; and, lastly, when the fire is pushed to red heat, the oil and water, which had been formed in the early part of the process, become again decomposed, the oxygen and charcoal unite to form carbonic acid, a large quantity of hydrogen gas is set free, and nothing but charcoal remains in the retort.

A great part of these phenomena occur during the combustion of vegetables in the open air; but, in this case, the presence of the air introduces three new substances, the oxygen and azote of the air, and caloric, of which two at least produce considerable changes in the results of the operation. In proportion as the hydrogen of the vegetable, or that which results from the decomposition of the water, is forced out in the form of hydrogen gas by the progress of the fire, it is set on fire immediately upon getting in contact with the air, water is again

formed, and the greater part of the caloric of the two gases becoming free produces flame. When all the hydrogen gas is driven out, burnt, and again reduced to water, the remaining charcoal continues to burn, but without flame; it is formed into carbonic acid, which carries off a portion of caloric sufficient to give it the gaseous form; the rest of the caloric, from the oxygen of the air, being set free, produces the heat and light observed during the combustion of charcoal. The whole vegetable is thus reduced into water and carbonic acid, and nothing remains but a small portion of gray earthy matter called *ashes*, being the only really fixed principles which enter into the constitution of vegetables.

The earth, or rather ashes, which seldom exceeds a twentieth part of the weight of the vegetable, contains a substance of a particular nature, known under the name of *fixed vegetable alkali* or *potash*. To obtain it, water is poured upon the ashes, which dissolves the potash and leaves the ashes which are insoluble; by afterwards evaporating the water, we obtain the potash in a white concrete form: it is very fixed even in a very high degree of heat. I do not mean here to describe the art of preparing potash, or the method of procuring it in a state of purity, but have entered upon the above detail that I might not use any word not previously explained.

The potash obtained by this process is always less or more saturated with carbonic acid, which is easily accounted for. As the potash does not form, or at least is not set free, but in proportion as the charcoal of the vegetable is converted into carbonic acid by the addition of oxygen, either from the air or the water, it follows that each particle of potash, at the instant of its formation, or at least of its liberation, is in contact with a particle of carbonic acid, and, as there is a considerable affinity between these two substances, they naturally combine together. Although the carbonic acid has less affinity with potash than any other acid, yet it is difficult to separate the last portions from it. The most usual method of accomplishing this is to dissolve the potash in water; to this solution add two or three times its weight of quicklime, then filtrate the liquor and evaporate it in close vessels; the saline substance left by the evaporation is potash almost entirely deprived of carbonic acid. In this state it is soluble in an equal weight of water, and even attracts the moisture of the air with great avidity; by this property it furnishes us with an excellent means

[1] Perhaps my thus rejecting the alkalies from the class of salts may be considered as a capital defect in the method I have adopted, and I am ready to admit the charge; but this inconvenience is compensated by so many advantages, that I could not think it of sufficient consequence to make me alter my plan.— AUTHOR.

of rendering air or gas dry by exposing them to its action. In this state it is soluble in alcohol, though not when combined with carbonic acid; and M. Berthollet employs this property as a method of procuring potash in the state of perfect purity.

All vegetables yield less or more of potash in consequence of combustion, but it is furnished in various degrees of purity by different vegetables; usually, indeed, from all of them it is mixed with different salts from which it is easily separable. We can hardly entertain a doubt that the ashes or earth which is left by vegetables in combustion pre-existed in them before they were burnt, forming what may be called the skeleton or osseous part of the vegetable. But it is quite otherwise with potash; this substance has never yet been procured from vegetables but by means of processes or intermedia capable of furnishing oxygen and azote, such as combustion, or by means of nitric acid; so that it is not yet demonstrated that potash may not be a produce from these operations. I have begun a series of experiments upon this object and hope soon to be able to give an account of their results.

Of Soda

Soda, like potash, is an alkali procured by lixiviation from the ashes of burnt plants, but only from those which grow upon the seaside, and especially from the herb *kali*, whence is derived the name *alkali* given to this substance by the Arabians. It has some properties in common with potash and others which are entirely different. In general, these two substances have peculiar characters in their saline combinations which are proper to each and consequently distinguish them from each other; thus soda, which, as obtained from marine plants, is usually entirely saturated with carbonic acid, does not attract the humidity of the atmosphere like potash, but, on the contrary, desiccates, its crystals effloresce and are converted into a white powder having all the properties of soda, which it really is, having only lost its water of crystallization.

We are not better acquainted with the constituent elements of soda than with those of potash, being equally uncertain whether it previously existed ready formed in the vegetable or is a combination of elements effected by combustion. Analogy leads us to suspect that azote is a constituent element of all the alkalies, as is the case with ammonia; but we have only slight presumptions, unconfirmed by any decisive experiments, respecting the composition of potash and soda.

Of Ammonia

We have, however, very accurate knowledge of the composition of ammonia, or volatile alkali as it is called by the old chemists. M. Berthollet, in the *Recueil de l'Académie* for 1784, p. 316, has proved by analysis, that 1000 parts of this substance consist of about 807 parts of azote combined with 193 parts of hydrogen.

Ammonia is chiefly procurable from animal substances by distillation, during which process the azote and hydrogen necessary to its formation unite in proper proportions; it is not, however, procured pure by this process, being mixed with oil and water and mostly saturated with carbonic acid. To separate these substances it is first combined with an acid, the muriatic for instance, and then disengaged from that combination by the addition of lime or potash. When ammonia is thus produced in its greatest degree of purity, it can only exist under the gaseous form, at least in the usual temperature of the atmosphere; it has an excessively penetrating smell, is absorbed in large quantities by water, especially if cold and assisted by compression. Water thus saturated with ammonia has usually been termed *volatile alkaline fluor;* we shall call it either simply *ammonia*, or *liquid ammonia*, and *ammoniacal gas* when it exists in the aeriform state.

Of Lime, Magnesia, Barytes, and Argill

The composition of these four earths is totally unknown, and, until by new discoveries their constituent elements are ascertained, we are certainly authorised to consider them as simple bodies. Art has no share in the production of these earths, as they are all procured ready formed from nature; but, as they have all, especially the three first, great tendency to combination, they are never found pure. Lime is usually saturated with carbonic acid in the state of chalk, calcareous spars, most of the marbles, &c.; sometimes with sulphuric acid, as in gypsum and plaster stones; at other times with fluoric acid forming vitreous or fluor spars; and, lastly, it is found in the waters of the sea, and of saline springs, combined with muriatic acid. Of all the salifiable bases it is the most universally spread through nature.

Magnesia is found in mineral waters, for the most part combined with sulphuric acid; it is likewise abundant in sea-water, united with muriatic acid; and it exists in a great number of stones of different kinds.

Barytes is much less common than the three preceding earths; it is found in the mineral kingdom, combined with sulphuric acid, forming heavy spars, and sometimes, though rarely, united to carbonic acid.

Argill, or the base of alum, having less tendency to combination than the other earths, is often found in the state of argill, uncombined with any acid. It is chiefly procurable from clays, of which, properly speaking, it is the base or chief ingredient.

Of Metallic Bodies

The metals, except gold and sometimes silver, are rarely found in the mineral kingdom in their metallic state, being usually less or more saturated with oxygen, or combined with sulphur, arsenic, sulphuric acid, muriatic acid, carbonic acid, or phosphoric acid. Metallurgy, or the docimastic art, teaches the means of separating them from these foreign matters; and for this purpose we refer to such chemical books as treat upon these operations.

We are probably only acquainted as yet with a part of the metallic substances existing in nature, as all those which have a stronger affinity to oxygen than charcoal possesses are incapable of being reduced to the metallic state and, consequently, being only presented to our observation under the form of oxides, are confounded with earths. It is extremely probable that barytes, which we have just now arranged with earths, is in this situation; for in many experiments it exhibits properties nearly approaching to those of metallic bodies. It is even possible that all the substances we call earths may be only metallic oxides, irreducible by any hitherto known process.

Those metallic bodies we are at present acquainted with, and which we can reduce to the metallic or reguline state, are the following seventeen:

1. Arsenic	7. Bismuth	13. Copper
2. Molybdenum	8. Antimony	14. Mercury
3. Tungsten	9. Zinc	15. Silver
4. Manganese	10. Iron	16. Platinum
5. Nickel	11. Tin	17. Gold
6. Cobalt	12. Lead	

I only mean to consider these as salifiable bases, without entering at all upon the consideration of their properties in the arts and for the uses of society. In these points of view each metal would require a complete treatise, which would lead me far beyond the bounds I have prescribed for this work.

CHAPTER XVII

Continuation of the Observations upon Salifiable Bases and the Formation of Neutral Salts

IT is necessary to remark that earths and alkalies unite with acids to form neutral salts without the intervention of any medium, whereas metallic substances are incapable of forming this combination without being previously less or more oxygenated; strictly speaking, therefore, metals are not soluble in acids but only metallic oxides. Hence, when we put a metal into an acid for solution, it is necessary, in the first place, that it become oxygenated, either by attracting oxygen from the acid or from the water; or, in other words, that a metal cannot be dissolved in an acid unless the oxygen, either of the acid or of the water mixed with it, has a stronger affinity to the metal than to the hydrogen or the acidifiable base; or, which amounts to the same thing, that no metallic solution can take place without a previous decomposition of the water or the acid in which it is made. The explanation of the principal phenomena of metallic solution depends entirely upon this simple observation, which was overlooked even by the illustrious Bergman.

The first and most striking of these is the effervescence, or, to speak less equivocally, the disengagement of gas which takes place during the solution; in the solutions made in nitric acid this effervescence is produced by the disengagement of nitrous gas; in solutions with sulphuric acid it is either sulphurous acid gas or hydrogen gas, according as the oxidation of the metal happens to be made at the expense of the sulphuric acid or of the water. As both nitric acid and water are composed of elements which, when separate, can only exist in the gaseous form, at least in the common temperature of the atmosphere, it is evident that, whenever either of these is deprived of its oxygen, the remaining element must instantly expand and assume the state of gas; the effervescence is occasioned by this sudden conversion from the liquid to the gaseous state. The same decomposition, and consequent formation of gas, takes place when solutions of metals are made in sulphuric acid. In general, especially by the humid way, metals do not attract all the oxygen it contains; they therefore reduce it, not into sulphur, but into sulphurous acid, and as this acid can only exist as gas in the usual temperature it is disengaged and occasions effervescence.

The second phenomenon is that when the metals have been previously oxidated they all dissolve in acids without effervescence. This is easily explained; because, not having now any occasion for combining with oxygen, they neither decompose the acid nor the water by which, in the former case, the effervescence is occasioned.

A third phenomenon, which requires particular consideration, is that none of the metals produce effervescence by solution in oxygenated muriatic acid. During this process the metal, in the first place, carries off the excess of oxygen from the oxygenated muriatic acid, by which it becomes oxidated, and reduces the acid to the state of ordinary muriatic acid. In this case there is no production of gas, not that the muriatic acid does not tend to exist in the gaseous state in the common temperature, which it does equally with the acids formerly mentioned, but because this acid, which otherwise would expand into gas, finds more water combined with the oxygenated muriatic acid than is necessary to retain it in the liquid form; hence it does not disengage like the sulphurous acid, but remains and quietly dissolves and combines with the metallic oxide previously formed from its superabundant oxygen.

The fourth phenomenon is that metals are absolutely insoluble in such acids as have their bases joined to oxygen by a stronger affinity than these metals are capable of exerting upon that acidifying principle. Hence silver, mercury, and lead, in their metallic states, are insoluble in muriatic acid, but, when previously oxidated, they become readily soluble without effervescence.

From these phenomena it appears that oxygen is the bond of union between metals and acids; and from this we are led to suppose that oxygen is contained in all substances which have a strong affinity with acids. Hence it is very probable the four eminently salifiable earths contain oxygen, and their capability of uniting with acids is produced by the intermediation of that element. What I have formerly noticed relative to these earths is considerably strengthened by the above considerations, viz. that they may very possibly be metallic oxides, with which oxygen has a stronger affinity than with charcoal, and consequently not reducible by any known means.

All the acids hitherto known are enumerated in the following table, the first column of which contains the names of the acids according to the new nomenclature, and in the second column are placed the bases or radicals of these acids, with observations.

Names of the Acids	Names of the Bases, with Observations
1. Sulphurous 2. Sulphuric	Sulphur
3. Phosphorous 4. Phosphoric	Phosphorus
5. Muriatic 6. Oxygenated muriatic	Muriatic radical or base, hitherto unknown
7. Nitrous 8. Nitric 9. Oxygenated nitric	Azote
10. Carbonic	Charcoal
11. Acetous 12. Acetic 13. Oxalic 14. Tartarous 15. Pyro-tartarous 16. Citric 17. Malic 18. Pyro-lignous 19. Pyro-mucous	The bases or radicals of all these acids seem to be formed by a combination of charcoal and hydrogen; and the only difference seems to be owing to the different proportions in which these elements combine to form their bases, and to the different doses of oxygen in their acidification. A connected series of accurate experiments is still wanted upon this subject
20. Gallic 21. Prussic 22. Benzoic 23. Succinic 24. Camphoric 25. Lactic 26. Saccho-lactic	Our knowledge of the bases of these acids is hitherto imperfect; we only know that they contain hydrogen and charcoal as principal elements, and that the prussic acid contains azote
27. Bombic 28. Formic 29. Sebacic	The base of these and all the acids procured from animal substances seems to consist of charcoal, hydrogen, phosphorus, and azote
30. Boracic 31. Fluoric	The bases of these two are hitherto entirely unknown
32. Antimonic	Antimony
33. Argentic	Silver
34. Arseniac	Arsenic
35. Bismuthic	Bismuth
36. Cobaltic	Cobalt
37. Cupric	Copper
38. Stannic	Tin
39. Ferric	Iron
40. Munganic	Manganese
41. Mercuric	Mercury
42. Molybdic	Molybdenum
43. Nickolic	Nickel
44. Auric	Gold
45. Platinic	Platinum
46. Plumbic	Lead
47. Tungstic	Tungsten
48. Zincic	Zinc

In this list, which contains 48 acids, I have enumerated 17 metallic acids hitherto very imperfectly known, but upon which M. Berthollet is about to publish a very important work. It cannot be pretended that all the acids which exist in nature, or rather all the acidifiable bases, are yet discovered; but, on the other hand, there are considerable grounds for supposing that a more accurate investigation than has hitherto been attempted will diminish the number of the vegetable acids by showing that several of these, at present considered as distinct acids, are only modifications of others. All that can be done in the present state of our knowledge is to give a view of chemistry as it really is and to establish fundamental principles by which such bodies as may be discovered in future may receive names in conformity with one uniform system.

The known salifiable bases, or substances capable of being converted into neutral salts by union with acids, amount to 24; viz., 3 alkalies, 4 earths, and 17 metallic substances; so that, in the present state of chemical knowledge, the whole possible number of neutral salts amounts to 1152. This number is upon the supposition that the metallic acids are capable of dissolving other metals, which is a new branch of chemistry not hitherto investigated, upon which depends all the metallic combinations named *vitreous*. There is reason to believe that many of these supposable saline combinations are not capable of being formed, which must greatly reduce the real number of neutral salts producible by nature and art. Even if we suppose the real number to amount only to five or six hundred species of possible neutral salts, it is evident that, were we to distinguish them after the manner of the ancients, either by the names of their first discoverers or by terms derived from the substances from which they are procured, we should at last have such a confusion of arbitrary designations as no memory could possibly retain. This method might be tolerable in the early ages of chemistry, or even till within these twenty years, when only about thirty species of salts were known; but, in the present times, when the number is augmenting daily, when every new acid gives us 24 or 48 new salts according as it is capable of one or two degrees of oxygenation, a new method is certainly necessary. The method we have adopted, drawn from the nomenclature of the acids, is perfectly analogical and, following nature in the simplicity of her operations, gives a na-

tural and easy nomenclature applicable to every possible neutral salt.

In giving names to the different acids, we express the common property by the generical term *acid* and distinguish each species by the name of its peculiar acidifiable base. Hence the acids formed by the oxygenation of sulphur, phosphorus, charcoal, &c. are called *sulphuric acid, phosphoric acid, carbonic acid*, &c. We thought it likewise proper to indicate the different degrees of saturation with oxygen by different terminations of the same specific names. Hence we distinguish between sulphurous and sulphuric, and between phosphorous and phosphoric acids, &c.

By applying these principles to the nomenclature of neutral salts, we give a common term to all the neutral salts arising from the combination of one acid and distinguish the species by adding the name of the salifiable base. Thus, all the neutral salts having sulphuric acid in their composition are named *sulphates;* those formed by the phosphoric acid, *phosphates*, &c. The species being distinguished by the names of the salifiable bases gives us *sulphate of potash, sulphate of soda, sulphate of ammoniac, sulphate of lime, sulphate of iron*, &c. As we are acquainted with 24 salifiable bases, alkaline, earthy, and metallic, we have consequently 24 sulphates, as many phosphates, and so on through all the acids. Sulphur is, however, susceptible of two degrees of oxygenation, the first of which produces sulphurous and the second, sulphuric acid; and, as the neutral salts produced by these two acids have different properties and are in fact different salts, it becomes necessary to distinguish these by peculiar terminations; we have therefore distinguished the neutral salts formed by the acids in the first or lesser degree of oxygenation by changing the termination *ate* into *ite*, as *sulphites, phosphites*, &c. Thus, oxygenated or acidified sulphur, in its two degrees of oxygenation is capable of forming 48 neutral salts, 24 of which are sulphites, and as many sulphates; which is likewise the case with all the acids capable of two degrees of oxygenation.

It were both tiresome and unnecessary to follow these denominations through all the varieties of their possible application; it is enough to have given the method of naming the various salts which, when once well understood, is easily applied to every possible combination. The name of the combustible and acidifiable body being once known, the names of the acid it is capable of forming, and of all the neutral combinations the acid is susceptible of entering into, are most readily remembered. Such as require a more complete illustration of the methods in which the new nomenclature is applied will, in the second part of this book, find tables which contain a full enumeration of all the neutral salts and, in general, all the possible chemical combinations, so far as is consistent with the present state of our knowledge. To these I shall subjoin short explanations, containing the best and most simple means of procuring the different species of acids, and some account of the general properties of the neutral salts they produce.

I shall not deny that, to render this work more complete, it would have been necessary to add particular observations upon each species of salt, its solubility in water and alcohol, the proportions of acid and of salifiable base in its composition, the quantity of its water of crystallization, the different degrees of saturation it is susceptible of, and, finally, the degree of force or affinity with which the acid adheres to the base. This immense work has been already begun by MM. Bergman, Morveau, Kirwan, and other celebrated chemists, but is hitherto only in a moderate state of advancement; even the principles upon which it is founded are not perhaps sufficiently accurate.

These numerous details would have swelled this elementary treatise to much too great a size; besides that, to have gathered the necessary materials, and to have completed all the series of experiments requisite, must have retarded the publication of this book for many years. This is a vast field for employing the zeal and abilities of young chemists, whom I would advise to endeavour rather to do well than to do much, and to ascertain, in the first place, the composition of the acids, before entering upon that of the neutral salts. Every edifice which is intended to resist the ravages of time should be built upon a sure foundation; and, in the present state of chemistry, to attempt discoveries by experiments, either not perfectly exact or not sufficiently rigorous, will serve only to interrupt its progress, instead of contributing to its advancement.

SECOND PART

Of the combination of acids with salifiable bases,
and of the formation of neutral salts

INTRODUCTION

If I had strictly followed the plan I at first laid down for the conduct of this work, I would have confined myself, in the tables and accompanying observations which compose this second part, to short definitions of the several known acids and abridged accounts of the processes by which they are obtainable, with a mere nomenclature or enumeration of the neutral salts which result from the combination of these acids with the various salifiable bases. But I afterwards found that the addition of similar tables of all the simple substances which enter into the composition of the acids and oxides, together with the various possible combinations of these elements, would add greatly to the utility of this work without being any great increase to its size. These additions, which are all contained in the twelve first sections of this part and the tables annexed to these, form a kind of recapitulation of the first fifteen chapters of the first part. The rest of the tables and sections contain all the saline combinations.

It must be very apparent that, in this part of the work, I have borrowed greatly from what has been already published by M. de Morveau in the first volume of the *Encyclopedie par ordre des Matières*. I could hardly have discovered a better source of information, especially when the difficulty of consulting books in foreign languages is considered. I make this general acknowledgment on purpose to save the trouble of references to M. de Morveau's work in the course of the following part of mine.

Table *of Simple Substances Belonging to All the Kingdoms of Nature, Which May Be Considered as the Elements of Bodies*

New Names	Old Names
Light	Light
Caloric	Heat
	Principle or element of heat
	Fire, Igneous fluid
	Matter of fire and of heat
Oxygen	Dephlogisticated air
	Empyreal air
	Vital air, or base of vital air
Azote	Phlogisticated air or gas
	Mephitis, or its base
Hydrogen	Inflammable air or gas, or the base of inflammable air

Oxidable and Acidifiable Simple Substances Not Metallic

New Names	Old Names
Sulphur	
Phosphorus	The same names
Charcoal	
Muriatic radical	
Fluoric radical	Still unknown
Boracic radical	

TABLE *of Simple Substances, Continued*
Oxidable and Acidifiable Simple Metallic Bodies

New Names		Old Names
Antimony		Antimony
Arsenic		Arsenic
Bismuth		Bismuth
Cobalt		Cobalt
Copper		Copper
Gold		Gold
Iron	*Regulus of*	Iron
Lead		Lead
Manganese		Manganese
Mercury		Mercury
Molybdenum		Molybdenum
Nickel		Nickel
Platinum		Platinum
Silver		Silver
Tin		Tin
Tungsten		Tungsten
Zinc		Zinc

Salifiable Simple Earthy Substances

New Names	Old Names
Lime	Chalk, calcareous earth Quicklime
Magnesia	Magnesia, base of Epsom salt Calcined or caustic magnesia
Barytes	Barytes, or heavy earth
Argill	Clay, earth of alum
Silex	Siliceous or vitrifiable earth

SECTION I

Observations upon the Table of Simple Substances

The principal object of chemical experiments is to decompose natural bodies, so as separately to examine the different substances which enter into their composition. By consulting chemical systems, it will be found that this science of chemical analysis has made rapid progress in our own times. Formerly oil and salt were considered as elements of bodies, whereas later observation and experiment have shown that all salts, instead of being simple, are composed of an acid united to a base. The bounds of analysis have been greatly enlarged by modern discoveries;[1] the acids are shown to be composed of oxygen, as an acidifying principle common to all, united in each to a particular base. I have proved what M. Hassenfratz had before advanced, that these radicals of the acids are not all simple elements, many of them being, like the oily principle, composed of hydrogen and charcoal. Even the bases of neutral salts have been proved by M. Berthollet to be compounds, as he has shown that ammonia is composed of azote and hydrogen.

[1] See *Recueil de l'Académie* for 1776, p. 671; and for 1778, p. 535.—AUTHOR.

TABLE *of Compound Oxidable and Acidifiable Bases*

Names of the Radicals

	Names of the Radicals	
Oxidable or acidifiable base, from the mineral kingdom	Nitro-muriatic radical or base of the acid formerly called *aqua regia*	
Oxidable or acidifiable hydro-carbonous or carbono-hydrous radicals from the vegetable kingdom.[2]	Tartarous radical or base Malic Citric Pyro-lignous Pyro-mucous Pyro-tartarous Oxalic Acetous Succinic Benzoic Camphoric Gallic	*Radicals*
Oxidable or acidifiable radicals from the animal kingdom, which mostly contain azote, and frequently phosphorus	Lactic Saccholactic Formic Bombic Sebacic Lithic Prussic	

[2] *Note.* The radicals from the vegetable kingdom are converted by a first degree of oxygenation into vegetable oxides, such as sugar, starch, and gum or mucus: those of the animal kingdom by the same means form animal oxides, as lymph, &c.—AUTHOR.

Thus, as chemistry advances towards perfection, by dividing and subdividing, it is impossible to say where it is to end; and these things we at present suppose simple may soon be found quite otherwise. All we dare venture to affirm of any substance is that it must be considered as simple in the present state of our knowledge and so far as chemical analysis has been able to show. We may even presume that the earths must soon cease to be considered as simple bodies; they are the only bodies of the salifiable class which have no tendency to unite with oxygen; and I am much inclined to believe that this proceeds from their being already saturated with that element. If so, they will fall to be considered as compounds consisting of simple substances, perhaps metallic, oxidated to a certain degree. This is only hazarded as a conjecture; and I trust the reader will take care not to confound what I have related as truths, fixed on the firm basis of observation and experiment, with mere hypothetical conjectures.

The fixed alkalies, potash, and soda, are omitted in the foregoing table, because they are evidently compound substances, though we are ignorant as yet what are the elements they are composed of.

SECTION II

Observations upon the Table of Compound Radicals

The older chemists being unacquainted with the composition of acids and not suspecting them to be formed by a peculiar radical or base for each, united to an acidifying principle or element common to all, could not consequently give any name to substances of which they had not the most distant idea. We had therefore to invent a new nomenclature for this subject, though we were at the same time sensible that this nomenclature must be susceptible of great modification when the nature of the compound radicals shall be better understood.[1]

The compound oxidable and acidifiable radicals from the vegetable and animal kingdoms, enumerated in the foregoing table, are not reducible to systematic nomenclature, because their exact analysis is as yet unknown. We only know in general, by some experiments of my own and some made by

M. Hassenfratz, that most of the vegetable acids, such as the tartarous, oxalic, citric, malic, acetous, pyrotartarous, and pyromucous, have radicals composed of hydrogen and charcoal, combined in such a way as to form single bases, and that these acids only differ from each other by the proportions in which these two substances enter into the composition of their bases, and by the degree of oxygenation which these bases have received. We know further, chiefly from the experiments of M. Berthollet, that the radicals from the animal kingdom, and even some of those from vegetables, are of a more compound nature, and, besides hydrogen and charcoal, that they often contain azote, and sometimes phosphorus; but we were not possessed of sufficiently accurate experiments for calculating the proportions of these several substances. We are therefore forced, in the manner of the older chemists, still to name these acids after the substances from which they are procured. There can be little doubt that these names will be laid aside when our knowledge of these substances becomes more accurate and extensive; the terms *hydro-carbonous*, *hydro-carbonic*, *carbono-hydrous*, and *carbono-hydric*,[2] will then become substituted for those we now employ, which will then only remain as testimonies of the imperfect state in which this part of chemistry was transmitted to us by our predecessors.

It is evident that the oils, being composed of hydrogen and charcoal combined, are true carbono-hydrous or hydro-carbonous radicals; and, indeed, by adding oxygen, they are convertible into vegetable oxides and acids according to their degrees of oxygenation. We cannot, however, affirm that oils enter in their entire state into the composition of vegetable oxides and acids; it is possible that they previously lose a part either of their hydrogen or charcoal, and that the remaining ingredients no longer exist in the proportions necessary to constitute oils. We still require further experiments to elucidate these points.

Properly speaking, we are only acquainted with one compound radical from the mineral kingdom, the nitro-muriatic, which is formed by the combination of azote with the muriatic radical. The other compound mineral acids have been much less attended to, from their producing less striking phenomena.

[1] See Part 1, Chapter XI, upon this subject.— AUTHOR.

[2] See Part I, Chapter XI, upon the application of these names according to the proportions of the two ingredients.—AUTHOR.

TABLE of Binary Combinations of Oxygen With Simple Substances

Simple Substances	First degree of Oxygenation — New Names	First degree of Oxygenation — Old Names	Second Degree — New Names	Second Degree — Old Names	Third Degree — New Names	Third Degree — Old Names	Fourth Degree — New Names
Combinations of oxygen with simple non-metallic substances							
Caloric......	Oxygen gas......	Vital or dephlogisticated air					
Hydrogen......	Water[1]......						
Azote......	Nitrous oxide, or base of nitrous gas......	Nitrous gas or air......	Nitrous acid......	Smoking nitrous acid......	Nitric acid......	Pale or non-smoking nitrous acid	Oxygenated nitric acid
Charcoal......	Oxide of charcoal, or carbonic oxide......	Unknown......	Carbonous acid......	Unknown......	Carbonic acid......	Fixed air	— carbonic
Sulphur......	Oxide of sulphur......	Soft sulphur......	Sulphurous acid......	Sulphurous acid......	Sulphuric acid......	Vitriolic acid......	— sulphuric
Phosphorus......	Oxide of phosphorus......	Residuum from the combustion of phosphorus......	Phosphorous acid......	Volatile acid of phosphorus......	Phosphoric acid......	Phosphoric acid......	— phosphoric
Muriatic radical......	Muriatic oxide......	Unknown......	Muriatous acid......	Unknown......	Muriatic acid......	Marine acid......	— muriatic acid, Old Name: Dephlogisticated marine acid
Fluoric radical......	Fluoric oxide......	Unknown......	Fluorous acid......	Unknown......	Fluoric acid......	Unknown till lately	
Boracic radical......	Boracic oxide......	Unknown......	Boracous acid......	Unknown......	Boracic acid......	Homberg's sedative salt	
Combinations of oxygen with simple metallic substances							
Antimony......	Grey oxide of antimony......	Grey calx of antimony......	White oxide of antimony......	White calx of antimony, diaphoretic antimony......	Antimonic acid		
Silver......	Oxide of silver......	Calx of silver......			Argentic acid		
Arsenic......	Grey oxide of arsenic......	Grey calx of arsenic......	White oxide of arsenic......	White calx of arsenic......	Arseniac acid......	Acid of arsenic......	— arseniac acid
Bismuth......	Grey oxide of bismuth......	Grey calx of bismuth......	White oxide of bismuth......	White calx of bismuth......	Bismuthic acid		
Cobalt......	Grey oxide of cobalt......	Grey calx of cobalt......			Cobaltic acid		
Copper......	Brown oxide of copper......	Brown calx of copper......	Blue and green oxides of copper......	Blue and green calces of copper......	Cupric acid		
Tin......	Grey oxide of tin......	Grey calx of tin......	White oxide of tin......	White calx of tin, or putty of tin......	Stannic acid		
Iron......	Black oxide of iron......	Martial ethiops......	Yellow and red oxides of iron......	Ochre and rust of iron......	Ferric acid		
Manganese......	Black oxide of manganese......	Black calx of manganese......	White oxide of manganese......	White calx of manganese......	Manganesic acid		
Mercury......	Black oxide of mercury......	Ethiops mineral......	Yellow and red oxides of mercury......	Turbith mineral, red precipitate, calcined mercury, precipitate per se......	Mercuric acid		
Molybdenum......	Oxide of molybdenum......	Calx of molybdenum......			Molybdic acid......	Acid of molybdenum......	— molybdic
Nickel......	Oxide of nickel......	Calx of nickel......			Nickelic acid		
Gold......	Yellow oxide of gold......	Yellow calx of gold......	Red oxide of gold......	Red calx of gold, purple precipitate of cassius......	Auric acid		
Platinum......	Yellow oxide of platinum......	Yellow calx of platinum......			Platinic acid		
Lead......	Grey oxide of lead......	Grey calx of lead......	Yellow and red oxides of lead......	Massicot and minium......	Plumbic acid		
Tungsten......	Oxide of tungsten......	Calx of tungsten......			Tungstic acid......	Acid of tungsten......	— tungstic acid
Zinc......	Grey oxide of zinc......	Grey calx of zinc......	White oxide of zinc......	White calx of zinc, pompholix......	Zincic acid		

[1]Only one degree of oxygenation of hydrogen is known.—AUTHOR.

Section III

Observations upon the Combinations of Light and Caloric with Different Substances

I have not constructed any table of the combinations of light and caloric with the various simple and compound substances, because our conceptions of the nature of these combinations are not hitherto sufficiently accurate. We know, in general, that all bodies in nature are imbued, surrounded, and penetrated in every way with caloric, which fills up every interval left between their particles; that, in certain cases, caloric becomes fixed in bodies, so as to constitute a part even of their solid substance, though it more frequently acts upon them with a repulsive force, from which, or from its accumulation in bodies to a greater or lesser degree, the transformation of solids into fluids, and of fluids to aeriform elasticity, is entirely owing. We have employed the generic name *gas* to indicate this aeriform state of bodies produced by a sufficient accumulation of caloric, so that, when we wish to express the aeriform state of muriatic acid, carbonic acid, hydrogen, water, alcohol, &c. we do it by adding the word *gas* to their names; thus muriatic acid gas, carbonic acid gas, hydrogen gas, aqueous gas, alcoholic gas, &c.

The combinations of light, and its mode of acting upon different bodies, is still less known. By the experiments of M. Berthollet, it appears to have great affinity with oxygen, is susceptible of combining with it, and contributes alongst with caloric to change it into the state of gas. Experiments upon vegetation give reason to believe that light combines with certain parts of vegetables, and that the green of their leaves, and the various colours of their flowers, is chiefly owing to this combination. This much is certain, that plants which grow in darkness are perfectly white, languid, and unhealthy, and that to make them recover vigour, and to acquire their natural colours, the direct influence of light is absolutely necessary. Something similar takes place even upon animals: mankind degenerate to a certain degree when employed in sedentary manufactures, from living in crowded houses or in the narrow lanes of large cities; whereas they improve in their nature and constitution in most of the country labours which are carried on in the open air. Organization, sensation, spontaneous motion, and all the operations of life, only exist at the surface of the earth, and in places exposed to the influence of light. Without it nature itself would be lifeless and inanimate. By means of light, the benevolence of the Deity hath filled the surface of the earth with organization, sensation, and intelligence. The fable of Prometheus might perhaps be considered as giving a hint of this philosophical truth, which had even presented itself to the knowledge of the ancients. I have intentionally avoided any disquisitions relative to organized bodies in this work, for which reason the phenomena of respiration, sanguification, and animal heat, are not considered; but I hope, at some future time, to be able to elucidate these curious subjects.

Section IV

Observations upon the Combinations of Oxygen with the Simple Substances

Oxygen forms almost a third of the mass of our atmosphere and is consequently one of the most plentiful substances in nature. All the animals and vegetables live and grow in this immense magazine of oxygen gas, and from it we procure the greatest part of what we employ in experiments. So great is the reciprocal affinity between this element and other substances that we cannot procure it disengaged from all combination. In the atmosphere it is united with caloric, in the state of oxygen gas, and this again is mixed with about two thirds of its weight of azotic gas.

Several conditions are requisite to enable a body to become oxygenated or to permit oxygen to enter into combination with it. In the first place, it is necessary that the particles of the body to be oxygenated shall have less reciprocal attraction with each other than they have for the oxygen, which otherwise cannot possibly combine with them. Nature, in this case, may be assisted by art, as we have it in our power to diminish the attraction of the particles of bodies almost at will by heating them, or, in other words, by introducing caloric into the interstices between their particles; and, as the attraction of these particles for each other is diminished in the inverse ratio of their distance, it is evident that there must be a certain point of distance of particles when the affinity they possess with each other becomes less than that they have for oxygen, and at which oxygenation must necessarily take place if oxygen be present.

We can readily conceive that the degree of heat at which this phenomenon begins must be different in different bodies. Hence, on purpose to oxygenate most bodies, especially the greater part of the simple substances, it is only necessary to expose them to the influence of the air of the atmosphere in a convenient degree of temperature. With respect to lead, mercury, and tin, this needs be but little higher than the medium temperature of the earth; but it requires a more considerable degree of heat to oxygenate iron, copper, &c., by the dry way, or when this operation is not assisted by moisture. Sometimes oxygenation takes place with great rapidity and is accompanied by great sensible heat, light, and flame; such is the combustion of phosphorus in atmospheric air and of iron in oxygen gas. That of sulphur is less rapid; and the oxygenation of lead, tin, and most of the metals, takes place vastly slower, and consequently the disengagement of caloric, and more especially of light, is hardly perceptible.

Some substances have so strong an affinity with oxygen, and combine with it in such low degrees of temperature, that we cannot procure them in their unoxygenated state; such is the muriatic acid, which has not hitherto been decomposed by art, perhaps even not by nature, and which consequently has only been found in the state of acid. It is probable that many other substances of the mineral kingdom are necessarily oxygenated in the common temperature of the atmosphere, and that being already saturated with oxygen prevents their further action upon that element.

There are other means of oxygenating simple substances besides exposure to air in a certain degree of temperature, such as by placing them in contact with metals combined with oxygen and which have little affinity with that element. The red oxide of mercury is one of the best substances for this purpose, especially with bodies which do not combine with that metal. In this oxide the oxygen is united with very little force to the metal, and can be driven out by a degree of heat only sufficient to make glass red hot; wherefore such bodies as are capable of uniting with oxygen are readily oxygenated by means of being mixed with red oxide of mercury and moderately heated. The

TABLE *of the Combinations of Oxygen with the Compound Radicals*

Names of the Radicals	Names of the Resulting Acids	
	New Names	Old Names
Nitro-muriatic radical	Nitro-muriatic acid	*Aqua regia*
Tartaric	Tartarous acid	Unknown till lately
Malic	Malic acid	Ditto
Citric	Citric acid	Acid of lemons
Pyro-lignous	Pyro-lignous acid	Empyreumatic acid of wood
Pyro-mucous	Pyro-mucous acid	Empyr. acid of sugar
Pyro-tartarous	Pyro-tartarous acid	Empyr. acid of tartar
Oxalic	Oxalic acid	Acid of sorel
Acetic	Acetous acid	Vinegar, or acid of vinegar
	Acetic acid	Radical vinegar
Succinic	Succinic acid	Volatile salt of amber
Benzoic	Benzotic acid	Flowers of benzoin
Camphoric	Camphoric acid	Unknown till lately
Gallic	Gallic acid	The astringent principle of vegetables
Lactic	Lactic acid	Acid of sour whey
Saccholactic	Saccholactic acid	Unknown till lately
Formic	Formic acid	Acid of ants
Bombic	Bombic acid	Unknown till lately
Sebacic	Sebacic acid	Ditto
Lithic	Lithic acid	Urinary calculus
Prussic	Prussic acid	Colouring matter of Prussian blue

(Tartaric through Prussic bracketed: See Note 1 for Tartaric–Gallic; See Note 2 for Lactic–Prussic)

Note 1: These radicals by a first degree of oxygenation form vegetable oxides, as sugar, starch, mucus, &c.—AUTHOR.

Note 2: These radicals by a first degree of oxygenation form the animal oxides, as lymph, red part of the blood, animal secretions, &c.—AUTHOR.

same effect may be, to a certain degree, produced by means of the black oxide of manganese, the red oxide of lead, the oxides of silver, and by most of the metallic oxides, if we only take care to choose such as have less affinity with oxygen than the bodies they are meant to oxygenate. All the metallic reductions and revivifications belong to this class of operations, being nothing more than oxygenations of charcoal by means of the several metallic oxides. The charcoal combines with the oxygen and with caloric and escapes in form of carbonic acid gas, while the metal remains pure and revivified, or deprived of the oxygen which before combined with it in the form of oxide.

All combustible substances may likewise be oxygenated by means of mixing them with nitrate of potash or of soda, or with oxygenated muriate of potash, and subjecting the mixture to a certain degree of heat; the oxygen, in this case, quits the nitrate or the muriate, and combines with the combustible body. This species of oxygenation requires to be performed with extreme caution and only with very small quantities; because, as the oxygen enters into the composition of nitrates, and more especially of oxygenated muriates, combined with almost as much caloric as is necessary for converting it into oxygen gas, this immense quantity of caloric becomes suddenly free the instant of the combination of the oxygen with the combustible body and produces such violent explosions as are perfectly irresistible.

By the humid way we can oxygenate most combustible bodies, and convert most of the oxides of the three kingdoms of nature into acids. For this purpose we chiefly employ the nitric acid, which has a very slight hold of oxygen, and quits it readily to a great number of bodies by the assistance of a gentle heat. The oxygenated muriatic acid may be used for several operations of this kind, but not in them all.

I give the name of *binary* to the combinations of oxygen with the simple substances, because in these only two elements are combined. When three substances are united in one combination I call it *ternary*, and *quaternary* when the combination consists of four substances united.

Section V

Observations upon the Combinations of Oxygen with the Compound Radicals

I published a new theory of the nature and formation of acids in the *Recueil de l'Académie* for 1776, p. 671 and 1778, p. 535 in which I concluded that the number of acids must be greatly larger than was till then supposed. Since that time, a new field of inquiry has been opened to chemists; and, instead of five or six acids which were then known, near thirty new acids have been discovered, by which means the number of known neutral salts have been increased in the same proportion. The nature of the acidifiable bases or radicals of the acids, and the degrees of oxygenation they are susceptible of, still remain to be inquired into. I have already shown that almost all the oxidable and acidifiable radicals from the mineral kingdom are simple, and that, on the contrary, there hardly exists any radical in the vegetable, and more especially in the animal kingdom, but is composed of at least two substances, hydrogen and charcoal, and that azote and phosphorus are frequently united to these, by which we have compound radicals of two, three, and four bases or simple elements united.

From these observations, it appears that the vegetable and animal oxides and acids may differ from each other in three several ways: 1st, according to the number of simple acidifiable elements of which their radicals are composed: 2nd, according to the proportions in which these are combined together: and, 3rd, according to their different degrees of oxygenation: which circumstances are more than sufficient to explain the great variety which nature produces in these substances. It is not at all surprising, after this, that most of the vegetable acids are convertible into each other, nothing more being requisite than to change the proportions of the hydrogen and charcoal in their composition, and to oxygenate them in a greater or lesser degree. This has been done by M. Crell in some very ingenious experiments, which have been verified and extended by M. Hassenfratz. From these it appears that charcoal and hydrogen by a first oxygenation produce tartarous acid, oxalic acid by a second degree, and acetous or acetic acid by a third, or higher oxygenation; only, that charcoal seems to exist in a rather smaller proportion in the acetous and acetic acids. The citric and malic acids differ little from the preceding acids.

Ought we then to conclude that the oils are the radicals of the vegetable and animal acids? I have already expressed my doubts upon this subject: 1st, although the oils appear to be formed of nothing but hydrogen and charcoal, we do not know if these are in the precise proportion necessary for constituting the radicals of the acids: 2nd, since oxygen enters into the composition of these acids equally with hydrogen and charcoal, there is no more reason for supposing them to be composed of oil rather than of water or of carbonic acid. It is true that they contain the materials necessary for all these combinations, but then these do not take place in the common temperature of the atmosphere; all the three elements remain

either to a solid or liquid form. This is likewise one of the essential constituent elements of animal bodies, in which it is combined with charcoal and hydrogen, and sometimes with phosphorus; these are united together by a certain portion of oxygen, by which they are formed into oxides or acids according to the degree of oxygenation. Hence the animal sub-

TABLE *of the Binary Combinations of Azote with the Simple Substances*

Simple Substances	Results of the Combinations	
	New Names	Old Names
Caloric	Azotic gas	Phlogisticated air, or Mephitis
Hydrogen	Ammonia	Volatile alkali
Oxygen	Nitrous oxide	Base of Nitrous gas
	Nitrous acid	Smoking nitrous acid
	Nitric acid	Pale nitrous acid
	Oxygenated nitric acid	Unknown
Charcoal	This combination is unknown; should it ever be discovered, it will be called, according to the principles of our nomenclature, Azuret of Charcoal. Charcoal dissolves in azotic gas and forms carbonated azotic gas	
Phosphorus	Azuret of phosphorus. Still unknown	
Sulphur	Azuret of sulphur. Still unknown. We know that sulphur dissolves in azotic gas, forming sulphurated azotic gas	
Compound radicals	Azote combines with charcoal and hydrogen, and sometimes with phosphorus, in the compound oxydable and acidifiable bases, and is generally contained in the radicals of the animal acids	
Metallic substances	Such combinations are unknown; if ever discovered, they will form metallic azurets, as azuret of gold, of silver, &c.	
Lime Magnesia Barytes Argill Potash Soda	Entirely unknown. If ever discovered, they will form azuret of lime, azuret of magnesia, &c.	

combined in a state of equilibrium which is readily destroyed by a temperature only a little above that of boiling water.[1]

SECTION VI

Observations upon the Combinations of Azote with the Simple Substances

Azote is one of the most abundant elements; combined with caloric it forms azotic gas, or mephitis, which composes nearly two thirds of the atmosphere. This element is always in the state of gas in the ordinary pressure and temperature, and no degree of compression or of cold has been hitherto capable of reducing it

stances may be varied, in the same way with vegetables, in three different manners: 1st, according to the number of elements which enter into the composition of the base or radical; 2nd, according to the proportions of these elements; 3rd, according to the degree of oxygenation.

When combined with oxygen, azote forms the nitrous and nitric oxides and acids; when with hydrogen, ammonia is produced. Its combinations with the other simple elements are very little known; to these we give the name of *azurets*, preserving the termination in *uret* for all non-oxygenated compounds. It is extremely probable that all the alkaline substances may hereafter be found to belong to this genus of azurets.

[1] See Part I, Chapter XII, upon this subject —
AUTHOR.

The azotic gas may be procured from atmospheric air, by absorbing the oxygen gas which is mixed with it by means of a solution of sulphuret of potash, or sulphuret of lime. It requires twelve or fifteen days to complete this process, during which time the surface in contact must be frequently renewed by agitation and by breaking the pellicle which forms on the top of the solution. It may likewise be procured by dissolving animal substances in dilute nitric acid very little heated. In this operation the azote is disengaged in form of gas, which we receive under bell glasses filled with water in the pneumato-chemical apparatus. We may procure this gas by deflagrating nitre with charcoal, or any other combustible substance; when with charcoal, the azotic gas is mixed with carbonic acid gas, which may be absorbed by a solution of caustic alkali or by lime water, after which the azotic gas remains pure. We can procure it in a fourth manner from combinations of ammonia with metallic oxides, as pointed out by M. de Fourcroy: the hydrogen of the ammonia combines with the oxygen of the oxide, and forms water; whilst the azote being left free escapes in form of gas.

The combinations of azote were but lately discovered: M. Cavendish first observed it in nitrous gas and acid, and M. Berthollet in ammonia and the prussic acid. As no evidence of its decomposition has hitherto appeared, we are fully entitled to consider azote as a simple elementary substance.

Section VII

Observations upon Hydrogen and Its Combinations with Simple Substances

Hydrogen, as its name expresses, is one of the constituent elements of water, of which it forms fifteen hundredth parts by weight, combined with eighty-five hundredth parts of oxygen. This substance, the properties and even existence of which was unknown till lately, is very plentifully distributed in nature and acts a very considerable part in the processes of the animal and vegetable kingdoms. As it possesses so great affinity with caloric as only to exist in the state of gas, it is consequently impossible to procure it in the concrete or liquid state, independent of combination.

To procure hydrogen, or rather hydrogen gas, we have only to subject water to the action of a substance with which oxygen has greater affinity than it has to hydrogen; by this means the hydrogen is set free and, by uniting with caloric, assumes the form of hydrogen gas. Red hot iron is usually employed for this purpose: the iron, during the process, becomes oxidated, and is changed into a substance resembling the iron ore from the island of Elba. In this state of oxide it is much less attractible by the magnet, and dissolves in acids without effervescence.

Charcoal, in a red heat, has the same power of decomposing water, by attracting the oxygen from its combination with hydrogen. In

Table of the Binary Combinations of Hydrogen with Simple Substances

Simple Substances	Resulting Compounds	
	New Names	Old Names
Caloric	Hydrogen gas	Inflammable air
Azote	Ammonia	Volatile Alkali
Oxygen	Water	Water
Sulphur	Hydruret of sulphur, or sulphuret of hydrogen	Hitherto unknown[1]
Phosphorus	Hydruret of phosphorus, or phosphuret of hydrogen	
Charcoal	Hydro-carbonous, or carbono hydrous radicals[2]	Not known till lately
Metallic substances, as iron, &c	Metallic hydrurets[3], as hydruret of iron, &c	Hitherto unknown

[1] These combinations take place in the state of gas, and form, respectively, sulphurated and phosphorated oxygen gas.—AUTHOR.

[2] This combination of hydrogen with charcoal includes the fixed and volatile oils, and forms the radicals of a considerable part of the vegetable and animal oxides and acids. When it takes place in the state of gas it forms carbonated hydrogen gas.—AUTHOR.

[3] None of these combinations are known, and it is probable that they cannot exist, at least in the usual temperature of the atmosphere, owing to the great affinity of hydrogen for caloric.—AUTHOR.

this process carbonic acid gas is formed and mixes with the hydrogen gas but is easily separated by means of water or alkalies, which absorb the carbonic acid and leave the hydrogen gas pure. We may likewise obtain hydrogen gas by dissolving iron or zinc in dilute sulphuric acid. These two metals decompose water very slowly, and with great difficulty, when alone, but do it with great ease and rapidity when assisted by sulphuric acid; the hydrogen unites with caloric during the process and is disengaged in form of hydrogen gas, while the oxygen of the water unites with the metal in the form of oxide, which is immediately dissolved in the acid, forming a sulphate of iron or of zinc.

Some very distinguished chemists consider hydrogen as the *phlogiston* of Stahl; and as that celebrated chemist admitted the existence of phlogiston in sulphur, charcoal, metals, &c., they are, of course, obliged to suppose that hydrogen exists in all these substances, though they cannot prove their supposition; even if they could, it would not avail much, since this disengagement of hydrogen is quite insufficient to explain the phenomena of calcination and combustion. We must always recur to the examination of this question, "Are the heat and light which are disengaged during the different species of combustion furnished by the burning body or by the oxygen which combines in all these operations?" And certainly the supposition of hydrogen being disengaged throws no light whatever upon this question. Besides, it belongs to those who make suppositions to prove them; and, doubtless, a doctrine which

TABLE *of the Binary Combinations of Sulphur with Simple Substances*

Simple Substances	Resulting Compounds	
	New Names	Old Names
Caloric	Sulphuric gas	
Oxygen	Oxide of sulphur	Soft sulphur
	Sulphurous acid	Sulphureous acid
	Sulphuric acid	Vitriolic acid
Hydrogen	Sulphuret of hydrogen	
Azote	azote	Unknown combinations
Phosphorus	phosphorus	
Charcoal	charcoal	
Antimony	antimony	Crude antimony
Silver	silver	
Arsenic	arsenic	Orpiment, realgar
Bismuth	bismuth	
Cobalt	cobalt	
Copper	copper	Copper pyrites
Tin	tin	
Iron	iron	Iron pyrites
Manganese	manganese	
Mercury	mercury	Ethiops mineral, cinnabar
Molybdenum	molybdenum	
Nickel	nickel	
Gold	gold	
Platinum	platinum	
Lead	lead	Galena
Tungsten	tungsten	
Zinc	zinc	Blende
Potash	potash	Alkaline liver of sulphur with fixed vegetable alkali
Soda	soda	Alkaline liver of sulphur with fixed mineral alkali
Ammonia	ammonia	Volatile liver of sulphur, smoking liquor of Boyle
Lime	lime	Calcareous liver of sulphur
Magnesia	magnesia	Magnesian liver of sulphur
Barytes	barytes	Barytic liver of sulphur
Argill	argill	Yet unknown

without any supposition explains the phenomena as well and as naturally as theirs does by supposition has at least the advantage of greater simplicity.[1]

Section VIII

Observations on Sulphur and its Combinations

Sulphur is a combustible substance, having a very great tendency to combination; it is naturally in a solid state in the ordinary temperature, and requires a heat somewhat higher than boiling water to make it liquify. Sulphur is formed by nature in a considerable degree of purity in the neighbourhood of volcanos; we find it likewise, chiefly in the state of sulphuric acid, combined with argill in aluminous schist, with lime in gypsum, &c. From these combinations it may be procured in the state of sulphur, by carrying off its oxygen by means of charcoal in a red heat; carbonic acid is formed and escapes in the state of gas; the sulphur remains combined with the clay, lime, &c. in the state of sulphuret, which is decomposed by acids; the acid unites with the earth into a neutral salt, and the sulphur is precipitated.

Table *of the Binary Combinations of Phosphorus with the Simple Substances*

Simple Substances	Resulting Compounds
Caloric	Phosphoric gas
Oxygen	Oxide of phosphorus Phosphorous acid Phosphoric acid
Hydrogen	Phosphuret of hydrogen
Azote	Phosphuret of azote
Sulphur	Phosphuret of sulphur
Charcoal	Phosphuret of charcoal
Metallic substances	Phosphuret of metals[2]
Potash Soda Ammonia Lime Barytes Magnesia Argill	Phosphuret of Potash, Soda, &c.[3]

[1] Those who wish to see what has been said upon this great chemical question by MM. de Morveau, Berthollet, de Fourcroy, and myself may consult our translation of M. Kirwan's *Essay upon Phlogiston.*—Author.

[2] Of all these combinations of phosphorus with metals, that with iron only is hitherto known, forming the substance formerly called *siderite;* neither is it yet ascertained whether, in this combination, the phosphorus be oxygenated or not.—Author.

[3] These combinations of phosphorus with the alkalies and earths are not yet known; and, from the experiments of M. Gengembre, they appear to be impossible.—Author.

Section IX

Observations upon Phosphorus and its Combinations

Phosphorus is a simple combustible substance, which was unknown to chemists till 1667, when it was discovered by Brandt, who kept the process secret; soon after, Kunkel found out Brandt's method of preparation and made it public. It has been ever since known by the name of Kunkel's phosphorus. It was for a long time procured only from urine; and, though Homberg gave an account of the process in the *Recueil de l'Académie* for 1692, all the philosophers of Europe were supplied with it from England. It was first made in France in 1737, before a committee of the Academy at the Royal Garden. At present it is procured in a more commodious and more economical manner from animal bones, which are real calcareous phosphates, according to the process of MM. Gahn, Scheele, Rouelle, &c. The bones of adult animals, being calcined to whiteness, are pounded and passed through a fine silk sieve; pour upon the fine powder a quantity of dilute sulphuric acid, less than is sufficient for dissolving the whole. This acid unites with the calcareous earth of the bones into a sulphate of lime, and the phosphoric acid remains free in the liquor. The liquid is decanted off, and the residuum washed with boiling water; this water which has been used to wash out the adhering acid is joined with what was before decanted off, and the whole is gradually evaporated; the dissolved sulphate of lime crystallizes in form of silky threads, which are removed, and by continuing the evaporation we procure the phosphoric acid under the appearance of a white pellucid glass. When this is powdered and mixed with one third its weight of charcoal, we procure very pure phosphorus by sublimation. The phosphoric acid, as procured by the above process, is never so pure as that obtained by oxygenating pure phosphorus either by combustion or by means of nitric acid; wherefore this latter should always be employed in experiments of research.

Phosphorus is found in almost all animal substances, and in some plants which give a kind of animal analysis. In all these it is usually combined with charcoal, hydrogen, and azote, forming very compound radicals, which are, for the most part, in the state of oxides by a first degree of union with oxygen. The discovery of M. Hassenfratz, of phosphorus being contained in charcoal, gives reason to suspect that it is more common in the vegetable kingdom than has generally been supposed. It is certain that by proper processes it may be procured from every individual of some of the families of plants. As no experiment has hitherto given reason to suspect that phosphorus is a compound body, I have arranged it with the simple or elementary substances. It takes fire at the temperature of 32° (104°) of the thermometer.

In the business of charring wood, this is done by a less expensive process. The wood is disposed in heaps and covered with earth, so as to prevent the access of any more air than is absolutely necessary for supporting the fire, which is kept up till all the water and oil is driven off, after which the fire is extinguished by shutting up all the air-holes.

We may analyse charcoal either by combustion in air, or rather in oxygen gas, or by means

TABLE of Binary Combinations of Charcoal

Simple Substances	Resulting Compounds New Names	Old Names
Oxygen	Oxide of charcoal	Unknown
	Carbonic acid	Fixed air, chalky acid
Sulphur	Carburet of sulphur	
Phosphorus	Carburet of phosphorus	Unknown
Azote	Carburet of azote	
Hydrogen	Carbono-hydrous radical	
	Fixed and volatile oils	
Metallic substances	Carburets of metals	Of these only the carburets of iron and zinc are known, and were formerly called Plumbago
Alkalies and earths	Carburet of potash, &c.	Unknown

SECTION X

Observations upon Charcoal and its Combinations with Simple Substances

As charcoal has not been hitherto decomposed, it must, in the present state of our knowledge, be considered as a simple substance. By modern experiments it appears to exist ready formed in vegetables; and I have already remarked that in these it is combined with hydrogen, sometimes with azote and phosphorus, forming compound radicals which may be changed into oxides or acids according to their degree of oxygenation.

To obtain the charcoal contained in vegetable or animal substances, we subject them to the action of fire, at first moderate and afterwards very strong, on purpose to drive off the last portions of water, which adhere very obstinately to the charcoal. For chemical purposes, this is usually done in retorts of stoneware or porcelain, into which the wood, or other matter, is introduced, and then placed in a reverberatory furnace, raised gradually to its greatest heat. The heat volatilizes, or changes into gas, all the parts of the body susceptible of combining with caloric into that form, and the charcoal, being more fixed in its nature, remains in the retort combined with a little earth and some fixed salts.

of nitric acid. In either case we convert it into carbonic acid, and sometimes a little potash and some neutral salts remain. This analysis has hitherto been but little attended to by chemists; and we are not even certain if potash exists in charcoal before combustion or whether it be formed by means of some unknown combination during that process.

SECTION XI

Observations upon the Muriatic, Fluoric, and Boracic Radicals and their Combinations

As the combinations of these substances, either with each other or with the other combustible bodies, are entirely unknown, we have not attempted to form any table for their nomenclature. We only know that these radicals are susceptible of oxygenation, and of forming the muriatic, fluoric, and boracic acids, and that in the acid state they enter into a number of combinations, to be afterwards detailed. Chemistry has hitherto been unable to disoxygenate any of them, so as to produce them in a simple state. For this purpose, some substance must be employed to which oxygen has a stronger affinity than to their radicals, either by means of single affinity or by double elective attraction. All that is known relative to the origin of the radicals of these acids will be mentioned in the sections set apart for considering their combinations with the salifiable bases.

Observations upon the Combinations of Metals with Each Other

Before closing our account of the simple or elementary substances, it might be supposed necessary to give a table of alloys or combinations of metals with each other; but, as such a table would be both exceedingly voluminous and very unsatisfactory, without going into a series of experiments not yet attempted, I have thought it adviseable to omit it altogether. All that is necessary to be mentioned is that these alloys should be named according to the metal in largest proportion in the mixture or combination; thus the term *alloy of gold and silver*, or gold alloyed with silver, indicates that gold is the predominating metal.

Metallic alloys, like all other combinations, have a point of saturation. It would even appear, from the experiments of M. de la Briche, that they have two perfectly distinct degrees of saturation.

TABLE *of the Combinations of Azote, Completely Saturated with Oxygen, in the State of Nitric Acid, with the Salifiable Bases, in the Order of the Affinity with the Acid*

Bases	Names of the Resulting Neutral Salts	
	New Names	Old Names
Barytes	Nitrate of barytes	Nitre, with a base of heavy earth
Potash	potash	Nitre, Saltpetre; Nitre with base of potash
Soda	soda	Quadrangular nitre; Nitre with base of mineral alkali
Lime	lime	Calcareous nitre; Nitre with calcareous base; Mother water of nitre, or saltpetre
Magnesia	magnesia	Magnesian nitre; Nitre with base of magnesia
Ammonia	ammonia	Ammoniacal nitre
Argill	argill	Nitrous alum; Argillaceous nitre; Nitre with base of earth of alum
Oxide of zinc	zinc	Nitre of zinc
iron	iron	Nitre of iron; Martial nitre; Nitrated iron
manganese	manganese	Nitre of manganese
cobalt	cobalt	Nitre of cobalt
nickel	nickel	Nitre of nickel
lead	lead	Saturnine nitre; Nitre of lead
tin	tin	Nitre of tin
copper	copper	Nitre of copper or of Venus
bismuth	bismuth	Nitre of bismuth
antimony	antimony	Nitre of antimony
arsenic	arsenic	Arsenical nitre
mercury	mercury	Mercurial nitre
silver	silver	Nitre of silver or luna; Lunar caustic
gold	gold	Nitre of gold
platinum	platinum	Nitre of platinum

TABLE *of the Combinations of Azote in the State of Nitrous Acid with the Salifiable Bases, Arranged According to the Affinities of These Bases with the Acid*

Names of the Bases	Names of the Neutral Salts New Names	Notes
Barytes	Nitrite of barytes	
Potash	potash	
Soda	soda	These salts are only known of late and have received no particular name in the old nomenclature.
Lime	lime	
Magnesia	magnesia	
Ammonia	ammonia	
Argill	argill	
Oxide of zinc	zinc	
iron	iron	As metals dissolve both in nitrous and nitric acids, metallic salts must of consequence be formed having different degrees of oxygenation. Those wherein the metal is least oxygenated must be called Nitrites, when more so, Nitrates; but the limits of this distinction are difficultly ascertainable. The older chemists were not acquainted with any of these salts.
manganese	manganese	
cobalt	cobalt	
nickel	nickel	
lead	lead	
tin	tin	
copper	copper	
bismuth	bismuth	
antimony	antimony	
arsenic	arsenic	
mercury	mercury	
silver	It is extremely probable that gold, silver, and platinum only form nitrates, and cannot subsist in the state of nitrites.	
gold		
platinum		

SECTION XIII

Observations upon Nitrous and Nitric Acids and their Combinations with Salifiable Bases

The nitrous and nitric acids are procured from a neutral salt long known in the arts under the name of *saltpetre*. This salt is extracted by lixiviation from the rubbish of old buildings, from the earth of cellars, stables, or barns, and in general of all inhabited places. In these earths the nitric acid is usually combined with lime and magnesia, sometimes with potash, and rarely with argill. As all these salts, excepting the nitrate of potash, attract the moisture of the air, and consequently would be difficultly preserved, advantage is taken, in the manufactures of saltpetre and the royal refining-house, of the greater affinity of the nitric acid to potash than these other bases, by which means the lime, magnesia, and argill, are precipitated, and all these nitrates are reduced to the nitrate of potash or saltpetre.

The nitric acid is procured from this salt by distillation, from three parts of pure saltpetre decomposed by one part of concentrated sulphuric acid, in a retort with Woulfe's apparatus, (Plate IV, *Fig. 1*) having its bottles half filled with water, and all its joints carefully luted. The nitrous acid passes over in form of red vapours surcharged with nitrous gas, or, in other words, not saturated with oxygen. Part of the acid condenses in the recipient in form of a dark orange red liquid, while the rest combines with the water in the bottles. During the distillation, a large quantity of oxygen gas escapes, owing to the greater affinity of oxygen to caloric in a high temperature than to nitrous acid, though in the usual temperature of the atmosphere this affinity is reversed. It is from the disengagement of oxygen that the nitric acid of the neutral salt is in this operation converted into nitrous acid. It is brought back to the state of nitric acid by heating over a gentle fire, which drives off the superabundant nitrous gas, and leaves the nitric acid much diluted with water.

Nitric acid is procurable in a more concentrated state, and with much less loss, by mixing very dry clay with saltpetre. This mixture is put into an earthen retort and distilled with a strong fire. The clay combines with the potash, for which it has great affinity, and the nitric acid passes over, slightly impregnated with nitrous gas. This is easily disengaged by heating the acid gently in a retort; a small quantity of nitrous gas passes over into the recipient, and very pure concentrated nitric acid remains in the retort.

We have already seen that azote is the nitric radical. If to 20½ parts, by weight, of azote 43½ parts of oxygen be added, 64 parts of nitrous gas are formed; and, if to this we join 36 additional parts of oxygen, 100 parts of nitric acid result from the combination. Intermediate quantities of oxygen between these two extremes of oxygenation produce different species of nitrous acid, or, in other words, nitric acid less or more impregnated with nitrous gas. I ascertained the above proportions by means of decomposition; and, though I cannot answer for their absolute accuracy, they cannot be far removed from truth. M. Cavendish, who first showed by synthetic experiments that azote is the base of nitric acid, gives the proportions of azote a little larger than I have done; but, as it is not improbable that he produced the nitrous acid and not the nitric, that circumstance explains in some degree the difference in the results of our experiments.

As in all experiments of a philosophical nature the utmost possible degree of accuracy is required, we must procure the nitric acid for experimental purposes from nitre which has been previously purified from all foreign matter. If, after distillation, any sulphuric acid is suspected in the nitric acid, it is easily separated by dropping in a little nitrate of barytes, so

TABLE *of the Combinations of Sulphuric Acid with the Salifiable Bases, in the Order of Affinity*

Names of the Bases	Resulting Compounds New Names	Old Names
Barytes	Sulphate of barytes	Heavy spar; vitriol of heavy earth
Potash	potash	Vitriolated tartar; *sal de duobus; arcanum duplicatam*
Soda	soda	Glauber's salt
Lime	lime	Selenite, gypsum, calcareous vitriol
Magnesia	magnesia	Epsom salt, sedlitz salt, magnesian vitriol
Ammonia	ammonia	Glauber's secret sal ammoniac
Argill	argill	Alum
Oxide of zinc	zinc	White vitriol, goslar vitriol, white coperas, vitriol of zinc
iron	iron	Green coperas, green vitriol, martial vitriol, vitriol of iron
manganese	manganese	Vitriol of manganese
cobalt	cobalt	Vitriol of cobalt
nickel	nickel	Vitriol of nickel
lead	lead	Vitriol of lead
tin	tin	Vitriol of tin
copper	copper	Blue coperas, blue vitriol, Roman vitriol, vitriol of copper
bismuth	bismuth	Vitriol of bismuth
antimony	antimony	Vitriol of antimony
arsenic	arsenic	Vitriol of arsenic
mercury	mercury	Vitriol of mercury
silver	silver	Vitriol of silver
gold	gold	Vitriol of gold
platinum	platinum	Vitriol of platinum

long as any precipitation takes place; the sulphuric acid, from its greater affinity, attracts the barytes and forms with it an insoluble neutral salt, which falls to the bottom. It may be purified in the same manner from muriatic acid, by dropping in a little nitrate of silver so long as any precipitation of muriate of silver is produced. When these two precipitations are finished, distill off about seven-eighths of the acid by a gentle heat, and what comes over is in the most perfect degree of purity.

The nitric acid is one of the most prone to combination and is at the same time very easily decomposed. Almost all the simple substances, with the exception of gold, silver, and platinum, rob it less or more of its oxygen; some of them even decompose it altogether. It was very anciently known, and its combinations have been more studied by chemists than those of any other acid. These combinations were named *nitres* by MM. Macquer and Beaumé; but we have changed their names to nitrates and nitrites, according as they are formed by nitric or by nitrous acid, and have added the specific name of each particular base, to distinguish the several combinations from each other

SECTION XIV

Observations upon Sulphuric Acid and its Combinations

For a long time this acid was procured by distillation from sulphate of iron, in which sulphuric acid and oxide of iron are combined according to the process described by Basil Valentine in the fifteenth century; but, in modern times, it is procured more economically by the combustion of sulphur in proper vessels. Both to facilitate the combustion, and to assist the oxygenation of the sulphur, a little powdered saltpetre, nitrate of potash, is mixed with it; the nitre is decomposed and gives out its oxygen to the sulphur, which contributes to its conversion into acid. Notwithstanding this addition, the sulphur will only continue to burn in close vessels for a limited time; the combination ceases, because the oxygen is exhausted and the air of the vessels reduced almost to pure azotic gas, and because the acid itself remains long in the state of vapour and hinders the progress of combustion.

In the factories for making sulphuric acid in the large way, the mixture of nitre and sulphur is burnt in large close-built chambers lined with lead, having a little water at the bottom for facilitating the condensation of the vapours. Afterwards, by distillation in large retorts with a gentle heat, the water passes over, slightly impregnated with acid, and the sulphuric acid remains behind in a concentrated state. It is then pellucid, without any flavour, and nearly double the weight of an equal bulk of water. This process would be greatly facilitated, and the combustion much prolonged, by introducing fresh air into the chambers by means of several pairs of bellows directed towards the flame of the sulphur, and by allowing the nitrous gas to escape through long serpentine canals, in contact with water, to absorb any sulphuric or sulphurous acid gas it might contain.

By one experiment, M. Berthollet found that 69 parts of sulphur in combustion united with 31 parts of oxygen to form 100 parts of sulphuric acid; and, by another experiment, made in a different manner, he calculates that 100 parts of sulphuric acid consists of 72 parts sulphur, combined with 28 parts of oxygen, all by weight.

TABLE *of the Combinations of the Sulphurous Acid with the Salifiable Bases, in the Order of Affinity*

Names of the Bases	Names of the Neutral Salts
Barytes	Sulphite of barytes
Potash	potash
Soda	soda
Lime	lime
Magnesia	magnesia
Ammonia	ammonia
Argill	argill
Oxide of zinc	zinc
iron	iron
manganese	manganese
cobalt	cobalt
nickel	nickel
lead	lead
tin	tin
copper	copper
bismuth	bismuth
antimony	antimony
arsenic	arsenic
mercury	mercury
silver	silver
gold	gold
platinum	platinum

Note. The only one of these salts known to the old chemists was the sulphite of potash, under the name of *Stahl's sulphureous salt*. So that, before our new nomenclature, these compounds must have been named *Stahl's sulphureous salt*, having base of fixed vegetable alkali, and so of the rest.

In this table we have followed Bergman's order of affinity of the sulphuric acid, which is the same in regard to the earths and alkalies, but it is not certain if the order be the same for the metallic oxides.— AUTHOR.

This acid, in common with every other, can only dissolve metals when they have been previously oxidated; but most of the metals are capable of decomposing a part of the acid, so as to carry off a sufficient quantity of oxygen to render themselves soluble in the part of the acid which remains undecomposed. This happens with silver, mercury, iron, and zinc, in boiling concentrated sulphuric acid; they become first oxidated by decomposing part of the acid, and then dissolve in the other part; but they do not sufficiently disoxygenate the decomposed part of the acid to reconvert it into sulphur; it is only reduced to the state of sulphurous acid, which, being volatilised by the heat, flies off in form of sulphurous acid gas.

Silver, mercury, and all the other metals except iron and zinc, are insoluble in diluted sulphuric acid, because they have not sufficient affinity with oxygen to draw it off from its combination either with the sulphur, the sulphurous acid, or the hydrogen; but iron and zinc, being assisted by the action of the acid, decompose the water and become oxidated at its expense, without the help of heat.

Section XV

Observations upon Sulphurous Acid and its Combinations with Salifiable Bases

The sulphurous acid is formed by the union of oxygen with sulphur by a lesser degree of oxygenation than the sulphuric acid. It is procurable either by burning sulphur slowly, or by distilling sulphuric acid from silver, antimony, lead, mercury, or charcoal; by which operation a part of the oxygen quits the acid and unites to these oxidable bases, and the acid passes over in the sulphurous state of oxygenation. This acid, in the common pressure and temperature of the air, can only exist in form of gas; but it appears, from the experiments of M. Clouet, that, in a very low temperature, it condenses and becomes fluid. Water absorbs a great deal more of this gas than of carbonic acid gas, but much less than it does of muriatic acid gas.

That the metals cannot be dissolved in acids without being previously oxidated, or by procuring oxygen for that purpose from the acids during solution, is a general and well estab-

TABLE *of the Combinations of Phosphorous and Phosphoric Acids, with the Salifiable Bases, in Order of Affinity*

Names of the Bases	Names of the Neutral Salts formed by	
	Phosphorous Acid	Phosphoric Acid
Lime	Phosphites of lime[2]	Phosphates of lime[3]
Barytes	barytes	barytes
Magnesia	magnesia	magnesia
Potash	potash	potash
Soda	soda	soda
Ammonia	ammonia	ammonia
Argill	argill	argill
Oxides of zinc[1]	zinc	zinc
iron	iron	iron
manganese	manganese	manganese
cobalt	cobalt	cobalt
nickel	nickel	nickel
lead	lead	lead
tin	tin	tin
copper	copper	copper
bismuth	bismuth	bismuth
antimony	antimony	antimony
arsenic	arsenic	arsenic
mercury	mercury	mercury
silver	silver	silver
gold	gold	gold
platinum	platinum	platinum

[1] The existence of metallic phosphites supposes that metals are susceptible of solution in phosphoric acid at different degrees of oxygenation, which is not yet ascertained.—AUTHOR.

[2] All the phosphites were unknown till lately, and consequently have not yet received names.—AUTHOR.

[3] The greater part of the phosphates were only discovered of late, and have not yet been named.—AUTHOR.

lished fact which I have perhaps repeated too often. Hence, as sulphurous acid is already deprived of great part of the oxygen necessary for forming the sulphuric acid, it is more disposed to recover oxygen than to furnish it to the greatest part of the metals; and, for this reason, it cannot dissolve them unless previously oxidated by other means. From the same principle it is that the metallic oxides dissolve without effervescence, and with great facility, in sulphurous acid. This acid, like the muriatic, has even the property of dissolving metallic oxides surcharged with oxygen, and consequently insoluble in sulphuric acid, and in this way forms true sulphates. Hence we might be led to conclude that there are no metallic sulphites, were it not that the phenomena which accompany the solution of iron, mer-

cury, and some other metals, convince us that these metallic substances are susceptible of two degrees of oxidation, during their solution in acids. Hence the neutral salt in which the metal is least oxidated must be named *sulphite*, and that in which it is fully oxidated must be called *sulphate*. It is yet unknown whether this distinction is applicable to any of the metallic sulphates, except those of iron and mercury.

SECTION XVI

Observations upon Phosphorous and Phosphoric Acids and their Combinations with Salifiable Bases

Under the article Phosphorus, Part II, Section IX, we have already given a history of the discovery of that singular substance, with some

TABLE *of the Combinations of Carbonic Acid, with the Salifiable Bases, in the Order of Affinity*

Names of Bases[1]	New Names	Resulting Neutral Salts	
		Old Names	
Barytes	Carbonates of barytes	Aerated or effervescent heavy earth	
Lime	lime	Chalk, calcareous spar, aerated calcareous earth	
Potash	potash	Effervescing or aerated fixed vegetable alkali, mephitis of potash	
Soda	soda	Aerated or effervescing fixed mineral alkali, mephitic soda	
Magnesia	magnesia	Aerated, effervescing, mild, or mephitic magnesia	
Ammonia	ammonia	Aerated, effervescing, mild, or mephitic volatile alkali	
Argill	argill	Aerated or effervescing argillaceous earth, or earth of alum	
Oxide of zinc	zinc	Zinc spar, mephitic or aerated zinc	
iron	iron	Sparry iron-ore, mephitic or aerated iron	
manganese	manganese	Aerated manganese	
cobalt	cobalt	Aerated cobalt	
nickel	nickel	Aerated nickel	
lead	lead	Sparry lead-ore, or aerated lead	
tin	tin	Aerated tin	
copper	copper	Aerated copper	
bismuth	bismuth	Aerated bismuth	
antimony	antimony	Aerated antimony	
arsenic	arsenic	Aerated arsenic	
mercury	mercury	Aerated mercury	
silver	silver	Aerated silver	
gold	gold	Aerated gold	
platinum	platinum	Aerated platinum	

[1] As these salts have only been understood of late, they have not, properly speaking, any old names. M. Morveau, in the first volume of the *Encyclopedia*, calls them *Mephites;* M. Bergman gives them the name of *aerated;* and M. de Fourcroy, who calls the carbonic acid *chalky acid*, gives them the name of *chalks.*—AUTHOR.

observations upon the mode of its existence in vegetable and animal bodies. The best method of obtaining this acid in a state of purity is by burning well purified phosphorus under bell-glasses, moistened on the inside with distilled water; during combustion it absorbs twice and a half its weight of oxygen; so that 100 parts of phosphoric acid is composed of 28½ parts of phosphorus united to 71½ parts of oxygen. This acid may be obtained concrete, in form of white flakes which greedily attract the moisture of the air, by burning phosphorus in a dry glass over mercury.

To obtain phosphorous acid, which is phosphorus less oxygenated than in the state of phosphoric acid, the phosphorus must be burnt by a very slow spontaneous combustion over a glass-funnel leading into a crystal phial; after a few days, the phosphorus is found oxygenated, and the phosphorous acid, in proportion as it forms, has attracted moisture from the air and dropped into the phial. The phosphorous acid is readily changed into phosphoric acid by exposure for a long time to the free air; it absorbs oxygen from the air and becomes fully oxygenated.

As phosphorus has a sufficient affinity for oxygen to attract it from the nitric and muriatic acids, we may form phosphoric acid by means of these acids in a very simple and cheap manner. Fill a tubulated receiver half full of concentrated nitric acid and heat it gently, then throw in small pieces of phosphorus through the tube; these are dissolved with effervescence and red fumes of nitrous gas fly off; add phosphorus so long as it will dissolve, and then increase the fire under the retort to drive off the last particles of nitric acid; phosphoric acid, partly fluid and partly concrete, remains in the retort.

Section XVII

Observations upon Carbonic Acid and its Combinations with Salifiable Bases

Of all the known acids, the carbonic is the most abundant in nature; it exists ready formed in chalk, marble, and all the calcareous stones, in which it is neutralized by a particular earth called *lime*. To disengage it from this combination, nothing more is requisite than to add some sulphuric acid, or any other which has a stronger affinity for lime; a brisk effervescence ensues, which is produced by the disengagement of the carbonic acid which assumes the state of gas immediately upon being set free. This gas,

incapable of being condensed into the solid or liquid form by any degree of cold or of pressure hitherto known, unites to about its own bulk of water and thereby forms a very weak acid. It may likewise be obtained in great abundance from saccharine matter in fermentation but is then contaminated by a small portion of alcohol which it holds in solution.

As charcoal is the radical of this acid, we may form it artificially by burning charcoal in oxygen gas, or by combining charcoal and metallic oxides in proper proportions; the oxygen of the oxide combines with the charcoal, forming carbonic acid gas, and the metal being left free recovers its metallic or reguline form.

We are indebted for our first knowledge of this acid to Dr. Black, before whose time its property of remaining always in the state of gas had made it to elude the researches of chemistry.

It would be a most valuable discovery to society if we could decompose this gas by any cheap process, as by that means we might obtain, for economical purposes, the immense store of charcoal contained in calcareous earths, marbles, limestones, &c. This cannot be effected by single affinity, because to decompose the carbonic acid it requires a substance as

TABLE *of the Combinations of Oxygenated Muriatic Acid with the Salifiable Bases, in the Order of Affinity*

Names of the Bases	Neutral Salts, New Names
Barytes	Oxygenated muriate of barytes
Potash	potash
Soda	soda
Lime	lime
Magnesia	magnesia
Argill	argill
Oxide of zinc	zinc
iron	iron
manganese	manganese
cobalt	cobalt
nickel	nickel
lead	lead
tin	tin
copper	copper
bismuth	bismuth
antimony	antimony
arsenic	arsenic
mercury	mercury
silver	silver
gold	gold
platinum	platinum

This order of salts, entirely unknown to the ancient chemists, was discovered in 1786 by M. Berthollet.—AUTHOR.

TABLE *of the Combinations of Muriatic Acid with the*
Salifiable Bases in the Order of Affinity

Names of the Bases	New Names	Resulting Neutral Salts Old Names
Barytes	Muriate of barytes	Sea-salt, having base of heavy earth
Potash	potash	Febrifuge salt of Sylvius; Muriated vegetable fixed alkali
Soda	soda	Sea-salt
Lime	lime	Muriated lime Oil of lime
Magnesia	magnesia	Marine Epsom salt Muriated magnesia
Ammonia	ammonia	Sal ammoniac
Argill	argill	Muriated alum, sea-salt with base of earth of alum
Oxide of zinc	zinc	Sea-salt of, or muriatic zinc
iron	iron	Salt of iron, Martial sea-salt
manganese	manganese	Sea-salt of manganese
cobalt	cobalt	Sea-salt of cobalt
nickel	nickel	Sea-salt of nickel
lead	lead	Horny-lead; *plumbum corneum*
tin	smoking of tin solid of tin	Smoking liquor of Libavius Solid butter of tin
copper	copper	Sea-salt of copper
bismuth	bismuth	Sea-salt of bismuth
antimony	antimony	Sea-salt of antimony
arsenic	arsenic	Sea-salt of arsenic
mercury	sweet of mercury	Sweet sublimate of mercury, calomel, *aquila alba*
	corrosive of mercury	Corrosive sublimate of mercury
silver	silver	Horny silver, *argentum corneum, luna cornea*
gold	gold	Sea-salt of gold
platinum	platinum	Sea-salt of platinum

combustible as charcoal itself, so that we should only make an exchange of one combustible body for another not more valuable; but it may possibly be accomplished by double affinity, since this process is so readily performed by nature during vegetation from the most common materials.

Section XVIII

Observations upon Muriatic and Oxygenated Muriatic Acid and their Combinations with Salifiable Bases

Muriatic acid is very abundant in the mineral kingdom naturally combined with different salifiable bases, especially with soda, lime, and magnesia. In sea-water, and the water of several lakes, it is combined with these three bases, and in mines of rock-salt it is chiefly united to soda. This acid does not appear to have been hitherto decomposed in any chemical experiment; so that we have no idea whatever of the nature of its radical and only conclude from analogy with the other acids that it contains oxygen as its acidifying principle. M. Berthollet suspects the radical to be of a metallic nature; but, as nature appears to form this acid daily in inhabited places by combining miasmata with aeriform fluids, this must necessarily suppose a metallic gas to exist in the atmosphere, which is certainly not impossible but cannot be admitted without proof.

The muriatic acid has only a moderate adherence to the salifiable bases and can readily be driven from its combination with these by sulphuric acid. Other acids, as the nitric for instance, may answer the same purpose; but nitric acid being volatile would mix, during distillation, with the muriatic. About one part of sulphuric acid is sufficient to decompose two parts of decrepitated sea-salt. This operation is performed in a tubulated retort, having Woulfe's apparatus, (Plate IV, *Fig. 1*), adapted to it. When all the junctures are properly luted, the sea-salt is put into the retort through the tube, the sulphuric acid is poured on, and the opening immediately closed with its ground crystal stopper. As the muriatic acid can only subsist in the gaseous form in the ordinary temperature, we could not condense it without the presence of water. Hence the use of the water with which the bottles in Woulfe's apparatus are half filled; the muriatic acid gas, driven off from the sea-salt in the retort, combines with the water and forms what the old chemists called *smoking spirit of salt*, or *Glauber's spirit of sea-salt*, which we now name *muriatic acid*.

TABLE *of the Combinations of Nitro-Muriatic Acid with the Salifiable Bases in the Order of Affinity so Far as is Known*

Names of the Bases	Names of the Neutral Salts
Argill	Nitro-muriate of argill
Ammonia	ammonia
Oxide of antimony	antimony
silver	silver
arsenic	arsenic
Barytes	barytes
Oxide of bismuth	bismuth
Lime	lime
Oxide of cobalt	cobalt
copper	copper
tin	tin
iron	iron
Magnesia	magnesia
Oxide of manganese	manganese
mercury	mercury
molybdenum	molybdenum
nickel	nickel
gold	gold
platinum	platinum
lead	lead
Potash	potash
Soda	soda
Oxide of tungsten	tungsten
zinc	zinc

Note.—Most of these combinations, especially those with the earths and alkalies, have been little examined, and we are yet to learn whether they form a mixed salt in which the compound radical remains combined, or if the two acids separate to form two distinct neutral salts.—AUTHOR.

The acid obtained by the above process is still capable of combining with a further dose of oxygen, by being distilled from the oxides of manganese, lead, or mercury, and the resulting acid, which we name *oxygenated muriatic acid*, can only, like the former, exist in the gaseous form and is absorbed in a much smaller quantity by water. When the impregnation of water with this gas is pushed beyond a certain point, the superabundant acid precipitates to the bottom of the vessels in a concrete form. M. Berthollet has shown that this acid is capable of combining with a great number of the salifiable bases; the neutral salts which result from this union are susceptible of deflagrating with charcoal and many of the metallic substances; these deflagrations are very violent and dangerous, owing to the great quantity of caloric which the oxygen carries alongst with it into the composition of oxygenated muriatic acid.

SECTION XIX

Observations upon Nitro-Muriatic Acid and its Combinations with Salifiable Bases

The nitro-muriatic acid, formerly called *aqua regia*, is formed by a mixture of nitric and muriatic acids; the radicals of these two acids combine together and form a compound base, from which an acid is produced, having properties peculiar to itself and distinct from those of all other acids, especially the property of dissolving gold and platinum.

In dissolutions of metals in this acid, as in all other acids, the metals are first oxidated by attracting a part of the oxygen from the compound radical. This occasions a disengagement of a particular species of gas not hitherto described, which may be called *nitro-muriatic gas*; it has a very disagreeable smell and is fatal to animal life when respired; it attacks iron and causes it to rust; it is absorbed in considerable quantity by water, which thereby acquires some slight characters of acidity. I had occasion to make these remarks during a course of experiments upon platinum, in which I dissolved a considerable quantity of that metal in nitromuriatic acid.

I at first suspected that in the mixture of nitric and muriatic acids the latter attracted a part of the oxygen from the former and became converted into oxygenated muriatic acid, which gave it the property of dissolving gold; but several facts remain inexplicable upon this supposition. Were it so, we must be able to disengage nitrous gas by heating this acid, which however does not sensibly happen. From these considerations, I am led to adopt the opinion of M. Berthollet and to consider nitro-muriatic acid as a single acid, with a compound base or radical.

TABLE *of the Combinations of Fluoric Acid with the Salifiable Bases, in the Order of Affinity*

Names of the Bases	Names of the Neutral Salts
Lime	Fluat of lime
Barytes	barytes
Magnesia	magnesia
Potash	potash
Soda	soda
Ammonia	ammonia
Oxide of zinc	zinc
manganese	manganese
iron	iron
lead	lead
tin	tin
cobalt	cobalt
copper	copper
nickel	nickel
arsenic	arsenic
bismuth	bismuth
mercury	mercury
silver	silver
gold	gold
platinum	platinum

And by the dry way,

Argill	Fluat of argill

Note.—These combinations were entirely unknown to the old chemists, and consequently have no names in the old nomenclature.—AUTHOR.

SECTION XX

Observations upon the Fluoric Acid and its Combinations with Salifiable Bases

Fluoric exists ready formed by nature in the fluoric spars, combined with calcareous earth so as to form an insoluble neutral salt. To obtain it disengaged from that combination, fluor spar, or fluat of lime, is put into a leaden retort, with a proper quantity of sulphuric acid; a recipient likewise of lead, half full of water, is adapted, and fire is applied to the retort. The sulphuric acid, from its greater affinity, expels the fluoric acid which passes over and is absorbed by the water in the receiver. As fluoric acid is naturally in the gaseous form in the ordinary temperature, we can receive it in a pneumato-chemical apparatus over mercury. We are obliged to employ metallic vessels in this process, because fluoric acid dissolves glass and

silicious earth and even renders these bodies volatile, carrying them over with itself in distillation in the gaseous form.

We are indebted to M. Margraff for our first acquaintance with this acid, though, as he could never procure it free from combination with a considerable quantity of silicious earth, he was ignorant of its being an acid *sui generis.* The Duke de Liancourt, under the name of M. Boulanger, considerably increased our knowledge of its properties; and M. Scheele seems to have exhausted the subject. The only thing remaining is to endeavour to discover the nature of the fluoric radical, of which we cannot form any ideas as the acid does not appear to have been decomposed in any experiment. It is only by means of compound affinity that experiments can be made with this view with any probability of success.

TABLE *of the Combinations of Boracic Acid with the Salifiable Bases, in the Order of Affinity*

Bases	Neutral Salts
Lime	Borate of lime
Barytes	barytes
Magnesia	magnesia
Potash	potash
Soda	soda
Ammonia	ammonia
Oxide of zinc	zinc
iron	iron
lead	lead
tin	tin
cobalt	cobalt
copper	copper
nickel	nickel
mercury	mercury
Argill	argill

Note.—Most of these combinations were neither known nor named by the old chemists. The boracic acid was formerly called *sedative salt* and its compounds *borax*, with base of fixed vegetable alkali, &c.—AUTHOR.

SECTION XXI

Observations upon Boracic Acid and its Combinations with Salifiable Bases

This is a concrete acid extracted from a salt procured from India called *borax* or *tincall.* Although borax has been very long employed in the arts, we have as yet very imperfect knowledge of its origin and of the methods by which it is extracted and purified; there is reason to believe it to be a native salt, found in the earth in certain parts of the east and in the water of some lakes. The whole trade of borax is in the hands of the Dutch, who have been exclusively possessed of the art of purifying it till very lately when MM. L'Eguillier of Paris have rivalled them in the manufacture; but the process still remains a secret to the world.

By chemical analysis we learn that borax is a neutral salt with excess of base, consisting of soda, partly saturated with a peculiar acid long called *Homberg's sedative salt*, now *the boracic acid*. This acid is found in an uncombined state in the waters of certain lakes. That of Cherchiaio in Italy contains 94½ grains in each pint of water.

To obtain boracic acid, dissolve some borax in boiling water, filtrate the solution, and add sulphuric acid, or any other having greater affinity to soda than the boracic acid; this latter acid is separated and is procured in a crystalline form by cooling. This acid was long considered as being formed during the process by which it is obtained and was consequently supposed to differ according to the nature of the acid employed in separating it from the soda; but it is now universally acknowledged that it is identically the same acid, in whatever way procured, provided it be properly purified from mixture of other acids by washing and by re-

peated solution and crystallization. It is soluble both in water and alcohol and has the property of communicating a green colour to the flame of that spirit. This circumstance led to a suspicion of its containing copper, which is not confirmed by any decisive experiment. On the contrary, if it contain any of that metal, it must only be considered as an accidental mixture. It combines with the salifiable bases in the humid way; and though, in this manner, it is incapable of dissolving any of the metals directly, this combination is readily effected by compound affinity.

The table presents its combinations in the order of affinity in the humid way; but there is a considerable change in the order when we operate *via sicca*; for, in that case, argill, though the last in our list, must be placed immediately after soda.

The boracic radical is hitherto unknown; no experiments having as yet been able to decompose the acid; we conclude, from analogy with the other acids, that oxygen exists in its composition as the acidifying principle.

Section XXII

Observations upon Arseniac Acid and its Combinations with Salifiable Bases

In the *Recueil de l'Académie* for 1746, M. Macquer shows that when a mixture of white oxide of arsenic and nitre are subjected to the action of a strong fire a neutral salt is obtained, which he calls *neutral salt of arsenic*. At that time, the cause of this singular phenomenon, in which a metal acts the part of an acid, was quite unknown; but more modern experiments teach that during this process the arsenic becomes oxygenated, by carrying off the oxygen of the nitric acid; it is thus converted into a real acid and combines with the potash. There are other methods now known for oxygenating arsenic and obtaining its acid free from combination. The most simple and most effectual of these is as follows: dissolve white oxide of arsenic in three parts, by weight, of muriatic acid; to this solution, in a boiling state, add two parts of nitric acid and evaporate to dryness. In this process the nitric acid is decomposed, its oxygen unites with the oxide of arsenic and converts it into an acid, and the nitrous radical flies off in the state of nitrous gas; whilst the muriatic acid is converted by the heat into muriatic acid gas and may be collected in proper vessels. The arseniac acid is

TABLE *of the Combinations of Arseniac Acid with the Salifiable Bases, in the Order of Affinity*

Bases	Neutral Salts
Lime	Arseniate of lime
Barytes	barytes
Magnesia	magnesia
Potash	potash
Soda	soda
Ammonia	ammonia
Oxide of zinc	zinc
manganese	manganese
iron	iron
lead	lead
tin	tin
cobalt	cobalt
copper	copper
nickel	nickel
bismuth	bismuth
mercury	mercury
antimony	antimony
silver	silver
gold	gold
platinum	platinum
Argill	argill

Note.—This order of salts was entirely unknown to the ancient chemists. M. Macquer, in 1746, discovered the combinations of arseniac acid with potash and soda, to which he gave the name of *arsenical neutral salts.*—AUTHOR.

entirely freed from the other acids employed during the process by heating it in a crucible till it begins to grow red; what remains is pure concrete arseniac acid.

M. Scheele's process, which was repeated with great success by M. Morveau in the laboratory at Dijon, is as follows: distil muriatic acid from the black oxide of manganese; this converts it into oxygenated muriatic acid; by carrying off the oxygen from the manganese; receive this in a recipient containing white oxide of arsenic, covered by a little distilled water; the arsenic decomposes the oxygenated muriatic acid by carrying off its supersaturation of oxygen; the arsenic is converted into arseniac acid, and the oxygenated muriatic acid is brought back to the state of common muriatic acid. The two acids are separated by distillation, with a gentle heat increased towards the end of the operation; the muriatic acid passes over and the arseniac acid remains behind in a white concrete form.

The arseniac acid is considerably less volatile than white oxide of arsenic; it often contains white oxide of arsenic in solution, owing to its not being sufficiently oxygenated; this is prevented by continuing to add nitrous acid, as in the former process, till no more nitrous gas is produced. From all these observations I would give the following definition of arseniac acid. It is a white concrete metallic acid, formed by the combination of arsenic with oxygen, fixed in a red heat, soluble in water, and capable of combining with many of the salifiable bases.

Section XXIII

Observations upon Molybdic Acid and its Combinations with Salifiable Bases

Molybdenum is a particular metallic body, capable of being oxygenated so far as to become a true concrete acid.[1] For this purpose, one part ore of molybdenum, which is a natural sulphuret of that metal, is put into a retort with five or six parts nitric acid, diluted with a quarter of its weight of water, and heat is applied to the retort; the oxygen of the nitric acid acts both upon the molybdenum and the sulphur, converting the one into molybdic and the other into sulphuric acid; pour on fresh quantities of nitric acid so long as any red fumes of nitrous gas escape; the molybdenum

is then oxygenated as far as is possible and is found at the bottom of the retort in a pulverulent form, resembling chalk. It must be washed in warm water, to separate any adhering particles of sulphuric acid; and, as it is hardly soluble, we lose very little of it in this operation. All its combinations with salifiable bases were unknown to the ancient chemists.

TABLE *of the Combinations of Tungstic Acid with the Salifiable Bases*

Bases	Neutral Salts
Lime	Tungstate of lime
Barytes	barytes
Magnesia	magnesia
Potash	potash
Soda	soda
Ammonia	ammonia
Argill	argill
Oxide of antimony, &c.	antimony, &c.[2]

Section XXIV

Observations upon Tungstic Acid and its Combinations with Salifiable Bases

Tungsten is a particular metal, the ore of which has frequently been confounded with that of tin. The specific gravity of this ore is to water as 6 to 1; in its form of crystallization it resembles the garnet and varies in colour from a pearl-white to yellow and reddish; it is found in several parts of Saxony and Bohemia. The mineral called *wolfram*, which is frequent in the mines of Cornwall, is likewise an ore of this metal. In all these ores the metal is oxidated; and, in some of them, it appears even to be oxygenated to the state of acid, being combined with lime into a true tungstate of lime.

To obtain the acid free, mix one part of ore of tungsten with four parts of carbonate of potash and melt the mixture in a crucible; then powder and pour on twelve parts of boiling water, add nitric acid, and the tungstic acid precipitates in a concrete form. Afterwards, to insure the complete oxygenation of the metal, add more nitric acid and evaporate to dryness, repeating this operation so long as red fumes of nitrous gas are produced. To procure tungstic acid perfectly pure, the fusion of the ore with carbonate of potash must be made in a crucible of platinum, otherwise the earth of the com-

---

[1] This acid was discovered by M. Scheele, to whom chemistry is indebted for the discovery of several other acids.—AUTHOR.

[2] All these salts were unknown to the ancient chemists.—AUTHOR.

mon crucibles will mix with the products and adulterate the acid.

TABLE *of the Combinations of Tartarous Acid with the Salifiable Bases, in the Order of Affinity*

Bases	Neutral Salts
Lime	Tartarite of lime
Barytes	barytes
Magnesia	magnesia
Potash	potash
Soda	soda
Ammonia	ammonia
Argill	argill
Oxide of zinc	zinc
iron	iron
manganese	manganese
cobalt	cobalt
nickel	nickel
lead	lead
tin	tin
copper	copper
bismuth	bismuth
antimony	antimony
arsenic	arsenic
silver	silver
mercury	mercury
gold	gold
platinum	platinum

SECTION XXV

Observations upon Tartarous Acid and its Combinations with Salifiable Bases

Tartar, or the concretion which fixes to the inside of vessels in which the fermentation of wine is completed, is a well known salt, composed of a peculiar acid united in considerable excess to potash. M. Scheele first pointed out the method of obtaining this acid pure. Having observed that it has a greater affinity to lime than to potash, he directs us to proceed in the following manner. Dissolve purified tartar in boiling water and add a sufficient quantity of lime till the acid be completely saturated. The tartarite of lime which is formed, being almost insoluble in cold water, falls to the bottom and is separated from the solution of potash by decantation; it is afterwards washed in cold water and dried; then pour on some sulphuric acid, diluted with eight or nine parts of water, digest for twelve hours in a gentle heat, frequently stirring the mixture; the sulphuric acid combines with the lime, and the tartarous acid is left free. A small quantity of gas, not yet examined, is disengaged during this process. At the end of twelve hours, having decanted off the clear liquor, wash the sulphate of lime in cold water, which add to the decanted liquor, then evaporate the whole, and the tartarous acid is obtained in a concrete form. Two pounds of purified tartar, by means of from eight to ten ounces of sulphuric acid, yield about eleven ounces of tartarous acid.

As the combustible radical exists in excess, or as the acid from tartar is not fully saturated with oxygen, we call it *tartarous acid*, and the neutral salts formed by its combinations with salifiable bases *tartarites*. The base of the tartarous acid is a carbono-hydrous or hydro-carbonous radical, less oxygenated than in the oxalic acid; and it would appear, from the experiments of M. Hassenfratz, that azote enters into the composition of the tartarous radical even in considerable quantity. By oxygenating the tartarous acid, it is convertible into oxalic, malic, and acetous acids; but it is probable the proportions of hydrogen and charcoal in the radical are changed during these conversions, and that the difference between these acids does not alone consist in the different degrees of oxygenation.

The tartarous acid is susceptible of two degrees of saturation in its combinations with the fixed alkalies; by one of these a salt is formed with excess of acid, improperly called *cream of tartar*, which in our new nomenclature is named *acidulous tartarite of potash;* by a second or equal degree of saturation a perfectly neutral salt is formed, formerly called *vegetable salt*, which we name *tartarite of potash*. With soda this acid forms tartarite of soda, formerly called *sal de Seignette*, or *sal polychrest of Rochell*.

SECTION XXVI

Observations upon Malic Acid and its Combinations with Salifiable Bases

The malic acid exists ready formed in the sour juice of ripe and unripe apples, and many other fruits, and is obtained as follows: saturate the juice of apples with potash or soda and add a proper proportion of acetite of lead dissolved in water; a double decomposition takes place; the malic acid combines with the oxide of lead and precipitates, being almost insoluble, and the acetite of potash or soda remains in the liquor. The malate of lead being separated by decantation is washed with cold water, and some dilute sulphuric acid is added; this unites with the lead into an insoluble sulphate and the malic acid remains free in the liquor.

This acid, which is found mixed with citric and tartarous acid in a great number of fruits, is a kind of medium between oxalic and acetous acids, being more oxygenated than the former and less so than the latter. From this circumstance, M. Hermbstadt calls it *imperfect vinegar;* but it differs likewise from acetous acid, by having rather more charcoal and less hydrogen in the composition of its radical.

When an acid much diluted has been used in the foregoing process, the liquor contains oxalic as well as malic acid and probably a little tartarous; these are separated by mixing lime-water with the acids, oxalate, tartarite, and malate of lime are produced; the two former,

TABLE *of the Combinations of Citric Acid with the Salifiable Bases, in the Order of Affinity*[1]

Bases	Neutral Salts
Barytes	Citrate of barytes
Lime	lime
Magnesia	magnesia
Potash	potash
Soda	soda
Ammonia	ammonia
Oxide of zinc	zinc
manganesc	manganese
iron	iron
lead	lead
cobalt	cobalt
copper	copper
arsenic	arsenic
mercury	mercury
antimony	antimony
silver	silver
gold	gold
platinum	platinum
Argill	argill

being insoluble, are precipitated, and the malate of lime remains dissolved; from this the pure malic acid is separated by the acetite of lead and afterwards by sulphuric acid, as directed above.

Section XXVII

Observations upon Citric Acid and its Combinations with Salifiable Bases

The citric acid is procured by expression from lemons and is found in the juices of many

other fruits mixed with malic acid. To obtain it pure and concentrated, it is first allowed to depurate from the mucous part of the fruit by long rest in a cool cellar, and is afterwards concentrated by exposing it to the temperature of 4 or 5 degrees below zero, from 21° to 23° of Fahrenheit; the water is frozen, and the

TABLE *of the Combinations of Pyro-lignous Acid with the Salifiable Bases, in the Order of Affinity*[2]

Bases	Neutral Salts
Lime	Pyro-mucite of lime
Barytes	barytes
Potash	potash
Soda	soda
Magnesia	magnesia
Ammonia	ammonia
Oxide of zinc	zinc
manganese	manganese
iron	iron
lead	lead
tin	tin
cobalt	cobalt
copper	copper
nickel	nickel
arsenic	arsenic
bismuth	bismuth
mercury	mercury
antimony	antimony
silver	silver
gold	gold
platinum	platinum
Argill	argill

acid remains liquid, reduced to about an eighth part of its original bulk. A lower degree of cold would occasion the acid to be engaged amongst the ice, and render it difficultly separable. This process was pointed out by M. Georgius.

It is more easily obtained by saturating the lemon-juice with lime, so as to form a citrate of lime which is insoluble in water; wash this salt and pour on a proper quantity of sulphuric acid; this forms a sulphate of lime, which precipitates and leaves the citric acid free in the liquor.

Section XXVIII

Observations upon Pyro-lignous Acid and its Combinations with Salifiable Bases

The ancient chemists observed that most of the woods, especially the more heavy and compact ones, gave out a particular acid spirit, by distillation, in a naked fire; but, before M.

---

[1] These combinations were unknown to the ancient chemists. The order of affinity of the salifiable bases with this acid was determined by M. Bergman and by M. de Breney of the Dijon Academy.—AUTHOR.

[2] The above affinities were determined by MM. de Morveau and Elos Bourfier de Clervaux. These combinations were entirely unknown till lately.—AUTHOR.

Goetling, who gives an account of his experiments upon this subject in Crell's *Chemical Journal* for 1779, no one had ever made any inquiry into its nature and properties. This acid appears to be the same, whatever be the wood it is procured from. When first distilled, it is of a brown colour and considerably impregnated with charcoal and oil; it is purified from these by a second distillation. The pyrolignous radical is chiefly composed of hydrogen and charcoal.

Section XXIX

Observations upon Pyro-tartarous Acid and its Combinations with Salifiable Bases

The name of *Pyro-tartarous acid* is given to a dilute empyreumatic acid obtained from purified acidulous tartarite of potash by distillation in a naked fire. To obtain it, let a retort be half filled with powdered tartar, adapt a tubulated recipient, having a bent tube communicating with a bell-glass in a pneumato-chemical apparatus; by gradually raising the fire under the retort, we obtain the pyro-tartarous acid mixed with oil, which is separated by means of a funnel. A vast quantity of carbonic acid gas is disengaged during the distillation. The acid obtained by the above process is much contaminated with oil, which ought to be separated from it. Some authors advise to do this by a second distillation; but the Dijon academicians inform us that this is attended with great danger from explosions which take place during the process.

Section XXX

Observations upon Pyro-mucous Acid and its Combinations with Salifiable Bases

This acid is obtained by distillation in a naked fire from sugar and all the saccharine bodies; and, as these substances swell greatly in the fire, it is necessary to leave seven-eighths of the retort empty. It is of a yellow colour, verging to red, and leaves a mark upon the skin which will not remove but alongst with the epidermis. It may be procured less coloured, by means of a second distillation, and is concentrated by freezing, as is directed for the citric acid. It is chiefly composed of water and oil slightly oxygenated and is convertible into oxalic and malic acids by farther oxygenation with the nitric acid.

It has been pretended that a large quantity of gas is disengaged during the distillation of this acid, which is not the case if it be conducted slowly by means of moderate heat.

Section XXXI

Observations upon Oxalic Acid and its Combinations with Salifiable Bases

The oxalic acid is mostly prepared in Switzerland and Germany from the expressed juice

TABLE *of the Combinations of Pyro-mucous Acid, with the Salifiable Bases, in the Order of Affinity*[1]

Bases	Neutral Salts
Potash	Pyro-mucite of potash
Soda	soda
Barytes	barytes
Lime	lime
Magnesia	magnesia
Ammonia	ammonia
Argill	argill
Oxide of zinc	zinc
manganese	manganese
iron	iron
lead	lead
tin	tin
cobalt	cobalt
copper	copper
nickel	nickel
arsenic	arsenic
bismuth	bismuth
antimony	antimony

[1] All these combinations were unknown to the ancient chemists.—AUTHOR.

TABLE *of the Combinations of the Oxalic Acid, with the Salifiable Bases, in the Order of Affinity*[2]

Bases	Neutral Salts
Lime	Oxalate of lime
Barytes	barytes
Magnesia	magnesia
Potash	potash
Soda	soda
Ammonia	ammonia
Argill	argill
Oxide of zinc	zinc
iron	iron
manganese	manganese
cobalt	cobalt
nickel	nickel
lead	lead
copper	copper
bismuth	bismuth
antimony	antimony
arsenic	arsenic
mercury	mercury
silver	silver
gold	gold
platinum	platinum

[2] All unknown to the ancient chemists.—AUTHOR.

of sorrel, from which it crystallizes by being left long at rest; in this state it is partly saturated with potash, forming a true acidulous oxalate of potash, or salt with excess of acid. To obtain it pure, it must be formed artificially by oxygenating sugar, which seems to be the true oxalic radical. Upon one part of sugar pour six or eight parts of nitric acid and apply a gentle heat; a considerable effervescence takes place, and a great quantity of nitrous gas is disengaged; the nitric acid is decomposed, and its oxygen unites to the sugar. By allowing the liquor to stand at rest, crystals of pure oxalic acid are formed, which must be dried upon blotting paper to separate any remaining portions of nitric acid; and, to ensure the purity of the acid, dissolve the crystals in distilled water and crystallize them afresh.

From the liquor remaining after the first crystallization of the oxalic acid we may obtain malic acid by refrigeration. This acid is more oxygenated than the oxalic; and, by a further oxygenation, the sugar is convertible into acetous acid, or vinegar.

The oxalic acid, combined with a small quantity of soda or potash, has the property, like the tartarous acid, of entering into a number of combinations without suffering decomposi-

TABLE *of the Combinations of Acetous Acid with the Salifiable Bases in the Order of Affinity*

Bases	Neutral Salts	Names of the Resulting Neutral Salts According to the Old Names
Barytes	Acetite of barytes	Unknown to the ancients. Discovered by M. de Morveau, who calls it *barotic acéte.*
Potash	potash	*Secret terra foliata tartari* of Muller. *Arcanum tartari* of Basil Valentin and Paracelsus. *Purgative magistery of tartar* of Schroëder. *Essential salt of wine* of Zwelfer. *Regenerated tartar* of Tachenius. *Diuretic salt* of Sylvius and Wilson.
Soda	soda	Foliated earth with base of mineral alkali· Mineral or crystallizable foliated earth. Mineral acetous salt.
Lime	lime	Salt of chalk, coral, or crabs eyes; mentioned by Hartman.
Magnesia	magnesia	First mentioned by M. Wenzel.
Ammonia	ammonia	*Spiritus Mindereri.* Ammoniacal acetous salt·
Oxide of zinc	zinc	Known to Glauber, Schwedemberg, Respour, Pott, de Lassone, and Wenzel, but not named.
manganese	manganese	Unknown to the ancients.
iron	iron	Martial vinegar. Described by Monnet, Wenzel, and the Duke d'Ayen.
lead	lead	Sugar, vinegar, and salt of lead or Saturn.
tin	tin	Known to Lemery, Margraff, Monnet, Weslendorf, and Wenzel, but not named.
cobalt	cobalt	*Sympathetic ink* of M. Cadet.
copper	copper	Verdigris, crystals of verditer, verditer, distilled verdigris, crystals of Venus or of copper.
nickel	nickel	Unknown to the ancients.
arsenic	arsenic	Arsenico-acetous fuming liquor, *liquid phosphorus* of M. Cadet.
bismuth	Acetite of bismuth	*Sugar of bismuth* of M. Geoffroy. Known to Gellert, Pott, Weslendorf, Bergman. and de Morveau.
mercury	mercury	Mercurial foliated earth, Keyser's famous antivenereal remedy. Mentioned by Gebaver in 1748; known to Helot, Margraff, Baumé, Bergman, and de Morveau.
antimony	antimony	Unknown.
silver	silver	Described by Margraff, Monnet, and Wenzel; unknown to the ancients.
gold	gold	Little known, mentioned by Schroëder and Juncker.
platinum	platinum	Unknown.
Argill	argill	According to M. Wenzel, vinegar dissolves only a very small proportion of argill.

tion. These combinations form triple salts, or neutral salts with double bases, which ought to have proper names. The salt of sorrel, which is potash having oxalic acid combined in excess, is named acidulous oxalate of potash in our new nomenclature.

The acid procured from sorrel has been known to chemists for more than a century, being mentioned by M. Duclos in the *Recueil de l'Académie* for 1688, and was pretty accurately described by Boerhaave; but M. Scheele first showed that it contained potash and demonstrated its identity with the acid formed by the oxygenation of sugar.

SECTION XXXII

Observations upon Acetous Acid and its Combinations with Salifiable Bases

This acid is composed of charcoal and hydrogen united together and brought to the state of an acid by the addition of oxygen; it is consequently formed by the same elements with the tartarous oxalic, citric, malic acids, and others, but the elements exist in different proportions in each of these; and it would appear that the acetous acid is in a higher state of oxygenation than these other acids. I have some reason to believe that the acetous radical contains a small portion of azote; and, as this element is not contained in the radicals of any vegetable acid except the tartarous, this circumstance is one of the causes of difference. The acetous acid, or vinegar, is produced by exposing wine to a gentle heat, with the addition of some ferment: this is usually the dregs, or mother, which have separated from other vinegar during fermentation, or some similar matter. The spiritous part of the wine, which consists of charcoal and hydrogen, is oxygenated and converted into vinegar. This operation can only take place with free access of air and is always attended by a diminution of the air employed in consequence of the absorption of oxygen; wherefore, it ought always to be carried on in vessels only half filled with the vinous liquor submitted to the acetous fermentation. The acid formed during this process is very volatile, is mixed with a large proportion of water and with many foreign substances; and, to obtain it pure, it is distilled in stone or glass vessels by a gentle fire. The acid which passes over in distillation is somewhat changed by the process, and is not exactly of the same nature with what remains in the alembic, but seems less oxygenated. This circumstance has not been formerly observed by chemists.

Distillation is not sufficient for depriving this acid of all its unnecessary water; and, for this purpose, the best way is by exposing it to a degree of cold from 4° to 6° below the freezing point, from 19° to 23° of Fahrenheit; by this means the aqueous part becomes frozen and leaves the acid in a liquid state and considerably concentrated. In the usual temperature of the air, this acid can only exist in the gaseous form and can only be retained by combination with a large proportion of water. There are other chemical processes for obtaining the acetous acid, which consist in oxygenating the tartarous, oxalic, or malic acids, by means of nitric acid; but there is reason to believe the proportions of the elements of the radical are changed during this process. M. Hassenfratz is at present engaged in repeating the experiments by which these conversions are said to be produced.

The combinations of acetous acid with the various salifiable bases are very readily formed; but most of the resulting neutral salts are not crystallizable, whereas those produced by the tartarous and oxalic acids are, in general, hardly soluble. Tartarite and oxalate of lime are not soluble in any sensible degree. The malates are a medium between the oxalates and ace-

TABLE *of the Combinations of Acetic Acid with the Salifiable Bases, in the Order of Affinity*

Bases	Neutral Salts
Barytes	Acetate of barytes
Potash	potash
Soda	soda
Lime	lime
Magnesia	magnesia
Ammonia	ammonia
Oxide of zinc	zinc
manganese	manganese
iron	iron
lead	lead
tin	tin
cobalt	cobalt
copper	copper
nickel	nickel
arsenic	arsenic
bismuth	bismuth
mercury	mercury
antimony	antimony
silver	silver
gold	gold
platinum	platinum
Argill	argill

Note.—All these salts were unknown to the ancients; and even those chemists who are most versant in modern discoveries, are yet at a loss whether the greater part of the salts produced by the oxygenated acetic radical belong properly to the class of acetites, or to that of acetates.—AUTHOR.

tites, with respect to solubility, and the malic acid is in the middle degree of saturation between the oxalic and acetous acids. With this, as with all the acids, the metals require to be oxidated previous to solution.

The ancient chemists knew hardly any of the salts formed by the combinations of acetous acid with the salifiable bases, except the acetites of potash, soda, ammonia, copper, and lead. M. Cadet discovered the acetite of arsenic;[1] M. Wenzel, the Dijon academicians, M. de Lassone, and M. Proust, made us acquainted with the properties of the other acetites. From the property which acetite of potash possesses, of giving out ammonia in distillation, there is some reason to suppose that, besides charcoal and hydrogen, the acetous radical contains a small proportion of azote, though it is not impossible but the above production of ammonia may be occasioned by the decomposition of the potash.

Section XXXIII

Observations upon Acetic Acid and its Combinations with Salifiable Bases

We have given to radical vinegar the name of acetic acid, from supposing that it consists

TABLE *of the Combinations of Succinic Acid with the Salifiable Bases, in the Order of Affinity*

Bases	Neutral Salts
Barytes	Succinate of barytes
Lime	lime
Potash	potash
Soda	soda
Ammonia	ammonia
Magnesia	magnesia
Argill	argill
Oxide of zinc	zinc
iron	iron
manganese	manganese
cobalt	cobalt
nickel	nickel
lead	lead
tin	tin
copper	copper
bismuth	bismuth
antimony	antimony
arsenic	arsenic
mercury	mercury
silver	silver
gold	gold
platinum	platinum

Note.—All the succinates were unknown to the ancient chemists.—AUTHOR.

[1] *Savans Etrangers*, Vol. III.

of the same radical with that of the acetous acid but more highly saturated with oxygen. According to this idea, acetic acid is the highest degree of oxygenation of which the hydro-carbonous radical is susceptible; but, although this circumstance be extremely probable, it requires to be confirmed by further and more decisive experiments, before it be adopted as an absolute chemical truth. We procure this acid as follows: upon three parts acetite of potash or of copper pour one part of concentrated sulphuric acid, and, by distillation, a very highly concentrated vinegar is obtained, which we call *acetic acid*, formerly named *radical vinegar*. It is not rigorously proved that this acid is more highly oxygenated than the acetous acid, nor that the difference between them may not consist in a different proportion between the elements of the radical or base.

Section XXXIV

Observations upon Succinic Acid and its Combinations with Salifiable Bases

The succinic acid is drawn from amber by sublimation in a gentle heat and rises in a concrete form into the neck of the subliming vessel. The operation must not be pushed too far, or by too strong a fire, otherwise the oil of the amber rises alongst with the acid. The salt is dried upon blotting paper and purified by repeated solution and crystallization.

This acid is soluble in twenty-four times its weight of cold water and in a much smaller quantity of hot water. It possesses the qualities of an acid in a very small degree and only affects the blue vegetable colours very slightly. The affinities of this acid, with the salifiable bases, are taken from M. de Morveau, who is the first chemist that has endeavoured to ascertain them.

Section XXXV

Observations upon Benzoic Acid and its Combinations with Salifiable Bases

This acid was known to the ancient chemists under the name of *Flowers of Benjamin*, or of *Benzoin*, and was procured, by sublimation, from the gum or resin called *Benzoin*. The means of procuring it, *via humida*, was discovered by M. Geoffroy and perfected by M. Scheele. Upon benzoin, reduced to powder, pour strong lime-water, having rather an excess of lime; keep the mixture continually stirring and, after half an hour's digestion, pour off the liquor and use fresh portions of lime-water in the same manner, so long as there is any appearance of neutralization. Join all the decanted liquors and evaporate, as far as possible, without occasioning crystallization, and, when the liquor is cold, drop in muriatic acid till no more precipitate is formed. By the former part of the process a benzoate of lime is formed, and by the latter the muriatic acid combines with the lime, forming muriate of lime, which remains dissolved, while the benzoic acid, being insoluble, precipitates in a concrete state.

Section XXXVI

Observations upon Camphoric Acid and its Combinations with Salifiable Bases

Camphor is a concrete essential oil, obtained, by sublimation from a species of *laurus* which grows in China and Japan. By distilling nitric acid eight times from camphor, M. Kosegarten converted it into an acid analogous to the oxalic; but, as it differs from that acid in some circumstances, we have thought necessary to give it a particular name till its nature be more completely ascertained by farther experiment.

As camphor is a carbono-hydrous or hydro-carbonous radical, it is easily conceived that, by oxygenation, it should form oxalic, malic, and several other vegetable acids. This conjecture is rendered not improbable by the experiments of M. Kosegarten; and the principal phenomena exhibited in the combinations of camphoric acid with the salifiable bases, being very similar to those of the oxalic and malic acids, lead me to believe that it consists of a mixture of these two acids.

Section XXXVII

Observations upon Gallic Acid, and its Combinations with Salifiable Bases[1]

The gallic acid, formerly called *principle of astringency*, is obtained from gall nuts, either by infusion or decoction with water, or by distillation with a very gentle heat. This acid has only been attended to within these few years. The Committee of the Dijon Academy have followed it through all its combinations and give the best account of it hitherto produced.

[1] These combinations, which are called *gallates*, were all unknown to the ancients; and the order of their affinity is not established.—AUTHOR.

Its acid properties are very weak; it reddens the tincture of turnsole, decomposes sulphurets, and unites to all the metals when they have been previously dissolved in some other acid. Iron, by this combination, is precipitated of a very deep blue or violet colour. The radical of this acid, if it deserves the name of one, is hitherto entirely unknown; it is contained in oak willow, marsh iris, the strawberry, nymphea, Peruvian bark, the flowers and bark of pomegranate, and in many other woods and barks.

Section XXXVIII

Observations upon Lactic Acid and its Combinations with Salifiable Bases[2]

The only accurate knowledge we have of this acid is from the works of M. Scheele. It is contained in whey, united to a small quantity of earth, and is obtained as follows: reduce whey to one eighth part of its bulk by evaporation and filtrate, to separate all its cheesy matter; then add as much lime as is necessary to combine with the acid; the lime is afterwards disengaged by the addition of oxalic acid, which combines with it into an insoluble neutral salt. When the oxalate of lime has been separated by

TABLE *of the Combinations of Saccho-lactic Acid with the Salifiable Bases, in the Order of Affinity*

Bases	Neutral Salts
Lime	Saccholate of lime
Barytes	barytes
Magnesia	magnesia
Potash	potash
Soda	soda
Ammonia	ammonia
Argill	argill
Oxide of zinc	zinc
manganese	manganese
iron	iron
lead	lead
tin	tin
cobalt	cobalt
copper	copper
nickel	nickel
arsenic	arsenic
bismuth	bismuth
mercury	mercury
antimony	antimony
silver	silver

Note.—All these were unknown to the ancient chemists.—AUTHOR.

[2] These combinations are called *lactates;* they were all unknown to the ancient chemists and their affinities have not yet been ascertained.—AUTHOR.

decantation, evaporate the remaining liquor to the consistence of honey; the lactic acid is dissolved by alcohol, which does not unite with the sugar of milk and other foreign matters; these are separated by filtration from the alcohol and acid; and the alcohol being evaporated, or distilled off, leaves the lactic acid behind.

This acid unites with all the salifiable bases, forming salts which do not crystallize; and it seems considerably to resemble the acetous acid.

Section XXXIX

Observations upon Saccho-lactic Acid and its Combinations with Salifiable Bases

A species of sugar may be extracted, by evaporation, from whey, which has long been known in pharmacy, and which has a considerable resemblance to that procured from sugar canes. This saccharine matter, like ordinary sugar, may be oxygenated by means of nitric acid. For this purpose, several portions of nitric acid are distilled from it; the remaining liquid is evaporated and set to crystallize, by which means crystals of oxalic acid are procured; at the same time a very fine white powder precipitates, which is the saccholactic acid discovered by Scheele. It is susceptible of combining with the alkalies, ammonia, the earths, and even with the metals. Its action upon the latter is hitherto but little known, except that, with them, it forms difficultly soluble salts. The order of affinity in the table is taken from Bergman.

TABLE *of Combinations of Formic Acid with the Salifiable Bases, in the Order of Affinity*

Bases	Neutral Salts
Barytes	Formiate of barytes
Potash	potash
Soda	soda
Lime	lime
Magnesia	magnesia
Ammonia	ammonia
Oxide of zinc	zinc
manganese	manganese
iron	iron
lead	lead
tin	tin
cobalt	cobalt
copper	copper
nickel	nickel
bismuth	bismuth
silver	silver
Argill	argill

Note.—All unknown to the ancient chemists.—AUTHOR.

Section XL

Observations upon Formic Acid and its Combinations with Salifiable Bases

This acid was first obtained by distillation from ants in the last century, by Samuel Fisher. The subject was treated of by Margraff in 1749, and by MM. Ardwisson and Ochrn of Leipzig in 1777. The formic acid is drawn from a large species of red ants, *formica rufa*, *Lin.*, which form large ant hills in woody places. It is procured either by distilling the ants with a gentle heat in a glass retort or an alembic; or, after having washed the ants in cold water and dried them upon a cloth, by pouring on boiling water, which dissolves the acid; or the acid may be procured by gentle expression from the insects, in which case it is stronger than in any of the former ways. To obtain it pure, we must rectify, by means of distillation, which separates it from the uncombined oily and charry matter; and it may be concentrated by freezing, in the manner recommended for treating the acetous acid.

Section XLI

Observations upon Bombic Acid and its Combinations with Salifiable Bases[1]

The juices of the silk worm seem to assume an acid quality when that insect changes from

TABLE *of the Combinations of the Sebacic Acid with the Salifiable Bases, in the Order of Affinity*

Bases	Neutral Salts
Barytes	Sebate of barytes
Potash	potash
Soda	soda
Lime	lime
Magnesia	magnesia
Ammonia	ammonia
Argill	argill
Oxide of zinc	zinc
manganese	manganese
iron	iron
lead	lead
tin	tin
cobalt	cobalt
copper	copper
nickel	nickel
arsenic	arsenic
bismuth	bismuth
mercury	mercury
antimony	antimony
silver	silver

Note.—All these were unknown to the ancient chemists.—AUTHOR.

[1] These combinations named *bombates* were unknown to the ancient chemists; and the affinities of the salifiable bases with the bombic acid are undetermined.—AUTHOR.

a larva to a chrysalis. At the moment of its escape from the latter to the butterfly form, it emits a reddish liquor which reddens blue paper, and which was first attentively observed by M. Chaussier of the Dijon Academy, who obtains the acid by infusing silk worm chrysalids in alcohol, which dissolves their acid without being charged with any of the gummy parts of the insect; and, by evaporating the alcohol, the acid remains tolerably pure. The properties and affinities of this acid are not hitherto ascertained with any precision; and we have reason to believe that analogous acids may be procured from other insects. The radical of this acid is probably, like that of the other acids from the animal kingdom, composed of charcoal, hydrogen, and azote, with the addition, perhaps, of phosphorus.

Section XLII

Observations upon Sebacic Acid and its Combinations with Salifiable Bases

To obtain the sebacic acid, let some suet be melted in a skillet over the fire, alongst with some quicklime in fine powder, and constantly stirred, raising the fire towards the end of the operation, and taking care to avoid the vapours, which are very offensive. By this process the sebacic acid unites with the lime into a sebate of lime, which is with difficulty soluble in water; it is, however, separated from the fatty matters with which it is mixed by solution in a large quantity of boiling water. From this the neutral salt is separated by evaporation; and, to render it pure, is calcined, redissolved, and again crystallized. After this we pour on a proper quantity of sulphuric acid, and the sebacic acid passes over by distillation.

Section XLIII

Observations upon Lithic Acid and its Combinations with Salifiable Bases[1]

From the later experiments of Bergman and Scheele, the urinary calculus appears to be a species of salt with an earthy basis; it is slightly acidulous, and requires a large quantity of water for solution, three grains being scarcely soluble in a thousand grains of boiling water, and the greater part again crystallizes when cold. To this concrete acid, which M. de Morveau calls *lithiasic acid*, we give the name of

[1] All the combinations of this acid, should it finally turn out to be one, were unknown to the ancient chemists, and its affinities with the salifiable bases have not been determined.—AUTHOR.

lithic acid, the nature and properties of which are as yet very little known. There is some appearance that it is an acidulous neutral salt, or acid combined in excess with a salifiable base; and I have reason to believe that it really is an acidulous phosphate of lime; if so, it must be excluded from the class of peculiar acids.

TABLE *of the Combinations of the Prussic Acid with the Salifiable Bases, in the Order of Affinity*

Bases	Neutral Salts
Potash	Prussiate of potash
Soda	soda
Ammonia	ammonia
Lime	lime
Barytes	barytes
Magnesia	magnesia
Oxide of zinc	zinc
iron	iron
manganese	manganese
cobalt	cobalt
nickel	nickel
lead	lead
tin	tin
copper	copper
bismuth	bismuth
antimony	antimony
arsenic	arsenic
silver	silver
mercury	mercury
gold	gold
platinum	platinum

Note.—All these were unknown to former chemists.—AUTHOR.

Section XLIV

Observations upon the Prussic Acid and its Combinations with Salifiable Bases

As the experiments which have been made hitherto upon this acid seem still to leave a considerable degree of uncertainty with regard to its nature, I shall not enlarge upon its properties, and the means of procuring it pure and disengaged from combination. It combines with iron, to which it communicates a blue colour, and is equally susceptible of entering into combination with most of the other metals, which are precipitated from it by the alkalies, ammonia, and lime, in consequence of greater affinity. The prussic radical, from the experiments of Scheele, and especially from those of M. Berthollet, seems composed of charcoal and azote; hence it is an acid with a double base. The phosphorus which has been found combined with it appears, from the experiments of M. Hassenfratz, to be only accidental.

Although this acid combines with alkalies, earths, and metals, in the same way with other acids, it possesses only some of the properties we have been used to attribute to acids, and it may consequently be improperly ranked here in the class of acids; but, as I have already observed, it is difficult to form a decided opinion upon the nature of this substance until the subject has been farther elucidated by a greater number of experiments.

THIRD PART

Description of the instruments and operations
of chemistry

INTRODUCTION

In the two former parts of this work I designedly avoided being particular in describing the manual operations of chemistry, because I had found from experience that, in a work appropriated to reasoning, minute descriptions of processes and of plates interrupt the chain of ideas and render the attention necessary both difficult and tedious to the reader. On the other hand, if I had confined myself to the summary descriptions hitherto given, beginners could have only acquired very vague conceptions of practical chemistry from my work and must have wanted both confidence and interest in operations they could neither repeat nor thoroughly comprehend. This want could not have been supplied from books; for, besides that there are not any which describe the modern instruments and experiments sufficiently at large, any work that could have been consulted would have presented these things under a very different order of arrangement and in a different chemical language, which must greatly tend to injure the main object of my performance.

Influenced by these motives, I determined to reserve, for a third part of my work, a summary description of all the instruments and manipulations relative to elementary chemistry. I considered it as better placed at the end, rather than at the beginning of the book, because I must have been obliged to suppose the reader acquainted with circumstances which a beginner cannot know and must therefore have read the elementary part to become acquainted with. The whole of this third part may therefore be considered as resembling the explanations of plates which are usually placed at the end of academic memoirs that they may not interrupt the connection of the text by lengthened description. Though I have taken great pains to render this part clear and methodical and have not omitted any essential instrument or apparatus, I am far from pretending by it to set aside the necessity of attendance upon lectures and laboratories for such as wish to acquire accurate knowledge of the science of chemistry. These should familiarise themselves to the employment of apparatus, and to the performance of experiments by actual experience. *Nihil est in intellectu quod non prius fuerit in sensu*, the motto which the celebrated Rouelle caused to be painted in large characters in a conspicuous part of his laboratory, is an important truth never to be lost sight of either by teachers or students of chemistry.

Chemical operations may be naturally divided into several classes, according to the purposes they are intended for performing. Some may be considered as purely mechanical, such as the determination of the weight and bulk of bodies, trituration, levigation, searching, washing, filtration, &c. Others may be considered as real chemical operations, because they are performed by means of chemical powers and agents; such are solution, fusion, &c. Some of these are intended for separating the elements of bodies from each other, some for reuniting these elements together; and some, as combustion, produce both these effects during the same process.

Without rigorously endeavouring to follow the above method, I mean to give a detail of the chemical operations in such order of arrangement as seemed best calculated for conveying instruction. I shall be more particular in describing the apparatus connected with modern chemistry, because these are little known by men who have devoted much of their time to chemistry and even by many professors of the science.

CHAPTER I

Of the Instruments Necessary for Determining the Absolute and Specific Gravities of Solid and Liquid Bodies

The best method known for determining the quantities of substances submitted to chemical experiment or resulting from them, is by means of an accurately constructed beam and scales, with properly regulated weights, which well known operation is called *weighing*. The denomination and quantity of the weights used as an unit or standard for this purpose are extremely arbitrary, and vary not only in different kingdoms, but even in different provinces of the same kingdom, and in different cities of the same province. This variation is of infinite consequence to be well understood in commerce and in the arts; but, in chemistry, it is of no moment what particular denomination of weight be employed, provided the results of experiments be expressed in convenient fractions of the same denomination. For this purpose, until all the weights used in society be reduced to the same standard, it will be sufficient for chemists in different parts to use the common pound of their own country as the unit or standard, and to express all its fractional parts in decimals instead of the arbitrary divisions now in use. By this means the chemists of all countries will be thoroughly understood by each other, as, although the absolute weights of the ingredients and products cannot be known, they will readily, and without calculation, be able to determine the relative proportions of these to each other with the utmost accuracy; so that in this way we shall be possessed of an universal language for this part of chemistry.

With this view I have long projected to have the pound divided into decimal fractions, and I have of late succeeded through the assistance of M. Fourche, balance-maker at Paris, who has executed it for me with great accuracy and judgment. I recommend to all who carry on experiments to procure similar divisions of the pound, which they will find both easy and simple in its application, with a very small knowledge of decimal fractions.[1]

As the usefulness and accuracy of chemistry depend entirely upon the determination of the weights of the ingredients and products both before and after experiments, too much precision cannot be employed in this part of the subject; and, for this purpose, we must be provided with good instruments. As we are often obliged, in chemical processes, to ascertain, within a grain or less, the tare or weight of large and heavy instruments, we must have beams made with peculiar niceness by accurate

[1] M. Lavoisier's very accurate directions for reducing the common subdivisions of the French pound into decimal fractions, and *vice versa*, given in tables subjoined to this 3d part are not printed in this edition.—TRANSLATOR.

workmen, and these must always be kept apart from the laboratory in some place where the vapours of acids, or other corrosive liquors, cannot have access; otherwise the steel will rust, and the accuracy of the balance be destroyed. I have three sets, of different sizes, made by M. Fontin with the utmost nicety, and, excepting those made by M. Ramsden of London, I do not think any can compare with them for precision and sensitivity. The largest of these is about three feet long in the beam for large weights, up to fifteen or twenty pounds; the second, for weights of eighteen or twenty ounces, is exact to a tenth part of a grain; and the smallest, calculated only for weighing about one gros, is sensibly affected by the five hundredth part of a grain.

Besides these nicer balances, which are only used for experiments of research, we must have others of less value for the ordinary purposes of the laboratory. A large iron balance, capable of weighing forty or fifty pounds within half a dram, one of a middle size, which may ascertain eight or ten pounds, within ten or twelve grains, and a small one, by which about a pound may be determined, within one grain.

We must likewise be provided with weights divided into their several fractions, both vulgar and decimal, with the utmost nicety, and verified by means of repeated and accurate trials in the nicest scales; and it requires some experience, and to be accurately acquainted with the different weights, to be able to use them properly. The best way of precisely ascertaining the weight of any particular substance is to weigh it twice, once with the decimal divisions of the pound and another time with the common subdivisions or vulgar fractions, and, by comparing these, we attain the utmost accuracy.

By the specific gravity of any substance is understood the quotient of its absolute weight divided by its magnitude, or, what is the same, the weight of a determinate bulk of any body. The weight of a determinate magnitude of water has been generally assumed as unity for this purpose; and we express the specific gravity of gold, sulphuric acid, &c. by saying that gold is nineteen times, and sulphuric acid twice the weight of water, and so of other bodies.

It is the more convenient to assume water as unity in specific gravities, that those substances whose specific gravity we wish to determine are most commonly weighed in water for that purpose. Thus, if we wish to determine the specific gravity of gold flattened under the hammer, and supposing the piece of gold to weigh 8 *oz.* 4 *gros* 2½ *grs.* in the air,[1] it is suspended by means of a fine metallic wire under the scale of a hydrostatic balance so as to be entirely immersed in water and again weighed. The piece of gold in Mr. Brisson's experiment lost by this means 3 *gros* 37 *grs.;* and, as it is evident that the weight lost by a body weighed in water is precisely equal to the weight of the water displaced, or to that of an equal volume of water, we may conclude that, in equal magnitudes, gold weighs 4893½ *grs.* and water 253 *grs.* which, reduced to unity, gives 1.0000 as the specific gravity of water and 19.3617 for that of gold. We may operate in the same manner with all solid substances. We have rarely any occasion, in chemistry, to determine the specific gravity of solid bodies, unless when operating upon alloys or metallic glasses; but we have very frequent necessity to ascertain that of fluids, as it is often the only means of judging of their purity or degree of concentration.

This object may be very fully accomplished with the hydrostatic balance, by weighing a solid body; such, for example, as a little ball of rock crystal suspended by a very fine gold wire, first in the air, and afterwards in the fluid whose specific gravity we wish to discover. The weight lost by the crystal, when weighed in the liquor, is equal to that of an equal bulk of the liquid. By repeating this operation successively in water and different fluids, we can very readily ascertain, by a simple and easy calculation, the relative specific gravities of these fluids, either with respect to each other or to water. This method is not, however, sufficiently exact, or, at least, is rather troublesome, from its extreme delicacy, when used for liquids differing but little in specific gravity from water; such, for instance, as mineral waters, or any other water containing very small portions of salt in solution.

In some operations of this nature, which have not hitherto been made public, I employed an instrument of great sensitivity for this purpose with great advantage. It consists of a hollow cylinder *A b c f* (Plate VII, *Fig. 6*), of brass, or rather of silver, loaded at its bottom, *b c f*, with tin, as represented swimming in a jug of water, *l m n o*. To the upper part of the cylinder is attached a stalk of silver wire, not more

than three fourths of a line diameter, surmounted by a little cup *d*, intended for containing weights; upon the stalk a mark is made at *g*, the use of which we shall presently explain. This cylinder may be made of any size; but, to be accurate, ought at least to displace four pounds of water. The weight of tin with which this instrument is loaded ought to be such as will make it remain almost in equilibrium in distilled water and should not require more than half a dram, or a dram at most, to make it sink to *g*.

We must first determine, with great precision, the exact weight of the instrument and the number of additional grains requisite for making it sink, in distilled water of a determinate temperature, to the mark. We then perform the same experiment upon all the fluids of which we wish to ascertain the specific gravity, and, by means of calculation, reduce the observed differences to a common standard of cubic feet, pints or pounds, or of decimal fractions, comparing them with water. This method, joined to experiments with certain reagents, is one of the best for determining the quality of waters and is even capable of pointing out differences which escape the most accurate chemical analysis. I shall, at some future period, give an account of a very extensive set of experiments which I have made upon this subject.

These metallic hydrometers are only to be used for determining the specific gravities of such waters as contain only neutral salts or alkaline substances; and they may be constructed with different degrees of ballast for alcohol and other spiritous liquors. When the specific gravities of acid liquors are to be ascertained, we must use a glass hydrometer (Plate VII, *Fig. 14*). This consists of a hollow cylinder of glass, *a b c f*, hermetically sealed at its lower end, and drawn out at the upper into a capillary tube *a*, ending in the little cup or basin *d*. This instrument is ballasted with more or less mercury, at the bottom of the cylinder introduced through the tube, in proportion to the weight of the liquor intended to be examined. We may introduce a small graduated slip of paper into the tube *a d;* and, though these degrees do not exactly correspond to the fractions of grains in the different liquors, they may be rendered very useful in calculation.

What is said in this chapter may suffice, without further enlargement, for indicating the means of ascertaining the absolute and specific

---

[1] *Vide* Mr. Brisson's *Essay upon Specific Gravity*, p. 5.—AUTHOR.

gravities of solids and fluids, as the necessary instruments are generally known, and may easily be procured. But, as the instruments I have used for measuring the gases are not anywhere described, I shall give a more detailed account of these in the following chapter.

CHAPTER II

Of Gazometry, or the Measurement of the Weight and Volume of Aeriform Substances

SECTION I *Of the Pneumato-chemical Apparatus*

THE French chemists have of late applied the name of *pneumato-chemical apparatus* to the very simple and ingenious contrivance, invented by Dr. Priestley, which is now indispensably necessary to every laboratory. This consists of a wooden trough, of larger or smaller dimensions as is thought convenient, lined with plate-lead or tinned copper, as represented in perspective, Plate v. In *Fig. 1* the same trough or cistern is supposed to have two of its sides cut away, to show its interior construction more distinctly. In this apparatus, we distinguish between the shelf ABCD (*Figs. 1* and *2*) and the bottom or body of the cistern FGHI (*Fig. 2*). The jars or bell-glasses are filled with water in this deep part, and, being turned with their mouths downwards, are afterwards set upon the shelf ABCD, as shown (Plate x, *Fig. 1*, F) The upper parts of the sides of the cistern above the level of the shelf are called the *rim* or *borders*.

The cistern ought to be filled with water, so as to stand at least an inch and a half deep upon the shelf, and it should be of such dimensions as to admit of at least one foot of water in every direction in the well. This size is sufficient for ordinary occasions; but it is often convenient, and even necessary, to have more room. I would therefore advise such as intend to employ themselves usefully in chemical experiments, to have this apparatus made of considerable magnitude, where their place of operating will allow. The well of my principal cistern holds four cubic feet of water, and its shelf has a surface of fourteen square feet; yet, in spite of this size, which I at first thought immoderate, I am often straitened for room.

In laboratories, where a considerable number of experiments are performed, it is necessary to have several lesser cisterns, besides the large one, which may be called the *general mag-azine;* and even some portable ones, which may be moved, when necessary, near a furnace or wherever they may be wanted. There are likewise some operations which dirty the water of the apparatus and therefore require to be carried on in cisterns by themselves.

It were doubtless considerably cheaper to use cisterns, or iron-bound tubs, of wood simply dove-tailed, instead of being lined with lead or copper; and in my first experiments I used them made in that way; but I soon discovered their inconvenience. If the water be not always kept at the same level, such of the dovetails as are left dry shrink, and when more water is added it escapes through the joints, and runs out.

We employ crystal jars or bell-glasses, (Plate v, *Fig. 9*, A) for containing the gases in this apparatus; and, for transporting these, when full of gas, from one cistern to another, or for keeping them in reserve when the cistern is too full, we make use of a flat dish BC, surrounded by a standing up rim or border, with two handles DE for carrying it by.

After several trials of different materials, I have found marble the best substance for constructing the mercurial pneumato-chemical apparatus, as it is perfectly impenetrable by mercury, and is not liable, like wood, to separate at the junctures, or to allow the mercury to escape through chinks; neither does it run the risk of breaking, like glass, stone-ware, or porcelain. Take a block of marble BCDE (Plate v, *Figs. 3* and *4*), about two feet long, 15 or 18 inches broad, and ten inches thick, and cause it to be hollowed out as at *m n* (*Fig. 5*) about four inches deep, as a reservoir for the mercury; and, to be able more conveniently to fill the jars, cut the gutter TV (*Figs. 3, 4,* and *5*) at least four inches deeper; and, as this trench may sometimes prove troublesome, it is made capable of being covered at pleasure by thin boards, which slip into the grooves *x y*, (*Fig. 5*). I have two marble cisterns upon this construction, of different sizes, by which I can always employ one of them as a reservoir of mercury, which it preserves with more safety than any other vessel, being neither subject to overturn, nor to any other accident. We operate with mercury in this apparatus exactly as with water in the one before described; but the bell-glasses must be of smaller diameter and much stronger; or we may use glass tubes, having their mouths widened, as in *Fig. 7;* these are called *eudiometers* by the glass-men who sell them. One of the bell-glasses is represented,

Fig. 5, A, standing in its place, and what is called a *jar* is engraved *Fig. 6*.

The mercurial pneumato-chemical apparatus is necessary in all experiments wherein the disengaged gases are capable of being absorbed by water, as is frequently the case, especially in all combinations, excepting those of metals, in fermentation, &c.

SECTION II *Of the Gazometer*

I give the name of *gazometer* to an instrument which I invented and caused constructed, for the purpose of a kind of bellows which might furnish an uniform and continued stream of oxygen gas in experiments of fusion. M. Meusnier and I have since made very considerable corrections and additions, having converted it into what may be called an *universal instrument*, without which it is hardly possible to perform most of the very exact experiments. The name we have given the instrument indicates its intention for measuring the volume or quantity of gas submitted to it for examination.

It consists of a strong iron beam, DE (Plate VIII, *Fig. 1*), three feet long, having at each end, D and E, a segment of a circle, likewise strongly constructed of iron, and very firmly joined. Instead of being poised as in ordinary balances, this beam rests, by means of a cylindrical axis of polished steel F (*Fig. 9*), upon two large moveable brass friction-wheels, by which the resistance to its motion from friction is considerably diminished, being converted into friction of the second order. As an additional precaution, the parts of these wheels which support the axis of the beam are covered with plates of polished rock-crystal. The whole of this machinery is fixed to the top of the solid column of wood BC (*Fig. 1*). To one extremity D of the beam, a scale P for holding weights is suspended by a flat chain, which applies to the curvature of the arc *n*D*o*, in a groove made for the purpose. To the other extremity E of the beam is applied another flat chain, *i k m*, so constructed as to be incapable of lengthening or shortening, by being less or more charged with weight; to this chain, an iron trivet, with three branches, *a i*, *c i*, and *h i*, is strongly fixed at *i*, and these branches support a large inverted jar A, of hammered copper, of about 18 inches diameter and 20 inches deep. The whole of this machine is represented in perspective, Plate VIII, *Fig. 1*; and Plate IX, *Figs. 2* and *4* give perpendicular sections, which show its interior structure.

Round the bottom of the jar, on its outside, is fixed (Plate IX, *Fig. 2*) a border divided into compartments 1, 2, 3, 4, &c., intended to receive leaden weights separately represented 1, 2, 3, *Fig. 3*. These are intended for increasing the weight of the jar when a considerable pressure is requisite, as will be afterwards explained, though such necessity seldom occurs. The cylindrical jar A is entirely open below, *de* (Plate IX, *Fig. 4*); but is closed above with a copper lid, *a b c*, open at *bf*, and capable of being shut by the cock *g*. This lid, as may be seen by inspecting the figures, is placed a few inches within the top of the jar to prevent the jar from being ever entirely immersed in the water and covered over. Were I to have this instrument made over again, I should cause the lid to be considerably more flattened, so as to be almost level. This jar or reservoir of air is contained in the cylindrical copper vessel LMNO (Plate VIII, *Fig. 1*) filled with water.

In the middle of the cylindrical vessel LMNO (Plate IX, *Fig. 4*) are placed two tubes *st*, *xy*, which are made to approach each other at their upper extremities *ty*; these are made of such a length as to rise a little above the upper edge LM of the vessel LMNO, and when the jar *abcde* touches the bottom NO, their upper ends enter about half an inch into the conical hollow *b* leading to the stop-cock *g*.

The bottom of the vessel LMNO is represented, Plate IX, *Fig. 3*, in the middle of which a small hollow semispherical cap is soldered, which may be considered as the broad end of a funnel reversed, the two tubes *st*, *xy* (*Fig. 4*) are adapted to this cap at *s* and *x*, and by this means communicate with the tubes *mm*, *nn*, *oo*, *pp* (*Fig. 3*), which are fixed horizontally upon the bottom of the vessel, and all of which terminate in, and are united by, the spherical cap *sx*. Three of these tubes are continued out of the vessel, as in Plate VIII, *Fig. 1*. The first marked in that figure 1, 2, 3, is inserted at its extremity 3 by means of an intermediate stop-cock 4 to the jar V which stands upon the shelf of a small pneumato-chemical apparatus GHIK, the inside of which is shown Plate IX, *Fig. 1*. The second tube is applied against the outside of the vessel LMNO from 6 to 7, is continued at 8, 9, 10, and at 11 is engaged below the jar V. The former of these tubes is intended for conveying gas into the machine and the latter for conducting small quantities for trials under jars. The gas is made either to flow into or out of the machine, according to the degree of pressure it receives; and this pressure is varied at pleasure, by loading the scale P less or more by means of weights. When gas is to be introduced into the machine, the pressure is taken off, or even rendered negative; but, when gas is to be expelled, a pressure is made with such degree of force as is found necessary.

The third tube 12, 13, 14, 15, is intended for conveying air or gas to any necessary place or apparatus for combustions, combinations, or any other experiment in which it is required.

To explain the use of the fourth tube, I must enter into some discussions. Suppose the vessel LMNO (Plate VIII, *Fig. 1*) full of water, and the jar A partly filled with gas, and partly with water; it is evident that the weights in the basin P may be so adjusted as to occasion an exact equilibrium between the weight of the basin and of the jar, so that the external air shall not tend to enter into the jar nor the gas to escape from it; and in this case the water will stand exactly at the same level both within and without the jar. On the contrary, if the weight in the basin P be diminished, the jar will then press downwards from its own gravity, and the water will stand lower within the jar than it does without; in this case, the included air or gas will suffer a degree of compression above that experienced by the external air, exactly proportioned to the weight of a column of water, equal to the difference of the external and internal surfaces of the water. From these reflections, M. Meusnier contrived a method of determining the exact degree of pressure to which the gas contained in the jar is at any time exposed. For this purpose, he employs a double glass siphon 19, 20, 21, 22, 23, firmly cemented at 19 and 23. The extremity 19 of this siphon communicates freely with the water in the external vessel of the machine, and the extremity 23 communicates with the fourth tube at the bottom of the cylindrical vessel, and consequently, by means of the perpendicular tube *st* (Plate IX, *Fig. 4*) with the air contained in the jar. He likewise cements, at 16 (Plate VIII, *Fig. 1*), another glass tube 16, 17, 18, which communicates at 16 with the water in the exterior vessel LMNO, and, at its upper end 18, is open to the external air.

By these several contrivances, it is evident that the water must stand in the tube 16, 17, 18, at the same level with that in the cistern LMNO; and, on the contrary, that, in the branch 19, 20, 21, it must stand higher or lower according as the air in the jar is subjected to a greater or lesser pressure than the external air. To ascertain these differences, a brass scale di-

vided into inches and lines is fixed between these two tubes. It is readily conceived that, as air, and all other elastic fluids must increase in weight by compression, it is necessary to know their degree of condensation to be enabled to calculate their quantities and to convert the measure of their volumes into correspondent weights; and this object is intended to be fulfilled by the contrivance now described.

But, to determine the specific gravity of air or of gases, and to ascertain their weight in a known volume, it is necessary to know their temperature as well as the degree of pressure under which they subsist; and this is accomplished by means of a small thermometer, strongly cemented into a brass collet which screws into the lid of the jar A. This thermometer is represented separately, Plate VIII, *Fig. 10*, and in its place 24, 25, *Fig. 1* and Plate IX, *Fig. 4*. The bulb is in the inside of the jar A, and its graduated stalk rises on the outside of the lid.

The practice of gazometry would still have laboured under great difficulties without further precautions than those above described. When the jar A sinks in the water of the cistern LMNO, it must lose a weight equal to that of the water which it displaces; and consequently the compression which it makes upon the contained air or gas must be proportionally diminished. Hence the gas furnished, during experiments from the machine, will not have the same density towards the end that it had at the beginning, as its specific gravity is continually diminishing. This difference may, it is true, be determined by calculation; but this would have occasioned such mathematical investigations as must have rendered the use of this apparatus both troublesome and difficult. M. Meusnier has remedied this inconvenience by the following contrivance. A square rod of iron, 26, 27 (Plate VIII, *Fig. 1*), is raised perpendicular to the middle of the beam DE. This rod passes through a hollow box of brass 28, which opens, and may be filled with lead; and this box is made to slide alongst the rod by means of a toothed pinion playing in a rack, so as to raise or lower the box and to fix it at such places as is judged proper.

When the lever or beam DE stands horizontal, this box gravitates to neither side; but, when the jar A sinks into the cistern LMNO, so as to make the beam incline to that side, it is evident the loaded box 28, which then passes beyond the center of suspension, must gravitate to the side of the jar and augment its pressure upon the included air. This is increased in proportion as the box is raised towards 27, because the same weight exerts a greater power in proportion to the length of the lever by which it acts. Hence, by moving the box 28 alongst the rod 26, 27, we can augment or diminish the correction it is intended to make upon the pressure of the jar; and both experience and calculation show that this may be made to compensate very exactly for the loss of weight in the jar at all degrees of pressure.

I have not hitherto explained the most important part of the use of this machine, which is the manner of employing it for ascertaining the quantities of the air or gas furnished during experiments. To determine this with the most rigorous precision, and likewise the quantity supplied to the machine from experiments, we fixed to the arc which terminates the arm of the beam E (Plate VIII, *Fig. 1*), the brass sector *l m*, divided into degrees and half degrees, which consequently moves in common with the beam; and the lowering of this end of the beam is measured by the fixed index 29, 30, which has a nonius giving hundredth parts of a degree at its extremity 30.

The whole particulars of the different parts of the above described machine are represented in Plate VIII as follow:

Fig. 2 is the flat chain invented by M. Vaucanson and employed for suspending the scale or basin P, *Fig. 1*; but, as this lengthens or shortens according as it is more or less loaded, it would not have answered for suspending the jar A, *Fig. 1*.

Fig. 5 is the chain *i k m*, which in *Fig. 1* sustains the jar A. This is entirely formed of plates of polished iron interlaced into each other and held together by iron pins. This chain does not lengthen in any sensible degree, by any weight it is capable of supporting.

Fig. 6. The trivet, or three branched stirrup, by which the jar A is hung to the balance, with the screw by which it is fixed in an accurately vertical position.

Fig. 3. The iron rod 26, 27, which is fixed perpendicular to the center of the beam, with its box 28.

Figs. 7 & 8. The friction-wheels, with the plates of rock-crystal Z as points of contact by which the friction of the axis of the lever of the balance is avoided.

Fig. 4. The piece of metal which supports the axis of the friction-wheels.

Fig. 9. The middle of the lever or beam, with the axis upon which it moves.

Fig. 10. The thermometer for determining the temperature of the air or gas contained in the jar.

When this gazometer is to be used, the cistern or external vessel LMNO (Plate VIII, *Fig. 1*) is to be filled with water to a determinate height, which should be the same in all experiments. The level of the water should be taken when the beam of the balance stands horizontal; this level, when the jar is at the bottom of the cistern, is increased by all the water which it displaces and is diminished in proportion as the jar rises to its highest elevation. We next endeavour, by repeated trials, to discover at what elevation the box 28 must be fixed to render the pressure equal in all situations of the beam. I should have said nearly, because this correction is not absolutely rigorous; and differences of a quarter, or even of half a line, are not of any consequence. This height of the box 28 is not the same for every degree of pressure, but varies according as this is of one, two, three, or more inches. All these should be registered with great order and precision.

We next take a bottle which holds eight or ten pints, the capacity of which is very accurately determined by weighing the water it is capable of containing. This bottle is turned bottom upwards, full of water, in the cistern of the pneumato-chemical apparatus GHIK (*Fig. 1*), and is set on its mouth upon the shelf of the apparatus, instead of the glass jar V, having the extremity 11 of the tube 7, 8, 9, 10, 11, inserted into its mouth. The machine is fixed at zero of pressure, and the degree marked by the index 30 upon the sector *m l* is accurately observed; then, by opening the stop-cock 8, and pressing a little upon the jar A, as much air is forced into the bottle as fills it entirely. The degree marked by the index upon the sector is now observed, and we calculate what number of cubic inches correspond to each degree. We then fill a second and third bottle, and so on, in the same manner, with the same precautions, and even repeat the operation several times with bottles of different sizes, till at last, by accurate attention, we ascertain the exact gage or capacity of the jar A, in all its parts; but it is better to have it formed at first accurately cylindrical, by which we avoid these calculations and estimates.

The instrument I have been describing was constructed with great accuracy and uncommon skill by M. Meignié, Jr., engineer and physical instrument-maker. It is a most valuable instrument, from the great number of purposes to which it is applicable; and, indeed, there are many experiments which are almost impossible to perform without it. It becomes expensive, because, in many experiments, such as the formation of water and of nitric acid, it is absolutely necessary to employ two of the same machines. In the present advanced state of chemistry, very expensive and complicated instruments are become indispensably necessary for ascertaining the analysis and synthesis of bodies with the requisite precision as to quantity and proportion; it is certainly proper to endeavour to simplify these and to render them less costly; but this ought by no means to be attempted at the expense of their convenience of application, and much less of their accuracy.

SECTION III *Some Other Methods of Measuring the Volume of Gases*

The gazometer described in the foregoing section is too costly and too complicated for being generally used in laboratories for measuring the gases and is not even applicable to every circumstance of this kind. In numerous series of experiments, more simple and more readily applicable methods must be employed. For this purpose I shall describe the means I used before I was in possession of a gazometer and which I still use in preference to it in the ordinary course of my experiments.

Suppose that, after an experiment, there is a residuum of gas, neither absorbable by alkali nor water, contained in the upper part of the jar AEF (Plate IV, *Fig. 3*) standing on the shelf of a pneumato-chemical apparatus, of which we wish to ascertain the quantity. We must first mark the height to which the mercury or water rises in the jar with great exactness, by means of slips of paper pasted in several parts round the jar. If we have been operating in mercury, we begin by displacing the mercury from the jar by introducing water in its stead. This is readily done by filling a bottle quite full of water; having stopped it with your finger, turn it up, and introduce its mouth below the edge of the jar; then, turning down its body again, the mercury, by its gravity, falls into the bottle, and the water rises in the jar, and takes the place occupied by the mercury. When this is accomplished, pour so much water into the cistern ABCD as will stand about an inch over the surface of the mercury; then pass the dish BC (Plate V, *Fig. 9*) under the jar, and carry it to the water cistern (*Figs. 1* and *2*). We here exchange the gas into another jar, which has been previously graduated in the manner

to be afterwards described; and we thus judge of the quantity or volume of the gas by means of the degrees which it occupies in the graduated jar.

There is another method of determining the volume of gas, which may either be substituted in place of the one above described or may be usefully employed as a correction or proof of that method. After the air or gas is exchanged from the first jar, marked with slips of paper, into the graduated jar, turn up the mouth of the marked jar and fill it with water exactly to the marks EF (Plate IV, *Fig. 3*), and by weighing the water we determine the volume of the air or gas it contained, allowing one cubic foot, or 1728 cubic inches, of water for each 70 pounds, French weight.

The manner of graduating jars for this purpose is very easy, and we ought to be provided with several of different sizes, and even several of each size in case of accidents. Take a tall, narrow, and strong glass jar, and, having filled it with water in the cistern (Plate V, *Fig. 1*), place it upon the shelf ABCD; we ought always to use the same place for this operation, that the level of the shelf may be always exactly similar, by which almost the only error to which this process is liable will be avoided. Then take a narrow mouthed phial which holds exactly 6 *oz.* 3 *gros* 61 *grs.* of water, which corresponds to 10 cubic inches. If you have not one exactly of this dimension, choose one a little larger, and diminish its capacity to the size requisite by dropping in a little melted wax and rosin. This bottle serves the purpose of a standard for gauging the jars. Make the air contained in this bottle pass into the jar and mark exactly the place to which the water has descended; add another measure of air and again mark the place of the water, and so on, till all the water be displaced. It is of great consequence that, during the course of this operation, the bottle and jar be kept at the same temperature with the water in the cistern; and, for this reason, we must avoid keeping the hands upon either as much as possible; or, if we suspect they have been heated, we must cool them by means of the water in the cistern. The height of the barometer and thermometer during this experiment is of no consequence.

When the marks have been thus ascertained upon the jar for every ten cubic inches, we engrave a scale upon one of its sides by means of a diamond pencil. Glass tubes are graduated in the same manner for use in the mercurial apparatus, only they must be divided into cubic inches, and tenths of a cubic inch. The bottle used for gauging these must hold 8 *oz.* 6 *gros* 25 *grs.* of mercury, which exactly corresponds to a cubic inch of that metal.

The method of determining the volume of air or gas by means of a graduated jar has the advantage of not requiring any correction for the difference of height between the surface of the water within the jar and in the cistern; but it requires corrections with respect to the height of the barometer and thermometer. But, when we ascertain the volume of air by weighing the water which the jar is capable of containing, up to the marks EF, it is necessary to make a further correction for the difference between the surface of the water in the cistern and the height to which it rises within the jar. This will be explained in the fifth section of this chapter.

SECTION IV *Of the Method of Separating the Different Gases from Each Other*

As experiments often produce two, three, or more species of gas, it is necessary to be able to separate these from each other that we may ascertain the quantity and species of each. Suppose that under the jar A (Plate IV, *Fig. 3*), is contained a quantity of different gases mixed together and standing over mercury; we begin by marking with slips of paper, as before directed, the height at which the mercury stands within the glass; then introduce about a cubic inch of water into the jar, which will swim over the surface of the mercury. If the mixture of gas contains any muriatic or sulphurous acid gas, a rapid and considerable absorption will instantly take place, from the strong tendency these two gases have, especially the former, to combine with or be absorbed by water. If the water only produces a slight absorption of gas hardly equal to its own bulk, we conclude that the mixture neither contains muriatic acid, sulphuric acid, or ammoniacal gas, but that it contains carbonic acid gas, of which water only absorbs about its own bulk. To ascertain this conjecture, introduce some solution of caustic alkali, and the carbonic acid gas will be gradually absorbed in the course of a few hours; it combines with the caustic alkali or potash, and the remaining gas is left almost perfectly free from any sensible residuum of carbonic acid gas.

After each experiment of this kind, we must carefully mark the height at which the mercury stands within the jar by slips of paper pasted on and varnished over when dry, that they may not be washed off when placed in the water apparatus. It is likewise necessary to regis-

ter the difference between the surface of the mercury in the cistern and that in the jar, and the height of the barometer and thermometer, at the end of each experiment.

When all the gas or gases absorbable by water and potash are absorbed, water is admitted into the jar to displace the mercury; and, as is described in the preceding section, the mercury in the cistern is to be covered by one or two inches of water. After this, the jar is to be transported by means of the flat dish BC (Plate v, *Fig. 9*) into the water apparatus; and the quantity of gas remaining is to be ascertained by changing it into a graduated jar. After this, small trials of it are to be made by experiments in little jars, to ascertain nearly the nature of the gas in question. For instance, into a small jar full of the gas (Plate v, *Fig. 8*) a lighted taper is introduced; if the taper is not immediately extinguished, we conclude the gas to contain oxygen gas; and, in proportion to the brightness of the flame, we may judge if it contain less or more oxygen gas than atmospheric air contains. If, on the contrary, the taper be instantly extinguished, we have strong reason to presume that the residuum is chiefly composed of azotic gas. If, upon the approach of the taper, the gas takes fire and burns quietly at the surface with a white flame, we conclude it to be pure hydrogen gas; if this flame is blue, we judge it consists of carbonated hydrogen gas; and, if it takes fire with a sudden deflagration, that it is a mixture of oxygen and hydrogen gas. If, again, upon mixing a portion of the residuum with oxygen gas, red fumes are produced, we conclude that it contains nitrous gas.

These preliminary trials give some general knowledge of the properties of the gas and nature of the mixture, but are not sufficient to determine the proportions and quantities of the several gases of which it is composed. For this purpose all the methods of analysis must be employed; and, to direct these properly, it is of great use to have a previous approximation by the above methods. Suppose, for instance, we know that the residuum consists of oxygen and azotic gas mixed together; put a determinate quantity, 100 parts, into a graduated tube of ten or twelve lines diameter, introduce a solution of sulphuret of potash in contact with the gas, and leave them together for some days; the sulphuret absorbs the whole oxygen gas and leaves the azotic gas pure.

If it is known to contain hydrogen gas, a determinate quantity is introduced into Volta's eudiometer alongside with a known proportion of hydrogen gas; these are deflagrated together by means of the electrical spark; fresh portions of oxygen gas are successively added till no further deflagration takes place and till the greatest possible diminution is produced. By this process water is formed, which is immediately absorbed by the water of the apparatus; but, if the hydrogen gas contain charcoal, carbonic acid is formed at the same time, which is not absorbed so quickly; the quantity of this is readily ascertained by assisting its absorption, by means of agitation. If the residuum contains nitrous gas, by adding oxygen gas, with which it combines into nitric acid, we can very nearly ascertain its quantity from the diminution produced by this mixture.

I confine myself to these general examples, which are sufficient to give an idea of this kind of operation; a whole volume would not serve to explain every possible case. It is necessary to become familiar with the analysis of gases by long experience; we must even acknowledge that they mostly possess such powerful affinities to each other that we are not always certain of having separated them completely. In these cases, we must vary our experiments in every possible point of view, add new agents to the combination, and keep out others, and continue our trials till we are certain of the truth and exactitude of our conclusions.

SECTION V *Of the Necessary Corrections of the Volume of Gases, According to the Pressure of the Atmosphere*

All elastic fluids are compressible or condensable in proportion to the weight with which they are loaded. Perhaps this law, which is ascertained by general experience, may suffer some irregularity when these fluids are under a degree of condensation almost sufficient to reduce them to the liquid state, or when either in a state of extreme rarefaction or condensation; but we seldom approach either of these limits with most of the gases which we submit to our experiments. I understand this proposition of gases being compressible, in proportion to their superincumbent weights, as follows:

A barometer, which is an instrument generally known, is, properly speaking, a species of siphon, ABCD (Plate XII, *Fig. 16*), whose leg AB is filled with mercury, whilst the leg CD is full of air. If we suppose the branch CD indefinitely continued till it equals the height of our atmosphere, we can readily conceive that the barometer is, in reality, a sort of balance, in which a column of mercury stands in equilibri-

um with a column of air of the same weight. But it is unnecessary to prolongate the branch CD to such a height, as it is evident that the barometer, being immersed in air, the column of mercury AB will be equally in equilibrium with a column of air of the same diameter, though the leg CD be cut off at C, and the part CD be taken away altogether.

The medium height of mercury in equilibrium with the weight of a column of air, from the highest part of the atmosphere to the surface of the earth, is about twenty-eight French inches in the lower parts of the city of Paris; or, in other words, the air at the surface of the earth at Paris is usually pressed upon by a weight equal to that of a column of mercury twenty-eight inches in height. I must be understood in this way in the several parts of this publication when talking of the different gases, as, for instance, when the cubic foot of oxygen gas is said to weigh 1 *oz.* 4 *gros*, under 28 inches pressure. The height of this column of mercury, supported by the pressure of the air, diminishes in proportion as we are elevated above the surface of the earth, or rather above the level of the sea, because the mercury can only form an equilibrium with the column of air which is above it and is not in the smallest degree affected by the air which is below its level.

In what ratio does the mercury in the barometer descend in proportion to its elevation; or, which is the same thing, according to what law or ratio do the several strata of the atmosphere decrease in density? This question, which has exercised the ingenuity of natural philosophers during the last century, is considerably elucidated by the following experiment.

If we take the glass siphon ABCDE (Plate XII, *Fig. 17*), shut at E and open at A, and introduce a few drops of mercury, so as to intercept the communication of air between the leg AB and the leg BE, it is evident that the air contained in BCDE is pressed upon, in common with the whole surrounding air, by a weight or column of air equal to 28 inches of mercury. But, if we pour 28 inches of mercury into the leg AB, it is plain the air in the branch BCDE will now be pressed upon by a weight equal to twice 28 inches of mercury, or twice the weight of the atmosphere; and experience shows that, in this case, the included air, instead of filling the tube from B to E, only occupies from C to E, or exactly one half of the space it filled before. If to this first column of mercury we add two other portions of 28 inches each, in the branch AB, the air in the branch

BCDE will be pressed upon by four times the weight of the atmosphere, or four times the weight of 28 inches of mercury, and it will then only fill the space from D to E, or exactly one quarter of the space it occupied at the commencement of the experiment. From these experiments, which may be infinitely varied, has been deduced as a general law of nature, which seems applicable to all permanently elastic fluids, that they diminish in volume in proportion to the weights with which they are pressed upon; or, in other words: *"the volume of all elastic fluids is in the inverse ratio of the weight by which they are compressed."*

The experiments which have been made for measuring the heights of mountains by means of the barometer confirm the truth of these deductions; and, even supposing them in some degree inaccurate, these differences are so extremely small that they may be reckoned as nullities in chemical experiments. When this law of the compression of elastic fluids is once well understood, it becomes easily applicable to the corrections necessary in pneumato-chemical experiments upon the volume of gas in relation to its pressure. These corrections are of two kinds, the one relative to the variations of the barometer and the other for the column of water or mercury contained in the jars. I shall endeavour to explain these by examples, beginning with the most simple case.

Suppose that 100 cubic inches of oxygen gas are obtained at 10° (54.5°) of the thermometer, and at 28 inches 6 lines of the barometer, it is required to know what volume the 100 cubic inches of gas would occupy, under the pressure of 28 inches,[1] and what is the exact weight of the 100 inches of oxygen gas? Let the unknown volume, or the number of inches this gas would occupy at 28 inches of the barometer, be expressed by x; and, since the volumes are in the inverse ratio of their superincumbent weights, we have the following statement: 100 cubic inches is to x inversely as 28.5 inches of pressure is to 28.0 inches; or directly 28:28.5::100: $x = 101.786$—cubic inches, at 28 inches barometrical pressure; that is to say, the same gas or air which at 28.5 inches of the barometer occupies 100 cubic inches of volume, will occupy 101.786 cubic inches when the barometer is at 28 inches. It is equally easy to calculate the

weight of this gas occupying 100 cubic inches, under 28.5 inches of barometrical pressure; for, as it corresponds to 101.786 cubic inches at the pressure of 28, and as, at this pressure, and at 10° (54.5°) of temperature, each cubic inch of oxygen gas weighs half a grain, it follows that 100 cubic inches, under 28.5 barometrical pressure, must weigh 50.893 grains. This conclusion might have been formed more directly, as, since the volume of elastic fluids is in the inverse ratio of their compression, their weights must be in the direct ratio of the same compression: hence, since 100 cubic inches weigh 50 grains under the pressure of 28 inches, we have the following statement to determine the weight of 100 cubic inches of the same gas at 28.5 barometrical pressure; 28:50::28.5:x, the unknown quantity, $= 50.893$.

The following case is more complicated. Suppose the jar A (Plate XII, *Fig. 18*) to contain a quantity of gas in its upper part ACD, the rest of the jar below CD being full of mercury, and the whole standing in the mercurial basin or reservoir GHIK, filled with mercury up to EF, and that the difference between the surface CD of the mercury in the jar, and EF, that in the cistern, is six inches, while the barometer stands at 27.5 inches. It is evident from these data that the air contained in ACD is pressed upon by the weight of the atmosphere, diminished by the weight of the column of mercury CE, or by $27.5 - 6 = 21.5$ inches of barometrical pressure. This air is therefore less compressed than the atmosphere at the mean height of the barometer, and consequently occupies more space than it would occupy at the mean pressure, the difference being exactly proportional to the difference between the compressing weights. If, then, upon measuring the space ACD, it is found to be 120 cubic inches, it must be reduced to the volume which it would occupy under the mean pressure of 28 inches. This is done by the following statement: 120:x, the unknown volume, ::21.5:28 inversely; this gives

$$x = \frac{120 \times 21.5}{28} = 92.143 \text{ cubic inches.}$$

In these calculations we may either reduce the height of the mercury in the barometer, and the difference of level in the jar and basin, into lines or decimal fractions of the inch; but I prefer the latter, as it is more readily calculated. As, in these operations, which frequently recur, it is of great use to have means of abbreviation, I have given a table in the appendix for reducing lines and fractions of lines into decimal fractions of the inch.

[1] According to the proportion of 114 to 107, given between the French and English foot, 28 inches of the French barometer are equal to 29.83 inches of the English.—TRANSLATOR.

In experiments performed in the water-apparatus, we must make similar corrections to procure rigorously exact results, by taking into account, and making allowances for the difference of height of the water within the jar above the surface of the water in the cistern. But, as the pressure of the atmosphere is expressed in inches and lines of the mercurial barometer, and as homogeneous quantities only can be calculated together, we must reduce the observed inches and lines of water into correspondent heights of the mercury. I have given a table in the appendix for this conversion, upon the supposition that mercury is 13.5681 times heavier than water.[1]

SECTION VI *Of the Correction Relative to the Degrees of the Thermometer*

In ascertaining the weight of gases, besides reducing them to a mean of barometrical pressure, as directed in the preceding section, we must likewise reduce them to a standard thermometrical temperature; because, all elastic fluids being expanded by heat and condensed by cold, their weight in any determinate volume is thereby liable to considerable alterations. As the temperature of 10° (54.5°) is a medium between the heat of summer and the cold of winter, being the temperature of subterraneous places and that which is most easily approached to at all seasons, I have chosen that degree as a mean to which I reduce air or gas in this species of calculation.

M. de Luc found that atmospheric air was increased $\frac{1}{215}$ part of its bulk, by each degree of a mercurial thermometer, divided into 81 degrees, between the freezing and boiling points; this gives $\frac{1}{211}$ part for each degree of Reaumur's thermometer, which is divided into 80 degrees between these two points. The experiments of M. Monge seem to make this dilatation less for hydrogen gas, which he thinks is only dilated $\frac{1}{180}$. We have not any exact experiments hitherto published respecting the ratio of dilatation of the other gases; but, from the trials which have been made, their dilatation seems to differ little from that of atmospheric air. Hence I may take for granted, till further experiments give us better information upon this subject, that atmospherical air is dilated $\frac{1}{210}$ part, and hydrogen gas $\frac{1}{190}$ part for each degree of the thermometer; but, as there is still great uncertainty upon this point, we ought always to operate in a temperature as near as

[1] The appendix is omitted in this edition.—EDITOR.

possible to the standard of 10° (54.5°); by this means any errors in correcting the weight or volume of gases by reducing them to the common standard, will become of little moment.

The calculation for this correction is extremely easy. Divide the observed volume of air by 210 and multiply the quotient by the degrees of temperature above or below 10° (54.5°). This correction is negative when the actual temperature is above the standard and positive when below. By the use of logarithmical tables this calculation is much facilitated.

SECTION VII *Example for Calculating the Corrections Relative to the Variations of Pressure and Temperature*

CASE

In the jar A (Plate IV, *Fig. 3*), standing in a water-apparatus, is contained 353 cubic inches of air; the surface of the water within the jar at EF is 4½ inches above the water in the cistern, the barometer is at 27 inches 9½ lines, and the thermometer at 15° (65.75°). Having burnt a quantity of phosphorus in the air, by which concrete phosphoric acid is produced, the air after the combustion occupies 295 cubic inches, the water within the jar stands 7 inches above that in the cistern, the barometer is at 27 inches 9¼ lines, and the thermometer at 16° (68°). It is required from these data to determine the actual volume of air before and after combustion and the quantity absorbed during the process.

Calculation before Combustion

The air in the jar before combustion was 353 cubic inches, but it was only under a barometrical pressure of 27 inches 9½ lines, which, reduced to decimal fractions, gives 27.79167 inches; and from this we must deduct the difference of 4½ inches of water, which corresponds to 0.33166 inches of the barometer; hence the real pressure of the air in the jar is 27.46001. As the volume of elastic fluids diminish in the inverse ratio of the compressing weights, we have the following statement to reduce the 353 inches to the volume the air would occupy at 28 inches barometrical pressure.

353:x, the unknown volume, ::27.46001:28.

Hence, $x = \dfrac{353 \times 27.46001}{28} = 346.192$ cubic inches, which is the volume the same quantity of air would have occupied at 28 inches of the barometer.

The 210th part of this corrected volume is 1.65, which, for the five degrees of temperature above the standard gives 8.255 cubic inches; and, as this correction is subtractive, the real corrected volume of the air before combustion is 337.942 inches.

Calculation after Combustion

By a similar calculation upon the volume of air after combustion, we find its barometrical pressure $27.77083 - 0.51593 = 27.25490$. Hence, to have the volume of air under the pressure of 28 inches, $295 : x :: 27.77083 : 28$ inversely; or, x $=\dfrac{295 \times 27.25490}{28} = 287.150$. The 210th part of this corrected volume is 1.368, which, multiplied by 6 degrees of thermometrical difference, gives the subtractive correction for temperature 8.208, leaving the actual corrected volume of air after combustion 278.942 inches.

Result

The corrected volume before combustion 337.942
Ditto remaining after combustion 278.942

Volume absorbed during combustion   59.000.

Section VIII *Method of Determining the Absolute Gravity of the Different Gases*

Take a large balloon A (Plate v, *Fig. 10*) capable of holding 17 or 18 pints, or about half a cubic foot, having the brass cap *bcde* strongly cemented to its neck and to which the tube and stop-cock *fg* is fixed by a tight screw. This apparatus is connected by the double screw, represented separately at *Fig. 12* to the jar BCD, *Fig. 10*, which must be some pints larger in dimensions than the balloon. This jar is open at top and is furnished with the brass cap *hi* and stop-cock *lm*. One of these stop-cocks is represented separately at *Fig. 11*.

We first determine the exact capacity of the balloon by filling it with water and weighing it both full and empty. When emptied of water, it is dried with a cloth introduced through its neck *de*, and the last remains of moisture are removed by exhausting it once or twice in an air-pump.

When the weight of any gas is to be ascertained, this apparatus is used as follows: fix the balloon A to the plate of an air-pump by means of the screw of the stop-cock *fg*, which is left open; the balloon is to be exhausted as completely as possible, observing carefully the degree of exhaustion by means of the barom-

eter attached to the air-pump. When the vacuum is formed, the stop-cock *fg* is shut and the weight of the balloon determined with the most scrupulous exactitude. It is then fixed to the jar BCD, which we suppose placed in water in the shelf of the pneumato-chemical apparatus (*Fig. 1*); the jar is to be filled with the gas we mean to weigh, and then, by opening the stop-cocks *fg* and *lm*, the gas ascends into the balloon, whilst the water of the cistern rises at the same time into the jar. To avoid very troublesome corrections, it is necessary, during this first part of the operation, to sink the jar in the cistern till the surfaces of the water within the jar and without exactly correspond. The stop-cocks are again shut, and the balloon being unscrewed from its connection with the jar, is to be carefully weighed; the difference between this weight and that of the exhausted balloon is the precise weight of the air or gas contained in the balloon. Multiply this weight by 1728, the number of cubic inches in a cubic foot, and divide the product by the number of cubic inches contained in the balloon; the quotient is the weight of a cubic foot of the gas or air submitted to experiment.

Exact account must be kept of the barometrical height and temperature of the thermometer during the above experiment; and from these the resulting weight of a cubic foot is easily corrected to the standard of 28 inches and 10°, as directed in the preceding section. The small portion of air remaining in the balloon after forming the vacuum must likewise be attended to, which is easily determined by the barometer attached to the air-pump. If that barometer, for instance, remains at the hundredth part of the height it stood at before the vacuum was formed, we conclude that one hundredth part of the air originally contained remained in the balloon and consequently that only $\frac{99}{100}$ of gas was introduced from the jar into the balloon.

CHAPTER III

Description of the Calorimeter, or Apparatus for Measuring Caloric

THE calorimeter, or apparatus for measuring the relative quantities of heat contained in bodies, was described by M. de Laplace and me in the *Recueil de l'Académie* for 1780, p. 355, and from that essay the materials of this chapter are extracted.

If, after having cooled any body to the freezing point, it be exposed in an atmosphere of 25° (88.25°), the body will gradually become heated, from the surface inwards, till at last it acquires the same temperature with the surrounding air. But, if a piece of ice be placed in the same situation, the circumstances are quite different; it does not approach in the smallest degree towards the temperature of the circumambient air but remains constantly at zero (32°), or the temperature of melting ice, till the last portion of ice be completely melted.

This phenomenon is readily explained, as, to melt ice, or reduce it to water, it requires to be combined with a certain portion of caloric; the whole caloric attracted from the surrounding bodies, is arrested or fixed at the surface or external layer of ice which it is employed to dissolve, and combines with it to form water; the next quantity of caloric combines with the second layer to dissolve it into water, and so on successively till the whole ice be dissolved or converted into water by combination with caloric, the very last atom still remaining at its former temperature, because the caloric has never penetrated so far as long as any intermediate ice remained to melt.

Upon these principles, if we conceive a hollow sphere of ice at the temperature of zero (32°) placed in an atmosphere 10° (54.5°), and containing a substance at any degree of temperature above freezing, it follows, 1st, that the heat of the external atmosphere cannot penetrate into the internal hollow of the sphere of ice; 2nd, that the heat of the body placed in the hollow of the sphere cannot penetrate outwards beyond it, but will be stopped at the internal surface and continually employed to melt successive layers of ice, until the temperature of the body be reduced to zero (32°) by having all its superabundant caloric above that temperature carried off by the ice. If the whole water, formed within the sphere of ice during the reduction of the temperature of the included body to zero, be carefully collected, the weight of the water will be exactly proportional to the quantity of caloric lost by the body in passing from its original temperature to that of melting ice; for it is evident that a double quantity of caloric would have melted twice the quantity of ice; hence the quantity of ice melted is a very exact measure of the quantity of caloric employed to produce that effect and consequently of the quantity lost by the only substance that could possibly have supplied it.

I have made this supposition of what would take place in a hollow sphere of ice for the purpose of more readily explaining the method used in this species of experiment, which was first conceived by M. de Laplace. It would be difficult to procure such spheres of ice and inconvenient to make use of them when got; but, by means of the following apparatus, we have remedied that defect. I acknowledge the name of *calorimeter*, which I have given it, as derived partly from Greek and partly from Latin, is in some degree open to criticism; but, in matters of science, a slight deviation from strict etymology, for the sake of giving distinctness of idea, is excusable; and I could not derive the name entirely from Greek without approaching too near to the names of known instruments employed for other purposes.

The calorimeter is represented in Plate vi. It is shown in perspective at *Fig. 1*, and its interior structure is engraved in *Figs. 2* and *3;* the former being a horizontal, and the latter a perpendicular section. Its capacity or cavity is divided into three parts, which, for better distinction, I shall name the interior, middle, and external cavities. The interior cavity *ffff* (*Fig. 4*), into which the substances submitted to experiment are put, is composed of a grating or cage of iron wire supported by several iron bars; its opening or mouth LM is covered by the lid HG of the same materials. The middle cavity *bbbb* (*Figs. 2* and *3*) is intended to contain the ice which surrounds the interior cavity, and which is to be melted by the caloric of the substance employed in the experiment. The ice is supported by the grate *mm* at the bottom of the cavity, under which is placed the sieve *nn*. These two are represented separately in *Figs. 5* and *6*.

In proportion as the ice contained in the middle cavity is melted by the caloric disengaged from the body placed in the interior cavity, the water runs through the grate and sieve and falls through the conical funnel *ccd* (*Fig. 3*), and tube *xy*, into the receiver F (*Fig. 1*). This water may be retained or let out at pleasure, by means of the stop-cock *u*. The external cavity *aaaa* (*Figs. 2* and *3*), is filled with ice, to prevent any effect upon the ice in the middle cavity from the heat of the surrounding air, and the water produced from it is carried off through the pipe ST, which shuts by means of the stop-cock *r*. The whole machine is covered by the lid FF (*Fig. 7*), made of tin painted with oil colour to prevent rust.

When this machine is to be employed, the middle cavity *bbbb* (*Figs. 2* and *3*), the lid GH (*Fig. 4*) of the interior cavity, the external cavity *a a a a* (*Figs. 2* and *3*), and the general lid FF (*Fig. 7*), are all filled with pounded ice, well rammed so that no void spaces remain, and the ice of the middle cavity is allowed to drain. The machine is then opened, and the substance submitted to experiment being placed in the interior cavity, it is instantly closed. After waiting till the included body is completely cooled to the freezing point, and the whole melted ice has drained from the middle cavity, the water collected in the vessel F (*Fig. 1*) is accurately weighed. The weight of the water produced during the experiment is an exact measure of the caloric disengaged during the cooling of the included body, as this substance is evidently in a similar situation with the one formerly mentioned as included in a hollow sphere of ice; the whole caloric disengaged is stopped by the ice in the middle cavity, and that ice is preserved from being affected by any other heat by means of the ice contained in the general lid (*Fig. 7*) and in the external cavity. Experiments of this kind last from fifteen to twenty hours; they are sometimes accelerated by covering up the substance in the interior cavity with well drained ice, which hastens its cooling.

The substances to be operated upon are placed in the thin iron bucket (*Fig. 8*), the cover of which has an opening fitted with a cork, into which a small thermometer is fixed. When we use acids, or other fluids capable of injuring the metal of the instruments, they are contained in the matrass (*Fig. 10*), which has a similar thermometer in a cork fitted to its mouth, and which stands in the interior cavity upon the small cylindrical support RS (*Fig. 10*).

It is absolutely requisite that there be no communication between the external and middle cavities of the calorimeter, otherwise the ice melted by the influence of the surrounding air, in the external cavity, would mix with the water produced from the ice of the middle cavity, which would no longer be a measure of the caloric lost by the substance submitted to experiment.

When the temperature of the atmosphere is only a few degrees above the freezing point, its heat can hardly reach the middle cavity, being arrested by the ice of the cover (*Fig. 7*) and of the external cavity; but, if the temperature of the air be under the degree of freezing, it might cool the ice contained in the middle cavity by causing the ice in the external cavity to fall, in the first place, below zero (32°). It is therefore essential that this experiment be carried on in a temperature somewhat above freezing: hence, in time of frost, the calorimeter must be kept in an apartment carefully heated. It is likewise necessary that the ice employed be not under zero (32°); for which purpose it must be pounded and spread out thin for some time in a place of a higher temperature.

The ice of the interior cavity always retains a certain quantity of water adhering to its surface, which may be supposed to belong to the result of the experiment; but as, at the beginning of each experiment, the ice is already saturated with as much water as it can contain, if any of the water produced by the caloric should remain attached to the ice, it is evident that very nearly an equal quantity of what adhered to it before the experiment must have run down into the vessel F in its stead; for the inner surface of the ice in the middle cavity is very little changed during the experiment.

By any contrivance that could be devised, we could not prevent the access of the external air into the interior cavity when the atmosphere was 9° or 10° (52° or 54°) above zero. The air confined in the cavity, being in that case specifically heavier than the external air, escapes downwards through the pipe *x y* (*Fig. 3*), and is replaced by the warmer external air, which, giving out its caloric to the ice, becomes heavier and sinks in its turn; thus a current of air is formed through the machine, which is the more rapid in proportion as the external air exceeds the internal in temperature. This current of warm air must melt a part of the ice and injure the accuracy of the experiment. We may, in a great degree, guard against this source of error by keeping the stop-cock *u* continually shut; but it is better to operate only when the temperature of the external air does not exceed 3°, or at most 4° (39° to 41°); for we have observed that, in this case, the melting of the interior ice by the atmospheric air is perfectly insensible; so that we may answer for the accuracy of our experiments upon the specific heat of bodies to a fortieth part.

We have had constructed two of the above-described machines; one, which is intended for such experiments as do not require the interior air to be renewed, is precisely formed according to the description here given; the other, which answers for experiments upon combustion, respiration, &c. in which fresh quantities of air are indispensably necessary, differs from the former in having two small tubes in the two lids, by which a current of atmospheric air may be blown into the interior cavity of the machine.

It is extremely easy, with this apparatus, to determine the phenomena which occur in operations where caloric is either disengaged or absorbed. If we wish, for instance, to ascertain the quantity of caloric which is disengaged from a solid body in cooling a certain number of degrees, let its temperature be raised to 80° (212°); it is then placed in the interior cavity *ffff* (*Figs. 2* and *3*) of the calorimeter, and allowed to remain till we are certain that its temperature is reduced to zero (32°); the water produced by melting the ice during its cooling is collected and carefully weighed; and this weight, divided by the volume of the body submitted to experiment, multiplied into the degrees of temperature which it had above zero at the commencement of the experiment, gives the proportion of what the English philosophers call *specific heat.*

Fluids are contained in proper vessels, whose specific heat has been previously ascertained, and operated upon in the machine in the same manner as directed for solids, taking care to deduct, from the quantity of water melted during the experiment, the proportion which belongs to the containing vessel.

If the quantity of caloric disengaged during the combination of different substances is to be determined, these substances are to be previously reduced to the freezing degree by keeping them a sufficient time surrounded with pounded ice; the mixture is then to be made in the inner cavity of the calorimeter, in a proper vessel likewise reduced to zero (32°); and they are kept inclosed till the temperature of the combination has returned to the same degree. The quantity of water produced is a measure of the caloric disengaged during the combination.

To determine the quantity of caloric disengaged during combustion and during animal respiration, the combustible bodies are burnt, or the animals are made to breathe in the interior cavity, and the water produced is carefully collected. Guinea pigs, which resist the effects of cold extremely well, are well adapted for this experiment. As the continual renewal of air is absolutely necessary in such experiments, we blow fresh air into the interior cavity of the calorimeter by means of a pipe destined for that purpose and allow it to escape through another pipe of the same kind; and that the heat of this air may not produce errors in the results of the experiments, the tube which conveys it into the machine is made to pass through pounded ice, that it may be reduced to zero (32°) before it arrives at the calorimeter. The air which escapes must likewise be made to pass through a tube surrounded with ice, included in the interior cavity of the machine, and the water which is produced must make a part of what is collected, because the caloric disengaged from this air is part of the product of the experiment.

It is somewhat more difficult to determine the specific caloric contained in the different gases, on account of their small degree of density; for, if they are only placed in the calorimeter in vessels like other fluids, the quantity of ice melted is so small that the result of the experiment becomes at best very uncertain. For this species of experiment we have contrived to make the air pass through two metallic worms, or spiral tubes; one of these, through which the air passes and becomes heated in its way to the calorimeter, is contained in a vessel full of boiling water, and the other, through which the air circulates within the calorimeter to disengage its caloric, is placed in the interior cavity, *ffff,* of that machine. By means of a small thermometer placed at one end of the second worm, the temperature of the air, as it enters the calorimeter, is determined, and its temperature in getting out of the interior cavity is found by another thermometer placed at the other end of the worm. By this contrivance we are enabled to ascertain the quantity of ice melted by determinate quantities of air or gas, while losing a certain number of degrees of temperature, and, consequently, to determine their several degrees of specific caloric. The same apparatus, with some particular precautions, may be employed to ascertain the quantity of caloric disengaged by the condensation of the vapours of different liquids.

The various experiments which may be made with the calorimeter do not afford absolute conclusions, but only give us the measure of relative quantities; we have therefore to fix a unit, or standard point, from whence to form a scale of the several results. The quantity of caloric necessary to melt a pound of ice has been chosen as this unit; and, as it requires a pound of water of the temperature of 60° (167°) to melt a pound of ice, the quantity of caloric expressed by our unit or standard point is what raises a pound of water from zero (32°) to 60° (167°). When this unit is once determined, we have only to express the quantities of caloric disengaged from different bodies by cooling a certain number of degrees in analogous values.

The following is an easy mode of calculation for this purpose, applied to one of our earliest experiments.

We took 7 *lb.* 11 *oz.* 2 *gros* 36 *grs.* of plate-iron, cut into narrow slips and rolled up, or expressing the quantity in decimals, 7.7070319. These, being heated in a bath of boiling water to about 78° (207.5°), were quickly introduced into the interior cavity of the calorimeter. At the end of eleven hours, when the whole quantity of water melted from the ice had thoroughly drained off, we found that 1.109795 pounds of ice were melted. Hence, the caloric disengaged from the iron by cooling 78° (175.5°) having melted 1.109795 pounds of ice, how much would have been melted by cooling 60° (135°)? This question gives the following statement in direct proportion, 78:1.109795::60::x=0.8569. Dividing this quantity by the weight of the whole iron employed, viz. 7.7070319, the quotient 0.110770 is the quantity of ice which would have been melted by one pound of iron whilst cooling through 60° (135°) of temperature.

Fluid substances, such as sulphuric and nitric acids, &c., are contained in a matrass (Plate VI, *Fig. 9*) having a thermometer adapted to the cork, with its bulb immersed in the liquid. The matrass is placed in a bath of boiling water, and when, from the thermometer, we judge the liquid is raised to a proper temperature, the matrass is placed in the calorimeter. The calculation of the products, to determine the specific caloric of these fluids, is made as above directed, taking care to deduct from the water obtained the quantity which would have been produced by the matrass alone, which must be ascertained by a previous experiment. The table of the results obtained by these experiments is omitted, because not yet sufficiently complete, different circumstances having occasioned the series to be interrupted; it is not, however, lost sight of; and we are less or more employed upon the subject every winter.

CHAPTER IV

Of Mechanical Operations for Division of Bodies

SECTION I *Of Trituration, Levigation, and Pulverization*

THESE are, properly speaking, only preliminary mechanical operations for dividing and separating the particles of bodies and reducing them into very fine powder. These operations can never reduce substances into their primary, or elementary and ultimate particles; they do not even destroy the aggregation of bodies; for every particle, after the most accurate trituration, forms a small whole, resembling the original mass from which it was divided. The real chemical operations, on the contrary, such as solution, destroy the aggregation of bodies and separate their constituent and integrant particles from each other.

Brittle substances are reduced to powder by means of pestles and mortars. These are of brass or iron (Plate I, *Fig. 1*); of marble or granite (*Fig. 2*); of lignum vitae (*Fig. 3*); of glass (*Fig. 4*); of agate (*Fig. 5*); or of porcelain (*Fig. 6*). The pestles for each of these are represented in the plate, immediately below the mortars to which they respectively belong, and are made of hammered iron or brass, of wood, glass, porcelain, marble, granite, or agate, according to the nature of the substances they are intended to triturate. In every laboratory, it is requisite to have an assortment of these utensils, of various sizes and kinds. Those of porcelain and glass can only be used for rubbing substances to powder, by a dexterous use of the pestle round the sides of the mortar, as it would be easily broken by reiterated blows of the pestle.

The bottom of mortars ought to be in the form of a hollow sphere, and their sides should have such a degree of inclination as to make the substances they contain fall back to the bottom when the pestle is lifted, but not so perpendicular as to collect them too much together, otherwise too large a quantity would get below the pestle and prevent its operation. For this reason, likewise, too large a quantity of the substance to be powdered ought not to be put into the mortar at one time; and we must from time to time get rid of the particles already reduced to powder, by means of sieves to be afterwards described.

The most usual method of levigation is by means of a flat table ABCD (Plate 1, *Fig. 7*) of porphyry or other stone of similar hardness, upon which the substance to be reduced to powder is spread and is then bruised and rubbed by a muller M of the same hard materials, the bottom of which is made a small portion of a large sphere; and, as the muller tends continually to drive the substances towards the sides of the table, a thin flexible knife or spatula of iron, horn, wood, or ivory, is used for bringing them back to the middle of the stone.

In large works, this operation is performed by means of large rollers of hard stone, which turn upon each other, either horizontally, in the way of corn-mills, or by one vertical roller turning upon a flat stone. In the above operations, it is often requisite to moisten the substances a little, to prevent the fine powder from flying off.

There are many bodies which cannot be reduced to powder by any of the foregoing methods; such are fibrous substances, as woods; such as are tough and elastic, as the horns of animals, elastic gum, &c., and the malleable metals which flatten under the pestle, instead of being reduced to powder. For reducing the woods to powder, rasps (Plate 1, *Fig. 8*) are employed; files of a finer kind are used for horn, and still finer (Plate 1, *Figs. 9* and *10*) for metals.

Some of the metals, though not brittle enough to powder under the pestle, are too soft to be filed, as they clog the file and prevent its operation. Zinc is one of these, but it may be powdered when hot in a heated iron mortar, or it may be rendered brittle, by alloying it with a small quantity of mercury. One or other of these methods is used by fire-work makers for producing a blue flame by means of zinc. Metals may be reduced into grains, by pouring them when melted into water, which serves very well when they are not wanted in fine powder.

Fruits, potatoes, &c., of a pulpy and fibrous nature may be reduced to pulp by means of the grater (Plate 1, *Fig. 11*).

The choice of the different substances of which these instruments are made is a matter of importance; brass or copper are unfit for operations upon substances to be used as food or in pharmacy; and marble or metallic instruments must not be used for acid substances; hence mortars of very hard wood, and those of porcelain, granite, or glass, are of great utility in many operations.

Section II *Of Sifting and Washing Powdered Substances*

None of the mechanical operations employed for reducing bodies to powder is capable of producing it of an equal degree of fineness throughout; the powder obtained by the longest and most accurate trituration being still an assemblage of particles of various sizes. The coarser of these are removed, so as only to leave the finer and more homogeneous particles by means of sieves (Plate I, *Figs. 12, 13, 14, 15*) of different finenesses, adapted to the particular purposes they are intended for; all the powdered matter which is larger than the interstices of the sieve remains behind and is again submitted to the pestle, while the finer pass through. The sieve (*Fig. 12*) is made of hair-cloth, or of

silk gauze; and the one represented in *Fig. 13* is of parchment pierced with round holes of a proper size; this latter is employed in the manufacture of gun-powder. When very subtile or valuable materials are to be sifted, which are easily dispersed, or when the finer parts of the powder may be hurtful, a compound sieve (*Fig. 15*) is made use of, which consists of the sieve ABCD, with a lid EF, and receiver GH; these three parts are represented as joined together for use (*Fig. 14*).

There is a method of procuring powders of an uniform fineness, considerably more accurate than the sieve; but it can only be used with such substances as are not acted upon by water. The powdered substance is mixed and agitated with water, or other convenient fluid; the liquor is allowed to settle for a few moments, and is then decanted off; the coarsest powder remains at the bottom of the vessel, and the finer passes over with the liquid. By repeated decantations in this manner, various sediments are obtained of different degrees of fineness; the last sediment, or that which remains longest suspended in the liquor, being the finest. This process may likewise be used with advantage for separating substances of different degrees of specific gravity, though of the same fineness; this last is chiefly employed in mining, for separating the heavier metallic ores from the lighter earthy matters with which they are mixed.

In chemical laboratories, pans and jugs of glass or earthen ware are employed for this operation; sometimes, for decanting the liquor without disturbing the sediment, the glass siphon ABCHI (Plate II, *Fig. 11*) is used, which may be supported by means of the perforated board DE, at the proper depth in the vessel FG, to draw off all the liquor required into the receiver LM. The principles and application of this useful instrument are so well known as to need no explanation.

Section III *Of Filtration*

A filtre is a species of very fine sieve, which is permeable to the particles of fluids, but through which the particles of the finest powdered solids are incapable of passing; hence its use in separating fine powders from suspension in fluids. In pharmacy, very close and fine woollen cloths are chiefly used for this operation; these are commonly formed in a conical shape (Plate II, *Fig. 2*), which has the advantage of uniting all the liquor which drains through into a point A, where it may be readily collected in a narrow mouthed vessel. In large pharmaceutical laboratories, this filtring bag is stretched upon a wooden stand (Plate II, *Fig. 1*).

For the purposes of chemistry, as it is requisite to have the filtres perfectly clean, unsized paper is substituted instead of cloth or flannel; through this substance, no solid body, however finely it be powdered, can penetrate, and fluids percolate through it with the greatest readiness. As paper breaks easily when wet, various methods of supporting it are used according to circumstances. When a large quantity of fluid is to be filtrated, the paper is supported by the frame of wood (Plate II, *Fig. 3*) ABCD, having a piece of coarse cloth stretched over it by means of iron hooks. This cloth must be well cleaned each time it is used, or even new cloth must be employed, if there is reason to suspect its being impregnated with anything which can injure the subsequent operations. In ordinary operations, where moderate quantities of fluid are to be filtrated, different kinds of glass funnels are used for supporting the paper, as represented Plate II, *Figs. 5, 6*, and *7*. When several filtrations must be carried on at once, the board or shelf AB, *Fig. 9*, supported upon stands C and D, and pierced with round holes, is very convenient for containing the funnels.

Some liquors are so thick and clammy as not to be able to penetrate through paper without some previous preparation, such as clarification by means of white of eggs, which being mixed with the liquor, coagulates when brought to boil and, entangling the greater part of the impurities of the liquor, rises with them to the surface in the state of scum. Spiritous liquors may be clarified in the same manner by means of isinglass dissolved in water, which coagulates by the action of the alcohol without the assistance of heat.

As most of the acids are produced by distillation, and are consequently clear, we have rarely any occasion to filtrate them; but if, at any time, concentrated acids require this operation, it is impossible to employ paper, which would be corroded and destroyed by the acid. For this purpose, pounded glass, or rather quartz or rock-crystal, broken in pieces and grossly powdered, answers very well; a few of the larger pieces are put in the neck of the funnel; these are covered with the smaller pieces, the finer powder is placed over all, and the acid is poured on top. For the ordinary purposes of society, river-water is frequently filtrated by means of clean washed sand, to separate its impurities.

SECTION IV *Of Decantation*

This operation is often substituted instead of filtration for separating solid particles which are diffused through liquors. These are allowed to settle in conical vessels, ABCDE (Plate II, *Fig. 10*), the diffused matters gradually subside, and the clear fluid is gently poured off. If the sediment be extremely light, and apt to mix again with the fluid by the slightest motion, the siphon (*Fig. 11*) is used, instead of decantation, for drawing off the clear fluid.

In experiments where the weight of the precipitate must be rigorously ascertained, decantation is preferable to filtration, providing the precipitate be several times washed in a considerable proportion of water. The weight of the precipitate may indeed be ascertained, by carefully weighing the filtre before and after the operation; but, when the quantity of precipitate is small, the different proportions of moisture retained by the paper, in a greater or lesser degree of exsiccation, may prove a material source of error which ought carefully to be guarded against.

CHAPTER V

Of Chemical Means for Separating the Particles of Bodies from Each Other Without Decomposition, and for Uniting Them Again

I HAVE already shown that there are two methods of dividing the particles of bodies, the *mechanical* and *chemical*. The former only separates a solid mass into a great number of smaller masses; and for these purposes various species of forces are employed, according to circumstances, such as the strength of man or of animals, the weight of water applied through the means of hydraulic engines, the expansive power of steam, the force of the wind, &c. By all these mechanical powers, we can never reduce substances into powder beyond a certain degree of fineness; and the smallest particle produced in this way, though it seems very minute to our organs, is still in fact a mountain when compared with the ultimate elementary particles of the pulverized substance.

The chemical agents, on the contrary, divide bodies into their primitive particles. If, for instance, a neutral salt be acted upon by these, it is divided as far as is possible without ceasing to be a neutral salt. In this chapter, I mean to give examples of this kind of division of bodies, to which I shall add some account of the relative operations.

Section I *Of the Solution of Salts*

In chemical language, the terms of *solution* and *dissolution* have long been confounded and have very improperly been indiscriminately employed for expressing both the division of the particles of a salt in a fluid, such as water, and the division of a metal in an acid. A few reflections upon the effects of these two operations will suffice to show that they ought not to be confounded together. In the solution of salts, the saline particles are only separated from each other, whilst neither the salt nor the water are at all decomposed; we are able to recover both the one and the other in the same quantity as before the operation. The same thing takes place in the solution of resins in alcohol. During metallic dissolutions, on the contrary, a decomposition, either of the acid or of the water which dilutes it, always takes place; the metal combines with oxygen and is changed into an oxide, and a gaseous substance is disengaged; so that in reality none of the substances employed remain, after the operation, in the same state they were in before. This article is entirely confined to the consideration of solution.

To understand properly what takes place during the solution of salts, it is necessary to know that, in most of these operations, two distinct effects are complicated together, viz., solution by water, and solution by caloric; and, as the explanation of most of the phenomena of solution depends upon the distinction of these two circumstances, I shall enlarge a little upon their nature.

Nitrate of potash, usually called nitre or saltpetre, contains very little water of crystallization, perhaps even none at all; yet this salt liquefies in a degree of heat very little superior to that of boiling water. This liquefaction cannot therefore be produced by means of the water of crystallization, but in consequence of the salt being very fusible in its nature, and from its passing from the solid to the liquid state of aggregation when but a little raised above the temperature of boiling water. All salts are in this manner susceptible of being liquefied by caloric, but in higher or lower degrees of temperature. Some of these, as the acetites of potash and soda, liquefy with a very moderate heat, whilst others, as sulphate of potash, lime, &c., require the strongest fires we are capable of producing. This liquefaction of salts by caloric produces exactly the same phenomena with the melting of ice; it is accomplished in each salt by a determinate degree of heat, which remains invariably the same during the whole time of the liquefaction. Caloric is employed and becomes fixed during the melting of the salt, and is, on the contrary, disengaged when the salt coagulates. These are general phenomena which universally occur during the passage of every species of substance from the solid to the fluid state of aggregation, and from fluid to solid.

These phenomena arising from solution by caloric are always less or more conjoined with those which take place during solutions in water. We cannot pour water upon a salt, on purpose to dissolve it, without employing a compound solvent, both water and caloric; hence we may distinguish several different cases of solution, according to the nature and mode of existence of each salt. If for instance, a salt be with difficulty soluble in water, and readily so by caloric, it evidently follows that this salt will be with difficulty soluble in cold water, and considerably in hot water; such is nitrate of potash, and more especially oxygenated muriate of potash. If another salt be little soluble both in water and caloric, the difference of its solubility in cold and warm water will be very inconsiderable; sulphate of lime is of this kind. From these considerations, it follows that there is a necessary relation between the following circumstances; the solubility of a salt in cold water, its solubility in boiling water, and the degree of temperature at which the same salt liquefies by caloric, unassisted by water; and that the difference of solubility in hot and cold water is so much greater in proportion to its ready solution in caloric, or in proportion to its susceptibility of liquefying in a low degree of temperature.

The above is a general view of solution; but, for want of particular facts and sufficiently exact experiments, it is still nothing more than an approximation towards a particular theory. The means of completing this part of chemical science is extremely simple; we have only to ascertain how much of each salt is dissolved by a certain quantity of water at different degrees of temperature; and as, by the experiments published by M. de Laplace and me, the quantity of caloric contained in a pound of water at each degree of the thermometer is accurately known, it will be very easy to determine, by simple experiments, the proportion of water and caloric required for solution by each salt, what quantity of caloric is absorbed by each at the moment of liquefaction, and how much is disengaged at the moment of crystallization.

Hence the reason why salts are more rapidly soluble in hot than in cold water is perfectly evident. In all solutions of salts caloric is employed; when that is furnished intermediately from the surrounding bodies, it can only arrive slowly to the salt; whereas this is greatly accelerated when the requisite caloric exists ready combined with the water of solution.

In general, the specific gravity of water is augmented by holding salts in solution; but there are some exceptions to the rule. Some time hence, the quantities of radical, of oxygen, and of base, which constitute each neutral salt, the quantity of water and caloric necessary for solution, the increased specific gravity communicated to water, and the figure of the elementary particles of the crystals, will all be accurately known. From these all the circumstances and phenomena of crystallization will be explained, and by these means this part of chemistry will be completed. M. Seguin has formed the plan of a thorough investigation of this kind, which he is extremely capable of executing.

The solution of salts in water requires no particular apparatus; small glass phials of different sizes (Plate II, *Figs. 16* and *17*), pans of earthern ware A (*Figs. 1* and *2*), long-necked matrasses (*Fig. 14*), and pans or basins of copper or of silver (*Figs. 13* and *15*) answer very well for these operations.

Section II *Of Lixiviation*

This is an operation used in chemistry and manufactures for separating substances which are soluble in water from such as are insoluble. The large vat or tub (Plate II, *Fig. 12*), having a hole D near its bottom containing a wooden spigot and faucet or metallic stop-cock DE, is generally used for this purpose. A thin stratum of straw is placed at the bottom of the tub: over this, the substance to be lixiviated is laid and covered by a cloth, then hot or cold water, according to the degree of solubility of the saline matter, is poured on. When the water is supposed to have dissolved all the saline parts, it is let off by the stop-cock; and, as some of the water charged with salt necessarily adheres to the straw and insoluble matters, several fresh quantities of water are poured on. The straw serves to secure a proper passage for the water, and may be compared to the straws or glass rods used in filtrating to keep the paper from touching the sides of the funnel. The cloth which is laid over the matters under lixiviation prevents the water from making a hollow in these substances

where it is poured on, through which it might escape without acting upon the whole mass.

This operation is less or more imitated in chemical experiments; but as in these, especially with analytical views, greater exactness is required, particular precautions must be employed, so as not to leave any saline or soluble part in the residuum. More water must be employed than in ordinary lixiviations, and the substances ought to be previously stirred up in the water before the clear liquor is drawn off, otherwise the whole mass might not be equally lixiviated, and some parts might even escape altogether from the action of the water. We must likewise employ fresh portions of water in considerable quantity, until it comes off entirely free from salt, which we may ascertain by means of the hydrometer formerly described.

In experiments with small quantities, this operation is conveniently performed in jugs or matrasses of glass, and by filtrating the liquor through paper in a glass funnel. When the substance is in larger quantity, it may be lixiviated in a kettle of boiling water, and filtrated through paper supported by cloth in the wooden frame (Plate II, *Figs. 3* and *4*); and in operations in the large way, the tub already mentioned must be used.

Section III *Of Evaporation*

This operation is used for separating two substances from each other, of which one at least must be fluid, and whose degrees of volatility are considerably different. By this means we obtain a salt, which has been dissolved in water, in its concrete form; the water, by heating, becomes combined with caloric, which renders it volatile, while the particles of the salt being brought nearer to each other, and within the sphere of their mutual attraction, unite into the solid state.

As it was long thought that the air had great influence upon the quantity of fluid evaporated, it will be proper to point out the errors which this opinion has produced. There certainly is a constant slow evaporation from fluids exposed to the free air; and, though this species of evaporation may be considered in some degree as a solution in air, yet caloric has considerable influence in producing it, as is evident from the refrigeration which always accompanies this process; hence we may consider this gradual evaporation as a compound solution made partly in air and partly in caloric. But the evaporation which takes place from a fluid kept continually boiling, is quite different in its nature, and in it the evaporation produced by the action of the air is exceedingly inconsiderable in comparison with that which is occasioned by caloric. This latter species may be termed *vaporization* rather than *evaporation*. This process is not accelerated in proportion to the extent of evaporating surface, but in proportion to the quantities of caloric which combine with the fluid. Too free a current of cold air is often hurtful to this process, as it tends to carry off caloric from the water and consequently retards its conversion into vapour. Hence there is no inconvenience produced by covering, in a certain degree, the vessels in which liquids are evaporated by continual boiling, provided the covering body be of such a nature as does not strongly draw off the caloric, or, to use an expression of Dr. Franklin's, provided it be a bad conductor of heat. In this case, the vapours escape through such opening as is left, and at least as much is evaporated, frequently more than when free access is allowed to the external air.

As during evaporation the fluid carried off by caloric is entirely lost, being sacrificed for the sake of the fixed substances with which it was combined, this process is only employed where the fluid is of small value, as water, for instance. But, when the fluid is of more consequence, we have recourse to distillation, in which process we preserve both the fixed substance and the volatile fluid. The vessels employed for evaporation are basins or pans of copper, silver, or lead (Plate II, *Figs. 13* and *15*), or capsules of glass, porcelain, or stone ware (Plate II, A, *Figs. 1* and *2*; Plate III, *Figs. 3* and *4*). The best utensils for this purpose are made of the bottoms of glass retorts and matrasses, as their equal thinness renders them more fit than any other kind of glass vessel for bearing a brisk fire and sudden alterations of heat and cold without breaking.

As the method of cutting these glass vessels is nowhere described in books, I shall here give a description of it, that they may be made by chemists for themselves out of spoiled retorts, matrasses, and recipients, at a much cheaper rate than any which can be procured from glass manufacturers. The instrument (Plate III, *Fig. 5*), consisting of an iron ring AC, fixed to the rod AB, having a wooden handle D, is employed as follows: Make the ring red hot in the fire, and put it upon the matrass G (*Fig. 6*), which is to be cut; when the glass is sufficiently heated, throw on a little cold water, and it will generally break exactly at the circular line heated by the ring.

Small flasks or phials of thin glass are exceeding good vessels for evaporating small quantities of fluid: they are very cheap, and stand the fire remarkably. One or more of these may be placed upon a second grate above the furnace (Plate III, *Fig. 2*), where they will only experience a gentle heat. By this means a great number of experiments may be carried on at one time. A glass retort, placed in a sand-bath, and covered with a dome of baked earth (Plate III, *Fig. 1*), answers pretty well for evaporations; but in this way it is always considerably slower, and is even liable to accidents; as the sand heats unequally, and the glass cannot dilate in the same unequal manner, the retort is very liable to break. Sometimes the sand serves exactly the office of the iron ring formerly mentioned; for, if a single drop of vapour, condensed into liquid, happens to fall upon the heated part of the vessel, it breaks circularly at that place. When a very intense fire is necessary, earthen crucibles may be used; but we generally use the word *evaporation* to express what is produced by the temperature of boiling water or not much higher.

SECTION IV *Of Crystallization*

In this process the integrant parts of a solid body, separated from each other by the intervention of a fluid, are made to exert the mutual attraction of aggregation, so as to coalesce and reproduce a solid mass. When the particles of a body are only separated by caloric, and the substance is thereby retained in the liquid state, all that is necessary for making it crystallize is to remove a part of the caloric which is lodged between its particles, or, in other words, to cool it. If this refrigeration be slow, and the body be at the same time left at rest, its particles assume a regular arrangement, and crystallization, properly so called, takes place; but, if the refrigeration is made rapidly, or if the liquor be agitated at the moment of its passage to the concrete state, the crystallization is irregular and confused.

The same phenomena occur with watery solutions, or rather in those made partly in water and partly by caloric. So long as there remains a sufficiency of water and caloric to keep the particles of the body asunder beyond the sphere of their mutual attraction, the salt remains in the fluid state; but, whenever either caloric or water is not present in sufficient quantity, and the attraction of the particles for each other becomes superior to the power which keeps them asunder, the salt recovers its concrete form, and the crystals produced are the more regular in proportion as the evaporation has been slower and more tranquilly performed.

All the phenomena we formerly mentioned as taking place during the solution of salts, occur in a contrary sense during their crystallization. Caloric is disengaged at the instant of their assuming the solid state, which furnishes an additional proof of salt being held in solution by the compound action of water and caloric. Hence, to cause salts to crystallize which readily liquefy by means of caloric, it is not sufficient to carry off the water which held them in solution, but the caloric united to them must likewise be removed. Nitrate of potash, oxygenated muriate of potash, alum, sulphate of soda, &c., are examples of this circumstance, as, to make these salts crystallize, refrigeration must be added to evaporation. Such salts, on the contrary, as require little caloric for being kept in solution, and which, from that circumstance, are nearly equally soluble in cold and warm water, are crystallizable by simply carrying off the water which holds them in solution, and even recover their solid state in boiling water; such are sulphate of lime, muriate of potash and of soda, and several others.

The art of refining saltpetre depends upon these properties of salts, and upon their different degrees of solubility in hot and cold water. This salt, as produced in the manufactories by the first operation, is composed of many different salts: some are deliquescent and not susceptible of being crystallized, such as the nitrate and muriate of lime; others are almost equally soluble in hot and cold water, as the muriates of potash and of soda; and, lastly, the saltpetre, or nitrate of potash, is greatly more soluble in hot than it is in cold water. The operation is begun by pouring upon this mixture of salts as much water as will hold even the least soluble, the muriates of soda and of potash, in solution: so long as it is hot, this quantity readily dissolves all the saltpetre, but, upon cooling, the greater part of this salt crystallizes, leaving about a sixth part remaining dissolved, and mixed with the nitrate of lime and the two muriates. The nitre obtained by this process is still somewhat impregnated with other salts, because it has been crystallized from water in which these abound. It is completely purified from these by a second solution in a small quantity of boiling water, and second crystallization. The water remaining after these crystallizations of nitre is still loaded with a mixture of saltpetre, and other salts; by further evaporation, crude saltpetre, or rough-petre, as the workmen call it, is procured from it, and this is purified by two fresh solutions and crystallizations.

The deliquescent earthy salts which do not contain the nitric acid are rejected in this manufacture; but those which consist of that acid neutralized by an earthy base are dissolved in water, the earth is precipitated by means of potash, and allowed to subside; the clear liquor is then decanted, evaporated, and allowed to crystallize. The above management for refining saltpetre may serve as a general rule for separating salts from each other which happen to be mixed together. The nature of each must be considered, the proportion in which each dissolves in given quantities of water, and the different solubility of each in hot and cold water. If to these we add the property which some salts possess, of being soluble in alcohol, or in a mixture of alcohol and water, we have many resources for separating salts from each other by means of crystallization, though it must be allowed that it is extremely difficult to render this separation perfectly complete.

The vessels used for crystallization are pans of earthen ware A (Plate II, *Figs. 1* and *2*) and large flat dishes (Plate III, *Fig. 7*). When a saline solution is to be exposed to a slow evaporation in the heat of the atmosphere, with free access of air, vessels of some depth (Plate III, *Fig. 3*) must be employed, that there may be a considerable body of liquid; by this means the crystals produced are of considerable size, and remarkably regular in their figure.

Every species of salt crystallizes in a peculiar form, and even each salt varies in the form of its crystals according to circumstances, which take place during crystallization. We must not from thence conclude that the saline particles of each species are indeterminate in their figures. The primitive particles of all bodies, especially of salts, are perfectly constant in their specific forms; but the crystals which form in our experiments are composed of congeries of minute particles, which, though perfectly equal in size and shape, may assume very dissimilar arrangements and consequently produce a vast variety of regular forms, which have not the smallest apparent resemblance to each other nor to the original crystal. This subject has been very ably treated by the Abbé Haüy, in several *Mémoires* presented to the Academy and in his work upon the structure of crystals. It is only necessary to extend generally to the class of salts the principles he has particularly applied to some crystallized stones.

SECTION V *Of Simple Distillation*

As distillation has two distinct objects to accomplish, it is divisible into simple and compound; and, in this section, I mean to confine myself entirely to the former. When two bodies, of which one is more volatile than the other, or has more affinity to caloric, are submitted to distillation, our intention is to separate them from each other. The more volatile substance assumes the form of gas, and is afterwards condensed by refrigeration in proper vessels. In this case distillation, like evaporation, becomes a species of mechanical operation, which separates two substances from each other without decomposing or altering the nature of either. In evaporation, our only object is to preserve the fixed body, without paying any regard to the volatile matter; whereas, in distillation, our principal attention is generally paid to the volatile substance, unless when we intend to preserve both the one and the other. Hence, simple distillation is nothing more than evaporation produced in close vessels.

The most simple distilling vessel is a species of bottle or matrass A (Plate III, *Fig. 8*), which has been bent from its original form BC to BD, and which is then called a retort: when used, it is placed either in a reverberatory furnace (Plate XIII, *Fig. 2*) or in a sand bath under a dome of baked earth (Plate III, *Fig. 1*). To receive and condense the products, we adapt a recipient E (Plate III, *Fig. 9*), which is luted to the retort. Sometimes, more especially in pharmaceutical operations, the glass or stone ware cucurbit, A, with its capital B (Plate III, *Fig. 12*) or the glass alembic and capital (*Fig. 13*) of one piece, is employed. This latter is managed by means of a tubulated opening T, fitted with a ground stopper of crystal: the capital, both of the cucurbit and alembic, has a furrow or trench, *rr*, intended for conveying the condensed liquor into the beak RS by which it runs out. As, in almost all distillations, expansive vapours are produced, which might burst the vessels employed, we are under the necessity of having a small hole T (*Fig. 9*) in the balloon or recipient, through which these may find vent; hence, in this way of distilling, all the products which are permanently aeriform are entirely lost, and even such as with difficulty lose that state have not sufficient space to condense in the balloon. This apparatus is not, therefore, proper for experiments of investigation, and can only be admitted in the ordinary operations of the laboratory or in pharmacy.

In the article appropriated for compound distillation, I shall explain the various methods which have been contrived for preserving the whole products from bodies in this process.

As glass or earthen vessels are very brittle, and do not readily bear sudden alterations of heat and cold, every well regulated laboratory ought to have one or more alembics of metal for distilling water, spiritous liquors, essential oils, &c. This apparatus consists of a cucurbit and capital of tinned copper or brass (Plate III, *Figs. 15* and *16*), which, when judged proper, may be placed in the water bath D (*Fig. 17*). In distillations, especially of spiritous liquors, the capital must be furnished with a refrigeratory, SS (*Fig. 16*), kept continually filled with cold water; when the water becomes heated, it is let off by the stop-cock, R, and renewed with a fresh supply of cold water. As the fluid distilled is converted into gas by means of caloric furnished by the fire of the furnace, it is evident that it could not condense, and, consequently, that no distillation, properly speaking, could take place, unless it is made to deposit in the capital all the caloric it received in the cucurbit; with this view, the sides of the capital must always be preserved at a lower temperature than is necessary for keeping the distilling substance in the state of gas, and the water in the refrigeratory is intended for this purpose. Water is converted into gas by the temperature of 80° (212°), alcohol by 67° (182.75°), ether by 32° (104°): hence these substances cannot be distilled, or, rather, they will fly off in the state of gas, unless the temperature of the refrigeratory be kept under these respective degrees.

In the distillation of spiritous and other expansive liquors the above described refrigeratory is not sufficient for condensing all the vapours which arise; in this case, therefore, instead of receiving the distilled liquor immediately from the beak, TU, of the capital into a recipient, a worm is interposed between them. This instrument is represented Plate III, *Fig. 18*, contained in a worm tub of tinned copper; it consists of a metallic tube bent into a considerable number of spiral revolutions. The vessel which contains the worm is kept full of cold water, which is renewed as it grows warm. This contrivance is employed in all distilleries of spirits, without the intervention of a capital and refrigeratory, properly so called. The one represented in the plate is furnished with two worms, one of them being particularly appropriated to distillations of odoriferous substances.

In some simple distillations it is necessary to interpose an adopter between the retort and receiver, as shown (Plate III, *Fig. 11*). This may serve two different purposes, either to separate two products of different degrees of volatility, or to remove the receiver to a greater distance from the furnace, that it may be less heated. But these, and several other more complicated instruments of ancient contrivance, are far from producing the accuracy requisite in modern chemistry, as will be readily perceived when I come to treat of compound distillation.

Section VI *Of Sublimation*

This term is applied to the distillation of substances which condense in a concrete or solid form, such as the sublimation of sulphur, and of muriate of ammonia, or sal ammonia. These operations may be conveniently performed in the ordinary distilling vessels already described, though, in the sublimation of sulphur, a species of vessels, named *alludels*, have been usually employed. These are vessels of stone or porcelain ware, which adjust to each other over a cucurbit containing the sulphur to be sublimed. One of the best subliming vessels, for substances which are not very volatile, is a flask, or phial of glass, sunk about two thirds into a sand bath; but in this way we are apt to lose a part of the products. When these are wished to be entirely preserved, we must have recourse to the pneumato-chemical distilling apparatus, to be described in the following chapter.

CHAPTER VI

Of Pneumato-chemical Distillations, Metallic Dissolutions, and Some Other Operations Which Require Very Complicated Instruments

Section I *Of Compound and Pneumato-chemical Distillations*

In the preceding chapter, I have only treated of distillation as a simple operation, by which two substances, differing in degrees of volatility, may be separated from each other; but distillation often actually decomposes the substances submitted to its action and becomes one of the most complicated operations in chemistry. In every distillation, the substance distilled must be brought to the state of gas in the cucurbit or retort, by combination with caloric. In simple distillation, this caloric is given

out in the refrigeratory or in the worm, and the substance again recovers its liquid or solid form, but the substances submitted to compound distillation are absolutely decompounded; one part, as for instance the charcoal they contain, remains fixed in the retort, and all the rest of the elements are reduced to gases of different kinds. Some of these are susceptible of being condensed and of recovering their solid or liquid forms, whilst others are permanently aeriform; one part of these are absorbable by water, some by the alkalies, and others are not susceptible of being absorbed at all. An ordinary distilling apparatus, such as has been described in the preceding chapter, is quite insufficient for retaining or for separating these diversified products, and we are obliged to have recourse, for this purpose, to methods of a more complicated nature.

The apparatus I am about to describe is calculated for the most complicated distillations, and may be simplified according to circumstances. It consists of a tubulated glass retort A (Plate IV, *Fig. 1*), having its beak fitted to a tubulated balloon or recipient BC; to the upper orifice D of the balloon a bent tube DE*fg* is adjusted, which, at its other extremity *g*, is plunged into the liquor contained in the bottle L, with three necks *xxx*. Three other similar bottles are connected with this first one, by means of three similar bent tubes disposed in the same manner; and the farthest neck of the last bottle is connected with a jar in a pneumato-chemical apparatus, by means of a bent tube. A determinate weight of distilled water is usually put into the first bottle, and the other three have each a solution of caustic potash in water. The weight of all these bottles, and of the water and alkaline solution they contain, must be accurately ascertained. Every thing being thus disposed, the junctures between the retort and recipient, and of the tube D of the latter, must be luted with fat lute, covered over with slips of linen, spread with lime and white of egg; all the other junctures are to be secured by a lute made of wax and rosin melted together.

When all these dispositions are completed, and when, by means of heat applied to the retort A, the substance it contains becomes decomposed, it is evident that the least volatile products must condense or sublime in the beak or neck of the retort itself, where most of the concrete substances will fix themselves. The more volatile substances, as the lighter oils, ammonia, and several others, will condense in the recipient GC, whilst the gases, which are not susceptible of condensation by cold, will pass on by the tubes, and boil up through the liquors in the several bottles. Such as are absorbable by water will remain in the first bottle, and those which caustic alkali can absorb will remain in the others; whilst such gases as are not susceptible of absorption, either by water or alkalies, will escape by the tube RM, at the end of which they may be received into jars in a pneumato-chemical apparatus. The charcoal and fixed earth, &c. which form the substance or residuum, once called *caput mortuum*, remain behind in the retort.

In this manner of operating, we have always a very material proof of the accuracy of the analysis, as the whole weights of the products taken together, after the process is finished, must be exactly equal to the weight of the original substance submitted to distillation. Hence, for instance, if we have operated upon eight ounces of starch or gum arabic, the weight of the charry residuum in the retort, together with that of all the products gathered in its neck and the balloon, and of all the gas received into the jars by the tube RM added to the additional weight acquired by the bottles, must, when taken together, be exactly eight ounces. If the product be less or more, it proceeds from error, and the experiment must be repeated until a satisfactory result be procured, which ought not to differ more than six or eight grains in the pound from the weight of the substance submitted to experiment.

In experiments of this kind, I for a long time met with an almost insurmountable difficulty, which must at last have obliged me to desist altogether but for a very simple method of avoiding it, pointed out to me by M. Hassenfratz. The smallest diminution in the heat of the furnace, and many other circumstances inseparable from this kind of experiments, cause frequent reabsorptions of gas; the water in the cistern of the pneumato-chemical apparatus rushes into the last bottle through the tube RM, the same circumstance happens from one bottle into another, and the fluid is often forced even into the recipient C. This accident is prevented by using bottles having three necks, as represented in the plate, into one of which, in each bottle, a capillary glass-tube *St, st, st, st,* is adapted, so as to have its lower extremity *t* immersed in the liquor. If any absorption takes place, either in the retort or in any of the bottles, a sufficient quantity of external air enters,

by means of these tubes, to fill up the void; and we get rid of the inconvenience at the price of having a small mixture of common air with the products of the experiment, which is thereby prevented from failing altogether. Though these tubes admit the external air, they cannot permit any of the gaseous substances to escape, as they are always shut below by the water of the bottles.

It is evident that, in the course of experiments with this apparatus, the liquor of the bottles must rise in these tubes in proportion to the pressure sustained by the gas or air contained in the bottles; and this pressure is determined by the height and gravity of the column of fluid contained in all the subsequent bottles. If we suppose that each bottle contains three inches of fluid, and that there are three inches of water in the cistern of the connected apparatus above the orifice of the tube RM, and allowing the gravity of the fluids to be only equal to that of water, it follows that the air in the first bottle must sustain a pressure equal to twelve inches of water; the water must therefore rise twelve inches in the tube S, connected with the first bottle, nine inches in that belonging to the second, six inches in the third, and three in the last; wherefore these tubes must be made somewhat more than twelve, nine, six and three inches long respectively, allowance being made for oscillatory motions, which often take place in the liquids. It is sometimes necessary to introduce a similar tube between the retort and recipient; and, as the tube is not immersed in fluid at its lower extremity until some has collected in the progress of the distillation, its upper end must be shut at first with a little lute, so as to be opened according to necessity or after there is sufficient liquid in the recipient to secure its lower extremity.

This apparatus cannot be used in very accurate experiments, when the substances intended to be operated upon have a very rapid action upon each other or when one of them can only be introduced in small successive portions, as in such as produce violent effervescence when mixed together. In such cases, we employ a tubulated retort A (Plate VII, *Fig. 1*), into which one of the substances is introduced, preferring always the solid body, if any such is to be treated; we then lute to the opening of the retort a bent tube BCDA, terminating at its upper extremity B in a funnel, and at its other end A in a capillary opening. The fluid material of the experiment is poured into the retort by means of this funnel, which must be made of such a length, from B to C, that the column of liquid introduced may counterbalance the resistance produced by the liquors contained in all the bottles (Plate IV, *Fig. 1*).

Those who have not been accustomed to use the above described distilling apparatus may perhaps be startled at the great number of openings which require luting, and the time necessary for making all the previous preparations in experiments of this kind. It is very true that, if we take into account all the necessary weighings of materials and products, both before and after the experiments, these preparatory and succeeding steps require much more time and attention than the experiment itself. But, when the experiment succeeds properly, we are well rewarded for all the time and trouble bestowed, as by one process carried on in this accurate manner much more just and extensive knowledge is acquired of the nature of the vegetable or animal substance thus submitted to investigation than by many weeks assiduous labour in the ordinary method of proceeding.

When in want of bottles with three orifices, those with two may be used; it is even possible to introduce all the three tubes at one opening, so as to employ ordinary wide-mouthed bottles, provided the opening be sufficiently large. In this case we must carefully fit the bottles with corks very accurately cut and boiled in a mixture of oil, wax, and turpentine. These corks are pierced with the necessary holes for receiving the tubes by means of a round file, as in Plate IV, *Fig. 8*.

SECTION II *Of Metallic Dissolutions*

I have already pointed out the difference between solution of salts in water and metallic dissolutions. The former requires no particular vessels, whereas the latter requires very complicated vessels of late invention, that we may not lose any of the products of the experiment, and may thereby procure truly conclusive results of the phenomena which occur. The metals, in general, dissolve in acids with effervescence, which is only a motion excited in the solvent by the disengagement of a great number of bubbles of air or aeriform fluid, which proceed from the surface of the metal and break at the surface of the liquid.

M. Cavendish and Dr. Priestley were the first inventors of a proper apparatus for collecting these elastic fluids. That of Dr. Priestley is extremely simple and consists of a bottle

A (Plate VII, *Fig. 2*), with its cork B, through which passes the bent glass tube BC, which is engaged under a jar filled with water in the pneumato-chemical apparatus, or simply in a basin full of water. The metal is first introduced into the bottle, the acid is then poured over it, and the bottle is instantly closed with its cork and tube, as represented in the plate. But this apparatus has its inconveniences. When the acid is much concentrated, or the metal much divided, the effervescence begins before we have time to cork the bottle properly, and some gas escapes, by which we are prevented from ascertaining the quantity disengaged with rigorous exactness. In the next place, when we are obliged to employ heat, or when heat is produced by the process, a part of the acid distills and mixes with the water of the pneumato-chemical apparatus, by which means we are deceived in our calculation of the quantity of acid decomposed. Besides these, the water in the cistern of the apparatus absorbs all the gas produced which is susceptible of absorption and renders it impossible to collect these without loss.

To remedy these inconveniences, I at first used a bottle with two necks (Plate VII, *Fig. 3*), into one of which the glass funnel BC is luted so as to prevent any air escaping; a glass rod DE is fitted with emery to the funnel, so as to serve the purpose of a stopper. When it is used, the matter to be dissolved is first introduced into the bottle, and the acid is then permitted to pass in as slowly as we please, by raising the glass rod gently as often as is necessary until saturation is produced.

Another method has been since employed, which serves the same purpose, and is preferable to the last described in some instances. This consists in adapting to one of the mouths of the bottle A (Plate VII, *Fig. 4*), a bent tube DEFG, having a capillary opening at D, and ending in a funnel at G. This tube is securely luted to the mouth C of the bottle. When any liquid is poured into the funnel, it falls down to F; and, if a sufficient quantity be added, it passes by the curvature E and falls slowly into the bottle, so long as fresh liquor is supplied at the funnel. The liquor can never be forced out of the tube, and no gas can escape through it, because the weight of the liquid serves the purpose of an accurate cork.

To prevent any distillation of acid, especially in dissolutions accompanied with heat, this tube is adapted to the retort A (Plate VII, *Fig. 1*), and a small tubulated recipient, M, is applied, in which any liquor which may distill is condensed. On purpose to separate any gas that is absorbable by water, we add the double necked bottle L, half filled with a solution of caustic potash; the alkali absorbs any carbonic acid gas, and usually only one or two other gases pass into the jar of the connected pneumato-chemical apparatus through the tube NO. In the first chapter of this third part we have directed how these are to be separated and examined. If one bottle of alkaline solution be not thought sufficient, two, three, or more, may be added.

Section III *Apparatus Necessary in Experiments upon Vinous and Putrefactive Fermentations*

For these operations a peculiar apparatus, especially intended for this kind of experiment, is requisite. The one I am about to describe is finally adopted as the best calculated for the purpose, after numerous corrections and improvements. It consists of a large matrass, A (Plate x, *Fig. 1*), holding about twelve pints, with a cap of brass *a b*, strongly cemented to its mouth, and into which is screwed a bent tube *c d*, furnished with a stop-cock *e*. To this tube is joined the glass recipient B, having three openings, one of which communicates with the bottle C placed below it. To the posterior opening of this recipient is fitted a glass tube *g h i*, cemented at *g* and *i* to collets of brass, and intended to contain a very deliquescent concrete neutral salt, such as nitrate or muriate of lime, acetite of potash, &c. This tube communicates with two bottles D and E, filled to *x* and *y* with a solution of caustic potash.

All the parts of this machine are joined together by accurate screws, and the touching parts have greased leather interposed, to prevent any passage of air. Each piece is likewise furnished with two stop-cocks, by which its two extremities may be closed, so that we can weigh each separately at any period of the operation.

The fermentable matter, such as sugar, with a proper quantity of yeast and diluted with water, is put into the matrass. Sometimes, when the fermentation is too rapid, a considerable quantity of froth is produced, which not only fills the neck of the matrass, but passes into the recipient, and from thence runs down into the bottle C. On purpose to collect this scum and must, and to prevent it from reaching the tube filled with deliquescent salts, the recipient and connected bottle are made of considerable capacity.

In the vinous fermentation, only carbonic acid gas is disengaged, carrying with it a small proportion of water in solution. A great part of this water is deposited in passing through the tube *g h i*, which is filled with a deliquescent salt in gross powder, and the quantity is ascertained by the augmentation of the weight of the salt. The carbonic acid gas bubbles up through the alkaline solution in the bottle D, to which it is conveyed by the tube *k l m*. Any small portion which may not be absorbed by this first bottle is secured by the solution in the second bottle E, so that nothing, in general, passes into the jar F, except the common air contained in the vessels at the commencement of the experiment.

The same apparatus answers extremely well for experiments upon the putrefactive fermentation; but, in this case, a considerable quantity of hydrogen gas is disengaged through the tube *q r s t u*, by which it is conveyed into the jar F; and, as this disengagement is very rapid, especially in summer, the jar must be frequently changed. These putrefactive fermentations require constant attendance from the above circumstance, whereas the vinous fermentation hardly needs any. By means of this apparatus we can ascertain, with great precision, the weights of the substances submitted to fermentation, and of the liquid and aeriform products which are disengaged. What has been already said in Part I, Chapter XIII, upon the products of the vinous fermentation, may be consulted.

Section IV *Apparatus for the Decomposition of Water*

Having already given an account, in the first part of this work, of the experiments relative to the decomposition of water, I shall avoid any unnecessary repetitions and only give a few summary observations upon the subject in this section. The principal substances which have the power of decomposing water are iron and charcoal; for which purpose, they require to be made red hot, otherwise the water is only reduced into vapours and condenses afterwards by refrigeration without sustaining the smallest alteration. In a red heat, on the contrary, iron or charcoal carry off the oxygen from its union with hydrogen; in the first case, black oxide of iron is produced, and the hydrogen is disengaged pure in form of gas; in the other case, carbonic acid gas is formed, which disengages, mixed with the hydrogen gas; and this latter is commonly carbonated, or holds charcoal in solution.

A musket barrel, without its breach pin, answers exceedingly well for the decomposition of water by means of iron, and one should be chosen of considerable length and pretty strong. When too short, so as to run the risk of heating the lute too much, a tube of copper is to be strongly soldered to one end. The barrel is placed in a long furnace CDEF (Plate VII, *Fig. 11*), so as to have a few degrees of inclination from E to F; a glass retort, A, is luted to the upper extremity E, which contains water and is placed upon the furnace VVXX. The lower extremity F is luted to a worm SS, which is connected with the tubulated bottle H, in which any water distilled without decomposition, during the operation, collects, and the disengaged gas is carried by the tube KK to jars in a pneumato-chemical apparatus. Instead of the retort, a funnel may be employed, having its lower part shut by a stop-cock, through which the water is allowed to drop gradually into the gun-barrel. Immediately upon getting into contact with the heated part of the iron, the water is converted into steam, and the experiment proceeds in the same manner as if it were furnished in vapours from the retort.

In the experiment made by M. Meusnier and me before a committee of the Academy, we used every precaution to obtain the greatest possible precision in the result of our experiment, having even exhausted all the vessels employed before we began, so that the hydrogen gas obtained might be free from any mixture of azotic gas. The results of that experiment will hereafter be given at large in a particular *Mémoire*.

In numerous experiments, we are obliged to use tubes of glass, porcelain, or copper, instead of gun-barrels; but glass has the disadvantage of being easily melted and flattened, if the heat be in the smallest degree raised too high; and porcelain is mostly full of small minute pores, through which the gas escapes, especially when compressed by a column of water. For these reasons I procured a tube of brass, which M. de la Briche got cast and bored out of the solid for me at Strasburg, under his own inspection. This tube is extremely convenient for decomposing alcohol, which resolves into charcoal, carbonic acid gas, and hydrogen gas; it may likewise be used with the same advantage for decomposing water by means of charcoal, and in a great number of experiments of this nature.

CHAPTER VII

Of the Composition and Use of Lutes

THE necessity of properly securing the junctures of chemical vessels to prevent the escape of any of the products of experiments must be sufficiently apparent; for this purpose lutes are employed, which ought to be of such a nature as to be equally impenetrable to the most subtile substances, as glass itself through which only caloric can escape.

This first object of lutes is very well accomplished by bees wax, melted with about an eighth part of turpentine. This lute is very easily managed, sticks very closely to glass, and is very difficult to penetrate; it may be rendered more consistent, and less or more hard or pliable, by adding different kinds of resinous matters. Though this species of lute answers extremely well for retaining gases and vapours, there are many chemical experiments which produce considerable heat, by which this lute becomes liquefied, and consequently the expansive vapours must very readily force through and escape.

For such cases, the following fat lute is the best hitherto discovered, though not without its disadvantages, which shall be pointed out. Take very pure and dry unbaked clay reduced to a very fine powder; put this into a brass mortar and beat it for several hours with a heavy iron pestle, dropping in slowly some boiled linseed oil; this is oil which has been oxygenated, and has acquired a drying quality by being boiled with litharge. This lute is more tenacious, and applies better, if amber varnish be used instead of the above oil. To make this varnish, melt some yellow amber in an iron ladle, by which operation it loses a part of its succinic acid and essential oil, and mix it with linseed oil. Though the lute prepared with this varnish is better than that made with boiled oil, yet, as its additional expense is hardly compensated by its superior quality, it is seldom used.

The above fat lute is capable of sustaining a very violent degree of heat, is impenetrable by acids and spirituous liquors, and adheres exceedingly well to metals, stone ware, or glass, providing they have been previously rendered perfectly dry. But if, unfortunately, any of the liquor in the course of an experiment gets through, either between the glass and the lute or between the layers of the lute itself, so as to moisten the part, it is extremely difficult to close the opening. This is the chief inconvenience which attends the use of fat lute and perhaps the only one it is subject to. As it is apt to soften by heat, we must surround all the junctures with slips of wet bladder applied over the luting and fixed on by pack-thread tied round both above and below the joint; the bladder, and consequently the lute below, must be farther secured by a number of turns of pack-thread all over it. By these precautions, we are free from every danger of accident; and the junctures secured in this manner may be considered, in experiments, as hermetically sealed.

It frequently happens that the figure of the junctures prevents the application of ligatures, which is the case with the three-necked bottles formerly described; and it even requires great address to apply the twine without shaking the apparatus: so that, where a number of junctures require luting, we are apt to displace several while securing one. In these cases, we may substitute slips of linen, spread with white of egg and lime mixed together, instead of the wet bladder. These are applied while still moist, and very speedily dry and acquire considerable hardness. Strong glue dissolved in water may answer instead of white of egg. These fillets are usefully applied likewise over junctures luted together with wax and rosin.

Before applying a lute, all the junctures of the vessels must be accurately and firmly fitted to each other, so as not to admit of being moved. If the beak of a retort is to be luted to the neck of a recipient, they ought to fit pretty accurately; otherwise we must fix them, by introducing short pieces of soft wood or of cork. If the disproportion between the two be very considerable, we must employ a cork which fits the neck of the recipient, having a circular hole of proper dimensions to admit the beak of the retort. The same precaution is necessary in adapting bent tubes to the necks of bottles in the apparatus represented Plate IV, *Fig. 1*, and others of a similar nature. Each mouth of each bottle must be fitted with a cork, having a hole made with a round file of a proper size for containing the tube. And, when one mouth is intended to admit two or more tubes, which frequently happens when we have not a sufficient number of bottles with two or three necks, we must use a cork with two or three holes (Plate IV, *Fig. 8*).

When the whole apparatus is thus solidly joined, so that no part can play upon another, we begin to lute. The lute is softened by kneading and rolling it between the fingers, with the assistance of heat if necessary. It is rolled into little cylindrical pieces and applied to the junctures, taking great care to make it apply close and adhere firmly in every part; a second roll is applied over the first, so as to pass it on each side, and so on till each juncture be sufficiently covered; after this, the slips of bladder, or of linen, as above directed, must be carefully applied over all. Though this operation may appear extremely simple, yet it requires peculiar delicacy and management; great care must be taken not to disturb one juncture whilst luting another, and more especially when applying the fillets and ligatures.

Before beginning any experiment, the closeness of the luting ought always to be previously tried, either by slightly heating the retort A (Plate IV, *Fig. 1*), or by blowing in a little air by some of the perpendicular tubes *S s s s;* the alteration of pressure causes a change in the level of the liquid in these tubes. If the apparatus be accurately luted, this alteration of level will be permanent; whereas, if there be the smallest opening in any of the junctures, the liquid will very soon recover its former level. It must always be remembered that the whole success of experiments in modern chemistry depends upon the exactness of this operation, which therefore requires the utmost patience and most attentive accuracy.

It would be of infinite service to enable chemists, especially those who are engaged in pneumatic processes, to dispense with the use of lutes, or at least to diminish the number necessary in complicated instruments. I once thought of having my apparatus constructed so as to unite in all its parts by fitting with emery, in the way of bottles with crystal stoppers; but the execution of this plan was extremely difficult. I have since thought it preferable to substitute columns of a few lines of mercury in place of lutes, and have got an apparatus constructed upon this principle, which appears capable of very convenient application in a great number of circumstances.

It consists of a double necked bottle A (Plate XII, *Fig. 12*); the interior neck *bc* communicates with the inside of the bottle, and the exterior neck or rim *de* leaves an interval between the two necks, forming a deep gutter intended to contain the mercury. The cap or lid of glass B enters this gutter and is properly fitted to it, having notches in its lower edge for the passage of the tubes which convey the gas. These tubes, instead of entering directly into the bottles as in the ordinary apparatus, have a double bend for making them enter the gutter, as represented in *Fig. 13*, and for making them fit the notches of the cap B; they rise again from the gutter to enter the inside of the bottle over the border of the inner mouth. When the tubes are disposed in their proper places and the cap firmly fitted on, the gutter is filled with mercury, by which means the bottle is completely excluded from any communication, excepting through the tubes. This apparatus may be very convenient in many operations in which the substances employed have no action upon mercury. Plate XII, *Fig. 14*, represents an apparatus upon this principle properly fitted together.

M. Seguin, to whose active and intelligent assistance I have been very frequently much indebted, has bespoken for me, at the glasshouses, some retorts hermetically united to their recipients, by which luting will be altogether unnecessary.

CHAPTER VIII

Of Operations upon Combustion and Deflagration

SECTION I *Of Combustion in General*

COMBUSTION, according to what has been already said in the first part of this work, is the decomposition of oxygen gas produced by a combustible body. The oxygen which forms the base of this gas is absorbed by and enters into combination with the burning body, while the caloric and light are set free. Every combustion, therefore, necessarily supposes oxygenation; whereas, on the contrary, every oxygenation does not necessarily imply concomitant combustion; because combustion, properly so called, cannot take place without disengagement of caloric and light. Before combustion can take place, it is necessary that the base of oxygen gas should have greater affinity to the combustible body than it has to caloric; and this elective attraction, to use Bergman's expression, can only take place at a certain degree of temperature, which is different for each combustible substance; hence the necessity of giving a first motion or beginning to every combustion by the approach of a heated body. This necessity of heating any body we mean to burn depends upon certain considerations, which have not hitherto been attended to by any natural philosopher, for which reason I shall enlarge a little upon the subject in this place.

Nature is at present in a state of equilibrium, which cannot have been attained until all the spontaneous combustions or oxygenations possible in the ordinary degrees of temperature had taken place. Hence, no new combustions or oxygenations can happen without destroying this equilibrium and raising the combustible substances to a superior degree of temperature. To illustrate this abstract view of the matter by example: let us suppose the usual temperature of the earth a little changed, and that it is raised only to the degree of boiling water; it is evident that, in this case, phosphorus, which is combustible in a considerably lower degree of temperature, would no longer exist in nature in its pure and simple state but would always be procured in its acid or oxygenated state, and its radical would become one of the substances unknown to chemistry. By gradually increasing the temperature of the earth the same circumstance would successively happen to all the bodies capable of combustion; and, at last, every possible combustion having taken place, there would no longer exist any combustible body whatever, as every substance susceptible of that operation would be oxygenated and consequently incombustible.

There cannot therefore exist, so far as relates to us, any combustible body, except such as are incombustible in the ordinary temperatures of the earth; or, which is the same thing in other words, that it is essential to the nature of every combustible body not to possess the property of combustion, unless heated, or raised to the degree of temperature at which its combustion naturally takes place. When this degree is once produced, combustion commences, and the caloric which is disengaged by the decomposition of the oxygen gas keeps up the temperature necessary for continuing combustion. When this is not the case, that is, when the disengaged caloric is insufficient for keeping up the necessary temperature, the combustion ceases. This circumstance is expressed in common language by saying that a body burns ill or with difficulty.

Although combustion possesses some circumstances in common with distillation, especially with the compound kind of that operation, they differ in a very material point. In distillation there is a separation of one part of the elements of the substance from each other, and a combination of these in a new order, occasioned by the affinities which take place in the increased temperature produced during distillation. This likewise happens in combustion, but with this farther circumstance, that a new element, not originally in the body, is brought into action; oxygen is added to the substance submitted to the operation, and caloric is disengaged.

The necessity of employing oxygen in the state of gas in all experiments with combustion, and the rigorous determination of the quantities employed, render this kind of operations peculiarly troublesome. As almost all the products of combustion are disengaged in the state of gas, it is still more difficult to retain them than even those furnished during compound distillation; hence this precaution was entirely neglected by the ancient chemists; and this set of experiments exclusively belong to modern chemistry.

Having thus pointed out, in a general way, the objects to be had in view in experiments upon combustion, I proceed, in the following sections of this chapter, to describe the different instruments I have used with this view. The following arrangement is formed, not upon the nature of the combustible bodies, but upon that of the instruments necessary for combustion.

SECTION II *Of the Combustion of Phosphorus*

In these combustions we begin by filling a jar, capable at least of holding six pints, with oxygen gas in the water apparatus (Plate v, *Fig. 1*); when it is perfectly full, so that the gas begins to flow out below, the jar, A, is carried to the mercury apparatus (Plate IV, *Fig. 3*). We then dry the surface of the mercury, both within and without the jar, by means of blotting-paper, taking care to keep the paper for some time entirely immersed in the mercury before it is introduced under the jar, lest we let in any common air, which sticks very obstinately to the surface of the paper. The body to be submitted to combustion, being first very accurately weighed in nice scales, is placed in a small flat shallow dish, D, of iron or porcelain; this is covered by the larger cup P, which serves the office of a diving bell, and the whole is passed through the mercury into the jar, after which the larger cup is retired. The difficulty of passing the materials of combustion in this manner through the mercury may be avoided by raising one of the sides of the jar, A, for a moment, and slipping in the little cup, D, with the combustible body as quickly as possible. In this manner of operating, a small quantity of common air gets into the jar, but it is so very inconsiderable as not to injure either the progress or accuracy of the experiment in any sensible degree.

When the cup, D, is introduced under the jar, we suck out a part of the oxygen gas, so as to raise the mercury to EF, as formerly directed, Part I, Chapter V; otherwise, when the combustible body is set on fire, the gas becoming dilated would be in part forced out, and we should no longer be able to make any accurate calculation of the quantities before and after the experiment. A very convenient mode of drawing out the air is by means of an air-pump syringe adapted to the siphon, GHI, by which the mercury may be raised to any degree under twenty-eight inches. Very inflammable bodies, as phosphorus, are set on fire by means of the crooked iron wire MN (Plate IV, *Fig. 16*) made red hot and passed quickly through the mercury. Such as are less easily set on fire have a small portion of tinder, upon which a minute particle of phosphorus is fixed, laid upon them before using the red hot iron.

In the first moment of combustion the air, being heated, rarifies, and the mercury descends; but when, as in combustions of phosphorus and iron, no elastic fluid is formed, absorption becomes presently very sensible, and the mercury rises high into the jar. Great attention must be used not to burn too large a quantity of any substance in a given quantity of gas, otherwise, towards the end of the experiment the cup would approach so near the top of the jar as to endanger breaking it by the great heat produced and the sudden refrigeration from the cold mercury. For the methods of measuring the volume of the gases, and for correcting the measures according to the height of the barometer and thermometer, &c., see Chapter II, Sections V and VI of this part.

The above process answers very well for burning all the concrete substances, and even for the fixed oils. These last are burnt in lamps under the jar and are readily set on fire by means of tinder, phosphorus, and hot iron. But it is dangerous for substances susceptible of evaporating in a moderate heat, such as ether, alcohol, and the essential oils; these substances dissolve in considerable quantity in oxygen gas; and, when set on fire, a dangerous and sudden explosion takes place, which carries up the jar to a great height, and dashes it in a thousand pieces. From two such explosions some of the members of the Academy and myself escaped very narrowly. Besides, though this manner of operating is sufficient for determining pretty accurately the quantity of oxygen gas absorbed and of carbonic acid produced, as water is likewise formed in all experiments upon vegetable and animal matters which contain an excess of hydrogen, this apparatus can neither collect it nor determine its quantity. The experiment with phosphorus is even incomplete in this way, as it is impossible to demonstrate that the weight of the phosphoric acid produced is equal to the sum of the weights of the phosphorus burnt and oxygen gas absorbed during the process. I have been, therefore, obliged to vary the instruments according to circumstances, and to employ several of different kinds, which I shall describe in their order, beginning with that used for burning phosphorus.

Take a large balloon A (Plate IV, *Fig. 4*) of crystal or white glass, with an opening, EF, about two inches and a half or three inches diameter, to which a cap of brass is accurately fitted with emery, and which has two holes for the passage of the tubes xxx, yyy. Before shutting the balloon with its cover, place within it the stand, BC, supporting the cup of porcelain D, which contains the phosphorus. Then lute on the cap with fat lute and allow it to dry for some days and weigh the whole accurately; after this exhaust the balloon by means of an air-pump connected with the tube xxx, and fill it with oxygen gas by the tube yyy, from the gazometer (Plate VIII, *Fig. 1*) described Chapter II, Section II, of this part. The phosphorus is then set on fire by means of a burning-glass and is allowed to burn till the cloud of concrete phosphoric acid stops the combustion, oxygen gas being continually supplied from the gazometer. When the apparatus has cooled, it is weighed and unluted; the tare of the instrument being allowed, the weight is that of the phosphoric acid contained. It is proper, for greater accuracy, to examine the air or gas contained in the balloon after combustion, as it may happen to be somewhat heavier or lighter than common air; and this difference of weight must be taken into account in the calculations upon the results of the experiment.

SECTION III *Of the Combustion of Charcoal*

The apparatus I have employed for this process consists of a small conical furnace of hammered copper, represented in perspective, Plate XII, *Fig. 9*, and internally displayed *Fig. 11*. It is divided into the furnace, ABC, where the charcoal is burnt, the grate, de, and the ash-hole, F; the tube, GH, in the middle of the dome of the furnace serves to introduce the charcoal, and as a chimney for carrying off the air which has served for combustion. Through the tube, lmn, which communicates with the gazometer, the hydrogen gas, or air, intended for supporting the combustion, is conveyed into the ash-hole, F, whence it is forced, by the application of pressure to the gazometer, to pass through the grate, de, and to blow upon the burning charcoal placed immediately above.

Oxygen gas, which forms $^{28}/_{100}$ of atmospheric air, is changed into carbonic acid gas during combustion with charcoal, whilst the azotic gas of the air is not altered at all. Hence, after the combustion of charcoal in atmospheric air, a mixture of carbonic acid gas and azotic gas must remain; to allow this mixture to pass off, the tube, op, is adapted to the chimney, GH, by means of a screw at G, and conveys the gas into bottles half filled with solution of caustic potash. The carbonic acid gas is absorbed by the alkali, and the azotic gas is conveyed into a second gazometer where its quantity is ascertained.

The weight of the furnace, ABC, is first accurately determined; then introduce the tube RS, of known weight, by the chimney, GH, till its lower end S rests upon the grate, de, which it occupies entirely; in the next place, fill the furnace with charcoal and weigh the whole again, to know the exact quantity of charcoal submitted to experiment. The furnace is now put in its place, the tube, lmn, is screwed to that which communicates with the gazometer, and the tube, op, to that which communicates with the bottles of alkaline solution. Everything being in readiness, the stop-cock of the gazometer is opened, a small piece of burning charcoal is thrown into the tube, RS, which is instantly withdrawn, and the tube, op, is screwed to the chimney, GH. The little piece of charcoal falls upon the grate, and in this manner gets below the whole charcoal, and is kept on fire by the stream of air from the gazometer. To be certain that the combustion is begun, and goes on properly, the tube, qrs, is fixed to the furnace, having a piece of glass cemented to its upper extremity, s, through which we can see if the charcoal be on fire.

I neglected to observe above that the furnace and its appendages are plunged in water in the cistern TVXY (Plate XII, *Fig. 11*), to which ice may be added to moderate the heat, if necessary; though the heat is by no means very considerable, as there is no air but what comes from the gazometer, and no more of the charcoal burns at one time than what is immediately over the grate.

As one piece of charcoal is consumed another falls down into its place, in consequence of the declivity of the sides of the furnace; this gets into the stream of air from the grate, *d e*, and is burnt; and so on, successively, till the whole charcoal is consumed. The air which has served the purpose of the combustion passes through the mass of charcoal and is forced by the pressure of the gazometer to escape through the tube, *o p*, and to pass through the bottles of alkaline solution.

This experiment furnishes all the necessary data for a complete analysis of atmospheric air and of charcoal. We know the weight of charcoal consumed; the gazometer gives us the measure of the air employed; the quantity and quality of gas remaining after combustion may be determined as it is received, either in another gazometer, or in jars, in a pneumatochemical apparatus; the weight of ashes remaining in the ash-hole is readily ascertained; and, finally, the additional weight acquired by the bottles of alkaline solution gives the exact quantity of carbonic acid formed during the process. By this experiment we may likewise determine, with sufficient accuracy, the proportions in which charcoal and oxygen enter into the composition of carbonic acid.

In a future *Mémoire* I shall give an account to the Academy of a series of experiments I have undertaken with instrument upon all the vegetable and animal charcoals. By some very slight alterations, this machine may be made to answer for observing the principal phenomena of respiration.

Section IV *Of the Combustion of Oils*

Oils are more compound in their nature than charcoal, being formed by the combination of at least two elements, charcoal and hydrogen; of course, after their combustion in common air, water, carbonic acid gas, and azotic gas remain. Hence the apparatus employed for their combustion requires to be adapted for collecting these three products, and is consequently more complicated than the charcoal furnace.

The apparatus I employ for this purpose is composed of a large jar or pitcher A (Plate XII, *Fig. 4*), surrounded at its upper edge by a rim of iron properly cemented at DE and receding from the jar at BC so as to leave a furrow or gutter *x x* between it and the outside of the jar somewhat more than two inches deep. The cover or lid of the jar (*Fig. 5*) is likewise surrounded by an iron rim *f g*, which adjusts into the gutter *x x* (*Fig. 4*) which, being filled with mercury,

has the effect of closing the jar hermetically in an instant, without using any lute; and, as the gutter will hold about two inches of mercury, the air in the jar may be made to sustain the pressure of more than two feet of water, without danger of its escaping.

The lid has four holes, T*h i k*, for the passage of an equal number of tubes. The opening T is furnished with a leather box, through which passes the rod (*Fig. 3*) intended for raising and lowering the wick of the lamp, as will be afterwards directed. The three other holes are intended for the passage of three several tubes, one of which conveys the oil to the lamp, a second conveys air for keeping up the combustion, and the third carries off the air, after it has served for combustion. The lamp in which the oil is burnt is represented *Fig. 2; a* is the reservoir of oil, having a funnel by which it is filled; *b c d e f g h* is a siphon which conveys the oil to the lamp 11; 7, 8, 9, 10, is the tube which conveys the air for combustion from the gazometer to the same lamp. The tube *b c* is formed externally, at its lower end *b*, into a male screw, which turns in a female screw in the lid of the reservoir of oil *a;* so that, by turning the reservoir one way or the other, it is made to rise or fall, by which the oil is kept at the necessary level.

When the siphon is to be filled, and the communication formed between the reservoir of oil and the lamp, the stop-cock *c* is shut and that at *e* opened, oil is poured in by the opening *f* at the top of the siphon till it rises within three or four lines of the upper edge of the lamp; the stop-cock *k* is then shut and that at *c* opened: the oil is then poured in at *f*, till the branch *b c d* of the siphon is filled, and then the stop-cock *e* is closed. The two branches of the siphon being now completely filled, a communication is fully established between the reservoir and the lamp.

In Plate XII, *Fig. 1*, all the parts of the lamp 11 (*Fig. 2*) are represented magnified, to show them distinctly. The tube *i k* carries the oil from the reservoir to the cavity *a a a a*, which contains the wick; the tube 9, 10, brings the air from the gazometer for keeping up the combustion; this air spreads through the cavity *d d d d*, and, by means of the passages *c c c c* and *b b b b*, is distributed on each side of the wick, after the principles of the lamps constructed by Argand, Quinquet, and Lange.

To render the whole of this complicated apparatus more easily understood, and that its description may make all others of the same kind more readily followed, it is represented completely connected together for use in Plate XI. The gazometer P furnishes air for the combustion by the tube and stop-cock 1, 2; the tube 2, 3, communicates with a second gazometer, which is filled whilst the first one is emptying during the process, that there may be no interruption to the combustion; 4, 5, is a tube of glass filled with deliquescent salts, for drying the air as much as possible in its passage; and the weight of this tube and its contained salts, at the beginning of the experiment being known, it is easy to determine the quantity of water absorbed by them from the air. From this deliquescent tube the air is conducted through the pipe 5, 6, 7, 8, 9, 10, to the lamp 11, where it spreads on both sides of the wick, as before described, and feeds the flame. One part of this air, which serves to keep up the combustion of the oil, forms carbonic acid gas and water by oxygenating its elements. Part of this water condenses upon the sides of the pitcher A, and another part is held in solution in the air by means of caloric furnished by the combustion. This air is forced by the compression of the gazometer to pass through the tube 12, 13, 14, 15, into the bottle 16, and the worm 17, 18, where the water is fully condensed from the refrigeration of the air; and, if any water still remains in solution, it is absorbed by deliquescent salts contained in the tube 19, 20.

All these precautions are solely intended for collecting and determining the quantity of water formed during the experiment; the carbonic acid and azotic gas remains to be ascertained. The former is absorbed by caustic alkaline solution in the bottles 22 and 25. I have only represented two of these in the figure, but nine at least are requisite; and the last of the series may be half filled with lime-water, which is the most certain reagent for indicating the presence of carbonic acid; if the lime-water is not rendered turbid, we may be certain that no sensible quantity of that acid remains in the air.

The rest of the air which has served for combustion, and which chiefly consists of azotic gas, though still mixed with a considerable portion of oxygen gas which has escaped unchanged from the combustion, is carried through a third tube 28, 29, of deliquescent salts, to deprive it of any moisture it may have acquired in the bottles of alkaline solution and lime-water, and from thence by the tube 29, 30, into a gazometer, where its quantity is ascertained. Small essays are then taken from it, which are exposed to a solution of sulphuret of potash, to ascertain the proportions of oxygen and azotic gas it contains.

In the combustion of oils the wick becomes charred at last and obstructs the rise of the oil; besides, if we raise the wick above a certain height, more oil rises through its capillary tubes than the stream of air is capable of consuming, and smoke is produced. Hence it is necessary to be able to lengthen or shorten the wick without opening the apparatus; this is accomplished by means of the rod 31, 32, 33, 34, which passes through a leather-box and is connected with the support of the wick; and that the motion of this rod, and consequently of the wick, may be regulated with the utmost smoothness and facility, it is moved at pleasure by a pinion which plays in a toothed rack. The rod, with its appendages, are represented Plate XII, *Fig. 3*. It appeared to me that the combustion would be assisted by surrounding the flame of the lamp with a small glass jar open at both ends, as represented in its place in Plate XI.

I shall not enter into a more detailed description of the construction of this apparatus, which is still capable of being altered and modified in many respects, but shall only add that when it is to be used in experiment, the lamp and reservoir with the contained oil must be accurately weighed, after which it is placed as before directed and lighted; having then formed the connection between the air in the gazometer and the lamp, the external jar A (Plate XI) is fixed over all and secured by means of the board BC and two rods of iron which connect this board with the lid and are screwed to it. A small quantity of oil is burnt while the jar is adjusting to the lid, and the product of that combustion is lost; there is likewise a small portion of air from the gazometer lost at the same time. Both of these are of very inconsiderable consequence in extensive experiments, and they are even capable of being valued in our calculation of the results.

In a particular *Mémoire*, I shall give an account to the Academy of the difficulties inseparable from this kind of experiment. These are so insurmountable and troublesome that I have not hitherto been able to obtain any rigorous determination of the quantities of the products. I have sufficient proof, however, that the fixed oils are entirely resolved during combustion into water and carbonic acid gas, and consequently that they are composed of hydrogen and charcoal; but I have no certain knowledge respecting the proportions of these ingredients.

Section V *Of the Combustion of Alcohol*

The combustion of alcohol may be very readily performed in the apparatus already described for the combustion of charcoal and phosphorus. A lamp filled with alcohol is placed under the jar A (Plate iv, *Fig. 3*), a small morsel of phosphorus is placed upon the wick of the lamp, which is set on fire by means of the hot iron, as before directed. This process is, however, liable to considerable inconvenience; it is dangerous to make use of oxygen gas at the beginning of the experiment for fear of deflagration, which is even liable to happen when common air is employed. An instance of this had very near proved fatal to myself, in presence of some members of the Academy. Instead of preparing the experiment, as usual, at the time it was to be performed, I had disposed everything in order the evening before; the atmospheric air of the jar had thereby sufficient time to dissolve a good deal of the alcohol; and this evaporation had even been considerably promoted by the height of the column of mercury, which I had raised to EF (Plate iv, *Fig. 3*). The moment I attempted to set the little morsel of phosphorus on fire by means of the red hot iron, a violent explosion took place, which threw the jar with great violence against the floor of the laboratory and dashed it in a thousand pieces.

Hence we can only operate upon very small quantities, such as ten or twelve grains of alcohol, in this manner; and the errors which may be committed in experiments upon such small quantities prevents our placing any confidence in their results. I endeavoured to prolong the combustion, in the experiments contained in the *Recueil de l'Académie* for 1784, p. 593, by lighting the alcohol first in common air and furnishing oxygen gas afterwards to the jar, in proportion as it consumed; but the carbonic acid gas produced by the process became a great hinderance to the combustion, the more so that alcohol is but difficultly combustible, especially in worse than common air; so that even in this way very small quantities only could be burnt.

Perhaps this combustion might succeed better in the oil apparatus (Plate xi); but I have not hitherto ventured to try it. The jar A in which the combustion is performed is near 1400 cubic inches in dimension; and, were an explosion to take place in such a vessel, its consequences would be very terrible and very difficult to guard against. I have not, however, despaired of making the attempt.

From all these difficulties, I have been hitherto obliged to confine myself to experiments upon very small quantities of alcohol, or at least to combustions made in open vessels, such as that represented in Plate ix, *Fig. 5*, which will be described in Section VII of this chapter. If I am ever able to remove these difficulties, I shall resume this investigation.

Section VI *Of the Combustion of Ether*

Tho' the combustion of ether in close vessels does not present the same difficulties as that of alcohol, yet it involves some of a different kind, not more easily overcome, and which still prevent the progress of my experiments. I endeavoured to profit by the property which ether possesses of dissolving in atmospheric air and rendering it inflammable without explosion. For this purpose, I constructed the reservoir of ether *abcd* (Plate xii, *Fig. 8*), to which air is brought from the gazometer by the tube 1, 2, 3, 4. This air spreads, in the first place, in the double lid *ac* of the reservoir, from which it passes through seven tubes *ef*, *gh*, *ik*, &c., which descend to the bottom of the ether, and it is forced by the pressure of the gazometer to boil up through the ether in the reservoir. We may replace the ether in this first reservoir, in proportion as it is dissolved and carried off by the air, by means of the supplementary reservoir E, connected by a brass tube fifteen or eighteen inches long and shut by a stop-cock. This length of the connecting tube is to enable the descending ether to overcome the resistance occasioned by the pressure of the air from the gazometer.

The air, thus loaded with vapours of ether, is conducted by the tube 5, 6, 7, 8, 9, to the jar A, into which it is allowed to escape through a capillary opening, at the extremity of which it is set on fire. The air, when it has served the purpose of combustion, passes through the bottle 16 (Plate xi), the worm 17, 18, and the deliquescent tube 19, 20, after which it passes through the alkaline bottles; in these its carbonic acid gas is absorbed, the water formed during the experiment having been previously deposited in the former parts of the apparatus.

When I caused this apparatus constructed, I supposed that the combination of atmospheric air and ether formed in the reservoir *abcd* (Plate xii, *Fig. 8*) was in proper proportion for supporting combustion; but in this I was mistaken; for there is a very considerable quantity of excess of ether; so that an additional quantity of atmospheric air is necessary to enable it to burn fully. Hence a lamp constructed upon these principles will burn in common air, which furnishes the quantity of oxygen necessary for combustion, but will not burn in close vessels in which the air is not renewed. From this circumstance, my ether lamp went out soon after being lighted and shut up in the jar A (Plate XII, *Fig. 8*). To remedy this defect, I endeavoured to bring atmospheric air to the lamp by the lateral tube 10, 11, 12, 13, 14, 15, which I distributed circularly round the flame; but the flame is so exceedingly rare that it is blown out by the gentlest possible stream of air, so that I have not hitherto succeeded in burning ether. I do not, however, despair of being able to accomplish it by means of some changes I am about to have made upon this apparatus.

SECTION VII *Of the Combustion of Hydrogen Gas and the Formation of Water*

In the formation of water, two substances, hydrogen and oxygen, which are both in the aeriform state before combustion, are transformed into liquid or water by the operation. This experiment would be very easy and would require very simple instruments, if it were possible to procure the two gases perfectly pure, so that they might burn without any residuum. We might, in that case, operate in very small vessels and, by continually furnishing the two gases in proper proportions, might continue the combustion indefinitely. But, hitherto, chemists have only employed oxygen gas mixed with azotic gas; from which circumstance, they have only been able to keep up the combustion of hydrogen gas for a very limited time in close vessels, because, as the residuum of azotic gas is continually increasing, the air becomes at last so much contaminated that the flame weakens and goes out. This inconvenience is so much the greater in proportion as the oxygen gas employed is less pure. From this circumstance, we must either be satisfied with operating upon small quantities or must exhaust the vessels at intervals, to get rid of the residuum of azotic gas; but, in this case, a portion of the water formed during the experiment is evaporated by the exhaustion; and the resulting error is the more dangerous to the accuracy of the process, so that we have no certain means of valuing it.

These considerations make me desirous to repeat the principal experiments of pneumatic chemistry with oxygen gas entirely free from any admixture of azotic gas; and this may be procured from oxygenated muriate of potash. The oxygen gas extracted from this salt does not appear to contain azote, unless accident-ally, so that, by proper precautions, it may be obtained perfectly pure. In the mean time, the apparatus employed by M. Meusnier and me for the combustion of hydrogen gas, which is described in the experiment for recomposition of water, Part I, Chapter VIII, and need not be here repeated, will answer the purpose; when pure gases are procured, this apparatus will require no alterations, except that the capacity of the vessels may then be diminished. See Plate IV, *Fig. 5*.

The combustion, when once begun, continues for a considerable time but weakens gradually, in proportion as the quantity of azotic gas remaining from the combustion increases, till at last the azotic gas is in such over proportion that the combustion can no longer be supported, and the flame goes out. This spontaneous extinction must be prevented, because, as the hydrogen gas is pressed upon in its reservoir, by an inch and a half of water, whilst the oxygen gas suffers a pressure only of three lines, a mixture of the two would take place in the balloon, which would at last be forced by the superior pressure into the reservoir of oxygen gas. Wherefore the combustion must be stopped by shutting the stop-cock of the tube dDd whenever the flame grows very feeble; for which purpose it must be attentively watched.

There is another apparatus for combustion, which, though we cannot with it perform experiments with the same scrupulous exactness as with the preceding instruments, gives very striking results that are extremely proper to be shown in courses of philosophical chemistry. It consists of a worm EF (Plate IX, *Fig. 5*) contained in a metallic cooler ABCD. To the upper part of this worm E, the chimney GH is fixed, which is composed of two tubes, the inner of which is a continuation of the worm, and the outer one is a case of tin-plate, which surrounds it at about an inch distance, and the interval is filled up with sand. At the inferior extremity K of the inner tube, a glass tube is fixed, to which we adopt the Argand lamp LM for burning alcohol, &c.

Things being thus disposed, and the lamp being filled with a determinate quantity of alcohol, it is set on fire; the water which is formed during the combustion rises in the chimney KE, and, being condensed in the worm, runs out at its extremity F into the bottle P. The double tube of the chimney, filled with sand in the interstice, is to prevent the tube from cooling in its upper part and condensing the water; otherwise, it would fall back in the tube, and we should not be able to ascertain its quantity, and besides it might fall in drops upon the wick and extinguish the flame. The intention of this construction is to keep the chimney always hot and the worm always cool, that the water may be preserved in the state of vapour whilst rising and may be condensed immediately upon getting into the descending part of the apparatus. By this instrument, which was contrived by M. Meusnier, and which is described by me in the *Recueil de l'Académie* for 1784, p. 593, we may, with attention to keep the worm always cold, collect nearly seventeen ounces of water from the combustion of sixteen ounces of alcohol.

Section VIII *Of the Oxidation of Metals*

The term *oxidation* or *calcination* is chiefly used to signify the process by which metals exposed to a certain degree of heat are converted into oxides by absorbing oxygen from the air. This combination takes place in consequence of oxygen possessing a greater affinity to metals, at a certain temperature, than to caloric, which becomes disengaged in its free state; but, as this disengagement, when made in common air, is slow and progressive, it is scarcely evident to the senses. It is quite otherwise, however, when oxidation takes place in oxygen gas; for, being produced with much greater rapidity, it is generally accompanied with heat and light, so as evidently to show that metallic substances are real combustible bodies.

All the metals have not the same degree of affinity to oxygen. Gold, silver, and platinum, for instance, are incapable of taking it away from its combination with caloric, even in the greatest known heat; whereas the other metals absorb it in a larger or smaller quantity, until the affinities of the metal to oxygen, and of the latter to caloric, are in exact equilibrium. Indeed, this state of equilibrium of affinities may be assumed as a general law of nature in all combinations.

In all operations of this nature, the oxidation of metals is accelerated by giving free access to the air; it is sometimes much assisted by joining the action of a bellows, which directs a stream of air over the surface of the metal. This process becomes greatly more rapid if a stream of oxygen gas be used, which is readily done by means of the gazometer formerly described. The metal, in this case, throws out a brilliant flame, and the oxidation is very quickly accomplished; but this method can only be used in very confined experiments, on account of the expense of

procuring oxygen gas. In the essay of ores, and in all the common operations of the laboratory, the calcination or oxidation of metals is usually performed in a dish of baked clay (Plate IV, *Fig. 6*), commonly called a *roasting test*, placed in a strong furnace. The substances to be oxidated are frequently stirred, on purpose to present fresh surfaces to the air.

Whenever this operation is performed upon a metal which is not volatile, and from which nothing flies off into the surrounding air during the process, the metal acquires additional weight; but the cause of this increased weight during oxidation could never have been discovered by means of experiments performed in free air; and it is only since these operations have been performed in close vessels, and in determinate quantities of air, that any just conjectures have been formed concerning the cause of this phenomenon. The first method for this purpose is due to Dr. Priestley, who exposes the metal to be calcined in a porcelain cup N (Plate IV, *Fig. 11*), placed upon the stand IK, under a jar A, in the basin BCDE, full of water; the water is made to rise up to GH, by sucking out the air with a siphon, and the focus of a burning glass is made to fall upon the metal. In a few minutes the oxidation takes place, a part of the oxygen contained in the air combines with the metal, and a proportional diminution of the volume of air is produced; what remains is nothing more than azotic gas, still however mixed with a small quantity of oxygen gas. I have given an account of a series of experiments made with this apparatus in my *Physical and Chemical Essays*, first published in 1773. Mercury may be used instead of water in this experiment, whereby the results are rendered still more conclusive.

Another process for this purpose was invented by M. Boyle, of which I gave an account in the *Recueil de l'Académie* for 1774, p. 351. The metal is introduced into a retort (Plate III, *Fig. 20*), the beak of which is hermetically sealed; the metal is then oxidated by means of heat applied with great precaution. The weight of the vessel and its contained substances is not at all changed by this process, until the extremity of the neck of the retort is broken; but, when that is done, the external air rushes in with a hissing noise. This operation is attended with danger, unless a part of the air is driven out of the retort by means of heat before it is hermetically sealed, as otherwise the retort would be apt to burst by the dilation of the air when placed in the furnace. The quantity of air driven out may be received under a jar in the pneumato-chemical apparatus, by which its quantity and that of the air remaining in the retort is ascertained. I have not multiplied my experiments upon oxidation of metals so much as I could have wished; neither have I obtained satisfactory results with any metal except tin. It is much to be wished that some person would undertake a series of experiments upon oxidation of metals in the several gases; the subject is important and would fully repay any trouble which this kind of experiment might occasion.

As all the oxides of mercury are capable of revivifying without addition and restore the oxygen gas they had before absorbed, this seemed to be the most proper metal for becoming the subject of conclusive experiments upon oxidation. I formerly endeavoured to accomplish the oxidation of mercury in close vessels, by filling a retort, containing a small quantity of mercury, with oxygen gas, and adapting a bladder half full of the same gas to its beak; See Plate IV, *Fig. 12*. Afterwards, by heating the mercury in the retort for a very long time, I succeeded in oxidating a very small portion, so as to form a little red oxide floating upon the surface of the running mercury; but the quantity was so small that the smallest error committed in the determination of the quantities of oxygen gas before and after the operation must have thrown very great uncertainty upon the results of the experiment. I was, besides, dissatisfied with this process, and not without cause, lest any air might have escaped through the pores of the bladder, more especially as it becomes shrivelled by the heat of the furnace unless covered over with cloths kept constantly wet.

This experiment is performed with more certainty in the apparatus described in the *Recueil de l'Académie* for 1775, p. 580. This consists of a retort A (Plate IV, *Fig. 2*), having a crooked glass tube BCDE of ten or twelve lines internal diameter melted on to its beak, and which is engaged under the bell glass FG, standing with its mouth downwards in a basin filled with water or mercury. The retort is placed upon the bars of the furnace MMNN (Plate IV, *Fig. 2*), or in a sand bath, and by means of this apparatus we may, in the course of several days, oxidate a small quantity of mercury in common air; the red oxide floats upon the surface, from which it may be collected and revivified, so as to compare the quantity of oxygen gas obtained in revivification with the absorption which took place during oxidation. This kind

of experiment can only be performed upon a small scale, so that no very certain conclusions can be drawn from them.[1]

The combustion of iron in oxygen gas being a true oxidation of that metal, ought to be mentioned in this place. The apparatus employed by M. Ingenhousz for this operation is represented in Plate IV, *Fig. 17;* but, having already described it sufficiently in Chapter III, I shall refer the reader to what is said of it in that place. Iron may likewise be oxidated by combustion in vessels filled with oxygen gas, in the way already directed for phosphorus and charcoal. This apparatus is represented in Plate IV, *Fig. 3*, and described in the fifth chapter of the first part of this work. We learn from M. Ingenhousz that all the metals, except gold, silver, and mercury, may be burnt or oxidated in the same manner, by reducing them into very fine wire or very thin plates cut into narrow slips; these are twisted round with iron-wire, which communicates the property of burning to the other metals.

Mercury is even with difficulty oxidated in free air. In chemical laboratories, this process is usually carried on in a matrass A (Plate IV, *Fig. 10*), having a very flat body and a very long neck BC, which vessel is commonly called *Boyle's hell*. A quantity of mercury is introduced sufficient to cover the bottom, and it is placed in a sand bath, which keeps up a constant heat approaching to that of boiling mercury. By continuing this operation with five or six similar matrasses during several months, and renowing the mercury from time to time, a few ounces of red oxide are at last obtained. The great slowness and inconvenience of this apparatus arises from the air not being sufficiently renewed; but if, on the other hand, too free a circulation were given to the external air, it would carry off the mercury in solution in the state of vapour, so that in a few days none would remain in the vessel.

As, of all the experiments upon the oxidation of metals, those with mercury are the most conclusive, it were much to be wished that a simple apparatus could be contrived by which this oxidation and its results might be demonstrated in public courses of chemistry. This might, in my opinion, be accomplished by methods similar to those I have already described for the combustion of charcoal and the oils; but, from other pursuits, I have not been able hitherto to resume this kind of experiment.

[1] See an account of this experiment, Part I, Chapter III.—AUTHOR.

The oxide of mercury revives without addition, by being heated to a slightly red heat. In this degree of temperature, oxygen has greater affinity to caloric than to mercury, and forms oxygen gas. This is always mixed with a small portion of azotic gas, which indicates that the mercury absorbs a small portion of this latter gas during oxidation. It almost always contains a little carbonic acid gas, which must undoubtedly be attributed to the foulnesses of the oxide; these are charred by the heat, and convert a part of the oxygen gas into carbonic acid.

If chemists were reduced to the necessity of procuring all the oxygen gas employed in their experiments from mercury oxidated by heat without addition, or, as it is called, *calcined* or *precipitated per se*, the excessive dearness of that preparation would render experiments, even upon a moderate scale, quite impracticable. But mercury may likewise be oxidated by means of nitric acid; and in this way we procure a red oxide even more pure than that produced by calcination. I have sometimes prepared this oxide by dissolving mercury in nitric acid, evaporating to dryness, and calcining the salt, either in a retort or in capsules formed of pieces of broken matrasses and retorts, in the manner formerly described; but I have never succeeded in making it equally beautiful with what is sold by the druggists, and which is, I believe, brought from Holland. In choosing this, we ought to prefer what is in solid lumps composed of soft adhering scales, as when in powder it is sometimes adulterated with red oxide of lead.

To obtain oxygen gas from the red oxide of mercury, I usually employ a porcelain retort having a long glass tube adapted to its beak, which is engaged under jars in the water pneumato-chemical apparatus, and I place a bottle in the water, at the end of the tube, for receiving the mercury, in proportion as it revives and distils over. As the oxygen gas never appears till the retort becomes red, it seems to prove the principle established by M. Berthollet that an obscure heat can never form oxygen gas and that light is one of its constituent elements. We must reject the first portion of gas which comes over as being mixed with common air, from what was contained in the retort at the beginning of the experiment; but, even with this precaution, the oxygen gas procured is usually contaminated with a tenth part of azotic gas and with a very small portion of carbonic acid gas. This latter is readily got rid of, by making the gas pass through a solution of caustic alkali; but we know of no method for separating the azotic gas; its proportions may however be ascertained, by leaving a known quantity of the oxygen gas contaminated with it for a fortnight, in contact with sulphuret of soda or potash, which absorbs the oxygen gas so as to convert the sulphur into sulphuric acid and leaves the azotic gas remaining pure.

We may likewise procure oxygen gas from black oxide of manganese or nitrate of potash, by exposing them to a red heat in the apparatus already described for operating upon red oxide of mercury; only, as it requires such a heat as is at least capable of softening glass, we must employ retorts of stone or of porcelain. But the purest and best oxygen gas is what is disengaged from oxygenated muriate of potash by simple heat. This operation is performed in a glass retort, and the gas obtained is perfectly pure, provided that the first portions, which are mixed with the common air of the vessels, be rejected.

CHAPTER IX

Of Deflagration

I HAVE already shown, Part I, Chapter IX, that oxygen does not always part with the whole of the caloric it contained in the state of gas when it enters into combination with other bodies. It carries almost the whole of its caloric alongst with it in entering into the combinations which form nitric acid and oxygenated muriatic acid; so that in nitrates, and more especially in oxygenated muriates, the oxygen is, in a certain degree, in the state of oxygen gas, condensed, and reduced to the smallest volume it is capable of occupying.

In these combinations, the caloric exerts a constant action upon the oxygen to bring it back to the state of gas; hence the oxygen adheres but very slightly, and the smallest additional force is capable of setting it free; and, when such force is applied, it often recovers the state of gas instantaneously. This rapid passage from the solid to the aeriform state is called detonation, or fulmination, because it is usually accompanied with noise and explosion. Deflagrations are commonly produced by means of combinations of charcoal either with nitre or oxygenated muriate of potash; sometimes, to assist the inflammation, sulphur is added; and, upon the just proportion of these ingredients, and the proper manipulation of the mixture, depends the art of making gun-powder.

As oxygen is changed, by deflagration with charcoal, into carbonic acid, instead of oxygen gas, carbonic acid gas is disengaged, at least when the mixture has been made in just proportions. In deflagration with nitre, azotic gas is likewise disengaged, because azote is one of the constituent elements of nitric acid.

The sudden and instantaneous disengagement and expansion of these gases is not, however, sufficient for explaining all the phenomena of deflagration; because, if this were the sole operating power, gun-powder would always be so much the stronger in proportion as the quantity of gas disengaged in a given time was the more considerable, which does not always accord with experiment. I have tried some kinds which produced almost double the effect of ordinary gun-powder, although they gave out a sixth part less of gas during deflagration. It would appear that the quantity of caloric disengaged at the moment of detonation contributes considerably to the expansive effects produced; for, although caloric penetrates freely through the pores of every body in nature, it can only do so progressively, and in a given time; hence, when the quantity disengaged at once is too large to get through the pores of the surrounding bodies, it must necessarily act in the same way with ordinary elastic fluids and overturn everything that opposes its passage. This must, at least in part, take place when gun-powder is set on fire in a cannon; as, although the metal is permeable to caloric, the quantity disengaged at once is too large to find its way through the pores of the metal, it must therefore make an effort to escape on every side; and, as the resistance all around, excepting towards the muzzle, is too great to be overcome, this effort is employed for expelling the bullet.

The caloric produces a second effect, by means of the repulsive force exerted between its particles; it causes the gases, disengaged at the moment of deflagration, to expand with a degree of force proportioned to the temperature produced.

It is very probable that water is decomposed during the deflagration of gun-powder, and that part of the oxygen furnished to the nascent carbonic acid gas is produced from it. If so, a considerable quantity of hydrogen gas must be disengaged in the instant of deflagration which expands and contributes to the force of the explosion. It may readily be conceived how greatly this circumstance must increase the effect of powder, if we consider that a pint of hydrogen gas weighs only one grain and two thirds; hence a very small quantity in weight must occupy a very large space, and it must exert a prodigious expansive force in passing from the liquid to the aeriform state of existence.

In the last place, as a portion of undecomposed water is reduced to vapour during the deflagration of gun-powder, and as water, in the state of gas, occupies seventeen or eighteen hundred times more space than in its liquid state, this circumstance must likewise contribute largely to the explosive force of the powder.

I have already made a considerable series of experiments upon the nature of the elastic fluids disengaged during the deflagration of nitre with charcoal and sulphur, and have made some, likewise, with the oxygenated muriate of potash. This method of investigation leads to tolerably accurate conclusions with respect to the constituent elements of these salts. Some of the principal results of these experiments, and of the consequences drawn from them respecting the analysis of nitric acid, are reported in the collection of *Mémoires* presented to the Academy by foreign philosophers, Vol. XI, p. 625. Since then I have procured more convenient instruments, and I intend to repeat these experiments upon a larger scale, by which I shall procure more accurate precision in their results; the following, however, is the process I have hitherto employed. I would very earnestly advise such as intend to repeat some of these experiments to be very much upon their guard in operating upon any mixture which contains nitre, charcoal, and sulphur, and more especially with those in which oxygenated muriate of potash is mixed with these two materials.

I make use of pistol barrels, about six inches long and of five or six lines diameter, having the touch-hole spiked up with an iron nail strongly driven in and broken in the hole, and a little tin-smith's solder run in to prevent any possible issue for the air. These are charged with a mixture of known quantities of nitre and charcoal, or any other mixture capable of deflagration, reduced to an impalpable powder and formed into a paste with a moderate quantity of water. Every portion of the materials introduced must be rammed down with a rammer nearly of the same caliber with the barrel, four or five lines at the muzzle must be left empty, and about two inches of quick match are added at the end of the charge. The only difficulty in this experiment, especially when sulphur is contained in the mixture, is to discover the proper degree of moistening; for, if the paste be too much wetted, it will not take fire, and if too dry, the deflagration is apt to become too rapid and even dangerous.

When the experiment is not intended to be rigorously exact, we set fire to the match, and, when it is just about to communicate with the charge, we plunge the pistol below a large bell-glass full of water in the pneumato-chemical apparatus. The deflagration begins and continues in the water, and gas is disengaged with less or more rapidity, in proportion as the mixture is more or less dry. So long as the deflagration continues, the muzzle of the pistol must be kept somewhat inclined downwards, to prevent the water from getting into its barrel. In this manner I have sometimes collected the gas produced from the deflagration of an ounce and half, or two ounces, of nitre.

In this manner of operating it is impossible to determine the quantity of carbonic acid gas disengaged, because a part of it is absorbed by the water while passing through it; but, when the carbonic acid is absorbed, the azotic gas remains; and, if it be agitated for a few minutes in caustic alkaline solution, we obtain it pure and can easily determine its volume and weight. We may even, in this way, acquire a tolerably exact knowledge of the quantity of carbonic acid by repeating the experiment a great many times, and varying the proportions of charcoal, till we find the exact quantity requisite to deflagrate the whole nitre employed. Hence, by means of the weight of charcoal employed, we determine the weight of oxygen necessary for saturation and deduce the quantity of oxygen contained in a given weight of nitre.

I have used another process, by which the results of this experiment are considerably more accurate, which consists in receiving the disengaged gases in bell-glasses filled with mercury. The mercurial apparatus I employ is large enough to contain jars of from twelve to fifteen pints in capacity, which are not very readily managed when full of mercury and even require to be filled by a particular method. When the jar is placed in the cistern of mercury, a glass siphon is introduced, connected with a small air-pump by means of which the air is exhausted, and the mercury rises so as to fill the jar. After this, the gas of the deflagration is made to pass into the jar in the same manner as directed when water is employed.

I must again repeat that this species of experiment requires to be performed with the greatest possible precautions. I have sometimes seen, when the disengagement of gas proceeded with too great rapidity, jars filled with more than an hundred and fifty pounds of mercury driven off by the force of the explosion and broken to pieces, while the mercury was scattered about in great quantities.

When the experiment has succeeded and the gas is collected under the jar, its quantity in general, and the nature and quantities of the several species of gases of which the mixture is composed, are accurately ascertained by the methods already pointed out in the second chapter of this part of my work. I have been prevented from putting the last hand to the experiments I had begun upon deflagration, from their connection with the objects I am at present engaged in; and I am in hopes they will throw considerable light upon the operations belonging to the manufacture of gun-powder.

CHAPTER X

Of the Instruments Necessary for Operating upon Bodies in Very High Temperatures

SECTION I *Of Fusion*

WE have already seen that, by aqueous solution in which the particles of bodies are separated from each other, neither the solvent nor the body held in solution are at all decomposed; so that, whenever the cause of separation ceases, the particles reunite, and the saline substance recovers precisely the same appearance and properties it possessed before solution. Real solutions are produced by fire, or by introducing and accumulating a great quantity of caloric between the particles of bodies; and this species of solution in caloric is usually called *fusion*.

This operation is commonly performed in vessels called crucibles, which must necessarily be less fusible than the bodies they are intended to contain. Hence, in all ages, chemists have been extremely solicitous to procure crucibles of very refractory materials, or such as are capable of resisting a very high degree of heat. The best are made of very pure clay or of porcelain earth; whereas such as are made of clay mixed with calcareous or silicious earth are very fusible. All the crucibles made in the neighbourhood of Paris are of this kind and consequently unfit for most chemical experiments. The Hessian crucibles are tolerably good; but the best are made of Limoges earth, which seems absolutely infusible. We have, in France, a great many clays very fit for making crucibles; such, for instance, is the kind used for making melting-pots at the glass-manufactory of St. Gobin.

Crucibles are made of various forms, according to the operations they are intended to perform. Several of the most common kinds are represented Plate VII, *Figs. 7, 8, 9,* and *10;* the one represented at *Fig. 9* is almost shut at its mouth.

Though fusion may often take place without changing the nature of the fused body, this operation is frequently employed as a chemical means of decomposing and recompounding bodies. In this way all the metals are extracted from their ores; and, by this process, they are revivified, moulded, and alloyed with each other. By this process sand and alkali are combined to form glass, and by it likewise pastes, or coloured stones, enamels, &c. are formed.

The action of violent fire was much more frequently employed by the ancient chemists than it is in modern experiments. Since greater precision has been employed in philosophical researches, the *humid* has been preferred to the *dry* method of process, and fusion is seldom had recourse to until all the other means of analysis have failed.

SECTION II *Of Furnaces*

These are instruments of most universal use in chemistry; and, as the success of a great number of experiments depends upon their being well or ill constructed, it is of great importance that a laboratory be well provided in this respect. A furnace is a kind of hollow cylindrical tower, sometimes widened above (Plate XIII, *Fig. 1*). ABCD, which must have at least two lateral openings; one in its upper part F, which is the door of the fire-place, and one below G, leading to the ash hole. Between these the furnace is divided by a horizontal grate, intended for supporting the fuel, the situation of which is marked in the figure by the line HI. Though this be the least complicated of all the chemical furnaces, yet it is applicable to a great number of purposes. By it lead, tin, bismuth, and, in general, every substance which does not require a very strong fire, may be melted in crucibles; it will serve for metallic oxidations, for evaporatory vessels, and for sand baths, as in Plate III, *Figs. 1* and *2.* To render it proper for these purposes, several notches, *m m m m* (Plate XIII, *Fig. 1*), are made in its upper edge, as otherwise any pan which might be placed over the fire would stop the passage of the air, and prevent the fuel from burning. This furnace can only produce a moderate degree of heat, because the quantity of charcoal it is capable of consuming is limited by the quantity of air which is allowed to pass through the opening G of the ash-hole. Its power might be considerably augmented by enlarging this opening, but then the great stream of air which is convenient for some operations might be hurtful in others; wherefore we must have furnaces of different forms, constructed for different purposes, in our laboratories. There ought especially to be several of the kind now described of different sizes.

The reverberatory furnace (Plate XIII, *Fig. 2*) is perhaps more necessary. This, like the common furnace, is composed of the ash-hole HIKL, the fire-place KLMN, the laboratory MNOP, and the dome RRSS, with its funnel or chimney TTVV; and to this last several additional tubes may be adapted, according to the nature of the different experiments. The retort A is placed in the division called the laboratory and supported by two bars of iron which run across the furnace, and its beak comes out at a round hole in the side of the furnace, one half of which is cut in the piece called the laboratory and the other in the dome. In most of the ready-made reverberatory furnaces which are sold by the potters at Paris, the openings both above and below are too small. These do not allow a sufficient volume of air to pass through; hence, as the quantity of charcoal consumed, or, which is much the same thing, the quantity of caloric disengaged is nearly in proportion to the quantity of air which passes through the furnace, these furnaces do not produce a sufficient effect in a great number of experiments. To remedy this defect, there ought to be two openings GG to the ash-hole; one of these is shut up when only a moderate fire is required; and both are kept open when the strongest power of the furnace is to be exerted. The opening of the dome SS ought likewise to be considerably larger than is usually made.

It is of great importance not to employ retorts of too large size in proportion to the furnace, as a sufficient space ought always to be allowed for the passage of the air between the sides of the furnace and the vessel. The retort A in the figure is too small for the size of the furnace, yet I find it more easy to point out the error than to correct it. The intention of the dome is to oblige the flame and heat to surround and strike back or reverberate upon every part of the retort, whence the furnace gets the name of reverberatory. Without this circumstance the retort would only be heated in its bottom, the vapours raised from the contained substance would condense in the upper part, and a continual cohabitation would take place without anything passing over into the receiver; but, by means of the dome, the retort is equally heated in every part, and the vapours being forced out can only condense in the neck of the retort or in the recipient.

To prevent the bottom of the retort from being either heated or cooled too suddenly, it is sometimes placed in a small sand bath of baked clay, standing upon the cross bars of the furnace. Likewise, in many operations, the retorts are coated over with lutes, some of which are intended to preserve them from the too sudden influence of heat or of cold, while others are for sustaining the glass, or forming a kind of second retort, which supports the glass one during operations wherein the strength of the fire might soften it. The former is made of brick-clay with a little cow's hair beat up along with it, into a paste or mortar, and spread over the glass or stone retorts. The latter is made of pure clay and pounded stone-ware mixed together and used in the same manner. This dries and hardens by the fire, so as to form a true supplementary retort capable of retaining the materials, if the glass retort below should crack or soften. But, in experiments which are intended for collecting gases, this lute, being porous, is of no manner of use.

In a great many experiments wherein very violent fire is not required, the reverberatory furnace may be used as a melting one, by leaving out the piece called the laboratory and placing the dome immediately upon the fireplace, as represented Plate XIII, *Fig. 3*. The furnace represented in *Fig. 4* is very convenient for fusions; it is composed of the fire-place and ash-hole ABD, without a door, and having a hole E, which receives the muzzle of a pair of bellows strongly luted on, and the dome ABGH, which ought to be rather lower than is represented in the figure. This furnace is not capable of producing a very strong heat but is sufficient for ordinary operations and may be readily moved to any part of the laboratory where it is wanted. Though these particular furnaces are very convenient, every laboratory must be provided with a forge furnace, having a good pair of bellows, or, what is more necessary, a powerful melting furnace. I shall describe the one I use, with the principles upon which it is constructed.

The air circulates in a furnace in consequence of being heated in its passage through the burning coals; it dilates and, becoming lighter than the surrounding air, is forced to rise upwards by the pressure of the lateral columns of air,

and is replaced by fresh air from all sides, especially from below. This circulation of air even takes place when coals are burnt in a common chaffing dish; but we can readily conceive, that, in a furnace open on all sides, the mass of air which passes, all other circumstances being equal, cannot be so great as when it is obliged to pass through a furnace in the shape of a hollow tower, like most of the chemical furnaces, and consequently that the combustion must be more rapid in a furnace of this latter construction. Suppose, for instance, the furnace ABCDEF open above and filled with burning coals, the force with which the air passes through the coals will be in proportion to the difference between the specific gravity of two columns equal to AC, the one of cold air without, and the other of heated air within the furnace. There must be some heated air above the opening AB, and the superior levity of this ought likewise to be taken into consideration; but, as this portion is continually cooled and carried off by the external air, it cannot produce any great effect.

But, if we add to this furnace a large hollow tube GHAB of the same diameter, which preserves the air which has been heated by the burning coals from being cooled and dispersed by the surrounding air, the difference of specific gravity which causes the circulation will then be between two columns equal to GC. Hence, if GC be three times the length of AC, the circulation will have treble force. This is upon the supposition that the air in GHCD is as much heated as what is contained in ABCD, which is not strictly the case, because the heat must decrease between AB and GH; but, as the air in GHAB is much warmer than the external air, it follows that the addition of the tube must increase the rapidity of the stream of air, that a larger quantity must pass through the coals, and consequently that a greater degree of combustion must take place.

We must not, however, conclude from these principles, that the length of this tube ought to be indefinitely prolonged; for, since the heat of the air gradually diminishes in passing from AB to GH, even from the contact of the sides of the tube, if the tube were prolonged to a certain degree, we would at last come to a point where the specific gravity of the included air would be equal to the air without; and, in this case, as the cool air would no longer tend to rise upwards, it would become a gravitating mass, resisting the ascension of the air below. Besides, as this air, which has served for combustion, is necessarily mixed with carbonic acid gas, which is considerably heavier than common air, if the tube were made long enough, the air might at last approach so near to the temperature of the external air as even to gravitate downwards; hence we must conclude that the length of the tube added to a furnace must have some limit beyond which it weakens instead of strengthening the force of the fire.

From these reflections it follows that the first foot of tube added to a furnace produces more effect than the sixth, and the sixth more than the tenth; but we have no data to ascertain at what height we ought to stop. This limit of useful addition is so much the farther in proportion as the materials of the tube are weaker conductors of heat, because the air will thereby be so much less cooled; hence baked earth is much to be preferred to plate iron. It would be even of consequence to make the tube double, and to fill the interval with rammed charcoal, which is one of the worst conductors of heat known; by this the refrigeration of the air will be retarded, and the rapidity of the stream of air consequently increased; and, by this means, the tube may be made so much the longer.

As the fire-place is the hottest part of a furnace, and the part where the air is most dilated in its passage, this part ought to made with a considerable widening or belly. This is the more necessary, as it is intended to contain the charcoal and crucible, as well as for the passage of the air which supports, or rather produces the combustion; hence we only allow the interstices between the coals for the passage of the air.

From these principles my melting furnace is constructed, which I believe is at least equal in power to any hitherto made, though I by no means pretend that it possesses the greatest possible intensity that can be produced in chemical furnaces. The augmentation of the volume of air produced during its passage through a melting furnace not being hitherto ascertained from experiment, we are still unacquainted with the proportions which should exist between the inferior and superior apertures, and the absolute size of which these openings should be made is still less understood; hence data are wanting by which to proceed upon principle, and we can only accomplish the end in view by repeated trials.

This furnace, which, according to the above stated rules, is in form of an eliptical spheroid, is represented Plate XIII, *Fig. 6*, ABCD; it is cut off at the two ends by two planes, which

pass, perpendicular to the axis, through the foci of the elipse. From this shape it is capable of containing a considerable quantity of charcoal, while it leaves sufficient space in the intervals for the passage of the air. That no obstacle may oppose the free access of external air, it is perfectly open below, after the model of M. Macquer's melting furnace, and stands upon an iron tripod. The grate is made of flat bars set on edge, and with considerable interstices. To the upper part is added a chimney, or tube, of baked earth, ABFG, about eighteen feet long, and almost half the diameter of the furnace. Though this furnace produces a greater heat than any hitherto employed by chemists, it is still susceptible of being considerably increased in power by the means already mentioned, the principal of which is to render the tube as bad a conductor of heat as possible, by making it double, and filling the interval with rammed charcoal.

When it is required to know if lead contains any mixture of gold or silver, it is heated in a strong fire in capsules of calcined bones, which are called cupels. The lead is oxidated, becomes vitrified, and sinks into the substance of the cupel, while the gold or silver, being incapable of oxidation, remain pure. As lead will not oxidate without free access of air, this operation cannot be performed in a crucible placed in the middle of the burning coals of a furnace, because the internal air, being mostly already reduced by the combustion into azotic and carbonic acid gas, is no longer fit for the oxidation of metals. It was therefore necessary to contrive a particular apparatus, in which the metal should be at the same time exposed to the influence of violent heat and defended from contact with air rendered incombustible by its passage through burning coals. The furnace intended for answering this double purpose is called the cupelling or essay furnace. It is usually made of a square form, as represented Plate XIII, *Figs. 8* and *10*, having an ash-hole AABB, a fire-place BBCC, a laboratory CCDD, and a dome DDEE. The muffle or small oven of baked earth GH (*Fig. 9*) being placed in the laboratory of the furnace upon cross bars of iron, is adjusted to the opening GG, and luted with clay softened in water. The cupels are placed in this oven or muffle, and charcoal is conveyed into the furnace through the openings of the dome and fire-place. The external air enters through the openings of the ash-hole for supporting the combustion, and escapes by the superior opening or chimney at EE; and air is admitted through the door of the muffle GG for oxidating the contained metal.

Very little reflection is sufficient to discover the erroneous principles upon which this furnace is constructed. When the opening GG is shut, the oxidation is produced slowly and with difficulty, for want of air to carry it on; and, when this hole is open, the stream of cold air which is then admitted fixes the metal and obstructs the process. These inconveniences may be easily remedied, by constructing the muffle and furnace in such a manner that a stream of fresh external air should always play upon the surface of the metal, and this air should be made to pass through a pipe of clay kept continually red hot by the fire of the furnace. By this means the inside of the muffle will never be cooled, and processes will be finished in a few minutes which at present require a considerable space of time.

M. Sage remedies these inconveniences in a different manner; he places the cupel containing lead, alloyed with gold or silver, amongst the charcoal of an ordinary furnace and covered by a small porcelain muffle; when the whole is sufficiently heated, he directs the blast of a common pair of hand-bellows upon the surface of the metal and completes the cupellation in this way with great ease and exactness.

Section III *Of Increasing the Action of Fire by Using Oxygen Gas Instead of Atmospheric Air*

By means of large burning glasses, such as those of Tchirnausen and M. de Trudaine, a degree of heat is obtained somewhat greater than has hitherto been produced in chemical furnaces, or even in the ovens of furnaces used for baking hard porcelain. But these instruments are extremely expensive, and do not even produce heat sufficient to melt crude platinum; so that their advantages are by no means sufficient to compensate for the difficulty of procuring, and even of using them. Concave mirrors produce somewhat more effect than burning glasses of the same diameter, as is proved by the experiments of MM. Macquer and Beaumé with the speculum of the Abbé Bouriot; but, as the direction of the reflected rays is necessarily from below upwards, the substance to be operated upon must be placed in the air without any support, which renders most chemical experiments impossible to be performed with this instrument.

For these reasons, I first endeavoured to employ oxygen gas for combustion, by filling large bladders with it, and making it pass through a tube capable of being shut by a stop cock; and in this way I succeeded in causing it to support the combustion of lighted charcoal. The intensity of the heat produced, even in my first attempt, was so great as readily to melt a small quantity of crude platinum. To the success of this attempt is owing the idea of the gazometer, described p. 91 *et seq.*, which I substituted instead of the bladders; and, as we can give the oxygen gas any necessary degree of pressure, we can with this instrument keep up a continued stream and give it even a very considerable force.

The only apparatus necessary for experiments of this kind consists of a small table ABCD (Plate XII, *Fig. 15*), with a hole F, through which passes a tube of copper or silver, ending in a very small opening at G, and capable of being opened or shut by the stop-cock H. This tube is continued below the table at *l m n o* and is connected with the interior cavity of the gazometer. When we mean to operate, a hole of a few lines deep must be made with a chisel in a piece of charcoal, into which the substance to be treated is laid; the charcoal is set on fire by means of a candle and blow-pipe, after which it is exposed to a rapid stream of oxygen gas from the extremity G of the tube FG.

This manner of operating can only be used with such bodies as can be placed, without inconvenience, in contact with charcoal, such as metals, simple earths, &c. But, for bodies whose elements have affinity to charcoal, and which are consequently decomposed by that substance, such as sulphates, phosphates, and most of the neutral salts, metallic glasses, enamels, &c., we must use a lamp and make the stream of oxygen gas pass through its flame. For this purpose, we use the elbowed blow-pipe ST, instead of the bent one FG, employed with charcoal. The heat produced in this second manner is by no means so intense as in the former way and is very difficultly made to melt platinum. In this manner of operating with the lamp, the substances are placed in cupels of calcined bones, or little cups of porcelain, or even in metallic dishes. If these last are sufficiently large, they do not melt, because, metals being good conductors of heat, the caloric spreads rapidly through the whole mass, so that none of its parts are very much heated.

In the *Recueil de l'Académie* for 1782, p. 476, and for 1783, p. 573, the series of experiments I have made with this apparatus may be seen at large. The following are some of the principal results.

1. Rock crystal, or pure silicious earth, is infusible, but becomes capable of being softened or fused when mixed with other substances.

2. Lime, magnesia, and barytes, are infusible, either when alone, or when combined together; but, especially lime, they assist the fusion of every other body.

3. Argill, or pure base of alum, is completely fusible *per se* into a very hard opaque vitreous substance, which scratches glass like the precious stones.

4. All the compound earths and stones are readily fused into a brownish glass.

5. All the saline substances, even fixed alkali, are volatilized in a few seconds.

6. Gold, silver, and probably platinum, are slowly volatilized without any particular phenomenon.

7. All other metallic substances, except mercury, become oxidated, though placed upon charcoal, and burn with different coloured flames and at last dissipate altogether.

8. The metallic oxides likewise all burn with flames. This seems to form a distinctive character for these substances, and even leads me to believe, as was suspected by Bergman, that barytes is a metallic oxide, though we have not hitherto been able to obtain the metal in its pure or reguline state.

9. Some of the precious stones, as rubies, are capable of being softened and soldered together, without injuring their colour or even diminishing their weights. The hyacinth, tho' almost equally fixed with the ruby, loses its colour very readily. The Saxon and Brazilian topaz, and the Brazilian ruby, lose their colour very quickly and lose about a fifth of their weight, leaving a white earth, resembling white quartz or unglazed china. The emerald, chrysolite, and garnet, are almost instantly melted into an opaque and coloured glass.

10. The diamond presents a property peculiar to itself; it burns in the same manner with combustible bodies and is entirely dissipated.

There is yet another manner of employing oxygen gas for considerably increasing the force of fire, by using it to blow a furnace. M. Achard first conceived this idea; but the process he employed, by which he thought to dephlogisticate, as it is called, atmospheric air, or to deprive it of azotic gas, is absolutely unsatisfactory. I propose to construct a very simple furnace for this purpose, of very refractory earth, similar to the one represented Plate XIII, *Fig. 4*, but smaller in all its dimensions. It is to have two openings, as at E, through one of which the nozzle of a pair of bellows is to pass, by which the heat is to be raised as high as possible with common air; after which, the stream of common air from the bellows being suddenly stopped, oxygen gas is to be admitted by a tube at the other opening, communicating with a gazometer having the pressure of four or five inches of water. I can in this manner unite the oxygen gas from several gazometers, so as to make eight or nine cubic feet of gas pass through the furnace; and in this way I expect to produce a heat greatly more intense than any hitherto known. The upper orifice of the furnace must be carefully made of considerable dimensions, that the caloric produced may have free issue, lest the too sudden expansion of that highly elastic fluid should produce a dangerous explosion.

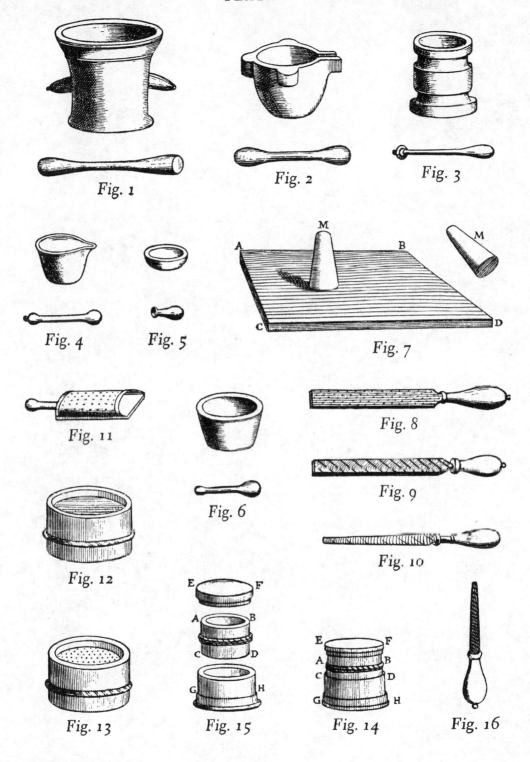

PLATE I

Fig. 1

Fig. 2

Fig. 3

Fig. 4

Fig. 5

Fig. 7

Fig. 11

Fig. 6

Fig. 8

Fig. 9

Fig. 10

Fig. 12

Fig. 13

Fig. 15

Fig. 14

Fig. 16

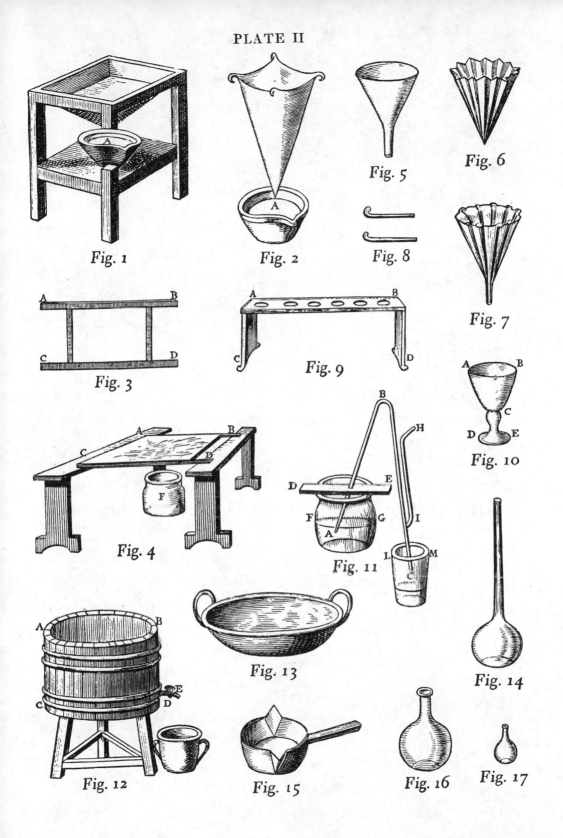

PLATE II

Fig. 1

Fig. 2

Fig. 5

Fig. 6

Fig. 3

Fig. 9

Fig. 7

Fig. 8

Fig. 4

Fig. 11

Fig. 10

Fig. 13

Fig. 14

Fig. 12

Fig. 15

Fig. 16

Fig. 17

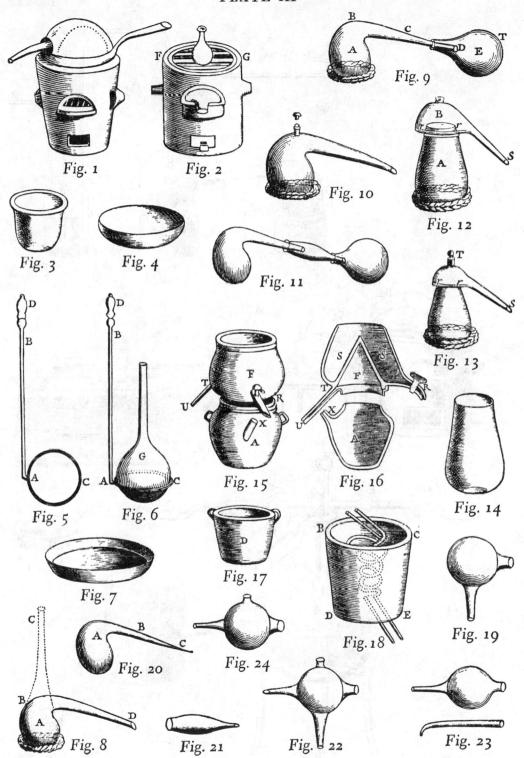

PLATE III

Fig. 1

Fig. 2

Fig. 9

Fig. 10

Fig. 12

Fig. 3

Fig. 4

Fig. 11

Fig. 13

Fig. 5

Fig. 6

Fig. 15

Fig. 16

Fig. 14

Fig. 7

Fig. 17

Fig. 18

Fig. 19

Fig. 20

Fig. 24

Fig. 8

Fig. 21

Fig. 22

Fig. 23

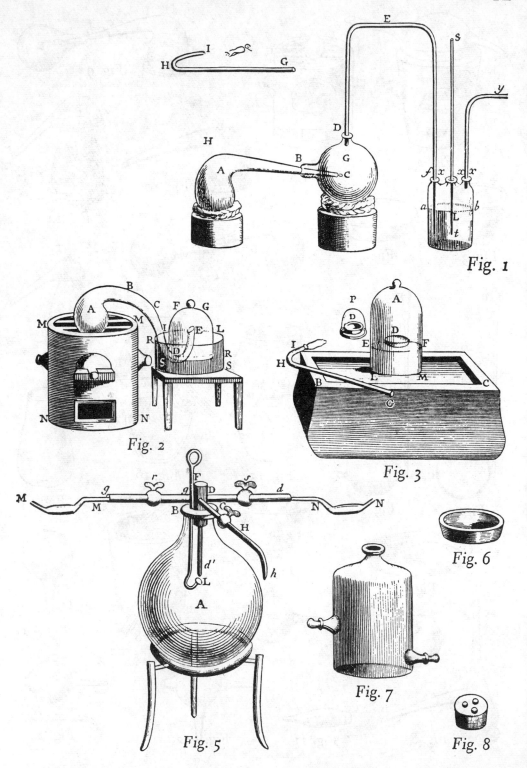

Fig. 1

Fig. 2

Fig. 3

Fig. 5

Fig. 6

Fig. 7

Fig. 8

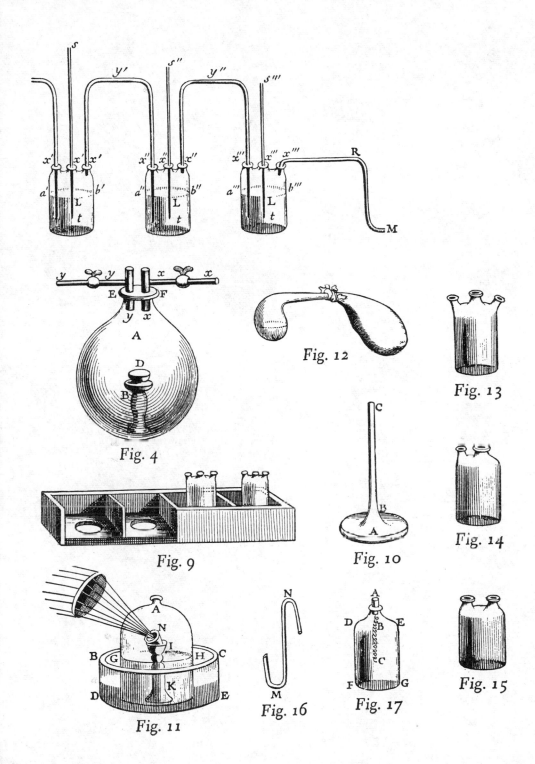

Fig. 12

Fig. 13

Fig. 4

Fig. 9

Fig. 10

Fig. 14

Fig. 11

Fig. 16

Fig. 17

Fig. 15

PLATE V

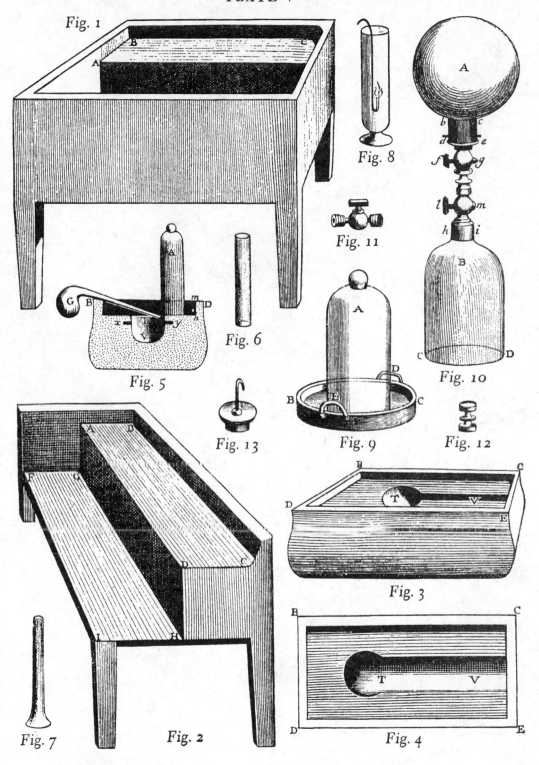

Fig. 1

Fig. 8

A

b c
d e
f g

l m
h i

B

C D

Fig. 10

G B
x y
A
V
m
D
n

Fig. 5

Fig. 6

Fig. 11

A

B E C

Fig. 9

Fig. 13

Fig. 12

A D

F G

D C

I H

Fig. 7

Fig. 2

B C
D T V E

Fig. 3

B C
T V
D E

Fig. 4

PLATE VI

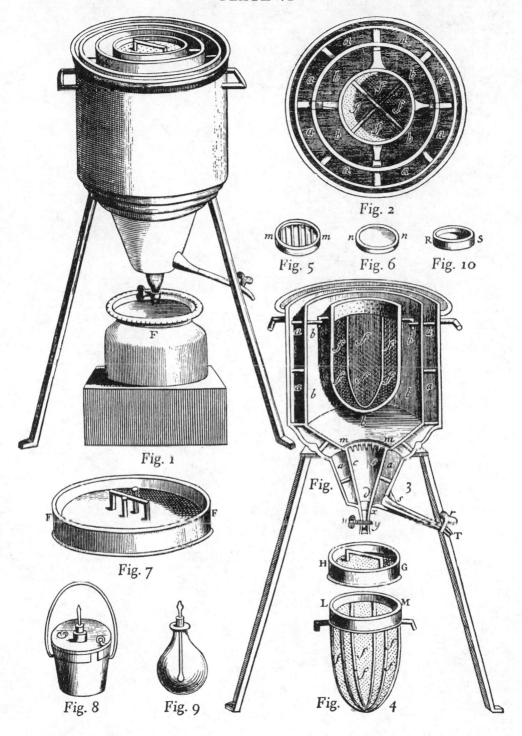

Fig. 2

Fig. 5   Fig. 6   Fig. 10

Fig. 1

Fig. 7

Fig. 3

Fig. 8   Fig. 9   Fig. 4

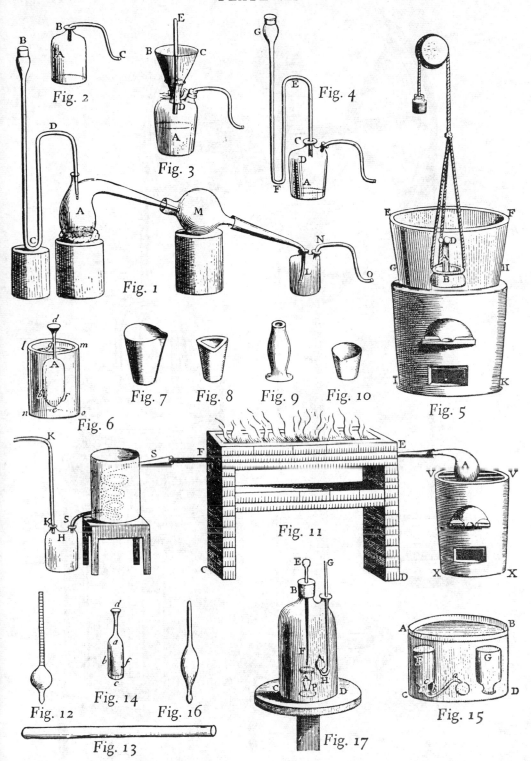

PLATE VII

Fig. 2

Fig. 3

Fig. 4

Fig. 1

Fig. 5

Fig. 6

Fig. 7

Fig. 8

Fig. 9

Fig. 10

Fig. 11

Fig. 12

Fig. 14

Fig. 16

Fig. 13

Fig. 17

Fig. 15

PLATE VIII

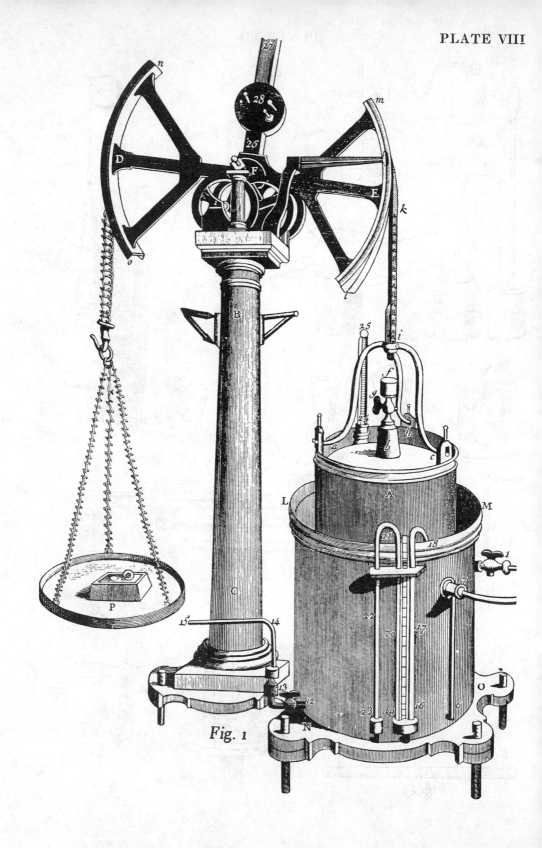

Fig. 1

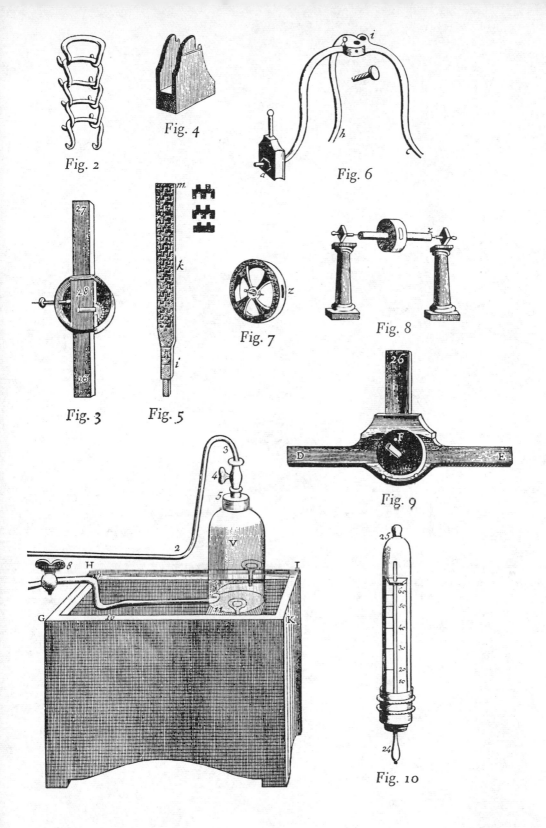

Fig. 2

Fig. 4

Fig. 6

Fig. 3

Fig. 5

Fig. 7

Fig. 8

Fig. 9

Fig. 10

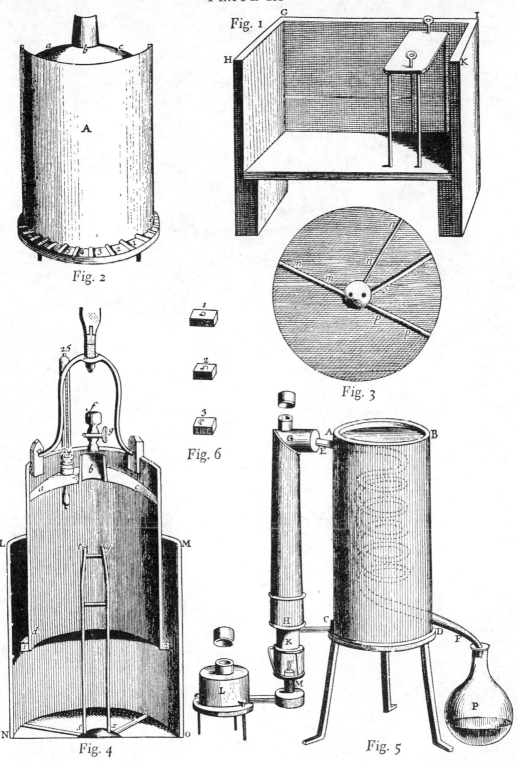

PLATE IX

Fig. 1

Fig. 2

Fig. 3

Fig. 4

Fig. 5

Fig. 6

PLATE X

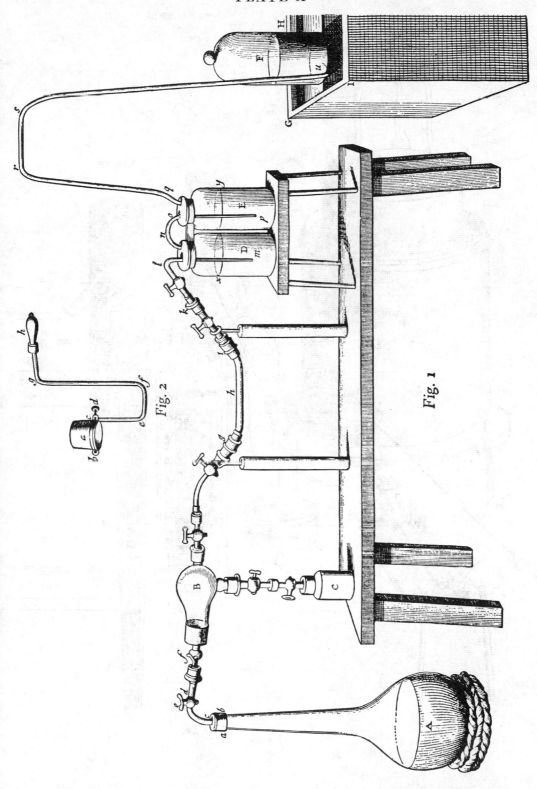

Fig. 1

Fig. 2

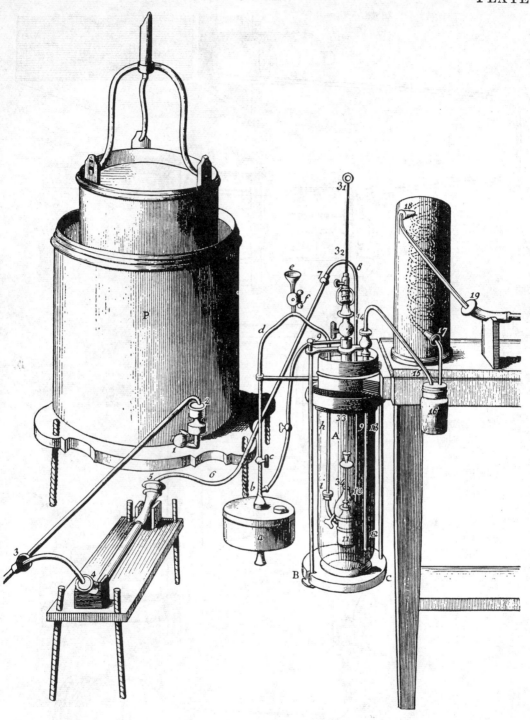

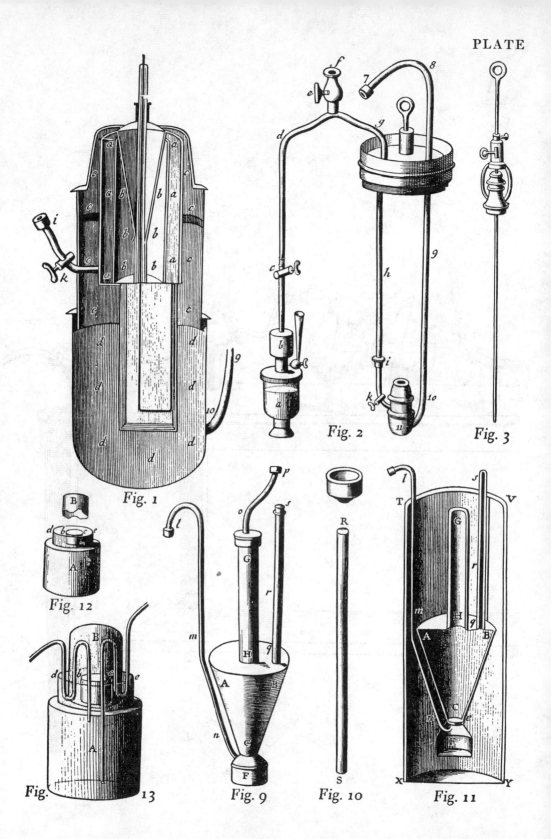

PLATE

Fig. 1

Fig. 2

Fig. 3

Fig. 12

Fig. 13

Fig. 9

Fig. 10

Fig. 11

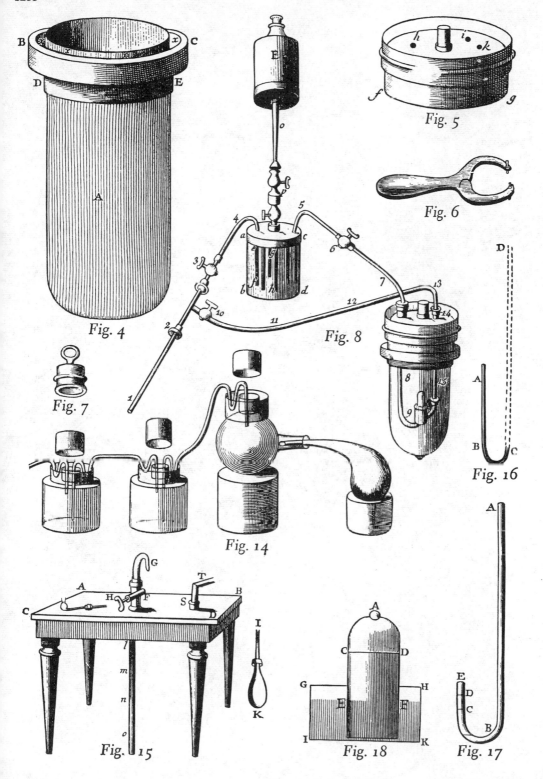

Fig. 4

Fig. 5

Fig. 6

Fig. 7

Fig. 8

Fig. 14

Fig. 15

Fig. 16

Fig. 17

Fig. 18

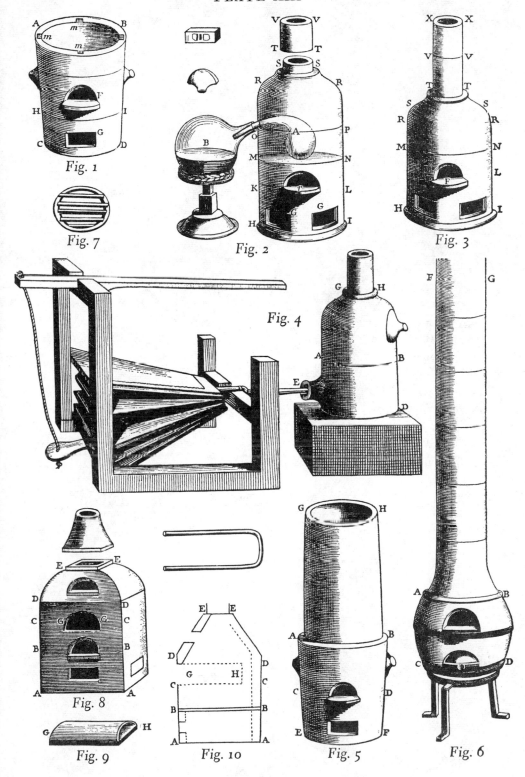

PLATE XIII

Fig. 1

Fig. 7

Fig. 2

Fig. 3

Fig. 4

Fig. 8

Fig. 9

Fig. 10

Fig. 5

Fig. 6

THEORY OF HEAT

BIOGRAPHICAL NOTE
Joseph Fourier, 1768-1830

Fourier was born at Auxerre March 21, 1768, the son of a poor tailor. An orphan at eight, he was recommended by a friend to the Bishop of Auxerre, who obtained admission for him in the local military school conducted by the Benedictines of Saint-Maur. He quickly distinguished himself as a student and showed distinct literary ability; at twelve he was writing sermons which were often used with great effect in Paris. At the age of thirteen mathematics began to attract him strongly. The prescribed hours of study did not suffice; he arose at night, concealed himself behind a screen, and by the light of candle-ends carefully collected during the day, pursued his mathematical studies. When he was twenty-one he delivered his first memoir before the Academy of Sciences on the resolution of numerical equations of all degrees.

Educated by monks in a military school, Fourier seems to have considered that only the army or the church could provide a career. With a strong recommendation from Legendre he applied for admission to the artillery. He was refused with the statement, "Fourier, not being of noble birth, cannot enter the artillery, not even if he is a second Newton." He then entered the Benedictine Order, where he remained as a novice from 1787 to 1789. Upon the outbreak of the Revolution he left the convent, although this did not result in any break with the Benedictines, since they immediately appointed him to the principal chair of mathematics at their school in Auxerre. When his colleagues became ill, he took their place, and besides teaching mathematics he also lectured on rhetoric, history, and philosophy.

At Auxerre, Fourier embraced the cause of the Revolution, joined the peoples' party, and served as publicist, recruiting agent, and member of the Citizens' Committee of Surveillance; in this last function he exercised such moderation that he was himself in danger from the Terror. When, in 1794, the Normal School was instituted at Paris to train a specially selected group of new teachers, Fourier was among the fifteen hundred that were chosen, and, although he began as a student, he was soon made a "master of conference." The school failed after a short time, but Fourier had so impressed the authorities that when the Polytechnic School was founded, he was appointed to its faculty, first as "superintendent of lectures on fortification" and then as "lecturer on analysis."

Napoleon sometimes attended the sessions at the Polytechnic School, and when he organized the expedition to Egypt in 1798, Fourier was asked to be a part of it, although he was not informed of the role he was expected to play. Fourier was in Egypt for three years, engaged in the most varied activities: organizing factories for the army, constructing machines, leading scientific expeditions, and executing numerous administrative tasks. He acted as the representative of the general-in-chief, receiving complaints from the Egyptian populace, and for one period was virtually governor of half of Egypt. On the death of General Kléber he was called upon to present a eulogy before the French Army. As secretary of the Institute of Cairo he instigated the collection of materials for the famous *Description of Egypt*. In collaboration with Napoleon he wrote the historical introduction to this work, which established his literary reputation and eventually won him membership in the French Academy.

On his return to France in 1802 Fourier was appointed prefect of the Département of Isère and for the next thirteen years lived at Grenoble. He composed the disputes between the different parties and brought order out of the confusion left by the Revolution in his province. As part of a general policy of public improvements, he initiated an extensive road-building project and undertook the reclamation of marsh-lands which had been the source of infection for thirty-seven communes. In recognition of his services he was created Baron of the Empire in 1808.

His many administrative duties as prefect of Isère did not interrupt his work as a mathematician and man of letters. He conducted investigations into the motions of heat in solid bodies with the aim of reducing them to mathematical formulation, and in 1807 submitted his first paper on the subject to the Academy of Sciences. To induce the author to extend and improve his researches the Academy assigned as the problem for its prize competition of 1812, "The mathematical theory of the laws of the propagation of heat and the comparison of the results of this theory with exact experiment." The judges were Laplace, Lagrange, and Legendre, and they awarded the prize to Fourier for his memoir in two parts, *Théorie des mouvements de la chaleur dans les corps solides*. The first part was republished in 1822 as the *Théorie Analytique de la Chaleur*.

Fourier continued to hold his position as prefect through the Revolution of 1814, but Napoleon's return from Elba proved to be his political downfall. As Napoleon was approaching Grenoble, Fourier went to Lyons to notify the Bourbons that the city would undoubtedly capitulate. They refused to believe him and made him responsible for the safety of the city. Upon his return to Grenoble, which had surrendered, he was taken prisoner and brought before the Emperor. Napoleon confronted him: "You also have declared war against me? . . . It only grieves me to see among my enemies an *Egyptian*, a man who has eaten along with me the bread of the bivouac, an old friend. How, moreover, could you have forgotten, Monsieur Fourier, that I have made you what you are?" Fourier's loyalty was re-established, although he did not share Napoleon's confidence of victory. The end of the Hundred Days and the Restoration found him deprived of political office, in disgrace, and almost penniless.

A friend and former pupil who was prefect of Paris made it possible for him to become Director of the Bureau of Statistics, which he remained until his death. His political past, however, did not prevent renewed recognition of his scientific abilities. In 1816 he was proposed for membership in the Academy of Sciences, and although Louis XVIII refused his consent at that time, he became a member the following year. He was made permanent secretary of the Division of Mathematical Sciences in 1822, member of the French Academy in 1826, and a year later succeeded Laplace as President of the Council for Improving the Polytechnic School. In 1828 he became a member of the government commission established for the encouragement of literature.

He died May 16, 1830, of aneurism of the heart, which had been aggravated by his habit of wrapping himself in all seasons like "an Egyptian mummy" and living in airless rooms at an excessively high temperature.

CONTENTS

CHAPTER II. EQUATIONS OF THE MOVEMENT OF HEAT

PRELIMINARY DISCOURSE

PRIMARY causes are unknown to us; but are subject to simple and constant laws, which may be discovered by observation, the study of them being the object of natural philosophy.

Heat, like gravity, penetrates every substance of the universe, its rays occupy all parts of space. The object of our work is to set forth the mathematical laws which this element obeys. The theory of heat will hereafter form one of the most important branches of general physics.

The knowledge of rational mechanics, which the most ancient nations had been able to acquire, has not come down to us, and the history of this science, if we except the first theorems in harmony, is not traced up beyond the discoveries of Archimedes. This great geometer explained the mathematical principles of the equilibrium of solids and fluids. About eighteen centuries elapsed before Galileo, the originator of dynamical theories, discovered the laws of motion of heavy bodies. Within this new science Newton comprised the whole system of the universe. The successors of these philosophers have extended these theories, and given them an admirable perfection: they have taught us that the most diverse phenomena are subject to a small number of fundamental laws which are reproduced in all the acts of nature. It is recognised that the same principles regulate all the movements of the stars, their form, the inequalities of their courses, the equilibrium and the oscillations of the seas, the harmonic vibrations of air and sonorous bodies, the transmission of light, capillary actions, the undulations of fluids, in fine the most complex effects of all the natural forces, and thus has the thought of Newton been confirmed: *quod tam paucis tam multa præstet geometria gloriatur.*

But whatever may be the range of mechanical theories, they do not apply to the effects of heat. These make up a special order of phenomena, which cannot be explained by the principles of motion and equilibrium. We have for a long time been in possession of ingenious instruments adapted to measure many of these effects; valuable observations have been collected; but in this manner partial results only have become known, and not the mathematical demonstration of the laws which include them all.

I have deduced these laws from prolonged study and attentive comparison of the facts known up to this time: all these facts I have observed afresh in the course of several years with the most exact instruments that have hitherto been used.

To found the theory, it was in the first place necessary to distinguish and define with precision the elementary properties which determine the action of heat. I then perceived that all the phenomena which depend on this action re-solve themselves into a very small number of general and simple facts; where-by every physical problem of this kind is brought back to an investigation of mathematical analysis. From these general facts I have concluded that to de-termine numerically the most varied movements of heat, it is sufficient to sub-mit each substance to three fundamental observations. Different bodies in fact do not possess in the same degree the power to *contain* heat, *to receive or trans-mit it across their surfaces*, nor to *conduct* it through the interior of their masses. These are the three specific qualities which our theory clearly distinguishes and shews how to measure.

It is easy to judge how much these researches concern the physical sciences and civil economy, and what may be their influence on the progress of the arts which require the employment and distribution of heat. They have also a necessary connection with the system of the world, and their relations become known when we consider the grand phenomena which take place near the sur-face of the terrestrial globe.

In fact. the radiation of the sun in which this planet is incessantly plunged, penetrates the air, the earth, and the waters; its elements are divided, change in direction every way, and, penetrating the mass of the globe, would raise its mean temperature more and more, if the heat acquired were not exactly bal-anced by that which escapes in rays from all points of the surface and expands through the sky.

Different climates, unequally exposed to the action of solar heat, have, after an immense time, acquired the temperatures proper to their situation. This effect is modified by several accessory causes, such as elevation, the form of the ground, the neighbourhood and extent of continents and seas, the state of the surface, the direction of the winds.

The succession of day and night, the alternations of the seasons occasion in the solid earth periodic variations, which are repeated every day or every year: but these changes become less and less sensible as the point at which they are measured recedes from the surface. No diurnal variation can be detected at the depth of about three metres [ten feet]; and the annual variations cease to be appreciable at a depth much less than sixty metres. The temperature at great depths is then sensibly fixed at a given place: but it is not the same at all points of the same meridian; in general it rises as the equator is approached.

The heat which the sun has communicated to the terrestrial globe, and which has produced the diversity of climates, is now subject to a movement which has become uniform. It advances within the interior of the mass which it penetrates throughout, and at the same time recedes from the plane of the equator, and proceeds to lose itself across the polar regions.

In the higher regions of the atmosphere the air is very rare and transparent, and retains but a minute part of the heat of the solar rays: this is the cause of the excessive cold of elevated places. The lower layers, denser and more heat-ed by the land and water, expand and rise up: they are cooled by the very fact of expansion. The great movements of the air, such as the trade winds which blow between the tropics, are not determined by the attractive forces of the moon and sun. The action of these celestial bodies produces scarcely percepti-ble oscillations in a fluid so rare and at so great a distance. It is the changes of temperature which periodically displace every part of the atmosphere.

The waters of the ocean are differently exposed at their surface to the rays of the sun, and the bottom of the basin which contains them is heated very unequally from the poles to the equator. These two causes, ever present, and combined with gravity and the centrifugal force, keep up vast movements in the interior of the seas. They displace and mingle all the parts, and produce those general and regular currents which navigators have noticed.

Radiant heat which escapes from the surface of all bodies, and traverses elastic media, or spaces void of air, has special laws, and occurs with widely varied phenomena. The physical explanation of many of these facts is already known; the mathematical theory which I have formed gives an exact measure of them. It consists, in a manner, in a new catoptrics which has its own theorems, and serves to determine by analysis all the effects of heat direct or reflected.

The enumeration of the chief objects of the theory sufficiently shews the nature of the questions which I have proposed to myself. What are the elementary properties which it is requisite to observe in each substance, and what are the experiments most suitable to determine them exactly? If the distribution of heat in solid matter is regulated by constant laws, what is the mathematical expression of those laws, and by what analysis may we derive from this expression the complete solution of the principal problems? Why do terrestrial temperatures cease to be variable at a depth so small with respect to the radius of the earth? Every inequality in the movement of this planet necessarily occasioning an oscillation of the solar heat beneath the surface, what relation is there between the duration of its period, and the depth at which the temperatures become constant?

What time must have elapsed before the climates could acquire the different temperatures which they now maintain; and what are the different causes which can now vary their mean heat? Why do not the annual changes alone in the distance of the sun from the earth, produce at the surface of the earth very considerable changes in the temperatures?

From what characteristic can we ascertain that the earth has not entirely lost its original heat; and what are the exact laws of the loss?

If, as several observations indicate, this fundamental heat is not wholly dissipated, it must be immense at great depths, and nevertheless it has no sensible influence at the present time on the mean temperature of the climates. The effects which are observed in them are due to the action of the solar rays. But independently of these two sources of heat, the one fundamental and primitive proper to the terrestrial globe, the other due to the presence of the sun, is there not a more universal cause, which determines *the temperature of the heavens*, in that part of space which the solar system now occupies? Since the observed facts necessitate this cause, what are the consequences of an exact theory in this entirely new question; how shall we be able to determine that constant value of *the temperature of space*, and deduce from it the temperature which belongs to each planet?

To these questions must be added others which depend on the properties of radiant heat. The physical cause of the reflection of cold, that is to say the reflection of a lesser degree of heat, is very distinctly known; but what is the mathematical expression of this effect?

On what general principles do the atmospheric temperatures depend, whether the thermometer which measures them receives the solar rays directly, on a surface metallic or unpolished, or whether this instrument remains exposed, during the night, under a sky free from clouds, to contact with the air.

to radiation from terrestrial bodies, and to that from the most distant and coldest parts of the atmosphere?

The intensity of the rays which escape from a point on the surface of any heated body varying with their inclination according to a law which experiments have indicated, is there not a necessary mathematical relation between this law and the general fact of the equilibrium of heat; and what is the physical cause of this inequality in intensity?

Lastly, when heat penetrates fluid masses, and determines in them internal movements by continual changes of the temperature and density of each molecule, can we still express, by differential equations, the laws of such a compound effect; and what is the resulting change in the general equations of hydrodynamics?

Such are the chief problems which I have solved, and which have never yet been submitted to calculation. If we consider further the manifold relations of this mathematical theory to civil uses and the technical arts, we shall recognize completely the extent of its applications. It is evident that it includes an entire series of distinct phenomena, and that the study of it cannot be omitted without losing a notable part of the science of nature.

The principles of the theory are derived, as are those of rational mechanics, from a very small number of primary facts, the causes of which are not considered by geometers, but which they admit as the results of common observations confirmed by all experiment.

The differential equations of the propagation of heat express the most general conditions, and reduce the physical questions to problems of pure analysis, and this is the proper object of theory. They are not less rigorously established than the general equations of equilibrium and motion. In order to make this comparison more perceptible, we have always preferred demonstrations analogous to those of the theorems which serve as the foundation of statics and dynamics. These equations still exist, but receive a different form, when they express the distribution of luminous heat in transparent bodies, or the movements which the changes of temperature and density occasion in the interior of fluids. The coefficients which they contain are subject to variations whose exact measure is not yet known, but in all the natural problems which it most concerns us to consider, the limits of temperature differ so little that we may omit the variations of these coefficients.

The equations of the movement of heat, like those which express the vibrations of sonorous bodies, or the ultimate oscillations of liquids, belong to one of the most recently discovered branches of analysis, which it is very important to perfect. After having established these differential equations their integrals must be obtained; this process consists in passing from a common expression to a particular solution subject to all the given conditions. This difficult investigation requires a special analysis founded on new theorems, whose object we could not in this place make known. The method which is derived from them leaves nothing vague and indeterminate in the solutions, it leads them up to the final numerical applications, a necessary condition of every investigation, without which we should only arrive at useless transformations.

The same theorems which have made known to us the equations of the movement of heat, apply directly to certain problems of general analysis and dynamics whose solution has for a long time been desired.

Profound study of nature is the most fertile source of mathematical discoveries. Not only has this study, in offering a determinate object to investigation, the advantage of excluding vague questions and calculations without issue; it is besides a sure method of forming analysis itself, and of discovering the elements which it concerns us to know, and which natural science ought always to preserve: these are the fundamental elements which are reproduced in all natural effects.

We see, for example, that the same expression whose abstract properties geometers had considered, and which in this respect belongs to general analysis, represents as well the motion of light in the atmosphere, as it determines the laws of diffusion of heat in solid matter, and enters into all the chief problems of the theory of probability.

The analytical equations, unknown to the ancient geometers, which Descartes was the first to introduce into the study of curves and surfaces, are not restricted to the properties of figures, and to those properties which are the object of rational mechanics; they extend to all general phenomena. There cannot be a language more universal and more simple, more free from errors and from obscurities, that is to say more worthy to express the invariable relations of natural things.

Considered from this point of view, mathematical analysis is as extensive as nature itself; it defines all perceptible relations, measures times, spaces, forces, temperatures; this difficult science is formed slowly, but it preserves every principle which it has once acquired; it grows and strengthens itself incessantly in the midst of the many variations and errors of the human mind.

Its chief attribute is clearness; it has no marks to express confused notions. It brings together phenomena the most diverse, and discovers the hidden analogies which unite them. If matter escapes us, as that of air and light, by its extreme tenuity, if bodies are placed far from us in the immensity of space, if man wishes to know the aspect of the heavens at successive epochs separated by a great number of centuries, if the actions of gravity and of heat are exerted in the interior of the earth at depths which will be always inaccessible, mathematical analysis can yet lay hold of the laws of these phenomena. It makes them present and measurable, and seems to be a faculty of the human mind destined to supplement the shortness of life and the imperfection of the senses; and what is still more remarkable, it follows the same course in the study of all phenomena; it interprets them by the same language, as if to attest the unity and simplicity of the plan of the universe, and to make still more evident that unchangeable order which presides over all natural causes.

The problems of the theory of heat present so many examples of the simple and constant dispositions which spring from the general laws of nature; and if the order which is established in these phenomena could be grasped by our senses, it would produce in us an impression comparable to the sensation of musical sound.

The forms of bodies are infinitely varied; the distribution of the heat which penetrates them seems to be arbitrary and confused; but all the inequalities are rapidly cancelled and disappear as time passes on. The progress of the phenomenon becomes more regular and simpler, remains finally subject to a definite law which is the same in all cases, and which bears no sensible impress of the initial arrangement.

All observation confirms these consequences. The analysis from which they are derived separates and expresses clearly: first, the general conditions, that is to say those which spring from the natural properties of heat; second, the effect, accidental but continued, of the form or state of the surfaces; third, the effect, not permanent, of the primitive distribution.

In this work we have demonstrated all the principles of the theory of heat, and solved all the fundamental problems. They could have been explained more concisely by omitting the simpler problems, and presenting in the first instance the most general results; but we wished to shew the actual origin of the theory and its gradual progress. When this knowledge has been acquired and the principles thoroughly fixed, it is preferable to employ at once the most extended analytical methods, as we have done in the later investigations. This is also the course which we shall hereafter follow in the memoirs which will be added to this work, and which will form in some manner its complement; and by this means we shall have reconciled, so far as it can depend on ourselves, the necessary development of principles with the precision which becomes the applications of analysis.

The subjects of these memoirs will be, the theory of radiant heat, the problem of the terrestrial temperatures, that of the temperature of dwellings, the comparison of theoretic results with those which we have observed in different experiments, lastly the demonstrations of the differential equations of the movement of heat in fluids.

The work which we now publish has been written a long time since; different circumstances have delayed and often interrupted the printing of it. In this interval, science has been enriched by important observations; the principles of our analysis, which had not at first been grasped, have become better known; the results which we had deduced from them have been discussed and confirmed. We ourselves have applied these principles to new problems, and have changed the form of some of the proofs. The delays of publication will have contributed to make the work clearer and more complete.

The subject of our first analytical investigations on the transfer of heat was its distribution amongst separated masses; these have been preserved in Chapter IV, Section II. The problems relative to continuous bodies, which form the theory rightly so called, were solved many years afterwards; this theory was explained for the first time in a manuscript work forwarded to the Institute of France at the end of the year 1807, an extract from which was published in the *Bulletin des Sciences* (*Société Philomatique*, year 1808, page 112). We added to this memoir, and successively forwarded very extensive notes, concerning the convergence of series, the diffusion of heat in an infinite prism, its emission in spaces void of air, the constructions suitable for exhibiting the chief theorems, and the analysis of the periodic movement at the surface of the earth. Our second memoir, on the propagation of heat, was deposited in the archives of the Institute, on the 28th of September, 1811. It was formed out of the preceding memoir and the notes already sent in; the geometrical constructions and those details of analysis which had no necessary relation to the physical problem were omitted, and to it was added the general equation which expresses the state of the surface. This second work was sent to press in the course of 1821, to be inserted in the collection of the Academy of Sciences. It is printed without any change or addition; the text agrees literally with the deposited manuscript, which forms part of the archives of the Institute.

In this memoir, and in the writings which preceded it, will be found a first explanation of applications which our actual work does not contain: they will be treated in the subsequent memoirs at greater length, and, if it be in our power, with greater clearness. The results of our labours concerning the same problems are also indicated in several articles already published. The extract inserted in the *Annales de Chimie et de Physique* shews the aggregate of our researches (Vol. III, page 350, year 1816). We published in the *Annales* two separate notes, concerning radiant heat (Vol. IV, page 128, year 1817, and Vol. VI, page 259, year 1817).

Several other articles of the same collection present the most constant results of theory and observation; the utility and the extent of thermological knowledge could not be better appreciated than by the celebrated editors of the *Annales*.[1]

In the *Bulletin des Sciences* (*Société philomatique* year 1818, page 1, and year 1820, page 60) will be found an extract from a memoir on the constant or variable temperature of dwellings, and an explanation of the chief consequences of our analysis of the terrestrial temperatures.

M. Alexandre de Humboldt, whose researches embrace all the great problems of natural philosophy, has considered the observations of the temperatures proper to the different climates from a novel and very important point of view (Memoir on Isothermal lines, *Société d'Arcueil*, Vol. III, page 462); (Memoir on the inferior limit of perpetual snow, *Annales de Chimie et de Physique*, Vol. V, page 102, year 1817).

As to the differential equations of the movement of heat in fluids mention has been made of them in the annual history of the Academy of Sciences. The extract from our memoir shews clearly its object and principle. (*Analyse des travaux de l'Académie des Sciences*, by M. De Lambre, year 1820.)

The examination of the repulsive forces produced by heat, which determine the statical properties of gases, does not belong to the analytical subject which we have considered. This question connected with the theory of radiant heat has just been discussed by the illustrious author of the *Mécanique céleste*, to whom all the chief branches of mathematical analysis owe important discoveries. (*Connaissance des Temps*, years 1824-5.)

The new theories explained in our work are united for ever to the mathematical sciences, and rest like them on invariable foundations; all the elements which they at present possess they will preserve, and will continually acquire greater extent. Instruments will be perfected and experiments multiplied. The analysis which we have formed will be deduced from more general, that is to say, more simple and more fertile methods common to many classes of phenomena. For all substances, solid or liquid, for vapours and permanent gases, determinations will be made of all the specific qualities relating to heat, and of the variations of the coefficients which express them. At different stations on the earth observations will be made, of the temperatures of the ground at different depths, of the intensity of the solar heat and its effects, constant or variable, in the atmosphere, in the ocean and in lakes; and the constant temperature of the heavens proper to the planetary regions will become known. The theory itself will direct all these measures, and assign their precision. No considerable progress can hereafter be made which is not founded on experiments such as these; for mathematical analysis can deduce from general and simple phenomena the expression of the laws of nature; but the special application of these laws to very complex effects demands a long series of exact observations.

[1]Gay-Lussac and Arago.

FIRST CHAPTER

INTRODUCTION

SECTION I. *Statement of the Object of the Work*

1. THE effects of heat are subject to constant laws which cannot be discovered without the aid of mathematical analysis. The object of the theory which we are about to explain is to demonstrate these laws; it reduces all physical researches on the propagation of heat, to problems of the integral calculus whose elements are given by experiment. No subject has more extensive relations with the progress of industry and the natural sciences; for the action of heat is always present, it penetrates all bodies and spaces, it influences the processes of the arts, and occurs in all the phenomena of the universe.

When heat is unequally distributed among the different parts of a solid mass, it tends to attain equilibrium, and passes slowly from the parts which are more heated to those which are less; and at the same time it is dissipated at the surface, and lost in the medium or in the void. The tendency to uniform distribution and the spontaneous emission which acts at the surface of bodies, change continually the temperature at their different points. The problem of the propagation of heat consists in determining what is the temperature at each point of a body at a given instant, supposing that the initial temperatures are known. The following examples will more clearly make known the nature of these problems.

2. If we expose to the continued and uniform action of a source of heat, the same part of a metallic ring, whose diameter is large, the molecules nearest to the source will be first heated, and, after a certain time, every point of the solid will have acquired very nearly the highest temperature which it can attain. This limit or greatest temperature is not the same at different points; it becomes less and less according as they become more distant from that point at which the source of heat is directly applied.

When the temperatures have become permanent, the source of heat supplies, at each instant, a quantity of heat which exactly compensates for that which is dissipated at all the points of the external surface of the ring.

If now the source be suppressed, heat will continue to be propagated in the interior of the solid, but that which is lost in the medium or the void, will no longer be compensated as formerly by the supply from the source, so that all the temperatures will vary and diminish incessantly until they have become equal to the temperatures of the surrounding medium.

3. Whilst the temperatures are permanent and the source remains, if at every point of the mean circumference of the ring an ordinate be raised perpendicular to the plane of the ring, whose length is proportional to the fixed temperature at that point, the curved line which passes through the ends of these ordinates will represent the permanent state of the temperatures, and it is very easy to determine by analysis the nature of this line. It is to be remarked

that the thickness of the ring is supposed to be sufficiently small for the temperature to be sensibly equal at all points of the same section perpendicular to the mean circumference. When the source is removed, the line which bounds the ordinates proportional to the temperatures at the different points will change its form continually. The problem consists in expressing, by one equation, the variable form of this curve, and in thus including in a single formula all the successive states of the solid.

4. Let z be the constant temperature at a point m of the mean circumference, x the distance of this point from the source, that is to say the length of the arc of the mean circumference, included between the point m and the point o which corresponds to the position of the source; z is the highest temperature which the point m can attain by virtue of the constant action of the source, and this permanent temperature z is a function $f(x)$ of the distance x. The first part of the problem consists in determining the function $f(x)$ which represents the permanent state of the solid.

Consider next the variable state which succeeds to the former state as soon as the source has been removed; denote by t the time which has passed since the suppression of the source, and by v the value of the temperature at the point m after the time t. The quantity v will be a certain function $F(x, t)$ of the distance x and the time t; the object of the problem is to discover this function $F(x, t)$, of which we only know as yet that the initial value is $f(x)$, so that we ought to have the equation $f(x) = F(x, O)$.

5. If we place a solid homogeneous mass, having the form of a sphere or cube, in a medium maintained at a constant temperature, and if it remains immersed for a very long time, it will acquire at all its points a temperature differing very little from that of the fluid. Suppose the mass to be withdrawn in order to transfer it to a cooler medium, heat will begin to be dissipated at its surface; the temperatures at different points of the mass will not be sensibly the same, and if we suppose it divided into an infinity of layers by surfaces parallel to its external surface, each of those layers will transmit, at each instant, a certain quantity of heat to the layer which surrounds it. If it be imagined that each molecule carries a separate thermometer, which indicates its temperature at every instant, the state of the solid will from time to time be represented by the variable system of all these thermometric heights. It is required to express the successive states by analytical formulæ, so that we may know at any given instant the temperatures indicated by each thermometer, and compare the quantities of heat which flow during the same instant, between two adjacent layers, or into the surrounding medium.

6. If the mass is spherical, and we denote by x the distance of a point of this mass from the centre of the sphere, by t the time which has elapsed since the commencement of the cooling, and by v the variable temperature of the point m, it is easy to see that all points situated at the same distance x from the centre of the sphere have the same temperature v. This quantity v is a certain function $F(x, t)$ of the radius x and of the time t; it must be such that it becomes constant whatever be the value of x, when we suppose t to be nothing; for by hypothesis, the temperature at all points is the same at the moment of emersion. The problem consists in determining that function of x and t which expresses the value of v.

7. In the next place it is to be remarked, that during the cooling, a certain quantity of heat escapes, at each instant, through the external surface, and

passes into the medium. The value of this quantity is not constant; it is greatest at the beginning of the cooling. If however we consider the variable state of the internal spherical surface whose radius is x, we easily see that there must be at each instant a certain quantity of heat which traverses that surface, and passes through that part of the mass which is more distant from the centre. This continuous flow of heat is variable like that through the external surface, and both are quantities comparable with each other; their ratios are numbers whose varying values are functions of the distance x, and of the time t which has elapsed. It is required to determine these functions.

8. If the mass, which has been heated by a long immersion in a medium, and whose rate of cooling we wish to calculate, is of cubical form, and if we determine the position of each point m by three rectangular co-ordinates x, y, z, taking for origin the centre of the cube, and for axes lines perpendicular to the faces, we see that the temperature v of the point m after the time t, is a function of the four variables x, y, z, and t. The quantities of heat which flow out at each instant through the whole external surface of the solid, are variable and comparable with each other; their ratios are analytical functions depending on the time t, the expression of which must be assigned.

9. Let us examine also the case in which a rectangular prism of sufficiently great thickness and of infinite length, being submitted at its extremity to a constant temperature, whilst the air which surrounds it is maintained at a less temperature, has at last arrived at a fixed state which it is required to determine. All the points of the extreme section at the base of the prism have, by hypothesis, a common and permanent temperature. It is not the same with a section distant from the source of heat; each of the points of this rectangular surface parallel to the base has acquired a fixed temperature, but this is not the same at different points of the same section, and must be less at points nearer to the surface exposed to the air. We see also that, at each instant, there flows across a given section a certain quantity of heat, which always remains the same, since the state of the solid has become constant. The problem consists in determining the permanent temperature at any given point of the solid, and the whole quantity of heat which, in a definite time, flows across a section whose position is given.

10. Take as origin of co-ordinates x, y, z, the centre of the base of the prism, and as rectangular axes, the axis of the prism itself, and the two perpendiculars on the sides: the permanent temperature v of the point m, whose co-ordinates are x, y, z, is a function of three variables $F(x, y, z)$: it has by hypothesis a constant value, when we suppose x nothing, whatever be the values of y and z. Suppose we take for the unit of heat that quantity which in the unit of time would emerge from an area equal to a unit of surface, if the heated mass which that area bounds, and which is formed of the same substance as the prism, were continually maintained at the temperature of boiling water, and immersed in atmospheric air maintained at the temperature of melting ice.

We see that the quantity of heat which, in the permanent state of the rectangular prism, flows, during a unit of time, across a certain section perpendicular to the axis, has a determinate ratio to the quantity of heat taken as unit. This ratio is not the same for all sections: it is a function $\phi(x)$ of the distance x, at which the section is situated. It is required to find an analytical expression of the function $\phi(x)$.

11. The foregoing examples suffice to give an exact idea of the different problems which we have discussed.

The solution of these problems has made us understand that the effects of the propagation of heat depend in the case of every solid substance, on three elementary qualities, which are, its capacity for heat, its own conductivity, and the exterior conductivity.

It has been observed that if two bodies of the same volume and of different nature have equal temperatures, and if the same quantity of heat be added to them, the increments of temperature are not the same; the ratio of these increments is the inverse ratio of their capacities for heat. In this manner, the first of the three specific elements which regulate the action of heat is exactly defined, and physicists have for a long time known several methods of determining its value. It is not the same with the two others; their effects have often been observed, but there is but one exact theory which can fairly distinguish, define, and measure them with precision.

The proper or interior conductivity of a body expresses the facility with which heat is propagated in passing from one internal molecule to another. The external or relative conductivity of a solid body depends on the facility with which heat penetrates the surface, and passes from this body into a given medium, or passes from the medium into the solid. The last property is modified by the more or less polished state of the surface; it varies also according to the medium in which the body is immersed; but the interior conductivity can change only with the nature of the solid.

These three elementary qualities are represented in our formulæ by constant numbers, and the theory itself indicates experiments suitable for measuring their values. As soon as they are determined, all the problems relating to the propagation of heat depend only on numerical analysis. The knowledge of these specific properties may be directly useful in several applications of the physical sciences; it is besides an element in the study and description of different substances. It is a very imperfect knowledge of bodies which ignores the relations which they have with one of the chief agents of nature. In general, there is no mathematical theory which has a closer relation than this with public economy, since it serves to give clearness and perfection to the practice of the numerous arts which are founded on the employment of heat.

12. The problem of the terrestrial temperatures presents one of the most beautiful applications of the theory of heat; the general idea to be formed of it is this. Different parts of the surface of the globe are unequally exposed to the influence of the solar rays; the intensity of their action depends on the latitude of the place; it changes also in the course of the day and in the course of the year, and is subject to other less perceptible inequalities. It is evident that, between the variable state of the surface and that of the internal temperatures, a necessary relation exists, which may be derived from theory. We know that, at a certain depth below the surface of the earth, the temperature at a given place experiences no annual variation: this permanent underground temperature becomes less and less according as the place is more and more distant from the equator. We may then leave out of consideration the exterior envelope, the thickness of which is incomparably small with respect to the earth's radius, and regard our planet as a nearly spherical mass, whose surface is subject to a temperature which remains constant at all points on a given parallel, but is not the same on another parallel. It follows from this that every internal

molecule has also a fixed temperature determined by its position. The mathematical problem consists in discovering the fixed temperature at any given point, and the law which the solar heat follows whilst penetrating the interior of the earth.

This diversity of temperature interests us still more, if we consider the changes which succeed each other in the envelope itself on the surface of which we dwell. Those alternations of heat and cold which are reproduced every day and in the course of every year, have been up to the present time the object of repeated observations. These we can now submit to calculation, and from a common theory derive all the particular facts which experience has taught us. The problem is reducible to the hypothesis that every point of a vast sphere is affected by periodic temperatures; analysis then tells us according to what law the intensity of these variations decreases according as the depth increases, what is the amount of the annual or diurnal changes at a given depth, the epoch of the changes, and how the fixed value of the underground temperature is deduced from the variable temperatures observed at the surface.

13. The general equations of the propagation of heat are partial differential equations, and though their form is very simple the known methods do not furnish any general mode of integrating them; we could not therefore deduce from them the values of the temperatures after a definite time. The numerical interpretation of the results of analysis is however necessary, and it is a degree of perfection which it would be very important to give to every application of analysis to the natural sciences. So long as it is not obtained, the solutions may be said to remain incomplete and useless, and the truth which it is proposed to discover is no less hidden in the formulæ of analysis than it was in the physical problem itself. We have applied ourselves with much care to this purpose, and we have been able to overcome the difficulty in all the problems of which we have treated, and which contain the chief elements of the theory of heat. There is not one of the problems whose solution does not provide convenient and exact means for discovering the numerical values of the temperatures acquired, or those of the quantities of heat which have flowed through, when the values of the time and of the variable coordinates are known. Thus will be given not only the differential equations which the functions that express the values of the temperatures must satisfy; but the functions themselves will be given under a form which facilitates the numerical applications.

14. In order that these solutions might be general, and have an extent equal to that of the problem, it was requisite that they should accord with the initial state of the temperatures, which is arbitrary. The examination of this condition shews that we may develop in convergent series, or express by definite integrals, functions which are not subject to a constant law, and which represent the ordinates or irregular or discontinuous lines. This property throws a new light on the theory of partial differential equations, and extends the employment of arbitrary functions by submitting them to the ordinary processes of analysis.

15. It still remained to compare the facts with theory. With this view, varied and exact experiments were undertaken, whose results were in conformity with those of analysis, and gave them an authority which one would have been disposed to refuse to them in a new matter which seemed subject to so much uncertainty. These experiments confirm the principle from which we started, and which is adopted by all physicists in spite of the diversity of their hypotheses on the nature of heat.

16. Equilibrium of temperature is effected not only by way of contact, it is established also between bodies separated from each other, which are situated for a long time in the same region. This effect is independent of contact with a medium; we have observed it in spaces wholly void of air. To complete our theory it was necessary to examine the laws which radiant heat follows, on leaving the surface of a body. It results from the observations of many physicists and from our own experiments, that the intensities of the different rays, which escape in all directions from any point in the surface of a heated body, depend on the angles which their directions make with the surface at the same point. We have proved that the intensity of a ray diminishes as the ray makes a smaller angle with the element of surface, and that it is proportional to the sine of that angle. This general law of emission of heat which different observations had already indicated, is a necessary consequence of the principle of the equilibrium of temperature and of the laws of propagation of heat in solid bodies.

Such are the chief problems which have been discussed in this work; they are all directed to one object only, that is to establish clearly the mathematical principles of the theory of heat, and to keep up in this way with the progress of the useful arts, and of the study of nature.

17. From what precedes it is evident that a very extensive class of phenomena exists, not produced by mechanical forces, but resulting simply from the presence and accumulation of heat. This part of natural philosophy cannot be connected with dynamical theories, it has principles peculiar to itself, and is founded on a method similar to that of other exact sciences. The solar heat, for example, which penetrates the interior of the globe, distributes itself therein according to a regular law which does not depend on the laws of motion, and cannot be determined by the principles of mechanics. The dilatations which the repulsive force of heat produces, observation of which serves to measure temperatures, are in truth dynamical effects; but it is not these dilatations which we calculate, when we investigate the laws of the propagation of heat.

18. There are other more complex natural effects, which depend at the same time on the influence of heat, and of attractive forces: thus, the variations of temperatures which the movements of the sun occasion in the atmosphere and in the ocean, change continually the density of the different parts of the air and the waters. The effect of the forces which these masses obey is modified at every instant by a new distribution of heat, and it cannot be doubted that this cause produces the regular winds, and the chief currents of the sea; the solar and lunar attractions occasioning in the atmosphere effects but slightly sensible, and not general displacements. It was therefore necessary, in order to submit these grand phenomena to calculation, to discover the mathematical laws of the propagation of heat in the interior of masses.

19. It will be perceived, on reading this work, that heat attains in bodies a regular disposition independent of the original distribution, which may be regarded as arbitrary.

In whatever manner the heat was at first distributed, the system of temperatures altering more and more, tends to coincide sensibly with a definite state which depends only on the form of the solid. In the ultimate state the temperatures of all the points are lowered in the same time, but preserve amongst each other the same ratios: in order to express this property the analytical formulæ contain terms composed of exponentials and of quantities analogous to trigonometric functions.

Several problems of mechanics present analogous results, such as the isochronism of oscillations, the multiple resonance of sonorous bodies. Common experiments had made these results remarked, and analysis afterwards demonstrated their true cause. As to those results which depend on changes of temperature, they could not have been recognised except by very exact experiments; but mathematical analysis has outrun observation, it has supplemented our senses, and has made us in a manner witnesses of regular and harmonic vibrations in the interior of bodies.

20. These considerations present a singular example of the relations which exist between the abstract science of numbers and natural causes.

When a metal bar is exposed at one end to the constant action of a source of heat, and every point of it has attained its highest temperature, the system of fixed temperatures corresponds exactly to a table of logarithms; the numbers are the elevations of thermometers placed at the different points, and the logarithms are the distances of these points from the source. In general, heat distributes itself in the interior of solids according to a simple law expressed by a partial differential equation common to physical problems of different order. The irradiation of heat has an evident relation to the tables of sines, for the rays which depart from the same point of a heated surface, differ very much from each other, and their intensity is rigorously proportional to the sine of the angle which the direction of each ray makes with the element of surface.

If we could observe the changes of temperature for every instant at every point of a solid homogeneous mass, we should discover in these series of observations the properties of recurring series, as of sines and logarithms; they would be noticed for example in the diurnal or annual variations of temperature of different points of the earth near its surface.

We should recognise again the same results and all the chief elements of general analysis in the vibrations of elastic media, in the properties of lines or of curved surfaces, in the movements of the stars, and those of light or of fluids. Thus the functions obtained by successive differentiations, which are employed in the development of infinite series and in the solution of numerical equations, correspond also to physical properties. The first of these functions, or the fluxion properly so called, expresses in geometry the inclination of the tangent of a curved line, and in dynamics the velocity of a moving body when the motion varies; in the theory of heat it measures the quantity of heat which flows at each point of a body across a given surface. Mathematical analysis has therefore necessary relations with sensible phenomena; its object is not created by human intelligence; it is a pre-existent element of the universal order, and is not in any way contingent or fortuitous; it is imprinted throughout all nature.

21. Observations more exact and more varied will presently ascertain whether the effects of heat are modified by causes which have not yet been perceived, and the theory will acquire fresh perfection by the continued comparison of its results with the results of experiment; it will explain some important phenomena which we have not yet been able to submit to calculation; it will shew how to determine all the thermometric effects of the solar rays, the fixed or variable temperature which would be observed at different distances from the equator, whether in the interior of the earth or beyond the limits of the atmosphere, whether in the ocean or in different regions of the air. From it will be derived the mathematical knowledge of the great movements which

result from the influence of heat combined with that of gravity. The same principles will serve to measure the conductivities, proper or relative, of different bodies, and their specific capacities, to distinguish all the causes which modify the emission of heat at the surface of solids, and to perfect thermometric instruments.

The theory of heat will always attract the attention of mathematicians, by the rigorous exactness of its elements and the analytical difficulties peculiar to it, and above all by the extent and usefulness of its applications; for all its consequences concern at the same time general physics, the operations of the arts, domestic uses and civil economy.

SECTION II. *Preliminary Definitions and General Notions*

22. Of the nature of heat uncertain hypotheses only could be formed, but the knowledge of the mathematical laws to which its effects are subject is independent of all hypothesis; it requires only an attentive examination of the chief facts which common observations have indicated, and which have been confirmed by exact experiments.

It is necessary then to set forth, in the first place, the general results of observation, to give exact definitions of all the elements of the analysis, and to establish the principles upon which this analysis ought to be founded.

The action of heat tends to expand all bodies, solid, liquid or gaseous; this is the property which gives evidence of its presence. Solids and liquids increase in volume, in most cases, if the quantity of heat which they contain increases; they contract if it diminishes.

When all the parts of a solid homogeneous body, for example those of a mass of metal, are equally heated, and preserve without any change the same quantity of heat, they have also and retain the same density. This state is expressed by saying that throughout the whole extent of the mass the molecules have a common and permanent temperature.

23. The thermometer is a body whose smallest changes of volume can be appreciated; it serves to measure temperatures by the dilatation of a fluid or of air. We assume the construction, use and properties of this instrument to be accurately known. The temperature of a body equally heated in every part, and which keeps its heat, is that which the thermometer indicates when it is and remains in *perfect contact* with the body in question.

Perfect contact is when the thermometer is completely immersed in a fluid mass, and, in general, when there is no point of the external surface of the instrument which is not touched by one of the points of the solid or liquid mass whose temperature is to be measured. In experiments it is not always necessary that this condition should be rigorously observed; but it ought to be assumed in order to make the definition exact.

24. Two fixed temperatures are determined on, namely: the temperature of melting ice which is denoted by 0, and the temperature of boiling water which we will denote by 1: the water is supposed to be boiling under an atmospheric pressure represented by a certain height of the barometer (76 centimetres), the mercury of the barometer being at the temperature 0.

25. Different quantities of heat are measured by determining how many times they contain a fixed quantity which is taken as the unit. Suppose a mass of ice having a definite weight (a kilogramme) to be at temperature 0, and to be converted into water at the same temperature 0 by the addition of a certain quantity of heat: the quantity of heat thus added is taken as the unit of measure. Hence the quantity of heat expressed by a number C contains C times the quantity required to melt a kilogramme of ice at the temperature zero into a mass of water at the same zero temperature.

26. To raise a metallic mass having a certain weight, a kilogramme of iron for example, from the temperature 0 to the temperature 1, a new quantity of heat must be added to that which is already contained in the mass. The number C which denotes this additional quantity of heat, is the specific capacity of iron for heat; the number C has very different values for different substances.

27. If a body of definite nature and weight (a kilogramme of mercury) occupies a volume V at temperature 0, it will occupy a greater volume $V+\Delta$, when it has acquired the temperature 1, that is to say, when the heat which it contained at the temperature 0 has been increased by a new quantity C, equal to the specific capacity of the body for heat. But if, instead of adding this quantity C, a quantity zC is added (z being a number positive or negative) the new volume will be $V+\delta$ instead of $V+\Delta$. Now experiments shew that if z is equal to $\frac{1}{2}$, the increase of volume δ is only half the total increment Δ, and that in general the value of δ is $z\Delta$, when the quantity of heat added is zC.

28. The ratio z of the two quantities zC and C of heat added, which is the same as the ratio of the two increments of volume δ and Δ, is that which is called the *temperature*; hence the quantity which expresses the actual temperature of a body represents the excess of its actual volume over the volume which it would occupy at the temperature of melting ice, unity representing the whole excess of volume which corresponds to the boiling point of water, over the volume which corresponds to the melting point of ice.

29. The increments of volume of bodies are in general proportional to the increments of the quantities of heat which produce the dilatations, but it must be remarked that this proportion is exact only in the case where the bodies in question are subjected to temperatures remote from those which determine their change of state. The application of these results to all liquids must not be relied on; and with respect to water in particular, dilatations do not always follow augmentations of heat.

In general the temperatures are numbers proportional to the quantities of heat added, and in the cases considered by us, these numbers are proportional also to the increments of volume.

30. Suppose that a body bounded by a plane surface having a certain area (a square metre) is maintained in any manner whatever at constant temperature 1, common to all its points, and that the surface in question is in contact with air maintained at temperature 0: the heat which escapes continuously at the surface and passes into the surrounding medium will be replaced always by the heat which proceeds from the constant cause to whose action the body is exposed; thus, a certain quantity of heat denoted by h will flow through the surface in a definite time (a minute).

This amount h, of a flow continuous and always similar to itself, which takes place at a unit of surface at a fixed temperature, is the measure of the external conducibility of the body, that is to say, of the facility with which its surface transmits heat to the atmospheric air.

The air is supposed to be continually displaced with a given uniform velocity: but if the velocity of the current increased, the quantity of heat communicated to the medium would vary also: the same would happen if the density of the medium were increased.

31. If the excess of the constant temperature of the body over the temperature of surrounding bodies, instead of being equal to 1, as has been supposed, had a less value, the quantity of heat dissipated would be less than h. The result of observation is, as we shall see presently, that this quantity of heat lost may be regarded as sensibly proportional to the excess of the temperature of the body over that of the air and surrounding bodies. Hence the quantity h having been determined by one experiment in which the surface heated is at temperature 1, and the medium at temperature 0; we conclude that hz would be the quantity, if the temperature of the surface were z, all the other circumstances remaining the same. This result must be admitted when z is a small fraction.

32. The value h of the quantity of heat which is dispersed across a heated surface is different for different bodies; and it varies for the same body according to the different states of the surface. The effect of irradiation diminishes as the surface becomes more polished; so that by destroying the polish of the surface the value of h is considerably increased. A heated metallic body will be more quickly cooled if its external surface is covered with a black coating such as will entirely tarnish its metallic lustre.

33. The rays of heat which escape from the surface of a body pass freely through spaces void of air; they are propagated also in atmospheric air: their directions are not disturbed by agitations in the intervening air: they can be reflected by metal mirrors and collected at their foci. Bodies at a high temperature, when plunged into a liquid, heat directly only those parts of the mass with which their surface is in contact. The molecules whose distance from this surface is not extremely small, receive no direct heat; it is not the same with aëriform fluids; in these the rays of heat are borne with extreme rapidity to considerable distances, whether it be that part of these rays traverses freely the layers of air, or whether these layers transmit the rays suddenly without altering their direction.

34. When the heated body is placed in air which is maintained at a sensibly constant temperature, the heat communicated to the air makes the layer of the fluid nearest to the surface of the body lighter; this layer rises more quickly the more intensely it is heated, and is replaced by another mass of cool air. A current is thus established in the air whose direction is vertical, and whose velocity is greater as the temperature of the body is higher. For this reason if the body cooled itself gradually the velocity of the current would diminish with the temperature, and the law of cooling would not be exactly the same as if the body were exposed to a current of air at a constant velocity.

35. When bodies are sufficiently heated to diffuse a vivid light, part of their radiant heat mixed with that light can traverse transparent solids or liquids, and is subject to the force which produces refraction. The quantity of heat which possesses this faculty becomes less as the bodies are less inflamed; it is, we may say, insensible for very opaque bodies however highly they may be heated. A thin transparent plate intercepts almost all the direct heat which proceeds from an ardent mass of metal; but it becomes heated in proportion as the intercepted rays are accumulated in it; whence, if it is formed of ice, it becomes liquid; but if this plate of ice is exposed to the rays of a torch it allows a sensible amount of heat to pass through with the light.

36. We have taken as the measure of the external conductivity of a solid body a coefficient h, which denotes the quantity of heat which would pass, in a definite time (a minute), from the surface of this body, into atmospheric air, supposing that the surface had a definite extent (a square metre), that the constant temperature of the body was 1, and that of the air 0, and that the heated surface was exposed to a current of air of a given invariable velocity. This value of h is determined by observation. The quantity of heat expressed by the coefficient is composed of two distinct parts which cannot be measured except by very exact experiments. One is the heat communicated by way of contact to the surrounding air: the other, much less than the first, is the radiant heat emitted. We must assume, in our first investigations, that the quantity of heat lost does not change when the temperatures of the body and of the medium are augmented by the same sufficiently small quantity.

37. Solid substances differ again, as we have already remarked, by their property of being more or less permeable to heat; this quality is their conductivity proper: we shall give its definition and exact measure, after having treated of the uniform and linear propagation of heat. Liquid substances possess also the property of transmitting heat from molecule to molecule, and the numerical value of their conductivity varies according to the nature of the substances: but this effect is observed with difficulty in liquids, since their molecules change places on change of temperature. The propagation of heat in them depends chiefly on this continual displacement, in all cases where the lower parts of the mass are most exposed to the action of the source of heat. If, on the contrary, the source of heat be applied to that part of the mass which is highest, as was the case in several of our experiments, the transfer of heat, which is very slow, does not produce any displacement, at least when the increase of temperature does not diminish the volume, as is indeed noticed in singular cases bordering on changes of state.

38. To this explanation of the chief results of observation, a general remark must be added on equilibrium of temperatures; which consists in this, that different bodies placed in the same region, all of whose parts are and remain equally heated, acquire also a common and permanent temperature.

Suppose that all the parts of a mass M have a common and constant temperature a, which is maintained by any cause whatever: if a smaller body m be placed in perfect contact with the mass M, it will assume the common temperature a.

In reality this result would not strictly occur except after an infinite time: but the exact meaning of the proposition is that if the body m had the temperature a before being placed in contact, it would keep it without any change. The same would be the case with a multitude of other bodies n, p, q, r each of which was placed separately in perfect contact with the mass M: all would acquire the constant temperature a. Thus a thermometer if successively applied to the different bodies m, n, p, q, r would indicate the same temperature.

39. The effect in question is independent of contact, and would still occur, if every part of the body m were enclosed in the solid M, as in an enclosure, without touching any of its parts. For example, if the solid were a spherical envelope of a certain thickness, maintained by some external cause at a temperature a, and containing a space entirely deprived of air, and if the body m could be placed in any part whatever of this spherical space, without touching

any point of the internal surface of the enclosure, it would acquire the common temperature a, or rather, it would preserve it if it had it already. The result would be the same for all the other bodies n, p, q, r, whether they were placed separately or all together in the same enclosure, and whatever also their substance and form might be.

40. Of all modes of presenting to ourselves the action of heat, that which seems simplest and most conformable to observation, consists in comparing this action to that of light. Molecules separated from one another reciprocally communicate, across empty space, their rays of heat, just as shining bodies transmit their light.

If within an enclosure closed in all directions, and maintained by some external cause at a fixed temperature a, we suppose different bodies to be placed without touching any part of the boundary, different effects will be observed according as the bodies, introduced into this space free from air, are more or less heated. If, in the first instance, we insert only one of these bodies, at the same temperature as the enclosure, it will send from all points of its surface as much heat as it receives from the solid which surrounds it, and is maintained in its original state by this exchange of equal quantities.

If we insert a second body whose temperature b is less than a, it will at first receive from the surfaces which surround it on all sides without touching it, a quantity of heat greater than that which it gives out: it will be heated more and more and will absorb through its surface more heat than in the first instance.

The initial temperature b continually rising, will approach without ceasing the fixed temperature a, so that after a certain time the difference will be almost insensible. The effect would be opposite if we placed within the same enclosure a third body whose temperature was greater than a.

41. All bodies have the property of emitting heat through their surface; the hotter they are the more they emit; the intensity of the emitted rays changes very considerably with the state of the surface.

42. Every surface which receives rays of heat from surrounding bodies reflects part and admits the rest: the heat which is not reflected, but introduced through the surface, accumulates within the solid; and so long as it exceeds the quantity dissipated by irradiation, the temperature rises.

43. The rays which tend to go out of heated bodies are arrested at the surface by a force which reflects part of them into the interior of the mass. The cause which hinders the incident rays from traversing the surface, and which divides these rays into two parts, of which one is reflected and the other admitted, acts in the same manner on the rays which are directed from the interior of the body towards external space.

If by modifying the state of the surface we increase the force by which it reflects the incident rays, we increase at the same time the power which it has of reflecting towards the interior of the body rays which are tending to go out. The incident rays introduced into the mass, and the rays emitted through the surface, are equally diminished in quantity.

44. If within the enclosure above mentioned a number of bodies were placed at the same time, separate from each other and unequally heated, they would receive and transmit rays of heat so that at each exchange their temperatures would continually vary, and would all tend to become equal to the fixed temperature of the enclosure.

This effect is precisely the same as that which occurs when heat is propagated within solid bodies; for the molecules which compose these bodies are separated by spaces void of air, and have the property of receiving, accumulating and emitting heat. Each of them sends out rays on all sides, and at the same time receives other rays from the molecules which surround it.

45. The heat given out by a point situated in the interior of a solid mass can pass directly to an extremely small distance only; it is, we may say, intercepted by the nearest particles; these particles only receive the heat directly and act on more distant points. It is different with gaseous fluids; the direct effects of radiation become sensible in them at very considerable distances.

46. Thus the heat which escapes in all directions from a part of the surface of a solid, passes on in air to very distant points; but is emitted only by those molecules of the body which are extremely near the surface. A point of a heated mass situated at a very small distance from the plane superficies which separates the mass from external space, sends to that space an infinity of rays, but they do not all arrive there; they are diminished by all that quantity of heat which is arrested by the intermediate molecules of the solid. The part of the ray actually dispersed into space becomes less according as it traverses a longer path within the mass. Thus the ray which escapes perpendicular to the surface has greater intensity than that which, departing from the same point, follows an oblique direction, and the most oblique rays are wholly intercepted.

The same consequences apply to all the points which are near enough to the surface to take part in the emission of heat, from which it necessarily follows that the whole quantity of heat which escapes from the surface in the normal direction is very much greater than that whose direction is oblique. We have submitted this question to calculation, and our analysis proves that the intensity of the ray is proportional to the sine of the angle which the ray makes with the element of surface. Experiments had already indicated a similar result.

47. This theorem expresses a general law which has a necessary connection with the equilibrium and mode of action of heat. If the rays which escape from a heated surface had the same intensity in all directions, a thermometer placed at one of the points of a space bounded on all sides by an enclosure maintained at a constant temperature would indicate a temperature incomparably greater than that of the enclosure. Bodies placed within this enclosure would not take a common temperature, as is always noticed; the temperature acquired by them would depend on the place which they occupied, or on their form, or on the forms of neighbouring bodies.

The same results would be observed, or other effects equally opposed to common experience, if between the rays which escape from the same point any other relations were admitted different from those which we have enunciated. We have recognised this law as the only one compatible with the general fact of the equilibrium of radiant heat.

48. If a space free from air is bounded on all sides by a solid enclosure whose parts are maintained at a common and constant temperature a, and if a thermometer, having the actual temperature a, is placed at any point whatever of the space, its temperature will continue without any change. It will receive therefore at each instant from the inner surface of the enclosure as much heat as it gives out to it. This effect of the rays of heat in a given space is, properly speaking, the measure of the temperature: but this consideration presupposes the mathematical theory of radiant heat.

If now between the thermometer and a part of the surface of the enclosure a body M be placed whose temperature is a, the thermometer will cease to receive rays from one part of the inner surface, but the rays will be replaced by those which it will receive from the interposed body M. An easy calculation proves that the compensation is exact, so that the state of the thermometer will be unchanged. It is not the same if the temperature of the body M is different from that of the enclosure. When it is greater, the rays which the interposed body M sends to the thermometer and which replace the intercepted rays convey more heat than the latter; the temperature of the thermometer must therefore rise.

If, on the contrary, the intervening body has a temperature less than a, that of the thermometer must fall; for the rays which this body intercepts are replaced by those which it gives out, that is to say, by rays cooler than those of the enclosure; thus the thermometer does not receive all the heat necessary to maintain its temperature a.

49. Up to this point abstraction has been made of the power which all surfaces have of reflecting part of the rays which are sent to them. If this property were disregarded we should have only a very incomplete idea of the equilibrium of radiant heat.

Suppose then that on the inner surface of the enclosure, maintained at a constant temperature, there is a portion which enjoys, in a certain degree, the power in question; each point of the reflecting surface will send into space two kinds of rays; the one go out from the very interior of the substance of which the enclosure is formed, the others are merely reflected by the same surface against which they had been sent. But at the same time that the surface repels on the outside part of the incident rays, it retains in the inside part of its own rays. In this respect an exact compensation is established, that is to say, every one of its own rays which the surface hinders from going out is replaced by a reflected ray of equal intensity.

The same result would happen, if the power of reflecting rays affected in any degree whatever other parts of the enclosure, or the surface of bodies placed within the same space and already at the common temperature.

Thus the reflection of heat does not disturb the equilibrium of temperatures, and does not introduce, whilst that equilibrium exists, any change in the law according to which the intensity of rays which leave the same point decreases proportionally to the sine of the angle of emission.

50. Suppose that in the same enclosure, all of whose parts maintain the temperature a, we place an isolated body M, and a polished metal surface R, which, turning its concavity towards the body, reflects great part of the rays which it received from the body; if we place a thermometer between the body M and the reflecting surface R, at the focus of this mirror, three different effects will be observed according as the temperature of the body M is equal to the common temperature a, or is greater or less.

In the first case, the thermometer preserves the temperature a; it receives 1^0, rays of heat from all parts of the enclosure not hidden from it by the body M or by the mirror; 2^0, rays given out by the body; 3^0, those which the surface R sends out to the focus, whether they come from the mass of the mirror itself, or whether its surface has simply reflected them; and amongst the last we may distinguish between those which have been sent to the mirror by the mass M, and those which it has received from the enclosure. All the rays in question proceed from surfaces which, by hypothesis, have a common temperature a, so that the thermometer is precisely in the same state as if the space bounded by the enclosure contained no other body but itself.

In the second case, the thermometer placed between the heated body M and the mirror, must acquire a temperature greater than a. In reality, it receives the same rays as in the first hypothesis; but with two remarkable differences: one arises from the fact that the rays sent by the body M to the mirror, and reflected upon the thermometer, contain more heat than in the first case. The other difference depends on the fact that the rays sent directly by the body M to the thermometer contain more heat than formerly. Both causes, and chiefly the first, assist in raising the temperature of the thermometer.

In the third case, that is to say, when the temperature of the mass M is less than a, the temperature must assume also a temperature less than a. In fact, it receives again all the varieties of rays which we distinguished in the first case: but there are two kinds of them which contain less heat than in this first hypothesis, that is to say, those which, being sent out by the body M, are reflected by the mirror upon the thermometer, and those which the same body M sends to it directly. Thus the thermometer does not receive all the heat which it requires to preserve its original temperature a. It gives out more heat than it receives. It is inevitable then that its temperature must fall to the point at which the rays which it receives suffice to compensate those which it loses. This last effect is what is called the reflection of cold, and which, properly speaking, consists in the reflection of too feeble heat. The mirror intercepts a certain quantity of heat, and replaces it by a less quantity.

51. If in the enclosure, maintained at a constant temperature a, a body M be placed, whose temperature a' is less than a, the presence of this body will lower the thermometer exposed to its rays, and we may remark that the rays sent to the thermometer from the surface of the body M, are in general of two kinds, namely, those which come from inside the mass M, and those which, coming from different parts of the enclosure, meet the surface M and are reflected upon the thermometer. The latter rays have the common temperature a, but those which belong to the body M contain less heat, and these are the rays which cool the thermometer. If now, by changing the state of the surface of the body M, for example, by destroying the polish, we diminish the power which it has of reflecting the incident rays, the thermometer will fall still lower, and will assume a temperature a'' less than a. In fact all the conditions would be the same as in the preceding case, if it were not that the body M gives out a greater quantity of its own rays and reflects a less quantity of the rays which it receives from the enclosure; that is to say, these last rays, which have the common temperature, are in part replaced by cooler rays. Hence the thermometer no longer receives so much heat as formerly.

If, independently of the change in the surface of the body M, we place a metal mirror adapted to reflect upon the thermometer the rays which have left M, the temperature will assume a value a''' less than a''. The mirror, in fact, intercepts from the thermometer part of the rays of the enclosure which all have the temperature a, and replaces them by three kinds of rays; namely, 1^0, those which come from the interior of the mirror itself, and which have the common temperature; 2^0, those which the different parts of the enclosure send to the mirror with the same temperature, and which are reflected to the focus; 3^0, those which, coming from the interior of the body M. fall upon the mirror, and are reflected upon the thermometer. The last rays have a temperature less than a; hence the thermometer no longer receives so much heat as it received before the mirror was set up.

Lastly, if we proceed to change also the state of the surface of the mirror, and by giving it a more perfect polish, increase its power of reflecting heat, the thermometer will fall still lower. In fact, all the conditions exist which occurred in the preceding case. Only, it happens that the mirror gives out a less quantity of its own rays, and replaces them by those which it reflects. Now, amongst these last rays, all those which proceed from the interior of the mass M are less intense than if they had come from the interior of the metal mirror; hence the thermometer receives still less heat than formerly: it will assume therefore a temperature a'''' less than a'''.

By the same principles all the known facts of the radiation of heat or of cold are easily explained.

52. The effects of heat can by no means be compared with those of an elastic fluid whose molecules are at rest.

It would be useless to attempt to deduce from this hypothesis the laws of propagation which we have explained in this work, and which all experience has confirmed. The free state of heat is the same as that of light; the active state of this element is then entirely different from that of gaseous substances. Heat acts in the same manner in a vacuum, in elastic fluids, and in liquid or solid masses, it is propagated only by way of radiation, but its sensible effects differ according to the nature of bodies.

53. Heat is the origin of all elasticity; it is the repulsive force which preserves the form of solid masses, and the volume of liquids. In solid masses, neighbouring molecules would yield to their mutual attraction, if its effect were not destroyed by the heat which separates them.

This elastic force is greater according as the temperature is higher; which is the reason why bodies dilate or contract when their temperature is raised or lowered.

54. The equilibrium which exists, in the interior of a solid mass, between the repulsive force of heat and the molecular attraction, is stable; that is to say, it re-establishes itself when disturbed by an accidental cause. If the molecules are arranged at distances proper for equilibrium, and if an external force begins to increase this distance without any change of temperature, the effect of attraction begins by surpassing that of heat, and brings back the molecules to their original position, after a multitude of oscillations which become less and less sensible.

A similar effect is exerted in the opposite sense when a mechanical cause diminishes the primitive distance of the molecules; such is the origin of the vibrations of sonorous or flexible bodies, and of all the effects of their elasticity.

55. In the liquid or gaseous state of matter, the external pressure is additional or supplementary to the molecular attraction, and, acting on the surface, does not oppose change of form, but only change of the volume occupied. Analytical investigation will best shew how the repulsive force of heat, opposed to the attraction of the molecules or to the external pressure, assists in the composition of bodies, solid or liquid, formed of one or more elements, and determines the elastic properties of gaseous fluids; but these researches do not belong to the object before us, and appear in dynamic theories.

56. It cannot be doubted that the mode of action of heat always consists, like that of light, in the reciprocal communication of rays, and this explana-

tion is at the present time adopted by the majority of physicists; but it is not necessary to consider the phenomena under this aspect in order to establish the theory of heat. In the course of this work it will be seen how the laws of equilibrium and propagation of radiant heat, in solid or liquid masses, can be rigorously demonstrated, independently of any physical explanation, as the necessary consequences of common observations.

SECTION III. *Principle of the Communication of Heat*

57. We now proceed to examine what experiments teach us concerning the communication of heat.

If two equal molecules are formed of the same substance and have the same temperature, each of them receives from the other as much heat as it gives up to it; their mutual action may then be regarded as null, since the result of this action can bring about no change in the state of the molecules. If, on the contrary, the first is hotter than the second, it sends to it more heat than it receives from it; the result of the mutual action is the difference of these two quantities of heat. In all cases we make abstraction of the two equal quantities of heat which any two material points reciprocally give up; we conceive that the point most heated acts only on the other, and that, in virtue of this action, the first loses a certain quantity of heat which is acquired by the second. Thus the action of the two molecules, or the quantity of heat which the hottest communicates to the other, is the difference of the two quantities which they give up to each other.

58. Suppose that we place in air a solid homogeneous body, whose different points have unequal actual temperatures; each of the molecules of which the body is composed will begin to receive heat from those which are at extremely small distances, or will communicate it to them. This action exerted during the same instant between all points of the mass, will produce an infinitesimal resultant change in all the temperatures: the solid will experience at each instant similar effects, so that the variations of temperature will become more and more sensible.

Consider only the system of two molecules, m and n, equal and extremely near, and let us ascertain what quantity of heat the first can receive from the second during one instant: we may then apply the same reasoning to all the other points which are near enough to the point m, to act directly on it during the first instant.

The quantity of heat communicated by the point n to the point m depends on the duration of the instant, on the very small distance between these points, on the actual temperature of each point, and on the nature of the solid substance; that is to say, if one of these elements happened to vary, all the other remaining the same, the quantity of heat transmitted would vary also. Now experiments have disclosed, in this respect, a general result: it consists in this, that all the other circumstances being the same, the quantity of heat which one of the molecules receives from the other is proportional to the difference of temperature of the two molecules. Thus the quantity would be double, triple, quadruple, if everything else remaining the same, the difference of the temperature of the point n from that of the point m became double, triple, or quadruple. To account for this result, we must consider that the action of n on m is always just as much greater as there is a greater difference between the temperatures of the two points: it is null, if the temperatures are equal, but if the molecule n contains more heat than the equal molecule m, that is to say, if the temperature of m being v, that of n is $v+\Delta$, a portion of the exceeding heat will pass from n to m. Now, if the excess of heat were double, or, which is the same thing, if the temperature of n were $v+2\Delta$, the exceeding heat would be composed of two equal parts corresponding to the two halves of the whole difference of temperature 2Δ; each of these parts would have its proper effect as if it alone existed: thus the quantity of heat communicated by n to m would be twice as great as when the difference of temperature is only Δ. This simultaneous action of the different parts of the exceeding heat is that which constitutes the principle of the communication of heat. It follows from it that the sum of the partial actions, or the total quantity of heat which m receives from n is porportional to the difference of the two temperatures.

59. Denoting by v and v' the temperatures of two equal molecules m and n, by p, their extremely small distance, and by dt, the infinitely small duration of the instant, the quantity of heat which m receives from n during this instant will be expressed by $(v'-v)\phi(p)\cdot dt$. We denote by $\phi(p)$ a certain function of the distance p which, in solid bodies and in liquids, becomes nothing when p has a sensible magnitude. The function is the same for every point of the same given substance; it varies with the nature of the substance.

60. The quantity of heat which bodies lose through their surface is subject to the same principle. If we denote by σ the area, finite or infinitely small, of the surface, all of whose points have the temperature v, and if a represents the temperature of the atmospheric air, the coefficient h being the measure of the external conducibility, we shall have $\sigma h(v-a)dt$ as the expression for the quantity of heat which this surface σ transmits to the air during the instant dt.

When the two molecules, one of which transmits to the other a certain quantity of heat, belong to the same solid, the exact expression for the heat communicated is that which we have given in the preceding article; and since the molecules are extremely near, the difference of the temperatures is extremely small. It is not the same when heat passes from a solid body into a gaseous medium. But the experiments teach us that if the difference is a quantity sufficiently small, the heat transmitted is sensibly proportional to that difference, and that the number h may, in these first researches, be considered as having a constant value, proper to each state of the surface, but independent of the temperature.

61. These propositions relative to the quantity of heat communicated have been derived from different observations. We see first, as an evident consequence of the expressions in question, that if we increased by a common quantity all the initial temperatures of the solid mass, and that of the medium in which it is placed, the successive changes of temperature would be exactly the same as if this increase had not been made. Now this result is sensibly in accordance with experiment; it has been admitted by the physicists who first have observed the effects of heat.

62. If the medium is maintained at a constant temperature, and if the heated body which is placed in that medium has dimensions sufficiently small for the temperature, whilst falling more and more, to remain sensibly the same at all points of the body, it follows from the same propositions, that a quantity of heat will escape at each instant through the surface of the body proportional

to the excess of its actual temperature over that of the medium. Whence it is easy to conclude, as will be seen in the course of this work, that the line whose abscissæ represent the times elapsed, and whose ordinates represent the temperatures corresponding to those times, is a logarithmic curve: now, observations also furnish the same result, when the excess of the temperature of the solid over that of the medium is a sufficiently small quantity.

63. Suppose the medium to be maintained at the constant temperature 0, and that the initial temperatures of different points a, b, c, d &c. of the same mass are α, β, γ, δ &c., that at the end of the first instant they have become α', β', γ', δ' &c., that at the end of the second instant they have become α'', β'', γ'', δ'' &c., and so on. We may easily conclude from the propositions enunciated, that if the initial temperatures of the same points had been $g\alpha$, $g\beta$, $g\gamma$, $g\delta$ &c. (g being any number whatever), they would have become, at the end of the first instant, by virtue of the action of the different points, $g\alpha'$, $g\beta'$, $g\gamma'$, $g\delta'$ &c., and at the end of the second instant, $g\alpha''$, $g\beta''$, $g\gamma''$, $g\delta''$ &c., and so on. For instance, let us compare the case when the initial temperatures of the points, a, b, c, d &c. were α, β, γ, δ &c. with that in which they are 2α, 2β, 2γ, 2δ &c., the medium preserving in both cases the temperature 0. In the second hypothesis, the difference of the temperatures of any two points whatever is double what it was in the first, and the excess of the temperature of each point, over that of each molecule of the medium, is also double; consequently the quantity of heat which any molecule whatever sends to any other, or that which it receives, is, in the second hypothesis, double of that which it was in the first. The change of temperature which each point suffers being proportional to the quantity of heat acquired, it follows that, in the second case, this change is double what it was in the first case. Now we have supposed that the initial temperature of the first point, which was α, became α' at the end of the first instant; hence if this initial temperature had been 2α, and if all the other temperatures had been doubled, it would have become $2\alpha'$. The same would be the case with all the other molecules b, c, d, and a similar result would be derived, if the ratio instead of being 2, were any number whatever g. It follows then, from the principle of the communication of heat, that if we increase or diminish in any given ratio all the initial temperatures, we increase or diminish in the same ratio all the successive temperatures.

This, like the two preceding results, is confirmed by observation. It could not have existed if the quantity of heat which passes from one molecule to another had not been, actually, proportional to the difference of the temperatures.

64. Observations have been made with accurate instruments, on the permanent temperatures at different points of a bar or of a metallic ring, and on the propagation of heat in the same bodies and in several other solids of the form of spheres or cubes. The results of these experiments agree with those which are derived from the preceding propositions. They would be entirely different if the quantity of heat transmitted from one solid molecule to another, or to a molecule of air, were not proportional to the excess of temperature. It is necessary first to know all the rigorous consequences of this proposition; by it we determine the chief part of the quantities which are the object of the problem. By comparing then the calculated values with those given by numerous and very exact experiments, we can easily measure the variations of the coefficients, and perfect our first researches.

SECTION IV. *On the Uniform and Linear Movement of Heat*

65. We shall consider, in the first place, the uniform movement of heat in the simplest case, which is that of an infinite solid enclosed between two parallel planes.

We suppose a solid body formed of some homogeneous substance to be enclosed between two parallel and infinite planes; the lower plane A is maintained, by any cause whatever, at a constant temperature a; we may imagine for example that the mass is prolonged, and that the plane A is a section common to the solid and to the enclosed mass, and is heated at all its points by a constant source of heat; the upper plane B is also maintained by a similar cause at a fixed temperature b, whose value is less than that of a; the problem is to determine what would be the result of this hypothesis if it were continued for an infinite time.

If we suppose the initial temperature of all parts of this body to be b, it is evident that the heat which leaves the source A will be propagated farther and farther and will raise the temperature of the molecules included between the two planes: but the temperature of the upper plane being unable, according to hypothesis to rise above b, the heat will be dispersed within the cooler mass, contact with which keeps the plane B at the constant temperature b. The system of temperatures will tend more and more to a final state, which it will never attain, but which would have the property, as we shall proceed to shew, of existing and keeping itself up without any change if it were once formed.

In the final and fixed state, which we are considering, the permanent temperature of a point of the solid is evidently the same at all points of the same section parallel to the base; and we shall prove that this fixed temperature, common to all the points of an intermediate section, decreases in arithmetic progression from the base to the upper plane, that is to say, if we represent the constant temperatures a and b by the ordinates $A\alpha$ and $B\beta$ (see Fig. 1), raised

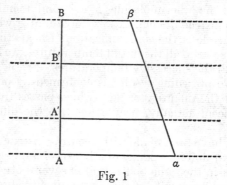

Fig. 1

perpendicularly to the distance AB between the two planes, the fixed temperatures of the intermediate layers will be represented by the ordinates of the straight line $\alpha\beta$ which joins the extremities α and β; thus, denoting by z the height of an intermediate section or its perpendicular distance from the plane A, by e the whole height or distance AB, and by v the temperature of the section whose height is z, we must have the equation $v = a + \dfrac{b-a}{e} z$.

In fact, if the temperatures were at first established in accordance with this law, and if the extreme surfaces A and B were always kept at the temperatures a and b, no change would happen in the state of the solid. To convince ourselves of this, it will be sufficient to compare the quantity of heat which would traverse an intermediate section A' with that which, during the same time, would traverse another section B'.

Bearing in mind that the final state of the solid is formed and continues, we see that the part of the mass which is below and plane A' must communicate heat to the part which is above that plane, since this second part is cooler than the first.

Imagine two points of the solid, m and m', very near to each other, and placed in any manner whatever, the one m below the plane A', and the other m' above this plane, to be exerting their action during an infinitely small instant: m the hottest point will communicate to m' a certain quantity of heat which will cross the plane A'. Let x, y, z be the rectangular coordinates of the point m, and x', y', z' the coordinates of the point m': consider also two other points n and n' very near to each other, and situated with respect to the plane B', in the same manner in which m and m' are placed with respect to the plane A': that is to say, denoting by ζ the perpendicular distance of the two sections A' and B', the coordinates of the point n will be x, y, $z+\zeta$ and those of the point n', x', y', $z'+\zeta$; the two distances mm' and nn' will be equal: further, the difference of the temperature v of the point m above the temperature v' of the point m' will be the same as the difference of temperature of the two points n and n'. In fact the former difference will be determined by substituting first z and then z' in the general equation

$$v = a + \frac{b-a}{e}\, z,$$

and subtracting the second equation from the first, whence the result $v-v'$ $= \dfrac{b-a}{e}\,(z-z')$. We shall then find, by the substitution of $z+\zeta$ and $z'+\zeta$, that the excess of temperature of the point n over that of the point n' is also expressed by

$$\frac{b-a}{e}\,(z-z').$$

It follows from this that the quantity of heat sent by the point m to the point m' will be the same as the quantity of heat sent by the point n to the point n', for all the elements which concur in determining this quantity of transmitted heat are the same.

It is manifest that we can apply the same reasoning to every system of two molecules which communicate heat to each other across the section A' or the section B'; whence, if we could sum up the whole quantity of heat which flows, during the same instant, across the section A' or the section B', we should find this quantity to be the same for both sections.

From this it follows that the part of the solid included between A' and B' receives always as much heat as it loses, and since this result is applicable to any portion whatever of the mass included between two parallel sections, it is evident that no part of the solid can acquire a temperature higher than that which it has at present. Thus, it has been rigorously demonstrated that the state of the prism will continue to exist just as it was at first.

Hence, the permanent temperatures of different sections of a solid enclosed between two parallel infinite planes, are represented by the ordinates of a straight line $\alpha\beta$, and satisfy the linear equation $v = a + \dfrac{b-a}{e}\, z$.

66. By what precedes we see distinctly what constitutes the propagation of heat in a solid enclosed between two parallel and infinite planes, each of which is maintained at a constant temperature. Heat penetrates the mass gradually across the lower plane: the temperatures of the intermediate sections are raised, but can never exceed nor even quite attain a certain limit which they approach nearer and nearer: this limit or final temperature is different for different intermediate layers, and decreases in arithmetic progression from the fixed temperature of the lower plane to the fixed temperature of the upper plane.

The final temperatures are those which would have to be given to the solid in order that its state might be permanent; the variable state which precedes it may also be submitted to analysis, as we shall see presently: but we are now considering only the system of final and permanent temperatures. In the last state, during each division of time, across a section parallel to the base, or a definite portion of that section, a certain quantity of heat flows, which is constant if the divisions of time are equal. This uniform flow is the same for all the intermediate sections; it is equal to that which proceeds from the source, and to that which is lost during the same time, at the upper surface of the solid, by virtue of the cause which keeps the temperature constant.

67. The problem now is to measure that quantity of heat which is propagated uniformly within the solid, during a given time, across a definite part of a section parallel to the base: it depends, as we shall see, on the two extreme temperatures a and b, and on the distance e between the two sides of the solid; it would vary if any one of these elements began to change, the other remaining the same. Suppose a second solid to be formed of the same substance as the first, and enclosed between two infinite parallel planes, whose perpendicular

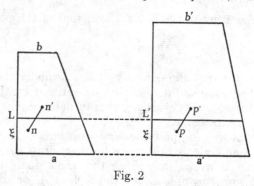

Fig. 2

distance is e' (see Fig. 2): the lower side is maintained at a fixed temperature a', and the upper side at the fixed temperature b'; both solids are considered to be in that final and permanent state which has the property of maintaining itself as soon as it has been formed. Thus the law of the temperatures is expressed for the first body by the equation $v = a + \dfrac{b-a}{e}\, z$, and for the second, by the equation $u = a' + \dfrac{b'-a'}{e'}\, z$, v in the first solid, and u in the second, being the temperature of the section whose height is z.

This arranged, we will compare the quantity of heat which, during the unit of time traverses a unit of area taken on an intermediate section L of the first solid, with that which during the same time traverses an equal area taken on the section L' of the second, ϵ being the height common to the two sections, that is to say, the distance of each of them from their own base. We shall consider two very near points n and n' in the first body, one of which n is below the plane L and the other n' above this plane: x, y, z are the co-ordinates of n: and x', y', z' the co-ordinates of n', ϵ being less than z', and greater than z.

We shall consider also in the second solid the instantaneous action of two points p and p', which are situated, with respect to the section L', in the same manner as the points n and n' with respect to the section L of the first solid. Thus the same co-ordinates x, y, z, and x', y', z' referred to three rectangular axes in the second body, will fix also the position of the points p and p'.

Now, the distance from the point n to the point n' is equal to the distance from the point p to the point p', and since the two bodies are formed of the same substance, we conclude, according to the principle of the communication of heat, that the action of n on n', or the quantity of heat given by n to n', and the action of p on p', are to each other in the same ratio as the differences of the temperature $v-v'$ and $u-u'$.

Substituting v and then v' in the equation which belongs to the first solid, and subtracting, we find $v-v' = \dfrac{b-a}{e}\,(z-z')$; we have also by means of the second equation $u-u' = \dfrac{b'-a'}{e'}\,(z-z')$, whence the ratio of the two actions in question is that of $\dfrac{a-b}{e}$ to $\dfrac{a'-b'}{e'}$.

We may now imagine many other systems of two molecules, the first of which sends to the second across the plane L, a certain quantity of heat, and each of these systems, chosen in the first solid, may be compared with a homologous system situated in the second, and whose action is exerted across the section L'; we can then apply again the previous reasoning to prove that the ratio of the two actions is always that of $\dfrac{a-b}{e}$ to $\dfrac{a'-b'}{e'}$.

Now, the whole quantity of heat which, during one instant, crosses the section L, results from the simultaneous action of a multitude of systems each of which is formed of two points; hence this quantity of heat and that which, in the second solid, crosses during the same instant the section L', are also to each other in the ratio of $\dfrac{a-b}{e}$ to $\dfrac{a'-b'}{e'}$.

It is easy then to compare with each other the intensities of the constant flows of heat which are propagated uniformly in the two solids, that is to say, the quantities of heat which, during unit of time, cross unit of surface of each of these bodies. The ratio of these intensities is that of the two quotients $\dfrac{a-b}{e}$ and $\dfrac{a'-b'}{e'}$. If the two quotients are equal, the flows are the same, whatever in other respects the values a, b, e, a', b', e', may be; in general, denoting the first flow by F and the second by F', we shall have $\dfrac{F}{F'} = \dfrac{a-b}{e} \div \dfrac{a'-b'}{e'}$.

68. Suppose that in the second solid, the permanent temperature a' of the lower plane is that of boiling water, 1; that the temperature e' of the upper plane is that of melting ice, 0; that the distance b' of the two planes is the unit of measure (a metre); let us denote by K the constant flow of heat which, during unit of time (a minute) would cross unit of surface in this last solid, if it were formed of a given substance; K expressing a certain number of units of heat, that is to say a certain number of times the heat necessary to convert a kilogramme of ice into water: we shall have, in general, to determine the constant flow F, in a solid formed of the same substance, the equation $\frac{F}{K} = \frac{a-b}{e}$ or $F = K\frac{a-b}{e}$.

The value of F denotes the quantity of heat which, during the unit of time, passes across a unit of area of the surface taken on a section parallel to the base.

Thus the thermometric state of a solid enclosed between two parallel infinite plane sides whose perpendicular distance is e, and which are maintained at fixed temperatures a and b, is represented by the two equations:

$$v = a + \frac{b-a}{e}\, z, \text{ and } F = K\frac{a-b}{e} \text{ or } F = -K\frac{dv}{dz}.$$

The first of these equations expresses the law according to which the temperatures decrease from the lower side to the opposite side, the second indicates the quantity of heat which, during a given time, crosses a definite part of a section parallel to the base.

69. We have taken this coefficient K, which enters into the second equation, to be the measure of the specific conducibility of each substance; this number has very different values for different bodies.

It represents, in general, the quantity of heat which, in a homogeneous solid formed of a given substance and enclosed between two infinite parallel planes, flows, during one minute, across a surface of one square metre taken on a section parallel to the extreme planes, supposing that these two planes are maintained, one at the temperature of boiling water, the other at the temperature of melting ice, and that all the intermediate planes have acquired and retain a permanent temperature.

We might employ another definition of conductivity, since we could estimate the capacity for heat by referring it to unit of volume, instead of referring it to unit of mass. All these definitions are equally good provided they are clear and precise.

We shall shew presently how to determine by observation the value K of the conducibility or conductibility in different substances.

70. In order to establish the equations which we have cited in Article 68, it would not be necessary to suppose the points which exert their action across the planes to be at extremely small distances.

The results would still be the same if the distances of these points had any magnitude whatever; they would therefore apply also to the case where the direct action of heat extended within the interior of the mass to very considerable distances, all the circumstances which constitute the hypothesis remaining in other respects the same.

We need only suppose that the cause which maintains the temperatures at the surface of the solid, affects not only that part of the mass which is extremely near to the surface, but that its action extends to a finite depth. The

equation $v = a - \dfrac{a-b}{e} z$ will still represent in this case the permanent temperatures of the solid. The true sense of this proposition is that, if we give to all
points of the mass the temperatures expressed by the equation, and if besides
any cause whatever, acting on the two extreme laminæ, retained always every
one of their molecules at the temperature which the same equation assigns to
them, the interior points of the solid would preserve without any change their
initial state.

If we supposed that the action of a point of the mass could extend to a finite
distance ϵ, it would be necessary that the thickness of the extreme laminæ,
whose state is maintained by the external cause, should be at least equal to ϵ.
But the quantity ϵ having in fact, in the natural state of solids, only an inappreciable value, we may make abstraction of this thickness; and it is sufficient
for the external cause to act on each of the two layers, extremely thin, which
bound the solid. This is always what must be understood by the expression, *to
maintain the temperature of the surface constant*.

71. We proceed further to examine the case in which the same solid would
be exposed, at one of its faces, to atmospheric air maintained at a constant
temperature.

Suppose then that the lower plane preserves the fixed temperature a, by
virtue of any external cause whatever, and that the upper plane, instead of
being maintained as formerly at a less temperature b, is exposed to atmospheric
air maintained at that temperature b, the perpendicular distance of the two
planes being denoted always by e: the problem is to determine the final temperatures.

Assuming that in the initial state of the solid, the common temperature of
its molecules is b or less than b, we can readily imagine that the heat which
proceeds incessantly from the source A penetrates the mass, and raises more
and more the temperatures of the intermediate sections; the upper surface is
gradually heated, and permits part of the heat which has penetrated the solid
to escape into the air. The system of temperatures continually approaches a
final state which would exist of itself if it were once formed; in this final state,
which is that which we are considering, the temperature of the plane B has a
fixed but unknown value, which we will denote by β, and since the lower plane
A preserves also a permanent temperature a, the system of temperatures is
represented by the general equation $v = a + \dfrac{\beta - a}{e} z$, v denoting always the fixed
temperature of the section whose height is z. The quantity of heat which flows
during unit of time across a unit of surface taken on any section whatever is
$K\dfrac{a - \beta}{e}$, k denoting the interior conducibility.

We must now consider that the upper surface B, whose temperature is β,
permits the escape into the air of a certain quantity of heat which must be
exactly equal to that which crosses any section whatever L of the solid. If it
were not so, the part of the mass included between this section L and the plane
B would not receive a quantity of heat equal to that which it loses; hence it
would not maintain its state, which is contrary to hypothesis; the constant
flow at the surface is therefore equal to that which traverses the solid: now, the
quantity of heat which escapes, during unit of time, from unit of surface taken
on the plane B, is expressed by $h(\beta - b)$, b being the fixed temperature of the

air. and h the measure of the conducibility of the surface B; we must therefore have the equation $K\dfrac{a-\beta}{e} = h(\beta - b)$, which will determine the value of β.

From this may be derived $a - \beta = \dfrac{he(a-b)}{he+K}$, an equation whose second member is known; for the temperatures a and b are given, as are also the quantities h, k, e.

Introducing this value of $a - \beta$ into the general equation $v = a + \dfrac{\beta - a}{e}\,z$, we shall have, to express the temperatures of any section of the solid, the equation $a - v = \dfrac{hz(a-b)}{he+K}$, in which known quantities only enter with the corresponding variables v and z.

72. So far we have determined the final and permanent state of the temperatures in a solid enclosed between two infinite and parallel plane surfaces, maintained at unequal temperatures. This first case is, properly speaking, the case of the linear and uniform propagation of heat, for there is no transfer of heat in the plane parallel to the sides of the solid; that which traverses the solid flows uniformly, since the value of the flow is the same for all instants and for all sections.

We will now restate the three chief propositions which result from the examination of this problem; they are susceptible of a great number of applications, and form the first elements of our theory.

1st. If at the two extremities of the thickness e of the solid we erect perpendiculars to represent the temperatures a and b of the two sides, and if we draw the straight line which joins the extremities of these two first ordinates, all the intermediate temperatures will be proportional to the ordinates of this straight line; they are expressed by the general equation $a - v = \dfrac{a-b}{e}\,z$, v denoting the temperature of the section whose height is z.

2nd. The quantity of heat which flows uniformly, during unit of time, across unit of surface taken on any section whatever parallel to the sides, all other things being equal, is directly proportional to the difference $a-b$ of the extreme temperatures, and inversely proportional to the distance e which separates these sides. The quantity of heat is expressed by $K\dfrac{a-b}{e}$, or $-K\dfrac{dv}{dz}$, if we derive from the general equation the value of $\dfrac{dv}{dz}$ which is constant; this uniform flow may always be represented, for a given substance and in the solid under examination, by the tangent of the angle included between the perpendicular e and the straight line whose ordinates represent the temperatures.

3rd. One of the extreme surfaces of the solid being submitted always to the temperature a, if the other plane is exposed to air maintained at a fixed temperature b; the plane in contact with the air acquires, as in the preceding case, a fixed temperature β, greater than b, and it permits a quantity of heat to escape into the air across unit of surface, during unit of time, which is expressed by $h(\beta - b)$, h denoting the external conducibility of the plane.

The same flow of heat $h(\beta - b)$ is equal to that which traverses the prism and whose value is $K(a - \beta)$; we have therefore the equation $h(\beta - b) = K\dfrac{a-\beta}{e}$, which gives the value of β.

SECTION V. *Law of the Permanent Temperatures in a Prism of Small Thickness*

73. We shall easily apply the principles which have just been explained to the following problem, very simple in itself, but one whose solution it is important to base on exact theory.

A metal bar, whose form is that of a rectangular parallelepiped infinite in length, is exposed to the action of a source of heat which produces a constant temperature at all points of its extremity A. It is required to determine the fixed temperatures at the different sections of the bar.

The section perpendicular to the axis is supposed to be a square whose side $2l$ is so small that we may without sensible error consider the temperatures to be equal at different points of the same section. The air in which the bar is placed is maintained at a constant temperature 0, and carried away by a current with uniform velocity.

Inside the solid, heat will pass successively all parts situated to the right or left (*pro re nata*) of the source, and not exposed directly to its action; they will be heated more and more, but the temperature of each point will not increase beyond a certain limit. This maximum temperature is not the same for every section; it in general decreases as the distance of the section from the origin increases: we shall denote by v the fixed temperature of a section perpendicular to the axis, and situated at a distance x from the origin A.

Before every point of the solid has attained its highest degree of heat, the system of temperatures varies continually, and approaches more and more to a fixed state, which is that which we consider. This final state is kept up of itself when it has once been formed. In order that the system of temperatures may be permanent, it is necessary that the quantity of heat which, during unit of time, crosses a section made at a distance x from the origin, should balance exactly all the heat which, during the same time, escapes through that part of the external surface of the prism which is situated to the right of the same section. The lamina whose thickness is dx, and whose external surface is $8ldx$, allows the escape into the air, during unit of time, of a quantity of heat expressed by $8hlv \cdot dx$, h being the measure of the external conducibility of the prism. Hence taking the integral $\int 8hlv \cdot dx$ from $x=0$ to $x=\infty$, we shall find the quantity of heat which escapes from the whole surface of the bar during unit of time; and if we take the same integral from $x=0$ to $x=x$, we shall have the quantity of heat lost through the part of the surface included between the source of heat and the section made at the distance x. Denoting the first integral by C, whose value is constant, and the variable value of the second by $\int 8hlv \cdot dx$; the difference $C - \int 8hlv \cdot dx$ will express the whole quantity of heat which escapes into the air across the part of the surface situated to the right of the section. On the other hand, the lamina of the solid, enclosed between two sections infinitely near at distances x and $x+dx$, must resemble an infinite solid, bounded by two parallel planes, subject to fixed temperatures v and $v+dv$, by hypothesis, the temperature does not vary throughout the whole extent of the same section. The thickness of the solid is dx, and the area of the section is $4l^2$: hence the quantity of heat which flows uniformly, during unit of time, across a section of this solid, is, according to the preceding principles,

$-4l^2 K \dfrac{dv}{dx}$, K being the specific internal conductivity: we must therefore have

the equation
$$-4l^2 K \frac{dv}{dx} = C - \int 8hlv \cdot dx,$$

whence
$$Kl \frac{d^2v}{dx^2} = 2hv.$$

74. We should obtain the same result by considering the equilibrium of heat in a single lamina infinitely thin, enclosed between two sections at distances x and $x+dx$. In fact, the quantity of heat which, during unit of time, crosses the first section situated at distance x, is $-4l^2 K \frac{dv}{dx}$. To find that which flows during the same time across the successive section situated at distance $x+dx$, we must in the preceding expression change x into $x+dx$, which gives $-4l^2 K \cdot \left[\frac{dv}{dx} + d\left(\frac{dv}{dx} \right) \right]$. If we subtract the second expression from the first we shall find how much heat is acquired by the lamina bounded by these two sections during unit of time; and since the state of the lamina is permanent, it follows that all the heat acquired is dispersed into the air across the external surface $8ldx$ of the same lamina: now the last quantity of heat is $8hlvdx$: we shall obtain therefore the same equation

$$8hlvdx - 4l^2 K d\left(\frac{dv}{dx} \right), \quad \text{whence} \quad \frac{d^2v}{dx^2} = \frac{2h}{Kl} v.$$

75. In whatever manner this equation is formed, it is necessary to remark that the quantity of heat which passes into the lamina whose thickness is dx, has a finite value, and that its exact expression is $-4l^2 K \frac{dv}{dx}$. The lamina being enclosed between two surfaces the first of which has a temperature v, and the second a lower temperature v', we see that the quantity of heat which it receives through the first surface depends on the difference $v-v'$, and is proportional to it: but this remark is not sufficient to complete the calculation. The quantity in question is not a differential: it has a finite value, since it is equivalent to all the heat which escapes through that part of the external surface of the prism which is situated to the right of the section. To form an exact idea of it, we must compare the lamina whose thickness is dx, with a solid terminated by two parallel planes whose distance is e, and which are maintained at unequal temperatures a and b. The quantity of heat which passes into such a prism across the hottest surface, is in fact proportional to the difference $a-b$ of the extreme temperatures, but it does not depend only on this difference: all other things being equal, it is less when the prism is thicker, and in general it is proportional to $\frac{a-b}{e}$. This is why the quantity of heat which passes through the first surface into the lamina, whose thickness is dx, is proportional to $\frac{v-v'}{dx}$.

We lay stress on this remark because the neglect of it has been the first obstacle to the establishment of the theory. If we did not make a complete analysis of the elements of the problem, we should obtain an equation not homogeneous, and, a fortiori, we should not be able to form the equations which express the movement of heat in more complex cases.

It was necessary also to introduce into the calculation the dimensions of the prism, in order that we might not regard, as general, consequences which observation had furnished in a particular case. Thus, it was discovered by experiment that a bar of iron, heated at one extremity, could not acquire, at a distance of six feet from the source, a temperature of one degree (octogesimal[1]); for to produce this effect, it would be necessary for the heat of the source to surpass considerably the point of fusion of iron; but this result depends on the thickness of the prism employed. If it had been greater, the heat would have been propagated to a greater distance, that is to say, the point of the bar which acquires a fixed temperature of one degree is much more remote from the source when the bar is thicker, all other conditions remaining the same. We can always raise by one degree the temperature of one end of a bar of iron, by heating the solid at the other end; we need only give the radius of the base a sufficient length: which is, we may say, evident, and of which besides a proof will be found in the solution of the problem (Art. 78).

76. The integral of the preceding equation is

$$v = A e^{-x \sqrt{\frac{2h}{Kl}}} + B e^{+x \sqrt{\frac{2h}{Kl}}},$$

A and B being two arbitrary constants; now, if we suppose the distance x infinite, the value of the temperature v must be infinitely small; hence the term $B e^{+x \sqrt{\frac{2h}{Kl}}}$ does not exist in the integral: thus the equation $v = A e^{-x \sqrt{\frac{2h}{Kl}}}$ represents the permanent state of the solid; the temperature at the origin is denoted by the constant A, since that is the value of v when x is zero.

This law according to which the temperatures decrease is the same as that given by experiment; several physicists have observed the fixed temperatures at different points of a metal bar exposed at its extremity to the constant action of a source of heat,[2] and they have ascertained that the distances from the origin represent logarithms, and the temperatures the corresponding numbers.

77. The numerical value of the constant quotient of two consecutive temperatures being determined by observation, we easily deduce the value of the ratio $\frac{h}{K}$; for, denoting by v_1, v_2 the temperatures corresponding to the distances x_1, x_2, we have

$$\frac{v_1}{v_2} = e^{-(x_1 - x_2) \sqrt{\frac{2h}{Kl}}}, \text{ whence } \sqrt{\frac{2h}{K}} = \frac{\log v_1 - \log v_2}{x_2 - x_1} \sqrt{l}.$$

As for the separate values of h and K, they cannot be determined by experiments of this kind: we must observe also the varying motion of heat.

78. Suppose two bars of the same material and different dimensions to be submitted at their extremities to the same temperature A; let l_1 be the side of a section in the first bar, and l_2 in the second, we shall have, to express the temperatures of these two solids, the equations

$$v_1 = A e^{-x_1 \sqrt{\frac{2h}{Kl_1}}} \text{ and } v_2 = A e^{-x_2 \sqrt{\frac{2h}{Kl_2}}},$$

v_1, in the first solid, denoting the temperature of a section made at distance x_1, and v_2, in the second solid, the temperature of a section made at distance x_2.

When these two bars have arrived at a fixed state, the temperature of a section of the first, at a certain distance from the source, will not be equal to

---

[1] Reaumer's scale of temperature.
[2] The conducting power K is not constant, but diminishes as the temperature increases.

the temperature of a section of the second at the same distance from the focus; in order that the fixed temperatures may be equal, the distances must be different. If we wish to compare with each other the distances x_1 and x_2 from the origin up to the points which in the two bars attain the same temperature, we must equate the second members of these equations, and from them we conclude that $\dfrac{x_1^2}{x_2^2} = \dfrac{l_1}{l_2}$. Thus the distances in question are to each other as the square roots of the thicknesses.

79. If two metal bars of equal dimensions, but formed of different substances, are covered with the same coating, which gives them the same external conducibility, and if they are submitted at their extremities to the same temperature, heat will be propagated most easily and to the greatest distance from the origin in that which has the greatest conductivity. To compare with each other the distances x_1 and x_2 from the common origin up to the points which acquire the same fixed temperature, we must, after denoting the respective conducibilities of the two substances by K_1 and K_2, write the equation

$$e^{-x_1 \sqrt{\frac{2h}{K_1 l}}} = e^{-x_2 \sqrt{\frac{2h}{K_2 l}}}, \text{ whence } \frac{x_1^2}{x_2^2} = \frac{K_1}{K_2}.$$

Thus the ratio of the two conductivities is that of the squares of the distances from the common origin to the points which attain the same fixed temperature.

80. It is easy to ascertain how much heat flows during unit of time through a section of the bar arrived at its fixed state: this quantity is expressed by $-4Kl^2 \dfrac{dv}{dx}$, or $4A\sqrt{2Khl^3} \cdot e^{-x}\sqrt{\frac{2h}{Kl}}$, and if we take its value at the origin, we shall have $4A\sqrt{2Khl^3}$ as the measure of the quantity of heat which passes from the source into the solid during unit of time; thus the expenditure of the source of heat is, all other things being equal, proportional to the square root of the cube of the thickness.

We should obtain the same result on taking the integral $\int 8hlv \cdot dx$ from x nothing to x infinite.

SECTION VI. *On the Heating of Closed Spaces*

81. We shall again make use of the theorems of Article 72 in the following problem, whose solution offers useful applications; it consists in determining the extent of the heating of closed spaces.

Imagine a closed space, of any form whatever, to be filled with atmospheric air and closed on all sides, and that all parts of the boundary are homogeneous and have a common thickness e, so small that the ratio of the external surface to the internal surface differs little from unity. The space which this boundary terminates is heated by a source whose action is constant; for example, by means of a surface whose area is σ maintained at a constant temperature α.

We consider here only the mean temperature of the air contained in the space, without regard to the unequal distribution of heat in this mass of air; thus we suppose that the existing causes incessantly mingle all the portions of air, and make their temperatures uniform.

We see first that the heat which continually leaves the source spreads itself in the surrounding air and penetrates the mass of which the boundary is formed, is partly dispersed at the surface, and passes into the external air, which we suppose to be maintained at a lower and permanent temperature n. The inner air is heated more and more: the same is the case with the solid boundary: the system of temperatures steadily approaches a final state which is the object of the problem, and has the property of existing by itself and of being kept up unchanged, provided the surface of the source σ be maintained at the temperature α, and the external air at the temperature n.

In the permanent state which we wish to determine the air preserves a fixed temperature m; the temperature of the inner surface s of the solid boundary has also a fixed value a; lastly, the outer surface s, which terminates the enclosure, preserves a fixed temperature b less than a, but greater than n. The quantities σ, α, s, e and n are known, and the quantities m, a and b are unknown.

The degree of heating consists in the excess of the temperature m over n, the temperature of the external air; this excess evidently depends on the area σ of the heating surface and on its temperature α; it depends also on the thickness e of the enclosure, on the area s of the surface which bounds it, on the facility with which heat penetrates the inner surface or that which is opposite to it; finally, on the specific conductivity of the solid mass which forms the enclosure: for if any one of these elements were to be changed, the others remaining the same, the degree of the heating would vary also. The problem is to determine how all these quantities enter into the value of $m - n$.

82. The solid boundary is terminated by two equal surfaces, each of which is maintained at a fixed temperature; every prismatic element of the solid enclosed between two opposite portions of these surfaces, and the normals raised round the contour of the bases, is therefore in the same state as if it belonged to an infinite solid enclosed between two parallel planes, maintained at unequal temperatures. All the prismatic elements which compose the boundary touch along their whole length. The points of the mass which are equidistant from the inner surface have equal temperatures, to whatever prism they belong; consequently there cannot be any transfer of heat in the direction perpendicular to the length of these prisms. The case is, therefore, the same as that of which we have already treated, and we must apply to it the linear equations which have been stated in former articles.

83. Thus in the permanent state which we are considering, the flow of heat which leaves the surface σ during a unit of time, is equal to that which, during the same time, passes from the surrounding air into the inner surface of the enclosure; it is equal also to that which, in a unit of time, crosses an intermediate section made within the solid enclosure by a surface equal and parallel to those which bound this enclosure; lastly, the same flow is again equal to that which passes from the solid enclosure across its external surface, and is dispersed into the air. If these four quantities of flow of heat were not equal, some variation would necessarily occur in the state of the temperatures, which is contrary to the hypothesis.

The first quantity is expressed by $\sigma\,(\alpha - m)\,g$, denoting by g the external conducibility of the surface σ, which belongs to the source of heat.

The second is $s(m - a)h$, the coefficient h being the measure of the external conducibility of the surface s, which is exposed to the action of the source of heat.

The third is $s\,\dfrac{a - b}{e}\,K$, the coefficient K being the measure of the conducibility proper to the homogeneous substance which forms the boundary.

The fourth is $s(b-n)H$, denoting by H the external conductivity of the surface s, which the heat quits to be dispersed into the air. The coefficients h and H may have very unequal values on account of the difference of the state of the two surfaces which bound the enclosure; they are supposed to be known, as also the coefficient K: we shall have then, to determine the three unknown quantities m, a and b. the three equations:

$$\sigma(\alpha-m)g = s(m-a)h,$$

$$\sigma(\alpha-m)g = s\frac{a-b}{e}K,$$

$$\sigma(\alpha-m)g = s(b-n)H.$$

84. The value of m is the special object of the problem. It may be found by writing the equations in the form

$$m-a = \frac{\sigma}{s}\frac{g}{h}(\alpha-m),$$

$$a-b = \frac{\sigma}{s}\frac{ge}{K}(\alpha-m),$$

$$b-n = \frac{\sigma}{s}\frac{g}{H}(\alpha-m);$$

adding, we have $\qquad m-n = (\alpha-m)\,P,$

denoting by P the known quantity $\dfrac{\sigma}{s}\left(\dfrac{g}{h}+\dfrac{ge}{K}+\dfrac{g}{H}\right);$

whence we conclude

$$m-n = (\alpha-n)\frac{P}{1+P} = \frac{(\alpha-n)\frac{\sigma}{s}\left(\frac{g}{h}+\frac{ge}{K}+\frac{g}{H}\right)}{1+\frac{\sigma}{s}\left(\frac{g}{h}+\frac{ge}{K}+\frac{g}{H}\right)}.$$

85. The result shews how $m-n$, the extent of the heating, depends on given quantities which constitute the hypothesis. We will indicate the chief results to be derived from it.

1st. The extent of the heating $m-n$ is directly proportional to the excess of the temperature of the source over that of the external air.

2nd. The value of $m-n$ does not depend on the form of the enclosure nor on its volume, but only on the ratio $\dfrac{\sigma}{s}$ of the surface from which the heat proceeds to the surface which receives it, and also on e the thickness of the boundary.

If we double σ the surface of the source of heat, the extent of the heating does not become double, but increases according to a certain law which the equation expresses.

3rd. All the specific coefficients which regulate the action of the heat, that is to say, g, K, H and h, compose, with the dimension e, in the value of $m-n$ a single element $\dfrac{g}{h}+\dfrac{ge}{K}+\dfrac{g}{H}$, whose value may be determined by observation.

If we doubled e the thickness of the boundary, we should have the same result if, in forming it, we employed a substance whose conductivity proper was twice as great. Thus the employment of substances which are bad conductors of heat permits us to make the thickness of the boundary small; the effect which is obtained depends only on the ratio $\dfrac{e}{K}$.

4th. If the conducibility K is nothing, we find $m = \alpha$; that is to say, the inner air assumes the temperature of the source: the same is the case if H is zero, or h zero. These consequences are otherwise evident, since the heat cannot then be dispersed into the external air.

5th. The values of the quantities g, H, h, K and α, which we supposed known, may be measured by direct experiments, as we shall shew in the sequel; but in the actual problem, it will be sufficient to notice the value of $m - n$ which corresponds to given values of σ and of α, and this value may be used to determine the whole coefficient $\dfrac{g}{h} + \dfrac{ge}{K} + \dfrac{g}{H}$, by means of the equation

$$m - n = (\alpha - n)\frac{\sigma}{s}\, p \div \left(1 + \frac{\sigma}{s}\, p\right)$$ in which p denotes the coefficient sought. We must substitute in this equation, instead of $\dfrac{\sigma}{s}$ and $\alpha - n$, the values of those quantities, which we suppose given, and that of $m - n$ which observation will have made known. From it may be derived the value of p, and we may then apply the formula to any number of other cases.

6th. The coefficient H enters into the value of $m - n$ in the same manner as the coefficient h; consequently the state of the surface, or that of the envelope which covers it, produces the same effect, whether it has reference to the inner or outer surface.

We should have considered it useless to take notice of these different consequences, if we were not treating here of entirely new problems, whose results may be of direct use.

86. We know that animated bodies retain a temperature sensibly fixed, which we may regard as independent of the temperature of the medium in which they live. These bodies are, after some fashion, constant sources of heat, just as inflamed substances are in which the combustion has become uniform. We may then, by aid of the preceding remarks, foresee and regulate exactly the rise of temperature in places where a great number of men are collected together. If we there observe the height of the thermometer under given circumstances, we shall determine in advance what that height would be, if the number of men assembled in the same space became very much greater.

In reality, there are several accessory circumstances which modify the results, such as the unequal thickness of the parts of the enclosure, the difference of their aspect, the effects which the outlets produce, the unequal distribution of heat in the air. We cannot therefore rigorously apply the rules given by analysis; nevertheless these rules are valuable in themselves, because they contain the true principles of the matter: they prevent vague reasonings and useless or confused attempts.

87. If the same space were heated by two or more sources of different kinds, or if the first enclosure were itself contained in a second enclosure separated from the first by a mass of air, we might easily determine in like manner the degree of heating and the temperature of the surfaces.

If we suppose that, besides the first source σ, there is a second heated surface π, whose constant temperature is β, and external conductivity j, we shall find, all the other denominations being retained, the following equation:

$$m-n= \frac{\frac{(\alpha-n)\sigma g + (\beta-n)\pi j}{s}\left(\frac{e}{K}+\frac{1}{H}+\frac{1}{h}\right)}{1+\frac{\sigma g+\pi j}{s}\left(\frac{e}{K}+\frac{1}{H}+\frac{1}{h}\right)}.$$

If we suppose only one source σ, and if the first enclosure is itself contained in a second, s', h', K', H', e', representing the elements of the second enclosure which correspond to those of the first which were denoted by s, h, K, H, e; we shall find, p denoting the temperature of the air which surrounds the external surface of the second enclosure, the following equation:

$$m-p= \frac{(\alpha-p)P}{1+P}.$$

The quantity P represents

$$\frac{\sigma}{s}\left(\frac{g}{h}+\frac{ge}{K}+\frac{g}{H}\right)+\frac{\sigma}{s'}\left(\frac{g}{h'}+\frac{ge'}{K'}+\frac{g}{H'}\right).$$

We should obtain a similar result if we had three or a greater number of successive enclosures; and from this we conclude that these solid envelopes, separated by air, assist very much in increasing the degree of heating, however small their thickness may be.

88. To make this remark more evident, we will compare the quantity of heat which escapes from the heated surface, with that which the same body would lose, if the surface which envelopes it were separated from it by an interval filled with air.

If the body A be heated by a constant cause, so that its surface preserves a fixed temperature b, the air being maintained at a less temperature a, the quantity of heat which escapes into the air in the unit of time across a unit of surface will be expressed by $h(b-a)$, h being the measure of the external conductivity. Hence in order that the mass may preserve a fixed temperature b, it is necessary that the source, whatever it may be, should furnish a quantity of heat equal to $hS(b-a)$, S denoting the area of the surface of the solid.

Suppose an extremely thin shell to be detached from the body A and separated from the solid by an interval filled with air; and suppose the surface of the same solid A to be still maintained at the temperature b. We see that the air contained between the shell and the body will be heated and will take a temperature a' greater than a. The shell itself will attain a permanent state and will transmit to the external air whose fixed temperature is a all the heat which the body loses. It follows that the quantity of heat escaping from the solid will be $hS(b-a')$, instead of being $hS(b-a)$, for we suppose that the new surface of the solid and the surfaces which bound the shell have likewise the same external conducibility h. It is evident that the expenditure of the source of heat will be less than it was at first. The problem is to determine the exact ratio of these quantities.

89. Let e be the thickness of the shell, m the fixed temperature of its inner surface, n that of its outer surface, and K its internal conductivity. We shall have, as the expression of the quantity of heat which leaves the solid through its surface, $hS(b-a')$.

As that of the quantity which penetrates the inner surface of the shell, $hS(a'-m)$.

As that of the quantity which crosses any section whatever of the same shell, $KS\dfrac{m-n}{e}$.

Lastly, as the expression of the quantity which passes through the outer surface into the air, $hS(n-a)$.

All these quantities must be equal, we have therefore the following equations:

$$h(n-a) = \frac{K}{e}\,(m-n),$$

$$h(n-a) = h(a'-m),$$

$$h(n-a) = h(b-a').$$

If moreover we write down the identical equation

$$h(n-a) = h(n-a),$$

and arrange them all under the forms

$$n-a = n-a,$$

$$m-n = \frac{he}{K}\,(n-a),$$

$$a'-m = n-a,$$

$$b-a' = n-a,$$

we find, on addition,

$$b-a = (n-a)\left(3+\frac{he}{K}\right).$$

The quantity of heat lost by the solid was $hS(b-a)$, when its surface communicated freely with the air, it is now $hS(b-a')$ or $hS(n-a)$, which is equivalent to $hS\dfrac{b-a}{3+\dfrac{he}{K}}$.

The first quantity is greater than the second in the ratio of $3+\dfrac{he}{K}$ to 1.

In order therefore to maintain at temperature b a solid whose surface communicates directly to the air, more than three times as much heat is necessary than would be required to maintain it at temperature b, when its extreme surface is not adherent but separated from the solid by any small interval whatever filled with air.

If we suppose the thickness e to be infinitely small, the ratio of the quantities of heat lost will be 3, which would also be the value if K were infinitely great.

We can easily account for this result, for the heat being unable to escape into the external air, without penetrating several surfaces, the quantity which flows out must diminish as the number of interposed surfaces increases; but we should have been unable to arrive at any exact judgment in this case, if the problem had not been submitted to analysis.

90. We have not considered, in the preceding article, the effect of radiation across the layer of air which separates the two surfaces; nevertheless this circumstance modifies the problem, since there is a portion of heat which

passes directly across the intervening air. We shall suppose then, to make the object of the analysis more distinct, that the interval between the surfaces is free from air, and that the heated body is covered by any number whatever of parallel laminæ separated from each other.

If the heat which escapes from the solid through its plane superficies maintained at a temperature b expanded itself freely in vacuo and was received by a parallel surface maintained at a less temperature a, the quantity which would be dispersed in unit of time across unit of surface would be proportional to $(b-a)$, the difference of the two constant temperatures: this quantity would be represented by $H(b-a)$, H being the value of the relative conducibility which is not the same as h.

The source which maintains the solid in its original state must therefore furnish, in every unit of time, a quantity of heat equal to $HS(b-a)$.

We must now determine the new value of this expenditure in the case where the surface of the body is covered by several successive laminæ separated by intervals free from air, supposing always that the solid is subject to the action of any external cause whatever which maintains its surface at the temperature b.

Imagine the whole system of temperatures to have become fixed; let m_1 be the temperature of the under surface of the first lamina which is consequently opposite to that of the solid, let n_1 be the temperature of the upper surface of the same lamina, e its thickness, and K its specific conductivity; denote also by m_1, n_1, m_2, n_2, m_3, n_3, m_4, n_4, &c. the temperatures of the under and upper surfaces of the different laminæ, and by K, e, the conductivity and thickness of the same laminæ; lastly suppose all these surfaces to be in a state similar to the surface of the solid, so that the value of the coefficient H is common to them.

The quantity of heat which penetrates the under surface of a lamina corresponding to any suffix i is $HS(n_{i-1}-m_i)$, that which crosses this lamina is $\dfrac{KS}{e}(m_i-n_i)$, and the quantity which escapes from its upper surface is $HS(n_i-m_{i+1})$. These three quantities, and all those which refer to the other laminæ are equal; we may therefore form the equation by comparing all these quantities in question with the first of them, which is $HS(b-m_1)$; we shall thus have, denoting the number of laminæ by j:

$$b-m_1=b-m_1,$$

$$m_1-n_1=\frac{He}{K}(b-m_1),$$

$$n_1-m_2=b-m_1,$$

$$m_2-n_2=\frac{He}{K}(b-m_1),$$

$$\cdot\quad\cdot\quad\cdot\quad\cdot$$

$$m_j-n_j=\frac{He}{K}(b-m_1),$$

$$n_j-a=b-m_1.$$

Adding these equations, we find

$$(b-a)=(b-m_1)j\left(1+\frac{He}{K}\right)+1.$$

The expenditure of the source of heat necessary to maintain the surface of the body A at the temperature b is $HS(b-a)$, when this surface sends its rays to a fixed surface maintained at the temperature a. The expenditure is

$HS(b-m_1)$ when we place between the surface of the body A, and the fixed surface maintained at temperature a, a number j of isolated laminæ; thus the quantity of heat which the source must furnish is very much less in the second hypotheses than in the first, and the ratio of the two quantities is $\dfrac{1}{j\left(1+\dfrac{He}{K}\right)+1}$.

If we suppose the thickness e of the laminæ to be infinitely small, the ratio is $\dfrac{1}{j+1}$. The expenditure of the source is then inversely as the number of laminæ which cover the surface of the solid.

91. The examination of these results and of those which we obtained when the intervals between successive enclosures were occupied by atmospheric air explain clearly why the separation of surfaces and the intervention of air assist very much in retaining heat.

Analysis furnishes in addition analogous consequences when we suppose the source to be external, and that the heat which emanates from it crosses successively different diathermanous envelopes and the air which they enclose. This is what has happened when experimenters have exposed to the rays of the sun thermometers covered by several sheets of glass within which different layers of air have been enclosed.

For similar reasons the temperature of the higher regions of the atmosphere is very much less than at the surface of the earth.

In general the theorems concerning the heating of air in closed spaces extend to a great variety of problems. It would be useful to revert to them when we wish to foresee and regulate temperature with precision, as in the case of green-houses, drying-houses, sheep-folds, work-shops, or in many civil establishments, such as hospitals, barracks, places of assembly.

In these different applications we must attend to accessory circumstances which modify the results of analysis, such as the unequal thickness of different parts of the enclosure, the introduction of air, &c.; but these details would draw us away from our chief object, which is the exact demonstration of general principles.

For the rest, we have considered only, in what has just been said, the permanent state of temperature in closed spaces. We can in addition express analytically the variable state which precedes, or that which begins to take place when the source of heat is withdrawn, and we can also ascertain in this way, how the specific properties of the bodies which we employ, or their dimensions affect the progress and duration of the heating; but these researches require a different analysis, the principles of which will be explained in the following chapters.

SECTION VII. *On the Uniform Movement of Heat in Three Dimensions*

92. Up to this time we have considered the uniform movement of heat in one dimension only, but it is easy to apply the same principles to the case in which heat is propagated uniformly in three directions at right angles.

Suppose the different points of a solid enclosed by six planes at right angles to have unequal actual temperatures represented by the linear equation $v = A + ax + by + cz$, x, y, z, being the rectangular co-ordinates of a molecule whose temperature is v. Suppose further that any external causes whatever acting on the six faces of the prism maintain every one of the molecules situated on the surface, at its actual temperature expressed by the general equation

$$v = A + ax + by + cz \cdot \cdot \cdot (a),$$

we shall prove that the same causes which, by hypothesis, keep the outer layers of the solid in their initial state, are sufficient to preserve also the actual temperatures of every one of the inner molecules, so that their temperatures do not cease to be represented by the linear equation.

The examination of this question is an element of the general theory, it will serve to determine the laws of the varied movement of heat in the interior of a solid of any form whatever, for every one of the prismatic molecules of which the body is composed is during an infinitely small time in a state similar to that which the linear equation (a) expresses. We may then, by following the ordinary principles of the differential calculus, easily deduce from the notion of uniform movement the general equations of varied movement.

93. In order to prove that when the extreme layers of the solid preserve their temperatures no change can happen in the interior of the mass, it is sufficient to compare with each other the quantities of heat which, during the same instant, cross two parallel planes.

Let b be the perpendicular distance of these two planes which we first suppose parallel to the horizontal plane of x and y. Let m and m' be two infinitely near molecules, one of which is above the first horizontal plane and the other below it: let x, y, z be the co-ordinates of the first molecule, and x', y', z' those of the second. In like manner let M and M' denote two infinitely near molecules, separated by the second horizontal plane and situated, relatively to that plane, in the same manner as m and m' are relatively to the first plane; that is to say, the co-ordinates of M are x, y, $z+\beta$, and those of M' are x', y', $z'+\beta$. It is evident that the distance mm' of the two molecules m and m' is equal to the distance MM' of the two molecules M and M'; further, let v be the temperature of m, and v' that of m', also let V and V' be the temperatures of M and M', it is easy to see that the two differences $v-v'$ and $V-V'$ are equal; in fact, substituting first the co-ordinates of m and m' in the general equation

$$v = A + ax + by + cz,$$

we find
$$v - v' = a(x-x') + b(y-y') + c(z-z'),$$

and then substituting the co-ordinates of M and M', we find also $V-V' = a(x-x') + b(y-y') + c(z-z')$. Now the quantity of heat which m sends to m' depends on the distance mm', which separates these molecules, and it is proportional to the difference $v-v'$ of their temperatures. This quantity of heat transferred may be represented by

$$q(v-v')dt;$$

the value of the coefficient q depends in some manner on the distance mm', and on the nature of the substance of which the solid is formed, dt is the duration of the instant. The quantity of heat transferred from M to M', or the action of M on M' is expressed likewise by $q(V-V')dt$, and the coefficient q is the same as in the expression $q(v-v')dt$, since the distance MM' is equal to mm' and the two actions are effected in the same solid: furthermore $V-V'$ is equal to $v-v'$, hence the two actions are equal.

If we choose two other points n and n', very near to each other, which transfer heat across the first horizontal plane, we shall find in the same manner that their action is equal to that of two homologous points N and N' which communicate heat across the second horizontal plane. We conclude then that the whole quantity of heat which crosses the first plane is equal to that which crosses the second plane during the same instant. We should derive the same result from the comparison of two planes parallel to the plane of x and z, or from the comparison of two other planes parallel to the plane of y and z. Hence any part whatever of the solid enclosed between six planes at right angles, receives through each of its faces as much heat as it loses through the opposite face; hence no portion of the solid can change temperature.

94. Thus, across one of these planes, a quantity of heat flows which is the same at all instants, and which is also the same for all other parallel sections.

In order to determine the value of this constant flow we shall compare it with the quantity of heat which flows uniformly in the most simple case, which has been already discussed. The case is that of an infinite solid enclosed between two infinite planes and maintained in a constant state. We have seen that the temperatures of the different points of the mass are in this case represented by the equation $v = A + cz$; we proceed to prove that the uniform flow of heat per unit area propagated in the vertical direction in the infinite solid is equal to that which flows in the same direction per unit area across the prism enclosed by six planes at right angles. This equality necessarily exists if the coefficient c in the equation $v = A + cz$, belonging to the first solid, is the same as the coefficient c in the more general equation $v = A + ax + by + cz$ which represents the state of the prism. In fact, denoting by H a plane in this prism perpendicular to z, and by m and μ two molecules very near to each other, the first of which m is below the plane H, and the second above this plane, let v be the temperature of m whose co-ordinates are x, y, z, and w the temperature of μ whose co-ordinates are $x + \alpha$, $y + \beta$, $z + \gamma$. Take a third molecule μ' whose co-ordinates are $x - \alpha$, $y - \beta$, $z + \gamma$, and whose temperature may be denoted by w'. We see that μ and μ' are on the same horizontal plane, and that the vertical drawn from the middle point of the line $\mu\mu'$, which joins these two points, passes through the point m, so that the distances $m\mu$ and $m\mu'$ are equal. The action of m on μ, or the quantity of heat which the first of these molecules sends to the other across the plane H, depends on the difference $v - w$ of their temperatures. The action of m on μ' depends in the same manner on the difference $v - w'$ of the temperatures of these molecules, since the distance of m from μ is the same as that of m from μ'. Thus, expressing by $q(v - w)$ the action of m on μ during the unit of time, we shall have $q(v - w')$ to express the action of m on μ', q being a common unknown factor, depending on the distance $m\mu$ and on the nature of the solid. Hence the sum of the two actions exerted during unit of time is $q(v - w + v - w')$.

If instead of x, y, and z, in the general equation

$$v = A + ax + by + cz,$$

we substitute the co-ordinates of m and then those of μ and μ', we shall find

$$v - w = -a\alpha - b\beta - c\gamma,$$
$$v - w = +a\alpha + b\beta - c\gamma.$$

The sum of the two actions of m on μ and of m on μ' is therefore $-2qc\gamma$.

Suppose then that the plane H belongs to the infinite solid whose temperature equation is $v = A + cz$, and that we denote also by m, μ and μ' those molecules in this solid whose co-ordinates are x, y, z for the first, $x + \alpha$, $y + \beta$, $z + \gamma$ for the second, and $x - \alpha$, $y - \beta$, $z + \gamma$ for the third: we shall have, as in the preceding case, $v - w + v - w' = -2c\gamma$. Thus the sum of the two actions of m on μ and of m on μ', is the same in the infinite solid as in the prism enclosed between the six planes at right angles.

We should obtain a similar result, if we considered the action of another point n below the plane H on two others ν and ν', situated at the same height above the plane. Hence, the sum of all the actions of this kind, which are exerted across the plane H, that is to say the whole quantity of heat which, during unit of time, passes to the upper side of this surface, by virtue of the action of very near molecules which it separates, is always the same in both solids.

95. In the second of these two bodies, that which is bounded by two infinite planes, and whose temperature equation is $v = A + cz$, we know that the quantity of heat which flows during unit of time across unit of area taken on any horizontal section whatever is $-cK$, c being the coefficient of z, and K the specific conductivity; hence, the quantity of heat which, in the prism enclosed between six planes at right angles, crosses during unit of time, unit of area taken on any horizontal section whatever, is also $-cK$, when the linear equation which represents the temperatures of the prism is

$$v = A + ax + by + cz.$$

In the same way it may be proved that the quantity of heat which, during unit of time, flows uniformly across unit of area taken on any section whatever perpendicular to x, is expressed by $-aK$, and that the whole quantity which, during unit of time, crosses unit of area taken on a section perpendicular to y, is expressed by $-bK$.

The theorems which we have demonstrated in this and the two preceding articles, suppose the direct action of heat in the interior of the mass to be limited to an extremely small distance, but they would still be true, if the rays of heat sent out by each molecule could penetrate directly to a quite appreciable distance, but it would be necessary in this case, as we have remarked in Article 70, to suppose that the cause which maintains the temperatures of the faces of the solid affects a part extending within the mass to a finite depth.

SECTION VIII. *Measure of the Movement of Heat at a Given Point of a Solid Mass*

96. It still remains for us to determine one of the principal elements of the theory of heat, which consists in defining and in measuring exactly the quantity of heat which passes through every point of a solid mass across a plane whose direction is given.

If heat is unequally distributed amongst the molecules of the same body, the temperatures at any point will vary every instant. Denoting by t the time which has elapsed, and by v the temperature attained after a time t by an infinitely small molecule whose co-ordinates are x, y, z; the variable state of the solid will be expressed by an equation similar to the following $v = F(x, y, z, t)$. Suppose the function F to be given, and that consequently we can determine at every instant the temperature of any point whatever; imagine that through the point m we draw a horizontal plane parallel to that of x and y, and that on this plane we trace an infinitely small circle ω, whose centre is at m; it is required to determine what is the quantity of heat which during the instant dt will pass across the circle ω from the part of the solid which is below the plane into the part above it.

All points extremely near to the point m and under the plane exert their action during the infinitely small instant dt, on all those which are above the plane and extremely near to the point m, that is to say, each of the points situated on one side of this plane will send heat to each of those which are situated on the other side.

We shall consider as positive an action whose effect is to transport a certain quantity of heat above the plane, and as negative that which causes heat to pass below the plane. The sum of all the partial actions which are exerted across the circle ω, that is to say, the sum of all the quantities of heat which, crossing any point whatever of this circle, pass from the part of the solid below the plane to the part above, compose the flow whose expression is to be found.

It is easy to imagine that this flow may not be the same throughout the whole extent of the solid, and that if at another point m' we traced a horizontal circle ω' equal to the former, the two quantities of heat which rise above these planes ω and ω' during the same instant might not be equal: these quantities are comparable with each other and their ratios are numbers which may be easily determined.

97. We know already the value of the constant flow for the case of linear and uniform movement; thus in the solid enclosed between two infinite horizontal planes, one of which is maintained at the temperature a and the other at the temperature b, the flow of heat is the same for every part of the mass; we may regard it as taking place in the vertical direction only. The value corresponding to unit of surface and to unit of time is $K\left(\dfrac{a-b}{e}\right)$, e denoting the perpendicular distance of the two planes, and K the specific conducibility: the temperatures at the different points of the solid are expressed by the equation

$$v = a - \left(\frac{a-b}{e}\right)z.$$

When the problem is that of a solid comprised between six rectangular planes, pairs of which are parallel, and the temperatures at the different points are expressed by the equation

$$v = A + ax + by + cz,$$

the propagation takes place at the same time along the directions of x, of y, of z; the quantity of heat which flows across a definite portion of a plane parallel to that of x and y is the same throughout the whole extent of the prism; its value corresponding to unit of surface, and to unit of time is $-cK$, in the direction of z, it is $-bK$, in the direction of y, and $-aK$ in that of x.

In general the value of the vertical flow in the two cases which we have just cited, depends only on the coefficient of z and on the specific conductivity K; this value is always equal to $-K\dfrac{dv}{dz}$.

The expression of the quantity of heat which, during the instant dt, flows across a horizontal circle infinitely small, whose area is ω, and passes in this manner from the part of the solid which is below the plane of the circle to the part above, is, for the two cases in question, $-K\dfrac{dv}{dz}\omega dt$.

98. It is easy now to generalise this result and to recognise that it exists in every case of the varied movement of heat expressed by the equation $v = F(x, y, z, t)$.

Let us in fact denote by x', y', z', the co-ordinates of this point m, and its actual temperature by v'. Let $x'+\xi$, $y'+\eta$, $z'+\zeta$, be the co-ordinates of a point μ infinitely near to the point m, and whose temperature is w; ξ, η, ζ are quantities infinitely small added to the co-ordinates x', y', z'; they determine the position of molecules infinitely near to the point m, with respect to three rectangular axes, whose origin is at m, parallel to the axes of x, y, and z. Differentiating the equation

$$v = F(x, y, z, t)$$

and replacing the differentials by ξ, η, ζ, we shall have, to express the value of w which is equivalent to $v+dv$, the linear equation $w = v' + \dfrac{dv'}{dx}\xi + \dfrac{dv'}{dy}\eta + \dfrac{dv'}{dz}\zeta$;

the coefficients v', $\dfrac{dv'}{dx}$, $\dfrac{dv'}{dy}$, $\dfrac{dv'}{dz}$, are functions of x, y, z, t, in which the given and constant values x', y', z', which belong to the point m, have been substituted for x, y, z.

Suppose that the same point m belongs also to a solid enclosed between six rectangular planes, and that the actual temperatures of the points of this prism, whose dimensions are finite, are expressed by the linear equation $w = A + a\xi + b\eta + c\zeta$; and that the molecules situated on the faces which bound the solid are maintained by some external cause at the temperature which is assigned to them by the linear equation. ξ, η, ζ are the rectangular co-ordinates of a molecule of the prism, whose temperature is w, referred to three axes whose origin is at m.

This arranged, if we take as the values of the constant coefficients A, a, b, c, which enter into the equation for the prism, the quantities v', $\dfrac{dv'}{dx}$, $\dfrac{dv'}{dy}$, $\dfrac{dv'}{dz}$, which belong to the differential equation; the state of the prism expressed by the equation

$$w = v' + \frac{dv'}{dx}\xi + \frac{dv'}{dy}\eta + \frac{dv'}{dz}\zeta$$

will coincide as nearly as possible with the state of the solid; that is to say, all the molecules infinitely near to the point m will have the same temperature, whether we consider them to be in the solid or in the prism. This coincidence of the solid and the prism is quite analogous to that of curved surfaces with the planes which touch them.

It is evident, from this, that the quantity of heat which flows in the solid across the circle ω, during the instant dt, is the same as that which flows in the prism across the same circle; for all the molecules whose actions concur in one effect or the other, have the same temperature in the two solids. Hence, the flow in question, in one solid or the other, is expressed by $-K\dfrac{dv}{dz}\omega dt$. It would be $-K\dfrac{dv}{dy}\omega dt$, if the circle ω, whose centre is m, were perpendicular to the axis of y, and $-K\dfrac{dv}{dx}\omega dt$, if this circle were perpendicular to the axis of x.

The value of the flow which we have just determined varies in the solid from one point to another, and it varies also with the time. We might imagine it to have, at all the points of a unit of surface, the same value as at the point m, and to preserve this value during unit of time; the flow would then be expressed by $-K\dfrac{dv}{dz}$, it would be $-K\dfrac{dv}{dy}$ in the direction of y, and $-K\dfrac{dv}{dx}$ in that of x. We shall ordinarily employ in calculation this value of the flow thus referred to unit of time and to unit of surface.

99. This theorem serves in general to measure the velocity with which heat tends to traverse a given point of a plane situated in any manner whatever in the interior of a solid whose temperatures vary with the time. Through the given point m, a perpendicular must be raised upon the plane, and at every point of this perpendicular ordinates must be drawn to represent the actual temperatures at its different points. A plane curve will thus be formed whose axis of abscissæ is the perpendicular. The fluxion of the ordinate of this curve, answering to the point m, taken with the opposite sign, expresses the velocity with which heat is transferred across the plane. This fluxion of the ordinate is known to be the tangent of the angle formed by the element of the curve with a parallel to the abscissæ.

The result which we have just explained is that of which the most frequent applications have been made in the theory of heat. We cannot discuss the different problems without forming a very exact idea of the value of the flow at every point of a body whose temperatures are variable. It is necessary to insist on this fundamental notion; an example which we are about to refer to will indicate more clearly the use which has been made of it in analysis.

100. Suppose the different points of a cubic mass, an edge of which has the length π, to have unequal actual temperatures represented by the equation $v = \cos x \cos y \cos z$. The co-ordinates x, y, z are measured on three rectangular axes, whose origin is at the centre of the cube, perpendicular to the faces. The points of the external surface of the solid are at the actual temperature 0, and it is supposed also that external causes maintain at all these points the actual temperature 0. On this hypothesis the body will be cooled more and more, the temperatures of all the points situated in the interior of the mass will vary, and, after an infinite time, they will all attain the temperature 0 of the surface. Now, we shall prove in the sequel, that the variable state of this solid is expressed by the equation

$$v = e^{-gt} \cos x \cos y \cos z,$$

the coefficient g is equal to $\dfrac{3K}{C \cdot D}$, K is the specific conductivity of the substance of which the solid is formed, D is the density and C the specific heat; t is the time elapsed.

We here suppose that the truth of this equation is admitted, and we proceed to examine the use which may be made of it to find the quantity of heat which crosses a given plane parallel to one of the three planes at the right angles.

If, through the point m, whose co-ordinates are x, y, z, we draw a plane perpendicular to z, we shall find, after the mode of the preceding article, that the value of the flow, at this point and across the plane, is $-K\dfrac{dv}{dz}$, or $Ke^{-gt}\cos x \cdot \cos y \cdot \sin z$. The quantity of heat which, during the instant dt, crosses an infinitely small rectangle, situated on this plane, and whose sides are dx and dy, is

$$K\ e^{-gt} \cos x \cos y \sin z\ dx\ dy\ dt.$$

Thus the whole heat which, during the instant dt, crosses the entire area of the same plane, is

$$K\ e^{-gt} \sin z \cdot dt \iint \cos x \cos y\ ax\ dy;$$

the double integral being taken from $x = -\frac{1}{2}\pi$ up to $x = \frac{1}{2}\pi$, and from $y = -\frac{1}{2}\pi$ up to $y = \frac{1}{2}\pi$. We find then for the expression of this total heat,

$$4\ K\ e^{-gt} \sin z \cdot dt.$$

If then we take the integral with respect to t, from $t = 0$ to $t = t$, we shall find the quantity of heat which has crossed the same plane since the cooling began up to the actual moment. This integral is $\dfrac{4K}{g} \sin z(1 - e^{-gt})$, its value at the surface is

$$\frac{4K}{g}(1 - e^{-gt}),$$

so that after an infinite time the quantity of heat lost through one of the faces is $\dfrac{4K}{g}$. The same reasoning being applicable to each of the six faces, we conclude that the solid has lost by its complete cooling a total quantity of heat equal to $\dfrac{24K}{g}$ or $8CD$, since g is equivalent to $\dfrac{3K}{CD}$. The total heat which is dissipated during the cooling must indeed be independent of the special conductivity K, which can only influence more or less the velocity of cooling.

100. A. We may determine in another manner the quantity of heat which the solid loses during a given time, and this will serve in some degree to verify the preceding calculation. In fact, the mass of the rectangular molecule whose dimensions are dx, dy, dz, is $D\ dx\ dy\ dz$, consequently the quantity of heat which must be given to it to bring it from the temperature 0 to that of boiling water is $CD\ dx\ dy\ dz$, and if it were required to raise this molecule to the temperature v, the expenditure of heat would be $v\ CD\ dx\ dy\ dz$.

It follows from this, that in order to find the quantity by which the heat of the solid, after time t, exceeds that which it contained at the temperature 0, we must take the multiple integral $\iiint v\ CD\ dx\ dy\ dz$, between the limits $x = -\frac{1}{2}\pi$, $x = \frac{1}{2}\pi$, $y = -\frac{1}{2}\pi$, $y = \frac{1}{2}\pi$, $z = -\frac{1}{2}\pi$, $z = \frac{1}{2}\pi$.

We thus find, on substituting for v its value, that is to say

$$e^{-gt} \cos x \cos y \cos z,$$

that the excess of actual heat over that which belongs to the temperature 0 is $8CDe^{-gt}$; or, at the start, $8CD$, as we found before.

We have described, in this introduction, all the elements which it is necessary to know in order to solve different problems relating to the movement of heat in solid bodies, and we have given some applications of these principles, in order to shew the mode of employing them in analysis; the most important use which we have been able to make of them, is to deduce from them the general equations of the propagation of heat, which is the subject of the next chapter.

SECOND CHAPTER

Equations of the Movement of Heat

SECTION I. *Equation of the Varied Movement of Heat in a Ring*

101. We might form the general equations which represent the movement of heat in solid bodies of any form whatever, and apply them to particular cases. But this method would often involve very complicated calculations which may easily be avoided. There are several problems which it is preferable to treat in a special manner by expressing the conditions which are appropriate to them; we proceed to adopt this course and examine separately the problems which have been enunciated in the first section of the introduction; we will limit ourselves at first to forming the differential equations, and shall give the integrals of them in the following chapters.

102. We have already considered the uniform movement of heat in a prismatic bar of small thickness whose extremity is immersed in a constant source of heat. This first case offered no difficulties, since there was no reference except to the permanent state of the temperatures, and the equation which expresses them is easily integrated. The following problem requires a more profound investigation; its object is to determine the variable state of a solid ring whose different points have received initial temperatures entirely arbitrary.

The solid ring or armlet is generated by the revolution of a rectangular section about an axis perpendicular to the plane of the ring (see figure 3), l is the perimeter of the section whose area is S, the coefficient h measures the external conductivity, K the internal conductivity, C the specific capacity for heat, D the density. The line $oxx'x''$ represents the mean circumference of the armlet, or that line which passes through the centres of figure of all the sections; the distance of a section from the origin o is measured by the arc whose length is x; R is the radius of the mean circumference.

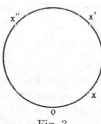

Fig. 3

It is supposed that on account of the small dimensions and of the form of the section, we may consider the temperature at the different points of the same section to be equal.

103. Imagine that initial arbitrary temperatures have been given to the different sections of the armlet, and that the solid is then exposed to air maintained at the temperature 0, and displaced with a constant velocity; the system of temperatures will continually vary, heat will be transmitted within the ring, and dispersed at the surface: it is required to determine what will be the state of the solid at any given instant.

Let v be the temperature which the section situated at distance x will have acquired after a lapse of time t; v is a certain function of x and t, into which all the initial temperatures also must enter: this is the function which is to be discovered.

221

104. We will consider the movement of heat in an infinitely small slice, enclosed between a section made at distance x and another section made at distance $x+dx$. The state of this slice for the duration of one instant is that of an infinite solid terminated by two parallel planes maintained at unequal temperatures; thus the quantity of heat which flows during this instant dt across the first section, and passes in this way from the part of the solid which precedes the slice into the slice itself, is measured according to the principles established in the introduction, by the product of four factors, that is to say, the conducibility K, the area of the section S, the ratio $-\dfrac{dv}{dx}$, and the duration of the instant; its expression is $-KS\dfrac{dv}{dx}\,dt$. To determine the quantity of heat which escapes from the same slice across the second section, and passes into the contiguous part of the solid, it is only necessary to change x into $x+dx$ in the preceding expression, or, which is the same thing, to add to this expression its differential taken with respect to x; thus the slice receives through one of its faces a quantity of heat equal to $-KS\dfrac{dv}{dx}\,dt$, and loses through the opposite face a quantity of heat expressed by

$$-KS\frac{dv}{dx}\,dt - KS\frac{d^2v}{dx^2}\,dx\,dt.$$

It acquires therefore by reason of its position a quantity of heat equal to the difference of the two preceding quantities, that is

$$KS\frac{d^2v}{dx^2}\,dx\,dt.$$

On the other hand, the same slice, whose external surface is ldx and whose temperature differs infinitely little from v, allows a quantity of heat equivalent to $hlv\,dx\,dt$ to escape into the air during the instant dt; it follows from this that this infinitely small part of the solid retains in reality a quantity of heat represented by $KS\dfrac{d^2v}{dx^2}\,dx\,dt - hlv\,dx\,dt$ which makes its temperature vary. The amount of this change must be examined.

105. The coefficient C expresses how much heat is required to raise unit of weight of the substance in question from temperature 0 up to temperature 1; consequently, multiplying the volume Sdx of the infinitely small slice by the density D, to obtain its weight, and by C the specific capacity for heat, we shall have $CDS\,dx$ as the quantity of heat which would raise the volume of the slice from temperature 0 up to temperature 1. Hence the increase of temperature which results from the addition of a quantity of heat equal to $KS\dfrac{d^2v}{dx^2}\,dx\,dt$ $-hlv\,dx\,dt$ will be found by dividing the last quantity by $CDS\,dx$. Denoting therefore, according to custom, the increase of temperature which takes place during the instant dt by $\dfrac{dv}{dt}\,dt$, we shall have the equation

$$\frac{dv}{dt} = \frac{K}{CD}\frac{d^2v}{dx^2} - \frac{hl}{CDS}v \cdot \cdot \cdot \cdot (b).$$

We shall explain in the sequel the use which may be made of this equation to determine the complete solution, and what the difficulty of the problem consists in; we limit ourselves here to a remark concerning the permanent state of the armlet.

106. Suppose that, the plane of the ring being horizontal, sources of heat, each of which exerts a constant action, are placed below different points m, n, p, q etc.; heat will be propagated in the solid, and that which is dissipated through the surface being incessantly replaced by that which emanates from the sources, the temperature of every section of the solid will approach more and more to a stationary value which varies from one section to another. In order to express by means of equation (b) the law of the latter temperatures, which would exist of themselves if they were once established, we must suppose that the quantity v does not vary with respect to t; which annuls the term $\dfrac{dv}{dt}$. We thus have the equation

$$\frac{d^2v}{dx^2} = \frac{hl}{KS}\, v, \text{ whence } v = M e^{-x\sqrt{\frac{hl}{KS}}} + N e^{+x\sqrt{\frac{hl}{KS}}},$$

M and N being two constants.

107. Suppose a portion of the circumference of the ring, situated between two successive sources of heat, to be divided into equal parts, and denote by v_1, v_2, v_3, v_4, &c., the temperatures at the points of division whose distances from the origin are x_1, x_2, x_3, x_4, &c.; the relation between v and x will be given by the preceding equation, after the two constants have been determined by means of the two values of v corresponding to the sources of heat. Denoting by α the quantity $e^{-\sqrt{\frac{hl}{KS}}}$, and by λ the distance $x_2 - x_1$ of two consecutive points of division, we shall have the equations:

$$v_1 = M\alpha^{x_1} + N\alpha^{-x_1},$$
$$v_2 = M\alpha^{\lambda} \cdot \alpha^{x_1} + N\alpha^{-\lambda}\alpha^{-x_1},$$
$$v_3 = M\alpha^{2\lambda}\alpha^{x_1} + N\alpha^{-2\lambda}\alpha^{-x_1},$$

whence we derive the following relation $\dfrac{v_1+v_3}{v_2} = \alpha^{\lambda} + \alpha^{-\lambda}$.

We should find a similar result for the three points whose temperatures are v_2, v_3, v_4, and in general for any three consecutive points. It follows from this that if we observed the temperatures v_1, v_2, v_3, v_4, v_5 &c. of several successive points, all situated between the same two sources m and n and separated by a constant interval λ, we should perceive that any three consecutive temperatures are always such that the sum of the two extremes divided by the mean gives a constant quotient $\alpha^{\lambda} + \alpha^{-\lambda}$.

108. If, in the space included between the next two sources of heat n and p, the temperatures of other different points separated by the same interval λ were observed, it would still be found that for any three consecutive points, the sum of the two extreme temperatures, divided by the mean, gives the same quotient $\alpha^{\lambda} + \alpha^{-\lambda}$. The value of this quotient depends neither on the position nor on the intensity of the sources of heat.

109. Let q be this constant value, we have the equation

$$v_3 = q v_2 - v_1;$$

we see by this that when the circumference is divided into equal parts, the temperatures at the points of division, included between two consecutive sources of heat, are represented by the terms of a recurring series whose scale of relation is composed of two terms q and -1.

Experiments have fully confirmed this result. We have exposed a metallic ring to the permanent and simultaneous action of different sources of heat, and we have observed the stationary temperatures of several points separated by constant intervals; we always found that the temperatures of any three consecutive points, not separated by a source of heat, were connected by the relation in question. Even if the sources of heat be multiplied, and in whatever manner they be disposed, no change can be effected in the numerical value of the quotient $\frac{v_1+v_3}{v_2}$; it depends only on the dimensions or on the nature of the ring, and not on the manner in which that solid is heated.

110. When we have found, by observation, the value of the constant quotient q or $\frac{v_1+v_3}{v_2}$, the value of α^λ may be derived from it by means of the equation $\alpha^\lambda+\alpha^{-\lambda}=q$. One of the roots is α^λ, and other root is $\alpha^{-\lambda}$. This quantity being determined, we may derive from it the value of the ratio $\frac{h}{K}$, which is $\frac{S}{l}(\log\alpha)^2$. Denoting α^λ by ω, we shall have $\omega^2-q\omega+1=0$. Thus the ratio of the two conductivities is found by multiplying $\frac{S}{l}$ by the square of the hyperbolic logarithm of one of the roots of the equation $\omega^2-q\omega+1=0$, and dividing the product by λ^2.

SECTION II. *Equation of the Varied Movement of Heat in a Solid Sphere*

111. A solid homogeneous mass, of the form of a sphere, having been immersed for an infinite time in a medium maintained at a permanent temperature 1, is then exposed to air which is kept at temperature 0, and displaced with constant velocity: it is required to determine the successive states of the body during the whole time of the cooling.

Denote by x the distance of any point whatever from the centre of the sphere, and by v the temperature of the same point, after a time t has elapsed; and suppose, to make the problem more general, that the initial temperature, common to all points situated at the distance x from the centre, is different for different values of x; which is what would have been the case if the immersion had not lasted for an infinite time.

Points of the solid, equally distant from the centre, will not cease to have a common temperature; v is thus a function of x and t. When we suppose $t=0$, it is essential that the value of this function should agree with the initial state which is given, and which is entirely arbitrary.

112. We shall consider the instantaneous movement of heat in an infinitely thin shell, bounded by two spherical surfaces whose radii are x and $x+dx$: the quantity of heat which, during an infinitely small instant dt, crosses the lesser surface whose radius is x, and so passes from that part of the solid which is nearest to the centre into the spherical shell, is equal to the product of four factors which are the conductivity K, the duration dt, the extent $4\pi x^2$ of surface, and the ratio $\frac{dv}{dx}$, taken with the negative sign; it is expressed by

$$-4K\pi x^2\frac{dv}{dx}dt.$$

To determine the quantity of heat which flows during the same instant through the second surface of the same shell, and passes from this shell into the part of the solid which envelops it, x must be changed into $x+dx$, in the preceding expression: that is to say, to the term $-4K\pi x^2 \dfrac{dv}{dx} dt$ must be added the differential of this term taken with respect to x. We thus find

$$-4K\pi x^2 \frac{dv}{dx} dt - 4K\pi d\left(x^2 \frac{dv}{dx}\right) \cdot dt$$

as the expression of the quantity of heat which leaves the spherical shell across its second surface; and if we subtract this quantity from that which enters through the first surface, we shall have $4K\pi d\left(x^2\dfrac{dv}{dx}\right) dt$. This difference is evidently the quantity of heat which accumulates in the intervening shell, and whose effect is to vary its temperature.

113. The coefficient C denotes the quantity of heat which is necessary to raise, from temperature 0 to temperature 1, a definite unit of weight; D is the weight of unit of volume, $4\pi x^2 dx$ is the volume of the intervening layer, differing from it only by a quantity which may be omitted: hence $4\pi C D x^2 dx$ is the quantity of heat necessary to raise the intervening shell from temperature 0 to temperature 1. Hence it is requisite to divide the quantity of heat which accumulates in this shell by $4\pi C D x^2 dx$, and we shall then find the increase of its temperature v during the time dt. We thus obtain the equation

$$dv = \frac{K}{CD} dt \cdot \frac{d\left(x^2 \dfrac{dv}{dx}\right)}{x^2 dx}.$$

or

$$\frac{dv}{dt} = \frac{K}{CD} \cdot \left(\frac{d^2v}{dx^2} + \frac{2}{x}\frac{dv}{dx}\right) \cdots (c)$$

114. The preceding equation represents the law of the movement of heat in the interior of the solid, but the temperatures of points in the surface are subject also to a special condition which must be expressed. This condition relative to the state of the surface may vary according to the nature of the problems discussed: we may suppose for example, that, after having heated the sphere, and raised all its molecules to the temperature of boiling water, the cooling is effected by giving to all points in the surface the temperature 0, and by retaining them at this temperature by any external cause whatever. In this case we may imagine the sphere, whose variable state it is desired to determine, to be covered by a very thin envelope on which the cooling agency exerts its action. It may be supposed, 1º, that this infinitely thin envelope adheres to the solid, that it is of the same substance as the solid and that it forms a part of it, like the other portions of the mass; 2º, that all the molecules of the envelope are subjected to temperature 0 by a cause always in action which prevents the temperature from ever being above or below zero. To express this condition theoretically, the function v, which contains x and t, must be made to become nul, when we give to x its complete value X equal to the radius of the sphere, whatever else the value of t may be. We should then have, on this

hypothesis, if we denote by $\phi(x, t)$ the function of x and t, which expresses the value of v, the two equations

$$\frac{dv}{dt} = \frac{K}{CD}\left(\frac{d^2v}{dx^2} + \frac{2}{x}\frac{dv}{dx}\right), \quad \text{and} \quad \phi(X, t) = 0.$$

Further, it is necessary that the initial state should be represented by the same function $\phi(x, t)$: we shall therefore have as a second condition $\phi(x, 0) = 1$. Thus the variable state of a solid sphere on the hypothesis which we have first described will be represented by a function v, which must satisfy the three preceding equations. The first is general, and belongs at every instant to all points of the mass; the second affects only the molecules at the surface, and the third belongs only to the initial state.

115. If the solid is being cooled in air, the second equation is different; it must then be imagined that the very thin envelope is maintained by some external cause, in a state such as to produce the escape from the sphere, at every instant, of a quantity of heat equal to that which the presence of the medium can carry away from it.

Now the quantity of heat which, during an infinitely small instant dt, flows within the interior of the solid across the spherical surface situate at distance x, is equal to $-4K\pi x^2 \frac{dv}{dx} dt$; and this general expression is applicable to all values of x. Thus, by supposing $x = X$ we shall ascertain the quantity of heat which in the variable state of the sphere would pass across the very thin envelope which bounds it; on the other hand, the external surface of the solid having a variable temperature, which we shall denote by V, would permit the escape into the air of a quantity of heat proportional to that temperature, and to the extent of the surface, which is $4\pi X^2$. The value of this quantity is $4h\pi X^2 V dt$.

To express, as is supposed, that the action of the envelope supplies the place, at every instant, of that which would result from the presence of the medium, it is sufficient to equate the quantity $4h\pi X^2 V dt$ to the value which the expression $-4K\pi X^2 \frac{dv}{dx} dt$ receives when we give to x its complete value X; hence we obtain the equation $\frac{dv}{dx} = -\frac{h}{K} v$, which must hold when in the functions $\frac{dv}{dx}$ and v we put instead of x its value X, which we shall denote by writing it in the form $K\frac{dV}{dx} + hV = 0$.

116. The value of $\frac{dv}{dx}$ taken when $x = X$, must therefore have a constant ratio $-\frac{h}{K}$ to the value of v, which corresponds to the same point. Thus we shall suppose that the external cause of the cooling determines always the state of the very thin envelope, in such a manner that the value of $\frac{dv}{dx}$ which results from this state, is proportional to the value of v, corresponding to $x = X$, and that the constant ratio of these two quantities is $-\frac{h}{K}$. This condition being fulfilled by means of some cause always present, which prevents the extreme

value of $\frac{dv}{dx}$ from being anything else but $-\frac{h}{K}v$, the action of the envelope will take the place of that of the air.

It is not necessary to suppose the envelope to be extremely thin, and it will be seen in the sequel that it may have an indefinite thickness. Here the thickness is considered to be indefinitely small, so as to fix the attention on the state of the surface only of the solid.

117. Hence it follows that the three equations which are required to determine the function $\phi(x, t)$ or v are the following,

$$\frac{dt}{dt} = \frac{K}{CD}\left(\frac{d^2v}{dx^2} + \frac{2}{x}\frac{dv}{dx}\right), \quad K\frac{dV}{dx} + hV = 0, \quad \phi(x, 0) = 1.$$

The first applies to all possible values of x and t; the second is satisfied when $x = X$, whatever be the value of t; and the third is satisfied when $t = 0$, whatever be the value of x.

It might be supposed that in the initial state all the spherical layers have not the same temperature: which is what would necessarily happen, if the immersion were imagined not to have lasted for an indefinite time. In this case, which is more general than the foregoing, the given function, which expresses the initial temperature of the molecules situated at distance x from the centre of the sphere, will be represented by $F(x)$; the third equation will then be replaced by the following, $\phi(x, 0) = F(x)$.

Nothing more remains than a purely analytical problem, whose solution will be given in one of the following chapters. It consists in finding the value of v, by means of the general condition, and the two special conditions to which it is subject.

SECTION III. *Equations of the Varied Movement of Heat in a Solid Cylinder*

118. A solid cylinder of infinite length, whose side is perpendicular to its circular base, having been wholly immersed in a liquid whose temperature is uniform, has been gradually heated, in such a manner that all points equally distant from the axis have acquired the same temperature; it is then exposed to a current of colder air; it is required to determine the temperatures of the different layers, after a given time.

x denotes the radius of a cylindrical surface, all of whose points are equally distant from the axis; X is the radius of the cylinder; v is the temperature which points of the solid, situated at distance x from the axis, must have after the lapse of a time denoted by t, since the beginning of the cooling. Thus v is a function of x and t, and if in it t be made equal to 0, the function of x which arises from this must necessarily satisfy the initial state, which is arbitrary.

119. Consider the movement of heat in an infinitely thin portion of the cylinder, included between the surface whose radius is x, and that whose radius is $x+dx$. The quantity of heat which this portion receives during the instant dt, from the part of the solid which it envelops, that is to say, the quantity which during the same time crosses the cylindrical surface whose radius is x, and whose length is supposed to be equal to unity, is expressed by

$$-2K\pi x \frac{dv}{dx}\, dt.$$

To find the quantity of heat which, crossing the second surface whose radius is $x+dx$, passes from the infinitely thin shell into the part of the solid which envelops it, we must, in the foregoing expression, change x into $x+dx$, or, which is the same thing, add to the term

$$-2K\pi x \frac{dv}{dx}\, dt,$$

the differential of this term, taken with respect to x. Hence the difference of the heat received and the heat lost, or the quantity of heat which accumulating in the infinitely thin shell determines the changes of temperature, is the same differential taken with the opposite sign, or

$$2K\pi \cdot dt \cdot d\left(x\frac{dv}{dx}\right);$$

on the other hand, the volume of this intervening shell is $2\pi x dx$, and $2CD\pi x dx$ expresses the quantity of heat required to raise it from the temperature 0 to the temperature 1, C being the specific heat, and D the density. Hence the quotient

$$\frac{2K\pi \cdot dt \cdot d\left(x\dfrac{dv}{dx}\right)}{2CD\pi x dx}$$

is the increment which the temperature receives during the instant dt. Whence we obtain the equation

$$\frac{dv}{dt} = \frac{K}{CD}\left(\frac{d^2v}{dx^2} + \frac{1}{x}\frac{dv}{dx}\right).$$

120. The quantity of heat which, during the instant dt, crosses the cylindrical surface whose radius is x, being expressed in general by $2K\pi x \dfrac{dv}{dx}\, dt$, we shall find that quantity which escapes during the same time from the surface of the solid, by making $x = X$ in the foregoing value; on the other hand, the same quantity, dispersed into the air, is, by the principle of the communication of heat, equal to $2\pi X h v dt$; we must therefore have at the surface the definite equation $-K\dfrac{dv}{dx} = hv$. The nature of these equations is explained at greater length, either in the articles which refer to the sphere, or in those wherein the general equations have been given for a body of any form whatever. The function v which represents the movement of heat in an infinite cylinder must therefore satisfy, 1st, the general equation $\dfrac{dv}{dt} = \dfrac{K}{CD}\left(\dfrac{d^2v}{dx^2} + \dfrac{1}{x}\dfrac{dv}{dx}\right)$, which applies whatever x and t may be; 2nd, the definite equation $\dfrac{h}{K}v + \dfrac{dv}{dx} = 0$, which is true, whatever the variable t may be, when $x = X$; 3rd, the definite equation $v = F(x)$. The last condition must be satisfied by all values of v, when t is made equal to 0, whatever the variable x may be. The arbitrary function $F(x)$ is supposed to be known; it corresponds to the initial state.

SECTION IV. *Equations of the Uniform Movement of Heat in a Solid Prism of Infinite Length*

121. A prismatic bar is immersed at one extremity in a constant source of heat which maintains that extremity at the temperature A; the rest of the bar, whose length is infinite, continues to be exposed to a uniform current of atmospheric air maintained at temperature 0; it is required to determine the highest temperature which a given point of the bar can acquire.

The problem differs from that of Article 73, since we now take into consideration all the dimensions of the solid, which is necessary in order to obtain an exact solution.

We are led, indeed, to suppose that in a bar of very small thickness all points of the same section would acquire sensibly equal temperatures; but some uncertainty may rest on the results of this hypothesis. It is therefore preferable to solve the problem rigorously, and then to examine, by analysis, up to what point, and in what cases, we are justified in considering the temperatures of different points of the same section to be equal.

122. The section made at right angles to the length of the bar, is a square whose side is $2l$, the axis of the bar is the axis of x, and the origin is at the extremity A. The three rectangular co-ordinates of a point of the bar are x, y, z, and v denotes the fixed temperature at the same point.

The problem consists in determining the temperatures which must be assigned to different points of the bar, in order that they may continue to exist without any change, so long as the extreme surface A, which communicates with the source of heat, remains subject, at all its points, to the permanent temperature A; thus v is a function of x, y, and z.

123. Consider the movement of heat in a prismatic molecule, enclosed between six planes perpendicular to the three axes of x, y, and z. The first three planes pass through the point m whose co-ordinates are x, y, z, and the others pass through the point m' whose co-ordinates are $x+dx$, $y+dy$, $z+dz$.

To find what quantity of heat enters the molecule during unit of time across the first plane passing through the point m and perpendicular to x, we must remember that the extent of the surface of the molecule on this plane is $dy\,dz$, and that the flow across this area is, according to the theorem of Article 98, equal to $-K\dfrac{dv}{dx}$; thus the molecule receives across the rectangle $dy\,dz$ passing through the point m a quantity of heat expressed by $-K\,dy\,dz\,\dfrac{dv}{dx}$. To find the quantity of heat which crosses the opposite face, and escapes from the molecule, we must substitute, in the preceding expression, $x+dx$ for x, or, which is the same thing, add to this expression its differential taken with respect to x only; whence we conclude that the molecule loses, at its second face perpendicular to x, a quantity of heat equal to

$$-K\,dydz\,\frac{dv}{dx} \;-K\,dydzd\!\left(\frac{dv}{dx}\right);$$

we must therefore subtract this from that which enters at the opposite face; the differences of these two quantities is

$$K\,dy\,dz\,d\!\left(\frac{dv}{dx}\right), \;\; \text{or,} \;\; K\,dx\,dy\,dz\,\frac{d^2v}{dx^2};$$

this expresses the quantity of heat accumulated in the molecule in consequence of the propagation in direction of x; which accumulated heat would make the temperature of the molecule vary, if it were not balanced by that which is lost in some other direction.

It is found in the same manner that a quantity of heat equal to $-K\,dz\,dx\,\dfrac{dv}{dy}$ enters the molecule across the plane passing through the point m perpendicular to y, and that the quantity which escapes at the opposite face is

$$-K\,dz\,dx\,\frac{dv}{dy} - K\,dz\,dx\,d\left(\frac{dv}{dy}\right),$$

the last differential being taken with respect to y only. Hence the difference of the two quantities, or $K\,dx\,dy\,dz\,\dfrac{d^2v}{dy^2}$, expresses the quantity of heat which the molecule acquires, in consequence of the propagation in direction of y.

Lastly, it is proved in the same manner that the molecule acquires, in consequence of the propagation in direction of z, a quantity of heat equal to $K\,dx\,dy\,dz\,\dfrac{d^2v}{dz^2}$. Now, in order that there may be no change of temperature, it is necessary for the molecule to retain as much heat as it contained at first, so that the heat it acquires in one direction must balance that which it loses in another. Hence the sum of the three quantities of heat acquired must be nothing; thus we form the equation

$$\frac{d^2v}{dx^2} + \frac{d^2v}{dy^2} + \frac{d^2v}{dz^2} = 0.$$

124. It remains now to express the conditions relative to the surface. If we suppose the point m to belong to one of the faces of the prismatic bar, and the face to be perpendicular to z, we see that the rectangle $dx\,dy$, during unit of time, permits a quantity of heat equal to $V\,h\,dx\,dy$ to escape into the air, V denoting the temperature of the point m of the surface, namely what $\phi\,(x, y, z)$ the function sought becomes when z is made equal to l, half the dimension of the prism. On the other hand, the quantity of heat which, by virtue of the action of the molecules, during unit of time, traverses an infinitely small surface ω, situated within the prism, perpendicular to z, is equal to $-K\omega\,\dfrac{dv}{dz}$, according to the theorems quoted above. This expression is general, and applying it to points for which the co-ordinate z has its complete value l, we conclude from it that the quantity of heat which traverses the rectangle $dx\,dy$ taken at the surface is $-K\,dx\,dy\,\dfrac{dv}{dz}$, giving to z in the function $\dfrac{dv}{dz}$ its complete value l. Hence the two quantities $-K\,dx\,dy\,\dfrac{dv}{dz}$, and $h\,dx\,dy\,v$, must be equal, in order that the action of the molecules may agree with that of the medium. This equality must also exist when we give to z in the functions $\dfrac{dv}{dz}$ and v the value $-l$, which it has at the face opposite to that first considered. Further, the quantity of heat which crosses an infinitely small surface ω, perpendicular to the axis of y, being $-K\omega\,\dfrac{dv}{dy}$, it follows that that which flows across a

rectangle $dz\,dx$ taken on a face of the prism perpendicular to y is $-K\,dz\,dx\,\dfrac{dv}{dy}$

giving to y in the function $\dfrac{dv}{dy}$ its complete value l. Now this rectangle $dz\,dx$ permits a quantity of heat expressed by $hv\,dx\,dz$ to escape into the air; the equation $hv=-K\dfrac{dv}{dy}$ becomes therefore necessary, when y is made equal to l or $-l$ in the functions v and $\dfrac{dv}{dy}$.

125. The value of the function v must by hypothesis be equal to A, when we suppose $x=0$, whatever be the values of y and z. Thus the required function v is determined by the following conditions: 1st, for all values of x, y, z, it satisfies the general equation

$$\frac{d^2v}{dx^2} + \frac{d^2v}{dy^2} + \frac{d^2v}{dz^2} = 0;$$

2nd, it satisfies the equation $\dfrac{h}{K}v + \dfrac{dv}{dy} = 0$, when y is equal to l or $-l$, whatever x and z may be, or satisfies the equation $\dfrac{h}{K}v + \dfrac{dv}{dz} = 0$, when z is equal to l or $-l$, whatever x and y may be; 3rd, it satisfies the equation $v=A$, when $x=0$ whatever y and z may be.

SECTION V. *Equations of the Varied Movement of Heat in a Solid Cube*

126. A solid in the form of a cube, all of whose points have acquired the same temperature, is placed in a uniform current of atmospheric air, maintained at temperature 0. It is required to determine the successive states of the body during the whole time of the cooling.

The centre of the cube is taken as the origin of rectangular coordinates; the three perpendiculars dropped from this point on the faces, are the axes of x, y, and z; $2l$ is the side of the cube, v is the temperature to which a point whose coordinates are x, y, z, is lowered after the time t has elapsed since the commencement of the cooling: the problem consists in determining the function v, which depends on x, y, z and t.

127. To form the general equation which v must satisfy, we must ascertain what change of temperature an infinitely small portion of the solid must experience during the instant dt, by virtue of the action of the molecules which are extremely near to it. We consider then a prismatic molecule enclosed between six planes at right angles; the first three pass through the point m, whose co-ordinates are x, y, z, and the three others, through the point m', whose co-ordinates are

$$x+dx,\ y+dy,\ z+dz.$$

The quantity of heat which during the instant dt passes into the molecule across the first rectangle $dy\,dz$ perpendicular to x, is $-K\,dy\,dz\,\dfrac{dv}{dx}\,dt$, and that which escapes in the same time from the molecule, through the opposite face, is found by writing $x+dx$ in place of x in the preceding expression, it is

$$-K\,dy\,dz\left(\frac{dv}{dx}\right)dt - K\,dy\,dz\,d\left(\frac{dv}{dx}\right)dt,$$

the differential being taken with respect to x only. The quantity of heat which during the instant dt enters the molecule, across the first rectangle $dz\, dx$ perpendicular to the axis of y, is $-K\, dz\, dx\, \dfrac{dv}{dy}\, dt$, and that which escapes from the molecule during the same instant, by the opposite face, is

$$-K\, dz\, dx\, \frac{dv}{dy}\, dt - K\, dz\, dx\, d\left(\frac{dv}{dy}\right) dt,$$

the differential being taken with respect to y only. The quantity of heat which the molecule receives during the instant dt, through its lower face, perpendicular to the axis of z, is $-K\, dx\, dy\, \dfrac{dv}{dz}\, dt$, and that which it loses through the opposite face is

$$-K\, dx\, dy\, \frac{dv}{dz}\, dt - K\, dx\, dy\, d\left(\frac{dv}{dz}\right) dt,$$

the differential being taken with respect to z only.

The sum of all the quantities of heat which escape from the molecule must now be deducted from the sum of the quantities which it receives, and the difference is that which determines its increase of temperature during the instant: this difference is

$$K\, dy\, dz\, d\left(\frac{dv}{dx}\right) dt + K\, dz\, dx\, d\left(\frac{dv}{dy}\right) dt + K\, dx\, dy\, d\left(\frac{dv}{dz}\right) dt,$$

$$\text{or } K\, dx\, dy\, dz \left\{ \frac{d^2v}{dx^2} + \frac{d^2v}{dy^2} + \frac{d^2v}{dz^2} \right\} dt.$$

128. If the quantity which has just been found be divided by that which is necessary to raise the molecule from the temperature 0 to the temperature 1, the increase of temperature which is effected during the instant dt will become known. Now, the latter quantity is $CD\, dx\, dy\, dz$: for C denotes the capacity of the substance for heat; D its density, and $dx\, dy\, dz$ the volume of the molecule. The movement of heat in the interior of the solid is therefore expressed by the equation

$$\frac{dv}{dt} = \frac{K}{CD}\left(\frac{d^2v}{dx^2} + \frac{d^2v}{dy^2} + \frac{d^2v}{dz^2} \right) \cdots (d).$$

129. It remains to form the equations which relate to the state of the surface, which presents no difficulty, in accordance with the principles which we have established. In fact, the quantity of heat which, during the instant dt, crosses the rectangle $dz\, dy$, traced on a plane perpendicular to x, is $-K\, dy\, dz\, \dfrac{dv}{dx}\, dt$. This result, which applies to all points of the solid, ought to hold when the value of x is equal to l, half the thickness of the prism. In this case, the rectangle $dy\, dz$ being situated at the surface, the quantity of heat which crosses it, and is dispersed into the air during the instant dt, is expressed by $hv\, dy\, dz\, dt$, we ought therefore to have, when $x = l$, the equation $hv = -K\, \dfrac{dv}{dx}$. This condition must also be satisfied when $x = -l$.

It will be found also that, the quantity of heat which crosses the rectangle

$dz\,dx$ situated on a plane perpendicular to the axis of y being in general $-K\,dz\,dx\,\dfrac{dv}{dy}$, and that which escapes at the surface into the air across the same rectangle being $hv\,dz\,dx\,dt$, we must have the equation $hv+K\,\dfrac{dv}{dy}=0$, when $y=l$ or $-l$. Lastly, we obtain in like manner the definite equation

$$hv+K\,\frac{dv}{dz}=0,$$

which is satisfied when $z=l$ or $-l$.

130. The function sought, which expresses the varied movement of heat in the interior of a solid of cubic form, must therefore be determined by the following conditions:

1st. It satisfies the general equation

$$\frac{dv}{dt}=\frac{K}{C\cdot D}\left(\frac{d^2v}{dx^2}+\frac{d^2v}{dy^2}+\frac{d^2v}{dz^2}\right);$$

2nd. It satisfies the three definite equations

$$hv+K\,\frac{dv}{dx}=0,\quad hv+K\,\frac{dv}{dy}=0,\quad hv+K\,\frac{dv}{dz}=0,$$

which hold when $x=\pm l,\ y=\pm l,\ z=\pm l$;

3rd. If in the function v which contains x, y, z, t, we make $t=0$, whatever be the values of x, y, and z, we ought to have, according to hypothesis, $v=A$, which is the initial and common value of the temperature.

131. The equation arrived at in the preceding problem represents the movement of heat in the interior of all solids. Whatever, in fact, the form of the body may be, it is evident that, by decomposing it into prismatic molecules, we shall obtain this result. We may therefore limit ourselves to demonstrating in this manner the equation of the propagation of heat. But in order to make the exhibition of principles more complete, and that we may collect into a small number of consecutive articles the theorems which serve to establish the general equation of the propagation of heat in the interior of solids, and the equations which relate to the state of the surface, we shall proceed, in the two following sections, to the investigation of these equations, independently of any particular problem, and without reverting to the elementary propositions which we have explained in the introduction.

SECTION VI. *General equation of the Propagation of Heat in the Interior of Solids*

132. **Theorem I.** *If the different points of a homogeneous solid mass, enclosed between six planes at right angles, have actual temperatures determined by the linear equation*

$$v=A-ax-by-cz,\ \cdots\ ,\ (a),$$

and if the molecules situated at the external surface on the six planes which bound the prism are maintained, by any case whatever, at the temperature expressed by the equation (a): all the molecules situated in the interior of the mass will of themselves retain their actual temperatures, so that there will be no change in the state of the prism.

v denotes the actual temperature of the point whose co-ordinates are x, y, z; A, a, b, c, are constant coefficients.

To prove this proposition, consider in the solid any three points whatever $mM\mu$, situated on the same straight line $m\mu$, which the point M divides into two equal parts; denote by x, y, z the co-ordinates of the point M, and its temperature by v, the co-ordinates of the point μ by $x+\alpha$, $y+\beta$, $z+\gamma$, and its temperature by w, the co-ordinates of the point m by $x-\alpha$, $y-\beta$, $z-\gamma$, and its temperature by u, we shall have

$$v = A - ax - by - cz,$$
$$w = A - a(x+\alpha) - b(y+\beta) - c(z+\gamma),$$
$$u = A - a(x-\alpha) - b(y-\beta) - c(z-\gamma),$$

whence we conclude that,

$$v - w = a\alpha + b\beta + c\gamma, \text{ and } u - v = a\alpha + b\beta + c\gamma;$$

therefore $$v - w = u - v.$$

Now the quantity of heat which one point receives from another depends on the distance between the two points and on the difference of their temperatures. Hence the action of the point M on the point μ is equal to the action of m on M; thus the point M receives as much heat from m as it gives up to the point μ.

We obtain the same result, whatever be the direction and magnitude of the line which passes through the point M, and is divided into two equal parts. Hence it is impossible for this point to change its temperature, for it receives from all parts as much heat as it gives up.

The same reasoning applies to all other points; hence no change can happen in the state of the solid.

133. CorollaRY I. A solid being enclosed between two infinite parallel planes A and B, if the actual temperature of its different points is supposed to be expressed by the equation $v = 1 - z$, and the two planes which bound it are maintained by any cause whatever, A at the temperature 1, and B at the temperature 0; this particular case will then be included in the preceding theorem, if we make $A = 1$, $a = 0$, $b = 0$, $c = 1$.

134. CorollaRY II. If in the interior of the same solid we imagine a plane M parallel to those which bound it, we see that a certain quantity of heat flows across this plane during unit of time; for two very near points, such as m and n, one of which is below the plane and the other above it, are unequally heated; the first, whose temperature is highest, must therefore send to the second, during each instant, a certain quantity of heat which, in some cases, may be very small, and even insensible, according to the nature of the body and the distance of the two molecules.

The same is true for any two other points whatever separated by the plane. That which is most heated sends to the other a certain quantity of heat, and the sum of these partial actions, or of all the quantities of heat sent across the plane, composes a continual flow whose value does not change, since all the molecules preserve their temperatures. It is easy to prove *that this flow, or the quantity of heat which crosses the plane M during the unit of time, is equivalent to that which crosses, during the same time, another plane N parallel to the first.* In fact, the part of the mass which is enclosed between the two surfaces M and N will receive continually, across the plane M, as much heat as it loses across the plane N. If the quantity of heat, which in passing the plane M enters the part of the mass which is considered, were not equal to that which escapes by the opposite surface N, the solid enclosed between the two surfaces would acquire fresh heat, or would lose a part of that which it has, and its temperatures would not be constant; which is contrary to the preceding corollary.

135. The measure of the specific conducibility of a given substance is taken to be the quantity of heat which, in an infinite solid, formed of this substance, and enclosed between two parallel planes, flows during unit of time across unit of surface, taken on any intermediate plane whatever, parallel to the external planes, the distance between which is equal to unit of length, one of them being maintained at temperature 1, and the other at temperature 0. This constant flow of the heat which crosses the whole extent of the prism is denoted by the coefficient K, and is the measure of the conductivity.

136. LEMMA. *If we suppose all the temperatures of the solid in question under the preceding article, to be multiplied by any number whatever g, so that the equation of temperatures is v = g − gz, instead of being v = 1 − z, and if the two external planes are maintained, one at the temperature g, and the other at temperature 0, the constant flow of heat, in this second hypothesis, or the quantity which during unit of time crosses unit of surface taken on an intermediate plane parallel to the bases, is equal to the product of the first flow multiplied by g.*

In fact, since all the temperatures have been increased in the ratio of 1 to g, the differences of the temperatures of any two points whatever m and μ, are increased in the same ratio. Hence, according to the principle of the communication of heat, in order to ascertain the quantity of heat which m sends to μ on the second hypothesis, we must multiply by g the quantity which the same point m sends to μ on the first hypothesis. The same would be true for any two other points whatever. Now, the quantity of heat which crosses a plane M results from the sum of all the actions which the points m, m', m'', m''', etc., situated on the same side of the plane, exert on the points μ, μ', μ'', μ''', etc., situated on the other side. Hence, if in the first hypothesis the constant flow is denoted by K, it will be equal to gK, when we have multiplied all the temperatures by g.

137. THEOREM II. *In a prism whose constant temperatures are expressed by the equation v = A − ax − by − cz, and which is bounded by six planes at right angles all of whose points are maintained at constant temperatures determined by the preceding equation, the quantity of heat which, during unit of time, crosses unit of surface taken on any intermediate plane whatever perpendicular to z, is the same as the constant flow in a solid of the same substance would be, if enclosed between two infinite parallel planes, and for which the equation of constant temperatures is v = c − cz.*

To prove this, let us consider in the prism, and also in the infinite solid, two extremely near points m and μ, separated by the plane M perpendicular to the axis of z; μ being above the plane, and m below it (see Fig. 4), and below the

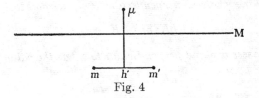

Fig. 4

same plane let us take a point m' such that the perpendicular dropped from the point μ on the plane may also be perpendicular to the distance mm' at its middle point h'. Denote by x, y, $z+h$, the co-ordinates of the point μ, whose temperature is w, by $x-\alpha$, $y-\beta$, z, the co-ordinates of m, whose temperature is v, and by $x+\alpha$, $y+\beta$, z, the co-ordinates of m', whose temperature is v'.

The action of m on μ, or the quantity of heat which m sends to μ during a certain time, may be expressed by $q(v-w)$. The factor q depends on the distance $m\mu$, and on the nature of the mass. The action of m' on μ will therefore be expressed by $q(v'-w)$; and the factor q is the same as in the preceding expression; hence the sum of the two actions of m on μ, and of m' on μ, or the quantity of heat which μ receives from m and from m', is expressed by

$$q(v-w+v'-w).$$

Now, if the points m, μ, m' belong to the prism, we have

$$w=A-ax-by-c(z+h),\ v=A-a(x-\alpha)-b(y-\beta)-cz,$$

and

$$v'=A-a(x+\alpha)-b(y+\beta)-cz;$$

and if the same points belonged to an infinite solid, we should have, by hypothesis,

$$w=c-c(z+h),\ v=c-cz,\ \text{and}\ v'=c-cz.$$

In the first case, we find

$$q(v-w+v'-w)=2qch,$$

and, in the second case, we still have the same result. Hence the quantity of heat which μ receives from m and from m' on the first hypothesis, when the equation of constant temperatures is $v=A-ax-by-cz$, is equivalent to the quantity of heat which μ receives from m and from m' when the equation of constant temperatures is $v=c-cz$.

The same conclusion might be drawn with respect to any three other points whatever m', μ', m'', provided that the second μ' be placed at equal distances from the other two, and the altitude of the isosceles triangle $m'\mu'm''$ be parallel to z. Now, the quantity of heat which crosses any plane whatever M, results from the sum of the actions which all the points m, m', m'', m''' etc., situated on one side of this plane, exert on all the points μ, μ', μ'', μ''', etc., situated on the other side: hence the constant flow, which, during unit of time, crosses a definite part of the plane M in the infinite solid, is equal to the quantity of heat which flows in the same time across the same portion of the plane M in the prism, all of whose temperatures are expressed by the equation

$$v=A-ax-by-cz.$$

138. COROLLARY. The flow has the value cK in the infinite solid, when the part of the plane which it crosses has unit of surface. *In the prism also it has the same value cK or $-K\dfrac{dv}{dz}$*. It is proved in the same manner, *that the constant flow which takes place, during unit of time, in the same prism across unit of surface, on any plane whatever perpendicular to y, is equal to*

$$bK\ \ or\ \ -K\frac{dv}{dy}\ ;$$

and that which crosses a plane perpendicular to x has the value

$$aK\ \ or\ \ -K\frac{dv}{dx}.$$

139. The propositions which we have proved in the preceding articles apply also to the case in which the instantaneous action of a molecule is exerted in the interior of the mass up to an appreciable distance. In this case, we must suppose that the cause which maintains the external layers of the body in the state expressed by the linear equation, affects the mass up to a finite depth. All observation concurs to prove that in solids and liquids the distance in question is extremely small.

140. THEOREM III. If the temperatures at the points of a solid are expressed by the equation $v = f(x, y, z, t)$, in which x, y, z are the co-ordinates of a molecule whose temperature is equal to v after the lapse of a time t; the flow of heat which crosses part of a plane traced in the solid, perpendicular to one of the three axes, is no longer constant; its value is different for different parts of the plane, and it varies also with the time. This variable quantity may be determined by analysis.

Let ω be an infinitely small circle whose centre coincides with the point m of the solid, and whose plane is perpendicular to the vertical co-ordinate z; during the instant dt there will flow across this circle a certain quantity of heat which will pass from the part of the circle below the plane of the solid into the upper part. This flow is composed of all the rays of heat which depart from a lower point and arrive at an upper point, by crossing a point of the small surface ω. We proceed to shew *that the expression of the value of the flow is*

$$-K \frac{dy}{dz} \omega dt.$$

Let us denote by x', y', z' the co-ordinates of the point m whose temperature is v'; and suppose all the other molecules to be referred to this point m chosen as the origin of new axes parallel to the former axes: let ξ, η, ζ, be the three co-ordinates of a point referred to the origin m; in order to express the actual temperature w of a molecule infinitely near to m, we shall have the linear equation

$$w = v' + \xi \frac{dv'}{dx} + \eta \frac{dv'}{dy} + \zeta \frac{dv'}{dz}.$$

The coefficients v', $\frac{dv'}{dx}$, $\frac{dv'}{dy}$, $\frac{dv'}{dz}$ are the values which are found by substituting in the functions v, $\frac{dv}{dx}$, $\frac{dv}{dy}$, $\frac{dv}{dz}$, for the variables x, y, z, the constant quantities x', y', z', which measure the distances of the point m from the first three axes of x, y, and z.

Suppose now that the point m is also an internal molecule of a rectangular prism, enclosed between six planes perpendicular to the three axes whose origin is m; that w the actual temperature of each molecule of this prism, whose dimensions are finite, is expressed by the linear equation $w = A + a\xi + b\eta + c\zeta$, and that the six faces which bound the prism are maintained at the fixed temperatures which the last equation assigns to them. The state of the internal molecules will also be permanent, and a quantity of heat measured by the expression $-Kc\, wdt$ will flow during the instant dt across the circle ω.

This arranged, if we take as the values of the constants A, a, b, c, the quantities v', $\frac{dv'}{dx}$, $\frac{dv'}{dy}$, $\frac{dv'}{dz}$, the fixed state of the prism will be expressed by the equation

$$w = v' + \frac{dv'}{dx}\xi + \frac{dv'}{dy}\eta + \frac{dv'}{dz}\zeta.$$

Thus the molecules infinitely near to the point m will have, during the instant dt, the same actual temperature in the solid whose state is variable, and in the prism whose state is constant. Hence the flow which exists at the point m, during the instant dt, across the infinitely small circle ω, is the same in either solid; it is therefore expressed by $-K\dfrac{dv'}{dz}\omega dt$.

From this we derive the following proposition

If in a solid whose internal temperatures vary with the time, by virtue of the action of the molecules, we trace any straight line whatever, and erect (see Fig. 5), at the different points of this line, the ordinates pm of a plane curve equal to the temperatures of these points taken at the same moment; the flow of heat, at each point p of the straight line, will be proportional to the tangent of the angle α which the element of the curve makes with the parallel to the abscissæ; that is to say, if at the point p we place the centre of an infinitely small circle ω perpendicular

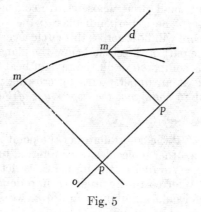

Fig. 5

to the line, the quantity of heat which has flowed during the instant dt, across this circle, in the direction in which the abscissæ op increase, will be measured by the product of four factors, which are, the tangent of the angle α, a constant coefficient K, the area ω of the circle, and the duration dt of the instant.

141. COROLLARY. If we represent by ϵ the abscissa of this curve or the distance of a point p of the straight line from a fixed point o, and by v the ordinate which represents the temperature of the point p, v will vary with the distance ϵ and will be a certain function $f(\epsilon)$ of that distance; the quantity of heat which would flow across the circle ω, placed at the point p perpendicular to the line, will be $-K\dfrac{dv}{d\epsilon}\omega dt$, or

$$-Kf'(\epsilon)\omega dt,$$

denoting the function $\dfrac{df(\epsilon)}{d\epsilon}$ by $f'(\epsilon)$.

We may express this result in the following manner, which facilitates its application.

To obtain the actual flow of heat at a point p of a straight line drawn in a solid whose temperatures vary by action of the molecules, we must divide the difference of the temperatures at two points infinitely near to the point p by the distance between these points. The flow is proportional to the quotient.

142. THEOREM IV. From the preceding Theorems it is easy to deduce the general equations of the propagation of heat.

Suppose the different points of a homogeneous solid of any form whatever, to have received initial temperatures which vary successively by the effect of the mutual action of the molecules, and suppose the equation v=f(x, y, z, t) to represent the successive states of the solid, it may now be shewn that v a function of four variables necessarily satisfies the equation

$$\frac{dv}{dt} = \frac{K}{CD}\left(\frac{d^2v}{dx^2} + \frac{d^2v}{dy^2} + \frac{d^2v}{dz^2}\right)$$

In fact, let us consider the movement of heat in a molecule enclosed between six planes at right angles to the axes of x, y, and z; the first three of these planes pass through the point m whose coordinates are x, y, z, the other three pass through the point m', whose coordinates are $x+dx$, $y+dy$, $z+dz$.

During the instant dt, the molecule receives, across the lower rectangle $dxdy$, which passes through the point m, a quantity of heat equal to $-K\,dx\,dy\,\frac{dv}{dz}\,dt$.

To obtain the quantity which escapes from the molecule by the opposite face, it is sufficient to change z into $z+dz$ in the preceding expression, that is to say, to add to this expression its own differential taken with respect to z only; we then have

$$-K\,dx\,dy\,\frac{dv}{dz}\,dt - K\,dx\,dy\,\frac{d\left(\frac{dv}{dz}\right)}{dz}\,dz\,dt$$

as the value of the quantity which escapes across the upper rectangle. The same molecule receives also across the first rectangle $dz\,dx$ which passes through the point m, a quantity of heat equal to $-K\,\frac{dv}{dy}\,dz\,dx\,dt$; and if we add to this expression its own differential taken with respect to y only, we find that the quantity which escapes across the opposite face $dz\,dx$ is expressed by

$$-K\,\frac{dv}{dy}\,dz\,dx\,dt - K\,\frac{d\left(\frac{dv}{dy}\right)}{dy}\,dy\,dz\,dx\,dt.$$

Lastly, the molecule receives through the first rectangle $dy\,dz$ a quantity of heat equal to $-K\,\frac{dv}{dx}\,dy\,dz\,dt$, and that which it loses across the opposite rectangle which passes through m' is expressed by

$$-K\,\frac{dv}{dx}\,dy\,dz\,dt - K\,\frac{d\left(\frac{dv}{dx}\right)}{dx}\,dx\,dy\,dz\,dt.$$

We must now take the sum of the quantities of heat which the molecule receives and subtract from it the sum of those which it loses. Hence it appears that during the instant dt, a total quantity of heat equal to

$$K\left(\frac{d^2v}{dx^2} + \frac{d^2v}{dy^2} + \frac{d^2v}{dz^2}\right)dx\,dy\,dz\,dt$$

accumulates in the interior of the molecule. It remains only to obtain the increase of temperature which must result from this addition of heat.

D being the density of the solid, or the weight of unit of volume, and C the specific capacity, or the quantity of heat which raises the unit of weight from the temperature 0 to the temperature 1; the product $CD\,dx\,dy\,dz$ expresses the quantity of heat required to raise from 0 to 1 the molecule whose volume is $dx\,dy\,dz$. Hence dividing by this product the quantity of heat which the molecule has just acquired, we shall have its increase of temperature. Thus we obtain the general equation

$$\frac{dv}{dt} = \frac{K}{CD}\left(\frac{d^2v}{dx^2} + \frac{d^2v}{dy^2} + \frac{d^2v}{dz^2}\right)\cdots\text{(A)},$$

which is the equation of the propagation of heat in the interior of all solid bodies.

143. Independently of this equation the system of temperatures is often subject to several definite conditions, of which no general expression can be given, since they depend on the nature of the problem.

If the dimensions of the mass in which heat is propagated are finite, and if the surface is maintained by some special cause in a given state; for example, if all its points retain, by virtue of that cause, the constant temperature 0, we shall have, denoting the unknown function v by $\phi\,(x,\,y,\,z,\,t)$, the equation of condition $\phi(x,\,y,\,z,\,t)=0$; which must be satisfied by all values of $x,\,y,\,z$ which belong to points of the external surface, whatever be the value of t. Further, if we suppose the initial temperatures of the body to be expressed by the known function $F(x,\,y,\,z)$, we have also the equation $\phi(x,\,y,\,z,\,0)=F(x,\,y,\,z)$; the condition expressed by this equation must be fulfilled by all values of the co-ordinates $x,\,y,\,z$ which belong to any point whatever of the solid.

144. Instead of submitting the surface of the body to a constant temperature, we may suppose the temperature not to be the same at different points of the surface, and that it varies with the time according to a given law; which is what takes place in the problem of terrestrial temperature. In this case the equation relative to the surface contains the variable t.

145. In order to examine by itself, and from a very general point of view, the problem of the propagation of heat, the solid whose initial state is given must be supposed to have all its dimensions infinite; no special condition disturbs then the diffusion of heat, and the law to which this principle is submitted becomes more manifest; it is expressed by the general equation

$$\frac{dv}{dt} = \frac{K}{CD}\left(\frac{d^2v}{dx^2} + \frac{d^2v}{dy^2} + \frac{dv^2}{dz^2}\right),$$

to which must be added that which relates to the initial arbitrary state of the solid.

Suppose the initial temperature of a molecule, whose co-ordinates are $x,\,y,\,z$, to be a known function $F(x,\,y,\,z)$, and denote the unknown value v by $\phi(x,\,y,\,z,\,t)$, we shall have the definite equation $\phi(x,\,y,\,z,\,0)=F(x,\,y,\,z)$; thus the problem is reduced to the integration of the general equation (A) in such a manner that it may agree, when the time is zero, with the equation which contains the arbitrary function F.

SECTION VII. *General Equation Relative to the Surface*

146. If the solid has a definite form, and if its original heat is dispersed gradually into atmospheric air maintained at a constant temperature, a third condition relative to the state of the surface must be added to the general equation (A) and to that which represents the initial state.

We proceed to examine, in the following articles, the nature of the equation which expresses this third condition.

Consider the variable state of a solid whose heat is dispersed into air, maintained at the fixed temperature 0. Let ω be an infinitely small part of the external surface, and μ a point of ω, through which a normal to the surface is drawn; different points of this line have at the same instant different temperatures.

Let v be the actual temperature of the point μ, taken at a definite instant, and w the corresponding temperature of a point ν of the solid taken on the normal, and distant from μ by an infinitely small quantity α. Denote by x, y, z the co-ordinates of the point μ, and those of the point ν by $x+\delta x$, $y+\delta y$, $z+\delta z$; let $f(x, y, z)=0$ be the known equation to the surface of the solid, and $v=\phi(x, y, z, t)$ the general equation which ought to give the value of v as a function of the four variables x, y, z, t. Differentiating the equation $f(x, y, z)=0$, we shall have

$$m\,dx+n\,dy+p\,dz=0;$$

m, n, p being functions of x, y, z.

It follows from the corollary enunciated in Article 141, that the flow in direction of the normal, or the quantity of heat which during the instant dt would cross the surface ω, if it were placed at any point whatever of this line, at right angles to its direction, is proportional to the quotient which is obtained by dividing the difference of temperature of two points infinitely near by their distance. Hence the expression for the flow at the end of the normal is

$$-K\,\frac{w-v}{\alpha}\,\omega\,dt;$$

K denoting the specific conducibility of the mass. On the other hand, the surface ω permits a quantity of heat to escape into the air, during the time dt, equal to $hv\omega\,dt$; h being the conductivity relative to atmospheric air. Thus the flow of heat at the end of the normal has two different expressions, that is to say:

$$hv\omega\,dt \quad\text{and}\quad -K\,\frac{w-v}{\alpha}\,\omega\,dt;$$

hence these two quantities are equal; and it is by the expression of this equality that the condition relative to the surface is introduced into the analysis.

147. We have

$$w=v+\delta v=v+\frac{dv}{dx}\,\delta x+\frac{dv}{dy}\,\delta y+\frac{dv}{dz}\,\delta z.$$

Now it follows from the principles of geometry, that the co-ordinates δx, δy, δz, which fix the position of the point ν of the normal relative to the point μ satisfy the following conditions:

$$p\,\delta x=m\,\delta z, \qquad p\,\delta y=n\,\delta z.$$

We have therefore

$$w-v\frac{1}{p}\left(m\,\frac{dv}{dx}+n\,\frac{dv}{dy}+p\,\frac{dv}{dz}\right)\delta z:$$

we have also

$$\alpha=\sqrt{\delta x^2+\delta y^2+\delta z^2}=\frac{1}{p}\,(m^2+n^2+p^2)^{\frac{1}{2}}\delta z,$$

or $\qquad \alpha = \dfrac{q}{p}\,\delta z$, denoting by q the quantity $(m^2+n^2+p^2)^{\frac{1}{2}}$,

hence $\qquad \dfrac{w-v}{\alpha} = \left(m\,\dfrac{dv}{dx} + n\,\dfrac{dv}{dy} + p\,\dfrac{dv}{dz} \right)\dfrac{1}{q}$;

consequently the equation

$$ hv\omega dt = -K\left(\dfrac{w-v}{\alpha} \right)\omega dt $$

becomes the following:

$$ m\,\frac{dv}{dx} + n\,\frac{dv}{dy} + p\,\frac{dv}{dz} + \frac{h}{K}\,vq = 0 \cdot \cdot \cdot \text{(B)}. $$

This equation is definite and applies only to points at the surface; it is that which must be added to the general equation of the propagation of heat (A), and to the condition which determines the initial state of the solid; m, n, p, q, are known functions of the co-ordinates of the points on the surface.

148. The equation (B) signifies in general that the decrease of the temperature, in the direction of the normal, at the boundary of the solid, is such that the quantity of heat which tends to escape by virtue of the action of the molecules, is equivalent always to that which the body must lose in the medium.

The mass of the solid might be imagined to be prolonged, in such a manner that the surface, instead of being exposed to the air, belonged at the same time to the body which it bounds, and to the mass of a solid envelope which contained it. If, on this hypothesis, any cause whatever regulated at every instant the decrease of the temperatures in the solid envelope, and determined it in such a manner that the condition expressed by the equation (B) was always satisfied, the action of the envelope would take the place of that of the air, and the movement of heat would be the same in either case: we can suppose then that this cause exists, and determine on this hypothesis the variable state of the solid; which is what is done in the employment of the two equations (A) and (B).

By this it is seen how the interruption of the mass and the action of the medium, disturb the diffusion of heat by submitting it to an accidental condition.

149. We may also consider the equation (B), which relates to the state of the surface, under another point of view: but we must first derive a remarkable consequence from Theorem III. (Art. 140). We retain the construction referred to in the corollary of the same theorem (Art. 141). Let x, y, z be the co-ordinates of the point p, and

$$ x+\delta x,\; y+\delta y,\; z+\delta z $$

those of a point q infinitely near to p, and taken on the straight line in question: if we denote by v and w the temperatures of the two points p and q taken at the same instant, we have

$$ w = v+\delta v = v + \frac{dv}{dx}\,\delta x + \frac{dv}{dy}\,\delta y + \frac{dv}{dz}\,\delta z\,; $$

hence the quotient

$$ \frac{\delta v}{\delta \epsilon} = \frac{dv}{dx}\,\frac{\delta x}{\delta \epsilon} + \frac{dv}{dy}\,\frac{\delta y}{\delta \epsilon} + \frac{dv}{dz}\,\frac{\delta z}{\delta \epsilon},\; \text{ and } \delta\epsilon = \sqrt{\delta x^2+\delta y^2+\delta z^2}\,; $$

thus the quantity of heat which flows across the surface ω placed at the point p, perpendicular to the straight line, is

$$-K\omega dt\left\{\frac{dv}{dx}\frac{\delta x}{\delta\epsilon}+\frac{dv}{dy}\frac{\delta y}{\delta\epsilon}+\frac{dv}{dz}\frac{\delta z}{\delta\epsilon}\right\}.$$

The first term is the product of $-K\dfrac{dv}{dx}$ by dt and by $\omega\dfrac{\delta x}{\delta\epsilon}$. The latter quantity is, according to the principles of geometry, the area of the projection of ω on the plane of y and z; thus the product represents the quantity of heat which would flow across the area of the projection, if it were placed at the point p perpendicular to the axis of x.

The second term $-K\dfrac{dv}{dy}\omega\dfrac{\delta y}{\delta\epsilon}dt$ represents the quantity of heat which would cross the projection of ω, made on the plane of x and z, if this projection were placed parallel to itself at the point p.

Lastly, the third term $-K\dfrac{dv}{dz}\omega\dfrac{\delta z}{\delta\epsilon}dt$ represents the quantity of heat which would flow during the instant dt, across the projection of ω on the plane of x and y, if this projection were placed at the point p, perpendicular to the co-ordinate z.

By this it is seen *that the quantity of heat which flows across every infinitely small part of a surface drawn in the interior of the solid, can always be decomposed into three other quantities of flow, which penetrate the three orthogonal projections of the surface, along the directions perpendicular to the planes of the projections.* The result gives rise to properties analogous to those which have been noticed in the theory of forces.

150. The quantity of heat which flows across a plane surface ω, infinitely small, given in form and position, being equivalent to that which would cross its three orthogonal projections, it follows that, if in the interior of the solid an element be imagined of any form whatever, the quantities of heat which pass into this polyhedron by its different faces, compensate each other reciprocally: or more exactly, the sum of the terms of the first order, which enter into the expression of the quantities of heat received by the molecule, is zero; so that the heat which is in fact accumulated in it, and makes its temperature vary, cannot be expressed except by terms infinitely smaller than those of the first order.

This result is distinctly seen when the general equation (A) has been established, by considering the movement of heat in a prismatic molecule (Articles 127 and 142); the demonstration may be extended to a molecule of any form whatever, by substituting for the heat received through each face, that which its three projections would receive.

In other respects it is necessary that this should be so: for, if one of the molecules of the solid acquired during each instant a quantity of heat expressed by a term of the first order, the variation of its temperature would be infinitely greater than that of other molecules, that is to say, during each infinitely small instant its temperature would increase or decrease by a finite quantity, which is contrary to experience.

151. We proceed to apply this remark to a molecule situated at the external surface of the solid.

Through a point a (see Fig. 6), taken on the plane of x and y, draw two planes perpendicular, one to the axis of x the other to the axis of y. Through a point b of the same plane, infinitely near to a, draw two other planes parallel to the two preceding planes; the ordinates z, raised at the points a, b, c, d, up to the

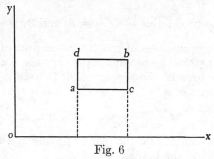

Fig. 6

external surface of the solid, will mark on this surface four points a', b', c', d', and will be the edges of a truncated prism, whose base is the rectangle $abcd$. If through the point a' which denotes the least elevated of the four points a', b', c', d', a plane be drawn parallel to that of x and y, it will cut off from the truncated prism a molecule, one of whose faces, that is to say $a'b'c'd'$, coincides with the surface of the solid. The values of the four ordinates aa', cc', dd', bb' are the following:

$$aa' = z,$$

$$cc' = z + \frac{dz}{dx}\, dx,$$

$$dd' = z + \frac{dz}{dy}\, dy,$$

$$bb' = z + \frac{dz}{dx}\, dx + \frac{dz}{dy}\, dy.$$

152. One of the faces perpendicular to x is a triangle, and the opposite face is a trapezium. The area of the triangle is

$$\tfrac{1}{2} dy\, \frac{dz}{dy}\, dy,$$

and the flow of heat in the direction perpendicular to this surface being $-K\dfrac{dv}{dx}$ we have, omitting the factor dt

$$-K \frac{dv}{dx}\, \tfrac{1}{2} dy\, \frac{dz}{dy}\, dy,$$

as the expression of the quantity of heat which in one instant passes into the molecule, across the triangle in question.

The area of the opposite face is

$$\tfrac{1}{2} dy \left(\frac{dz}{dx}\, dx + \frac{dz}{dx}\, dx + \frac{dz}{dy}\, dy \right),$$

and the flow perpendicular to this face is also $-K\dfrac{dv}{dx}$, suppressing terms of the second order infinitely smaller than those of the first; subtracting the quantity of heat which escapes by the second face from that which enters by the first we find

$$K \frac{dv}{dx} \frac{dz}{dx} dx\, dy.$$

This term expresses the quantity of heat the molecule receives through the faces perpendicular to x.

It will be found, by a similar process, that the same molecule receives, through the faces perpendicular to y, a quantity of heat equal to $K \dfrac{dv}{dy} \dfrac{dz}{dy} dx\, dy$.

The quantity of heat which the molecule receives through the rectangular base is $-K \dfrac{dv}{dz} dx\, dy$. Lastly, across the upper surface $a'b'c'd'$, a certain quantity of heat is permitted to escape, equal to the product of hv into the extent ω of that surface. The value of ω is, according to known principles, the same as that of $dx\, dy$ multiplied by the ratio $\dfrac{\epsilon}{z}$; ϵ denoting the length of the normal between the external surface and the plane of x and y, and

$$\epsilon = z \left\{ 1 + \left(\frac{dz}{dx} \right)^2 + \left(\frac{dz}{dy} \right)^2 \right\}^{\frac{1}{2}},$$

hence the molecule loses across its surface $a'b'c'd'$ a quantity of heat equal to $hv\, dx\, dy \dfrac{\epsilon}{z}$.

Now, the terms of the first order which enter into the expression of the total quantity of heat acquired by the molecule, must cancel each other, in order that the variation of temperature may not be at each instant a finite quantity; we must then have the equation

$$K \left(\frac{dv}{dx} \frac{dz}{dx} dx\, dy + \frac{dv}{dy} \frac{dz}{dy} dx\, dy + \frac{dv}{dz} dx\, dy \right) \quad hv \frac{\epsilon}{z} dx\, dy - 0,$$

$$\text{or} \quad \frac{h}{K} v \frac{\epsilon}{z} = \frac{dv}{dx} \frac{dz}{dx} + \frac{dv}{dy} \frac{dz}{dy} - \frac{dv}{dz}.$$

153. Substituting for $\dfrac{dz}{dx}$ and $\dfrac{dz}{dy}$ their values derived from the equation

$$m\, dx + n\, dy + p\, dz = 0,$$

and denoting by q the quantity

$$(m^2 + n^2 + p^2),$$

we have

$$K \left(m \frac{dv}{dx} + n \frac{dv}{dy} + p \frac{dv}{dz} \right) + hvq = 0 \cdot \cdot \cdot \text{(B)},$$

thus we know distinctly what is represented by each of the terms of this equation.

Taking them all with contrary signs and multiplying them by $dx\, dy$, the first expresses how much heat the molecule receives through the two faces perpendicular to x, the second how much it receives through its two faces perpendicular to y, the third how much it receives through the face perpendicular to z, and the fourth how much it receives from the medium. The equation therefore expresses that the sum of all the terms of the first order is zero, and that the heat acquired cannot be represented except by terms of the second order.

154. To arrive at equation (B), we in fact consider one of the molecules whose base is in the surface of the solid, as a vessel which receives or loses heat through its different faces. The equation signifies that all the terms of the first order which enter into the expression of the heat acquired cancel each other; so that the gain of heat cannot be expressed except by terms of the second order. We may give to the molecule the form, either of a right prism whose axis is normal to the surface of the solid, or that of a truncated prism, or any form whatever.

The general equation (A), (Art. 142) supposes that all the terms of the first order cancel each other in the interior of the mass, which is evident for prismatic molecules enclosed in the solid. The equation (B), (Art. 147) expresses the same result for molecules situated at the boundaries of bodies.

Such are the general points of view from which we may look at this part of the theory of heat.

The equation $\dfrac{dv}{dt} = \dfrac{K}{CD}\left(\dfrac{d^2v}{dx^2} + \dfrac{d^2v}{dy^2} + \dfrac{d^2v}{dz^2}\right)$ represents the movement of heat

in the interior of bodies. It enables us to ascertain the distribution from instant to instant in all substances solid or liquid; from it we may derive the equation which belongs to each particular case.

In the two following articles we shall make this application to the problem of the cylinder, and to that of the sphere.

SECTION VIII. *Application of the General Equations*

155. Let us denote the variable radius of any cylindrical envelope by r, and suppose, as formerly, in Article 118, that all the molecules equally distant from the axis have at each instant a common temperature; v will be a function of r and t; r is a function of y, z, given by the equation $r^2 = y^2 + z^2$. It is evident in the first place that the variation of v with respect to x is nul; thus the term $\dfrac{d^2v}{dx^2}$ must be omitted. We shall have then, according to the principles of the differential calculus, the equations

$$\frac{dv}{dy} = \frac{dv}{dr}\frac{dr}{dy} \text{ and } \frac{d^2v}{dy^2} = \frac{d^2v}{dr^2}\left(\frac{dr}{dy}\right)^2 + \frac{dv}{dr}\left(\frac{d^2r}{dy^2}\right),$$

$$\frac{dv}{dz} = \frac{dv}{dr}\frac{dr}{dz} \text{ and } \frac{d^2v}{dz^2} = \frac{d^2v}{dr^2}\left(\frac{dr}{dz}\right)^2 + \frac{dv}{dr}\left(\frac{d^2r}{dz^2}\right);$$

whence

$$\frac{d^2v}{dy^2} + \frac{d^2v}{dz^2} = \frac{d^2v}{dr^2}\left\{\left(\frac{dr}{dy}\right)^2 + \left(\frac{dr}{dz}\right)^2\right\} + \frac{dv}{dr}\left(\frac{d^2r}{dy^2} + \frac{d^2r}{dz^2}\right) \cdots (a).$$

In the second member of the equation, the quantities

$$\frac{dr}{dy}, \ \frac{dr}{dz}, \ \frac{d^2r}{dy^2}, \ \frac{d^2r}{dz^2},$$

must be replaced by their respective values; for which purpose we derive from the equation $y^2 + z^2 = r^2$,

$$y = r\frac{dr}{dy} \quad \text{and} \quad 1 = \left(\frac{dr}{dy}\right)^2 + r\frac{d^2r}{dy^2},$$

$$z = r\frac{dr}{dz} \quad \text{and} \quad 1 = \left(\frac{dr}{dz}\right)^2 + r\frac{d^2r}{dz^2},$$

and consequently

$$y^2 + z^2 = r^2\left\{\left(\frac{dr}{dy}\right)^2 + \left(\frac{dr}{dz}\right)^2\right\},$$

$$2 = \left(\frac{dr}{dy}\right)^2 + \left(\frac{dr}{dz}\right)^2 + r\left\{\frac{d^2r}{dy^2} + \frac{d^2r}{dz^2}\right\}.$$

The first equation, whose first member is equal to r^2, gives

$$\left(\frac{dr}{dy}\right)^2 + \left(\frac{dr}{dz}\right)^2 = 1 \cdot \cdot \cdot (b);$$

the second gives, when we substitute for

$$\left(\frac{dr}{dy}\right)^2 + \left(\frac{dr}{dz}\right)^2$$

its value 1,

$$\frac{d^2r}{dy^2} + \frac{d^2r}{dz^2} = \frac{1}{r} \cdot \cdot \cdot (c).$$

If the values given by equations (b) and (c) be now substituted in (a), we have

$$\frac{d^2v}{dy^2} + \frac{d^2v}{dz^2} = \frac{d^2v}{dr^2} + \frac{1}{r}\frac{dv}{dr}.$$

Hence the equation which expresses the movement of heat in the cylinder, is

$$\frac{dv}{dt} = \frac{K}{CD}\left(\frac{d^2v}{dr^2} + \frac{1}{r}\frac{dv}{dr}\right),$$

as was found formerly, Art. 119.

We might also suppose that particles equally distant from the centre have not received a common initial temperature; in this case we should arrive at a much more general equation.

156. To determine, by means of equation (A), the movement of heat in a sphere which has been immersed in a liquid, we shall regard v as a function of r and t; r is a function of x, y, z, given by the equation

$$r^2 = x^2 + y^2 + z^2,$$

r being the variable radius of an envelope. We have then

$$\frac{dv}{dx} = \frac{dv}{dr}\frac{dr}{dx} \quad \text{and} \quad \frac{d^2v}{dx^2} = \frac{d^2v}{dr^2}\left(\frac{dr}{dx}\right)^2 + \frac{dv}{dr}\frac{d^2r}{dx^2},$$

$$\frac{dv}{dy} = \frac{dv}{dr}\frac{dr}{dy} \quad \text{and} \quad \frac{d^2v}{dy^2} = \frac{d^2v}{dr^2}\left(\frac{dr}{dy}\right)^2 + \frac{dv}{dr}\frac{d^2r}{dy^2},$$

$$\frac{dv}{dz} = \frac{dv}{dr}\frac{dr}{dz} \quad \text{and} \quad \frac{d^2v}{dz^2} = \frac{d^2v}{dr^2}\left(\frac{dr}{dz}\right)^2 + \frac{dv}{dr}\frac{d^2r}{dz^2}.$$

Making these substitutions in the equation

$$\frac{dv}{dt} = \frac{K}{CD}\left\{\frac{d^2v}{dx^2} + \frac{d^2v}{dy^2} + \frac{d^2v}{dz^2}\right\},$$

we shall have

$$\frac{dv}{dt} = \frac{K}{CD}\left[\frac{d^2v}{dr^2}\left\{\left(\frac{dr}{dx}\right)^2 + \left(\frac{dr}{dy}\right)^2 + \left(\frac{dr}{dz}\right)^2\right\} + \frac{dv}{dr}\left\{\frac{d^2r}{dx^2} + \frac{d^2r}{dy^2} + \frac{d^2r}{dz^2}\right\}\right] \quad (a).$$

The equation $x^2+y^2+z^2=r^2$ gives the following results:

$$x = r\frac{dr}{dx} \quad \text{and} \quad 1 = \left(\frac{dr}{dx}\right)^2 + r\frac{d^2r}{dx^2},$$

$$y = r\frac{dr}{dy} \quad \text{and} \quad 1 = \left(\frac{dr}{dy}\right)^2 + r\frac{d^2r}{dy^2},$$

$$z = r\frac{dr}{dz} \quad \text{and} \quad 1 = \left(\frac{dr}{dz}\right)^2 + r\frac{d^2r}{dz^2}.$$

The three equations of the first order give:

$$x^2+y^2+z^2 = r^2\left\{\left(\frac{dr}{dx}\right)^2 + \left(\frac{dr}{dy}\right)^2 + \left(\frac{dr}{dz}\right)^2\right\}.$$

The three equations of the second order give:

$$3 = \left(\frac{dr}{dx}\right)^2 + \left(\frac{dr}{dy}\right)^2 + \left(\frac{dr}{dz}\right)^2 + r\left\{\frac{d^2r}{dx^2} + \frac{d^2r}{dy^2} + \frac{d^2r}{dz^2}\right\}:$$

and substituting for

$$\left(\frac{dr}{dx}\right)^2 + \left(\frac{dr}{dy}\right)^2 + \left(\frac{dr}{dz}\right)^2$$

its value 1, we have

$$\frac{d^2r}{dx^2} + \frac{d^2r}{dy^2} + \frac{d^2r}{dz^2} = \frac{2}{r}.$$

Making these substitutions in the equation (a) we have the equation

$$\frac{dv}{dt} = \frac{K}{CD}\left\{\frac{d^2v}{dr^2} + \frac{2}{r}\frac{dv}{dr}\right\},$$

which is the same as that of Art. 114.

The equation would contain a greater number of terms, if we supposed molecules equally distant from the centre not to have received the same initial temperature.

We might also deduce from the definite equation (B), the equations which express the state of the surface in particular cases, in which we suppose solids of given form to communicate their heat to the atmospheric air; but in most cases these equations present themselves at once, and their form is very simple, when the co-ordinates are suitably chosen.

SECTION IX. *General Remarks*

157. The investigation of the laws of movement of heat in solids now consists in the integration of the equations which we have constructed; this is the object of the following chapters. We conclude this chapter with general remarks on the nature of the quantities which enter into our analysis.

In order to measure these quantities and express them numerically, they must be compared with different kinds of units, five in number, namely, the unit of length, the unit of time, that of temperature, that of weight, and finally the unit which serves to measure quantities of heat. For the last unit, we might have chosen the quantity of heat which raises a given volume of a certain substance from the temperature 0 to the temperature 1. The choice of this unit would have been preferable in many respects to that of the quantity of heat required to convert a mass of ice of a given weight, into an equal mass of water at 0, without raising its temperature. We have adopted the last unit only because it had been in a manner fixed beforehand in several works on physics; besides this supposition would introduce no change into the results of analysis.

158. The specific elements which in every body determine the measurable effects of heat are three in number, namely, the conductivity proper to the body, the conductivity relative to the atmospheric air, and the capacity for heat. The numbers which express these quantities are, like the specific gravity, so many natural characters proper to different substances.

We have already remarked, Art. 36, that the conductivity of the surface would be measured in a more exact manner, if we had sufficient observations on the effects of radiant heat in spaces deprived of air.

It may be seen, as has been mentioned in the first section of Chapter I, Art. 11, that only three specific coefficients, K, h, C, enter into the investigation; they must be determined by observation; and we shall point out in the sequel the experiments adapted to make them known with precision.

159. The number C which enters into the analysis, is always multiplied by the density D, that is to say, by the number of units of weight which are equivalent to the weight of unit of volume; thus the product CD may be replaced by the coefficient c. In this case we must understand by the specific capacity for heat, the quantity required to raise from temperature 0 to temperature 1 unit of volume of a given substance, and not unit of weight of that substance.

With the view of not departing from the common definition, we have referred the capacity for heat to the weight and not to the volume; but it would be preferable to employ the coefficient c which we have just defined; magnitudes measured by the unit of weight would not then enter into the analytical expressions: we should have to consider only, 1st, the linear dimension x, the temperature v, and the time t; 2nd, the coefficients c, h, and K. The three first quantities are undetermined, and the three others are, for each substance, constant elements which experiment determines. As to the unit of surface and the unit of volume, they are not absolute, but depend on the unit of length.

160. It must now be remarked that every undetermined magnitude or constant has one *dimension* proper to itself, and that the terms of one and the same equation could not be compared, if they had not the same *exponent of dimension*. We have introduced this consideration into the theory of heat, in order to make our definitions more exact, and to serve to verify the analysis;

it is derived from primary notions on quantities; for which reason, in geometry and mechanics, it is the equivalent of the fundamental lemmas which the Greeks have left us without proof.

161. In the analytical theory of heat, every equation (E) expresses a necessary relation between the existing magnitudes x, t, v, c, h, K. This relation depends in no respect on the choice of the unit of length, which from its very nature is contingent, that is to say, if we took a different unit to measure the linear dimensions, the equation (E) would still be the same. Suppose then the unit of length to be changed, and its second value to be equal to the first divided by m. Any quantity whatever x which in the equation (E) represents a certain line ab, and which, consequently, denotes a certain number of times the unit of length, becomes mx, corresponding to the same length ab; the value t of the time, and the value v of the temperature will not be changed; the same is not the case with the specific elements h, K, c: the first, h, becomes $\dfrac{h}{m^2}$; for it expresses the quantity of heat which escapes, during the unit of time, from the unit of surface at the temperature 1. If we examine attentively the nature of the coefficient K, as we have defined it in Articles 68 and 135, we perceive that it becomes $\dfrac{K}{m}$; for the flow of heat varies directly as the area of the surface, and inversely as the distance between two infinite planes (Art. 72). As to the coefficient c which represents the product CD, it also depends on the unit of length and becomes $\dfrac{c}{m^3}$; hence equation (E) must undergo no change when we write mx instead of x, and at the same time $\dfrac{K}{m}$, $\dfrac{h}{m^2}$, $\dfrac{c}{m^3}$, instead of K, h, c; the number m disappears after these substitutions: thus the dimension of x with respect to the unit of length is 1, that of K is -1, that of h is -2, and that of c is -3. If we attribute to each quantity its own *exponent of dimension*, the equation will be homogeneous, since every term will have the same total exponent. Numbers such as S, which represent surfaces or solids, are of two dimensions in the first case, and of three dimensions in the second. Angles, sines, and other trigonometrical functions, logarithms or exponents of powers, are, according to the principles of analysis, *absolute* numbers which do not change with the unit of length; their dimensions must therefore be taken equal to 0, which is the dimension of all abstract numbers.

If the unit of time, which was at first 1, becomes $\dfrac{1}{n}$, the number t will become nt, and the numbers x and v will not change. The coefficients K, h, c will become $\dfrac{K}{n}$, $\dfrac{h}{n}$, c. Thus the dimensions of x, t, v with respect to the unit of time are 0, 1, 0, and those of K, h, c are -1, -1, 0.

If the unit of temperature be changed, so that the temperature 1 becomes that which corresponds to an effect other than the boiling of water; and if that effect requires a less temperature, which is to that of boiling water in the ratio of 1 to the number p; v will become vp, x and t will keep their values, and the coefficients K, h, c will become $\dfrac{K}{p}$, $\dfrac{h}{p}$, $\dfrac{c}{p}$.

The following table indicates the dimensions of the three undetermined quantities and the three constants, with respect to each kind of unit.

Quantity or Constant	Length	Duration	Temperature
Exponent of dimension of x..............	1	0	0
" " " " t..............	0	1	0
" " " " v..............	0	0	1
The specific conducibility, K..............	−1	−1	−1
The surface conducibility, h..............	−2	−1	−1
The capacity for heat, c..............	−3	0	−1

162. If we retained the coefficients C and D, whose product has been represented by c, we should have to consider the unit of weight, and we should find that the exponent of dimension, with respect to the unit of length, is -3 for the density D, and 0 for C.

On applying the preceding rule to the different equations and their transformations, it will be found that they are homogeneous with respect to each kind of unit, and that the dimension of every angular or exponential quantity is nothing. If this were not the case, some error must have been committed in the analysis, or abridged expressions must have been introduced

If, for example, we take equation (b) of Art. 105,

$$\frac{dv}{dt} = \frac{K}{CD}\frac{d^2v}{dx^2} - \frac{hl}{CDS}v,$$

we find that, with respect to the unit of length, the dimension of each of the three terms is 0; it is 1 for the unit of temperature, and -1 for the unit of time.

In the equation $v = Ae^{-x\sqrt{\frac{2h}{Kl}}}$ of Art. 76, the linear dimension of each term is 0, and it is evident that the dimension of the exponent $x\sqrt{\frac{2h}{Kl}}$ is always nothing, whatever be the units of length, time, or temperature.

EXPERIMENTAL RESEARCHES
IN ELECTRICITY

BIOGRAPHICAL NOTE
MICHAEL FARADAY, 1791-1867

FARADAY was born September 22, 1791, in Newington, Surrey, the son of a blacksmith. When he was five, the family moved to London, and he grew up in such poverty that, as he later recalled, the loaf of bread his mother gave him had to last a week. "My education," he wrote, "was of the most ordinary description, consisting of little more than the rudiments of reading, writing, and arithmetic at a common day school. My hours out of school were passed at home and in the streets."

At the age of twelve he became an errand-boy for a bookseller and bookbinder, and a year later he was accepted because of exemplary conduct as an apprentice without fee. His scientific education began while he was engaged in binding books. As he later wrote to a friend: "It was in those books, in the hours after work, that I found the beginning of my philosophy. There were two that especially helped me, the *Encyclopaedia Britannica*, from which I gained my first notions of electricity, and Mrs. Marcet's *Conversations on Chemistry*, which gave me my foundation in that science." With what money he could spare he bought materials for experiments, and by 1812 was conducting investigations in electrolytic decomposition. In the spring of that year, through the generosity of a customer, he was able to attend a series of four lectures by Sir Humphry Davy at the Royal Institution. He took careful notes, wrote them out in fuller form, and bound them into a book. He sent the notes to Davy with a request for employment at the Royal Institution in any capacity connected with science. Davy advised him not to give up a skilled trade for something in which there was neither security, money, nor opportunity for advancement, but a few months later, on the dismissal of a laboratory assistant, he offered the post to Faraday. He became Davy's assistant in March, 1813, and in October of that year accompanied him on a tour of the universities and laboratories of France, Italy, and Switzerland, which lasted until April, 1815.

Upon his return to England and the Institution, Faraday continued as Davy's assistant and began research of his own. In 1816 he made his first contribution in the form of an analysis of caustic lime from Tuscany, which was published in the *Quarterly Journal of Science*. From that time he wrote an increasing number of notes and memoirs. In 1821 he began work upon electromagnetism; he first collected and repeated all the known experiments, published an account of them in the *Annals of Philosophy*, and proceeded to make his own investigations. His experiments were meticulously recorded in numbered paragraphs, and in 1831 he started the first section of his *Experimental Researches in Electricity*, which was to occupy him intermittently for the next twenty-three years. First published in the form of monographs in the *"Transactions of the Royal Society,"* they were later brought out in three volumes (1844, 1847, 1855).

Faraday was occupied during these years with many things in addition to research in electricity. Pursuing the chemical investigations he had begun as Davy's assistant, he made a special study of chlorine, discovered two new chlorides of carbon, initiated experiments on the diffusion of gases, and was among the first to succeed in their liquefaction. Many of his discoveries had industrial applications, some of which he investigated, such as the alloys of steel and the manufacture of glass. He was also called upon to act as a consultant on many works of public concern, and for thirty years he was adviser to Trinity House on the supervision of the lighthouses of England. In 1823 he was elected to the Royal Society over Davy's strong opposition, which, however, Faraday did not permit to interfere with their friendship. In 1833 he was made the Fullerian professor of chemistry for life, and although he was not obliged to lecture, he frequently did so in order to increase the stability and influence of the Institution. His celebrated *Chemical History of a Candle* was one of the series of Christmas lectures for children which he had started at the Institution. He received honorary degrees and scientific tributes from all parts of the world, and both the Royal Society and the Royal Institution tried in vain to persuade him to accept the presidency. As he told his friend Tyndall in refusing the Royal Society's offer, "I must remain plain Michael Faraday to the last."

After he had become famous for his discoveries, Faraday's services were eagerly sought by industry and commerce. For a few years he did a little "professional business," as he called it, and in 1830 received more than a thousand pounds in return. It is estimated that this work might easily have yielded five thousand pounds in 1832, but he then felt, as he later told Tyndall, that he had to decide whether to make wealth or science the pursuit of his life. He chose science and lived and died a poor man

Faraday married in 1821, "an event," he wrote, "which more than any other contributed to my earthly happiness and healthful state of mind." The marriage was childless, but Faraday's lodgings in the Royal Institution were always full of his wife's nieces and nephews, for he enjoyed the company of children and liked to take part in their games. Faraday's parents belonged to the small dissident Presbyterian sect known as Sandemanians, and Faraday himself attended their meetings from childhood; he made a formal declaration of faith at thirty and for two different periods discharged the office of elder.

Faraday's last years were spent in seriously declining health. As early as 1841, as a result of overwork, he had suffered a serious breakdown and was compelled to take a complete rest for a period of several years. Although he was back in the laboratory by 1845 and for fifteen years engaged in some of his most important research, his health was never completely restored. When at length he found his memory failing and his powers declining, he yielded to others whatever parts of his work he could no longer accomplish according to his own standard of efficiency. Queen Victoria, in 1858, provided him with a house at Hampton Court which had rooms so arranged that he had no stairs to climb. In 1862 he delivered his last lecture and performed his last experiment. He died August 25, 1867.

CONTENTS

CONTENTS

PREFACES FROM ORIGINAL THREE-VOLUME EDITION

Preface to Volume I

I HAVE been induced by various circumstances to collect in one volume the Fourteen Series of *Experimental Researches in Electricity*, which have appeared in the *Philosophical Transactions* during the last seven years: the chief reason has been the desire to supply at a moderate price the whole of these papers, with an index, to those who may desire to have them.

The readers of the volume will, I hope, do me the justice to remember that it was not written as a *whole*, but in parts; the earlier portions rarely having any known relation at the time to those which might follow. If I had rewritten the work, I perhaps might have considerably varied the form, but should not have altered much of the real matter: it would not, however, then have been considered a faithful reprint or statement of the course and results of the whole investigation, which only — I desired to supply.

I may be allowed to express my great satisfaction at finding, that the different parts, written at intervals during seven years, harmonize so well as they do. There would have been nothing particular in this, if the parts had related only to matters well ascertained before any of them were written:—but as each professes to contain something of original discovery, or of correction of received views, it does surprise even my partiality, that they should have the degree of consistency and apparent general accuracy which they seem to me to present.

I have made some alterations in the text, but they have been altogether of a typographical or grammatical character; and even where greatest, have been intended to explain the sense, not to alter it. I have often added Notes at the bottom of the page, as to paragraphs 59, 360, 439, 521, 552, 555, 598, 657, 883, for the correction of errors, and also the purpose of illustration: but these are all distinguished from the Original Notes of the *Researches* by the date of *Dec. 1838.*

The date of a scientific paper containing any pretensions to discovery is frequently a matter of serious importance, and it is a great misfortune that there are many most valuable communications, essential to the history and progress of science, with respect to which this point cannot now be ascertained. This arises from the circumstance of the papers having no dates attached to them individually, and of the journals in which they appear having such as are inaccurate, i.e. dates of a period earlier than that of publication. I may refer to the note at the end of the First Series, as an illustration of the kind of confusion thus produced. These circumstances have induced me to affix a date at the top of every other page, and I have thought myself justified in using that placed by the Secretary of the Royal Society on each paper as it was received. An author has no right, perhaps, to claim an earlier one, unless it has received confirmation by some public act or officer.

Before concluding these lines I would beg leave to make a reference or two; first, to my own "Papers on Electro-magnetic Rotations" in the *Quarterly Journal of Science*, 1822. XII, 74, 186, 283, 416, and also to my "Letter on Magneto-electric Induction" in the *Annales de Chimie*, LI, p. 404. These might, as to the matter, very properly have appeared in this volume, but they would have interfered with it as a simple reprint of the *Experimental Researches* of the *Philosophical Transactions*.

Then I wish to refer, in relation to the Fourth Series on a new law of Electric Conduction, to Franklin's experiments on the non-conduction of ice, which have been very properly separated and set forth by Professor Bache (*Journal of the Franklin Institute*, 1836. XVII, 183). These, which I did not at all remember as to the extent of the effect, though they in no way anticipate the expression of the law I state as to the general effect of liquefaction on electrolytes, still should never be forgotten when speaking of that law as applicable to the case of water.

There are two papers which I am anxious to refer to, as corrections or criticisms of parts of the *Experimental Researches*. The first of these is one by Jacobi (*Philosophical Magazine*, 1838. XIII, 401), relative to the possible production of a spark on completing the junction of the two metals of a single pair of plates (915). It is an excellent paper, and though I have not repeated the experiments, the description of them convinces me that I must have been in error. The second is by that excellent philosopher Marianini (*Memoria della Societa Italiana di Modena*, XXI, 205), and is a critical and experimental examination of Series VIII, and of the question whether metallic contact is or is not *productive* of a part of the electricity of the voltaic pile. I see no reason as yet to alter the opinion I have given; but the paper is so very valuable, comes to the question so directly, and the point itself is of such great importance, that I intend at the first opportunity renewing the inquiry, and, if I can, rendering the proofs either on the one side or the other undeniable to all.

Other parts of these researches have received the honour of critical attention from various philosophers, to all of whom I am obliged, and some of whose corrections I have acknowledged in the foot notes. There are, no doubt, occasions on which I have not felt the force of the remarks, but time and the progress of science will best settle such cases; and, although I cannot honestly say that I *wish* to be found in error, yet I do fervently hope that the progress of science in the hands of its many zealous present cultivators will be such, as by giving us new and other developments, and laws more and more general in their applications, will even make me think that what is written and illustrated in these experimental researches, belongs to the by-gone parts of science.

MICHAEL FARADAY

Royal Institution, March, 1839

Preface to Volume II

FOR reasons stated in the former volume of *Experimental Researches in Electricity*, I have been induced to gather the remaining Series together, and to add to them certain other papers devoted to Electrical research.

To the prefatory remarks containing these reasons, I would recall the recollection of those who may honour these *Researches* with any further attention.

I have printed the papers in this volume, as before, with little or no alteration, except that I have placed the fair and just date of each at the top of the pages.

I regret the presence of those papers which partake of a controversial character, but could not help it; some of them contain much new, important and explanatory matter. The introduction of matter due to other parties than myself, as Nobili and Antinori, or Hare, was essential to the comprehension of the further development given in the replies.

I owe many thanks to the Royal Society, to Mr. Murray, and to Mr. Taylor, for the great kindness I have received in the loan of plates, &c., and in other facilities granted to me for the printing of the volume.

As the Index belongs both to the *Experimental Researches* and to the miscellaneous papers, its references are of necessity made in two ways; those to the *Researches* are, as before, to the numbers of the Paragraphs, and are easily recognised by the greatness of the numbers: the other references are to the pages, and being always preceded by *p.* or *pp.*, are known by that mark.

Michael Faraday

Preface to Volume III

For reasons stated in the First Volume of these *Experimental Researches*, I have been induced to gather the remaining Series together, and to add to them certain other papers devoted to Electrical and Magnetic Research.

To the prefatory remarks containing these reasons, I would recall the recollection of those who may honour these *Researches* with any further attention. I have printed the papers in this volume, as before, with little or no alteration, except that I have placed the fair and just date of each at the top of the pages.

As regards magnecrystallic action, which commences at paragraph 2454, the reader will see the gradual change and enlargement of view respecting its nature in the course of long investigations at the following places, 2550, 2562, 2576, 2584, &c., 2591, 2639, 2797, 2818, 2836, &c. I would refer readers to the paper by Tyndall and Knoblauch in the *Philosophical Magazine*, 1850, Vol. XXXVII, p. 1, for a very philosophical account of the physical cause of the magnecrystallic action,[1] and to the paper by Professor W. Thomson on the theory of magnetic induction in crystalline and non-crystalline substances in the *Philosophical Magazine*, 1851, Vol. I, p. 177, as being in all parts in perfect accordance with the various experimental results which I have at different times obtained.

With respect to paragraph 2967, and the intentions there expressed of experimenting with oxygen at low temperatures, I have endeavoured to carry these intentions out; but the extreme difficulty of working on such attenuated matter as gases at low temperatures, without the production of air-currents able to influence the very delicate torsion-balance and apparatus required to measure the result, is so great as to have prevented me as yet from obtaining any results worthy of confidence.

I owe many thanks to the Royal Society and to the Proprietors of the *Philosophical Magazine*, for the great kindness I have received in the loan of plates, &c., and in other facilities granted to me for the printing of the volume.

[1] Marchand and Scheerer say that bismuth is expanded by pressure and has its structure changed. Gmelin's Handbook, iv. p. 428.

As the Index belongs both to the *Experimental Researches* and to the other papers, its references are of necessity made in two ways; those to the *Researches* are, as before, to the numbers of the paragraphs, and are easily recognized by the greatness of the numbers: the other references are to the pages, and being always preceded by *p.* or *pp.*, are known by that mark.

MICHAEL FARADAY

January, 1855

FIRST SERIES

§ 1. *On the Induction of Electric Currents* § 2. *On the Evolution of Electricity from Magnetism* § 3. *New Electrical Condition of Matter* § 4. *Explication of* Arago's *Magnetic Phenomena*

READ NOVEMBER 24, 1831

1. THE power which electricity of tension possesses of causing an opposite electrical state in its vicinity has been expressed by the general term Induction; which, as it has been received into scientific language, may also, with propriety, be used in the same general sense to express the power which electrical currents may possess of inducing any particular state upon matter in their immediate neighbourhood, otherwise indifferent. It is with this meaning that I purpose using it in the present paper.

2. Certain effects of the induction of electrical currents have already been recognised and described: as those of magnetization; Ampère's experiments of bringing a copper disc near to a flat spiral; his repetition with electromagnets of Arago's extraordinary experiments, and perhaps a few others. Still it appeared unlikely that these could be all the effects which induction by currents could produce; especially as, upon dispensing with iron, almost the whole of them disappear, whilst yet an infinity of bodies, exhibiting definite phenomena of induction with electricity of tension, still remain to be acted upon by the induction of electricity in motion.

3. Further: Whether Ampère's beautiful theory were adopted, or any other, or whatever reservation were mentally made, still it appeared very extraordinary, that as every electric current was accompanied by a corresponding intensity of magnetic action at right angles to the current, good conductors of electricity, when placed within the sphere of this action, should not have any current induced through them, or some sensible effect produced equivalent in force to such a current.

4. These considerations, with their consequence, the hope of obtaining electricity from ordinary magnetism, have stimulated me at various times to investigate experimentally the inductive effect of electric currents. I lately arrived at positive results; and not only had my hopes fulfilled, but obtained a key which appeared to me to open out a full explanation of Arago's magnetic phenomena, and also to discover a new state, which may probably have great influence in some of the most important effects of electric currents.

5. These results I purpose describing, not as they were obtained, but in such a manner as to give the most concise view of the whole.

§ 1. *On the Induction of Electric Currents*

6. About twenty-six feet of copper wire one twentieth of an inch in diameter were wound round a cylinder of wood as a helix, the different spires of which were prevented from touching by a thin interposed twine. This helix was covered with calico, and then a second wire applied in the same manner. In this way twelve helices were superposed, each containing an average length of wire of twenty-seven feet, and all in the same direction. The first, third, fifth, seventh, ninth, and eleventh of these helices were connected at their extremities end to end, so as to form one helix; the others were connected in a similar manner; and thus two principal helices were produced, closely interposed, having the same direction, not touching anywhere, and each containing one hundred and fifty-five feet in length of wire.

7. One of these helices was connected with a galvanometer, the other with a voltaic battery of ten pairs of plates four inches square, with double coppers and well charged; yet not the slightest sensible deflection of the galvanometer-needle could be observed.

8. A similar compound helix, consisting of six lengths of copper and six of soft iron wire, was constructed. The resulting iron helix contained two hundred and fourteen feet of wire, the resulting copper helix two hundred and eight feet; but whether the current from the trough was passed through the copper or the iron helix, no effect upon the other could be perceived at the galvanometer.

9. In these and many similar experiments

no difference in action of any kind appeared between iron and other metals.

10. Two hundred and three feet of copper wire in one length were coiled round a large block of wood; other two hundred and three feet of similar wire were interposed as a spiral between the turns of the first coil, and metallic contact everywhere prevented by twine. One of these helices was connected with a galvanometer, and the other with a battery of one hundred pairs of plates four inches square, with double coppers, and well charged. When the contact was made, there was a sudden and very slight effect at the galvanometer, and there was also a similar slight effect when the contact with the battery was broken. But whilst the voltaic current was continuing to pass through the one helix, no galvanometrical appearances nor any effect like induction upon the other helix could be perceived, although the active power of the battery was proved to be great, by its heating the whole of its own helix, and by the brilliancy of the discharge when made through charcoal.

11. Repetition of the experiments with a battery of one hundred and twenty pairs of plates produced no other effects; but it was ascertained, both at this and the former time, that the slight deflection of the needle occurring at the moment of completing the connexion, was always in one direction, and that the equally slight deflection produced when the contact was broken, was in the other direction; and also, that these effects occurred when the first helices were used (6, 8).

12. The results which I had by this time obtained with magnets led me to believe that the battery current through one wire, did, in reality, induce a similar current through the other wire, but that it continued for an instant only, and partook more of the nature of the electrical wave passed through from the shock of a common Leyden jar than of the current from a voltaic battery, and therefore might magnetise a steel needle, although it scarcely affected the galvanometer.

13. This expectation was confirmed; for on substituting a small hollow helix, formed round a glass tube, for the galvanometer, introducing a steel needle, making contact as before between the battery and the inducing wire (7, 10), and then removing the needle before the battery contact was broken, it was found magnetised.

14. When the battery contact was first made, then an unmagnetised needle introduced into the small indicating helix (13), and lastly the battery contact broken, the needle was found magnetised to an equal degree apparently as before; but the poles were of the contrary kind.

15. The same effects took place on using the large compound helices first described (6, 8).

16. When the unmagnetised needle was put into the indicating helix, before contact of the inducing wire with the battery, and remained there until the contact was broken, it exhibited little or no magnetism; the first effect having been nearly neutralised by the second (13, 14). The force of the induced current upon making contact was found always to exceed that of the induced current at breaking of contact; and if therefore the contact was made and broken many times in succession, whilst the needle remained in the indicating helix, it at last came out not unmagnetised, but a needle magnetised as if the induced current upon making contact had acted alone on it. This effect may be due to the accumulation (as it is called) at the poles of the unconnected pile, rendering the current upon first making contact more powerful than what it is afterwards, at the moment of breaking contact.

17. If the circuit between the helix or wire under induction and the galvanometer or indicating spiral was not rendered complete *before* the connexion between the battery and the inducing wire was completed or broken, then no effects were perceived at the galvanometer. Thus, if the battery communications were first made, and then the wire under induction connected with the indicating helix, no magnetising power was there exhibited. But still retaining the latter communications, when those with the battery were broken, a magnet was formed in the helix, but of the second kind (14), i.e., with poles indicating a current in the same direction to that belonging to the battery current, or to that always induced by that current at its cessation.

18. In the preceding experiments the wires were placed near to each other, and the contact of the inducing one with the battery made when the inductive effect was required; but as the particular action might be supposed to be exerted only at the moments of making and breaking contact, the induction was produced in another way. Several feet of copper wire were stretched in wide zigzag forms, representing the letter W, on one surface of a broad board; a second wire was stretched in precisely similar forms on a second board, so that when brought near the first, the wires should every-

where touch, except that a sheet of thick paper was interposed. One of these wires was connected with the galvanometer, and the other with a voltaic battery. The first wire was then moved towards the second, and as it approached, the needle was deflected. Being then removed, the needle was deflected in the opposite direction. By first making the wires approach and then recede, simultaneously with the vibrations of the needle, the latter soon became very extensive; but when the wires ceased to move from or towards each other, the galvanometer-needle soon came to its usual position.

19. As the wires approximated, the induced current was in the *contrary* direction to the inducing current. As the wires receded, the induced current was in the *same* direction as the inducing current. When the wires remained stationary, there was no induced current (54).

20. When a small voltaic arrangement was introduced into the circuit between the galvanometer (10) and its helix or wire, so as to cause a permanent deflection of 30° or 40°, and then the battery of one hundred pairs of plates connected with the inducing wire, there was an instantaneous action as before (11); but the galvanometer-needle immediately resumed and retained its place unaltered, notwithstanding the continued contact of the inducing wire with the trough: such was the case in whichever way the contacts were made (33).

21. Hence it would appear that collateral currents, either in the same or in opposite directions, exert no permanent inducing power on each other, affecting their quantity or tension.

22. I could obtain no evidence by the tongue, by spark, or by heating fine wire or charcoal, of the electricity passing through the wire under induction; neither could I obtain any chemical effects, though the contacts with metallic and other solutions were made and broken alternately with those of the battery, so that the second effect of induction should not oppose or neutralise the first (13, 16).

23. This deficiency of effect is not because the induced current of electricity cannot pass fluids, but probably because of its brief duration and feeble intensity; for on introducing two large copper plates into the circuit on the induced side (20), the plates being immersed in brine, but prevented from touching each other by an interposed cloth, the effect at the indicating galvanometer, or helix, occurred as before. The induced electricity could also pass through a voltaic trough (20). When, however, the quantity of interposed fluid was reduced to a drop, the galvanometer gave no indication.

24. Attempts to obtain similar effects by the use of wires conveying ordinary electricity were doubtful in the results. A compound helix similar to that already described, containing eight elementary helices (6), was used. Four of the helices had their similar ends bound together by wire, and the two general terminations thus produced connected with the small magnetising helix containing an unmagnetised needle (13). The other four helices were similarly arranged, but their ends connected with a Leyden jar. On passing the discharge, the needle was found to be a magnet; but it appeared probable that a part of the electricity of the jar had passed off to the small helix, and so magnetised the needle. There was indeed no reason to expect that the electricity of a jar possessing as it does great tension, would not diffuse itself through all the metallic matter interposed between the coatings.

25. Still it does not follow that the discharge of ordinary electricity through a wire does not produce analogous phenomena to those arising from voltaic electricity; but as it appears impossible to separate the effects produced at the moment when the discharge begins to pass, from the equal and contrary effects produced when it ceases to pass (16), inasmuch as with ordinary electricity these periods are simultaneous, so there can be scarcely any hope that in this form of the experiment they can be perceived.

26. Hence it is evident that currents of voltaic electricity present phenomena of induction somewhat analogous to those produced by electricity of tension, although, as will be seen hereafter, many differences exist between them. The result is the production of other currents, (but which are only momentary), parallel, or tending to parallelism, with the inducing current. By reference to the poles of the needle formed in the indicating helix (13, 14) and to the deflections of the galvanometer-needle (11), it was found in all cases that the induced current, produced by the first action of the inducing current, was in the contrary direction to the latter, but that the current produced by the cessation of the inducing current was in the same direction (19). For the purpose of avoiding periphrasis, I propose to call this action of the current from the voltaic battery, *volta-electric induction*. The properties of the second wire, after induction has developed the first

PLATE I

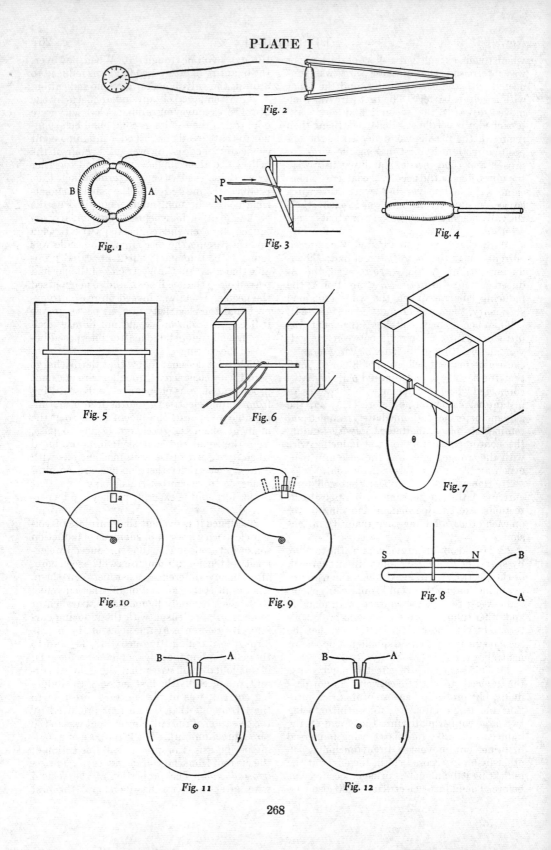

Fig. 2

Fig. 1

Fig. 3

Fig. 4

Fig. 5

Fig. 6

Fig. 7

Fig. 10

Fig. 9

Fig. 8

Fig. 11

Fig. 12

current, and whilst the electricity from the battery continues to flow through its inducing neighbour (10, 18), constitute a peculiar electric condition, the consideration of which will be resumed hereafter (60). All these results have been obtained with a voltaic apparatus consisting of a single pair of plates.

§ 2. *On the Evolution of Electricity from Magnetism*

27. A welded ring was made of soft round bar-iron, the metal being seven-eighths of an inch in thickness, and the ring six inches in external diameter. Three helices were put round one part of this ring, each containing about twenty-four feet of copper wire one-twentieth of an inch thick; they were insulated from the iron and each other, and superposed in the manner before described (6), occupying about nine inches in length upon the ring. They could be used separately or conjointly; the group may be distinguished by the letter A (Pl. I, *Fig. 1*). On the other part of the ring about sixty feet of similar copper wire in two pieces were applied in the same manner, forming a helix B, which had the same common direction with the helices of A, but being separated from it at each extremity by about half an inch of the uncovered iron.

28. The helix B was connected by copper wires with a galvanometer three feet from the ring. The helices of A were connected end to end so as to form one common helix, the extremities of which were connected with a battery of ten pairs of plates four inches square. The galvanometer was immediately affected, and to a degree far beyond what has been described when with a battery of tenfold power helices *without iron* were used (10); but though the contact was continued, the effect was not permanent, for the needle soon came to rest in its natural position, as if quite indifferent to the attached electro-magnetic arrangement. Upon breaking the contact with the battery, the needle was again powerfully deflected, but in the contrary direction to that induced in the first instance.

29. Upon arranging the apparatus so that B should be out of use, the galvanometer be connected with one of the three wires of A (27), and the other two made into a helix through which the current from the trough (28) was passed, similar but rather more powerful effects were produced.

30. When the battery contact was made in one direction, the galvanometer-needle was de-

flected on the one side; if made in the other direction, the deflection was on the other side. The deflection on breaking the battery contact was always the reverse of that produced by completing it. The deflection on making a battery contact always indicated an induced current in the opposite direction to that from the battery; but on breaking the contact the deflection indicated an induced current in the same direction as that of the battery. No making or breaking of the contact at B side, or in any part of the galvanometer circuit, produced any effect at the galvanometer. No continuance of the battery current caused any deflection of the galvanometer-needle. As the above results are common to all these experiments, and to similar ones with ordinary magnets to be hereafter detailed, they need not be again particularly described.

31. Upon using the power of one hundred pairs of plates (10) with this ring, the impulse at the galvanometer, when contact was completed or broken, was so great as to make the needle spin round rapidly four or five times, before the air and terrestrial magnetism could reduce its motion to mere oscillation.

32. By using charcoal at the ends of the B helix, a minute *spark* could be perceived when the contact of the battery with A was completed. This spark could not be due to any diversion of a part of the current of the battery through the iron to the helix B; for when the battery contact was continued, the galvanometer still resumed its perfectly indifferent state (28). The spark was rarely seen on breaking contact. A small platina[1] wire could not be ignited by this induced current; but there seems every reason to believe that the effect would be obtained by using a stronger original current or a more powerful arrangement of helices.

33. A feeble voltaic current was sent through the helix B and the galvanometer, so as to deflect the needle of the latter 30° or 40°, and then the battery of one hundred pairs of plates connected with A; but after the first effect was over, the galvanometer-needle resumed exactly the position due to the feeble current transmitted by its own wire. This took place in whichever way the battery contacts were made, and shows that here again (20) no permanent influence of the currents upon each other, as to their quantity and tension, exists.

34. Another arrangement was then employed connecting the former experiments on volta-

[1]*Platina*: early form for *platinum*, used often in this work.—ED.

electric induction (6—26) with the present. A combination of helices like that already described (6) was constructed upon a hollow cylinder of pasteboard: there were eight lengths of copper wire, containing altogether 220 feet; four of these helices were connected end to end, and then with the galvanometer (7); the other intervening four were also connected end to end, and the battery of one hundred pairs discharged through them. In this form the effect on the galvanometer was hardly sensible (11), though magnets could be made by the induced current (13). But when a soft iron cylinder seven-eighths of an inch thick, and twelve inches long, was introduced into the pasteboard tube, surrounded by the helices, then the induced current affected the galvanometer powerfully and with all the phenomena just described (30). It possessed also the power of making magnets with more energy, apparently, than when no iron cylinder was present.

35. When the iron cylinder was replaced by an equal cylinder of copper, no effect beyond that of the helices alone was produced. The iron cylinder arrangement was not so powerful as the ring arrangement already described (27).

36. Similar effects were then produced with *ordinary magnets:* thus the hollow helix just described (34) had all its elementary helices connected with the galvanometer by two copper wires, each five feet in length; the soft iron cylinder was introduced into its axis; a couple of bar magnets, each twenty-four inches long, were arranged with their opposite poles at one end in contact, so as to resemble a horse-shoe magnet, and then contact made between the other poles and the ends of the iron cylinder, so as to convert it for the time into a magnet (Pl. I, *Fig. 2*): by breaking the magnetic contacts, or reversing them, the magnetism of the iron cylinder could be destroyed or reversed at pleasure.

37. Upon making magnetic contact, the needle was deflected; continuing the contact, the needle became indifferent, and resumed its first position; on breaking the contact, it was again deflected, but in the opposite direction to the first effect, and then it again became indifferent. When the magnetic contacts were reversed the deflections were reversed.

38. When the magnetic contact was made, the deflection was such as to indicate an induced current of electricity in the opposite direction to that fitted to form a magnet, having the same polarity as that really produced by contact with the bar magnets. Thus when the marked and unmarked poles were placed as in Pl. I, *Fig. 3*, the current in the helix was in the direction represented, P being supposed to be the end of the wire going to the positive pole of the battery, or that end towards which the zinc plates face, and N the negative wire. Such a current would have converted the cylinder into a magnet of the opposite kind to that formed by contact with the poles A and B; and such a current moves in the opposite direction to the currents which in M. Ampère's beautiful theory are considered as constituting a magnet in the position figured.[1]

39. But as it might be supposed that in all the preceding experiments of this section, it was by some peculiar effect taking place during the formation of the magnet, and not by its mere virtual approximation, that the momentary induced current was excited, the following experiment was made. All the similar ends of the compound hollow helix (34) were bound together by copper wire, forming two general terminations, and these were connected with the galvanometer. The soft iron cylinder (34) was removed, and a cylindrical magnet, three-quarters of an inch in diameter and eight inches and a half in length, used instead. One end of this magnet was introduced into the axis of the helix (Pl. I, *Fig. 4*), and then the galvanometer-needle being stationary, the magnet was suddenly thrust in; immediately the needle was deflected in the same direction as if the magnet had been formed by either of the two preceding processes (34, 36). Being left in, the needle resumed its first position, and then the magnet being withdrawn the needle was deflected in the opposite direction. These effects were not great; but by introducing and withdrawing the magnet, so that the impulse each time should be added to those previously communicated to the needle, the latter could be made to vibrate through an arc of 180° or more.

[1] The relative position of an electric current and a magnet is by most persons found very difficult to remember, and three or four helps to the memory have been devised by M. Ampère and others. I venture to suggest the following as a very simple and effectual assistance in these and similar latitudes. Let the experimenter think he is looking down upon a dipping-needle, or upon the pole of the earth, and then let him think upon the direction of the motion of the hands of a watch, or of a screw moving direct; currents in that direction round a needle would make it into such a magnet as the dipping needle, or would themselves constitute an electro-magnet of similar qualities; or if brought near a magnet would tend to make it take that direction; or would themselves be moved into that position by a magnet so placed; or in M. Ampère's theory are considered as moving in that direction in the magnet. These two points of the position of the dipping-needle and the motion of the watch hands being remembered, any other relation of the current and magnet can be at once deduced from it.

40. In this experiment the magnet must not be passed entirely through the helix, for then a second action occurs. When the magnet is introduced, the needle at the galvanometer is deflected in a certain direction; but being in, whether it be pushed quite through or withdrawn, the needle is deflected in a direction the reverse of that previously produced. When the magnet is passed in and through at one continuous motion, the needle moves one way, is then suddenly stopped, and finally moves the other way.

41. If such a hollow helix as that described (34) be laid east and west (or in any other constant position), and a magnet be retained east and west, its marked pole always being one way; then whichever end of the helix the magnet goes in at, and consequently whichever pole of the magnet enters first, still the needle is deflected the same way: on the other hand, whichever direction is followed in withdrawing the magnet, the deflection is constant, but contrary to that due to its entrance.

42. These effects are simple consequences of the *law* hereafter to be described (114).

43. When the eight elementary helices were made one long helix, the effect was not so great as in the arrangement described. When only one of the eight helices was used, the effect was also much diminished. All care was taken to guard against any direct action of the inducing magnet upon the galvanometer, and it was found that by moving the magnet in the same direction, and to the same degree on the outside of the helix, no effect on the needle was produced.

44. The Royal Society are in possession of a large compound magnet formerly belonging to Dr. Gowin Knight, which, by permission of the President and Council, I was allowed to use in the prosecution of these experiments: it is at present in the charge of Mr. Christie, at his house at Woolwich, where, by Mr. Christie's kindness, I was at liberty to work; and I have to acknowledge my obligations to him for his assistance in all the experiments and observations made with it. This magnet is composed of about 450 bar magnets, each fifteen inches long, one inch wide, and half an inch thick, arranged in a box so as to present at one of its extremities two external poles (Pl. I, *Fig. 5*). These poles projected horizontally six inches from the box, were each twelve inches high and three inches wide. They were nine inches apart; and when a soft iron cylinder, three-quarters of an inch in diameter and twelve inches long, was put across from one to the other, it required a

force of nearly one hundred pounds to break the contact. The pole to the left in the figure is the marked pole.[1]

45. The indicating galvanometer, in all experiments made with this magnet, was about eight feet from it, not directly in front of the poles, but about 16° or 17° on one side. It was found that on making or breaking the connexion of the poles by soft iron, the instrument was slightly affected; but all error of observation arising from this cause was easily and carefully avoided.

46. The electrical effects exhibited by this magnet were very striking. When a soft iron cylinder thirteen inches long was put through the compound hollow helix, with its ends arranged as two general terminations (39), these connected with the galvanometer, and the iron cylinder brought in contact with the two poles of the magnet (Pl. I, *Fig. 5*), so powerful a rush of electricity took place that the needle whirled round many times in succession.[2]

47. Notwithstanding this great power, if the contact was continued, the needle resumed its natural position, being entirely uninfluenced by the position of the helix (30). But on breaking the magnetic contact, the needle was whirled round in the opposite direction with a force also equal to the former.

48. A piece of copper plate wrapped *once* round the iron cylinder like a socket, but with interposed paper to prevent contact, had its edges connected with the wires of the galvanometer. When the iron was brought in contact with the poles the galvanometer was strongly affected.

49. Dismissing the helices and sockets, the galvanometer wire was passed over, and consequently only half round the iron cylinder (Pl. I, *Fig. 6*); but even then a strong effect upon the needle was exhibited, when the magnetic contact was made or broken.

50. As the helix with its iron cylinder was brought towards the magnetic poles, but *without making contact*, still powerful effects were produced. When the helix, without the iron cyl-

---

[1] To avoid any confusion as to the poles of the magnet, I shall designate the pole pointing to the north as the marked pole; I may occasionally speak of the north and south ends of the needle, but do not mean thereby north and south poles. That is by many considered the true north pole of a needle which points to the south; but in this country it is often called the south pole.

[2] A soft iron bar in the form of a lifter to a horseshoe magnet, when supplied with a coil of this kind round the middle of it, becomes, by juxtaposition with a magnet, a ready source of a brief but determinate current of electricity.

inder, and consequently containing no metal but copper, was approached to, or placed between the poles (44), the needle was thrown 80°, 90°, or more, from its natural position. The inductive force was of course greater, the nearer the helix, either with or without its iron cylinder, was brought to the poles; but otherwise the same effects were produced, whether the helix, &c. was or was not brought into contact with the magnet; i.e., no permanent effect on the galvanometer was produced; and the effects of approximation and removal were the reverse of each other (30).

51. When a bolt of copper corresponding to the iron cylinder was introduced, no greater effect was produced by the helix than without it. But when a thick iron wire was substituted, the magneto-electric induction was rendered sensibly greater.

52. The direction of the electric current produced in all these experiments with the helix, was the same as that already described (38) as obtained with the weaker bar magnets.

53. A spiral containing fourteen feet of copper wire, being connected with the galvanometer, and approximated directly towards the marked pole in the line of its axis, affected the instrument strongly; the current induced in it was in the reverse direction to the current theoretically considered by M. Ampère as existing in the magnet (38), or as the current in an electro-magnet of similar polarity. As the spiral was withdrawn, the induced current was reversed.

54. A similar spiral had the current of eighty pairs of 4-inch plates sent through it so as to form an electro-magnet, and then the other spiral connected with the galvanometer (53) approximated to it; the needle vibrated, indicating a current in the galvanometer spiral the reverse of that in the battery spiral (18, 26). On withdrawing the latter spiral, the needle passed in the opposite direction.

55. Single wires, approximated in certain directions towards the magnetic pole, had currents induced in them. On their removal, the currents were inverted. In such experiments the wires should not be removed in directions different to those in which they were approximated; for then occasionally complicated and irregular effects are produced, the causes of which will be very evident in the fourth part of this paper.

56. All attempts to obtain chemical effects by the induced current of electricity failed, though the precautions before described (22),

and all others that could be thought of, were employed. Neither was any sensation on the tongue, or any convulsive effect upon the limbs of a frog, produced. Nor could charcoal or fine wire be ignited (133). But upon repeating the experiments more at leisure at the Royal Institution, with an armed loadstone belonging to Professor Daniell and capable of lifting about thirty pounds, a frog was very *powerfully convulsed* each time magnetic contact was made. At first the convulsions could not be obtained on breaking magnetic contact; but conceiving the deficiency of effect was because of the comparative slowness of separation, the latter act was effected by a blow, and then the frog was convulsed strongly. The more instantaneous the union or disunion is effected, the more powerful the convulsion. I thought also I could perceive the *sensation* upon the tongue and the *flash* before the eyes; but I could obtain no evidence of chemical decomposition.

57. The various experiments of this section prove, I think, most completely the production of electricity from ordinary magnetism. That its intensity should be very feeble and quantity small, cannot be considered wonderful, when it is remembered that like thermo-electricity it is evolved entirely within the substance of metals retaining all their conducting power. But an agent which is conducted along metallic wires in the manner described; which whilst so passing possesses the peculiar magnetic actions and force of a current of electricity; which can agitate and convulse the limbs of a frog; and which, finally, can produce a spark[1] by its discharge through charcoal (32), can only be electricity. As all the effects can be produced by ferruginous electro-magnets (34), there is no doubt that arrangements like the magnets of Professors Moll, Henry, Ten Eyke, and others, in which as many as two thousand pounds have been lifted, may be used for these experiments; in which case not only a brighter spark may be obtained, but wires also ignited, and, as the current can pass liquids (23), chemical action be produced. These effects are still more likely to be obtained when the magneto-electric arrangements to be explained in the fourth section are excited by the powers of such apparatus.

[1] For a mode of obtaining the spark from the common magnet which I have found effectual, see the *Philosophical Magazine* for June, 1832, p. 5. In the same journal for November, 1834, Vol. V, p. 349, will be found a method of obtaining the magneto-electric spark, still simpler in its principle, the use of soft iron being dispensed with altogether.—*Dec.* 1838.

58. The similarity of action, almost amounting to identity, between common magnets and either electro-magnets or volta-electric currents, is strikingly in accordance with and confirmatory of M. Ampère's theory, and furnishes powerful reasons for believing that the action is the same in both cases; but, as a distinction in language is still necessary, I propose to call the agency thus exerted by ordinary magnets, *magneto-electric* or *magnelectric* induction (26).

59. The only difference which powerfully strikes the attention as existing between volta-electric and magneto-electric induction, is the suddenness of the former, and the sensible time required by the latter; but even in this early state of investigation there are circumstances which seem to indicate that upon further inquiry this difference will, as a philosophical distinction, disappear (68).[1]

§ 3. *New Electrical State or Condition of Matter*[2]

60. Whilst the wire is subject to either volta-electric or magneto-electric induction, it appears to be in a peculiar state; for it resists the formation of an electrical current in it, whereas, if in its common condition, such a current would be produced; and when left uninfluenced it has the power of originating a current, a power which the wire does not possess under common circumstances. This electrical condition of matter has not hitherto been recognised, but it probably exerts a very important influence in many if not most of the phenomena produced by currents of electricity. For reasons which will immediately appear (71), I have, after advising with several learned friends, ventured to designate it as the *electro-tonic state.*

61. This peculiar condition shows no known electrical effects whilst it continues; nor have I yet been able to discover any peculiar powers exerted, or properties possessed, by matter whilst retained in this state.

62. It shows no reaction by attractive or repulsive powers. The various experiments which

have been made with powerful magnets upon such metals, as copper, silver, and generally those substances not magnetic, prove this point; for the substances experimented upon, if electrical conductors, must have acquired this state; and yet no evidence of attractive or repulsive powers has been observed. I have placed copper and silver discs, very delicately suspended on torsion balances *in vacuo* near to the poles of very powerful magnets, yet have not been able to observe the least attractive or repulsive force.

63. I have also arranged a fine slip of gold-leaf very near to a bar of copper, the two being in metallic contact by mercury at their extremities. These have been placed *in vacuo*, so that metal rods connected with the extremities of the arrangement should pass through the sides of the vessel into the air. I have then moved powerful magnetic poles, about this arrangement, in various directions, the metallic circuit on the outside being sometimes completed by wires, and sometimes broken. But I never could obtain any sensible motion of the gold-leaf, either directed to the magnet or towards the collateral bar of copper, which must have been, as far as induction was concerned, in a similar state to itself.

64. In some cases it has been supposed that, under such circumstances, attractive and repulsive forces have been exhibited, i.e., that such bodies have become slightly magnetic. But the phenomena now described, in conjunction with the confidence we may reasonably repose in M. Ampère's theory of magnetism, tend to throw doubt on such cases; for if magnetism depend upon the attraction of electrical currents, and if the powerful currents at first excited, both by volta-electric and magneto-electric induction, instantly and naturally cease (12, 28, 47), causing at the same time an entire cessation of magnetic effects at the galvanometer needle, then there can be little or no expectation that any substances not partaking of the peculiar relation in which iron, nickel, and one or two other bodies, stand, should exhibit magneto-attractive powers. It seems far more probable, that the extremely feeble permanent effects observed have been due to traces of iron, or perhaps some other unrecognised cause not magnetic.

65. This peculiar condition exerts no retarding or accelerating power upon electrical currents passing through metal thus circumstanced (20, 33). Neither could any such power upon the inducing current itself be detected; for

[1] For important additional phenomena and developments of the induction of electrical currents, see now the ninth series, 1048–1118.—*Dec.* 1838.

[2] This section having been read at the Royal Society and reported upon, and having also, in consequence of a letter from myself to M. Hachette, been noticed at the French Institute, I feel bound to let it stand as part of the paper; but later investigations (intimated 73, 76, 77) of the laws governing these phenomena, induce me to think that the latter can be fully explained without admitting the electro-tonic state. My views on this point will appear in the second series of these researches.—M. F.

when masses of metal, wires, helices, &c., were arranged in all possible ways by the side of a wire or helix, carrying a current measured by the galvanometer (20), not the slightest permanent change in the indication of the instrument could be perceived. Metal in the supposed peculiar state, therefore, conducts electricity in all directions with its ordinary facility, or, in other words, its conducting power is not sensibly altered by it.

66. All metals take on the peculiar state. This is proved in the preceding experiments with copper and iron (9), and with gold, silver, tin, lead, zinc, antimony, bismuth, mercury, &c., by experiments to be described in the fourth part (132), admitting of easy application. With regard to iron, the experiments prove the thorough and remarkable independence of these phenomena of induction, and the ordinary magnetical appearances of that metal.

67. This state is altogether the effect of the induction exerted, and ceases as soon as the inductive force is removed. It is the same state, whether produced by the collateral passage of voltaic currents (26), or the formation of a magnet (34, 36), or the mere approximation of a magnet (39, 50); and is a strong proof in addition to those advanced by M. Ampère, of the identity of the agents concerned in these several operations. It probably occurs, momentarily, during the passage of the common electric spark (24), and may perhaps be obtained hereafter in bad conductors by weak electrical currents or other means (74, 76).

68. The state appears to be instantly assumed (12), requiring hardly a sensible portion of time for that purpose. The *difference* of time between volta-electric and magneto-electric induction, rendered evident by the galvanometer (59), may probably be thus explained. When a voltaic current is sent through one of two parallel wires, as those of the hollow helix (34), a current is produced in the other wire, as brief in its continuance as the time required for a single action of this kind, and which, by experiment, is found to be inappreciably small. The action will seem still more instantaneous, because, as there is an accumulation of power in the poles of the battery before contact, the first rush of electricity in the wire of communication is greater than that sustained after the contact is completed; the wire of induction becomes at the moment electro-tonic to an equivalent degree, which the moment after sinks to the state in which the continuous current can sustain it, but in sinking, causes an opposite in-

duced current to that at first produced. The consequence is that the first induced wave of electricity more resembles that from the discharge of an electric jar than it otherwise would do.

69. But when the iron cylinder is put into the same helix (34), previous to the connexion being made with the battery, then the current from the latter may be considered as active in inducing innumerable currents of a similar kind to itself in the iron, rendering it a magnet. This is known by experiment to occupy time; for a magnet so formed, even of soft iron, does not rise to its fullest intensity in an instant, and it may be because the currents within the iron are successive in their formation or arrangement. But as the magnet can induce, as well as the battery current, the combined action of the two continues to evolve induced electricity, until their joint effect is at a maximum, and thus the existence of the deflecting force is prolonged sufficiently to overcome the inertia of the galvanometer needle.

70. In all those cases where the helices or wires are advanced towards or taken from the magnet (50, 55), the direct or inverted current of induced electricity continues for the time occupied in the advance or recession; for the electro-tonic state is rising to a higher or falling to a lower degree during that time, and the change is accompanied by its corresponding evolution of electricity; but these form no objections to the opinion that the electro-tonic state is instantly assumed.

71. This peculiar state appears to be a state of tension, and may be considered as *equivalent* to a current of electricity, at least equal to that produced either when the condition is induced or destroyed. The current evolved, however, first or last, is not to be considered a measure of the degree of tension to which the electro-tonic state has risen; for as the metal retains its conducting powers unimpaired (65), and as the electricity evolved is but for a moment, (the peculiar state being instantly assumed and lost [68]), the electricity which may be led away by long wire conductors, offering obstruction in their substance proportionate to their small lateral and extensive linear dimensions, can be but a very small portion of that really evolved within the mass at the moment it assumes this condition. Insulated helices and portions of metal instantly assumed the state; and no traces of electricity could be discovered in them, however quickly the contact with the electrometer was made, after they were put under induction, either by the current

from the battery or the magnet. A single drop of water or a small piece of moistened paper (23, 56) was obstacle sufficient to stop the current through the conductors, the electricity evolved returning to a state of equilibrium through the metal itself, and consequently in an unobserved manner.

72. The tension of this state may therefore be comparatively very great. But whether great or small, it is hardly conceivable that it should exist without exerting a reaction upon the original inducing current, and producing equilibrium of some kind. It might be anticipated that this would give rise to a retardation of the original current; but I have not been able to ascertain that this is the case. Neither have I in any other way as yet been able to distinguish effects attributable to such a reaction.

73. All the results favour the notion that the electro-tonic state relates to the particles, and not to the mass, of the wire or substance under induction, being in that respect different to the induction exerted by electricity of tension. If so, the state may be assumed in liquids when no electrical current is sensible, and even in non-conductors; the current itself, when it occurs, being as it were a contingency due to the existence of conducting power, and the momentary propulsive force exerted by the particles during their arrangement. Even when conducting power is equal, the currents of electricity, which as yet are the only indicators of this state, may be unequal, because of differences as to numbers, size, electrical condition, &c., &c., in the particles themselves. It will only be after the laws which govern this new state are ascertained, that we shall be able to predict what is the true condition of, and what are the electrical results obtainable from, any particular substance.

74. The current of electricity which induces the electro-tonic state in a neighbouring wire, probably induces that state also in its own wire; for when by a current in one wire a collateral wire is made electro-tonic, the latter state is not rendered any way incompatible or interfering with a current of electricity passing through it (62). If, therefore, the current were sent through the second wire instead of the first, it does not seem probable that its inducing action upon the second would be less, but on the contrary more, because the distance between the agent and the matter acted upon would be very greatly diminished. A copper bolt had its extremities connected with a galvanometer, and then the poles of a battery of one hun-

dred pairs of plates connected with the bolt, so as to send the current through it; the voltaic circuit was then suddenly broken, and the galvanometer observed for any indications of a return current through the copper bolt due to the discharge of its supposed electro-tonic state. No effect of the kind was obtained, nor indeed, for two reasons, ought it to be expected; for first, as the cessation of induction and the discharge of the electro-tonic condition are simultaneous, and not successive, the return current would only be equivalent to the neutralization of the last portion of the inducing current, and would not therefore show any alteration of direction; or assuming that time did intervene, and that the latter current was really distinct from the former, its short, sudden character (12, 26) would prevent it from being thus recognised.

75. No difficulty arises, I think, in considering the wire thus rendered electro-tonic by its own current more than by any external current, especially when the apparent non-interference of that state with currents is considered (62, 71). The simultaneous existence of the conducting and electro-tonic states finds an analogy in the manner in which electrical currents can be passed through magnets, where it is found that both the currents passed, and those of the magnets, preserve all their properties distinct from each other, and exert their mutual actions.

76. The reason given with regard to metals extends also to fluids and all other conductors, and leads to the conclusion that when electric currents are passed through them they also assume the electro-tonic state. Should that prove to be the case, its influence in voltaic decomposition, and the transference of the elements to the poles, can hardly be doubted. In the electro-tonic state the homogenoeus particles of matter appear to have assumed a regular but forced electrical arrangement in the direction of the current, which if the matter be undecomposable, produces, when relieved, a return current; but in decomposable matter this forced state may be sufficient to make an elementary particle leave its companion, with which it is in a constrained condition, and associate with the neighbouring similar particle, in relation to which it is in a more natural condition, the forced electrical arrangement being itself discharged or relieved, at the same time, as effectually as if it had been freed from induction. But as the original voltaic current is continued, the electro-tonic state may be instantly

renewed, producing the forced arrangement of the compound particles, to be as instantly discharged by a transference of the elementary particles of the opposite kind in opposite directions, but parallel to the current. Even the differences between common and voltaic electricity, when applied to effect chemical decomposition, which Dr. Wollaston has pointed out,[1] seem explicable by the circumstances connected with the induction of electricity from these two sources (25). But as I have reserved this branch of the inquiry, that I might follow out the investigations contained in the present paper, I refrain (though much tempted) from offering further speculations.

77. Marianini has discovered and described a peculiar affection of the surfaces of metallic discs, when, being in contact with humid conductors, a current of electricity is passed through them; they are then capable of producing a reverse current of electricity, and Marianini has well applied the effect in explanation of the phenomena of Ritter's piles.[2] M. A. de la Rive has described a peculiar property acquired by metallic conductors, when being immersed in a liquid as poles, they have completed, for some time, the voltaic circuit, in consequence of which, when separated from the battery and plunged into the same fluid, they by themselves produce an electric current.[3] M. A. Van Beek has detailed cases in which the electrical relation of one metal in contact with another has been preserved after separation, and accompanied by its corresponding chemical effects.[4] These states and results appear to differ from the electro-tonic state and its phenomena; but the true relation of the former to the latter can only be decided when our knowledge of all these phenomena has been enlarged.

78. I had occasion in the commencement of this paper (2) to refer to an experiment by Ampère, as one of those dependent upon the electrical induction of currents made prior to the present investigation, and have arrived at conclusions which seem to imply doubts of the accuracy of the experiment (62, &c.); it is therefore due to M. Ampère that I should attend to it more distinctly. When a disc of copper (says M. Ampère) was suspended by a silk thread and surrounded by a helix or spiral, and when the charge of a powerful voltaic battery was sent through the spiral, a strong magnet at the same time being presented to the copper disc,

[1] *Philosophical Transactions*, 1801, p. 247.
[2] *Annales de Chimie*, XXXVIII. 5.
[3] *Ibid.*, XXVIII. 190.
[4] *Annales de Chimie*, XXXVIII. 49.

the latter turned at the moment to take a position of equilibrium, exactly as the spiral itself would have turned had it been free to move. I have not been able to obtain this effect, nor indeed any motion; but the cause of my failure in the *latter* point may be due to the momentary existence of the current not allowing time for the inertia of the plate to be overcome (11, 12). M. Ampère has perhaps succeeded in obtaining motion from the superior delicacy and power of his electro-magnetical apparatus, or he may have obtained only the motion due to cessation of action. But all my results tend to invert the sense of the proposition stated by M. Ampère, "that a current of electricity tends to put the electricity of conductors near which it passes in motion in the same direction," for they indicate an opposite direction for the produced current (26, 53); and they show that the effect is momentary, and that it is also produced by magnetic induction, and that certain other extraordinary effects follow thereupon.

79. The momentary existence of the phenomena of induction now described is sufficient to furnish abundant reasons for the uncertainty or failure of the experiments, hitherto made to obtain electricity from magnets, or to effect chemical decomposition or arrangement by their means.[5]

80. It also appears capable of explaining fully the remarkable phenomena observed by M. Arago between metals and magnets when neither are moving (120), as well as most of the results obtained by Sir John Herschel, Messrs. Babbage, Harris, and others, in repeating his experiments; accounting at the same time perfectly for what at first appeared inexplicable; namely, the non-action of the same metals and magnets when at rest. These results, which also

[5] *The Lycée*, No. 36, for January 1st, has a long and rather premature article, in which it endeavours to show anticipations by French philosophers of my researches. It however mistakes the erroneous results of MM. Fresnel and Ampère for true ones, and then imagines my true results are like those erroneous ones. I notice it here, however, for the purpose of doing honour to Fresnel in a much higher degree than would have been merited by a feeble anticipation of the present investigations. That great philosopher, at the same time with myself and fifty other persons, made experiments which the present paper proves could give no expected result. He was deceived for the moment, and published his imaginary success; but on more carefully repeating his trials, he could find no proof of their accuracy; and, in the high and pure philosophic desire to remove error as well as discover truth, he recanted his first statement. The example of Berzelius regarding the first Thorina is another instance of this fine feeling; and as occasions are not rare, it would be to the dignity of science if such examples were more frequently followed.—February 10th, 1832.

afford the readiest means of obtaining electricity from magnetism, I shall now proceed to describe.

§ 4. *Explication of Arago's Magnetic Phenomena*

81. If a plate of copper be revolved close to a magnetic needle, or magnet, suspended in such a way that the latter may rotate in a plane parallel to that of the former, the magnet tends to follow the motion of the plate; or if the magnet be revolved, the plate tends to follow its motion; and the effect is so powerful, that magnets or plates of many pounds weight may be thus carried round. If the magnet and plate be at rest relative to each other, not the slightest effect, attractive or repulsive, or of any kind, can be observed between them (62). This is the phenomenon discovered by M. Arago; and he states that the effect takes place not only with all metals, but with solids, liquids, and even gases, i.e., with all substances (130).

82. Mr. Babbage and Sir John Herschel, on conjointly repeating the experiments in this country,[1] could obtain the effects only with the metals, and with carbon in a peculiar state (from gas retorts), i.e., only with excellent conductors of electricity. They refer the effect to magnetism induced in the plate by the magnet; the pole of the latter causing an opposite pole in the nearest part of the plate, and round this a more diffuse polarity of its own kind (120). The essential circumstance in producing the rotation of the suspended magnet is, that the substance revolving below it shall acquire and lose its magnetism in sensible time, and not instantly (124). This theory refers the effect to an attractive force, and is not agreed to by the discoverer, M. Arago, nor by M. Ampère, who quote against it the absence of all attraction when the magnet and metal are at rest (62, 126), although the induced magnetism should still remain; and who, from experiments made with a long dipping-needle, conceive the action to be always repulsive (125).

83. Upon obtaining electricity from magnets by the means already described (36, 46), I hoped to make the experiment of M. Arago a new source of electricity; and did not despair, by reference to terrestrial magneto-electric induction, of being able to construct a new electrical machine. Thus stimulated, numerous experiments were made with the magnet of the Royal Society at Mr. Christie's house, in all of which I had the advantage of his assistance. As

[1] *Philosophical Transactions*, 1825, p. 467.

many of these were in the course of the investigation superseded by more perfect arrangements, I shall consider myself at liberty to rearrange them in a manner calculated to convey most readily what appears to me to be a correct view of the nature of the phenomena.

84. The magnet has been already described (44). To concentrate the poles, and bring them nearer to each other, two iron or steel bars, each about six or seven inches long, one inch wide, and half an inch thick, were put across the poles as in Pl. I, *Fig. 7*, and being supported by twine from slipping, could be placed as near to or far from each other as was required. Occasionally two bars of soft iron were employed, so bent that when applied, one to each pole, the two smaller resulting poles were vertically over each other, either being uppermost at pleasure.

85. A disc of copper, twelve inches in diameter, and about one-fifth of an inch in thickness, fixed upon a brass axis, was mounted in frames so as to allow of revolution either vertically or horizontally, its edge being at the same time introduced more or less between the magnetic poles Pl. I, (*Fig. 7*). The edge of the plate was well-amalgamated for the purpose of obtaining a good but moveable contact, and a part round the axis was also prepared in a similar manner.

86. Conductors or electric collectors of copper and lead were constructed so as to come in contact with the edge of the copper disc (85), or with other forms of plates hereafter to be described (101). These conductors were about four inches long, one third of an inch wide, and one-fifth of an inch thick; one end of each was slightly grooved, to allow of more exact adaptation to the somewhat convex edge of the plates, and then amalgamated. Copper wires, one-sixteenth of an inch in thickness, attached, in the ordinary manner, by convolutions to the other ends of these conductors, passed away to the galvanometer.

87. The galvanometer was roughly made, yet sufficiently delicate in its indications. The wire was of copper covered with silk, and made sixteen or eighteen convolutions. Two sewing-needles were magnetized and fixed on to a stem of dried grass parallel to each other, but in opposite directions, and about half an inch apart; this system was suspended by a fibre of unspun silk, so that the lower needle should be between the convolutions of the multiplier, and the upper above them. The latter was by much the most powerful magnet, and gave terrestrial direction to the whole; Pl. I, *Fig. 8.* represents

PLATE II

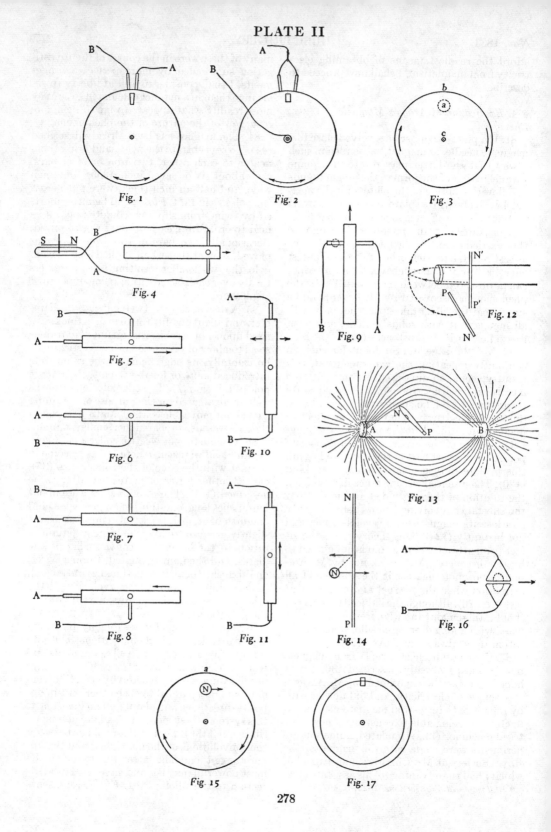

Fig. 1

Fig. 2

Fig. 3

Fig. 4

Fig. 5

Fig. 6

Fig. 7

Fig. 8

Fig. 9

Fig. 10

Fig. 11

Fig. 12

Fig. 13

Fig. 14

Fig. 15

Fig. 16

Fig. 17

the direction of the wire and of the needles when the instrument was placed in the magnetic meridian: the ends of the wires are marked A and B for convenient reference hereafter. The letters S and N designate the south and north ends of the needle when affected merely by terrestrial magnetism; the end N is therefore the marked pole (44). The whole instrument was protected by a glass jar, and stood, as to position and distance relative to the large magnet, under the same circumstances as before (45).

88. All these arrangements being made, the copper disc was adjusted as in Pl. I, *Fig. 7*, the small magnetic poles being about half an inch apart, and the edge of the plate inserted about half their width between them. One of the galvanometer wires was passed twice or thrice loosely round the brass axis of the plate, and the other attached to a conductor (86), which itself was retained by the hand in contact with the amalgamated edge of the disc at the part immediately between the magnetic poles. Under these circumstances all was quiescent, and the galvanometer exhibited no effect. But the instant the plate moved, the galvanometer was influenced, and by revolving the plate quickly the needle could be deflected 90° or more.

89. It was difficult under the circumstances to make the contact between the conductor and the edge of the revolving disc uniformly good and extensive; it was also difficult in the first experiments to obtain a regular velocity of rotation: both these causes tended to retain the needle in a continual state of vibration, but no difficulty existed in ascertaining to which side it was deflected, or generally, about what line it vibrated. Afterwards, when the experiments were made more carefully, a permanent deflection of the needle of nearly 45° could be sustained.

90. Here therefore was demonstrated the production of a permanent current of electricity by ordinary magnets (57).

91. When the motion of the disc was reversed, every other circumstance remaining the same, the galvanometer needle was deflected with equal power as before; but the deflection was on the opposite side, and the current of electricity evolved, therefore, the reverse of the former.

92. When the conductor was placed on the edge of the disc a little to the right or left, as in the dotted positions Pl. I, *Fig. 9*, the current of electricity was still evolved, and in the same direction as at first (88, 91). This occurred to a considerable distance, i.e., 50° or 60° on each side of the place of the magnetic poles. The current gathered by the conductor and conveyed to the galvanometer was of the same kind on both sides of the place of greatest intensity, but gradually diminished in force from that place. It appeared to be equally powerful at equal distances from the place of the magnetic poles, not being affected in that respect by the direction of the rotation. When the rotation of the disc was reversed, the direction of the current of electricity was reversed also; but the other circumstances were not affected.

93. On raising the plate, so that the magnetic poles were entirely hidden from each other by its intervention, (*a*, Pl. I, *Fig. 10*), the same effects were produced in the same order, and with equal intensity as before. On raising it still higher, so as to bring the place of the poles to *c*, still the effects were produced, and apparently with as much power as at first.

94. When the conductor was held against the edge as if fixed to it, and with it moved between the poles, even though but for a few degrees, the galvanometer needle moved and indicated a current of electricity, the same as that which would have been produced if the wheel had revolved in the same direction, the conductor remaining stationary.

95. When the galvanometer connexion with the axis was broken, and its wires made fast to two conductors, both applied to the edge of the copper disc, then currents of electricity were produced, presenting more complicated appearances, but in perfect harmony with the above results. Thus, if applied as in Pl. I, *Fig. 11*, a current of electricity through the galvanometer was produced; but if their place was a little shifted, as in Pl. I, *Fig. 12*, a current in the contrary direction resulted; the fact being, that in the first instance the galvanometer indicated the difference between a strong current through A and a weak one through B, and in the second, of a weak current through A and a strong one through B (92), and therefore produced opposite deflections.

96. So also when the two conductors were equidistant from the magnetic poles, as in Pl. II, *Fig. 1*, no current at the galvanometer was perceived, whichever way the disc was rotated, beyond what was momentarily produced by irregularity of contact; because equal currents in the same direction tended to pass into both. But when the two conductors were connected with one wire, and the axis with the other wire, (Pl. II, *Fig. 2*) then the galvanometer showed

a current according with the direction of rotation (91); both conductors now acting consentaneously, and as a single conductor did before (88).

97. All these effects could be obtained when only one of the poles of the magnet was brought near to the plate; they were of the same kind as to direction, &c., but by no means so powerful.

98. All care was taken to render these results independent of the earth's magnetism, or of the mutual magnetism of the magnet and galvanometer needles. The contacts were made in the magnetic equator of the plate, and at other parts; the plate was placed horizontally, and the poles vertically; and other precautions were taken. But the absence of any interference of the kind referred to, was readily shown by the want of all effect when the disc was removed from the poles, or the poles from the disc; every other circumstance remaining the same.

99. The *relation of the current* of electricity produced, to the magnetic pole, to the direction of rotation of the plate, &c., &c., may be expressed by saying, that when the unmarked pole (44, 84) is beneath the edge of the plate, and the latter revolves horizontally, screw-fashion, the electricity which can be collected at the edge of the plate nearest to the pole is positive. As the pole of the earth may mentally be considered the unmarked pole, this relation of the rotation, the pole, and the electricity evolved, is not difficult to remember. Or if, in Pl. II, *Fig. 3*, the circle represent the copper disc revolving in the direction of the arrows, and *a* the outline of the unmarked pole placed beneath the plate, then the electricity collected at *b* and the neighbouring parts is positive, whilst that collected at the centre *c* and other parts is negative (88). The currents in the plate are therefore from the centre by the magnetic poles towards the circumference.

100. If the marked pole be placed above, all other things remaining the same, the electricity at *b*, Pl. II, *Fig. 3*, is still positive. If the marked pole be placed below, or the unmarked pole above, the electricity is reversed. If the direction of revolution in any case is reversed, the electricity is also reversed.

101. It is now evident that the rotating plate is merely another form of the simpler experiment of passing a piece of metal between the magnetic poles in a rectilinear direction, and that in such cases currents of electricity are produced at right angles to the direction of the motion, and crossing it at the place of the magnetic pole or poles. This was sufficiently shown by the following simple experiment: A piece of copper plate one-fifth of an inch thick, one inch and a half wide, and twelve inches long, being amalgamated at the edges, was placed between the magnetic poles, whilst the two conductors from the galvanometer were held in contact with its edges; it was then drawn through between the poles of the conductors in the direction of the arrow, Pl. II, *Fig. 4*; immediately the galvanometer needle was deflected, its north or marked end passed eastward, indicating that the wire A received negative and the wire B positive electricity; and as the marked pole was above, the result is in perfect accordance with the effect obtained by the rotatory plate (99).

102. On reversing the motion of the plate, the needle at the galvanometer was deflected in the opposite direction, showing an opposite current.

103. To render evident the character of the electrical current existing in various parts of the moving copper plate, differing in their relation to the inducing poles, one collector (86) only was applied at the part to be examined near to the pole, the other being connected with the end of the plate as the most neutral place: the results are given at Pl. II, *Figs. 5–8*, the marked pole being above the plate. In *Fig. 5*, B received positive electricity; but the plate moving in the same direction, it received on the opposite side, *Fig. 6*, negative electricity: reversing the motion of the latter, as in *Fig. 8*, B received positive electricity; or reversing the motion of the first arrangement, that of *Fig. 5* to *Fig. 7*, B received negative electricity.

104. When the plates were previously removed sideways from between the magnets, as in Pl. II, *Fig. 9*, so as to be quite out of the polar axis, still the same effects were produced, though not so strongly.

105. When the magnetic poles were in contact, and the copper plate was drawn between the conductors near to the place, there was but very little effect produced. When the poles were opened by the width of a card, the effect was somewhat more, but still very small.

106. When an amalgamated copper wire, one-eighth of an inch thick, was drawn through between the conductors and poles (101), it produced a very considerable effect, though not so much as the plates.

107. If the conductors were held permanently against any particular parts of the copper

plates, and carried between the magnetic poles with them, effects the same as those described were produced, in accordance with the results obtained with the revolving disc (94).

108. On the conductors being held against the ends of the plates, and the latter then passed between the magnetic poles, in a direction transverse to their length, the same effects were produced (Pl. II, *Fig. 10*). The parts of the plates towards the end may be considered either as mere conductors, or as portions of metal in which the electrical current is excited, according to their distance and the strength of the magnet; but the results were in perfect harmony with those before obtained. The effect was as strong as when the conductors were held against the sides of the plate (101).

109. When a mere wire, connected with the galvanometer so as to form a complete circuit, was passed through between the poles, the galvanometer was affected; and upon moving the wire to and fro, so as to make the alternate impulses produced correspond with the vibrations of the needle, the latter could be increased to 20° or 30° on each side of the magnetic meridian.

110. Upon connecting the ends of a plate of metal with the galvanometer wires, and then carrying it between the poles from end to end (as in Pl. II, *Fig. 11*), in either direction, no effect whatever was produced upon the galvanometer. But the moment the motion became transverse, the needle was deflected.

111. These effects were also obtained from *electro-magnetic poles*, resulting from the use of copper helices or spirals, either alone or with iron cores (34, 54). The directions of the motions were precisely the same; but the action was much greater when the iron cores were used, than without.

112. When a flat spiral was passed through edgewise between the poles, a curious action at the galvanometer resulted; the needle first went strongly one way, but then suddenly stopped, as if it struck against some solid obstacle, and immediately returned. If the spiral were passed through from above downwards, or from below upwards, still the motion of the needle was in the same direction, then suddenly stopped, and then was reversed. But on turning the spiral half-way round, i.e., edge for edge, then the directions of the motions were reversed, but still were suddenly interrupted and inverted as before. This double action depends upon the halves of the spiral (divided by a line passing through its centre perpendicular to the direc-

tion of its motion) acting in opposite directions; and the reason why the needle went to the same side, whether the spiral passed by the poles in the one or the other direction, was the circumstance, that upon changing the motion, the direction of the wires in the approaching half of the spiral was changed also. The effects, curious as they appear when witnessed, are immediately referable to the action of single wires (40, 109).

113. Although the experiments with the revolving plate, wires, and plates of metal, were first successfully made with the large magnet belonging to the Royal Society, yet they were all ultimately repeated with a couple of bar magnets two feet long, one inch and a half wide, and half an inch thick; and, by rendering the galvanometer (87) a little more delicate, with the most striking results. Ferro-electro-magnets, as those of Moll, Henry, &c. (57), are very powerful. It is very essential, when making experiments on different substances, that thermo-electric effects (produced by contact of the fingers, &c.) be avoided, or at least appreciated and accounted for; they are easily distinguished by their permanency, and their independence of the magnets, or of the direction of the motion.

114. The relation which holds between the magnetic pole, the moving wire or metal, and the direction of the current evolved, i.e., *the law* which governs the evolution of electricity by magneto-electric induction, is very simple, although rather difficult to express. If in Pl. II, *Fig. 12*, PN represent a horizontal wire passing by a marked magnetic pole, so that the direction of its motion shall coincide with the curved line proceeding from below upwards; or if its motion parallel to itself be in a line tangential to the curved line, but in the general direction of the arrows; or if it pass the pole in other directions, but so as to cut the magnetic curves[1] in the same general direction, or on the same side as they would be cut by the wire if moving along the dotted curved line—then the current of electricity in the wire is from P to N. If it be carried in the reverse directions, the electric current will be from N to P. Or if the wire be in the vertical position, figured P′ N′, and it be carried in similar directions, coinciding with the dotted horizontal curve so far, as to cut the magnetic curves on the same side

[1] By magnetic curves, I mean the lines of magnetic forces, however modified by the juxtaposition of poles, which would be depicted by iron filings; or those to which a very small magnetic needle would form a tangent.

with it, the current will be from P' to N'. If the wire be considered a tangent to the curved surface of the cylindrical magnet, and it be carried round that surface into any other position, or if the magnet itself be revolved on its axis, so as to bring any part opposite to the tangential wire—still, if afterwards the wire be moved in the directions indicated, the current of electricity will be from P to N; or if it be moved in the opposite direction, from N to P; so that as regards the motions of the wire past the pole, they may be reduced to two, directly opposite to each other, one of which produces a current from P to N, and the other from N to P.

115. The same holds true of the unmarked pole of the magnet, except that if it be substituted for the one in the figure, then, as the wires are moved in the direction of the arrows, the current of electricity would be from N to P, and when they move in the reverse direction, from P to N.

116. Hence the current of electricity which is excited in metal when moving in the neighbourhood of a magnet, depends for its direction altogether upon the relation of the metal to the resultant of magnetic action, or to the magnetic curves, and may be expressed in a popular way thus: Let A B (Pl. II, *Fig. 13*) represent a cylinder magnet, A being the marked pole, and B the unmarked pole; let P N be a silver knife-blade, resting across the magnet with its edge upward, and with its marked or notched side towards the pole A; then in whatever direction or position this knife be moved edge foremost, either about the marked or the unmarked pole, the current of electricity produced will be from P to N, provided the intersected curves proceeding from A abut upon the notched surface of the knife, and those from B upon the unnotched side. Or if the knife be moved with its back foremost, the current will be from N to P in every possible position and direction, provided the intersected curves abut on the same surfaces as before. A little model is easily constructed, by using a cylinder of wood for a magnet, a flat piece for the blade, and a piece of thread connecting one end of the cylinder with the other, and passing through a hole in the blade, for the magnetic curves: this readily gives the result of any possible direction.

117. When the wire under induction is passing by an electro-magnetic pole, as for instance one end of a copper helix traversed by the electric current (34), the direction of the current in the approaching wire is the same with that of the current in the parts or sides of the spirals nearest to it, and in the receding wire the reverse of that in the parts nearest to it.

118. All these results show that the power of inducing electric currents is circumferentially exerted by a magnetic resultant or axis of power, just as circumferential magnetism is dependent upon and is exhibited by an electric current.

119. The experiments described combine to prove that when a piece of metal (and the same may be true of all conducting matter [213]) is passed either before a single pole, or between the opposite poles of a magnet, or near electromagnetic poles, whether ferruginous or not, electrical currents are produced across the metal transverse to the direction of motion; and which therefore, in Arago's experiments, will approximate towards the direction of radii. If a single wire be moved like the spoke of a wheel near a magnetic pole, a current of electricity is determined through it from one end towards the other. If a wheel be imagined, constructed of a great number of these radii, and this revolved near the pole, in the manner of the copper disc (85), each radius will have a current produced in it as it passes by the pole. If the radii be supposed to be in contact laterally, a copper disc results, in which the directions of the currents will be generally the same, being modified only by the coaction which can take place between the particles, now that they are in metallic contact.

120. Now that the existence of these currents is known, Arago's phenomena may be accounted for without considering them as due to the formation in the copper, of a pole of the opposite kind to that approximated, surrounded by a diffuse polarity of the same kind (82); neither is it essential that the plate should acquire and lose its state in a finite time; nor on the other hand does it seem necessary that any repulsive force should be admitted as the cause of the rotation (82).

121. The effect is precisely of the same kind as the electro-magnetic rotations which I had the good fortune to discover some years ago.[1] According to the experiments then made which have since been abundantly confirmed, if a wire P N, (Pl. II, *Fig. 14*) be connected with the positive and negative ends of a voltaic battery, so that the positive electricity shall pass from P to N, and a marked magnetic pole N be placed near the wire between it and the spec-

[1] *Quarterly Journal of Science*, Vol. XII, pp. 74, 186, 416, 283.

tator, the pole will move in a direction tangential to the wire, i.e., towards the right, and the wire will move tangentially towards the left, according to the directions of the arrows. This is exactly what takes place in the rotation of a plate beneath a magnetic pole; for let N (Pl. II, *Fig. 15*) be a marked pole above the circular plate, the latter being rotated in the direction of the arrow: immediately currents of positive electricity set from the central parts in the general direction of the radii by the pole to the parts of the circumference *a* on the other side of that pole (99, 119), and are therefore exactly in the same relation to it as the current in the wire (PN, *Fig. 14*), and therefore the pole in the same manner moves to the right hand.

122. If the rotation of the disc be reversed, the electric currents are reversed (91), and the pole therefore moves to the left hand. If the contrary pole be employed, the effects are the same, i. e. in the same direction, because currents of electricity, the reverse of those described, are produced, and by reversing both poles and currents, the visible effects remain unchanged. In whatever position the axis of the magnet be placed, provided the same pole be applied to the same side of the plate, the electric current produced is in the same direction, in consistency with the law already stated (114, &c.); and thus every circumstance regarding the direction of the motion may be explained.

123. These currents are *discharged or return* in the parts of the plate on each side of and more distant from the place of the pole, where, of course, the magnetic induction is weaker; and when the collectors are applied, and a current of electricity is carried away to the galvanometer (88), the deflection there is merely a repetition, by the same current or part of it, of the effect of rotation in the magnet over the plate itself.

124. It is under the point of view just put forth that I have ventured to say it is not necessary that the plate should acquire and lose its state in a finite time (120); for if it were possible for the current to be fully developed the instant *before* it arrived at its state of nearest approximation to the vertical pole of the magnet, instead of opposite to or a little beyond it, still the relative motion of the pole and plate would be the same, the resulting force being in fact tangential instead of direct.

125. But it is possible (though not necessary for the rotation) that *time* may be required for the development of the maximum current in the plate, in which case the resultant of all the forces would be in advance of the magnet when the plate is rotated, or in the rear of the magnet when the latter is rotated, and many of the effects with pure electro-magnetic poles tend to prove this is the case. Then, the tangential force may be resolved into two others, one parallel to the plane of rotation, and the other perpendicular to it; the former would be the force exerted in making the plate revolve with the magnet, or the magnet with the plate; the latter would be a repulsive force, and is probably that, the effects of which M. Arago has also discovered (82).

126. The extraordinary circumstance accompanying this action, which has seemed so inexplicable, namely, the cessation of all phenomena when the magnet and metal are brought to rest, now receives a full explanation (82); for then the electrical currents which cause the motion cease altogether.

127. All the effects of solution of metallic continuity, and the consequent diminution of power described by Messrs. Babbage and Herschel,[1] now receive their natural explanation, as well also as the resumption of power when the cuts were filled up by metallic substances, which, though conductors of electricity, were themselves very deficient in the power of influencing magnets. And new modes of cutting the plate may be devised, which shall almost entirely destroy its power. Thus, if a copper plate (81) be cut through at about a fifth or sixth of its diameter from the edge, so as to separate a ring from it, and this ring be again fastened on, but with a thickness of paper intervening (Pl. II, *Fig. 17*), and if Arago's experiment be made with this compound plate so adjusted that the section shall continually travel opposite the pole, it is evident that the magnetic currents will be greatly interfered with, and the plate probably lose much of its effect.[2]

An elementary result of this kind was obtained by using two pieces of thick copper, shaped as in *Fig. 16*. When the two neighbouring edges were amalgamated and put together, and the arrangement passed between the poles of the magnet, in a direction parallel to these edges, a current was urged through the wires attached to the outer angles, and the galvanometer became strongly affected; but when a single film of paper was interposed, and the exper-

---

[1] *Philosophical Transactions*, 1825, p. 481.

[2] This experiment has actually been made by Mr. Christie, with the results here described, and is recorded in the *Philosophical Transactions* for 1827, p. 82.

iment repeated, no sensible effect could be produced.

128. A section of this kind could not interfere much with the induction of magnetism, supposed to be of the nature ordinarily received by iron.

129. The effect of rotation or deflection of the needle, which M. Arago obtained by ordinary magnets, M. Ampère succeeded in procuring by electro-magnets. This is perfectly in harmony with the results relative to volta-electric and magneto-electric induction described in this paper. And by using flat spirals of copper wire, through which electric currents were sent, in place of ordinary magnetic poles (111), sometimes applying a single one to one side of the rotating plate, and sometimes two to opposite sides, I obtained the induced currents of electricity from the plate itself, and could lead them away to, and ascertain their existence by, the galvanometer.

130. The cause which has now been assigned for the rotation in Arago's experiment, namely, the production of electrical currents, seems abundantly sufficient in all cases where the metals, or perhaps even other conductors, are concerned; but with regard to such bodies as glass, resins, and, above all, gases, it seems impossible that currents of electricity, capable of producing these effects, should be generated in them. Yet Arago found that the effects in question were produced by these and by all bodies tried (81). Messrs. Babbage and Herschel, it is true, did not observe them with any substance not metallic, except carbon, in a highly conducting state (82). Mr. Harris has ascertained their occurrence with wood, marble, freestone and annealed glass, but obtained no effect with sulphuric acid and saturated solution of sulphate of iron, although these are better conductors of electricity than the former substances.

131. Future investigations will no doubt explain these difficulties, and decide the point whether the retarding or dragging action spoken of is always simultaneous with electric currents.[1] The existence of the action in metals, only whilst the currents exist, i.e., whilst motion is given (82, 88), and the explication of the repulsive action observed by M. Arago

(82, 125), are powerful reasons for referring it to this cause; but it may be combined with others which occasionally act alone.

132. Copper, iron, tin, zinc, lead, mercury, and all the metals tried, produced electrical currents when passed between the magnetic poles: the mercury was put into a glass tube for the purpose. The dense carbon deposited in coal gas retorts, also produced the current, but ordinary charcoal did not. Neither could I obtain any sensible effects with brine, sulphuric acid, saline solutions, &c., whether rotated in basins, or inclosed in tubes and passed between the poles.

133. I have never been able to produce any sensation upon the tongue by the wires connected with the conductors applied to the edges of the revolving plate (88) or slips of metal (101). Nor have I been able to heat a fine platina wire, or produce a spark, or convulse the limbs of a frog. I have failed also to produce any chemical effects by electricity thus evolved (22, 56).

134. As the electric current in the revolving copper plate occupies but a small space, proceeding by the poles and being discharged right and left at very small distances comparatively (123); and as it exists in a thick mass of metal possessing almost the highest conducting power of any, and consequently offering extraordinary facility for its production and discharge; and as, notwithstanding this, considerable currents may be drawn off which can pass through narrow wires, forty, fifty, sixty, or even one hundred feet long; it is evident that the current existing in the plate itself must be a very powerful one, when the rotation is rapid and the magnet strong. This is also abundantly proved by the obedience and readiness with which a magnet ten or twelve pounds in weight follows the motion of the plate and will strongly twist up the cord by which it is suspended.

135. Two rough trials were made with the intention of constructing *magneto-electric machines*. In one, a ring one inch and a half broad and twelve inches external diameter, cut from a thick copper plate, was mounted so as to revolve between the poles of the magnet and represent a plate similar to those formerly used (101), but of interminable length; the inner and outer edges were amalgamated, and the conductors applied one to each edge, at the place of the magnetic poles. The current of electricity evolved did not appear by the galvanometer to be stronger, if so strong, as that from the circular plate (88).

[1] Experiments which I have since made convince me that this particular action is always due to the electrical currents formed; and they supply a test by which it may be distinguished from the action of ordinary magnetism, or any other cause, including those which are mechanical or irregular, producing similar effects (254).

136. In the other, small thick discs of copper or other metal, half an inch in diameter, were revolved rapidly near to the poles, but with the axis of rotation out of the polar axis; the electricity evolved was collected by conductors applied as before to the edges (86). Currents were procured, but of strength much inferior to that produced by the circular plate.

137. The latter experiment is analogous to those made by Mr. Barlow with a rotating iron shell, subject to the influence of the earth.[1] The effects obtained by him have been referred by Messrs. Babbage and Herschel to the same cause as that considered as influential in Arago's experiment,[2] but it would be interesting to know how far the electric current which might be produced in the experiment would account for the deflexion of the needle. The mere inversion of a copper wire six or seven times near the poles of the magnet, and isochronously with the vibrations of the galvanometer needle connected with it, was sufficient to make the needle vibrate through an arc of 60° or 70°. The rotation of a copper shell would perhaps decide the point, and might even throw light upon the more permanent, though somewhat analogous effects obtained by Mr. Christie.

138. The remark which has already been made respecting iron (66), and the independence of the ordinary magnetical phenomena of that substance and the phenomena now described of magneto-electric induction in that and other metals, was fully confirmed by many results of the kind detailed in this section. When an iron plate similar to the copper one formerly described (101) was passed between the magnetic poles, it gave a current of electricity like the copper plate, but decidedly of less power; and in the experiments upon the induction of electric currents (9), no difference in the kind of action between iron and other metals could be perceived. The power therefore of an iron plate to drag a magnet after it, or to intercept magnetic action, should be carefully distinguished from the similar power of such metals as silver, copper, &c., &c., inasmuch as in the iron by far the greater part of the effect is due to what may be called ordinary magnetic action. There can be no doubt that the cause assigned by Messrs. Babbage and Herschel in explication of Arago's phenomena is the true one, when iron is the metal used.

[1] *Philosophical Transactions*, 1825, p. 317.
[2] *Ibid.*, 1825, p. 485.

139. The very feeble powers which were found by those philosophers to belong to bismuth and antimony, when moving, of affecting the suspended magnet, and which has been confirmed by Mr. Harris, seem at first disproportionate to their conducting powers; whether it be so or not must be decided by future experiment (73).[3] These metals are highly crystalline, and probably conduct electricity with different degrees of facility in different directions; and it is not unlikely that where a mass is made up of a number of crystals heterogeneously associated, an effect approaching to that of actual division may occur (127); or the currents of electricity may become more suddenly deflected at the confines of similar crystalline arrangements, and so be more readily and completely discharged within the mass.

Royal Institution, November 1831.

Note. In consequence of the long period which has intervened between the reading and printing of the foregoing paper, accounts of the experiments have been dispersed, and, through a letter of my own to M. Hachette, have reached France and Italy. That letter was translated (with some errors), and read to the Academy of Sciences at Paris, 26th December, 1831. A copy of it in *Le Temps* of the 28th December quickly reached Signor Nobili, who, with Signor Antinori, immediately experimented upon the subject, and obtained many of the results mentioned in my letter; others they could not obtain or understand, because of the brevity of my account. These results by Signor Nobili and Antinori have been embodied in a paper dated 31st January, 1832, and printed and published in the number of the *Antologia* dated November, 1831 (according at least to the copy of the paper kindly sent me by Signor Nobili). It is evident the work could not have been then printed; and though Signor Nobili, in his paper, has inserted my letter as the text of his experiments, yet the circumstance of back date has caused many here, who have heard of Nobili's experiments by report only, to imagine his results were anterior to, instead of being dependent upon, mine.

I may be allowed under these circumstances to remark, that I experimented on this subject several years ago, and have published results. (See *Quarterly Journal of Science* for July, 1825, p. 338.) The following also is an extract from my note-book, dated November 28, 1825: "Experiments on induction by connecting wire of voltaic battery: a battery of four troughs, ten pairs of plates, each arranged side by side—the poles connected by a wire about four feet long, parallel to which was another similar wire separated from it only by two thicknesses of paper, the ends of the latter were attached to a galvanometer: exhibited no action, &c., &c., &c. Could not in any way render any induction evident from the connecting wire." The cause of failure at that time is now evident (79).—M. F. *April,* 1832.

[3] I have since been able to explain these differences, and prove, with several metals, that the effect is in the order of the conducting power; for I have been able to obtain, by magneto-electric induction, currents of electricity which are proportionate in strength to the conducting power of the bodies experimented with (211).

SECOND SERIES

§ 5. *Terrestrial Magneto-electric Induction* § 6. *General Remarks and Illustrations of the Force and Direction of Magneto-electric Induction*

THE BAKERIAN LECTURE, Read January 12, 1832

§ 5. *Terrestrial Magneto-electric Induction*

140. WHEN the general facts described in the former paper were discovered, and the *law* of magneto-electric induction relative to direction was ascertained (114), it was not difficult to perceive that the earth would produce the same effect as a magnet, and to an extent that would, perhaps, render it available in the construction of new electrical machines. The following are some of the results obtained in pursuance of this view.

141. The hollow helix already described (6) was connected with a galvanometer by wires eight feet long; and the soft iron cylinder (34) after being heated red-hot and slowly cooled, to remove all traces of magnetism, was put into the helix so as to project equally at both ends, and fixed there. The combined helix and bar were held in the magnetic direction or line of dip, and (the galvanometer needle being motionless) were then inverted, so that the lower end should become the upper, but the whole still correspond to the magnetic direction; the needle was immediately deflected. As the latter returned to its first position, the helix and bar were again inverted; and by doing this two or three times, making the inversions and vibrations to coincide, the needle swung through an arc of 150° or 160°.

142. When one end of the helix, which may be called A, was uppermost at first (B end consequently being below), then it mattered not in which direction it proceeded during the inversion, whether to the right hand or left hand, or through any other course; still the galvanometer needle passed in the same direction. Again, when B end was uppermost, the inversion of the helix and bar in any direction always caused the needle to be deflected one way; that way being the opposite to the course of the deflection in the former case.

143. When the helix with its iron core in any given position was inverted, the effect was as if a magnet with its marked pole downwards had been introduced from above into the inverted helix. Thus, if the end B were upwards, such a magnet introduced from above would make the marked end of the galvanometer needle pass west. Or the end B being downwards, and the soft iron in its place, inversion of the whole produced the same effect.

144. When the soft iron bar was taken out of the helix and inverted in various directions within four feet of the galvanometer, not the slightest effect upon it was produced.

145. These phenomena are the necessary consequence of the inductive magnetic power of the earth, rendering the soft iron cylinder a magnet with its marked pole downwards. The experiment is analogous to that in which two bar magnets were used to magnetize the same cylinder in the same helix (36), and the inversion of position in the present experiment is equivalent to a change of the poles in that arrangement. But the result is not less an instance of the evolution of electricity by means of the magnetism of the globe.

146. The helix alone was then held permanently in the magnetic direction, and the soft iron cylinder afterwards introduced; the galvanometer needle was instantly deflected; by withdrawing the cylinder as the needle returned, and continuing the two actions simultaneously, the vibrations soon extended through an arc of 180°. The effect was precisely the same as that obtained by using a cylinder magnet with its marked pole downwards; and the direction of motion, &c. was perfectly in accordance with the results of former experiments obtained with such a magnet (39). A magnet in that position being used, gave the same deflections, but stronger. When the helix was put at right angles to the magnetic direction or dip, then the introduction or removal of the soft iron cylinder produced no effect at the needle. Any inclination to the dip gave results of the same kind as those already described,

286

but increasing in strength as the helix approximated to the direction of the dip.

147. A cylinder magnet, although it has great power of affecting the galvanometer when moving into or out of the helix, has no power of continuing the deflection (39); and therefore, though left in, still the magnetic needle comes to its usual place of rest. But upon repeating (with the magnet) the experiment of inversion in the direction of the dip (141), the needle was affected as powerfully as before; the disturbance of the magnetism in the steel magnet, by the earth's inductive force upon it, being thus shown to be nearly, if not quite, equal in amount and rapidity to that occurring in soft iron. It is probable that in this way magneto-electrical arrangements may become very useful in indicating the disturbance of magnetic forces, where other means will not apply; for it is not the whole magnetic power which produces the visible effect, but only the difference due to the disturbing causes.

148. These favourable results led me to hope that the direct magneto-electric induction of the earth might be rendered sensible; and I ultimately succeeded in obtaining the effect in several ways. When the helix just referred to (141, 6) was placed in the magnetic dip, but without any cylinder of iron or steel, and was then inverted, a feeble action at the needle was observed. Inverting the helix ten or twelve times, and at such periods that the deflecting forces exerted by the currents of electricity produced in it should be added to the momentum of the needle (39), the latter was soon made to vibrate through an arc of 80° or 90°. Here, therefore, currents of electricity were produced by the direct inductive power of the earth's magnetism, without the use of any ferruginous matter, and upon a metal not capable of exhibiting any of the ordinary magnetic phenomena. The experiment in everything represents the effects produced by bringing the same helix to one or both poles of any powerful magnet (50).

149. Guided by the law already expressed (114), I expected that all the electric phenomena of the revolving metal plate could now be produced without any other magnet than the earth. The plate so often referred to (85) was therefore fixed so as to rotate in a horizontal plane. The magnetic curves of the earth (114, *note*), i.e., the dip, passes through this plane at angles of about 70°, which it was expected would be an approximation to perpendicularity, quite enough to allow of magneto-electric induction sufficiently powerful to produce a current of electricity.

150. Upon rotation of the plate, the currents ought, according to the law (114, 121), to tend to pass in the direction of the radii, through *all* parts of the plate, either from the centre to the circumference, or from the circumference to the centre, as the direction of the rotation of the plate was one way or the other. One of the wires of the galvanometer was therefore brought in contact with the axis of the plate, and the other attached to a leaden collector or conductor (86), which itself was placed against the amalgamated edge of the disc. On rotating the plate there was a distinct effect at the galvanometer needle; on reversing the rotation, the needle went in the opposite direction; and by making the action of the plate coincide with the vibrations of the needle, the arc through which the latter passed soon extended to half a circle.

151. Whatever part of the edge of the plate was touched by the conductor, the electricity was the same, provided the direction of rotation continued unaltered.

152. When the plate revolved *screw-fashion*, or as the hands of a watch, the current of electricity (150) was from the centre to the circumference; when the direction of rotation was *unscrew*, the current was from the circumference to the centre. These directions are the same with those obtained when the unmarked pole of a magnet was placed beneath the revolving plate (99).

153. When the plate was in the magnetic meridian, or in any other plane *coinciding* with the magnetic dip, then its rotation produced no effect upon the galvanometer. When inclined to the dip but a few degrees, electricity began to appear upon rotation. Thus when standing upright in a plane perpendicular to the magnetic meridian, and when consequently its own plane was inclined only about 20° to the dip, revolution of the plate evolved electricity. As the inclination was increased, the electricity became more powerful until the angle formed by the plane of the plate with the dip was 90°, when the electricity for a given velocity of the plate was a maximum.

154. It is a striking thing to observe the revolving copper plate become thus a *new electrical machine;* and curious results arise on comparing it with the common machine. In the one, the plate is of the best non-conducting substance that can be applied; in the other, it is the most perfect conductor: in the one, insu-

lation is essential; in the other, it is fatal. In comparison of the quantities of electricity produced, the metal machine does not at all fall below the glass one; for it can produce a constant current capable of deflecting the galvanometer needle, whereas the latter cannot. It is quite true that the force of the current thus evolved has not as yet been increased so as to render it available in any of our ordinary applications of this power; but there appears every reasonable expectation that this may hereafter be effected; and probably by several arrangements. Weak as the current may seem to be, it is as strong as, if not stronger than, any thermo-electric current; for it can pass fluids (23), agitate the animal system, and in the case of an electro-magnet has produced sparks (32).

155. A disc of copper, one-fifth of an inch thick and only one inch and a half in diameter, was amalgamated at the edge; a square piece of sheet lead (copper would have been better) of equal thickness had a circular hole cut in it, into which the disc loosely fitted; a little mercury completed the metallic communication of the disc and its surrounding ring; the latter was attached to one of the galvanometer wires, and the other wire dipped into a little metallic cup containing mercury, fixed upon the top of the copper axis of the small disc. Upon rotating the disc in a horizontal plane, the galvanometer needle could be affected, although the earth was the only magnet employed, and the radius of the disc but three-quarters of an inch; in which space only the current was excited.

156. On putting the pole of a magnet under the revolving disc, the galvanometer needle could be permanently deflected.

157. On using copper wires one-sixth of an inch in thickness instead of the smaller wires (86) hitherto constantly employed, far more powerful effects were obtained. Perhaps if the galvanometer had consisted of fewer turns of thick wire instead of many convolutions of thinner, more striking effects would have been produced.

158. One form of apparatus which I purpose having arranged, is to have several discs superposed; the discs are to be metallically connected, alternately at the edges and at the centres, by means of mercury; and are then to be revolved alternately in opposite directions, i.e., the first, third, fifth, &c., to the right hand, and the second, fourth, sixth, &c., to the left hand; the whole being placed so that the discs are perpendicular to the dip, or intersect most directly the magnetic curves of powerful magnets. The electricity will be from the centre to the circumference in one set of discs, and from the circumference to the centre in those on each side of them; thus the action of the whole will conjoin to produce one combined and more powerful current.

159. I have rather, however, been desirous of discovering new facts and new relations dependent on magneto-electric induction, than of exalting the force of those already obtained; being assured that the latter would find their full development hereafter.

160. I referred in my former paper to the probable influence of terrestrial magneto-electric induction (137) in producing, either altogether or in part, the phenomena observed by Messrs. Christie and Barlow,[1] whilst revolving ferruginous bodies; and especially those observed by the latter when rapidly rotating an iron shell, which were by that philosopher referred to a change in the ordinary disposition of the magnetism of the ball. I suggested also that the rotation of a copper globe would probably insulate the effects due to electric currents from those due to mere derangement of magnetism, and throw light upon the true nature of the phenomena.

161. Upon considering the law already referred to (114), it appeared impossible that a metallic globe could revolve under natural circumstances, without having electric currents produced within it, circulating round the revolving globe in a plane at right angles to the plane of revolution, provided its axis of rotation did not coincide with the dip; and it appeared that the current would be most powerful when the axis of revolution was perpendicular to the dip of the needle: for then all those parts of the ball below a plane passing through its centre and perpendicular to the dip, would in moving cut the magnetic curves in one direction, whilst all those parts above that plane would intersect them in the other direction: currents therefore would exist in these moving parts, proceeding from one pole of rotation to the other; but the currents above would be in the reverse direction to those below, and in conjunction with them would produce a continued circulation of electricity.

162. As the electric currents are nowhere interrupted in the ball, powerful effects were expected, and I endeavoured to obtain them with simple apparatus. The ball I used was of brass:

[1] Christie, *Phil. Trans.*, 1825, pp. 58, 347, &c. Barlow. *Phil. Trans.*, 1825, p. 317.

it had belonged to an old electrical machine, was hollow, thin (too thin), and four inches in diameter; a brass wire was screwed into it, and the ball either turned in the hand by the wire, or sometimes, to render it more steady, supported by its wire in a notched piece of wood, and motion again given by the hand. The ball gave no signs of magnetism when at rest.

163. A compound magnetic needle was used to detect the currents. It was arranged thus: a sewing-needle had the head and point broken off, and was then magnetised; being broken in halves, the two magnets thus produced were fixed on a stem of dried grass, so as to be perpendicular to it, and about four inches asunder; they were both in one plane, but their similar poles in contrary directions. The grass was attached to a piece of unspun silk about six inches long, the latter to a stick passing through a cork in the mouth of a cylindrical jar; and thus a compound arrangement was obtained, perfectly sheltered from the motion of the air, but little influenced by the magnetism of the earth, and yet highly sensible to magnetic and electric forces, when the latter were brought into the vicinity of the one or the other needle.

164. Upon adjusting the needles to the plane of the magnetic meridian; arranging the ball on the outside of the glass jar to the west of the needles, and at such a height that its centre should correspond horizontally with the upper needle, whilst its axis was in the plane of the magnetic meridian, but perpendicular to the dip; and then rotating the ball, the needle was immediately affected. Upon inverting the direction of rotation, the needle was again affected, but in the opposite direction. When the ball revolved from east over to west, the marked pole went eastward; when the ball revolved in the opposite direction, the marked pole went westward or towards the ball. Upon placing the ball to the east of the needles, still the needle was deflected in the same way; i.e., when the ball revolved from east over to west, the marked pole went eastward (or towards the ball); when the rotation was in the opposite direction, the marked pole went westward.

165. By twisting the silk of the needles, the latter were brought into a position perpendicular to the plane of the magnetic meridian; the ball was again revolved, with its axis parallel to the needles; the upper was affected as before, and the deflection was such as to show that both here and in the former case the needle was influenced solely by currents of electricity existing in the brass globe.

166. If the upper part of the revolving ball be considered as a wire moving from east to west, over the unmarked pole of the earth, the current of electricity in it should be from north to south (99, 114, 150); if the under part be considered as a similar wire, moving from west to east over the same pole, the electric current should be from south to north; and the circulation of electricity should therefore be from north above to south, and below back to north, in a metal ball revolving from east above to west in these latitudes. Now these currents are exactly those required to give the directions of the needle in the experiments just described; so that the coincidence of the theory from which the experiments were deduced, with the experiments themselves, is perfect.

167. Upon inclining the axis of rotation considerably, the revolving ball was still found to affect the magnetic needle; and it was not until the angle which it formed with the magnetic dip was rendered small, that its effects, even upon this apparatus, were lost (153). When revolving with its axis parallel to the dip, it is evident that the globe becomes analogous to the copper plate; electricity of one kind might be collected at its equator, and of the other kind at its poles.

168. A current in the ball, such as that described above (161), although it ought to deflect a needle the same way whether it be to the right or the left of the ball and of the axis of rotation, ought to deflect it the contrary way when above or below the ball; for then the needle is, or ought to be, acted upon in a contrary direction by the current. This expectation was fulfilled by revolving the ball beneath the magnetic needle, the latter being still inclosed in its jar. When the ball was revolved from east over to west, the marked pole of the needle, instead of passing eastward, went westward; and when revolved from west over to east, the marked pole went eastward.

169. The deflections of the magnetic needle thus obtained with a brass ball are exactly in the same direction as those observed by Mr. Barlow in the revolution of the iron shell; and from the manner in which iron exhibits the phenomena of magneto-electric induction like any other metal, and distinct from its peculiar magnetic phenomena (132), it is impossible but that electric currents must have been excited, and become active in those experiments. What proportion of the whole effect obtained is due to this cause, must be decided by a more elaborate investigation of all the phenomena.

PLATE III

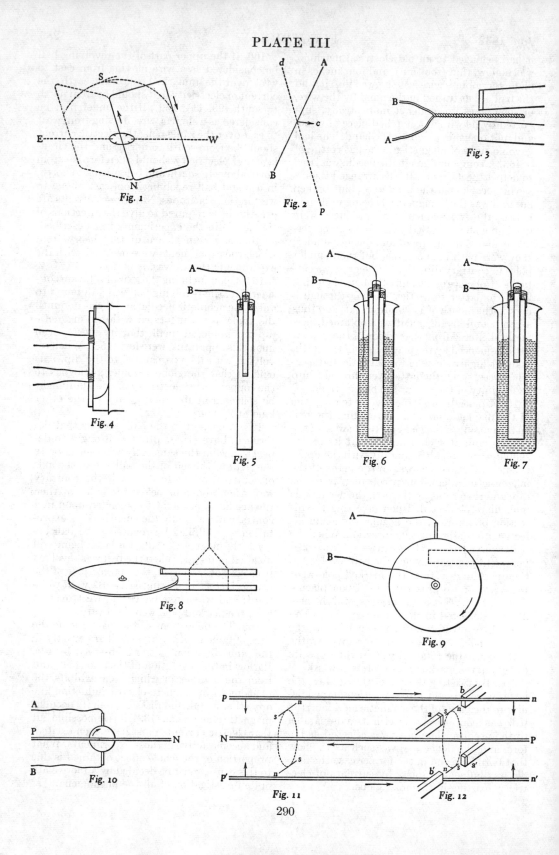

Fig. 1

Fig. 2

Fig. 3

Fig. 4

Fig. 5

Fig. 6

Fig. 7

Fig. 8

Fig. 9

Fig. 10

Fig. 11

Fig. 12

170. These results, in conjunction with the general law before stated (114), suggested an experiment of extreme simplicity, which yet, on trial, was found to answer perfectly. The exclusion of all extraneous circumstances and complexity of arrangement, and the distinct character of the indications afforded, render this single experiment an epitome of nearly all the facts of magneto-electric induction.

171. A piece of common copper wire, about eight feet long and one-twentieth of an inch in thickness, had one of its ends fastened to one of the terminations of the galvanometer wire, and the other end to the other termination; thus it formed an endless continuation of the galvanometer wire: it was then roughly adjusted into the shape of a rectangle, or rather of a loop, the upper part of which could be carried to and fro over the galvanometer, whilst the lower part, and the galvanometer attached to it, remained steady (Pl. III, *Fig. 1*). Upon moving this loop over the galvanometer from right to left, the magnetic needle was immediately deflected; upon passing the loop back again, the needle passed in the contrary direction to what it did before; upon repeating these motions of the loop in accordance with the vibrations of the needle (39), the latter soon swung through 90° or more.

172. The relation of the current of electricity produced in the wire, to its motion, may be understood by supposing the convolutions at the galvanometer away, and the wire arranged as a rectangle, with its lower edge horizontal and in the plane of the magnetic meridian, and a magnetic needle suspended above and over the middle part of this edge, and directed by the earth (*Fig. 1*). On passing the upper part of the rectangle from west to east into the position represented by the dotted line, the marked pole of the magnetic needle went west; the electric current was therefore from north to south in the part of the wire passing under the needle, and from south to north in the moving or upper part of the parallelogram. On passing the upper part of the rectangle from east to west over the galvanometer, the marked pole of the needle went east, and the current of electricity was therefore the reverse of the former.

173. When the rectangle was arranged in a plane east and west, and the magnetic needle made parallel to it, either by the torsion of its suspension thread or the action of a magnet, still the general effects were the same. On moving the upper part of the rectangle from north to south, the marked pole of the needle went north; when the wire was moved in the opposite direction, the marked pole went south. The same effect took place when the motion of the wire was in any other azimuth of the line of dip; the direction of the current always being conformable to the law formerly expressed (114), and also to the directions obtained with the rotating ball (164).

174. In these experiments it is not necessary to move the galvanometer or needle from its first position. It is quite sufficient if the wire of the rectangle is distorted where it leaves the instrument, and bent so as to allow the moving upper part to travel in the desired direction.

175. The moveable part of the wire was then arranged *below* the galvanometer, but so as to be carried across the dip. It affected the instrument as before, and in the same direction; i.e., when carried from west to east under the instrument, the marked end of the needle went west, as before. This should, of course, be the case; for when the wire is cutting the magnetic dip in a certain direction, an electric current also in a certain direction should be induced in it.

176. If, in Pl. III, *Fig. 2*, *d p* be parallel to the dip, and B A be considered as the upper part of the rectangle (171), with an arrow *c* attached to it, both these being retained in a plane perpendicular to the dip—then, however B A with its attached arrow is moved upon *d p* as an axis, if it afterwards proceed in the direction of the arrow, a current of electricity will move along it from B towards A.

177. When the moving part of the wire was carried up or down parallel to the dip, no effect was produced on the galvanometer. When the direction of motion was a little inclined to the dip, electricity manifested itself; and was at a maximum when the motion was perpendicular to the magnetic direction.

178. When the wire was bent into other forms and moved, equally strong effects were obtained, especially when instead of a rectangle a double catenarian curve was formed of it on one side of the galvanometer, and the two single curves or halves were swung in opposite directions at the same time; their action then combined to affect the galvanometer: but all the results were reducible to those above described.

179. The longer the extent of the moving wire, and the greater the space through which it moves, the greater is the effect upon the galvanometer.

180. The facility with which electric currents are produced in metals when moving under the influence of magnets, suggests that henceforth precautions should always be taken, in experiments upon metals and magnets, to guard against such effects. Considering the universality of the magnetic influence of the earth, it is a consequence which appears very extraordinary to the mind, that scarcely any piece of metal can be moved in contact with others, either at rest, or in motion with different velocities or in varying directions, without an electric current existing within them. It is probable that amongst arrangements of steam-engines and metal machinery, some curious accidental magneto-electric combinations may be found, producing effects which have never been observed, or, if noticed, have never as yet been understood.

181. Upon considering the effects of terrestrial magneto-electric induction which have now been described, it is almost impossible to resist the impression that similar effects, but infinitely greater in force, may be produced by the action of the globe, as a magnet, upon its own mass, in consequence of its diurnal rotation. It would seem that if a bar of metal be laid in these latitudes on the surface of the earth parallel to the magnetic meridian, a current of electricity tends to pass through it from south to north, in consequence of the travelling of the bar from west to east (172), by the rotation of the earth; that if another bar in the same direction be connected with the first by wires, it cannot discharge the current of the first, because it has an equal tendency to have a current in the same direction induced within itself: but that if the latter be carried from east to west, which is equivalent to a diminution of the motion communicated to it from the earth (172), then the electric current from south to north is rendered evident in the first bar, in consequence of its discharge, at the same time, by means of the second.

182. Upon the supposition that the rotation of the earth tended, by magneto-electric induction, to cause currents in its own mass, these would, according to the law (114) and the experiments, be, upon the surface at least, from the parts in the neighbourhood of or towards the plane of the equator, in opposite directions to the poles; and if collectors could be applied at the equator and at the poles of the globe, as has been done with the revolving copper plate (150), and also with magnets (220), then neg-

ative electricity would be collected at the equator, and positive electricity at both poles (222). But without the conductors, or something equivalent to them, it is evident these currents could not exist, as they could not be discharged.

183. I did not think it impossible that some natural difference might occur between bodies, relative to the intensity of the current produced or tending to be produced in them by magneto-electric induction, which might be shown by opposing them to each other; especially as Messrs. Arago, Babbage, Herschel, and Harris, have all found great differences, not only between the metals and other substances, but between the metals themselves, in their power of receiving motion from or giving it to a magnet in trials by revolution (130). I therefore took two wires, each one hundred and twenty feet long, one of iron and the other of copper. These were connected with each other at their ends, and then extended in the direction of the magnetic meridian, so as to form two nearly parallel lines, nowhere in contact except at the extremities. The copper wire was then divided in the middle, and examined by a delicate galvanometer, but no evidence of an electrical current was obtained.

184. By favour of His Royal Highness the President of the Society, I obtained the permission of His Majesty to make experiments at the lake in the gardens of Kensington Palace, for the purpose of comparing, in a similar manner, water and metal. The basin of this lake is artificial; the water is supplied by the Chelsea Company; no springs run into it, and it presented what I required, namely, a uniform mass of still pure water, with banks ranging nearly from east to west, and from north to south.

185. Two perfectly clean bright copper plates, each exposing four square feet of surface, were soldered to the extremities of a copper wire; the plates were immersed in the water, north and south of each other, the wire which connected them being arranged upon the grass of the bank. The plates were about four hundred and eighty feet from each other, in a right line; the wire was probably six hundred feet long. This wire was then divided in the middle, and connected by two cups of mercury with a delicate galvanometer.

186. At first, indications of electric currents were obtained; but when these were tested by inverting the direction of contact, and in other ways, they were found to be due to other causes

than the one sought for. A little difference in temperature; a minute portion of the nitrate of mercury used to amalgamate the wires, entering into the water employed to reduce the two cups of mercury to the same temperature, was sufficient to produce currents of electricity, which affected the galvanometer, notwithstanding they had to pass through nearly five hundred feet of water. When these and other interfering causes were guarded against, no effect was obtained; and it appeared that even such dissimilar substances as water and copper, when cutting the magnetic curves of the earth with equal velocity, perfectly neutralized each other's action.

187. Mr. Fox of Falmouth has obtained some highly important results respecting the electricity of metalliferous veins in the mines of Cornwall, which have been published in the *Philosophical Transactions*.[1] I have examined the paper with a view to ascertain whether any of the effects were probably referable to magneto-electric induction; but, though unable to form a very strong opinion, believe they are not. When parallel veins running east and west were compared, the general tendency of the electricity *in the wires* was from north to south; when the comparison was made between parts towards the surface and at some depth, the current of electricity in the wires was from above downwards. If there should be any natural difference in the force of the electric currents produced by magneto-electric induction in different substances, or substances in different positions moving with the earth, and which might be rendered evident by increasing the masses acted upon, then the wires and veins experimented with by Mr. Fox might perhaps have acted as dischargers to the electricity of the mass of strata included between them, and the directions of the currents would agree with those observed as above.

188. Although the electricity obtained by magneto-electric induction in a few feet of wire is of but small intensity, and has not yet been observed except in metals, and carbon in a particular state, still it has power to pass through brine (23); and, as increased length in the substance acted upon produces increase of intensity, I hoped to obtain effects from extensive moving masses of water, though quiescent water gave none. I made experiments therefore (by favour) at Waterloo Bridge, extending a copper wire nine hundred and sixty feet in length upon the parapet of the bridge, and

dropping from its extremities other wires with extensive plates of metal attached to them to complete contact with the water. Thus the wire and the water made one conducting circuit; and as the water ebbed or flowed with the tide, I hoped to obtain currents analogous to those of the brass ball (161).

189. I constantly obtained deflections at the galvanometer, but they were very irregular, and were, in succession, referred to other causes than that sought for. The different condition of the water as to purity on the two sides of the river; the difference in temperature; slight differences in the plates, in the solder used, in the more or less perfect contact made by twisting or otherwise; all produced effects in turn: and though I experimented on the water passing through the middle arches only; used platina plates instead of copper; and took every other precaution, I could not after three days obtain any satisfactory results.

190. Theoretically, it seems a necessary consequence, that where water is flowing, there electric currents should be formed; thus, if a line be imagined passing from Dover to Calais through the sea, and returning through the land beneath the water to Dover, it traces out a circuit of conducting matter, one part of which, when the water moves up or down the channel, is cutting the magnetic curves of the earth, whilst the other is relatively at rest. This is a repetition of the wire experiment (171), but with worse conductors. Still there is every reason to believe that electric currents do run in the general direction of the circuit described, either one way or the other, according as the passage of the waters is up or down the channel. Where the lateral extent of the moving water is enormously increased, it does not seem improbable that the effect should become sensible; and the gulf stream may thus, perhaps, from electric currents moving across it, by magneto-electric induction from the earth, exert a sensible influence upon the forms of the lines of magnetic variation.[2]

191. Though positive results have not yet been obtained by the action of the earth upon water and aqueous fluids, yet, as the experiments are very limited in their extent, and as such fluids do yield the current by artificial magnets (23), (for transference of the current

---

[1] 1830, p. 399.

[2] Theoretically, even a ship or a boat when passing on the surface of the water, in northern or southern latitudes, should have currents of electricity running through it directly across the line of her motion; or if the water is flowing past the ship at anchor, similar currents should occur.

is proof that it may be produced (213),) the supposition made, that the earth produces these induced currents within itself (181) in consequence of its diurnal rotation, is still highly probable (222, 223); and when it is considered that the moving masses extend for thousands of miles across the magnetic curves, cutting them in various directions within its mass, as well as at the surface, it is possible the electricity may rise to considerable intensity.

192. I hardly dare venture, even in the most hypothetical form, to ask whether the Aurora Borealis and Australis may not be the discharge of electricity, thus urged towards the poles of the earth, from whence it is endeavouring to return by natural and appointed means above the earth to the equatorial regions. The non-occurrence of it in very high latitudes is not at all against the supposition; and it is remarkable that Mr. Fox, who observed the deflections of the magnetic needle at Falmouth, by the Aurora Borealis, gives that direction of it which perfectly agrees with the present view. He states that all the variations at night were towards the east,[1] and this is what would happen if electric currents were setting from south to north in the earth under the needle, or from north to south in space above it.

§ 6. *General Remarks and Illustrations of the Force and Direction of Magneto-electric Induction*

193. In the repetition and variation of Arago's experiment by Messrs. Babbage, Herschel, and Harris, these philosophers directed their attention to the differences of force observed amongst the metals and other substances in their action on the magnet. These differences were very great,[2] and led me to hope that by mechanical combinations of various metals important results might be obtained (183). The following experiments were therefore made, with a view to obtain, if possible, any such difference of the action of two metals.

194. A piece of soft iron bonnet-wire covered with cotton was laid bare and cleaned at one extremity, and there fastened by metallic contact with the clean end of a copper wire. Both wires were then twisted together like the strands of a rope, for eighteen or twenty inches; and the remaining parts being made to diverge, their extremities were connected with the wires of the galvanometer. The iron wire was about two feet long, the continuation to the galvanometer being copper.

195. The twisted copper and iron (touching each other nowhere but at the extremity) were then passed between the poles of a powerful magnet arranged horse-shoe fashion (Pl. III, *Fig. 3*); but not the slightest effect was observed at the galvanometer, although the arrangement seemed fitted to show any electrical difference between the two metals relative to the action of the magnet.

196. A soft iron cylinder was then covered with paper at the middle part, and the twisted portion of the above compound wire coiled as a spiral around it, the connexion with the galvanometer still being made at the ends A and B. The iron cylinder was then brought in contact with the poles of a powerful magnet capable of raising thirty pounds; yet no signs of electricity appeared at the galvanometer. Every precaution was applied in making and breaking contact to accumulate effect, but no indications of a current could be obtained.

197. Copper and tin, copper and zinc, tin and zinc, tin and iron, and zinc and iron, were tried against each other in a similar manner (194), but not the slightest sign of electric currents could be procured.

198. Two flat spirals, one of copper and the other of iron, containing each eighteen inches of wire, were connected with each other and with the galvanometer, and then put face to face so as to be in contrary directions. When brought up to the magnetic pole (53), no electrical indications at the galvanometer were observed. When one was turned round so that both were in the same direction, the effect at the galvanometer was very powerful.

199. The compound helix of copper and iron wire formerly described (8) was arranged as a double helix, one of the helices being all iron and containing two hundred and fourteen feet, the other all copper and containing two hundred and eight feet. The two similar ends A A of the copper and iron helix were connected together, and the other ends B B of each helix connected with the galvanometer; so that when a magnet was introduced into the centre of the arrangement, the induced currents in the iron and copper would tend to proceed in contrary directions. Yet when a magnet was inserted, or a soft iron bar within made a magnet by contact with poles, no effect at the needle was produced.

200. A glass tube about fourteen inches long was filled with strong sulphuric acid. Twelve inches of the end of a clean copper wire were bent up into a bundle and inserted into the

---

[1] *Philosophical Transactions*, 1831, p. 202.
[2] *Ibid.*, 1825, p. 472; 1831, p. 78.

tube, so as to make good superficial contact with the acid, and the rest of the wire passed along the outside of the tube and away to the galvanometer. A wire similarly bent up at the extremity was immersed in the other end of the sulphuric acid, and also connected with the galvanometer, so that the acid and copper wire were in the same parallel relation to each other in this experiment as iron and copper were in the first (194). When this arrangement was passed in a similar manner between the poles of the magnet, not the slightest effect at the galvanometer could be perceived.

201. From these experiments it would appear, that when metals of different kinds connected in one circuit are equally subject in every circumstance to magneto-electric induction, they exhibit exactly equal powers with respect to the currents which either are formed, or tend to form, in them. The same even appears to be the case with regard to fluids, and probably all other substances.

202. Still it seemed impossible that these results could indicate the relative inductive power of the magnet upon the different metals; for that the effect should be in some relation to the conducting power seemed a necessary consequence (139), and the influence of rotating plates upon magnets had been found to bear a general relation to the conducting power of the substance used.

203. In the experiments of rotation (81), the electric current is excited and discharged in the same substance, be it a good or bad conductor; but in the experiments just described the current excited in iron could not be transmitted but through the copper, and that excited in copper had to pass through iron: i. e. supposing currents of dissimilar strength to be formed in the metals proportionate to their conducting power, the stronger current had to pass through the worst conductor, and the weaker current through the best.

204. Experiments were therefore made in which different metals insulated from each other were passed between the poles of the magnet, their opposite ends being connected with the same end of the galvanometer wire, so that the currents formed and led away to the galvanometer should oppose each other; and when considerable lengths of different wires were used, feeble deflections were obtained.

205. To obtain perfectly satisfactory results a new galvanometer was constructed, consisting of two independent coils, each containing eighteen feet of silked copper wire. These coils were exactly alike in shape and number of turns, and were fixed side by side with a small interval between them, in which a double needle could be hung by a fibre of silk exactly as in the former instrument (87). The coils may be distinguished by the letters K L, and when electrical currents were sent through them in the same direction, acted upon the needle with the sum of their powers; when in opposite directions, with the difference of their powers.

206. The compound helix (199, 8) was now connected, the ends A and B of the iron with A and B ends of galvanometer coil K, and the ends A and B of the copper with B and A ends of galvanometer coil L, so that the currents excited in the two helices should pass in opposite directions through the coils K and L. On introducing a small cylinder magnet within the helices, the galvanometer needle was powerfully deflected. On disuniting the iron helix, the magnet caused with the copper helix alone still stronger deflection in the same direction. On reuniting the iron helix, and unconnecting the copper helix, the magnet caused a moderate deflection in the contrary direction. Thus it was evident that the electric current induced by a magnet in a copper wire was far more powerful than the current induced by the same magnet in an equal iron wire.

207. To prevent any error that might arise from the greater influence, from vicinity or other circumstances, of one coil on the needle beyond that of the other, the iron and copper terminations were changed relative to the galvanometer coils K L, so that the one which before carried the current from the copper now conveyed that from the iron, and vice versa. But the same striking superiority of the copper was manifested as before. This precaution was taken in the rest of the experiments with other metals to be described.

208. I then had wires of iron, zinc, copper, tin, and lead, drawn to the same diameter (very nearly one-twentieth of an inch), and I compared exactly equal lengths, namely sixteen feet, of each in pairs in the following manner: The ends of the copper wire were connected with the ends A and B of galvanometer coil K, and the ends of the zinc wire with the terminations A and B of the galvanometer coil L. The middle part of each wire was then coiled six times round a cylinder of soft iron covered with paper, long enough to connect the poles of Daniell's horse-shoe magnet (56) (Pl. III, *Fig. 4*), so that similar helices of copper and zinc, each of six turns, surrounded the bar at

two places equidistant from each other and from the poles of the magnet: but these helices were purposely arranged so as to be in contrary directions, and therefore send contrary currents through the galvanometer coils K and L.

209. On making and breaking contact between the soft iron bar and the poles of the magnet, the galvanometer was strongly affected; on detaching the zinc it was still more strongly affected in the same direction. On taking all the precautions before alluded to (207), with others, it was abundantly proved that the current induced by the magnet in copper was far more powerful than in zinc.

210. The copper was then compared in a similar manner with tin, lead, and iron, and surpassed them all, even more than it did zinc. The zinc was then compared experimentally with the tin, lead, and iron, and found to produce a more powerful current than any of them. Iron in the same manner proved superior to tin and lead. Tin came next, and lead the last.

211. Thus the order of these metals is copper, zinc, iron, tin, and lead. It is exactly their order with respect to conducting power for electricity, and, with the exception of iron, is the order presented by the magneto-rotation experiments of Messrs. Babbage, Herschel, Harris, &c. The iron has additional power in the latter kind of experiments, because of its ordinary magnetic relations, and its place relative to magneto-electric action of the kind now under investigation cannot be ascertained by such trials. In the manner above described it may be correctly ascertained.[1]

212. It must still be observed that in these experiments the whole effect between different metals is not obtained; for of the thirty-four feet of wire included in each circuit, eighteen feet are copper in both, being the wire of the galvanometer coils; and as the whole circuit is concerned in the resulting force of the current, this circumstance must tend to diminish the difference which would appear between the metals if the circuits were of the same substances throughout. In the present case the difference obtained is probably not more than a half of that which would be given if the whole of each circuit were of one metal.

[1] Mr. Christie, who being appointed reporter upon this paper, had it in his hands before it was complete, felt the difficulty (202); and to satisfy his mind, made experiments upon iron and copper with the large magnet (44), and came to the same conclusions as I have arrived at. The two sets of experiments were perfectly independent of each other, neither of us being aware of the other's proceedings.

213. These results tend to prove that the currents produced by magneto-electric induction in bodies is proportional to their conducting power. That they are *exactly* proportional to and altogether dependent upon the conducting power, is, I think, proved by the perfect neutrality displayed when two metals or other substances, as acid, water, &c. &c. (201, 186), are opposed to each other in their action. The feeble current which tends to be produced in the worse conductor, has its transmission favoured in the better conductor, and the stronger current which tends to form in the latter has its intensity diminished by the obstruction of the former; and the forces of generation and obstruction are so perfectly balanced as to neutralize each other exactly. Now as the obstruction is inversely as the conducting power, the tendency to generate a current must be directly as that power to produce this perfect equilibrium.

214. The cause of the equality of action under the various circumstances described, where great extent of wire (183) or wire and water (184) were connected together, which yet produced such different effects upon the magnet, is now evident and simple.

215. The effects of a rotating substance upon a needle or magnet ought, where ordinary magnetism has no influence, to be directly as the conducting power of the substance; and I venture now to predict that such will be found to be the case; and that in all those instances where non-conductors have been supposed to exhibit this peculiar influence, the motion has been due to some interfering cause of an ordinary kind; as mechanical communication of motion through the parts of the apparatus, or otherwise (as in the case Mr. Harris has pointed out)[2]; or else to ordinary magnetic attractions. To distinguish the effects of the latter from those of the induced electric currents, I have been able to devise a most perfect test, which shall be almost immediately described (243).

216. There is every reason to believe that the magnet or magnetic needle will become an excellent measurer of the conducting power of substances rotated near it; for I have found by careful experiment, that when a constant current of electricity was sent successively through a series of wires of copper, platina, zinc, silver, lead, and tin, drawn to the same diameter; the deflection of the needle was exactly equal by them all. It must be remembered that when

[2] *Philosophical Transactions*, 1831, p. 68.

bodies are rotated in a horizontal plane, the magnetism of the earth is active upon them. As the effect is general to the whole of the plate, it may not interfere in these cases; but in some experiments and calculations may be of important consequence.

217. Another point which I endeavoured to ascertain, was, whether it was essential or not that the moving part of the wire should, in cutting the magnetic curves, pass into positions of greater or lesser magnetic force; or whether, always intersecting curves of equal magnetic intensity, the mere motion was sufficient for the production of the current. That the latter is true has been proved already in several of the experiments on terrestrial magneto-electric induction. Thus the electricity evolved from the copper plate (149), the currents produced in the rotating globe (161, &c.), and those passing through the moving wire (171), are all produced under circumstances in which the magnetic force could not but be the same during the whole experiments.

218. To prove the point with an ordinary magnet, a copper disc was cemented upon the end of a cylinder magnet, with paper intervening; the magnet and disc were rotated together, and collectors (attached to the galvanometer) brought in contact with the circumference and the central part of the copper plate. The galvanometer needle moved as in former cases, and the *direction* of motion was the *same* as that which would have resulted, if the copper only had revolved, and the magnet been fixed. Neither was there any apparent difference in the quantity of deflection. Hence, rotating the magnet causes no difference in the results; for a rotatory and a stationary magnet produce the same effect upon the moving copper.

219. A copper cylinder, closed at one extremity, was then put over the magnet, one half of which it inclosed like a cap; it was firmly fixed, and prevented from touching the magnet anywhere by interposed paper. The arrangement was then floated in a narrow jar of mercury, so that the lower edge of the copper cylinder touched the fluid metal; one wire of the galvanometer dipped into this mercury, and the other into a little cavity in the centre of the end of the copper cap. Upon rotating the magnet and its attached cylinder, abundance of electricity passed through the galvanometer, and in the same direction as if the cylinder had rotated only, the magnet being still. The results therefore were the same as those with the disc (218).

220. That the metal of the magnet itself might be substituted for the moving cylinder, disc, or wire, seemed an inevitable consequence, and yet one which would exhibit the effects of magneto-electric induction in a striking form. A cylinder magnet had therefore a little hole made in the centre of each end to receive a drop of mercury, and was then floated pole upwards in the same metal, contained in a narrow jar. One wire from the galvanometer dipped into the mercury of the jar, and the other into the drop contained in the hole at the upper extremity of the axis. The magnet was then revolved by a piece of string passed round it, and the galvanometer-needle immediately indicated a powerful current of electricity. On reversing the order of rotation, the electrical current was reversed. The direction of the electricity was the same as if the copper cylinder (219) or a copper wire had revolved round the fixed magnet in the same direction as that which the magnet itself had followed. Thus a *singular independence* of the magnetism and the bar in which it resides is rendered evident.

221. In the above experiment the mercury reached about half way up the magnet; but when its quantity was increased until within one-eighth of an inch of the top, or diminished until equally near the bottom, still the same effects and the *same direction* of electrical current was obtained. But in those extreme proportions the effects did not appear so strong as when the surface of the mercury was about the middle, or between that and an inch from each end. The magnet was eight inches and a half long, and three-quarters of an inch in diameter.

222. Upon inversion of the magnet, and causing rotation in the same direction, i.e., always screw or always unscrew, then a contrary current of electricity was produced. But when the motion of the magnet was continued in a direction constant in relation to its *own axis*, then electricity of the same kind was collected at both poles, and the opposite electricity at the equator, or in its neighbourhood, or in the parts corresponding to it. If the magnet be held parallel to the axis of the earth, with its unmarked pole directed to the pole star, and then rotated so that the parts at its southern side pass from west to east in conformity to the motion of the earth; then positive electricity may be collected at the extremities of the magnet, and negative electricity at or about the middle of its mass.

223. When the galvanometer was very sensible, the mere spinning of the magnet in the air,

whilst one of the galvanometer wires touched the extremity, and the other the equatorial parts, was sufficient to evolve a current of electricity and deflect the needle.

224. Experiments were then made with a similar magnet, for the purpose of ascertaining whether any return of the electric current could occur at the central or axial parts, they having the same angular velocity of rotation as the other parts (259); the belief being that it could not.

225. A cylinder magnet, seven inches in length, and three quarters of an inch in diameter, had a hole pierced in the direction of its axis from one extremity, a quarter of an inch in diameter, and three inches deep. A copper cylinder, surrounded by paper and amalgamated at both extremities, was introduced so as to be in metallic contact at the bottom of the hole, by a little mercury, with the middle of the magnet; insulated at the sides by the paper; and projecting about a quarter of an inch above the end of the steel. A quill was put over the copper rod, which reached to the paper, and formed a cup to receive mercury for the completion of the circuit. A high paper edge was also raised round that end of the magnet and mercury put within it, which however had no metallic connexion with that in the quill, except through the magnet itself and the copper rod (Pl. III, *Fig. 5*). The wires A and B from the galvanometer were dipped into these two portions of mercury; any current through them could, therefore, only pass down the magnet towards its equatorial parts, and then up the copper rod; or vice versa.

226. When thus arranged and rotated screw fashion, the marked end of the galvanometer needle went west, indicating that there was a current through the instrument from A to B and consequently from B through the magnet and copper rod to A (*Fig. 5*).

227. The magnet was then put into a jar of mercury (Pl. III, *Fig. 6*) as before (219); the wire A left in contact with the copper axis, but the wire B dipped in the mercury of the jar, and therefore in metallic communication with the equatorial parts of the magnet instead of its polar extremity. On revolving the magnet screw fashion, the galvanometer needle was deflected in the same direction as before, but far more powerfully. Yet it is evident that the parts of the magnet from the equator to the pole were out of the electric circuit.

228. Then the wire A was connected with the mercury on the extremity of the magnet, the wire B still remaining in contact with that in the jar (Pl. III, *Fig. 7*), so that the copper axis was altogether out of the circuit. The magnet was again revolved screw fashion, and again caused the same deflection of the needle, the current being as strong as it was in the last trial (227), and much stronger than at first (226).

229. Hence it is evident that there is no discharge of the current at the centre of the magnet, for the current, now freely evolved, is up through the magnet; but in the first experiment (226) it was down. In fact, at that time, it was only the part of the moving metal equal to a little disc extending from the end of the wire B in the mercury to the wire A that was efficient, i.e., moving with a different angular velocity to the rest of the circuit (258); and for that portion the direction of the current is consistent with the other results.

230. In the two after experiments, the *lateral* parts of the magnet or of the copper rod are those which move relative to the other parts of the circuit, i.e., the galvanometer wires; and being more extensive, intersecting more curves, or moving with more velocity, produce the greater effect. For the discal part, the direction of the induced electric current is the same in all, namely, from the circumference towards the centre.

231. The law under which the induced electric current excited in bodies moving relatively to magnets, is made dependent on the intersection of the magnetic curves by the metal (114) being thus rendered more precise and definite (217, 220, 224), seem now even to apply to the cause in the first section of the former paper (26); and by rendering a perfect reason for the effects produced, take away any for supposing that peculiar condition, which I ventured to call the electro-tonic state (60).

232. When an electrical current is passed through a wire, that wire is surrounded at every part by magnetic curves, diminishing in intensity according to their distance from the wire, and which in idea may be likened to rings situated in planes perpendicular to the wire or rather to the electric current within it. These curves, although different in form, are perfectly analogous to those existing between two contrary magnetic poles opposed to each other; and when a second wire, parallel to that which carries the current, is made to approach the latter (18), it passes through magnetic curves exactly of the same kind as those it would intersect when carried between opposite mag-

netic poles (109) in one direction; and as it recedes from the inducing wire, it cuts the curves around it in the same manner that it would do those between the same poles if moved in the other direction.

233. If the wire N P (Pl. III, *Fig. 11*) have an electric current passed through it in the direction from P to N, then the dotted ring may represent a magnetic curve round it, and it is in such a direction that if small magnetic needles be placed as tangents to it, they will become arranged as in the figure, *n* and *s* indicating north and south ends (44 *note*).

234. But if the current of electricity were made to cease for a while, and magnetic poles were used instead to give direction to the needles, and make them take the same position as when under the influence of the current, then they must be arranged as at Pl. III, *Fig. 12;* the marked and unmarked poles *a b* above the wire, being in opposite directions to those *a' b'* below. In such a position therefore the magnetic curves between the poles *a b* and *a' b'* have the same general direction with the corresponding parts of the ring magnetic curve surrounding the wire N P carrying an electric current.

235. If the second wire *p n* (*Fig. 11*) be now brought towards the principal wire, carrying a current, it will cut an infinity of magnetic curves, similar in direction to that figured, and consequently similar in direction to those between the poles *a b* of the magnets (*Fig. 12*), and it will intersect these current curves in the same manner as it would the magnet curves, if it passed from above between the poles downwards. Now, such an intersection would, with the magnets, induce an electric current in the wire from *p* to *n* (114); and therefore as the curves are alike in arrangement, the same effect ought to result from the intersection of the magnetic curves dependent on the current in the wire N P; and such is the case, for on approximation the induced current is in the opposite direction to the principal current (19).

236. If the wire *p' n'* be carried up from below, it will pass in the opposite direction between the magnetic poles; but then also the magnetic poles themselves are reversed (*Fig. 12*), and the induced current is therefore (114) still in the same direction as before. It is also, for equally sufficient and evident reasons, in the same direction, if produced by the influence of the curves dependent upon the wire.

237. When the second wire is retained at rest in the vicinity of the principal wire, no current is induced through it, for it is intersecting no magnetic curves. When it is removed from the principal wire, it intersects the curves in the opposite direction to what it did before (235); and a current in the opposite direction is induced, which therefore corresponds with the direction of the principal current (19). The same effect would take place if by inverting the direction of motion of the wire in passing between either set of poles (*Fig. 12*), it were made to intersect the curves there existing in the opposite direction to what it did before.

238. In the first experiments (10, 13), the inducing wire and that under induction were arranged at a fixed distance from each other, and then an electric current sent through the former. In such cases the magnetic curves themselves must be considered as moving (if I may use the expression) across the wire under induction, from the moment at which they begin to be developed until the magnetic force of the current is at its utmost; expanding as it were from the wire outwards, and consequently being in the same relation to the fixed wire under induction as if *it* had moved in the opposite direction across them, or towards the wire carrying the current. Hence the first current induced in such cases was in the contrary direction to the principal current (17, 235). On breaking the battery contact, the magnetic curves (which are mere expressions for arranged magnetic forces) may be conceived as contracting upon and returning towards the failing electrical current, and therefore move in the opposite direction across the wire, and cause an opposite induced current to the first.

239. When, in experiments with ordinary magnets, the latter, in place of being moved past the wires, were actually made near them (27, 36), then a similar progressive development of the magnetic curves may be considered as having taken place, producing the effects which would have occurred by motion of the wires in one direction; the destruction of the magnetic power corresponds to the motion of the wire in the opposite direction.

240. If, instead of intersecting the magnetic curves of a straight wire carrying a current, by approximating or removing a second wire (235), a revolving plate be used, being placed for that purpose near the wire, and, as it were, amongst the magnetic curves, then it ought to have continuous electric currents induced within it; and if a line joining the wire with the centre of the plate were perpendicular to both, then the induced current ought to be, according to the law (114), directly across the plate, from one

side to the other, and at right angles to the direction of the inducing current.

241. A single metallic wire one-twentieth of an inch in diameter had an electric current passed through it, and a small copper disc one inch and a half in diameter revolved near to and under, but not in actual contact with it (Pl. III, *Fig. 10*). Collectors were then applied at the opposite edges of the disc, and wires from them connected with the galvanometer. As the disc revolved in one direction, the needle was deflected on one side; and when the direction of revolution was reversed, the needle was inclined on the other side, in accordance with the results anticipated.

242. Thus the reasons which induce me to suppose a particular state in the wire (60) have disappeared; and though it still seems to me unlikely that a wire at rest in the neighbourhood of another carrying a powerful electric current is entirely indifferent to it, yet I am not aware of any distinct *facts* which authorize the conclusion that it is in a particular state.

243. In considering the nature of the cause assigned in these papers to account for the mutual influence of magnets and moving metals (120), and comparing it with that heretofore admitted, namely, the induction of a feeble magnetism like that produced in iron, it occurred to me that a most decisive experimental test of the two views could be applied (215).

244. No other known power has like direction with that exerted between an electric current and a magnetic pole; it is tangential, while all other forces, acting at a distance, are direct. Hence, if a magnetic pole on one side of a revolving plate follow its course by reason of its obedience to the tangential force exerted upon it by the very current of electricity which it has itself caused, a similar pole on the opposite side of the plate should immediately set it free from this force; for the currents which tend to be formed by the action of the two poles are in opposite directions; or rather no current tends to be formed, or no magnetic curves are intersected (114); and therefore the magnet should remain at rest. On the contrary, if the action of a north magnetic pole were to produce a southness in the nearest part of the copper plate, and a diffuse northness elsewhere (82), as is really the case with iron; then the use of another north pole on the opposite side of the same part of the plate should double the effect instead of destroying it, and double the tendency of the first magnet to move with the plate.

245. A thick copper plate (85) was therefore fixed on a vertical axis, a bar magnet was suspended by a plaited silk cord, so that its marked pole hung over the edge of the plate, and a sheet of paper being interposed, the plate was revolved; immediately the magnetic pole obeyed its motion and passed off in the same direction. A second magnet of equal size and strength was then attached to the first, so that its marked pole should hang *beneath* the edge of the copper plate in a corresponding position to that above, and at an equal distance (Pl. III, *Fig. 8*). Then a paper sheath or screen being interposed as before, and the plate revolved, the poles were found entirely indifferent to its motion, although either of them alone would have followed the course of rotation.

246. On turning one magnet round, so that *opposite* poles were on each side of the plate, then the mutual action of the poles and the moving metal was a maximum.

247. On suspending one magnet so that its axis was level with the plate, and either pole opposite its edge, the revolution of the plate caused no motion of the magnet. The electrical currents dependent upon induction would now tend to be produced in a vertical direction across the thickness of the plate, but could not be so discharged, or at least only to so slight a degree as to leave all effects insensible; but ordinary magnetic induction, or that on an iron plate, would be equally if not more powerfully developed in such a position (251).

248. Then, with regard to the production of electricity in these cases: whenever motion was communicated by the plate to the magnets, currents existed; when it was not communicated, they ceased. A marked pole of a large bar magnet was put under the edge of the plate; collectors (86) applied at the axis and edge of the plate as on former occasions (Pl. III, *Fig. 9*), and these connected with the galvanometer; when the plate was revolved, abundance of electricity passed to the instrument. The unmarked pole of a similar magnet was then put over the place of the former pole, so that contrary poles were above and below; on revolving the plate, the electricity was more powerful than before. The latter magnet was then turned end for end, so that marked poles were both above and below the plate, and then, upon revolving it, scarcely any electricity was procured. By adjusting the distance of the poles so as to correspond with their relative force, they at last were brought so perfectly to neutralize each other's inductive action upon the

plate that no electricity could be obtained with the most rapid motion.

249. I now proceeded to compare the effect of similar and dissimilar poles upon iron and copper, adopting for the purpose Mr. Sturgeon's very useful form of Arago's experiment. This consists in a circular plate of metal supported in a vertical plane by a horizontal axis, and weighted a little at one edge or rendered eccentric so as to vibrate like a pendulum. The poles of the magnets are applied near the side and edges of these plates, and then the number of vibrations, required to reduce the vibrating arc a certain constant quantity, noted. In the first description of this instrument[1] it is said that opposite poles produced the greatest retarding effect, and similar poles none; and yet within a page of the place the effect is considered as of the same kind with that produced in iron.

250. I had two such plates mounted, one of copper, one of iron. The copper plate alone gave sixty vibrations, in the average of several experiments, before the arc of vibration was reduced from one constant mark to another. On placing opposite magnetic poles near to, and on each side of, the same place, the vibrations were reduced to fifteen. On putting similar poles on each side of it, they rose to fifty; and on placing two pieces of wood of equal size with the poles equally near, they became fifty-two. So that, when similar poles were used, the magnetic effect was little or none, (the obstruction being due to the confinement of the air, rather), whilst with opposite poles it was the greatest possible. When a pole was presented to the edge of the plate, no retardation occurred.

251. The iron plate alone made thirty-two vibrations, whilst the arc of vibration diminished a certain quantity. On presenting a magnetic pole to the edge of the plate (247), the vibrations were diminished to eleven; and when the pole was about half an inch from the edge, to five.

252. When the marked pole was put at the side of the iron plate at a certain distance, the number of vibrations was only five. When the marked pole of the second bar was put on the opposite side of the plate at the same distance (250), the vibrations were reduced to two. But when the second pole was an unmarked one, yet occupying exactly the same position, the vibrations rose to twenty-two. By removing the stronger of these two opposite poles a little way from the plate, the vibrations increased to thirty-one, or nearly the original number. But

[1] *Edin. Phil. Journal*, 1825, p. 124.

on removing it *altogether*, they fell to between five and six.

253. Nothing can be more clear, therefore, than that with iron, and bodies admitting of ordinary magnetic induction, *opposite* poles on opposite sides of the edge of the plate neutralize each other's effect, whilst *similar* poles exalt the action; a single pole end on is also sufficient. But with copper, and substances not sensible to ordinary magnetic impressions, *similar* poles on opposite sides of the plate neutralize each other· *opposite* poles exalt the action; and a single pole at the edge or end on does nothing.

254. Nothing can more completely show the thorough independence of the effects obtained with the metals by Arago, and those due to ordinary magnetic forces; and henceforth, therefore, the application of two poles to various moving substances will, if they appear at all magnetically affected, afford a proof of the nature of that affection. If opposite poles produce a greater effect than one pole, the result will be due to electric currents. If similar poles produce more effect than one, then the power is *not* electrical; it is not like that active in the metals and carbon when they are moving, and in most cases will probably be found to be not even magnetical, but the result of irregular causes not anticipated and consequently not guarded against.

255. The result of these investigations tends to show that there are really but very few bodies that are magnetic in the manner of iron. I have often sought for indications of this power in the common metals and other substances; and once in illustration of Arago's objection (82), and in hopes of ascertaining the existence of currents in metals by the momentary approach of a magnet, suspended a disc of copper by a single fibre of silk in an excellent vacuum, and approximated powerful magnets on the outside of the jar, making them approach and recede in unison with a pendulum that vibrated as the disc would do: but no motion could be obtained; not merely, no indication of ordinary magnetic powers, but none of *any electric current* occasioned in the metal by the approximation and recession of the magnet. I therefore venture to arrange substances in three classes as regards their relation to magnets; first, those which are affected when at rest, like iron, nickel, &c., being such as possess ordinary magnetic properties; then, those which are affected when in motion, being conductors of electricity in which are produced electric currents by the inductive force of the magnet; and,

lastly, those which are perfectly indifferent to the magnet, whether at rest or in motion.

256. Although it will require further research, and probably close investigation, both experimental and mathematical, before the exact mode of action between a magnet and metal moving relatively to each other is ascertained; yet many of the results appear sufficiently clear and simple to allow of expression in a somewhat general manner. If a terminated wire move so as to cut a magnetic curve, a power is called into action which tends to urge an electric current through it; but this current cannot be brought into existence unless provision be made at the ends of the wire for its discharge and renewal.

257. If a second wire move in the same direction as the first, the same power is exerted upon it, and it is therefore unable to alter the condition of the first: for there appear to be no natural differences among substances when connected in a series, by which, when moving under the same circumstances relative to the magnet, one tends to produce a more powerful electric current in the whole circuit than another (201, 214).

258. But if the second wire move with a different velocity, or in some other direction, then variations in the force exerted take place; and if connected at their extremities, an electric current passes through them.

259. Taking, then, a mass of metal or an endless wire, and referring to the pole of the magnet as a centre of action (which though perhaps not strictly correct may be allowed for facility of expression, at present), if all parts move in the same direction, and with the same angular velocity, and through magnetic curves of constant intensity, then no electric currents are produced. This point is easily observed with masses subject to the earth's magnetism, and may be proved with regard to small magnets; by rotating them, and leaving the metallic arrangements stationary, no current is produced.

260. If one part of the wire or metal cut the magnetic curves, whilst the other is stationary, then currents are produced. All the results obtained with the galvanometer are more or less of this nature, the galvanometer extremity being the fixed part. Even those with the wire, galvanometer, and earth (170), may be considered so without any error in the result.

261. If the motion of the metal be in the same direction, but the angular velocity of its parts relative to the pole of the magnet different, then currents are produced. This is the case in Arago's experiment, and also in the wire subject to the earth's induction (172), when it was moved from west to east.

262. If the magnet moves not directly to or from the arrangement, but laterally, then the case is similar to the last.

263. If different parts move in opposite directions across the magnetic curves, then the effect is a maximum for equal velocities.

264. All these in fact are variations of one simple condition, namely, that all parts of the mass shall not move in the same direction across the curves, and with the same angular velocity. But they are forms of expression which, being retained in the mind, I have found useful when comparing the consistency of particular phenomena with general results.

Royal Institution, December 21, 1831

THIRD SERIES

§ 7. *Identity of Electricities Derived from Different Sources* § 8. *Relation by Measure of Common and Voltaic Electricity*

READ JANUARY 10TH and 17TH, 1833

§ 7. *Identity of Electricities Derived from Different Sources*

265. THE progress of the electrical researches which I have had the honour to present to the Royal Society, brought me to a point at which it was essential for the further prosecution of my inquiries that no doubt should remain of the identity or distinction of electricities excited by different means. It is perfectly true that Cavendish,[1] Wollaston,[2] Colladon,[3] and others, have in succession removed some of the greatest objections to the acknowledgement of the identity of common, animal and voltaic

[1] *Phil. Trans.*, 1776, p. 196.
[2] *Ibid.*, 1801, p. 434.
[3] *Annales de Chimie*, 1826, p. 62, &c.

electricity, and I believe that most philosophers consider these electricities as really the same. But on the other hand it is also true that the accuracy of Wollaston's experiments has been denied;[1] and also that one of them, which really is no proper proof of chemical decomposition by common electricity (309, 327), has been that selected by several experimenters as the test of chemical action (336, 346). It is a fact, too, that many philosophers are still drawing distinctions between the electricities from different sources; or at least doubting whether their identity is proved. Sir Humphry Davy, for instance, in his paper on the Torpedo,[2] thought it probable that animal electricity would be found of a peculiar kind; and referring to it, to common electricity, voltaic electricity and magnetism, has said, "Distinctions might be established in pursuing the various modifications or properties of electricity in these different forms, &c." Indeed I need only refer to the last volume of the *Philosophical Transactions* to show that the question is by no means considered as settled.[3]

[1] *Phil. Trans.*, 1832, p. 282, note.
[2] *Phil. Trans.*, 1829, p. 17. "Common electricity is excited upon non-conductors, and is readily carried off by conductors and imperfect conductors. Voltaic electricity is excited upon combinations of perfect and imperfect conductors, and is only transmitted by perfect conductors or imperfect conductors of the best kind. Magnetism, if it be a form of electricity, belongs only to perfect conductors; and, in its modifications, to a peculiar class of them.[a] Animal electricity resides only in the imperfect conductors forming the organs of living animals, &c."
[a] Dr. Ritchie has shown this is not the case, *Phil. Trans.*, 1832, p. 294.
[3] *Phil. Trans.*, 1832, p. 259. Dr. Davy, in making experiments on the torpedo, obtains effects the same as those produced by common and voltaic electricity, and says that in its magnetic and chemical power it does not seem to be essentially peculiar,—p. 274; but he then says, p. 275, there are other points of difference; and after referring to them, adds, "How are these differences to be explained? Do they admit of explanation similar to that advanced by Mr. Cavendish in his theory of the torpedo; or may we suppose, according to the analogy of the solar ray, that the electrical power, whether excited by the common machine, or by the voltaic battery, or by the torpedo, is not a simple power, but a combination of powers, which may occur variously associated, and produce all the varieties of electricity with which we are acquainted?"
At p. 279 of the same volume of *Transactions* is Dr. Ritchie's paper, from which the following are extracts: "Common electricity is diffused over the surface of the metal;—voltaic electricity exists within the metal. Free electricity is conducted over the surface of the thinnest gold leaf as effectually as over a mass of metal having the same surface;—voltaic electricity requires thickness of metal for its conduction," p. 280: and again, "The supposed analogy between common and voltaic electricity, which was so eagerly traced after the invention of the pile, completely fails in this case, which was thought to afford the most striking resemblance." p. 291.

266. Notwithstanding, therefore, the general impression of the identity of electricities, it is evident that the proofs have not been sufficiently clear and distinct to obtain the assent of all those who were competent to consider the subject; and the question seemed to me very much in the condition of that which Sir H. Davy solved so beautifully—namely, whether voltaic electricity in all cases merely eliminated, or did not in some actually produce, the acid and alkali found after its action upon water. The same necessity that urged him to decide the doubtful point, which interfered with the extension of his views, and destroyed the strictness of his reasoning, has obliged me to ascertain the identity or difference of common and voltaic electricity. I have satisfied myself that they are identical, and I hope the experiments which I have to offer and the proofs flowing from them, will be found worthy the attention of the Royal Society.

267. The various phenomena exhibited by electricity may, for the purposes of comparison, be arranged under two heads; namely, those connected with electricity of tension, and those belonging to electricity in motion. This distinction is taken at present not as philosophical, but merely as convenient. The effect of electricity of tension, at rest, is either attraction or repulsion at sensible distances. The effects of electricity in motion or electrical currents may be considered as 1st, evolution of heat; 2nd, magnetism; 3rd, chemical decomposition; 4th, physiological phenomena; 5th, spark. It will be my object to compare electricities from different sources, and especially common and voltaic electricities, by their power of producing these effects.

1. *Voltaic Electricity*

268. *Tension.* When a voltaic battery of 100 pairs of plates has its extremities examined by the ordinary electrometer, it is well known that they are found positive and negative, the gold leaves at the same extremity repelling each other, the gold leaves at different extremities attracting each other, even when half an inch or more of air intervenes.

269. That ordinary electricity is discharged by points with facility through air: that it is readily transmitted through highly rarefied air, and also through heated air, as for instance a flame; is due to its high tension. I sought, therefore, for similar effects in the discharge of voltaic electricity, using as a test of the passage of the electricity either the galvanometer

PLATE IV

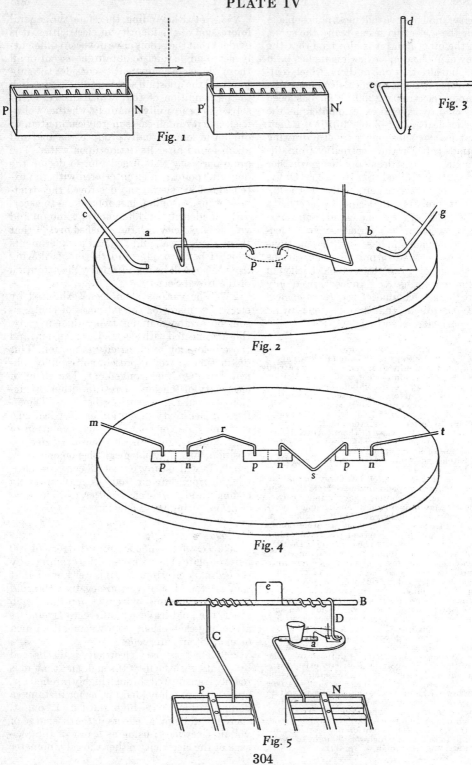

Fig. 1

Fig. 3

Fig. 2

Fig. 4

Fig. 5

or chemical action produced by the arrangement hereafter to be described (312, 316).

270. The voltaic battery I had at my disposal consisted of 140 pairs of plates four inches square, with double coppers. It was insulated throughout, and diverged a gold leaf electrometer about one-third of an inch. On endeavouring to discharge this battery by delicate points very nicely arranged and approximated, either in the air or in an exhausted receiver, I could obtain no indications of a current, either by magnetic or chemical action. In this, however, was found no point of discordance between voltaic and common electricity; for when a Leyden battery (291) was charged so as to deflect the gold leaf electrometer to the same degree, the points were found equally unable to discharge it with such effect as to produce either magnetic or chemical action. This was not because common electricity could not produce both these effects (307, 310), but because when of such low intensity the quantity required to make the effects visible (being enormously great (371, 375),) could not be transmitted in any reasonable time. In conjunction with the other proofs of identity hereafter to be given, these effects of points also prove identity instead of difference between voltaic and common electricity.

271. As heated air discharges common electricity with far greater facility than points, I hoped that voltaic electricity might in this way also be discharged. An apparatus was therefore constructed (Pl. IV, *Fig. 5*), in which A B is an insulated glass rod upon which two copper wires, C, D, are fixed firmly; to these wires are soldered two pieces of fine platina wire, the ends of which are brought very close to each other at *e*, but without touching; the copper wire C was connected with the positive pole of a voltaic battery, and the wire D with a decomposing apparatus (312, 316), from which the communication was completed to the negative pole of the battery. In these experiments only two troughs, or twenty pairs of plates, were used.

272. Whilst in the state described, no decomposition took place at the point *a*, but when the side of a spirit-lamp flame was applied to the two platina extremities at *e*, so as to make them bright red-hot, decomposition occurred; iodine soon appeared at the point *a*, and the transference of electricity through the heated air was established. On raising the temperature of the points *e* by a blowpipe, the discharge was rendered still more free, and decomposition

took place instantly. On removing the source of heat, the current immediately ceased. On putting the ends of the wires very close by the side of and parallel to each other, but not touching, the effects were perhaps more readily obtained than before. On using a larger voltaic battery (270), they were also more freely obtained.

273. On removing the decomposing apparatus and interposing a galvanometer instead, heating the points *e* as the needle would swing one way, and removing the heat during the time of its return (302), feeble deflections were soon obtained: thus also proving the current through heated air; but the instrument used was not so sensible under the circumstances as chemical action.

274. These effects, not hitherto known or expected under this form, are only cases of the discharge which takes place through air between the charcoal terminations of the poles of a powerful battery, when they are gradually separated after contact. Then the passage is through heated air exactly as with common electricity, and Sir H. Davy has recorded that with the original battery of the Royal Institution this discharge passed through a space of at least four inches.[1] In the exhausted receiver the electricity would *strike* through nearly half an inch of space, and the combined effects of rarefaction and heat were such upon the inclosed air as to enable it to conduct the electricity through a space of six or seven inches.

275. The instantaneous charge of a Leyden battery by the poles of a voltaic apparatus is another proof of the tension, and also the quantity, of electricity evolved by the latter. Sir H. Davy says,[2] "When the two conductors from the ends of the combination were connected with a Leyden battery, one with the internal, the other with the external coating, the battery instantly became charged; and on removing the wires and making the proper connexions, either a shock or a *spark* could be perceived: and the least possible time of contact was sufficient to renew the charge to its full intensity."

276. *In Motion;* i. *Evolution of Heat.* The evolution of heat in wires and fluids by the voltaic current is matter of general notoriety.

277. ii. *Magnetism.* No fact is better known to philosophers than the power of the voltaic current to deflect the magnetic needle, and to make magnets according to *certain laws;* and

---

[1] *Elements of Chemical Philosophy*, p. 153.
[2] *Ibid.*, p. 154.

no effect can be more distinctive of an electrical current.

278. iii. *Chemical Decomposition*. The chemical powers of the voltaic current, and their subjection to *certain laws*, are also perfectly well known.

279. iv. *Physiological Effects*. The power of the voltaic current, when strong, to shock and convulse the whole animal system, and when weak to affect the tongue and the eyes, is very characteristic.

280. v. *Spark*. The brilliant star of light produced by the discharge of a voltaic battery is known to all as the most beautiful light that man can produce by art.

281. That these effects may be almost infinitely varied, some being exalted whilst others are diminished, is universally acknowledged; and yet without any doubt of the identity of character of the voltaic currents thus made to differ in their effect. The beautiful explication of these variations afforded by Cavendish's theory of quantity and intensity requires no support at present, as it is not supposed to be doubted.

282. In consequence of the comparisons that will hereafter arise between wires carrying voltaic and ordinary electricities, and also because of certain views of the condition of a wire or any other conducting substance connecting the poles of a voltaic apparatus, it will be necessary to give some definite expression of what is called the voltaic current, in contradistinction to any supposed peculiar state of arrangement, not progressive, which the wire or the electricity within it may be supposed to assume. If two voltaic troughs P N, P′ N′, Pl. IV, *Fig. 1*, be symmetrically arranged and insulated, and the ends N P′ connected by a wire, over which a magnetic needle is suspended, the wire will exert no effect over the needle; but immediately that the ends P N′ are connected by another wire, the needle will be deflected, and will remain so as long as the circuit is complete. Now if the troughs merely act by causing a peculiar arrangement in the wire either of its particles or its electricity, that arrangement constituting its electrical and magnetic state, then the wire N P′ should be in a similar state of arrangement *before* P and N′ were connected, to what it is afterwards, and should have deflected the needle, although less powerfully, perhaps to one-half the extent which would result when the communication is complete throughout. But if the magnetic effects depend upon a current, then it is evident why they could not

be produced in *any* degree before the circuit was complete; because prior to that no current could exist.

283. By *current*, I mean anything progressive, whether it be a fluid of electricity, or two fluids moving in opposite directions, or merely vibrations, or, speaking still more generally, progressive forces. By *arrangement*, I understand a local adjustment of particles, or fluids, or forces, not progressive. Many other reasons might be urged in support of the view of a *current* rather than an *arrangement*, but I am anxious to avoid stating unnecessarily what will occur to others at the moment.

II. *Ordinary Electricity*

284. By ordinary electricity I understand that which can be obtained from the common machine, or from the atmosphere, or by pressure, or cleavage of crystals, or by a multitude of other operations; its distinctive character being that of great intensity, and the exertion of attractive and repulsive powers, not merely at sensible but at considerable distances.

285. *Tension*. The attractions and repulsions at sensible distances, caused by ordinary electricity, are well known to be so powerful in certain cases, as to surpass, almost infinitely, the similar phenomena produced by electricity otherwise excited. But still those attractions and repulsions are exactly of the same nature as those already referred to under the head *Tension, Voltaic electricity* (268); and the difference in degree between them is not greater than often occurs between cases of ordinary electricity only. I think it will be unnecessary to enter minutely into the proofs of the identity of this character in the two instances. They are abundant; are generally admitted as good; and lie upon the surface of the subject: and whenever in other parts of the comparison I am about to draw, a similar case occurs, I shall content myself with a mere announcement of the similarity, enlarging only upon those parts where the great question of distinction or identity still exists.

286. The discharge of common electricity through heated air is a well-known fact. The parallel case of voltaic electricity has already been described (272, &c.).

287. *In Motion*. i. *Evolution of Heat*. The heating power of common electricity, when passed through wires or other substances, is perfectly well known. The accordance between it and voltaic electricity is in this respect complete. Mr. Harris has constructed and describ-

ed[1] a very beautiful and sensible instrument on this principle, in which the heat produced in a wire by the discharge of a small portion of common electricity is readily shown, and to which I shall have occasion to refer for experimental proof in a future part of this paper (344).

288. ii. *Magnetism.* Voltaic electricity has most extraordinary and exalted magnetic powers. If common electricity be identical with it, it ought to have the same powers. In rendering needles or bars magnetic, it is found to agree with voltaic electricity, and the *direction* of the magnetism, in both cases, is the same; but in deflecting the magnetic needle, common electricity has been found deficient, so that sometimes its power has been denied altogether, and at other times distinctions have been hypothetically assumed for the purpose of avoiding the difficulty.[2]

289. M. Colladon, of Geneva, considered that the difference might be due to the use of insufficient quantities of common electricity in all the experiments before made on this head; and in a *Mémoire* read to the Académie des Sciences in 1826,[3] describes experiments, in which, by the use of a battery, points, and a delicate galvanometer, he succeeded in obtaining deflections, and thus establishing identity in that respect. MM. Arago, Ampère, and Savary, are mentioned in the paper as having witnessed a successful repetition of the experiments. But as no other one has come forward in confirmation, MM. Arago, Ampère, and Savary, not having themselves published (that I am aware of) their admission of the results, and as some have not been able to obtain them, M. Colladon's conclusions have been occasionally doubted or denied; and an important point with me was to establish their accuracy, or remove them entirely from the body of received experimental research. I am happy to say that my results fully confirm those by M. Colladon, and I should have had no occasion to describe them, but that they are essential as proofs of the accuracy of the final and general conclusions I am enabled to draw respecting the magnetic and chemical action of electricity (360, 366, 367, 377, &c.).

290. The plate electrical machine I have used is fifty inches in diameter; it has two sets of rubbers; its prime conductor consists of two brass cylinders connected by a third, the whole length being twelve feet, and the surface in contact with air about 1422 square inches. When in good excitation, one revolution of the plate will give ten or twelve sparks from the conductors, each an inch in length. Sparks or flashes from ten to fourteen inches in length may easily be drawn from the conductors. Each turn of the machine, when worked moderately, occupies about ⅘ths of a second.

291. The electric battery consisted of fifteen equal jars. They are coated eight inches upwards from the bottom, and are twenty-three inches in circumference, so that each contains one hundred and eighty-four square inches of glass, coated on both sides: this is independent of the bottoms, which are of thicker glass, and contain each about fifty square inches.

292. A good *discharging train* was arranged by connecting metallically a sufficiently thick wire with the metallic gas pipes of the house, with the metallic gas pipes belonging to the public gas works of London; and also with the metallic water pipes of London. It was so effectual in its office as to carry off instantaneously electricity of the feeblest tension, even that of a single voltaic trough, and was essential to many of the experiments.

293. The galvanometer was one or the other of those formerly described (87, 205), but the glass jar covering it and supporting the needle was coated inside and outside with tinfoil, and the upper part (left uncoated, that the motions of the needle might be examined), was covered with a frame of wirework, having numerous sharp points projecting from it. When this frame and the two coatings were connected with the discharging train (292), an insulated point or ball, connected with the machine when most active, might be brought within an inch of any part of the galvanometer, yet without affecting the needle within by ordinary electrical attraction or repulsion.

294. In connexion with these precautions, it may be necessary to state that the needle of the galvanometer is very liable to have its magnetic power deranged, diminished, or even inverted by the passage of a shock through the instrument. If the needle be at all oblique, in the wrong direction, to the coils of the galvanometer when the shock passes, effects of this kind are sure to happen.

295. It was to the retarding power of bad conductors, with the intention of diminishing its *intensity* without altering its *quantity*, that I first looked with the hope of being able to

---

[1] *Philosophical Transactions*, 1827, p. 18. *Edinburgh Transactions*, 1831, Harris on a New Electrometer, &c. &c.

[2] Demonferrand's *Manuel d'electricité dynamique*, p. 121.

[3] *Annales de Chimie*, XXXIII, p. 62.

make common electricity assume more of the characters and power of voltaic electricity, than it is usually supposed to have.

296. The coating and armour of the galvanometer were first connected with the discharging train (292); the end B (87) of the galvanometer wire was connected with the outside coating of the battery, and then both these with the discharging train; the end A of the galvanometer wire was connected with a discharging rod by a wet thread four feet long; and finally, when the battery (291) had been positively charged by about forty turns of the machine, it was discharged by the rod and the thread through the galvanometer. The needle immediately moved.

297. During the time that the needle completed its vibration in the first direction and returned, the machine was worked, and the battery recharged; and when the needle in vibrating resumed its first direction, the discharge was again made through the galvanometer. By repeating this action a few times, the vibrations soon extended to above 40° on each side of the line of rest.

298. This effect could be obtained at pleasure. Nor was it varied, apparently, either in direction or degree, by using a short thick string, or even four short thick strings in place of the long fine thread. With a more delicate galvanometer, an excellent swing of the needle could be obtained by one discharge of the battery.

299. On reversing the galvanometer communications so as to pass the discharge through from B to A, the needle was equally well deflected, but in the opposite direction.

300. The deflections were in the same direction as if a voltaic current had been passed through the galvanometer, i.e., the positively charged surface of the electric battery coincided with the positive end of the voltaic apparatus (268), and the negative surface of the former with the negative end of the latter.

301. The battery was then thrown out of use, and the communications so arranged that the current could be passed from the prime conductor, by the discharging rod held against it, through the wet string, through the galvanometer coil, and into the discharging train (292), by which it was finally dispersed. This current could be stopped at any moment, by removing the discharging rod, and either stopping the machine or connecting the prime conductor by another rod with the discharging train; and could be as instantly renewed. The needle was so adjusted, that whilst vibrating

in moderate and small arcs, it required time equal to twenty-five beats of a watch to pass in one direction through the arc, and of course an equal time to pass in the other direction.

302. Thus arranged, and the needle being stationary, the current, direct from the machine, was sent through the galvanometer for twenty-five beats, then interrupted for other twenty-five beats, renewed for twenty-five beats more, again interrupted for an equal time, and so on continually. The needle soon began to vibrate visibly, and after several alternations of this kind, the vibration increased to 40° or more.

303. On changing the direction of the current through the galvanometer, the direction of the deflection of the needle was also changed. In all cases the motion of the needle was in direction the same as that caused either by the use of the electric battery or a voltaic trough (300).

304. I now rejected the wet string, and substituted a copper wire, so that the electricity of the machine passed at once into wires communicating directly with the discharging train, the galvanometer coil being one of the wires used for the discharge. The effects were exactly those obtained above (302).

305. Instead of passing the electricity through the system, by bringing the discharging rod at the end of it into contact with the conductor, four points were fixed on to the rod; when the current was to pass, they were held about twelve inches from the conductor, and when it was not to pass, they were turned away. Then operating as before (302), except with this variation, the needle was soon powerfully deflected, and in perfect consistency with the former results. Points afforded the means by which Colladon, in all cases, made his discharges.

306. Finally, I passed the electricity first through an exhausted receiver, so as to make it there resemble the aurora borealis, and then through the galvanometer to the earth; and it was found still effective in deflecting the needle, and apparently with the same force as before.

307. From all these experiments, it appears that a current of common electricity, whether transmitted through water or metal, or rarefied air, or by means of points in common air, is still able to deflect the needle; the only requisite being, apparently, to allow time for its action: that it is, in fact, just as magnetic in every respect as a voltaic current, and that in this character therefore no distinction exists.

308. Imperfect conductors, as water, brine, acids, &c., &c., will be found far more convenient for exhibiting these effects than other modes of discharge, as by points or balls; for the former convert at once the charge of a powerful battery into a feeble spark discharge, or rather continuous current, and involve little or no risk of deranging the magnetism of the needles (294).

309. iii. *Chemical Decomposition.* The chemical action of voltaic electricity is characteristic of that agent, but not more characteristic than are the *laws* under which the bodies evolved by decomposition arrange themselves at the poles. Dr. Wollaston showed[1] that common electricity resembled it in these effects, and "that they are both essentially the same"; but he mingled with his proofs an experiment having a resemblance, and nothing more, to a case of voltaic decomposition, which however he himself partly distinguished; and this has been more frequently referred to by some, on the one hand, to prove the occurrence of electro-chemical decomposition, like that of the pile, and by others to throw doubt upon the whole paper, than the more numerous and decisive experiments which he has detailed.

310. I take the liberty of describing briefly my results, and of thus adding my testimony to that of Dr. Wollaston on the identity of voltaic and common electricity as to chemical action, not only that I may facilitate the repetition of the experiments, but also lead to some new consequences respecting electro-chemical decomposition (376, 377).

311. I first repeated Wollaston's fourth experiment,[2] in which the ends of coated silver wires are immersed in a drop of sulphate of copper. By passing the electricity of the machine through such an arrangement, that end in the drop which received the electricity became coated with metallic copper. One hundred turns of the machine produced an evident effect; two hundred turns a very sensible one. The decomposing action was however very feeble. Very little copper was precipitated, and no sensible trace of silver from the other pole appeared in the solution.

312. A much more convenient and effectual arrangement for chemical decompositions by common electricity, is the following. Upon a glass plate, Pl. IV, *Fig. 2*, placed over, but raised above a piece of white paper, so that shadows may not interfere, put two pieces of

tinfoil *a, b;* connect one of these by an insulated wire *c*, or wire and string (301) with the machine, and the other *g*, with the discharging train (292) or the negative conductor; provide two pieces of fine platina wire, bent as in Pl. IV, *Fig. 3*, so that the part *d, f* shall be nearly upright, whilst the whole is resting on the three bearing points *p, e, f;* place these as in *Fig. 2;* the points *p, n* then become the decomposing poles. In this way surfaces of contact, as minute as possible, can be obtained at pleasure, and the connexion can be broken or renewed in a moment, and the substances acted upon examined with the utmost facility.

313. A coarse line was made on the glass with solution of sulphate of copper, and the terminations *p* and *n* put into it; the foil *a* was connected with the positive conductor of the machine by wire and wet string, so that no sparks passed: twenty turns of the machine caused the precipitation of so much copper on the end *n*, that it looked like copper wire; no apparent change took place at *p*.

314. A mixture of equal parts of muriatic acid and water was rendered deep blue by sulphate of indigo, and a large drop put on the glass, *Fig. 2*, so that *p* and *n* were immersed at opposite sides: a single turn of the machine showed bleaching effects round *p*, from evolved chlorine. After twenty revolutions no effect of the kind was visible at *n*, but so much chlorine had been set free at *p*, that when the drop was stirred the whole became colourless.

315. A drop of solution of iodide of potassium mingled with starch was put into the same position at *p* and *n;* on turning the machine, iodine was evolved at *p*, but not at *n*.

316. A still further improvement in this form of apparatus consists in wetting a piece of filtering paper in the solution to be experimented on, and placing that under the points *p* and *n*, on the glass: the paper retains the substance evolved at the point of evolution, by its whiteness renders any change of colour visible, and allows of the point of contact between it and the decomposing wires being contracted to the utmost degree. A piece of paper moistened in the solution of iodide of potassium and starch, or of the iodide alone, with certain precautions (322), is a most admirable test of electro-chemical action; and when thus placed and acted upon by the electric current, will show iodine evolved at *p* by only half a turn of the machine. With these adjustments and the use of iodide of potassium on paper, chemical action is sometimes a more delicate test of electrical currents

[1] *Philosophical Transactions*, 1801, pp. 427, 434.
[2] *Ibid.*, 1801, p. 429.

than the galvanometer (273). Such cases occur when the bodies traversed by the current are bad conductors, or when the quantity of electricity evolved or transmitted in a given time is very small.

317. A piece of litmus paper moistened in solution of common salt or sulphate of soda, was quickly reddened at p. A similar piece moistened in muriatic acid was very soon bleached at p. No effects of a similar kind took place at n.

318. A piece of turmeric paper moistened in solution of sulphate of soda was reddened at n by two or three turns of the machine, and in twenty or thirty turns plenty of alkali was there evolved. On turning the paper round, so that the spot came under p, and then working the machine, the alkali soon disappeared, the place became yellow, and a brown alkaline spot appeared in the new part under n.

319. On combining a piece of litmus with a piece of turmeric paper, wetting both with solution of sulphate of soda, and putting the paper on the glass, so that p was on the litmus and n on the turmeric, a very few turns of the machine sufficed to show the evolution of acid at the former and alkali at the latter, exactly in the manner effected by a volta-electric current.

320. All these decompositions took place equally well, whether the electricity passed from the machine to the foil a, through water, or through wire only; by *contact* with the conductor, or by *sparks* there; provided the sparks were not so large as to cause the electricity to pass in sparks from p to n, or towards n; and I have seen no reason to believe that in cases of true electro-chemical decomposition by the machine, the electricity passed in sparks from the conductor, or at any part of the current, is able to do more, because of its tension, than that which is made to pass merely as a regular current.

321. Finally, the experiment was extended into the following form, supplying in this case the fullest analogy between common and voltaic electricity. Three compound pieces of litmus and turmeric paper (319) were moistened in solution of sulphate of soda, and arranged on a plate of glass with platina wires, as in Pl. IV, *Fig. 4*. The wire m was connected with the prime conductor of the machine, the wire t with the discharging train, and the wires r and s entered into the course of the electrical current by means of the pieces of moistened paper; they were so bent as to rest each on three points, n, r, p; n, s, p, the points r and s being supported by the glass, and the others by the papers; the three terminations p, p, p rested on the litmus, and the other three n, n, n on the turmeric paper. On working the machine for a short time only, acid was evolved at *all* the poles or terminations p, p, p, by which the electricity entered the solution, and alkali at the other poles n, n, n, by which the electricity left the solution.

322. In all experiments of electro-chemical decomposition by the common machine and moistened papers (316), it is necessary to be aware of and to avoid the following important source of error. If a spark passes over moistened litmus and turmeric paper, the litmus paper (provided it be delicate and not too alkaline), is reddened by it; and if several sparks are passed, it becomes powerfully reddened. If the electricity pass a little way from the wire over the surface of the moistened paper, before it finds mass and moisture enough to conduct it, then the reddening extends as far as the ramifications. If similar ramifications occur at the termination n, on the turmeric paper, they *prevent* the occurrence of the red spot due to the alkali, which would otherwise collect there: sparks or ramifications from the points n will also redden litmus paper. If paper moistened by a solution of iodide of potassium (which is an admirably delicate test of electro-chemical action), be exposed to the sparks or ramifications, or even a feeble stream of electricity through the air from either the point p or n, iodine will be immediately evolved.

323. These effects must not be confounded with those due to the true electro-chemical powers of common electricity, and must be carefully avoided when the latter are to be observed. No sparks should be passed, therefore, in any part of the current, nor any increase of intensity allowed, by which the electricity may be induced to pass between the platina wires and the moistened papers, otherwise than by conduction; for if it burst through the air, the effect referred to above (322) ensues.

324. The effect itself is due to the formation of nitric acid by the combination of the oxygen and nitrogen of the air, and is, in fact, only a delicate repetition of Cavendish's beautiful experiment. The acid so formed, though small in quantity, is in a high state of concentration as to water, and produces the consequent effects of reddening the litmus paper; or preventing the exhibition of alkali on the turmeric paper; or, by acting on the iodide of potassium, evolving iodine.

325. By moistening a very small slip of litmus paper in solution of caustic potassa,[1] and then passing the electric spark over its length in the air, I gradually neutralized the alkali, and ultimately rendered the paper red; on drying it, I found that nitrate of potassa had resulted from the operation, and that the paper had become touch-paper.

326. Either litmus paper or white paper, moistened in a strong solution of iodide of potassium, offers therefore a very simple, beautiful, and ready means of illustrating Cavendish's experiment of the formation of nitric acid from the atmosphere.

327. I have already had occasion to refer to an experiment (265, 309) made by Dr. Wollaston, which is insisted upon too much, both by those who oppose and those who agree with the accuracy of his views respecting the identity of voltaic and ordinary electricity. By covering fine wires with glass or other insulating substances, and then removing only so much matter as to expose the point, or a section of the wires, and by passing electricity through two such wires the guarded points of which were immersed in water, Wollaston found that the water could be decomposed even by the current from the machine, without sparks, and that two streams of gas arose from the points, exactly resembling, in appearance, those produced by voltaic electricity, and, like the latter, giving a mixture of oxygen and hydrogen gases. But Dr. Wollaston himself points out that the effect is different from that of the voltaic pile, inasmuch as both oxygen and hydrogen are evolved from *each* pole; he calls it "a very close *imitation* of the galvanic phenomena," but adds that "in fact the resemblance is not complete," and does not trust to it to establish the principles correctly laid down in his paper.

328. This experiment is neither more nor less than a repetition, in a refined manner, of that made by Dr. Pearson in 1797,[2] and previously by MM. Paets Van Troostwyk and Deiman in 1789 or earlier. That the experiment should never be quoted as proving true electro-chemical decomposition, is sufficiently evident from the circumstance, that the *law* which regulates the transference and final place of the evolved bodies (278, 309) has no influence here. The water is decomposed at both poles independently of each other, and the oxygen and hydrogen evolved at the wires are the elements of the water existing the instant before in those places. That the poles, or rather points, have no mutual decomposing dependence, may be shown by substituting a wire, or the finger, for one of them, a change which does not at all interfere with the other, though it stops all action at the changed pole. This fact may be observed by turning the machine for some time; for though bubbles will rise from the point left unaltered, in quantity sufficient to cover entirely the wire used for the other communication, if they could be applied to it, yet not a single bubble will appear on that wire.

329. When electro-chemical decomposition takes place, there is great reason to believe that the *quantity* of matter decomposed is not proportionate to the intensity, but to the quantity of electricity passed (320). Of this I shall be able to offer some proofs in a future part of this paper (375, 377). But in the experiment under consideration, this is not the case. If, with a constant pair of points, the electricity be passed from the machine in sparks, a certain proportion of gas is evolved; but if the sparks be rendered shorter, less gas is evolved; and if no sparks be passed, there is scarcely a sensible portion of gases set free. On substituting solution of sulphate of soda for water, scarcely a sensible quantity of gas could be procured even with powerful sparks, and nearly none with the mere current; yet the quantity of electricity in a given time was the same in all these cases.

330. I do not intend to deny that with such an apparatus common electricity can decompose water in a manner analogous to that of the voltaic pile; I believe at present that it can. But when what I consider the true effect only was obtained, the quantity of gas given off was so small that I could not ascertain whether it was, as it ought to be, oxygen at one wire and hydrogen at the other. Of the two streams one seemed more copious than the other, and on turning the apparatus round, still the same side in relation to the machine gave the largest stream. On substituting solution of sulphate of soda for pure water (329), these minute streams were still observed. But the quantities were so small, that on working the machine for half an hour I could not obtain at either pole a bubble of gas larger than a small grain of sand. If the conclusion which I have drawn (377) relating to the amount of chemical action be correct, this ought to be the case.

331. I have been the more anxious to assign the true value of this experiment as a test of

[1] *Potassa caustica* or caustic potash, now known as potassium hydroxide.—Ed.
[2] *Nicholson's Journal*, 4to, Vol. 1, pp. 241, 299, 349.

electro-chemical action, because I shall have occasion to refer to it in cases of supposed chemical action by magneto-electric and other electric currents (336, 346) and elsewhere. But, independent of it, there cannot be now a doubt that Dr. Wollaston was right in his general conclusion; and that voltaic and common electricity have powers of chemical decomposition, alike in their nature, and governed by the same law of arrangement.

332. iv. *Physiological Effects*. The power of the common electric current to shock and convulse the animal system, and when weak to affect the tongue and the eyes, may be considered as the same with the similar power of voltaic electricity, account being taken of the intensity of the one electricity and duration of the other. When a wet thread was interposed in the course of the current of common electricity from the battery (291) charged by eight or ten[1] revolutions of the machine in good action (290), and the discharge made by platina spatulas through the tongue or the gums, the effect upon the tongue and eyes was exactly that of a momentary feeble voltaic circuit.

333. v. *Spark*. The beautiful flash of light attending the discharge of common electricity is well known. It rivals in brilliancy, if it does not even very much surpass, the light from the discharge of voltaic electricity; but it endures for an instant only, and is attended by a sharp noise like that of a small explosion. Still no difficulty can arise in recognising it to be the same spark as that from the voltaic battery, especially under certain circumstances. The eye cannot distinguish the difference between a voltaic and a common electricity spark, if they be taken between amalgamated surfaces of metal, at intervals only, and through the same distance of air.

334. When the Leyden battery (291) was discharged through a wet string placed in some part of the circuit away from the place where the spark was to pass, the spark was yellowish, flamy, having a duration sensibly longer than if the water had not been interposed, was about three-fourths of an inch in length, was accompanied by little or no noise, and whilst losing part of its usual character had approximated in some degree to the voltaic spark. When the electricity retarded by water was discharged between pieces of charcoal, it was exceedingly luminous and bright upon both surfaces of the charcoal, resembling the brightness of the voltaic discharge on such surfaces. When the discharge

of the unretarded electricity was taken upon charcoal, it was bright upon both the surfaces (in that respect resembling the voltaic spark), but the noise was loud, sharp, and ringing.

335. I have assumed, in accordance, I believe, with the opinion of every other philosopher, that atmospheric electricity is of the same nature with ordinary electricity (284), and I might therefore refer to certain published statements of chemical effects produced by the former as proofs that the latter enjoys the power of decomposition in common with voltaic electricity. But the comparison I am drawing is far too rigorous to allow me to use these statements without being fully assured of their accuracy; yet I have no right to suppress them, because, if accurate, they establish what I am labouring to put on an undoubted foundation, and have priority to my results.

336. M. Bonijol of Geneva[2] is said to have constructed very delicate apparatus for the decomposition of water by common electricity. By connecting an insulated lightning rod with his apparatus, the decomposition of the water proceeded in a continuous and rapid manner even when the electricity of the atmosphere was not very powerful. The apparatus is not described; but as the diameter of the wire is mentioned as very small, it appears to have been similar in construction to that of Wollaston (327); and as that does not furnish a case of true polar electro-chemical decomposition (328), this result of M. Bonijol does not prove the identity in chemical action of common and voltaic electricity.

337. At the same page of the *Bibliothèque Universelle*, M. Bonijol is said to have decomposed *potash*, and also chloride of silver, by putting them into very narrow tubes and passing electric sparks from an ordinary machine over them. It is evident that these offer no analogy to cases of true voltaic decomposition, where the electricity only decomposes when it is *conducted* by the body acted upon, and ceases to decompose, according to its ordinary laws, when it passes in sparks. These effects are probably partly analogous to that which takes place with water in Pearson's or Wollaston's apparatus, and may be due to very high temperature acting on minute portions of matter; or they may be connected with the results in air (322). As nitrogen can combine directly with oxygen under the influence of the electric spark (324), it is not impossible that it should even take it from the potassium of the potash, especially as

---

[1] Or even from thirty to forty.

there would be plenty of potassa in contact with the acting particles to combine with the nitric acid formed. However distinct all these actions may be from true polar electro-chemical decompositions, they are still highly important, and well-worthy of investigation.

338. The late Mr. Barry communicated a paper to the Royal Society[1] last year, so distinct in the details that it would seem at once to prove the identity in chemical action of common and voltaic electricity; but, when examined, considerable difficulty arises in reconciling certain of the effects with the remainder. He used two tubes, each having a wire within it passing through the closed end, as is usual for voltaic decompositions. The tubes were filled with solution of sulphate of soda, coloured with syrup of violets, and connected by a portion of the same solution, in the ordinary manner; the wire in one tube was connected by a *gilt thread* with the string of an insulated electrical kite, and the wire in the other tube by a similar *gilt thread* with the ground. Hydrogen soon appeared in the tube connected with the kite, and oxygen in the other, and in ten minutes the liquid in the first tube was green from the alkali evolved, and that in the other red from free acid produced. The only indication of the strength or intensity of the atmospheric electricity is in the expression, "the usual shocks were felt on touching the string."

339. That the electricity in this case does not resemble that from any ordinary source of common electricity is shown by several circumstances. Wollaston could not effect the decomposition of water by such an arrangement, and obtain the gases in *separate* vessels, using common electricity; nor have any of the numerous philosophers, who have employed such an apparatus, obtained any such decomposition, either of water or of a neutral salt, by the use of the machine. I have lately tried the large machine (290) in full action for a quarter of an hour, during which time seven hundred revolutions were made, without producing any sensible effects, although the shocks that it would then give must have been far more powerful and numerous than could have been taken, with any chance of safety, from an electrical kite-string; and by reference to the comparison hereafter to be made (371), it will be seen that for common electricity to have produced the effect, the quantity must have been awfully great, and apparently far more than could have been conducted to the earth by a gilt thread,

and at the same time only have produced the "usual shocks."

340. That the electricity was apparently not analogous to voltaic electricity is evident, for the "usual shocks" only were produced, and nothing like the terrible sensation due to a voltaic battery, even when it has a tension so feeble as not to strike through the eighth of an inch of air.

341. It seems just possible that the air which was passing by the kite and string, being in an electrical state sufficient to produce the "usual shocks" only, could still, when the electricity was drawn off below, renew the charge, and so continue the current. The string was 1500 feet long, and contained two double threads. But when the enormous quantity which must have been thus collected is considered (371, 376), the explanation seems very doubtful. I charged a voltaic battery of twenty pairs of plates four inches square with double coppers very strongly, insulated it, connected its positive extremity with the discharging train (292), and its negative pole with an apparatus like that of Mr. Barry, communicating by a wire inserted three inches into the wet soil of the ground. This battery thus arranged produced feeble decomposing effects, as nearly as I could judge answering the description Mr. Barry has given. Its intensity was, of course, far lower than the electricity of the kite-string, but the supply of quantity from the discharging train was unlimited. It gave no shocks to compare with the "usual shocks" of a kite-string.

342. Mr. Barry's experiment is a very important one to repeat and verify. If confirmed, it will be, as far as I am aware, the first recorded case of true electro-chemical decomposition of water by common electricity, and it will supply a form of electrical current, which, both in quantity and intensity, is exactly intermediate with those of the common electrical machine and the voltaic pile.

III. *Magneto-electricity*

343. *Tension.* The attractions and repulsions due to the tension of ordinary electricity have been well observed with that evolved by magneto-electric induction. M. Pixii, by using an apparatus, clever in its construction and powerful in its action,[2] was able to obtain great divergence of the gold leaves of an electrometer.[3]

344. *In Motion:* i. *Evolution of Heat.* The current produced by magneto-electric induction

[1] *Philosophical Transactions*, 1831, p. 165.

[2] *Annales de Chimie*, L, p. 322.
[3] *Ibid.*, LI, p. 77.

can heat a wire in the manner of ordinary electricity. At the British Association of Science at Oxford, in June of the present year, I had the pleasure, in conjunction with Mr. Harris, Professor Daniell, Mr. Duncan, and others, of making an experiment, for which the great magnet in the museum, Mr. Harris's new electrometer (287), and the magneto-electric coil described in my first paper (34), were put in requisition. The latter had been modified in the manner I have elsewhere described,[1] so as to produce an electric spark when its contact with the magnet was made or broken. The terminations of the spiral, adjusted so as to have their contact with each other broken when the spark was to pass, were connected with the wire in the electrometer, and it was found that each time the magnetic contact was made and broken, expansion of the air within the instrument occurred, indicating an increase, at the moment, of the temperature of the wire.

345. ii. *Magnetism.* These currents were discovered by their magnetic power.

346. iii. *Chemical Decomposition.* I have made many endeavours to effect chemical decomposition by magneto-electricity, but unavailingly. In July last I received an anonymous letter (which has since been published)[2] describing a magneto-electric apparatus, by which the decomposition of water was effected. As the term "guarded points" is used, I suppose the apparatus to have been Wollaston's (327 &c.), in which case the results did not indicate polar electro-chemical decomposition. Signor Botto has recently published certain results which he has obtained;[3] but they are, as at present described, inconclusive. The apparatus he used was apparently that of Dr. Wollaston, which gives only fallacious indications (327, &c.). As magneto-electricity can produce sparks, it would be able to show the effects proper to this apparatus. The apparatus of M. Pixii already referred to (343) has however, in the hands of himself[4] and M. Hachette,[5] given decisive chemical results, so as to complete this link in the chain of evidence. Water was decomposed by it, and the oxygen and hydrogen obtained in separate tubes according to the law governing volta-electric and machine-electric decomposition.

347. iv. *Physiological Effects.* A frog was convulsed in the earliest experiments on these currents (56). The sensation upon the tongue, and the flash before the eyes, which I at first obtained only in a feeble degree (56), have been since exalted by more powerful apparatus, so as to become even disagreeable.

348. v. *Spark.* The feeble spark which I first obtained with these currents (32), has been varied and strengthened by Signori Nobili and Antinori, and others, so as to leave no doubt as to its identity with the common electric spark.

IV. *Thermo-electricity*

349. With regard to thermo-electricity, (that beautiful form of electricity discovered by Seebeck), the very conditions under which it is excited are such as to give no ground for expecting that it can be raised like common electricity to any high degree of tension; the effects, therefore, due to that state are not to be expected. The sum of evidence respecting its analogy to the electricities already described, is, I believe, as follows:—*Tension.* The attractions and repulsions due to a certain degree of tension have not been observed. *In Currents:* i. *Evolution of Heat.* I am not aware that its power of raising temperature has been observed. ii. *Magnetism.* It was discovered, and is best recognised, by its magnetic powers. iii. *Chemical Decomposition* has not been effected by it. iv. *Physiological Effects.* Nobili has shown[6] that these currents are able to cause contractions in the limbs of a frog. v. *Spark.* The spark has not yet been seen.

350. Only those effects are weak or deficient which depend upon a certain high degree of intensity: and if common electricity be reduced in that quality to a similar degree with the thermo-electricity, it can produce no effects beyond the latter.

V. *Animal Electricity*

351. After an examination of the experiments of Walsh,[7] Ingenhousz,[8] Cavendish,[9] Sir H. Davy, [10] and Dr. Davy,[11] no doubt remains on my mind as to the identity of the electricity of the torpedo with common and voltaic electricity; and I presume that so little will remain on the minds of others as to justify my refraining from entering at length into the philosophical proofs of that identity. The doubts raised by Sir H. Davy have been removed by his brother Dr.

---

[1] *Phil. Mag. and Annals*, 1832, Vol. XI, p. 405.
[2] *Lond. and Edinb. Phil. Mag. and Journ.*, 1832, Vol. I, p. 161.
[3] *Ibid.*, 1832, Vol. I, p. 441.
[4] *Annales de Chimie*, LI, p. 77.
[5] *Ibid.*, LI, p. 72.

[6] *Bibliothèque Universelle*, XXXVII, 15.
[7] *Philosophical Transactions*, 1773, p. 461
[8] *Ibid.*, 1775, p. 1.
[9] *Ibid.*, 1776, p. 196.
[10] *Ibid.*, 1829, p. 15.
[11] *Ibid.*, 1832, p. 259.

Davy: the results of the latter being the reverse of those of the former. At present the sum of evidence is as follows:

352. *Tension.* No sensible attractions or repulsions due to tension have been observed.

353. *In Motion:* i. *Evolution of Heat;* not yet observed; I have little or no doubt that Harris's electrometer would show it (287, 359).

354. ii. *Magnetism.* Perfectly distinct. According to Dr. Davy,[1] the current deflected the needle and made magnets under the same law, as to direction, which governs currents of ordinary and voltaic electricity.

355. iii. *Chemical Decomposition.* Also distinct; and though Dr. Davy used an apparatus of similar construction with that of Dr. Wollaston (327), still no error in the present case is involved, for the decompositions were polar, and in their nature truly electro-chemical. By the direction of the magnet it was found that the under surface of the fish was negative, and the upper positive; and in the chemical decompositions, silver and lead were precipitated on the wire connected with the under surface, and not on the other; and when these wires were either steel or silver, in solution of common salt, gas (hydrogen?) rose from the negative wire, but none from the positive.

356. Another reason for the decomposition being electro-chemical is, that a Wollaston's apparatus constructed with *wires,* coated by sealing-wax, would most probably not have decomposed water, even in its own peculiar way, unless the electricity had risen high enough in intensity to produce sparks in some part of the circuit; whereas the torpedo was not able to produce sensible sparks. A third reason is, that the purer the water in Wollaston's apparatus, the more abundant is the decomposition; and I have found that a machine and wire points which succeeded perfectly well with distilled water, failed altogether when the water was rendered a good conductor by sulphate of soda, common salt, or other saline bodies. But in Dr. Davy's experiments with the torpedo, *strong* solutions of salt, nitrate of silver, and superacetate of lead were used successfully, and there is no doubt with more success than weaker ones.

357. iv. *Physiological Effects.* These are so characteristic, that by them the peculiar powers of the torpedo and *gymnotus* are principally recognised.

358. v. *Spark.* The electric spark has not yet been obtained, or at least I think not; but per-

haps I had better refer to the evidence on this point. Humboldt, speaking of results obtained by M. Fahlberg, of Sweden, says, "This philosopher has seen an electric spark, as Walsh and Ingenhousz had done before him in London, by placing the *gymnotus* in the air, and interrupting the conducting chain by two gold leaves pasted upon glass, and a line distant from each other."[2] I cannot, however, find any record of such an observation by either Walsh or Ingenhousz, and do not know where to refer to that by M. Fahlberg. M. Humboldt could not himself perceive any luminous effect.

Again, Sir John Leslie, in his dissertation on the progress of mathematical and physical science, prefixed to the seventh edition of the *Encyclopædia Britannica* (Edinb., 1830, p. 622), says, "From a healthy specimen" of the *Silurus electricus,* meaning rather the *gymnotus,* "exhibited in London, vivid sparks were drawn in a darkened room"; but he does not say he saw them himself, nor state who did see them; nor can I find any account of such a phenomenon; so that the statement is doubtful.[3]

359. In concluding this summary of the powers of torpedinal electricity, I cannot refrain from pointing out the enormous absolute quantity of electricity which the animal must put in circulation at each effort. It is doubtful whether any common electrical machine has as yet been able to supply electricity sufficient in a reasonable time to cause true electro-chemical decomposition of water (330, 339), yet the current from the torpedo has done it. The same high proportion is shown by the magnetic effects (296, 371). These circumstances indicate that the torpedo has power (in the way probably that Cavendish describes) to continue the evolution for a sensible time, so that its successive discharges rather resemble those of a voltaic arrangement, intermitting in its action, than those of a Leyden apparatus, charged and discharged many times in succession. In reality, however, there is *no philosophical difference* between these two cases.

360. The *general conclusion* which must, I think, be drawn from this collection of facts is, that *electricity, whatever may be its source, is identical in its nature.* The phenomena in the five kinds or species quoted, differ, not in their character but only in degree; and in that respect vary in proportion to the variable circum-

[1] *Philosophical Transactions,* 1832, p. 260.

[2] *Edinburgh Phil. Journal,* II, p. 249.
[3] Mr. Brayley, who referred me to these statements, and has extensive knowledge of recorded facts, is unacquainted with any further account relating to them.

stances of *quantity* and *intensity*[1] which can at pleasure be made to change in almost any one of the kinds of electricity, as much as it does between one kind and another.

Table of the Experimental Effects Common to the Electricites Derived from Different Sources[2]

	Physiological Effects	Magnetic Deflection	Magnets made	Spark	Heating Power	True chemical Action	Attraction and Repulsion	Discharge by Hot Air
1. Voltaic Electricity	×	×	×	×	×	×	×	×
2. Common Electricity	×	×	×	×	×	×	×	×
3. Magneto-electricity	×	×	×	×	×	×	×	
4. Thermo-electricity	×	×	+	+	+	+		
5. Animal electricity	×	×	×	+	+	×		

§ 8. *Relation by Measure of Common and Voltaic Electricity*[3]

361. Believing the point of identity to be satisfactorily established, I next endeavoured to obtain a common measure, or a known relation as to quantity, of the electricity excited by a machine, and that from a voltaic pile; for the purpose not only of confirming their identity (378), but also of demonstrating certain general principles (366, 377, &c.), and creating an extension of the means of investigating and ap-

[1] The term *quantity* in electricity is perhaps sufficiently definite as to sense; the term *intensity* is more difficult to define strictly. I am using the terms in their ordinary and accepted meaning.

[2] Many of the spaces in this table originally left blank may now be filled. Thus with *thermo-electricity*, Botto made magnets and obtained polar chemical decomposition: Antinori produced the spark; and if it has not been done before, Mr. Watkins has recently heated a wire in Harris's thermo-electrometer. In respect to *animal electricity*, Matteucci and Linari have obtained the spark from the torpedo, and I have recently procured it from the *gymnotus*: Dr. Davy has observed the heating power of the current from the torpedo. I have therefore filled up these spaces with crosses, in a different position to the others originally in the table. There remain but five spaces unmarked, two under *attraction* and *repulsion*, and three under *discharge by hot air*; and though these effects have not yet been obtained, it is a necessary conclusion that they must be possible, since the *spark* corresponding to them has been procured. For when a discharge across cold air can occur, that intensity which is the only essential additional requisite for the other effects must be present.
—*Dec.* 13, 1838.

[3] In further illustration of this subject see 855–873 in Series VII.—*Dec.* 1838.

plying the chemical powers of this wonderful and subtile agent.

362. The first point to be determined was, whether the same absolute quantity of ordinary electricity, sent through a galvanometer, under different circumstances, would cause the same deflection of the needle. An arbitrary scale was therefore attached to the galvanometer, each division of which was equal to about 4°, and the instrument arranged as in former experiments (296). The machine (290), battery (291), and other parts of the apparatus were brought into good order, and retained for the time as nearly as possible in the same condition. The experiments were alternated so as to indicate any change in the condition of the apparatus and supply the necessary corrections.

363. Seven of the battery jars were removed, and eight retained for present use. It was found that about forty turns would fully charge the eight jars. They were then charged by thirty turns of the machine, and discharged through the galvanometer, a thick wet string, about ten inches long, being included in the circuit. The needle was immediately deflected five divisions and a half, on the one side of the zero, and in vibrating passed as nearly as possible through five divisions and a half on the other side.

364. The other seven jars were then added to the eight, and the whole fifteen charged by thirty turns of the machine. The Henley's electrometer stood not quite half as high as before; but when the discharge was made through the galvanometer, previously at rest, the needle immediately vibrated, passing *exactly* to the same division as in the former instance. These experiments with eight and with fifteen jars were repeated several times alternately with the same results.

365. Other experiments were then made, in which all the battery was used, and its charge (being fifty turns of the machine), sent through the galvanometer: but it was modified by being passed sometimes through a mere wet thread, sometimes through thirty-eight inches of thin string wetted by distilled water, and sometimes through a string of twelve times the thickness, only twelve inches in length, and soaked in dilute acid (298). With the thick string the charge passed at once: with the thin string it occupied a sensible time, and with the thread it required two or three seconds before the electrometer fell entirely down. The current therefore must have varied extremely in intensity in these different cases, and yet the deflection of the needle was sensibly the same in all of them. If any

difference occurred, it was that the thin string and thread caused greatest deflection: and if there is any lateral transmission, as M. Colladon says, through the silk in the galvanometer coil, it ought to have been so, because then the intensity is lower and the lateral transmission less.

366. Hence it would appear that *if the same absolute quantity of electricity pass through the galvanometer, whatever may be its intensity, the deflecting force upon the magnetic needle is the same.*

367. The battery of fifteen jars was then charged by sixty revolutions of the machine, and discharged, as before, through the galvanometer. The deflection of the needle was now as nearly as possible to the eleventh division, but the graduation was not accurate enough for me to assert that the arc was exactly double the former arc; to the eye it appeared to be so. The probability is, that *the deflecting force of an electric current is directly proportional to the absolute quantity of electricity passed*, at whatever intensity that electricity may be.[1]

368. Dr. Ritchie has shown that in a case where the intensity of the electricity remained the same, the deflection of the magnetic needle was directly as the quantity of electricity passed through the galvanometer.[2] Mr. Harris has shown that the *heating* power of common electricity on metallic wires is the same for the same quantity of electricity whatever its intensity might have previously been.[3]

369. The next point was to obtain a *voltaic* arrangement producing an effect equal to that just described (367). A platina and a zinc wire were passed through the same hole of a draw-plate, being then one-eighteenth of an inch in diameter; these were fastened to a support, so that their lower ends projected, were parallel, and five-sixteenths of an inch apart. The upper ends were well-connected with the galvanometer wires. Some acid was diluted, and, after various preliminary experiments, that adopted as a standard which consisted of one drop strong sulphuric acid in four ounces distilled water. Finally, the time was noted which the needle

---

[1] The great and general value of the galvanometer, as an actual measure of the electricity passing through it, either continuously or interruptedly, must be evident from a consideration of these two conclusions. As constructed by Professor Ritchie with glass threads (see *Philosophical Transactions*, 1830, p. 218, and *Quarterly Journal of Science*, New Series, Vol. I, p. 29), it apparently seems to leave nothing unsupplied in its own department.

[2] *Quarterly Journal of Science*, New Series, Vol. I, p. 33.

[3] *Plymouth Transactions*, p. 22.

required in swinging either from right to left or left to right: it was equal to seventeen beats of my watch, the latter giving one hundred and fifty in a minute. The object of these preparations was to arrange a voltaic apparatus, which, by immersion in a given acid for a given time, much less than that required by the needle to swing in one direction, should give equal deflection to the instrument with the discharge of ordinary electricity from the battery (363, 364); and a new part of the zinc wire having been brought into position with the platina, the comparative experiments were made.

370. On plunging the zinc and platina wires five-eighths of an inch deep into the acid, and retaining them there for eight beats of the watch, (after which they were quickly withdrawn), the needle was deflected, and continued to advance in the same direction some time after the voltaic apparatus had been removed from the acid. It attained the five-and-a-half division, and then returned swinging an equal distance on the other side. This experiment was repeated many times, and always with the same result.

371. Hence, as an approximation, and judging from *magnetic force* only at present (376), it would appear that two wires, one of platina and one of zinc, each one-eighteenth of an inch in diameter, placed five-sixteenths of an inch apart and immersed to the depth of five-eighths of an inch in acid, consisting of one drop oil of vitriol and four ounces distilled water, at a temperature about 60°, and connected at the other extremities by a copper wire eighteen feet long and one-eighteenth of an inch thick (being the wire of the galvanometer coils), yield as much electricity in eight beats of my watch, or in $\frac{8}{150}$ ths of a minute, as the electrical battery charged by thirty turns of the large machine, in excellent order (363, 364). Notwithstanding this apparently enormous disproportion, the results are perfectly in harmony with those effects which are known to be produced by variations in the intensity and quantity of the electric fluid.

372. In order to procure a reference to *chemical action*, the wires were now retained immersed in the acid to the depth of five-eighths of an inch, and the needle, when stationary, observed; it stood, as nearly as the unassisted eye could decide, at 5⅓ division. Hence a permanent deflection to that extent might be considered as indicating a constant voltaic current, which in eight beats of my watch (369) could supply as much electricity as the elec-

trical battery charged by thirty turns of the machine.

373. The following arrangements and results are selected from many that were made and obtained relative to chemical action. A platina wire one-twelfth of an inch in diameter, weighing two hundred and sixty grains, had the extremity rendered plain, so as to offer a definite surface equal to a circle of the same diameter as the wire; it was then connected in turn with the conductor of the machine, or with the voltaic apparatus (369), so as always to form the positive pole, and at the same time retain a perpendicular position, that it might rest, with its whole weight, upon the test paper to be employed. The test paper itself was supported upon a platina spatula, connected either with the discharging train (292), or with the negative wire of the voltaic apparatus, and it consisted of four thicknesses, moistened at all times to an equal degree in a standard solution of hydriodate of potassa (316).

374. When the platina wire was connected with the prime conductor of the machine, and the spatula with the discharging train, ten turns of the machine had such decomposing power as to produce a pale round spot of iodine of the diameter of the wire; twenty turns made a much darker mark, and thirty turns made a dark brown spot penetrating to the second thickness of the paper. The difference in effect produced by two or three turns, more or less, could be distinguished with facility.

375. The wire and spatula were then connected with the voltaic apparatus (369), the galvanometer being also included in the arrangement; and, a stronger acid having been prepared, consisting of nitric acid and water, the voltaic apparatus was immersed so far as to give a permanent deflection of the needle to the 5⅕ division (372), the fourfold moistened paper intervening as before.[1] Then by shifting the end of the wire from place to place upon the test paper, the effect of the current for five, six, seven, or any number of the beats of the watch (369) was observed, and compared with that of the machine. After alternating and repeating the experiments of comparison many times, it was constantly found that this standard current of voltaic electricity, continued for eight beats of the watch, was equal, in chemical effect, to thirty turns of the machine; twenty-eight revolutions of the machine were sensibly too few.

376. Hence it results that both in *magnetic deflection* (371) and in *chemical force*, the current of electricity of the standard voltaic battery for eight beats of the watch was equal to that of the machine evolved by thirty revolutions.

377. It also follows that for this case of electro-chemical decomposition, and it is probable for all cases, that the *chemical power, like the magnetic force* (366), *is in direct proportion to the absolute quantity of electricity* which passes.

378. Hence arises still further confirmation, if any were required, of the identity of common and voltaic electricity, and that the differences of intensity and quantity are quite sufficient to account for what were supposed to be their distinctive qualities.

379. The extension which the present investigations have enabled me to make of the facts and views constituting the theory of electro-chemical decomposition, will, with some other points of electrical doctrine, be almost immediately submitted to the Royal Society in another series of these *Researches*.

Royal Institution, Dec. 15, 1832

NOTE. I am anxious, and am permitted, to add to this paper a correction of an error which I have attributed to M. Ampère in the first series of these *Experimental Researches*. In referring to his experiment on the induction of electrical currents (78), I have called that a disc which I should have called a circle or a ring. M. Ampère used a ring, or a very short cylinder made of a narrow plate of copper bent into a circle, and he tells me that by such an arrangement the motion is very readily obtained. I have not doubted that M. Ampère obtained the motion he described; but merely mistook the kind of mobile conductor used, and so far I described his *experiment* erroneously.

In the same paragraph I have stated that M. Ampère says the disc turned "to take a position of equilibrium exactly as the spiral itself would have turned had it been free to move"; and farther on I have said that my results tended to invert the sense of the proposition "stated by M. Ampère, *that a current of electricity tends to put the electricity of conductors near which it passes in motion in the same direction.*" M. Ampère tells me in a letter which I have just received from him, that he carefully avoided, when describing the experiment, any reference to the direction of the induced current; and on looking at the passages he quotes to me, I find that to be the case. I have therefore done him injustice in the above statements, and am anxious to correct my error.

But that it may not be supposed I lightly wrote those passages, I will briefly refer to my reasons for understanding them in the sense I did. At first the experiment failed. When re-made successfully about a year afterwards, it was at Geneva in company with M. A. De la Rive: the latter philosopher described the results,[2] and says that the plate of copper bent into a circle which was used as the mobile conductor "sometimes advanced between the two branches of the (horse-shoe) magnet, and sometimes was repelled, *according* to the direction of the current in the surrounding conductors."

---

[1] Of course the heightened power of the voltaic battery was necessary to compensate for the bad conductor now interposed.

[2] *Bibliothèque Universelle*, XXI, p. 48.

I have been in the habit of referring to Demonferrand's *Manuel d'Electricité Dynamique*, as a book of authority in France; containing the general results and laws of this branch of science, up to the time of its publication, in a well-arranged form. At p. 173, the author, when describing this experiment, says, "The mobile circle turns to take a position of equilibrium as a conductor would do in which the current moved in the *same direction* as in the spiral"; and in the same paragraph he adds, "It is therefore proved *that a current of electricity tends to put the electricity of conductors, near which it passes, in motion in the same direction.*" These are the words I quoted in my paper (78).

Le Lycée of 1st of January, 1832, No. 36, in an article written after the receipt of my first unfortunate letter to M. Hachette, and before my papers were printed, reasons upon the direction of the induced currents, and says, that there ought to be "an elementary current produced in the same direction as the corresponding portion of the producing current." A little further on it says, "therefore we ought to obtain currents, moving in the *same direction*, produced upon a metallic wire, either by a magnet or a current. M. Ampère *was so thoroughly persuaded that such ought to be the direction of the currents by influence, that he neglected to assure himself of it in his* experiment at Geneva."

It was the precise statements in Demonferrand's *Manuel*, agreeing as they did with the expression in M. De la Rive's paper, (which, however, I now understand as only meaning that when the inducing current was changed, the motion of the mobile circle changed also), and not in discordance with anything expressed by M. Ampère himself where he speaks of the experiment, which made me conclude, when I wrote the paper, that what I wrote was really his avowed opinion; and when the Number of the *Lycée* referred to appeared, which was before my paper was printed, it could excite no suspicion that I was in error.

Hence the mistake into which I unwittingly fell. I am proud to correct it and do full justice to the acuteness and accuracy which, as far as I can understand the subjects, M. Ampère carries into all the branches of philosophy which he investigates.

Finally, my note to (79) says that the *Lycée*, No. 36, "mistakes the erroneous results of MM. Fresnel and Ampère for true ones," &c. &c. In calling M. Ampère's results erroneous, I spoke of the results described in, and referred to by the *Lycée* itself; but *now* that the expression of the direction of the induced current is to be separated, the term *erroneous* ought no longer to be attached to them.—M. F. *April* 29, 1833

FOURTH SERIES

§ 9. *On a New Law of Electric Conduction*   § 10. *On Conducting Power Generally*

RECEIVED APRIL 24, READ MAY 23, 1833

§ 9. *On a New Law of Electric Conduction*[1]

380. IT was during the progress of investigations relating to electro-chemical decomposition, which I still have to submit to the Royal Society, that I encountered effects due to a very *general law* of electric conduction not hitherto recognised; and though they prevented me from obtaining the condition I sought for, they afforded abundant compensation for the momentary disappointment, by the new and important interest which they gave to an extensive part of electrical science.

381. I was working with ice, and the solids resulting from the freezing of solutions, arranged either as barriers across a substance to be decomposed, or as the actual poles of a voltaic battery, that I might trace and catch certain elements in their transit, when I was suddenly stopped in my progress by finding that ice was in such circumstances a non-conductor of electricity; and that as soon as a thin film of it was interposed, in the circuit of a very powerful voltaic battery, the transmission of electricity was prevented, and all decomposition ceased.

[1] In reference to this law see further considerations at 910, 1358, 1705.—*Dec.* 1838.

382. At first the experiments were made with common ice, during the cold freezing weather of the latter end of January 1833; but the results were fallacious, from the imperfection of the arrangements, and the following more unexceptionable form of experiment was adopted.

383. Tin vessels were formed, five inches deep, one inch and a quarter wide in one direction, of different widths from three-eighths to five-eighths of an inch in the other, and open at one extremity. Into these were fixed by corks, plates of platina, so that the latter should not touch the tin cases; and copper wires having previously been soldered to the plate, these were easily connected, when required, with a voltaic pile. Then distilled water, previously boiled for three hours, was poured into the vessels, and frozen by a mixture of salt and snow, so that pure transparent solid ice intervened between the platina and tin; and finally these metals were connected with the opposite extremities of the voltaic apparatus, a galvanometer being at the same time included in the circuit.

384. In the first experiment, the platina pole was three inches and a half long, and seven-eighths of an inch wide; it was wholly immersed

in the water or ice, and as the vessel was four-eighths of an inch in width, the average thickness of the intervening ice was only a quarter of an inch, whilst the surface of contact with it at both poles was nearly fourteen square inches. After the water was frozen, the vessel was still retained in the frigorific mixture, whilst contact between the tin and platina respectively was made with the extremities of a well-charged voltaic battery, consisting of twenty pair of four-inch plates, each with double coppers. Not the slightest deflection of the galvanometer needle occurred.

385. On taking the frozen arrangement out of the cold mixture, and applying warmth to the bottom of the tin case, so as to melt part of the ice, the connexion with the battery being in the mean time retained, the needle did not at first move; and it was only when the thawing process had extended so far as to liquefy part of the ice touching the platina pole, that conduction took place; but then it occurred effectually, and the galvanometer needle was permanently deflected nearly 70°.

386. In another experiment, a platina spatula, five inches in length and seven-eighths of an inch in width, had four inches fixed in the ice, and the latter was only three-sixteenths of an inch thick between one metallic surface and the other; yet this arrangement insulated as perfectly as the former.

387. Upon pouring a little water in at the top of this vessel on the ice, still the arrangement did not conduct; yet fluid water was evidently there. This result was the consequence of the cold metals having frozen the water where they touched it, and thus insulating the fluid part; and it well illustrates the non-conducting power of ice, by showing how thin a film could prevent the transmission of the battery current. Upon thawing parts of this thin film, at *both* metals, conduction occurred.

388. Upon warming the tin case and removing the piece of ice, it was found that a cork having slipped, one of the edges of the platina had been all but in contact with the inner surface of the tin vessel; yet, notwithstanding the extreme thinness of the interfering ice in this place, no sensible portion of electricity had passed.

389. These experiments were repeated many times with the same results. At last a battery of fifteen troughs, or one hundred and fifty pairs of four-inch plates, powerfully charged, was used; yet even here no sensible quantity of electricity passed the thin barrier of ice.

390. It seemed at first as if occasional departures from these effects occurred; but they could always be traced to some interfering circumstances. The water should in every instance be well-frozen; for though it is not necessary that the ice should reach from pole to pole, since a barrier of it about one pole would be quite sufficient to prevent conduction, yet, if part remain fluid, the mere necessary exposure of the apparatus to the air or the approximation of the hands, is sufficient to produce, at the *upper surface* of the water and ice, a film of fluid, extending from the platina to the tin; and then conduction occurs. Again, if the corks used to block the platina in its place are damp or wet within, it is necessary that the cold be sufficiently well applied to freeze the water in them, or else when the surfaces of their contact with the tin become slightly warm by handling, that part will conduct, and the interior being ready to conduct also, the current will pass. The water should be pure, not only that unembarrassed results may be obtained, but also that, as the freezing proceeds, a minute portion of concentrated saline solution may not be formed, which remaining fluid, and being interposed in the ice, or passing into cracks resulting from contraction, may exhibit conducting powers independent of the ice itself.

391. On one occasion I was surprised to find that after thawing much of the ice the conducting power had not been restored; but I found that a cork which held the wire just where it joined the platina, dipped so far into the ice, that with the ice itself it protected the platina from contact with the melted part long after that contact was expected.

392. This insulating power of ice is not effective with electricity of exalted intensity. On touching a diverged gold-leaf electrometer with a wire connected with the platina, whilst the tin case was touched by the hand or another wire, the electrometer was instantly discharged (419).

393. But though electricity of an intensity so low that it cannot diverge the electrometer, can still pass (though in very limited quantities [419]) through ice; the comparative relation of water and ice to the electricity of the voltaic apparatus is not less extraordinary on that account, or less important in its consequences.

394. As it did not seem likely that this *law of the assumption of conducting power during liquefaction, and loss of it during congelation,* would be peculiar to water, I immediately pro-

ceeded to ascertain its influence in other cases, and found it to be very general. For this purpose bodies were chosen which were solid at common temperatures, but readily fusible; and of such composition as, for other reasons connected with electro-chemical action, led to the conclusion that they would be able when fused to replace water as conductors. A voltaic battery of two troughs, or twenty pairs of four-inch plates (384), was used as the source of electricity, and a galvanometer introduced into the circuit to indicate the presence or absence of a current.

395. On fusing a little chloride of lead by a spirit lamp on a fragment of a Florence flask, and introducing two platina wires connected with the poles of the battery, there was instantly powerful action, the galvanometer was most violently affected, and the chloride rapidly decomposed. On removing the lamp, the instant the chloride solidified all current and consequent effects ceased, though the platina wires remained inclosed in the chloride not more than the one-sixteenth of an inch from each other. On renewing the heat, as soon as the fusion had proceeded far enough to allow liquid matter to connect the poles, the electrical current instantly passed.

396. On fusing the chloride, with one wire introduced, and then touching the liquid with the other, the latter being cold, caused a little knob to concrete on its extremity, and no current passed; it was only when the wire became so hot as to be able to admit or allow of contact with the liquid matter, that conduction took place, and then it was very powerful.

397. When chloride of silver and chlorate of potassa were experimented with, in a similar manner, exactly the same results occurred.

398. Whenever the current passed in these cases, there was decomposition of the substances; but the electro-chemical part of this subject I purpose connecting with more general views in a future paper.[1]

399. Other substances, which could not be melted on glass, were fused by the lamp and blowpipe on platina connected with one pole of the battery, and then a wire, connected with

[1] In 1801, Sir H. Davy knew that "dry nitre, caustic potash, and soda are conductors of galvanism when rendered fluid by a high degree of heat," (*Journals of the Royal Institution*, 1802, p. 53), but was not aware of the general law which I have been engaged in developing. It is remarkable, that eleven years after that, he should say, "There are no fluids known except such as contain water, which are capable of being made the medium of connexion between the metal or metals of the voltaic apparatus." *Elements of Chemical Philosophy*, p. 169.

the other, dipped into them. In this way chloride of sodium, sulphate of soda, protoxide of lead, mixed carbonates of potash and soda, &c., &c., exhibited exactly the same phenomena as those already described: whilst liquid, they conducted and were decomposed; whilst solid, though very hot, they insulated the battery current even when four troughs were used.

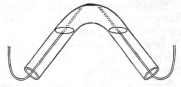

400. Occasionally the substances were contained in small bent tubes of green glass, and when fused, the platina poles introduced, one on each side. In such cases the same general results as those already described were procured; but a further advantage was obtained, namely, that whilst the substance was conducting and suffering decomposition, the final arrangement of the elements could be observed. Thus, iodides of potassium and lead gave iodine at the positive pole, and potassium or lead at the negative pole. Chlorides of lead and silver gave chlorine at the positive, and metals at the negative pole. Nitre and chlorate of potassa gave oxygen, &c., at the positive, and alkali, or even potassium, at the negative pole.

401. A fourth arrangement was used for substances requiring very high temperatures for their fusion. A platina wire was connected with one pole of the battery; its extremity bent into a small ring, in the manner described by Berzelius for blowpipe experiments; a little of the salt, glass, or other substance, was melted on this ring by the ordinary blowpipe, or even in some cases by the oxy-hydrogen blowpipe, and when the drop, retained in its place by the ring, was thoroughly hot and fluid, a platina wire from the opposite pole of the battery was made to touch it, and the effects observed.

402. The following are various substances, taken from very different classes chemically considered, which are subject to this law. The list might, no doubt, be enormously extended; but I have not had time to do more than confirm the law by a sufficient number of instances.

First, *water*.

Amongst *oxides;* potassa, protoxide of lead, glass of antimony, protoxide of antimony, oxide of bismuth.

Chlorides of potassium, sodium, barium, strontium, calcium, magnesium, manganese, zinc, copper (proto-), lead, tin (proto-), antimony, silver.

Iodides of potassium, zinc and lead, protiodide of tin, periodide of mercury; *fluoride* of potassium; *cyanide* of potassium; *sulpho-cyanide* of potassium.

Salts. Chlorate of potassa; nitrates of potassa, soda, baryta, strontia, lead, copper, and silver; sulphates of soda and lead, proto-sulphate of mercury; phosphates of potassa, soda, lead, copper, phosphoric glass or acid phosphate of lime; carbonates of potassa and soda, mingled and separate; borax, borate of lead, perborate of tin; chromate of potassa, bichromate of potassa, chromate of lead; acetate of potassa.

Sulphurets.[1] Sulphuret of antimony, sulphuret of potassium made by reducing sulphate of potassa by hydrogen; ordinary sulphuret of potassa.

Silicated potassa; chameleon mineral.

403. It is highly interesting in the instances of those substances which soften before they liquefy, to observe at what period the conducting power is acquired, and to what degree it is exalted by perfect fluidity. Thus, with the borate of lead, when heated by the lamp upon glass, it becomes as soft as treacle, but it did not conduct, and it was only when urged by the blowpipe and brought to a fair red heat, that it conducted. When rendered quite liquid, it conducted with extreme facility.

404. I do not mean to deny that part of the increased conducting power in these cases of softening was probably due to the elevation of temperature (432, 455); but I have no doubt that by far the greater part was due to the influence of the general law already demonstrated, and which in these instances came gradually, instead of suddenly, into operation.

405. The following are bodies which acquired no conducting power upon assuming the liquid state:

Sulphur, phosphorus; iodide of sulphur, periodide of tin; orpiment, realgar; glacial acetic acid, mixed margaric and oleic acids, artificial camphor; caffeine, sugar, adipocere, stearine of cocoanut oil, spermaceti, camphor, naphthaline, resin, gum sandarac, shall lac.

406. Perchloride of tin, chloride of arsenic, and the hydrated chloride of arsenic, being liquids, had no sensible conducting power indicated by the galvanometer, nor were they decomposed.

407. Some of the above substances are sufficiently remarkable as exceptions to the general law governing the former cases. These are orpiment, realgar, acetic acid, artificial camphor, periodide of tin, and the chlorides of tin and arsenic. I shall have occasion to refer to these cases in the paper on Electro-chemical Decomposition.

408. Boracic acid was raised to the highest possible temperature by an oxy-hydrogen flame (401), yet it gained no conducting powers sufficient to affect the galvanometer, and underwent no apparent voltaic decomposition. It seemed to be quite as bad a conductor as air. Green bottle-glass, heated in the same manner, did not gain conducting power sensible to the galvanometer. Flint glass, when highly heated, did conduct a little and decompose; and as the proportion of potash or oxide of lead was increased in the glass, the effects were more powerful. Those glasses, consisting of boracic acid on the one hand, and oxide of lead or potassa on the other, show the assumption of conducting power upon fusion and the accompanying decomposition very well.

409. I was very anxious to try the general experiment with sulphuric acid, of about specific gravity 1.783, containing that proportion of water which gives it the power of crystallizing at 40° Fahr.; but I found it impossible to obtain it so that I could be sure the whole would congeal even at 0° Fahr. A ten-thousandth part of water, more or less than necessary, would, upon cooling the whole, cause a portion of uncongealable liquid to separate, and that remaining in the interstices of the solid mass, and moistening the planes of division, would prevent the correct observation of the phenomena due to entire solidification and subsequent liquefaction.

410. With regard to the substances on which conducting power is thus conferred by liquidity, the degree of power so given is generally very great. Water is that body in which this acquired power is feeblest. In the various oxides, chlorides, salts, &c., &c., it is given in a much higher degree. I have not had time to measure the conducting power in these cases, but it is apparently some hundred times that of pure water. The increased conducting power known to be given to water by the addition of salts, would seem to be in a great degree dependent upon the high conducting power of these bodies when in the liquid state, that state being given them for the time, not by heat but solution in the water.[2]

---

[1] *Sulphuret:* a sulphide. The *-uret* ending was formerly used for all binary compounds.—ED.

[2] See a doubt on this point at 1356.—Dec. 1838.

411. Whether the conducting power of these liquefied bodies is a consequence of their decomposition or not (413), or whether the two actions of conduction and decomposition are essentially connected or not, would introduce no difference affecting the probable accuracy of the preceding statement.

412. This *general assumption of conducting power* by bodies as soon as they pass from the solid to the liquid state, offers a new and extraordinary character, the existence of which, as far as I know, has not before been suspected; and it seems importantly connected with some properties and relations of the particles of matter which I may now briefly point out.

413. In almost all the instances, as yet observed, which are governed by this law, the substances experimented with have been those which were not only compound bodies, but such as contain elements known to arrange themselves at the opposite poles; and were also such as could be *decomposed* by the electrical current. When conduction took place, decomposition occurred; when decomposition ceased, conduction ceased also; and it becomes a fair and an important question: Whether the conduction itself may not, wherever the law holds good, be a consequence not merely of the capability, but of the act of decomposition? And that question may be accompanied by another, namely: Whether solidification does not prevent conduction, merely by chaining the particles to their places, under the influence of aggregation, and preventing their final separation in the manner necessary for decomposition?

414. But, on the other hand, there is one substance (and others may occur), the *periodide of mercury*, which, being experimented with like the others (400), was found to insulate when solid, and to acquire conducting power when fluid; yet it did not seem to undergo decomposition in the latter case.

415. Again, there are many substances which contain elements such as would be expected to arrange themselves at the opposite poles of the pile, and therefore in that respect fitted for decomposition, which yet do not conduct. Amongst these are the iodide of sulphur, periodide of zinc, perchloride of tin, chloride of arsenic, hydrated chloride of arsenic, acetic acid, orpiment, realgar, artificial camphor, &c.; and from these it might perhaps be assumed that decomposition is dependent upon conducting power, and not the latter upon the former. The true relation, however, of conduction and decomposition in those bodies governed by the general

law which it is the object of this paper to establish, can only be satisfactorily made out from a far more extensive series of observations than those I have yet been able to supply.[1]

416. The relation, under this *law*, of the conducting power for electricity to that for heat, is very remarkable, and seems to imply a natural dependence of the two. As the solid becomes a fluid, it loses almost entirely the power of conduction for heat, but gains in a high degree that for electricity; but as it reverts back to the solid state, it gains the power of conducting heat, and loses that of conducting electricity. If, therefore, the properties are not incompatible, still they are most strongly contrasted, one being lost as the other is gained. We may hope, perhaps, hereafter to understand the physical reason of this very extraordinary relation of the two conducting powers, both of which appear to be directly connected with the corpuscular condition of the substances concerned.

417. The assumption of conducting power and a decomposable condition by liquefaction, promises new opportunities of, and great facilities in, voltaic decomposition. Thus, such bodies as the oxides, chlorides, cyanides, sulphocyanides, fluorides, certain vitreous mixtures, &c., &c., may be submitted to the action of the voltaic battery under new circumstances; and indeed I have already been able, with ten pairs of plates, to decompose common salt, chloride of magnesium, borax, &c., &c., and to obtain sodium, magnesium, boron, &c., in their separate states.

§ 10. *On Conducting Power Generally*[2]

418. It is not my intention here to enter into an examination of all the circumstances connected with conducting power, but to record certain facts and observations which have arisen during recent inquiries, as additions to the general stock of knowledge relating to this point of electrical science.

419. I was anxious, in the first place, to obtain some idea of the conducting power of ice and solid salts for electricity of high tension (392), that a comparison might be made between it and the large accession of the same power gained upon liquefaction. For this purpose the large electrical machine (290) was brought into excellent action, its conductor

---

[1] See 679, &c., &c.—*Dec.* 1838.
[2] In reference to this § refer to 983 in series **VIII**, and the results connected with it.—*Dec.* 1838.

connected with a delicate gold-leaf electrometer, and also with the platina inclosed in the
ice (383), whilst the tin case was connected
with the discharging train (292). On working
the machine moderately, the gold leaves barely
separated; on working it rapidly, they could be
opened nearly two inches. In this instance the
tin case was five-eighths of an inch in width;
and as, after the experiment, the platina plate
was found very nearly in the middle of the ice,
the average thickness of the latter had been
five-sixteenths of an inch, and the extent of
surface of contact with tin and platina fourteen square inches (384). Yet, under these circumstances, it was but just able to conduct the
small quantity of electricity which this machine could evolve (371), even when of a tension competent to open the leaves two inches;
no wonder, therefore, that it could not conduct
any sensible portion of the electricity of the
troughs (384), which, though almost infinitely
surpassing that of the machine in quantity,
had a tension so low as not to be sensible to an
electrometer.

420. In another experiment, the tin case was
only four-eighths of an inch in width, and it
was found afterwards that the platina had been
not quite one-eighth of an inch distant in the
ice from one side of the tin vessel. When this
was introduced into the course of the electricity from the machine (419), the gold leaves
could be opened, but not more than half an
inch; the thinness of the ice favouring the conduction of the electricity, and permitting the
same quantity to pass in the same time, though
of a much lower tension.

421. Iodide of potassium which had been fused
and cooled was introduced into the course of
the electricity from the machine. There were
two pieces, each about a quarter of an inch in
thickness, and exposing a surface on each side
equal to about half a square inch; these were
placed upon platina plates, one connected with
the machine and electrometer (419), and the
other with the discharging train, whilst a fine
platina wire connected the two pieces, resting
upon them by its two points. On working the
electrical machine, it was possible to open the
electrometer leaves about two-thirds of an inch.

422. As the platina wire touched only by
points, the facts show that this salt is a far better conductor than ice; but as the leaves of the
electrometer opened, it is also evident with
what difficulty conduction, even of the small
portion of electricity produced by the machine,
is effected by this body in the solid state, when

compared to the facility with which enormous
quantities at very low tensions are transmitted
by it when in the fluid state.

432. In order to confirm these results by
others, obtained from the voltaic apparatus, a
battery of one hundred and fifty plates, four
inches square, was well-charged: its action was
good; the shock from it strong; the discharge
would *continue* from copper to copper through
four-tenths of an inch of air, and the gold-leaf
electrometer before used could be opened nearly a quarter of an inch.

424. The ice vessel employed (420) was half
an inch in width; as the extent of contact of the
ice with the tin and platina was nearly fourteen square inches, the whole was equivalent
to a plate of ice having a surface of seven square
inches, of perfect contact at each side, and only
one-fourth of an inch thick. It was retained in
a freezing mixture during the experiment.

425. The order of arrangement in the course
of the electric current was as follows. The positive pole of the battery was connected by a
wire with the platina plate in the ice; the plate
was in contact with the ice, the ice with the tin
jacket, the jacket with a wire, which communicated with a piece of tin foil, on which rested
one end of a bent platina wire (312), the other
or decomposing end being supported on paper
moistened with solution of iodide of potassium
(316): the paper was laid flat on a platina spatula connected with the negative end of the battery. All that part of the arrangement between
the ice vessel and the decomposing wire point,
including both these, was insulated, so that no
electricity might pass through the latter which
had not traversed the former also.

426. Under these circumstances, it was found
that a pale brown spot of iodine was slowly
formed under the decomposing platina point,
thus indicating that ice could conduct a little
of the electricity evolved by a voltaic battery
charged up to the degree of intensity indicated
by the electrometer. But it is quite evident
that notwithstanding the enormous quantity
of electricity which the battery could furnish,
it was, under present circumstances, a very inferior instrument to the ordinary machine; for
the latter could send as much through the ice
as it could carry, being of a far higher intensity,
i.e., able to open the electrometer leaves half
an inch or more (419, 420).

427. The decomposing wire and solution of
iodide of potassium were then removed, and
replaced by a very delicate galvanometer (205);
it was so nearly astatic, that it vibrated to and

fro in about sixty-three beats of a watch giving one hundred and fifty beats in a minute. The same feebleness of current as before was still indicated; the galvanometer needle was deflected, but it required to break and make contact three or four times (297), before the effect was decided.

428. The galvanometer being removed, two platina plates were connected with the extremities of the wires, and the tongue placed between them, so that the whole charge of the battery, so far as the ice would let it pass, was free to go through the tongue. Whilst standing on the stone floor, there was shock, &c., but when insulated, I could feel no sensation. I think a frog would have been scarcely, if at all, affected.

429. The ice was now removed, and experiments made with other solid bodies, for which purpose they were placed under the end of the decomposing wire instead of the solution of iodide of potassium (425). For instance, a piece of dry iodide of potassium was placed on the spatula connected with the negative pole of the battery, and the point of the decomposing wire placed upon it, whilst the positive end of the battery communicated with the latter. A brown spot of iodine very slowly appeared, indicating the passage of a little electricity, and agreeing in that respect with the results obtained by the use of the electrical machine (421). When the galvanometer was introduced into the circuit at the same time with the iodide, it was with difficulty that the action of the current on it could be rendered sensible.

430. A piece of common salt previously fused and solidified being introduced into the circuit was sufficient almost entirely to destroy the action on the galvanometer. Fused and cooled chloride of lead produced the same effect. The conducting power of these bodies, *when fluid*, is very great (395, 402).

431. These effects, produced by using the common machine and the voltaic battery, agree therefore with each other, and with the law laid down in this paper (394); and also with the opinion I have supported, in the Third Series of these *Researches*, of the identity of electricity derived from different sources (360).

432. The effect of heat in increasing the conducting power of many substances, especially for electricity of high tension, is well known. I have lately met with an extraordinary case of this kind, for electricity of low tension, or that of the voltaic pile, and which is in direct contrast with the influence of heat upon me-

tallic bodies, as observed and described by Sir Humphry Davy.[1]

433. The substance presenting this effect is sulphuret of silver. It was made by fusing a mixture of precipitated silver and sublimed sulphur, removing the film of silver by a file from the exterior of the fused mass, pulverizing the sulphuret, mingling it with more sulphur, and fusing it again in a green glass tube, so that no air should obtain access during the process. The surface of the sulphuret being again removed by a file or knife, it was considered quite free from uncombined silver.

434. When a piece of this sulphuret, half an inch in thickness, was put between surfaces of platina, terminating the poles of a voltaic battery of twenty pairs of four-inch plates, a galvanometer being also included in the circuit, the needle was slightly deflected, indicating a feeble conducting power. On pressing the platina poles and sulphuret together with the fingers, the conducting power increased as the whole became warm. On applying a lamp under the sulphuret between the poles, the conducting power rose rapidly with the heat, and at last the galvanometer needle jumped into a fixed position, and the sulphuret was found conducting in the manner of a metal. On removing the lamp and allowing the heat to fall, the effects were reversed, the needle at first began to vibrate a little, then gradually left its transverse direction, and at last returned to a position very nearly that which it would take when no current was passing through the galvanometer.

435. Occasionally, when the contact of the sulphuret with the platina poles was good, the battery freshly charged, and the commencing temperature not too low, the mere current of electricity from the battery was sufficient to raise the temperature of the sulphuret; and then, without any application of extraneous heat, it went on increasing conjointly in temperature and conducting power, until the cooling influence of the air limited the effects. In such cases it was generally necessary to cool the whole purposely, to show the returning series of phenomena.

436. Occasionally, also, the effects would sink of themselves, and could not be renewed until a fresh surface of the sulphuret had been applied to the positive pole. This was in consequence of peculiar results of decomposition, to which I shall have occasion to revert in the section on Electro-chemical Decomposition, and

[1] *Philosophical Transactions*, 1821, p. 431.

was conveniently avoided by inserting the ends of two pieces of platina wire into the opposite extremities of a portion of sulphuret fused in a glass tube, and placing this arrangement between the poles of the battery.

437. The hot sulphuret of silver conducts sufficiently well to give a bright spark with charcoal, &c., &c., in the manner of a metal.

438. The native grey sulphuret of silver, and the ruby silver ore, both presented the same phenomena. The native malleable sulphuret of silver presented precisely the same appearances as the artificial sulphuret.

439. There is no other body with which I am acquainted, that, like sulphuret of silver, can compare with metals in conducting power for electricity of low tension when hot, but which, unlike them, during cooling, loses in power, whilst they, on the contrary, gain. Probably, however, many others may, when sought for, be found.[1]

440. The proto-sulphuret of iron, the native per-sulphuret of iron, arsenical sulphuret of iron, native yellow sulphuret of copper and iron, grey artificial sulphuret of copper, artificial sulphuret of bismuth, and artificial grey sulphuret of tin, all conduct the voltaic battery current when cold, more or less, some giving sparks like the metals, others not being sufficient for that high effect. They did not seem to conduct better when heated, than before; but I had not time to enter accurately into the investigation of this point. Almost all of them became much heated by the transmission of the current, and present some very interesting phenomena in that respect. The sulphuret of antimony does not conduct the same current sensibly either hot or cold, but is amongst those bodies acquiring conducting power when fused (402). The sulphuret of silver and perhaps some others decompose whilst in the solid state; but the phenomena of this decomposition will be reserved for its proper place in the next series of these *Researches*.

441. Notwithstanding the extreme dissimilarity between sulphuret of silver and gases or vapours, I cannot help suspecting the action of heat upon them to be the same, bringing them all into the same class as conductors of electricity, although with those great differences in degree, which are found to exist under common circumstances. When gases are heated, they increase in conducting power, both for common and voltaic electricity (271); and it is probable that if we could compress and con-

dense them at the same time, we should still further increase their conducting power. Cagniard de la Tour has shown that a substance, for instance water, may be so expanded by heat whilst in the liquid state, or condensed whilst in the vaporous state, that the two states shall coincide at one point, and the transition from one to the other be so gradual that no line of demarcation can be pointed out,[2] that, in fact, the two states shall become one; which one state presents us at different times with differences in degree as to certain properties and relations; and which differences are, under ordinary circumstances, so great as to be equivalent to two different states.

442. I cannot but suppose at present that at that point where the liquid and the gaseous state coincide, the conducting properties are the same for both; but that they diminish as the expansion of the matter into a rarer form takes place by the removal of the necessary pressure; still, however, retaining, as might be expected, the capability of having what feeble conducting power remains, increased by the action of heat.

443. I venture to give the following summary of the conditions of electric conduction in bodies, not however without fearing that I may have omitted some important points.[3]

444. All bodies conduct electricity in the same manner, from metals to lac and gases, but in very different degrees.

445. Conducting power is in some bodies powerfully increased by heat, and in others diminished, yet without our perceiving any accompanying essential electrical difference, either in the bodies or in the changes occasioned by the electricity conducted.

446. A numerous class of bodies, insulating electricity of low intensity when solid, conduct it very freely when fluid, and are then decomposed by it.

447. But there are many fluid bodies which do not sensibly conduct electricity of this low intensity; there are some which conduct it and are not decomposed; nor is fluidity essential to decomposition.[4]

448. There is but one body yet discovered[5] which, insulating a voltaic current when solid,

[1] See now on this subject, 1340, 1341.—*Dec.* 1838.

[2] *Annales de Chimie*, XXI. pp. 127, 178.
[3] See now in relation to this subject, 1320–1342.—*Dec.* 1838.
[4] See the next series of these *Experimental Researches*.
[5] It is just possible that this case may, by more delicate experiment, hereafter disappear. (See now, 1340, 1341, in relation to this note.—*Dec.* 1838.)

and conducting it when fluid, is not decomposed in the latter case (414).

449. There is no strict electrical distinction of conduction which can, as yet, be drawn between bodies supposed to be elementary and those known to be compounds.

Royal Institution, April 15, 1833

FIFTH SERIES

§ 11. *On Electro-chemical Decomposition* ¶ i. *New Conditions of Electro-chemical Decomposition* ¶ ii. *Influence of Water in Electro-chemical Decomposition* ¶ iii. *Theory of Electro-chemical Decomposition*

RECEIVED JUNE 18, READ JUNE 20, 1833

§ 11. *On Electro-Chemical Decomposition*[1]

450. I HAVE in a recent series of these *Researches* (265) proved (to my own satisfaction, at least), the identity of electricities derived from different sources, and have especially dwelt upon the proofs of the sameness of those obtained by the use of the common electrical machine and the voltaic battery.

451. The great distinction of the electricities obtained from these two sources is the very high tension to which the small quantity obtained by aid of the machine may be raised, and the enormous quantity (371, 376) in which that of comparatively low tension, supplied by the voltaic battery, may be procured; but as their actions, whether magnetical, chemical, or of any other nature, are essentially the same (360), it appeared evident that we might reason from the former as to the manner of action of the latter; and it was, to me, a probable consequence, that the use of electricity of such intensity as that afforded by the machine, would, when applied to effect and elucidate electro-chemical decomposition, show some new conditions of that action, evolve new views of the internal arrangements and changes of the substances under decomposition, and perhaps give efficient powers over matter as yet undecomposed.

452. For the purpose of rendering the bearings of the different parts of this series of researches more distinct, I shall divide it into several heads.

¶ i. *New Conditions of Electro-chemical Decomposition*

453. The tension of machine electricity causes it, however small in quantity, to pass through any length of water, solutions, or other substances classing with these as conductors, as

[1] Refer to the note after 1047, Series VIII.—*Dec.* 1838.

fast as it can be produced, and therefore, in relation to quantity, as fast as it could have passed through much shorter portions of the same conducting substance. With the voltaic battery the case is very different, and the passing current of electricity supplied by it suffers serious diminution in any substance, by considerable extension of its length, but especially in such bodies as those mentioned above.

454. I endeavoured to apply this facility of transmitting the current of electricity through any length of a conductor, to an investigation of the transfer of the elements in a decomposing body, in contrary directions, towards the poles. The general form of apparatus used in these experiments has been already described (312, 316); and also a particular experiment (319), in which, when a piece of litmus paper and a piece of turmeric paper were combined and moistened in solution of sulphate of soda, the point of the wire from the machine (representing the positive pole) put upon the litmus paper, and the receiving point from the discharging train (292, 316), representing the negative pole, upon the turmeric paper, a very few turns of the machine sufficed to show the evolution of acid at the former, and alkali at the latter, exactly in the manner effected by a volta-electric current.

455. The pieces of litmus and turmeric paper were *now* placed each upon a separate plate of glass, and connected by an insulated string four feet long, moistened in the same solution of sulphate of soda: the terminal decomposing wire points were placed upon the papers as before. On working the machine, the same evolution of acid and alkali appeared as in the former instance, and with equal readiness, notwithstanding that the places of their appearance were four feet apart from each other. Finally, a piece of string, seventy feet long, was

PLATE V

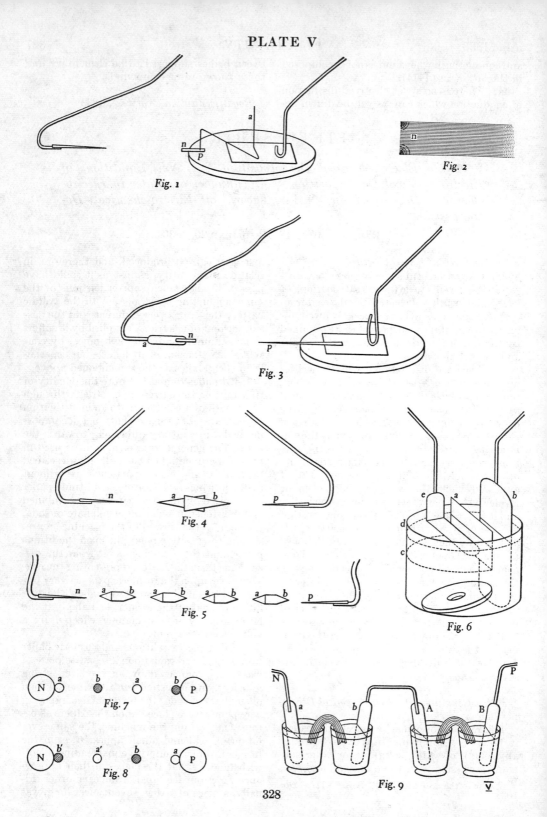

Fig. 1

Fig. 2

Fig. 3

Fig. 4

Fig. 5

Fig. 6

Fig. 7

Fig. 8

Fig. 9

used. It was insulated in the air by suspenders of silk, so that the electricity passed through its entire length: decomposition took place exactly as in former cases, alkali and acid appearing at the two extremities in their proper places.

456. Experiments were then made both with sulphate of soda and iodide of potassium, to ascertain if any diminution of decomposing effect was produced by such great extension as those just described of the moist conductor or body under decomposition; but whether the contact of the decomposing point connected with the discharging train was made with turmeric paper touching the prime conductor, or with other turmeric paper connected with it through the seventy feet of string, the spot of alkali for an equal number of turns of the machine had equal intensity of colour. The same results occurred at the other decomposing wire, whether the salt or the iodide were used: and it was fully proved that this great extension of the distance between the poles produced no effect whatever on the amount of decomposition, provided the same *quantity* of electricity were passed in both cases (377).

457. The negative point of the discharging train, the turmeric paper, and the string were then removed; the positive point was left resting upon the litmus paper, and the latter touched by a piece of moistened string held in the hand. A few turns of the machine evolved acid at the positive point as freely as before.

458. The end of the moistened string, instead of being held in the hand, was suspended by glass in the air. On working the machine the electricity proceeded from the conductor through the wire point to the litmus paper, and thence away by the intervention of the string to the air, so that there was (as in the last experiment) but one metallic pole; still acid was evolved there as freely as in any former case.

459. When any of these experiments were repeated with electricity from the negative conductor, corresponding effects were produced whether one or two decomposing wires were used. The results were always constant, considered in relation to the *direction* of the electric current.

460. These experiments were varied so as to include the action of only one metallic pole, but that not the pole connected with the machine. Turmeric paper was moistened in solution of sulphate of soda, placed upon glass, and connected with the discharging train (292) by a decomposing wire (312); a piece of wet string was hung from it, the lower extremity of

which was brought opposite a point connected with the positive prime conductor of the machine. The machine was then worked for a few turns, and alkali immediately appeared at the point of the discharging train which rested on the turmeric paper. Corresponding effects took place at the negative conductor of a machine.

461. These cases are abundantly sufficient to show that electro-chemical decomposition does not depend upon the simultaneous action of two metallic poles, since a single pole might be used, decomposition ensue, and one or other of the elements liberated pass to the pole, according as it was positive or negative. In considering the course taken by, and the final arrangement of, the other element, I had little doubt that I should find it had receded towards the other extremity, and that the air itself had acted as a pole, an expectation which was fully confirmed in the following manner.

462. A piece of turmeric paper, not more than 0.4 of an inch in length and 0.5 of an inch in width, was moistened with sulphate of soda and placed upon the edge of a glass plate opposite to, and about two inches from, a point connected with the discharging train (Pl. V, *Fig. 1*); a piece of tinfoil, resting upon the same glass plate, was connected with the machine, and also with the turmeric paper, by a decomposing wire *a* (312). The machine was then worked, the positive electricity passing into the turmeric paper at the point *p*, and out at the extremity *n*. After forty or fifty turns of the machine, the extremity *n* was examined, and the two points or angles found deeply coloured by the presence of free alkali (Pl. V, *Fig. 2*).

463. A similar piece of litmus paper, dipped in solution of sulphate of soda *n*, Pl. V, *Fig. 3*, was now supported upon the end of the discharging train *a*, and its extremity brought opposite to a point *p*, connected with the conductor of the machine. After working the machine for a short time, acid was developed at both the corners towards the point, i.e., at both the corners receiving the electricities from the air. Every precaution was taken to prevent this acid from being formed by sparks or brushes passing through the air (322); and these, with the accompanying general facts, are sufficient to show that the acid was really the result of electro-chemical decomposition (466).

464. Then a long piece of turmeric paper, large at one end and pointed at the other, was moistened in the saline solution, and immediately connected with the conductor of the machine, so that its pointed extremity was oppo-

site a point upon the discharging train. When the machine was worked, alkali was evolved at that point; and even when the discharging train was removed, and the electricity left to be diffused and carried off altogether by the air, still alkali was evolved where the electricity left the turmeric paper.

465. Arrangements were then made in which no metallic communication with the decomposing matter was allowed, but both poles (if they might now be called by that name) formed of air only. A piece of turmeric paper a, Pl. V, *Fig. 4*, and a piece of litmus paper b, were dipped in solution of sulphate of soda, put together so as to form one moist pointed conductor, and supported on wax between two needle points, one, p, connected by a wire with the conductor of the machine, and the other, n, with the discharging train. The interval in each case between the points was about half an inch; the positive point p was opposite the litmus paper; the negative point n opposite the turmeric. The machine was then worked for a time, upon which evidence of decomposition quickly appeared, for the point of the litmus b became reddened from acid evolved there, and the point of the turmeric a red from a similar and simultaneous evolution of alkali.

466. Upon turning the paper conductor round, so that the litmus point should now give off the positive electricity, and the turmeric point receive it, and working the machine for a short time, both the red spots disappeared, and as on continuing the action of the machine no red spot was re-formed at the litmus extremity, it proved that in the first instance (463) the effect was not due to the action of brushes or mere electric discharges causing the formation of nitric acid from the air (322).

467. If the combined litmus and turmeric paper in this experiment be considered as constituting a conductor independent of the machine or the discharging train, and the final places of the elements evolved be considered in relation to this conductor, then it will be found that the acid collects at the *negative* or receiving end or pole of the arrangement, and the alkali at the *positive* or delivering extremity.

468. Similar litmus and turmeric paper points were now placed upon glass plates, and connected by a string six feet long, both string and paper being moistened in solution of sulphate of soda; a needle point connected with the machine was brought opposite the litmus paper point, and another needle point connected with the discharging train brought opposite the tur-

meric paper. On working the machine, acid appeared on the litmus, and alkali on the turmeric paper; but the latter was not so abundant as in former cases, for much of the electricity passed off from the string into the air, and diminished the quantity discharged at the turmeric point.

469. Finally, a series of four small compound conductors, consisting of litmus and turmeric paper (Pl. V, *Fig. 5*) moistened in solution of sulphate of soda, were supported on glass rods, in a line at a little distance from each other, between the points p and n of the machine and discharging train, so that the electricity might pass in succession through them, entering in at the litmus points b, b, and passing out at the turmeric points a, a. On working the machine carefully, so as to avoid sparks and brushes (322), I soon obtained evidence of decomposition in each of the moist conductors, for all the litmus points exhibited free acid, and the turmeric points equally showed free alkali.

470. On using solutions of iodide of potassium, acetate of lead, &c., similar effects were obtained; but as they were all consistent with the results above described, I refrain from describing the appearances minutely.

471. These cases of electro-chemical decomposition are in their nature exactly of the same kind as those affected under ordinary circumstances by the voltaic battery, notwithstanding the great differences as to the presence or absence, or at least as to the nature of the parts usually called poles; and also of the final situation of the elements eliminated at the electrified boundary surface (467). They indicate at once an internal action of the parts suffering decomposition, and appear to show that the power which is effectual in separating the elements is exerted there and not at the poles. But I shall defer the consideration of this point for a short time (493, 518), that I may previously consider another supposed condition of electro-chemical decomposition.[1]

[1] I find (since making and describing these results,) from a note to Sir Humphry Davy's paper in the *Philosophical Transactions*, 1807, p. 31, that that philosopher, in repeating Wollaston's experiment of the decomposition of water by common electricity (327, 330) used an arrangement somewhat like some of those I have described. He immersed a guarded platina point connected with the machine in distilled water, and dissipated the electricity from the water into the air by moistened filaments of cotton. In this way he states that he obtained oxygen and hydrogen *separately* from each other. This experiment, had I known of it, ought to have been quoted in an earlier series of these *Researches* (342); but it does not remove any of the objections I have made to the use of Wollaston's apparatus as a test of true chemical action (331).

¶ ii. *Influence of Water in Electro-chemical Decomposition*

472. It is the opinion of several philosophers, that the presence of water is essential in electro-chemical decomposition, and also for the evolution of electricity in the voltaic battery itself. As the decomposing cell is merely one of the cells of the battery, into which particular substances are introduced for the purpose of experiment, it is probable that what is an essential condition in the one case is more or less so in the other. The opinion, therefore, that water is necessary to decomposition, may have been founded on the statement made by Sir Humphry Davy that "there are no fluids known, except such as contain water, which are capable of being made the medium of connexion between the metals or metal of the voltaic apparatus";[1] and again, "when any substance rendered fluid by heat, consisting of *water*, oxygen, and inflammable or metallic matter, is exposed to those wires, similar phenomena (of decomposition) occur."[2]

473. This opinion has, I think, been shown by other philosophers not to be accurate, though I do not know where to refer for a contradiction of it. Sir Humphry Davy himself said in 1801,[3] that dry nitre, caustic potash and soda are conductors of galvanism when rendered fluid by a high degree of heat; but he must have considered them, or the nitre at least, as not suffering decomposition, for the statements above were made by him eleven years subsequently. In 1826 he also pointed out, that bodies not containing water, as *fused litharge* and *chlorate of potassa*, were sufficient to form, with platina and zinc, powerful electromotive circles;[4] but he is here speaking of the *production* of electricity in the pile, and not of its effects when evolved; nor do his words at all imply that any correction of his former distinct statements relative to *decomposition* was required.

474. I may refer to the last series of these *Experimental Researches* (380, 402) as setting the matter at rest, by proving that there are hundreds of bodies equally influential with water in this respect: that amongst binary compounds, oxides, chlorides, iodides, and even sulphurets (402) were effective; and that amongst more complicated compounds, cyanides and salts, of equal efficacy, occurred in great numbers (402).

475. Water, therefore, is in this respect merely one of a very numerous class of substances, instead of being the *only one* and *essential;* and it is of that class one of the *worst* as to its capability of facilitating conduction and suffering decomposition. The reasons why it obtained for a time an exclusive character which it so little deserved are evident, and consist in the general necessity of a fluid condition (394); in its being the *only one* of this class of bodies existing in the fluid state at common temperatures; its abundant supply as the great natural solvent; and its constant use in that character in philosophical investigations, because of its having a smaller interfering, injurious, or complicating action upon the bodies, either dissolved or evolved, than any other substance.

476. The analogy of the decomposing or experimental cell to the other cells of the voltaic battery renders it nearly certain that any of those substances which are decomposable when fluid, as described in my last paper (402), would, if they could be introduced between the metallic plates of the pile, be equally effectual with water, if not more so. Sir Humphry Davy found that litharge and chlorate of potassa were thus effectual.[5] I have constructed various voltaic arrangements, and found the above conclusion to hold good. When any of the following substances in a fused state were interposed between copper and platina, voltaic action more or less powerful was produced. Nitre; chlorate of potassa; carbonate of potassa; sulphate of soda; chloride of lead, of sodium, of bismuth, of calcium, iodide of lead, oxide of bismuth: oxide of lead: the electric current was in the same direction as if acids had acted upon the metals. When any of the same substances, or phosphate of soda, were made to act on platina and iron, still more powerful voltaic combinations of the same kind were produced. When either nitrate of silver or chloride of silver was the fluid substance interposed, there was voltaic action, but the electric current was in the reverse direction.

¶ iii. *Theory of Electro-chemical Decomposition*

477. The extreme beauty and value of electro-chemical decompositions have given to that power which the voltaic pile possesses of causing their occurrence an interest surpassing that of any other of its properties; for the power is not only intimately connected with the continuance, if not with the production, of the electrical phenomena, but it has furnished us

---

[1] *Elements of Chemical Philosophy*, p. 169, &c.
[2] *Ibid.*, pp. 144, 145.
[3] *Journal of the Royal Institution*, 1802, p. 53.
[4] *Philosophical Transactions*, 1826, p. 406.
[5] *Philosophical Transactions*, 1826, p. 406.

with the most beautiful demonstrations of the nature of many compound bodies: has in the hands of Becquerel been employed in compounding substances: has given us several new combinations, and sustains us with the hope that when thoroughly understood it will produce many more.

478. What may be considered as the general facts of electro-chemical decomposition are agreed to by nearly all who have written on the subject. They consist in the separation of the decomposable substance acted upon into its proximate or sometimes ultimate principles, whenever both poles of the pile are in contact with that substance in a proper condition: in the evolution of these principles at distant points, i.e., at the poles of the pile, where they are either finally set free or enter into union with the substance of the poles; and in the constant determination of the evolved elements or principles to particular poles according to certain well-ascertained laws.

479. But the views of men of science vary much as to the nature of the action by which these effects are produced; and as it is certain that we shall be better able to apply the power when we really understand the manner in which it operates, this difference of opinion is a strong inducement to further inquiry. I have been led to hope that the following investigations might be considered, not as an increase of that which is doubtful, but a real addition to this branch of knowledge.

480. It will be needful that I briefly state the views of electro-chemical decomposition already put forth, that their present contradictory and unsatisfactory state may be seen before I give that which seems to me more accurately to agree with facts; and I have ventured to discuss them freely, trusting that I should give no offence to their high-minded authors; for I felt convinced that if I were right, they would be pleased that their views should serve as stepping-stones for the advance of science; and that if I were wrong, they would excuse the zeal which misled me, since it was exerted for the service of that great cause whose prosperity and progress they have desired.

481. Grotthuss, in the year 1805, wrote expressly on the decomposition of liquids by voltaic electricity.[1] He considers the pile as an electric magnet, i.e., as an attractive and repulsive agent; the poles having *attractive* and *repelling* powers. The pole from whence resinous electricity issues attracts hydrogen and repels

oxygen, whilst that from which vitreous electricity proceeds attracts oxygen and repels hydrogen; so that each of the elements of a particle of water, for instance, is subject to an attractive and a repulsive force, acting in contrary directions, the centres of action of which are reciprocally opposed. The action of each force in relation to a molecule of water situated in the course of the electric current is in the inverse ratio of the square of the distance at which it is exerted, thus giving (it is stated) for such a molecule a *constant force*.[2] He explains the appearance of the elements at a distance from each other by referring to a succession of decompositions and recompositions occurring amongst the intervening particles,[3] and he thinks it probable that those which are about to separate at the poles unite to the two electricities there, and in consequence become gases.[4]

482. Sir Humphry Davy's celebrated Bakerian Lecture on some chemical agencies of electricity was read in November 1806, and is almost entirely occupied in the consideration of *electro-chemical decompositions*. The facts are of the utmost value, and, with the general points established, are universally known. The *mode of action* by which the effects take place is stated very generally, so generally, indeed, that probably a dozen precise schemes of electro-chemical action might be drawn up, differing essentially from each other, yet all agreeing with the statement there given.

483. When Sir Humphry Davy uses more particular expressions, he seems to refer the decomposing effects to the attractions of the poles. This is the case in the "general expression of facts" given at pp. 28 and 29 of the *Philosophical Transactions* for 1807, also at p. 30. Again at p. 160 of the *Elements of Chemical Philosophy*, he speaks of the great attracting powers of the surfaces of the poles. He mentions the probability of a succession of decompositions and recompositions throughout the fluid, agreeing in that respect with Grotthuss;[5] and supposes that the attractive and repellent agencies may be communicated from the metallic surfaces throughout the whole of the menstruum,[6] being communicated from *one particle to another particle of the same kind*,[7] and diminishing in strength from the place of the poles to the middle point, which is necessarily

---

[1] *Annales de Chimie*, 1806, Vol. LVIII. p. 64.

[2] *Ibid.*, pp. 66, 67; also Vol. LXIII. p. 20.
[3] *Ibid.*, Vol. LVIII. p. 68; Vol. LXIII. p. 20.
[4] *Ibid.*, Vol. LXIII. p. 34.
[5] *Philosophical Transactions*, 1807, pp. 29, 30.
[6] *Ibid.*, p. 39.   [7] *Ibid.*, p. 29.

neutral.[1] In reference to this diminution of power at increased distances from the poles, he states that in a circuit of ten inches of water, solution of sulphate of potassa placed four inches from the positive pole, did not decompose; whereas when only two inches from that pole, it did render up its elements.[2]

484. When in 1826 Sir Humphry Davy wrote again on this subject, he stated that he found nothing to alter in the fundamental theory laid down in the original communication,[3] and uses the terms *attraction* and *repulsion* apparently in the same sense as before.[4]

485. Messrs. Riffault and Chompré experimented on this subject in 1807. They came to the conclusion that the voltaic current caused decompositions throughout its whole course in the humid conductor, not merely as preliminary to the recompositions spoken of by Grotthuss and Davy, but producing final separation of the elements in the *course* of the current, and elsewhere than at the poles. They considered the *negative* current as collecting and carrying the acids, &c., to the *positive* pole, and the *positive* current as doing the same duty with the bases, and collecting them at the *negative* pole. They likewise consider the currents as *more powerful* the nearer they are to their respective poles, and state that the positive current is *superior* in power to the negative current.[5]

486. M. Biot is very cautious in expressing an opinion as to the cause of the separation of the elements of a compound body.[6] But as far as the effects can be understood, he refers them to the opposite electrical states of the portions of the decomposing substance in the neighbourhood of the two poles. The fluid is most positive at the positive pole; that state gradually diminishes to the middle distance, where the fluid is neutral or not electrical; but from thence to the negative pole it becomes more and more negative. When a particle of salt is decomposed at the negative pole, the acid particle is considered as acquiring a negative electrical state from the pole, stronger than that of the surrounding *undecomposed* particles, and is therefore repelled from amongst them, and from out of that portion of the liquid towards the positive pole, towards which also it is drawn by the attraction of the pole itself and the particles of positive *undecomposed* fluid around it.[8]

487. M. Biot does not appear to admit the successive decompositions and recompositions spoken of by Grotthuss, Davy, &c., &c.; but seems to consider the substance whilst in transit as combined with, or rather attached to, the electricity for the time,[9] and though it communicates this electricity to the surrounding undecomposed matter with which it is in contact, yet it retains during the transit a little superiority with respect to that kind which it first received from the pole, and is, by virtue of that difference, carried forward through the fluid to the opposite pole.[10]

488. This theory implies that decomposition takes place at both poles upon distinct portions of fluid, and not at all in the intervening parts. The latter serve merely as imperfect conductors, which, assuming an electric state, urge particles electrified more highly at the poles through them in opposite directions, by virtue of a series of ordinary electrical attractions and repulsions.[11]

489. M. A. de la Rive investigated this subject particularly, and published a paper on it in 1825.[12] He thinks those who have referred the phenomena to the attractive powers of the poles, rather express the general fact than give any explication of it. He considers the results as due to an actual combination of the elements, or rather of half of them, with the electricities passing from the poles in consequence of a kind of play of affinities between the matter and electricity.[13] The current from the positive pole combining with the hydrogen, or the bases it finds there, leaves the oxygen and acids at liberty, but carries the substances it is united with across to the negative pole, where, because of the peculiar character of the metal as a conductor,[14] it is separated from them, entering the metal and leaving the hydrogen or bases upon its surface. In the same manner the electricity from the negative pole sets the hydrogen and bases which it finds there, free, but combines with the oxygen and acids, carries them across to the positive pole, and there deposits them.[15] In this respect M. de la Rive's hypothesis accords in part with that of MM. Riffault and Chompré (485).

490. M. de la Rive considers the portions of matter which are decomposed to be those contiguous to *both* poles.[16] He does not admit with

[1] *Ibid.*, p. 42.   [3] *Ibid.*, 1826, p. 383.
[2] *Ibid.*, p. 42.   [4] *Ibid.*, pp. 389, 407, 415.
[5] *Annales de Chimie*, 1807, Vol. LXIII, p. 83, &c.
[6] *Précis Elémentaire de Physique*, 3me édition, 1824, Vol. I., p. 641.
[7] *Ibid.*, p. 637.   [8] *Ibid.*, pp. 641, 642.

[9] *Ibid.*, p. 636.   [10] *Ibid.*, p. 642.
[11] *Ibid.*, pp. 638, 642.
[12] *Annales de Chimie*, Vol. XXVIII, p. 190.
[13] *Annales de Chimie*, Vol. XXVIII, pp. 200, 202
[14] *Ibid.*, p. 202.   [15] *Ibid.*, p. 201.
[16] *Ibid.*, pp. 197, 198.

others the successive decompositions and re-compositions in the whole course of the electricity through the humid conductor,[1] but thinks the middle parts are in themselves unaltered, or at least serve only to conduct the two contrary currents of electricity and matter which set off from the opposite poles.[2] The decomposition, therefore, of a particle of water, or a particle of salt, may take place at either pole, and when once effected, it is final for the time, no recombination taking place, except the momentary union of the transferred particle with the electricity be so considered.

491. The latest communication that I am aware of on the subject is by M. Hachette: its date is October 1832.[3] It is incidental to the description of the decomposition of water by the magneto-electric currents (346). One of the results of the experiment is, that "it is not necessary, as has been supposed, that for the chemical decomposition of water, the action of the two electricities, positive and negative, should be simultaneous."

492. It is more than probable that many other views of electro-chemical decomposition may have been published, and perhaps amongst them some which, differing from those above, might, even in my own opinion, were I acquainted with them, obviate the necessity for the publication of my views. If such be the case, I have to regret my ignorance of them, and apologize to the authors.

493. That electro-chemical decomposition does not depend upon any direct attraction and repulsion of the poles (meaning thereby the metallic terminations either of the voltaic battery, or ordinary electrical machine arrangements [312]), upon the elements in contact with or near to them, appeared very evident from the experiments made in air (462, 465, &c.), when the substances evolved did not collect about any poles, but, in obedience to the direction of the current, were evolved, and I would say ejected, at the extremities of the decomposing substance. But notwithstanding the extreme dissimilarity in the character of air and metals, and the almost total difference existing between them as to their mode of conducting electricity, and becoming charged with it, it might perhaps still be contended, although quite hypothetically, that the bounding portions of air were now the surfaces or places of attraction, as the metals had been supposed to be before. In illustration of this and other points, I endeavoured to devise an arrangement by which I could decompose a body against a surface of water, as well as against air or metal, and succeeded in doing so unexceptionably in the following manner. As the experiment for very natural reasons requires many precautions, to be successful, and will be referred to hereafter in illustration of the views I shall venture to give, I must describe it minutely.

494. A glass basin (Pl. V, *Fig.* 6), four inches in diameter and four inches deep, had a division of mica *a*, fixed across the upper part so as to descend one inch and a half below the edge, and be perfectly water-tight at the sides: a plate of platina *b*, three inches wide, was put into the basin on one side of the division *a*, and retained there by a glass block below, so that any gas produced by it in a future stage of the experiment should not ascend beyond the mica, and cause currents in the liquid on that side. A strong solution of sulphate of magnesia was carefully poured without splashing into the basin, until it rose a little above the lower edge of the mica division *a*, great care being taken that the glass or mica on the unoccupied or *c* side of the division in the figure, should not be moistened by agitation of the solution above the level to which it rose. A thin piece of clean cork, well-wetted in distilled water, was then carefully and lightly placed on the solution at the *c* side, and distilled water poured gently on to it until a stratum the eighth of an inch in thickness appeared over the sulphate of magnesia; all was then left for a few minutes, that any solution adhering to the cork might sink away from it, or be removed by the water on which it now floated; and then more distilled water was added in a similar manner, until it reached nearly to the top of the glass. In this way solution of the sulphate occupied the lower part of the glass, and also the upper on the right-hand side of the mica; but on the left-hand side of the division a stratum of water from *c* to *d*, one inch and a half in depth, reposed upon it, the two presenting, when looked through horizontally, a comparatively definite plane of contact. A second platina pole *e*, was arranged so as to be just under the surface of the water, in a position nearly horizontal, a little inclination being given to it, that gas evolved during decomposition might escape: the part immersed was three inches and a half long by one inch wide, and about seven-eighths of an inch of water intervened between it and the solution of sulphate of magnesia.

[1] *Ibid.*, pp. 192, 199.
[2] *Ibid.*, p. 200.
[3] *Ibid.*, Vol. LI, p. 73.

495. The latter pole *e* was now connected with the negative end of a voltaic battery, of forty pairs of plates four inches square, whilst the former pole *b* was connected with the positive end. There was action and gas evolved at both poles; but from the intervention of the pure water, the decomposition was very feeble compared to what the battery would have effected in a uniform solution. After a little while (less than a minute), magnesia also appeared at the negative side: *it did not make its appearance at the negative metallic pole, but in the water*, at the plane where the solution and the water met; and on looking at it horizontally, it could be there perceived lying in the water upon the solution, not rising more than the fourth of an inch above the latter, whilst the water between it and the negative pole was perfectly clear. On continuing the action, the bubbles of hydrogen rising upwards from the negative pole impressed a circulatory movement on the stratum of water, upwards in the middle, and downwards at the side, which gradually gave an ascending form to the cloud of magnesia in the part just under the pole, having an appearance as if it were there attracted to it: but this was altogether an effect of the currents, and did not occur until long after the phenomena looked for were satisfactorily ascertained.

496. After a little while the voltaic communication was broken, and the platina poles removed with as little agitation as possible from the water and solution, for the purpose of examining the liquid adhering to them. The pole *e*, when touched by turmeric paper, gave no traces of alkali, nor could anything but pure water be found upon it. The pole *b*, though drawn through a much greater depth and quantity of fluid, was found so acid as to give abundant evidence to litmus paper, the tongue, and other tests. Hence there had been no interference of alkaline salts in any way, undergoing first decomposition, and then causing the separation of the magnesia at a distance from the pole by mere chemical agencies. This experiment was repeated again and again, and always successfully.

497. As, therefore, the substances evolved in cases of electro-chemical decomposition may be made to appear against air (465, 469)—which, according to common language, is not a conductor, nor is decomposed, or against water (495), which is a conductor, and can be decomposed—as well as against the metal poles, which are excellent conductors, but undecomposable, there appears but little reason to con-

sider the phenomena generally, as due to the *attraction* or attractive powers of the latter, when used in the ordinary way, since similar attractions can hardly be imagined in the former instances.

498. It may be said that the surfaces of air or of water in these cases become the poles, and exert attractive powers; but what proof is there of that, except the fact that the matters evolved collect there, which is the point to be explained, and cannot be justly quoted as its own explanation? Or it may be said that any section of the humid conductor, as that in the present case, where the solution and the water meet, may be considered as representing the pole. But such does not appear to me to be the view of those who have written on the subject, certainly not of some of them, and is inconsistent with the supposed laws which they have assumed, as governing the diminution of power at increased distances from the poles.

499. Grotthuss, for instance, describes the poles as centres of attractive and repulsive forces (481), these forces varying inversely as the squares of the distances, and says, therefore, that a particle placed anywhere between the poles will be acted upon by a constant force. But the compound force, resulting from such a combination as he supposes, would be anything but a constant force; it would evidently be a force greatest at the poles, and diminishing to the middle distance. Grotthuss is right, however, *in the fact*, according to my experiments (502, 505), that the particles are acted upon by equal force everywhere in the circuit, when the conditions of the experiment are the simplest possible; but the fact is against his theory, and is also, I think, against all theories that place the decomposing effect in the attractive power of the poles.

500. Sir Humphry Davy, who also speaks of the *diminution* of power with increase of distance from the poles[1] (483), supposes, that when both poles are acting on substances to decompose them, still the power of decomposition *diminishes* to the middle distance. In this statement of fact he is opposed to Grotthuss, and quotes an experiment in which sulphate of potassa, placed at different distances from the poles in a humid conductor of constant length, decomposed when near the pole, but not when at a distance. Such a consequence would necessarily result theoretically from considering the poles as centres of attraction and repulsion; but I have not found the statement borne out

[1] *Philosophical Transactions*, 1807, p. 42.

by other experiments (505); and in the one quoted by him the effect was doubtless due to some of the many interfering causes of variation which attend such investigations.

501. A glass vessel had a platina plate fixed perpendicularly across it, so as to divide it into two cells: a head of mica was fixed over it, so as to collect the gas it might evolve during experiments; then each cell, and the space beneath the mica, was filled with dilute sulphuric acid. Two poles were provided, consisting each of a platina wire terminated by a plate of the same metal; each was fixed into a tube passing through its upper end by an air-tight joint, that it might be moveable, and yet that the gas evolved at it might be collected. The tubes were filled with the acid, and one immersed in each cell. Each platina pole was equal in surface to one side of the dividing plate in the middle glass vessel, and the whole might be considered as an arrangement between the poles of the battery of a humid decomposable conductor divided in the middle by the interposed platina diaphragm. It was easy, when required, to draw one of the poles further up the tube, and then the platina diaphragm was no longer in the middle of the humid conductor. But whether it were thus arranged at the middle, or towards one side, it always evolved a quantity of oxygen and hydrogen equal to that evolved by both the extreme plates.[1]

502. If the wires of a galvanometer be terminated by plates, and these be immersed in dilute acid, contained in a regularly formed rectangular glass trough, connected at each end with a voltaic battery by poles equal to the section of the fluid, a part of the electricity will pass through the instrument and cause a certain deflection. And if the plates are always retained at the *same distance from each other* and from the sides of the trough, are always parallel to each other, and uniformly placed relative to the fluid, then, whether they are immersed near the middle of the decomposing solution, or at one end, still the instrument will indicate the same deflection, and consequently the same electric influence.

503. It is very evident, that when the width of the decomposing conductor varies, as is always the case when mere wires or plates, as poles, are dipped into or are surrounded by solution, no constant expression can be given as

to the action upon a single particle placed in the course of the current, nor any conclusion of use, relative to the supposed attractive or repulsive force of the poles, be drawn. The force will vary as the distance from the pole varies; as the particle is directly between the poles, or more or less on one side; and even as it is nearer to or farther from the sides of the containing vessels, or as the shape of the vessel itself varies; and, in fact, by making variations in the form of the arrangement, the force upon any single particle may be made to increase, or diminish, or remain constant, whilst the distance between the particle and the pole shall remain the same; or the force may be made to increase, or diminish, or remain constant, either as the distance increases or as it diminishes.

504. From numerous experiments, I am led to believe the following general expression to be correct; but I purpose examining it much further, and would therefore wish not to be considered at present as pledged to its accuracy. The *sum of chemical decomposition is constant* for any section taken across a decomposing conductor, uniform in its nature, at whatever distance the poles may be from each other or from the section; or however that section may intersect the currents, whether directly across them, or so oblique as to reach almost from pole to pole, or whether it be plane, or curved, or irregular in the utmost degree; provided the current of electricity be retained constant in quantity (377), and that the section passes through every part of the current through the decomposing conductor.

505. I have reason to believe that the statement might be made still more general, and expressed thus: That *for a constant quantity of electricity, whatever the decomposing conductor may be, whether water, saline solutions, acids, fused bodies, &c., the amount of electro-chemical action is also a constant quantity, i.e., would always be equivalent to a standard chemical effect founded upon ordinary chemical affinity.* I have this investigation in hand, with several others, and shall be prepared to give it in the next series but one of these *Researches*.

506. Many other arguments might be adduced against the hypotheses of the attraction of the poles being the cause of electro-chemical decomposition; but I would rather pass on to the view I have thought more consistent with facts, with this single remark; that if decomposition by the voltaic battery depended upon the attraction of the poles, or the parts about them, being stronger than the mutual attrac-

[1] There are certain precautions, in this and such experiments, which can only be understood and guarded against by a knowledge of the phenomena to be described in the first part of the Sixth Series of these *Researches*.

tion of the particles separated, it would follow that the weakest *electrical* attraction was stronger than, if not the strongest, yet very strong *chemical* attraction, namely, such as exists between oxygen and hydrogen, potassium and oxygen, chlorine and sodium, acid and alkali, &c., a consequence which, although perhaps not impossible, seems in the present state of the subject very unlikely.

507. The view which M. de la Rive has taken (489), and also MM. Riffault and Chompré (485), of the manner in which electro-chemical decomposition is effected, is very different to that already considered, and is not affected by either the arguments or facts urged against the latter. Considering it as stated by the former philosopher, it appears to me to be incompetent to account for the experiments of decomposition against surfaces of air (462, 469) and water (495), which I have described; for if the physical differences between metals and humid conductors, which M. de la Rive supposes to account for the transmission of the compound of matter and electricity in the latter, and the transmission of the electricity only with the rejection of the matter in the former, be allowed for a moment, still the analogy of air to metal is, electrically considered, so small, that instead of the former replacing the latter (462), an effect the very reverse might have been expected. Or if even that were allowed, the experiment with water (495), at once sets the matter at rest, the decomposing pole being now of a substance which is admitted as competent to transmit the assumed compound of electricity and matter.

508. With regard to the views of MM. Riffault and Chompré (485), the occurrence of decomposition alone in the *course* of the current is so contrary to the well-known effects obtained in the forms of experiment adopted up to this time, that it must be proved before the hypothesis depending on it need be considered.

509. The consideration of the various theories of electro-chemical decomposition, whilst it has made me diffident, has also given me confidence to add another to the number; for it is because the one I have to propose appears, after the most attentive consideration, to explain and agree with the immense collection of facts belonging to this branch of science, and to remain uncontradicted by, or unopposed to, any of them, that I have been encouraged to give it.

510. Electro-chemical decomposition is well known to depend essentially upon the *current* of electricity. I have shown that in certain

cases (375) the decomposition is proportionate to the quantity of electricity passing, whatever may be its intensity or its source, and that the same is probably true for all cases (377) even when the utmost generality is taken on the one hand, and great precision of expression on the other (505).

511. In speaking of the current, I find myself obliged to be still more particular than on a former occasion (283), in consequence of the variety of views taken by philosophers, all agreeing in the effect of the current itself. Some philosophers, with Franklin, assume but one electric fluid; and such must agree together in the general uniformity and character of the electric current. Others assume two electric fluids; and here singular differences have arisen.

512. MM. Riffault and Chompré, for instance, consider the positive and negative currents each as causing decomposition, and state that the positive current is *more powerful* than the negative current,[1] the nitrate of soda being, under similar circumstances, decomposed by the former, but not by the latter.

513. M. Hachette states[2] that "it is not necessary, as has been believed, that the action of the two electricities, positive and negative, should be simultaneous for the decomposition of water." The passage implying, if I have caught the meaning aright, that one electricity can be obtained, and can be applied in effecting decompositions, independent of the other.

514. The view of M. de la Rive to a certain extent agrees with that of M. Hachette, for he considers that the two electricities decompose separate portions of water (490).[3] In one passage he speaks of the two electricities as two influences, wishing perhaps to avoid offering a decided opinion upon the independent existence of electric fluids; but as these influences are considered as combining with the elements set free as by a species of chemical affinity, and for the time entirely masking their character, great vagueness of idea is thus introduced, inasmuch as such a species of combination can only be conceived to take place between things having independent existences. The two elementary electric currents, moving in opposite directions, from pole to pole, constitute the ordinary *voltaic current*.

515. M. Grotthuss is inclined to believe that the elements of water, when about to separate at the poles, combine with the electricities, and

[1] *Annales de Chimie*, 1807, Vol. LXIII, p. 84.
[2] *Ibid.*, 1832, Vol. LI, p. 73.
[3] *Ibid.*, 1825, Vol. XXVIII, pp. 197, 201.

so become gases. M. de la Rive's view is the exact reverse of this: whilst passing through the fluid, they are, according to him, compounds with the electricities; when evolved at the poles, they are de-electrified.

516. I have sought amongst the various experiments quoted in support of these views, or connected with electro-chemical decompositions or electric currents, for any which might be considered as sustaining the theory of two electricities rather than that of one, but have not been able to perceive a single fact which could be brought forward for such a purpose: or, admitting the hypothesis of two electricities, much less have I been able to perceive the slightest grounds for believing that one electricity in a current can be more powerful than the other, or that it can be present without the other, or that one can be varied or in the slightest degree affected, without a corresponding variation in the other.[1] If, upon the supposition of two electricities, a current of one can be obtained without the other, or the current of one be exalted or diminished more than the other, we might surely expect some variation either of the chemical or magnetical effects, or of both; but no such variations have been observed. If a current be so directed that it may act chemically in one part of its course, and magnetically in another, the two actions are always found to take place together. A current has not, to my knowledge, been produced which could act chemically and not magnetically, nor any which can act on the magnet, and not *at the same time* chemically.[2]

517. *Judging from facts only*, there is not as yet the slightest reason for considering the influence which is present in what we call the electric current,—whether in metals or fused bodies or humid conductors, or even in air, flame, and rarefied elastic media,—as a compound or complicated influence. It has never been resolved into simpler or elementary influences, and may perhaps best be conceived of as *an axis of power having contrary forces, exactly equal in amount, in contrary directions.*

518. Passing to the consideration of electro-chemical decomposition, it appears to me that the effect is produced by an *internal corpuscular action*, exerted according to the direction of the

[1] See now in relation to this subject, 1627–1645.— *Dec.* 1838.
[2] Thermo-electric currents are of course no exception, because when they fail to act chemically they also fail to be currents

electric current, and that it is due to a force either *super-added to*, or *giving direction to the ordinary chemical affinity* of the bodies present. The body under decomposition may be considered as a mass of acting particles, all those which are included in the course of the electric current contributing to the final effect; and it is because the ordinary chemical affinity is relieved, weakened, or partly neutralized by the influence of the electric current in one direction parallel to the course of the latter, and strengthened or added to in the opposite direction, that the combining particles have a tendency to pass in opposite courses.

519. In this view the effect is considered as *essentially dependent* upon the *mutual chemical affinity* of the particles of opposite kinds. Particles a a, Pl. V, *Fig. 7*, could not be transferred or travel from one pole N towards the other P, unless they found particles of the opposite kind b b ready to pass in the contrary direction: for it is by virtue of their increased affinity for those particles, combined with their diminished affinity for such as are behind them in their course, that they are urged forward: and when any one particle a, Pl. V, *Fig. 8*, arrives at the pole, it is excluded or set free, because the particle b of the opposite kind, with which it was the moment before in combination, has, under the superinducing influence of the current, a greater attraction for the particle a', which is before it in its course, than for the particle a, towards which its affinity has been weakened.

520. As far as regards any single compound particle, the case may be considered as analogous to one of ordinary decomposition, for, in *Fig. 8*, a may be conceived to be expelled from the compound a b by the superior attraction of a' for b, that superior attraction belonging to it in consequence of the relative position of a' b and a to the direction of the axis of electric power (517) superinduced by the current. But as all the compound particles in the course of the current, except those actually in contact with the poles, act conjointly, and consist of elementary particles, which, whilst they are in one direction expelling, are in the other being expelled, the case becomes more complicated, but not more difficult of comprehension.

521. It is not here assumed that the acting particles must be in a right line between the poles. The lines of action which may be supposed to represent the electric currents passing through a decomposing liquid, have in many experiments very irregular forms; and even in the simplest case of two wires or points im-

mersed as poles in a drop or larger single portion of fluid, these lines must diverge rapidly from the poles; and the direction in which the chemical affinity between particles is most powerfully modified (519, 520) will vary with the direction of these lines, according constantly with them. But even in reference to these lines or currents, it is not supposed that the particles which mutually affect each other must of necessity be parallel to them, but only that they shall accord generally with their direction. Two particles, placed in a line perpendicular to the electric current passing in any particular place, are not supposed to have their ordinary chemical relations towards each other affected; but as the line joining them is inclined one way to the current their mutual affinity is increased; as it is inclined in the other direction it is diminished; and the effect is a maximum, when that line is parallel to the current.[1]

522. That the actions, of whatever kind they may be, take place frequently in oblique directions is evident from the circumstance of those particles being included which in numerous cases are not in a line between the poles. Thus, when wires are used as poles in a glass of solution, the decompositions and recompositions occur to the right or left of the direct line between the poles, and indeed in every part to which the currents extend, as is proved by many experiments, and must therefore often occur between particles obliquely placed as respects the current itself; and when a metallic vessel containing the solution is made one pole, whilst a mere point or wire is used for the other, the decompositions and recompositions must frequently be still more oblique to the course of the currents.

523. The theory which I have ventured to put forth (almost) requires an admission, that in a compound body capable of electro-chemical decomposition the elementary particles have a mutual relation to, and influence upon each other, extending beyond those with which they are immediately combined. Thus in water, a particle of hydrogen in combination with oxygen is considered as not altogether indifferent to other particles of oxygen, although they are combined with other particles of hydrogen; but to have an affinity or attraction towards them, which, though it does not at all approach in force, under ordinary circumstances, to that by which it is combined with its own particle, can, under the electric influence, exerted in a definite direction, be made even to surpass it. This general relation of particles already in combination to other particles with which they are not combined, is sufficiently distinct in numerous results of a purely chemical character; especially in those where partial decompositions only take place, and in Berthollet's experiments on the effects of quantity upon affinity: and it probably has a direct relation to, and connexion with, attraction of aggregation, both in solids and fluids. It is a remarkable circumstance, that in gases and vapours, where the attraction of aggregation ceases, there likewise the decomposing powers of electricity apparently cease, and there also the chemical action of quantity is no longer evident. It seems not unlikely that the inability to suffer decomposition in these cases may be dependent upon the absence of that mutual attractive relation of the particles which is the cause of aggregation.

524. I hope I have now distinctly stated, although in general terms, the view I entertain of the cause of electro-chemical decomposition, *as far as that cause can at present be traced and understood*. I conceive the effects to arise from forces which are *internal*, relative to the matter under decomposition—and not *external*, as they might be considered, if directly dependent upon the poles. I suppose that the effects are due to a modification, by the electric current, of the chemical affinity of the particles through or by which that current is passing, giving them the power of acting more forcibly in one direction than in another, and consequently making them travel by a series of successive decompositions and recompositions in opposite directions, and finally causing their expulsion or exclusion at the boundaries of the body under decomposition, in the direction of the current, *and that* in larger or smaller quantities, according as the current is more or less powerful (377). I think, therefore, it would be more philosophical, and more directly expressive of the facts, to speak of such a body in relation to the current passing through it, rather than to the poles, as they are usually called, in contact with it; and say that whilst under decomposition, oxygen, chlorine, iodine, acids, &c., are rendered at its negative extremity, and combustibles, metals, alkalies, bases, &c., at its positive extremity (467). I do not believe that a substance can be transferred in the electric current beyond the point where it ceases to find particles with which it can combine;

---

[1] In reference to this subject see now electrolytic induction and discharge, Series XII, ¶ viii. 1343-1351, &c.—*Dec.* 1838.

and I may refer to the experiments made in air (465) and in water (495), already quoted, for facts illustrating these views in the first instance; to which I will now add others.

525. In order to show the dependence of the decomposition and transfer of elements upon the chemical affinity of the substances present, experiments were made upon sulphuric acid in the following manner. Dilute sulphuric acid was prepared: its specific gravity was 1021.2. A solution of sulphate of soda was also prepared, of such strength that a measure of it contained exactly as much sulphuric acid as an equal measure of the diluted acid just referred to. A solution of pure soda, and another of pure ammonia, were likewise prepared, of such strengths that a measure of either should be exactly neutralized by a measure of the prepared sulphuric acid.

526. Four glass cups were then arranged, as in Pl. V, *Fig. 9*; seventeen measures of the free sulphuric acid (525) were put into each of the vessels *a* and *b*, and seventeen measures of the solution of sulphate of soda into each of the vessels A and B. Asbestos, which had been well-washed in acid, acted upon by the voltaic pile, well-washed in water, and dried by pressure, was used to connect *a* with *b* and A with B, the portions being as equal as they could be made in quantity, and cut as short as was consistent with their performing the part of effectual communications. *b* and A were connected by two platina plates or poles soldered to the extremities of one wire, and the cups *a* and B were by similar platina plates connected with a voltaic battery of forty pairs of plates four inches square, that in *a* being connected with the negative, and that in B with the positive pole. The battery, which was not powerfully charged, was retained in communication above half an hour. In this manner it was certain that the same electric current had passed through *a b* and A B, and that in each instance the same quantity and strength of acid had been submitted to its action, but in one case merely dissolved in water, and in the other dissolved and also combined with an alkali.

527. On breaking the connexion with the battery, the portions of asbestos were lifted out, and the drops hanging at the ends allowed to fall each into its respective vessel. The acids in *a* and *b* were then first compared, for which purpose two evaporating dishes were balanced, and the acid from *a* put into one, and that from *b* into the other; but as one was a little heavier than the other, a small drop was transferred from the heavier to the lighter, and the two

rendered equal in weight. Being neutralized by the addition of the soda solution (525), that from *a*, or the negative vessel, required 15 parts of the soda solution, and that from *b*, or the positive vessel, required 16.3 parts. That the sum of these is not 34 parts is principally due to the acid removed with the asbestos; but taking the mean of 15.65 parts, it would appear that a twenty-fourth part of the acid originally in the vessel *a* had passed, through the influence of the electric current, from *a* into *b*.

528. In comparing the difference of acid in A and B, the necessary equality of weight was considered as of no consequence, because the solution was at first neutral, and would not, therefore, affect the test liquids, and all the evolved acid would be in B, and the free alkali in A. The solution in A required 3.2 measures of the prepared acid (525) to neutralize it, and the solution in B required also 3.2 measures of the soda solution (525) to neutralize it. As the asbestos must have removed a little acid and alkali from the glasses, these quantities are by so much too small; and therefore it would appear that about a tenth of the acid originally in the vessel A had been transferred into B during the continuance of the electric action.

529. In another similar experiment, whilst a thirty-fifth part of the acid passed from *a* to *b* in the free acid vessels, between a tenth and an eleventh passed from A to B in the combined acid vessels. Other experiments of the same kind gave similar results.

530. The variation of electro-chemical decomposition, the transfer of elements and their accumulation at the poles, according as the substance submitted to action consists of particles opposed more or less in their chemical affinity, together with the consequent influence of the latter circumstances, are sufficiently obvious in these cases, where sulphuric acid is acted upon in the *same quantity* by the *same* electric current, but in one case opposed to the comparatively weak affinity of water for it, and in the other to the stronger one of soda. In the latter case the quantity transferred is from two and a half to three times what it is in the former; and it appears therefore very evident that the transfer is greatly dependent upon the mutual action of the particles of the decomposing bodies.[1]

531. In some of the experiments the acid from the vessels *a* and *b* was neutralized by ammonia, then evaporated to dryness, heated to redness, and the residue examined for sulphates.

[1] See the note to 675.—*Dec.* 1838.

In these cases more sulphate was always obtained from *a* than from *b;* showing that it had been impossible to exclude saline bases (derived from the asbestos, the glass, or perhaps impurities originally in the acid), and that they had helped in transferring the acid into *b*. But the quantity was small, and the acid was principally transferred by relation to the water present.

532. I endeavoured to arrange certain experiments by which saline solutions should be decomposed against surfaces of water and at first worked with the electric machine upon a piece of bibulous paper, or asbestos moistened in the solution, and in contact at its two extremities with pointed pieces of paper moistened in pure water, which served to carry the electric current to and from the solution in the middle piece. But I found numerous interfering difficulties. Thus, the water and solutions in the pieces of paper could not be prevented from mingling at the point where they touched. Again, sufficient acid could be derived from the paper connected with the discharging train, or it may be even from the air itself, under the influence of electric action, to neutralize the alkali developed at the positive extremity of the decomposing solution, and so not merely prevent its appearance, but actually transfer it on to the metal termination: and, in fact, when the paper points were not allowed to touch there, and the machine was worked until alkali was evolved at the delivering or positive end of the turmeric paper, containing the sulphate of soda solution, it was merely necessary to place the opposite receiving point of the paper connected with the discharging train, which had been moistened by distilled water, upon the brown turmeric point and press them together, when the alkaline effect immediately disappeared.

533. The experiment with sulphate of magnesia already described (495) is a case in point, however, and shows most clearly that the sulphuric acid and magnesia contributed to each other's transfer and final evolution, exactly as the same acid and soda affected each other in the results just given (527, &c.); and that so soon as the magnesia advanced beyond the reach of the acid, and found no other substance with which it could combine, it appeared in its proper character, and was no longer able to continue its progress towards the negative pole.

534. The theory I have ventured to put forth appears to me to explain all the prominent features of electro-chemical decomposition in a satisfactory manner.

535. In the first place, it explains why, in all ordinary cases, the evolved substances *appear only at the poles;* for the poles are the limiting surfaces of the decomposing substance, and except at them, every particle finds other particles having a contrary tendency with which it can combine.

536. Then it explains why, in numerous cases, the elements or evolved substances are not *retained* by the poles; and this is no small difficulty in those theories which refer the decomposing effect directly to the attractive power of the poles. If, in accordance with the usual theory, a piece of platina be supposed to have sufficient power to attract a particle of hydrogen from the particle of oxygen with which it was the instant before combined, there seems no sufficient reason, nor any fact, except those to be explained, which show why it should not, according to analogy with all ordinary attractive forces, as those of gravitation, magnetism, cohesion, chemical affinity, &c., *retain* that particle which it had just before taken from a distance and from previous combination. Yet it does not do so, but allows it to escape freely. Nor does this depend upon its assuming the gaseous state, for acids and alkalies, &c., are left equally at liberty to diffuse themselves through the fluid surrounding the pole, and show no particular tendency to combine with or adhere to the latter. And though there are plenty of cases where combination with the pole does take place, they do not at all explain the instances of non-combination, and do not therefore in their particular action reveal the general principle of decomposition.

537. But in the theory that I have just given, the effect appears to be a natural consequence of the action: the evolved substances are *expelled* from the decomposing mass (518, 519), not *drawn out by an attraction* which ceases to act on one particle without any assignable reason, while it continues to act on another of the same kind: and whether the poles be metal, water, or air, still the substances are evolved, and are sometimes set free, whilst at others they unite to the matter of the poles, according to the chemical nature of the latter, i.e., their chemical relation to those particles which are leaving the substance under operation.

538. The theory accounts for the *transfer of elements* in a manner which seems to me at present to leave nothing unexplained; and it was, indeed, the phenomena of transfer in the numerous cases of decomposition of bodies rendered fluid by heat (380, 402), which, in

conjunction with the experiments in air, led to its construction. Such cases as the former where binary compounds of easy decomposability are acted upon, are perhaps the best to illustrate the theory.

539. Chloride of lead, for instance, fused in a bent tube (400), and decomposed by platina wires, evolves lead, passing to what is usually called the negative pole, and chlorine, which being evolved at the positive pole, is in part set free, and in part combines with the platina. The chloride of platina formed, being soluble in the chloride of lead, is subject to decomposition, and the platina itself is gradually transferred across the decomposing matter, and found with the lead at the negative pole.

540. Iodide of lead evolves abundance of lead at the negative pole, and abundance of iodine at the positive pole.

541. Chloride of silver furnishes a beautiful instance, especially when decomposed by silver wire poles. Upon fusing a portion of it on a piece of glass, and bringing the poles into contact with it, there is abundance of silver evolved at the negative pole, and an equal abundance absorbed at the positive pole, for no chlorine is set free: and by careful management, the negative wire may be withdrawn from the fused globule as the silver is reduced there, the latter serving as the continuation of the pole, until a wire or thread of revived silver, five or six inches in length, is produced; at the same time the silver at the positive pole is as rapidly dissolved by the chlorine, which seizes upon it, so that the wire has to be continually advanced as it is melted away. The whole experiment includes the action of only two elements, silver and chlorine, and illustrates in a beautiful manner their progress in opposite directions, parallel to the electric current, which is for the time giving a uniform general direction to their mutual affinities (524).

542. According to my theory, an element or a substance not decomposable under the circumstances of the experiment, (as for instance, a dilute acid or alkali), should not be transferred, or pass from pole to pole, unless it be in chemical relation to some other element or substance tending to pass in the opposite direction, for the effect is considered as essentially due to the mutual relation of such particles. But the theories attributing the determination of the elements to the attractions and repulsions of the poles require no such condition, i.e., there is no reason apparent why the attraction of the positive pole, and the repulsion

of the negative pole, upon a particle of free acid, placed in water between them, should not (with equal currents of electricity) be as strong as if that particle were previously combined with alkali; but, on the contrary, as they have not a powerful chemical affinity to overcome, there is every reason to suppose they would be stronger, and would sooner bring the acid to rest at the positive pole.[1] Yet such is not the case, as has been shown by the experiments on free and combined acid (526, 528).

543. Neither does M. de la Rive's theory, as I understand it, *require* that the particles should be in combination: it does not even admit, where there are two sets of particles capable of combining with and passing by each other, that they do combine, but supposes that they travel as separate compounds of matter and electricity. Yet in fact the free substance *cannot* travel, the combined one *can*.

544. It is very difficult to find cases amongst solutions or fluids which shall illustrate this point, because of the difficulty of finding two fluids which shall conduct, shall not mingle, and in which an element evolved from one shall not find a combinable element in the other. *Solutions* of acids or alkalies will not answer, because they exist by virtue of an attraction; and increasing the solubility of a body in one direction, and diminishing it in the opposite, is just as good a reason for transfer as modifying the affinity between the acids and alkalies themselves.[2] Nevertheless the case of sulphate of magnesia is in point (494, 495), and shows that *one element or principle only* has no power of transference or of passing towards either pole.

545. Many of the metals, however, in their solid state, offer very fair instances of the kind required. Thus, if a plate of platina be used as the positive pole in a solution of sulphuric acid, oxygen will pass towards it, and so will acid; but these are not substances having such chemical relation to the platina as, even under the favourable condition superinduced by the current (518, 524), to combine with it; the platina therefore remains where it was first placed, and has no tendency to pass towards the negative pole. But if a plate of iron, zinc or copper, be substituted for the platina, then the oxygen and acid can combine with these, and the metal immediately begins to travel (as an oxide) to the opposite pole, and is finally deposited there.

---

[1] Even Sir Humphry Davy considered the attraction of the pole as being communicated from one particle to another of the *same* kind (483).
[2] See the note to 675.—*Dec.* 1838.

Or if, retaining the platina pole, a fused chloride, as of lead, zinc, silver, &c., be substituted for the sulphuric acid, then, as the platina finds an element it can combine with, it enters into union, acts as other elements do in cases of voltaic decomposition, is rapidly transferred across the melted matter, and expelled at the negative pole.

546. I can see but little reason in the theories referring the electro-chemical decomposition to the attractions and repulsions of the poles, and I can perceive none in M. de la Rive's theory, why the metal of the positive pole should not be transferred across the intervening conductor, and deposited at the negative pole, even when it cannot act chemically upon the element of the fluid surrounding it. It cannot be referred to the attraction of cohesion preventing such an effect; for if the pole be made of the lightest spongy platina, the effect is the same. Or if gold precipitated by sulphate of iron be diffused through the solution, still accumulation of it at the negative pole will not take place; and yet in it the attraction of cohesion is almost perfectly overcome, the particles are so small as to remain for hours in suspension, and are perfectly free to move by the slightest impulse towards either pole; and *if in relation* by chemical affinity to any substance present, are powerfully determined to the negative pole.[1]

547. In support of these arguments, it may be observed, that as yet no determination of a substance to a pole, or tendency to obey the electric current, has been observed (that I am aware of) in cases of mere mixture; i.e., a substance diffused through a fluid, but having no sensible chemical affinity with it, or with substances that may be evolved from it during the action, does not in any case seem to be affected by the electric current. Pulverised charcoal was diffused through dilute sulphuric acid, and subjected with the solution to the action of a voltaic battery, terminated by platina poles; but not the slightest tendency of the charcoal to

the negative pole could be observed. Sublimed sulphur was diffused through similar acid, and submitted to the same action, a silver plate being used as the negative pole; but the sulphur had no tendency to pass to that pole, the silver was not tarnished, nor did any sulphuretted hydrogen appear. The case of magnesia and water (495, 533), with those of comminuted metals in certain solutions (546), are also of this kind; and, in fact, substances which have the instant before been powerfully determined towards the pole, as magnesia from sulphate of magnesia, become entirely *indifferent to it* the moment they assume their independent state, and pass away, diffusing themselves through the surrounding fluid.

548. There are, it is true, many instances of insoluble bodies being acted upon, as glass, sulphate of baryta, marble, slate, basalt, &c., but they form no exception; for the substances they give up are in direct and strong relation as to chemical affinity with those which they find in the surrounding solution, so that these decompositions enter into the class of ordinary effects.

549. It may be expressed as a general consequence, that the more directly bodies are opposed to each other in chemical affinity, the more *ready* is their separation from each other in cases of electro-chemical decomposition, i.e., provided other circumstances, as insolubility, deficient conducting power, proportions, &c., do not interfere. This is well known to be the case with water and saline solutions; and I have found it to be equally true with *dry* chlorides, iodides, salts, &c., rendered subject to electro-chemical decomposition by fusion (402). So that in applying the voltaic battery for the purpose of decomposing bodies not yet resolved into forms of matter simpler than their own, it must be remembered, that success may depend not upon the weakness, or failure upon the strength, of the affinity by which the elements sought for are held together, but contrariwise; and then modes of application may be devised, by which, in *association* with ordinary chemical powers, and the assistance of fusion (394, 417), we may be able to penetrate much further than at present into the constitution of our chemical elements.

550. Some of the most beautiful and surprising cases of electro-chemical decomposition and *transfer* which Sir Humphry Davy described in his celebrated paper,[2] were those in which acids were passed through alkalies, and alkalies or

---

[1] In making this experiment, care must be taken that no substance be present that can act chemically on the gold. Although I used the metal very carefully washed, and diffused through dilute sulphuric acid, yet in the first instance I obtained gold at the negative pole, and the effect was repeated when the platina poles were changed. But on examining the clear liquor in the cell, after subsidence of the metallic gold, I found a little of that metal in solution, and a little chlorine was also present. I therefore well washed the gold which had thus been subjected to voltaic action, diffused it through other pure dilute sulphuric acid, and then found, that on subjecting it to the action of the pile, not the slightest tendency to the negative pole could be perceived.

[2] *Philosophical Transactions*, 1807, p. 1.

earths through acids;[1] and the way in which substances having the most powerful attractions for each other were thus prevented from combining, or, as it is said, had their natural affinity destroyed or suspended throughout the whole of the circuit, excited the utmost astonishment. But if I be right in the view I have taken of the effects, it will appear, that that which made the *wonder*, is in fact the *essential condition* of transfer and decomposition, and that the more alkali there is in the course of an acid, the more will the transfer of that acid be facilitated from pole to pole; and perhaps a better illustration of the difference between the theory I have ventured, and those previously existing, cannot be offered than the views they respectively give of such facts as these.

551. The instances in which sulphuric acid could not be passed through baryta, or baryta through sulphuric acid,[2] because of the precipitation of sulphate of baryta, enter within the pale of the law already described (380, 412), by which liquidity is so generally required for conduction and decomposition. In assuming the solid state of sulphate of baryta, these bodies became virtually non-conductors to electricity of so low a tension as that of the voltaic battery, and the power of the latter over them was almost infinitely diminished.

552. The theory I have advanced accords in a most satisfactory manner with the fact of an element or substance finding its place of rest, or rather of evolution, sometimes at one pole and sometimes at the other. Sulphur illustrates this effect very well.[3] When sulphuric acid is decomposed by the pile, sulphur is evolved at the negative pole; but when sulphuret of silver is decomposed in a similar way (436), then the sulphur appears at the positive pole; and if a hot platina pole be used so as to vaporize the sulphur evolved in the latter case, then the relation of that pole to the sulphur is exactly the same as the relation of the same pole to oxygen upon its immersion in water. In both cases the element evolved is liberated at the pole, but not retained by it; but by virtue of its elastic, uncombinable, and immiscible condition passes away into the surrounding medium. The sulphur is evidently determined in these opposite directions by its opposite chemical relations to oxygen and silver; and it is to such relations

generally that I have referred all electro-chemical phenomena. Where they do not exist, no electro-chemical action can take place. Where they are strongest, it is most powerful; where they are reversed, the direction of transfer of the substance is reversed with them.

553. *Water* may be considered as one of those substances which can be made to pass to *either* pole. When the poles are immersed in dilute sulphuric acid (527), acid passes towards the positive pole, and water towards the negative pole; but when they are immersed in dilute alkali, the alkali passes towards the negative pole, and water towards the positive pole.

554. Nitrogen is another substance which is considered as determinable to either pole; but in consequence of the numerous compounds which it forms, some of which pass to one pole, and some to the other, I have not always found it easy to determine the true circumstances of its appearance. A pure strong solution of ammonia is so bad a conductor of electricity that it is scarcely more decomposable than pure water; but if sulphate of ammonia be dissolved in it, then decomposition takes place very well; nitrogen almost pure, and in some cases quite, is evolved at the positive pole, and hydrogen at the negative pole.

555. On the other hand, if a strong solution of nitrate of ammonia be decomposed, oxygen appears at the positive pole, and hydrogen, with sometimes nitrogen, at the negative pole. If fused nitrate of ammonia be employed, hydrogen appears at the negative pole, mingled with a little nitrogen. Strong nitric acid yields plenty of oxygen at the positive pole, but no gas (only nitrous acid) at the negative pole. Weak nitric acid yields the oxygen and hydrogen of the water present, the acid apparently remaining unchanged. Strong nitric acid with nitrate of ammonia dissolved in it, yields a gas at the negative pole, of which the greater part is hydrogen, but apparently a little nitrogen is present. I believe, that in some of these cases a little nitrogen appeared at the negative pole. I suspect, however, that in all these, and in all former cases, the appearance of the nitrogen at the positive or negative pole is entirely a secondary effect, and not an immediate consequence of the decomposing power of the electric current.[4]

556. A few observations on what are called the *poles* of the voltaic battery now seem necessary. The poles are merely the surfaces or

---

[1] *Ibid.*, p. 24, &c.   [2] *Ibid.*, p. 25, &c.
[3] At 681 and 757 of Series VII will be found corrections of the statement here made respecting sulphur and sulphuric acid. At present there is no well-ascertained fact which proves that the same body can go directly to *either* of the two poles at pleasure.—*Dec.* 1838.

[4] Refer for proof of the truth of this supposition to 748, 752, &c.—*Dec.* 1838.

doors by which the electricity enters into or passes out of the substance suffering decomposition. They limit the extent of that substance in the course of the electric current, being its *terminations* in that direction: hence the elements evolved pass so far and no farther.

557. Metals make admirable poles, in consequence of their high conducting power, their immiscibility with the substances generally acted upon, their solid form, and the opportunity afforded of selecting such as are not chemically acted upon by ordinary substances.

558. Water makes a pole of difficult application, except in a few cases (494), because of its small conducting power, its miscibility with most of the substances acted upon, and its general relation to them in respect to chemical affinity. It consists of elements, which in their electrical and chemical relations are directly and powerfully opposed, yet combining to produce a body more neutral in its character than any other. So that there are but few substances which do not come into relation, by chemical affinity, with water or one of its elements; and therefore either the water or its elements are transferred and assist in transferring the infinite variety of bodies which, in association with it, can be placed in the course of the electric current. Hence the reason why it so rarely happens that the evolved substances rest at the first surface of the water, and why it therefore does not exhibit the ordinary action of a pole.

559. Air, however, and some gases are free from the latter objection, and may be used as poles in many cases (461, &c.); but, in consequence of the extremely low degree of conducting power belonging to them, they cannot be employed with the voltaic apparatus. This limits their use; for the voltaic apparatus is the only one as yet discovered which supplies sufficient quantity of electricity (371, 376) to effect electro-chemical decomposition with facility.

560. When the poles are liable to the chemical action of the substances evolved, either simply in consequence of their natural relation to them, or of that relation aided by the influence of the current (518), then they suffer corrosion, and the parts dissolved are subject to transference, in the same manner as the particles of the body originally under decomposition. An immense series of phenomena of this kind might be quoted in support of the view I have taken of the cause of electro-chemical decomposition, and the transfer and evolution of the elements. Thus platina being made the positive and negative poles in a solution of sulphate of soda, has no affinity or attraction for the oxygen, hydrogen, acid, or alkali evolved, and refuses to combine with or retain them. Zinc can combine with the oxygen and acid; at the positive pole it does combine, and immediately begins to travel as oxide towards the negative pole. Charcoal, which cannot combine with the metals, if made the negative pole in a metallic solution, refuses to unite to the bodies which are ejected from the solution upon its surface; but if made the positive pole in a dilute solution of sulphuric acid, it is capable of combining with the oxygen evolved there, and consequently unites with it, producing both carbonic acid and carbonic oxide in abundance.

561. A great advantage is frequently supplied, by the opportunity afforded amongst the metals of selecting a substance for the pole, which shall or shall not be acted upon by the elements to be evolved. The consequent use of platina is notorious. In the decomposition of sulphuret of silver and other sulphurets, a positive silver pole is superior to a platina one, because in the former case the sulphur evolved there combines with the silver, and the decomposition of the original sulphuret is rendered evident; whereas in the latter case it is dissipated, and the assurance of its separation at the pole not easily obtained.

562. The effects which take place when a succession of conducting decomposable and undecomposable substances are placed in the electric circuit, as, for instance, of wires and solutions, or of air and solutions (465, 469), are explained in the simplest possible manner by the theoretical view I have given. In consequence of the reaction of the constituents of each portion of decomposable matter, affected as they are by the supervention of the electric current (524), portions of the proximate or ultimate elements proceed in the direction of the current as far as they find matter of a contrary kind capable of effecting their transfer, and being equally affected by them; and where they cease to find such matter, they are evolved in their free state, i.e., upon the surfaces of metal or air bounding the extent of decomposable matter in the direction of the current.

563. Having thus given my theory of the mode in which electro-chemical decomposition is effected, I will refrain for the present from entering upon the numerous general considerations which it suggests, wishing first to submit it to the test of publication and discussion.

Royal Institution, June 1833.

PLATE VI

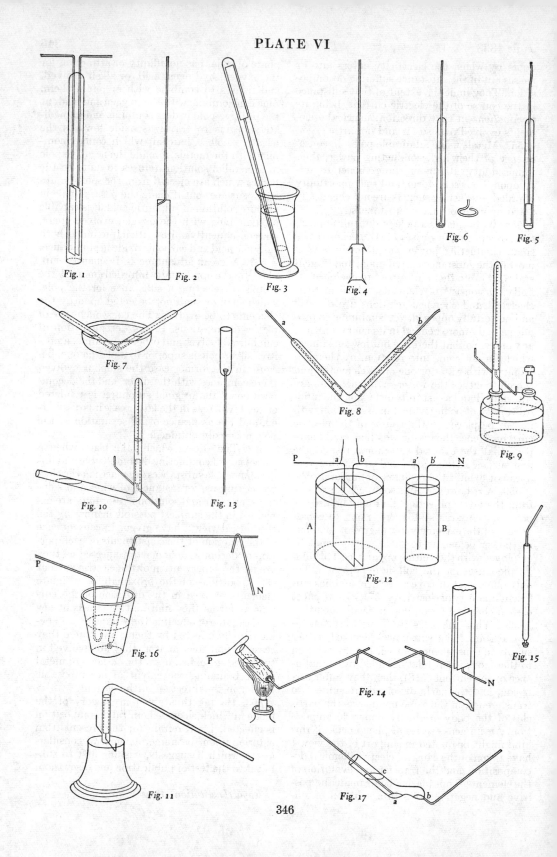

Fig. 1

Fig. 2

Fig. 3

Fig. 4

Fig. 5

Fig. 6

Fig. 7

Fig. 8

Fig. 9

Fig. 10

Fig. 13

Fig. 12

Fig. 16

Fig. 15

Fig. 14

Fig. 11

Fig. 17

SIXTH SERIES

§ 12. *On the Power of Metals and Other Solids to Induce the Combination of Gaseous Bodies*

Received November 30, 1833 Read January 11, 1834

564. The conclusion at which I have arrived in the present communication may seem to render the whole of it unfit to form part of a series of researches in electricity; since, remarkable as the phenomena are, the power which produces them is not to be considered as of an electric origin, otherwise than as all attraction of particles may have this subtile agent for their common cause. But as the effects investigated arose out of electrical researches, as they are directly connected with other effects which are of an electric nature, and must of necessity be understood and guarded against in a very extensive series of electro-chemical decompositions (707), I have felt myself fully justified in describing them in this place.

565. Believing that I had proved (by experiments hereafter to be described [705]), the constant and definite chemical action of a certain quantity of electricity, whatever its intensity might be, or however the circumstances of its transmission through either the body under decomposition or the more perfect conductors were varied, I endeavoured upon that result to construct a new measuring instrument, which from its use might be called, at least provisionally, a *Volta-electrometer* (739).[1]

566. During the course of the experiments made to render the instrument efficient, I was occasionally surprised at observing a deficiency of the gases resulting from the decompositions of water, and at last an actual disappearance of portions which had been evolved, collected, and measured. The circumstances of the disappearance were these. A glass tube, about twelve inches in length and ¾ths of an inch in diameter, had two platina poles fixed into its upper, hermetically sealed, extremity: the poles, where they passed through the glass, were of wire; but terminated below in plates, which were soldered to the wires with gold (Pl. VI, *Fig. 1*). The tube was filled with dilute sulphuric acid, and inverted in a cup of the same fluid; a voltaic battery was connected with the

[1] Or Voltameter.—*Dec.* 1838.

two wires, and sufficient oxygen and hydrogen evolved to occupy ⅘ths of the tube, or by the graduation, 116 parts. On separating the tube from the voltaic battery the volume of gas immediately began to diminish, and in about five hours only 13½ parts remained, and these ultimately disappeared.

567. It was found by various experiments, that this effect was not due to the escape or solution of the gas, nor to recombination of the oxygen or hydrogen in consequence of any peculiar condition *they* might be supposed to possess under the circumstances; but to be occasioned by the action of one or both of the poles within the tube upon the gas around them. On disuniting the poles from the pile after they had acted upon dilute sulphuric acid, and introducing them into separate tubes containing mixed oxygen and hydrogen, it was found that the *positive* pole effected the union of the gases, but the negative pole apparently not (588). It was ascertained also that no action of a sensible kind took place between the positive pole with oxygen or hydrogen alone.

568. These experiments reduced the phenomena to the consequence of a power possessed by the platina, after it had been the positive pole of a voltaic pile, of causing the combination of oxygen and hydrogen at common, or even at low, temperatures. This effect is, as far as I am aware, altogether new, and was immediately followed out to ascertain whether it was really of an electric nature, and how far it would interfere with the determination of the quantities evolved in the cases of electro-chemical decomposition required in the fourteenth section of these Researches.

569. Several platina plates were prepared (Pl. VI, *Fig. 2*). They were nearly half an inch wide, and two inches and a half long: some were ½₀₀th of an inch, others not more than ⅙₀₀th, whilst some were as much as ⅒th of an inch in thickness. Each had a piece of platina wire, about seven inches long, soldered to it by pure gold. Then a number of glass tubes were

347

prepared: they were about nine or ten inches in length, ⅝ths of an inch in internal diameter, were sealed hermetically at one extremity, and were graduated. Into these tubes was put a mixture of two volumes of hydrogen and one of oxygen, at the water pneumatic trough, and when one of the plates described had been connected with the positive or negative pole of the voltaic battery for a given time, or had been otherwise prepared, it was introduced through the water into the gas within the tube; the whole set aside in a test-glass (Pl. VI, *Fig. 3*), and left for a longer or shorter period, that the action might be observed.

570. The following result may be given as an illustration of the phenomenon to be investigated. Diluted sulphuric acid, of the specific gravity 1.336, was put into a glass jar, in which was placed also a large platina plate, connected with the negative end of a voltaic battery of forty pairs of four-inch plates, with double coppers, and moderately charged. One of the plates above described (569) was then connected with the positive extremity, and immersed in the same jar of acid for five minutes, after which it was separated from the battery, washed in distilled water, and introduced through the water of the pneumatic trough into a tube containing the mixture of oxygen and hydrogen (569). The volume of gases immediately began to lessen, the diminution proceeding more and more rapidly until about ¾ths of the mixture had disappeared. The upper end of the tube became quite warm, the plate itself so hot that the water boiled as it rose over it; and in less than a minute a cubical inch and a half of the gases were gone, having been combined by the power of the platina, and converted into water.

571. This extraordinary influence acquired by the platina at the positive pole of the pile, is exerted far more readily and effectively on oxygen and hydrogen than on any other mixture of gases that I have tried. One volume of nitrous gas was mixed with a volume of hydrogen, and introduced into a tube with a plate which had been made positive in the dilute sulphuric acid for four minutes (570). There was no sensible action in an hour: being left for thirty-six hours, there was a diminution of about one-eighth of the whole volume. Action had taken place, but it had been very feeble.

572. A mixture of two volumes of nitrous oxide with one volume of hydrogen was put with a plate similarly prepared into a tube (569, 570). This also showed no action immediately; but in thirty-six hours nearly a fourth of the whole had disappeared, i.e., about half of a cubical inch. By comparison with another tube containing the same mixture without a plate, it appeared that a part of the diminution was due to solution, and the other part to the power of the platina; but the action had been very slow and feeble.

573. A mixture of one volume olefiant gas and three volumes oxygen was not affected by such a platina plate, even though left together for several days (640, 641).

574. A mixture of two volumes carbonic oxide and one volume oxygen was also unaffected by the prepared platina plate in several days (645, &c.).

575. A mixture of equal volumes of chlorine and hydrogen was used in several experiments, with plates prepared in a similar manner (570). Diminution of bulk soon took place: but when after thirty-six hours the experiments were examined, it was found that nearly all the chlorine had disappeared, having been absorbed, principally by the water, and that the original volume of hydrogen remained unchanged. No combination of the gases, therefore, had here taken place.

576. Reverting to the action of the prepared plates on mixtures of oxygen and hydrogen (570), I found that the power, though gradually diminishing in all cases, could still be retained for a period, varying in its length with circumstances. When tubes containing plates (569) were supplied with fresh portions of mixed oxygen and hydrogen as the previous portions were condensed, the action was found to continue for above thirty hours, and in some cases slow combination could be observed even after eighty hours: but the continuance of the action greatly depended upon the purity of the gases used (638).

577. Some plates (569) were made positive for four minutes in dilute sulphuric acid of specific gravity 1.336: they were rinsed in distilled water, after which two were put into a small bottle and closed up, whilst others were left exposed to the air. The plates preserved in the limited portion of air were found to retain their power after eight days, but those exposed to the atmosphere had lost their force almost entirely in twelve hours, and in some situations, where currents existed, in a much shorter time.

578. Plates were made positive for five minutes in sulphuric acid, specific gravity 1.336. One of these was retained in similar acid for eight minutes after separation from the battery: it then acted on mixed oxygen and hydro-

¹ *Olefiant gas:* now known as *ethylene.*—ED.

gen with apparently undiminished vigour. Others were left in similar acid for forty hours, and some even for eight days, after the electrization, and then acted as well in combining oxygen and hydrogen gas as those which were used immediately after electrization.

579. The effect of a solution of caustic potassa in preserving the platina plates was tried in a similar manner. After being retained in such a solution for forty hours, they acted exceedingly well on oxygen and hydrogen, and one caused such rapid condensation of the gases, that the plate became much heated, and I expected the temperature would have risen to ignition.

580. When similarly prepared plates (569) had been put into distilled water for forty hours, and then introduced into mixed oxygen and hydrogen, they were found to act but very slowly and feebly as compared with those which had been preserved in acid or alkali. When, however, the quantity of water was but small, the power was very little impaired after three or four days. As the water had been retained in a wooden vessel, portions of it were redistilled in glass, and this was found to preserve prepared plates for a great length of time. Prepared plates were put into tubes with this water and closed up; some of them, taken out at the end of twenty-four days, were found very active on mixed oxygen and hydrogen; others, which were left in the water for fifty-three days, were still found to cause the combination of the gases. The tubes had been closed only by corks.

581. The act of combination always seemed to diminish, or apparently exhaust, the power of the platina plate. It is true, that in most, if not all instances, the combination of the gases, at first insensible, gradually increased in rapidity, and sometimes reached to explosion; but when the latter did not happen, the rapidity of combination diminished; and although fresh portions of gas were introduced into the tubes, the combination went on more and more slowly, and at last ceased altogether. The first effect of an increase in the rapidity of combination depended in part upon the water flowing off from the platina plate, and allowing a better contact with the gas, and in part upon the heat evolved during the progress of the combination (630). But notwithstanding the effect of these causes, diminution, and at last cessation of the power, always occurred. It must not, however, be unnoticed, that the purer the gases subjected to the action of the plate, the longer was its combining power retained. With the mixture evolved at the poles of the voltaic pile, in pure dilute sulphuric acid, it continued longest; and with oxygen and hydrogen, of perfect purity, it probably would not be diminished at all.

582. Different modes of treatment applied to the platina plate, after it had ceased to be the positive pole of the pile, affected its power very curiously. A plate which had been a positive pole in diluted sulphuric acid of specific gravity 1.336 for four or five minutes, if rinsed in water and put into mixed oxygen and hydrogen, would act very well, and condense perhaps one cubic inch and a half of gas in six or seven minutes; but if that same plate, instead of being merely rinsed, had been left in distilled water for twelve or fifteen minutes, or more, it would rarely fail, when put into the oxygen and hydrogen, of becoming, in the course of a minute or two, ignited, and would generally explode the gases. Occasionally the time occupied in bringing on the action extended to eight or nine minutes, and sometimes even to forty minutes, and yet ignition and explosion would result. This effect is due to the removal of a portion of acid which otherwise adheres firmly to the plate.[1]

583. Occasionally the platina plates (569), after being made the positive pole of the battery, were washed, wiped with filtering-paper or a cloth, and washed and wiped again. Being then introduced into mixed oxygen and hydrogen, they acted apparently as if they had been unaffected by the treatment. Sometimes the tubes containing the gas were opened in the air for an instant, and the plates put in dry; but no sensible difference in action was perceived, except that it commenced sooner.

584. The power of heat in altering the action of the prepared platina plates was also tried (595). Plates which had been rendered positive in dilute sulphuric acid for four minutes were well washed in water, and heated to redness in the flame of a spirit-lamp: after this they acted very well on mixed oxygen and hydrogen. Others, which had been heated more powerfully by the blowpipe, acted afterwards on the gases, though not so powerfully as the former. Hence it appears that heat does not take away the power acquired by the platina at the positive pole of the pile: the occasional diminution of force seemed always referable to other causes than the mere heat. If, for instance, the plate had not been well-washed from the acid, or if the flame used was carbonaceous, or was that of an alcohol lamp trimmed with spirit containing a little acid, or having a wick on which

[1] In proof that this is the case, refer to 1038. *Dec.* 1838.

salt, or other extraneous matter, had been placed, then the power of the plate was quickly and greatly diminished (634, 636).

585. This remarkable property was conferred upon platina when it was made the positive pole in sulphuric acid of specific gravity 1.336, or when it was considerably weaker, or when stronger, even up to the strength of oil of vitriol. Strong and dilute nitric acid, dilute acetic acid, solutions of tartaric, citric, and oxalic acids, were used with equal success. When muriatic acid was used, the plates acquired the power of condensing the oxygen and hydrogen, but in a much inferior degree.

586. Plates which were made positive in solution of caustic potassa did not show any sensible action upon the mixed oxygen and hydrogen. Other plates made positive in solutions of carbonates of potassa and soda exhibited the action, but only in a feeble degree.

587. When a neutral solution of sulphate of soda, or of nitre, or of chlorate of potassa, or of phosphate of potassa, or acetate of potassa, or sulphate of copper, was used, the plates, rendered positive in them for four minutes, and then washed in water, acted very readily and powerfully on the mixed oxygen and hydrogen.

588. It became a very important point, in reference to the *cause* of this action of the platina, to determine whether the *positive* pole *only* could confer it (567), or whether, notwithstanding the numerous contrary cases, the *negative* pole might not have the power when such circumstances as could interfere with or prevent the action were avoided. Three plates were therefore rendered negative, for four minutes in diluted sulphuric acid of specific gravity 1.336, washed in distilled water, and put into mixed oxygen and hydrogen. *All* of them *acted*, though not so strongly as they would have done if they had been rendered positive. Each combined about a cubical inch and a quarter of the gases in twenty-five minutes. On every repetition of the experiment the same result was obtained; and when the plates were retained in distilled water for ten or twelve minutes, before being introduced into the gas (582), the action was very much quickened.

589. But when there was any metallic or other substance present in the acid, which could be precipitated on the negative plate, then that plate ceased to act upon the mixed oxygen and hydrogen.

590. These experiments led to the expectation that the power of causing oxygen and hydrogen to combine, which could be conferred

upon any piece of platina by making it the positive pole of a voltaic pile, was not essentially dependent upon the action of the pile, or upon any structure or arrangement of parts it might receive whilst in association with it, but belonged to the platina *at all times*, and was *always effective* when the surface was *perfectly clean*. And though, when made the *positive* pole of the pile in acids, the circumstances might well be considered as those which would cleanse the surface of the platina in the most effectual manner, it did not seem impossible that ordinary operations should produce the same result, although in a less eminent degree.

591. Accordingly, a platina plate (569) was cleaned by being rubbed with a cork, a little water, and some coal-fire ashes upon a glass plate: being washed, it was put into mixed oxygen and hydrogen, and was found to act at first slowly, and then more rapidly. In an hour, a cubical inch and a half had disappeared.

592. Other plates were cleaned with ordinary sand-paper and water: others with chalk and water; others with emery and water; others, again, with black oxide of manganese and water; and others with a piece of charcoal and water. All of these acted in tubes of oxygen and hydrogen, causing combination of the gases. The action was by no means so powerful as that produced by plates having been in communication with the battery; but from one to two cubical inches of the gases disappeared, in periods extending from twenty-five to eighty or ninety minutes.

593. Upon cleaning the plates with a cork, ground emery, and dilute sulphuric acid, they were found to act still better. In order to simplify the conditions, the cork was dismissed, and a piece of platina foil used instead; still the effect took place. Then the acid was dismissed, and a solution of *potassa* used, but the effect occurred as before.

594. These results are abundantly sufficient to show that the mere mechanical cleansing of the surface of the platina is sufficient to enable it to exert its combining power over oxygen and hydrogen at common temperatures.

595. I now tried the effect of heat in conferring this property upon platina (584). Plates which had no action on the mixture of oxygen and hydrogen were heated by the flame of a freshly trimmed spirit-lamp, urged by a mouth blowpipe, and when cold were put into tubes of the mixed gases: they acted slowly at first, but after two or three hours condensed nearly all the gases.

596. A plate of platina, which was about one inch wide and two and three-quarters in length, and which had not been used in any of the preceding experiments, was curved a little so as to enter a tube, and left in a mixture of oxygen and hydrogen for thirteen hours: not the slightest action or combination of the gases occurred. It was withdrawn at the pneumatic trough from the gas through the water, heated red-hot by the spirit-lamp and blowpipe, and then returned when cold into the *same* portion of gas. In the course of a few minutes diminution of the gases could be observed, and in forty-five minutes about one cubical inch and a quarter had disappeared. In many other experiments platina plates when heated were found to acquire the power of combining oxygen and hydrogen.

597. But it happened not unfrequently that plates, after being heated, showed no power of combining oxygen and hydrogen gases, though left undisturbed in them for two hours. Sometimes also it would happen that a plate which, having been heated to dull redness, acted feebly, upon being heated to whiteness ceased to act; and at other times a plate which, having been slightly heated, did not act, was rendered active by a more powerful ignition.

598. Though thus uncertain in its action, and though often diminishing the power given to the plates at the positive pole of the pile (584), still it is evident that heat can render platina active, which before was inert (595). The cause of its occasional failure appears to be due to the surface of the metal becoming soiled, either from something previously adhering to it, which is made to adhere more closely by the action of the heat. or from matter communicated from the flame of the lamp, or from the air itself. It often happens that a polished plate of platina, when heated by the spirit-lamp and a blowpipe, becomes dulled and clouded on its surface by something either formed or deposited there; and this, and much less than this, is sufficient to prevent it from exhibiting the curious power now under consideration (634, 636). Platina also has been said to combine with carbon; and it is not at all unlikely that in processes of heating, where carbon or its compounds are present, a film of such a compound may be thus formed, and thus prevent the exhibition of the properties belonging to *pure* platina.[1]

[1] When heat does confer the property it is only by the destruction or dissipation of organic or other matter which had previously soiled the plate (632, 633, 634).—*Dec.* 1838.

599. The action of alkalies and acids in giving platina this property was now experimentally examined. Platina plates (569) having no action on mixed oxygen and hydrogen, being boiled in a solution of caustic potassa, washed, and then put into the gases, were found occasionally to act pretty well, but at other times to fail. In the latter case I concluded that the impurity upon the surface of the platina was of a nature not to be removed by the mere solvent action of the alkali, for when the plates were rubbed with a little emery, and the same solution of alkali (592), they became active.

600. The action of acids was far more constant and satisfactory. A platina plate was boiled in dilute nitric acid: being washed and put into mixed oxygen and hydrogen gases, it acted well. Other plates were boiled in strong nitric acid for periods extending from half a minute to four minutes, and then being washed in distilled water, were found to act very well, condensing one cubic inch and a half of gas in the space of eight or nine minutes, and rendering the tube warm (570).

601. Strong sulphuric acid was very effectual in rendering the platina active. A plate (569) was heated in it for a minute, then washed and put into the mixed oxygen and hydrogen, upon which it acted as well as if it had been made the positive pole of a voltaic pile (570).

602. Plates which, after being heated or electrized in alkali, or after other treatment, were found inert, immediately received power by being dipped for a minute or two, or even only for an instant, into hot oil of vitriol, and then into water.

603. When the plate was dipped into the oil of vitriol, taken out, and then heated so as to drive off the acid it did not act, in consequence of the impurity left by the acid upon its surface.

604. Vegetable acids, as acetic and tartaric, sometimes rendered inert platina active, at other times not. This, I believe, depended upon the character of the matter previously soiling the plates, and which may easily be supposed to be sometimes of such a nature as to be removed by these acids, and at other times not. Weak sulphuric acid showed the same difference, but strong sulphuric acid (601) never failed in its action.

605. The most favourable treatment, except that of making the plate a positive pole in strong acid, was as follows. The plate was held over a spirit-lamp flame, and when hot, rubbed with a piece of *potassa fusa* (caustic potash), which

melting, covered the metal with a coat of very strong alkali, and this was retained fused upon the surface for a second or two:[1] it was then put into water for four or five minutes to wash off the alkali, shaken, and immersed for about a minute in hot strong oil of vitriol; from this it was removed into distilled water, where it was allowed to remain ten or fifteen minutes to remove the last traces of acid (582). Being then put into a mixture of oxygen and hydrogen, combination immediately began, and proceeded rapidly; the tube became warm, the platina became red-hot, and the residue of the gases was inflamed. This effect could be repeated at pleasure, and thus the maximum phenomenon could be produced without the aid of the voltaic battery.

606. When a solution of tartaric or acetic acid was substituted, in this mode of preparation, for the sulphuric acid, still the plate was found to acquire the same power, and would often produce explosion in the mixed gases; but the strong sulphuric acid was most certain and powerful.

607. If borax, or a mixture of the carbonates of potash and soda, be fused on the surface of a platina plate, and that plate be well-washed in water, it will be found to have acquired the power of combining oxygen and hydrogen, but only in a moderate degree: but if, after the fusion and washing, it be dipped in the hot sulphuric acid (601), it will become very active.

608. Other metals than platina were then experimented with. Gold and palladium exhibited the power either when made the positive pole of the voltaic battery (570), or when acted on by hot oil of vitriol (601). When palladium is used, the action of the battery or acid should be moderated, as that metal is soon acted upon under such circumstances. Silver and copper could not be made to show any effect at common temperatures.

609. There can remain no doubt that the property of inducing combination, which can thus be conferred upon masses of platina and other metals by connecting them with the poles of the battery, or by cleansing processes either of a mechanical or chemical nature, is the same as that which was discovered by Dobereiner,[2] in 1823, to belong in so eminent a degree to spongy platina, and which was afterwards so well experimented upon and illustrated by

MM. Dulong and Thenard,[3] in 1823. The latter philosophers even quote experiments in which a very fine platina wire, which had been coiled up and digested in nitric, sulphuric, or muriatic acid, became ignited when put into a jet of hydrogen gas.[4] This effect I can now produce at pleasure with either wires or plates by the processes described (570, 601, 605); and by using a smaller plate cut so that it shall rest against the glass by a few points, and yet allow the water to flow off (Pl. VI, *Fig. 4*), the loss of heat is less, the metal is assimilated somewhat to the spongy state, and the probability of failure almost entirely removed.

610. M. Dobereiner refers the effect entirely to an electric action. He considers the platina and hydrogen as forming a voltaic element of the ordinary kind, in which the hydrogen, being very highly positive, represents the zinc of the usual arrangement, and like it, therefore, attracts oxygen and combines with it.[5]

611. In the two excellent experimental papers by MM. Dulong and Thenard,[6] those philosophers show that elevation of temperature favours the action, but does not alter its character; Sir Humphry Davy's incandescent platina wire being the same phenomenon with Dobereiner's spongy platina. They show that *all* metals have this power in a greater or smaller degree, and that it is even possessed by such bodies as charcoal, pumice, porcelain, glass, rock crystal, &c., when their temperatures are raised; and that another of Davy's effects, in which oxygen and hydrogen had combined slowly together at a heat below ignition, was really dependent upon the property of the heated glass, which it has in common with the bodies named above. They state that liquids do not show this effect, at least that mercury, at or below the boiling point, has not the power; that it is not due to porosity; that the same body varies very much in its action, according to its state; and that many other gaseous mixtures besides oxygen and hydrogen are affected, and made to act chemically, when the temperature is raised. They think it probable that spongy platina acquires its power from contact with the acid evolved during its reduction, or from the heat itself to which it is then submitted.

612. MM. Dulong and Thenard express themselves with great caution on the theory of this

[1] The heat need not be raised so much as to make the alkali tarnish the platina, although if that effect does take place it does not prevent the ultimate action.

[2] *Annales de Chimie*, Vol. XXIV, p. 93.

[3] *Ibid.*, Vol. XXIII, p. 440; Vol. XXIV, p. 380.

[4] *Ibid.*, Vol. XXIV, p. 383.

[5] *Ibid.*, Vol. XXIV, pp. 94, 95. Also *Bibliothèque Universelle*, Vol. XXIV, p. 54.

[6] *Ibid.*, Vol. XXIII, p. 440; Vol. XXIV, p. 380.

action; but, referring to the decomposing power of metals on ammonia when heated to temperatures not sufficient alone to affect the alkali, they remark that those metals which in this case are most efficacious, are the least so in causing the combination of oxygen and hydrogen; whilst platina, gold, &c., which have least power of decomposing ammonia, have most power of combining the elements of water: from which they are led to believe, that amongst gases, some tend to *unite* under the influence of metals, whilst others tend to *separate*, and that this property varies in opposite directions with the different metals. At the close of their second paper they observe, that the action is of a kind that cannot be connected with any known theory; and though it is very remarkable that the effects are transient, like those of most electrical actions, yet they state that the greater number of the results observed by them are inexplicable, by supposing them to be of a purely electric origin.

613. Dr. Fusinieri has also written on this subject, and given a theory which he considers as sufficient to account for the phenomena.[1] He expresses the immediate cause thus: "The platina determines upon its surface a continual renovation of *concrete laminæ* of the combustible substance of the gases or vapours, which flowing over it are burnt, pass away, and are renewed: this combustion at the surface raises and sustains the temperature of the metal." The combustible substance, thus reduced into imperceptible laminæ, of which the concrete parts are in contact with the oxygen, is presumed to be in a state combinable with the oxygen at a much lower temperature than when it is in the gaseous state, and more in analogy with what is called the nascent condition. That combustible gases should lose their elastic state, and become concrete, assuming the form of exceedingly attenuated but solid strata, is considered as proved by facts, some of which are quoted in the *Giornale di Fisica* for 1824;[2] and though the theory requires that they should assume this state at high temperatures, and though the *similar* films of aqueous and other matter are dissipated by the action of heat, still the facts are considered as justifying the conclusion against all opposition of reasoning.

614. The power or force which makes combustible gas or vapour abandon its elastic state in contact with a solid, that it may cover the latter with a thin stratum of its own proper

substance, is considered as being neither attraction nor affinity. It is able also to extend liquids and solids in concrete laminæ over the surface of the acting solid body, and consists in a *repulsion*, which is developed from the parts of the solid body by the simple fact of attenuation, and is highest when the attenuation is most complete. The force has a progressive development, and acts most powerfully, or at first, in the direction in which the dimensions of the attenuated mass decrease, and then in the direction of the angles or corners which from any cause may exist on the surface. This force not only causes spontaneous diffusion of gases and other substances over the surface, but is considered as very elementary in its nature, and competent to account for all the phenomena of capillarity, chemical affinity, attraction of aggregation, rarefaction, ebullition, volatilization, explosion, and other thermometric effects, as well as inflammation, detonation, &c., &c. It is considered as a form of heat to which the term *native caloric* is given, and is still further viewed as the principle of the two electricities and the two magnetisms.

615. I have been the more anxious to give a correct abstract of Dr. Fusinieri's view, both because I cannot form a distinct idea of the power to which he refers the phenomena, and because of my imperfect knowledge of the language in which the memoir is written. I would therefore beg to refer those who pursue the subject to the memoir itself.

616. Not feeling, however, that the problem has yet been solved, I venture to give the view which seems to me sufficient, upon *known principles*, to account for the effect.

617. It may be observed of this action, that, with regard to platina, it cannot be due to any peculiar, temporary condition, either of an electric or of any other nature: the activity of plates rendered either positive or negative by the pole, or cleaned with such different substances as acids, alkalies, or water; charcoal, emery, ashes, or glass; or merely heated, is sufficient to negative such an opinion. Neither does it depend upon the spongy and porous, or upon the compact and burnished, or upon the massive or the attenuated state of the metal, for in any of these states it may be rendered effective, or its action may be taken away. The only essential condition appears to be a *perfectly clean* and *metallic surface*, for whenever that is present the platina acts, whatever its form and condition in other respects may be; and though variations in the latter points will very

[1] *Giornale di Fisica,* &c., 1825, Vol. VIII, p. 259.
[2] pp. 138, 371.

much affect the rapidity, and therefore the visible appearances and secondary effects, of the action, i.e., the ignition of the metal and the inflammation of the gases, they, even in their most favourable state, cannot produce any effect unless the condition of a clean, pure, metallic surface be also fulfilled.

618. The effect is evidently produced by most, if not all, solid bodies, weakly perhaps by many of them, but rising to a high degree in platina. Dulong and Thenard have very philosophically extended our knowledge of the property to its possession by all the metals, and by earths, glass, stones, &c. (611); and every idea of its being a known and recognised electric action is in this way removed.

619. All the phenomena connected with this subject press upon my mind the conviction that the effects in question are entirely incidental and of a secondary nature; that they are dependent upon the *natural conditions* of gaseous elasticity, combined with the exertion of that attractive force possessed by many bodies, especially those which are solid, in an eminent degree, and probably belonging to all; by which they are drawn into association more or less close, without at the same time undergoing chemical combination, though often assuming the condition of adhesion; and which occasionally leads, under very favourable circumstances, as in the present instance, to the combination of bodies simultaneously subjected to this attraction. I am prepared myself to admit (and probably many others are of the same opinion), both with respect to the attraction of aggregation and of chemical affinity, that the sphere of action of particles extends beyond those other particles with which they are immediately and evidently in union (523), and in many cases produces effects rising into considerable importance: and I think that this kind of attraction is a determining cause of Dobereiner's effect, and of the many others of a similar nature.

620. Bodies which become wetted by fluids with which they do not combine chemically, or in which they do not dissolve, are simple and well-known instances of this kind of attraction.

621. All those cases of bodies which being insoluble in water and not combining with it are hygrometric, and condense its vapour around or upon their surface, are stronger instances of the same power, and approach a little nearer to the cases under investigation. If pulverized clay, protoxide or peroxide of iron, oxide of manganese, charcoal, or even metals, as spongy platina or precipitated silver, be put into an atmos-

phere containing vapour of water they soon become moist by virtue of an attraction which is able to condense the vapour upon, although not to combine it with, the substances; and if, as is well known, these bodies so damped be put into a dry atmosphere, as, for instance, one confined over sulphuric acid, or if they be heated, then they yield up this water again almost entirely, it not being in direct or permanent combination.[1]

622. Still better instances of the power I refer to, because they are more analogous to the cases to be explained, are furnished by the attraction existing between glass and air, so well known to barometer and thermometer makers, for here the adhesion or attraction is exerted between a solid and gases, bodies having very different physical conditions, having no power of combination with each other, and each retaining, during the time of action, its physical state unchanged.[2] When mercury is poured into a barometer tube, a film of air will remain between the metal and glass for months, or, as far as is known, for years, for it has never been displaced except by the action of means especially fitted for the purpose. These consist in boiling the mercury, or in other words, of forming an abundance of vapour, which coming in contact with every part of the glass and every portion of surface of the mercury, gradually mingles with, dilutes, and carries off the air attracted by, and adhering to, those surfaces, replacing it by other vapour, subject to an equal or perhaps greater attraction, but which when cooled condenses into the same liquid as that with which the tube is filled.

623. Extraneous bodies, which, acting as nuclei in crystallizing or depositing solutions, cause deposition of substances on them, when it does not occur elsewhere in the liquid, seem to produce their effects by a power of the same kind, i.e., a power of attraction extending to neighbouring particles, and causing them to become attached to the nuclei, although it is not strong enough to make them combine chemically with their substance.

624. It would appear from many cases of nuclei in solutions, and from the effects of bodies

---

[1] I met at Edinburgh with a case, remarkable as to its extent, of hygrometric action, assisted a little perhaps by very slight solvent power. Some turf had been well-dried by long exposure in a covered place to the atmosphere, but being then submitted to the action of a hydrostatic press, it yielded, *by the mere influence of the pressure,* 54 per cent of water.

[2] Fusinieri and Bellani consider the air as forming solid concrete films in these cases. *Giornale di Fisica,* Vol. VIII, p. 262, 1825.

put into atmospheres containing the vapours of water, or camphor, or iodine, &c., as if this attraction were in part elective, partaking in its characters both of the attraction of aggregation and chemical affinity: nor is this inconsistent with, but agreeable to, the idea entertained that it is the power of particles acting, not upon others with which they can immediately and intimately combine, but upon such as are either more distantly situated with respect to them, or which, from previous condition, physical constitution, or feeble relation are unable to enter into decided union with them.

625. Then, of all bodies, the gases are those which might be expected to show some *mutual* action whilst *jointly* under the attractive influence of the platina or other solid acting substance. Liquids, such as water, alcohol, &c., are in so dense and comparatively incompressible a state, as to favour no expectation that their particles should approach much closer to each other by the attraction of the body to which they adhere, and yet that attraction must (according to its effects) place their particles as near to those of the solid wetted body as they are to each other, and in many cases it is evident that the former attraction is the stronger. But gases and vapours are bodies competent to suffer very great changes in the relative distances of their particles by external agencies; and where they are in immediate contact with the platina, the approximation of the particles to those of the metal may be very great. In the case of the hygrometric bodies referred to (621), it is sufficient to reduce the vapour to the fluid state, frequently from atmospheres so rare that without this influence it would be needful to compress them by mechanical force into a bulk not more than $\frac{1}{10}$th or even $\frac{1}{20}$th of their original volume before the vapours would become liquids.

626. Another most important consideration in relation to this action of bodies, and which, as far as I am aware, has not hitherto been noticed, is the condition of elasticity under which the gases are placed against the acting surface. We have but very imperfect notions of the real and intimate conditions of the particles of a body existing in the solid, the liquid, and the gaseous state; but when we speak of the gaseous state as being due to the mutual repulsions of the particles or of their atmospheres, although we may err in imagining each particle to be a little nucleus to an atmosphere of heat, or electricity, or any other agent, we are still not likely to be in error in considering the

elasticity as dependent on *mutuality* of action. Now this mutual relation fails altogether on the side of the gaseous particles next to the platina, and we might be led to expect *à priori* a deficiency of elastic force there to at least one half; for if, as Dalton has shown, the elastic force of the particles of one gas cannot act against the elastic force of the particles of another, the two being as vacua to each other, so is it far less likely that the particles of the platina can exert any influence on those of the gas against it, such as would be exerted by gaseous particles of its own kind.

627. But the diminution of power to one-half on the side of the gaseous body towards the metal is only a slight result of what seems to me to flow as a necessary consequence of the known constitution of gases. An atmosphere of one gas or vapour, however dense or compressed, is in effect as a vacuum to another: thus, if a little water were put into a vessel containing a dry gas, as air, of the pressure of one hundred atmospheres, as much vapour of the water would *rise* as if it were in a perfect vacuum. Here the particles of watery vapour appear to have no difficulty in approaching within any distance of the particles of air, being influenced solely by relation to particles of their own kind; and if it be so with respect to a body having the same elastic powers as itself, how much more surely must it be so with particles, like those of the platina, or other limiting body, which at the same time that they have not these elastic powers, are also unlike it in nature! Hence it would seem to result that the particles of hydrogen or any other gas or vapour which are next to the platina, &c., must be in such contact with it as if they were in the liquid state, and therefore almost infinitely closer to it than they are to each other, even though the metal be supposed to exert no attractive influence over them.

628. A third and very important consideration in favour of the mutual action of gases under these circumstances is their perfect miscibility. If fluid bodies capable of combining together are also capable of mixture, *they do combine* when they are mingled, not waiting for any other determining circumstance; but if two such gases as oxygen and hydrogen are put together, though they are elements having such powerful affinity as to unite naturally under a thousand different circumstances, they do not combine by mere mixture. Still it is evident that, from their perfect association, the particles are in the most favourable state possible

for combination upon the supervention of any determining cause, such either as the negative action of the platina in suppressing or annihilating, as it were, their elasticity on its side; or the positive action of the metal in condensing them against its surface by an attractive force; or the influence of both together.

629. Although there are not many distinct cases of combination under the influence of forces external to the combining particles, yet there are sufficient to remove any difficulty which might arise on that ground. Sir James Hall found carbonic acid and lime to remain combined under pressure at temperatures at which they would not have remained combined if the pressure had been removed; and I have had occasion to observe a case of direct combination in chlorine,[1] which being compressed at common temperatures will combine with water, and form a definite crystalline hydrate, incapable either of being formed or of existing if that pressure be removed.

630. The course of events when platina acts upon, and combines oxygen and hydrogen, may be stated, according to these principles, as follows. From the influence of the circumstances mentioned (619, &c.), i.e., the deficiency of elastic power and the attraction of the metal for the gases, the latter, when they are in association with the former, are so far condensed as to be brought within the action of their mutual affinities at the existing temperature; the deficiency of elastic power, not merely subjecting them more closely to the attractive influence of the metal, but also bringing them into a more favourable state for union, by abstracting a part of that power (upon which depends their elasticity) which elsewhere in the mass of gases is opposing their combination. The consequence of their combination is the production of the vapour of water and an elevation of temperature. But as the attraction of the platina for the water formed is not greater than for the gases, if so great (for the metal is scarcely hygrometric), the vapour is quickly diffused through the remaining gases: fresh portions of the latter, therefore, come into juxtaposition with the metal, combine, and the fresh vapour formed is also diffused, allowing new portions of gas to be acted upon. In this way the process advances, but is accelerated by the evolution of heat, which is known by experiment to facilitate the combination in proportion to its intensity, and the temperature is thus gradually exalted until ignition results.

[1] *Philosophical Transactions*, 1823, p. 161.

631. The dissipation of the vapour produced at the surface of the platina, and the contact of fresh oxygen and hydrogen with the metal, form no difficulty in this explication. The platina is not considered as causing the combination of any particles with itself, but only associating them closely around it; and the compressed particles are as free to move from the platina, being replaced by other particles, as a portion of dense air upon the surface of the globe, or at the bottom of a deep mine, is free to move by the slightest impulse, into the upper and rarer parts of the atmosphere.

632. It can hardly be necessary to give any reasons why platina does not show this effect under ordinary circumstances. It is then not sufficiently clean (617), and the gases are prevented from touching it, and suffering that degree of effect which is needful to commence their combination at common temperatures and which they can only experience at its surface. In fact, the very power which causes the combination of oxygen and hydrogen is competent, under the usual casual exposure of platina, to condense extraneous matters upon its surface, which, soiling it, take away for the time its power of combining oxygen and hydrogen, by preventing their contact with it (598).

633. Clean platina, by which I mean such as has been made the positive pole of a pile (570), or has been treated with acid (605), and has then been put into distilled water for twelve or fifteen minutes, has a *peculiar friction* when one piece is rubbed against another. It wets freely with pure water, even after it has been shaken and dried by the heat of a spirit-lamp; and if made the pole of a voltaic pile in a dilute acid, it evolves minute bubbles from every part of its surface. But platina in its common state wants that peculiar friction: it will not wet freely with water as the clean platina does; and when made the positive pole of a pile, it for a time gives off large bubbles, which seem to cling or adhere to the metal, and are evolved at distinct and separate points of the surface. These appearances and effects, as well as its want of power on oxygen and hydrogen, are the consequences, and the indications, of a soiled surface.

634. I found also that platina plates which had been cleaned perfectly soon became soiled by mere exposure to the air; for after twenty-four hours they no longer moistened freely with water, but the fluid ran up into portions, leaving part of the surface bare, whilst other plates

which had been retained in water for the same time, when they were dried (580) did moisten, and gave the other indications of a clean surface.

635. Nor was this the case with platina or metals only, but also with earthy bodies. Rock crystal and obsidian would not wet freely upon the surface, but being moistened with strong oil of vitriol, then washed, and left in distilled water to remove all the acid, they did freely become moistened, whether they were previously dry or whether they were left wet; but being dried and left exposed to the air for twenty-four hours, their surface became so soiled that water would not then adhere freely to it, but ran up into partial portions. Wiping with a cloth (even the cleanest) was still worse than exposure to air; the surface either of the minerals or metals immediately became as if it were slightly greasy. The floating upon water of small particles of metals under ordinary circumstances is a consequence of this kind of soiled surface. The extreme difficulty of cleaning the surface of mercury when it has once been soiled or greased, is due to the same cause.

636. The same reasons explain why the power of the platina plates in some circumstances soon disappear, and especially upon use: MM. Dulong and Thenard have observed the same effect with the spongy metal,[1] as indeed have all those who have used Dobereiner's instantaneous light machines. If left in the air, if put into ordinary distilled water, if made to act upon ordinary oxygen and hydrogen, they can still find in all these cases *that* minute portion of impurity which, when once in contact with the surface of the platina, is retained there, and is sufficient to prevent its full action upon oxygen and hydrogen at common temperatures: a slight elevation of temperature is again sufficient to compensate this effect, and cause combination.

637. No state of a solid body can be conceived more favourable for the production of the effect than that which is possessed by platina obtained from the ammonio-muriate by heat. Its surface is most extensive and pure, yet very accessible to the gases brought in contact with it: if placed in impurity, the interior, as Thenard and Dulong have observed, is preserved clean by the exterior; and as regards temperature, it is so bad a conductor of heat, because of its divided condition, that almost all which is evolved by the combination of the first portions of gas is retained within the mass, exalt-

[1] *Annales de Chimie*, Vol. XXIV. p. 386.

ing the tendency of the succeeding portions to combine.

638. I have now to notice some very extraordinary interferences with this phenomenon, dependent, not upon the nature or condition of the metal or other acting solid, but upon the presence of certain substances mingled with the gases acted upon; and as I shall have occasion to speak frequently of a mixture of oxygen and hydrogen, I wish it always to be understood that I mean a mixture composed of one volume of oxygen to two volumes of hydrogen, being the proportions that form water. Unless otherwise expressed, the hydrogen was always that obtained by the action of dilute sulphuric acid on pure zinc, and the oxygen that obtained by the action of heat from the chlorate of potassa.

639. Mixtures of oxygen and hydrogen with *air*, containing one-fourth, one-half, and even two-thirds of the latter, being introduced with prepared platina plates (570, 605) into tubes, were acted upon almost as well as if no air were present: the retardation was far less than might have been expected from the mere dilution and consequent obstruction to the contact of the gases with the plates. In two hours and a half nearly all the oxygen and hydrogen introduced as mixture was gone.

640. But when similar experiments were made with *olefiant gas* (the platina plates having been made the positive poles of a voltaic pile [570] in acid), very different results occurred. A mixture was made of 29.2 volumes hydrogen and 14.6 volumes oxygen, being the proportions for water: and to this was added another mixture of 3 volumes oxygen and one volume olefiant gas, so that the olefiant gas formed but ¼₈th part of the whole; yet in this mixture the platina plate would not act in forty-five hours. The failure was not for want of any power in the plate, for when after that time it was taken out of this mixture and put into one of oxygen and hydrogen, it immediately acted, and in seven minutes caused explosion of the gas. This result was obtained several times, and when larger proportions of olefiant gas were used, the action seemed still more hopeless.

641. A mixture of forty-nine volumes oxygen and hydrogen (638) with one volume of olefiant gas had a well-prepared platina plate introduced. The diminution of gas was scarcely sensible at the end of two hours, during which it was watched; but on examination twenty-four hours afterwards, the tube was

found blown to pieces. The action, therefore, though it had been very much retarded, had occurred at last, and risen to a maximum.

642. With a mixture of ninety-nine volumes of oxygen and hydrogen (638) with one of olefiant gas, a feeble action was evident at the end of fifty minutes; it went on accelerating (630) until the eighty-fifth minute, and then became so intense that the gas exploded. Here also the retarding effect of the olefiant gas was very beautifully illustrated.

643. Plates prepared by alkali and acid (605) produced effects corresponding to those just described.

644. It is perfectly clear from these experiments, that *olefiant gas*, even in small quantities, has a very remarkable influence in preventing the combination of oxygen and hydrogen under these circumstances, and yet without at all injuring or affecting the power of the platina.

645. Another striking illustration of similar interference may be shown in *carbonic oxide;* especially if contrasted with *carbonic acid.* A mixture of one volume oxygen and hydrogen (638) with four volumes of carbonic acid was affected at once by a platina plate prepared with acid, &c. (605), and in one hour and a quarter nearly all the oxygen and hydrogen was gone. Mixtures containing less carbonic acid were still more readily affected.

646. But when carbonic oxide was substituted for the carbonic acid, not the slightest effect of combination was produced; and when the carbonic oxide was only one-eighth of the whole volume, no action occurred in forty and fifty hours. Yet the plates had not lost their power; for being taken out and put into pure oxygen and hydrogen, they acted well and at once.

647. Two volumes of carbonic oxide and one of oxygen were mingled with nine volumes of oxygen and hydrogen (638). This mixture was not affected by a plate which had been made positive in acid, though it remained in it fifteen hours. But when to the same volumes of carbonic oxide and oxygen were added thirty-three volumes of oxygen and hydrogen, the carbonic oxide being then only $\frac{1}{18}$th part of the whole, the plate acted, slowly at first, and at the end of forty-two minutes the gases exploded.

648. These experiments were extended to various gases and vapours, the general results of which may be given as follow. Oxygen, hydrogen, nitrogen, and nitrous oxide, when used to dilute the mixture of oxygen and hydrogen,

did not prevent the action of the plates even when they made four-fifths of the whole volume of gas acted upon. Nor was the retardation so great in any case as might have been expected from the mere dilution of the oxygen and hydrogen, and the consequent mechanical obstruction to its contact with the platina. The order in which carbonic acid and these substances seemed to stand was as follows, the first interfering least with the action; *nitrous oxide, hydrogen, carbonic acid, nitrogen, oxygen:* but it is possible the plates were not equally well prepared in all the cases, and that other circumstances also were unequal: consequently more numerous experiments would be required to establish the order accurately.

649. As to cases of *retardation*, the powers of olefiant gas and carbonic oxide have been already described. Mixtures of oxygen and hydrogen, containing from $\frac{1}{16}$th, to $\frac{1}{20}$th of sulphuretted hydrogen or phosphuretted hydrogen, seemed to show a little action at first, but were not further affected by the prepared plates, though in contact with them for seventy hours. When the plates were removed they had lost all power over pure oxygen and hydrogen, and the interference of these gases was therefore of a different nature from that of the two former, having permanently affected the plate.

650. A small piece of cork was dipped in sulphuret of carbon and passed up through water into a tube containing oxygen and hydrogen (638), so as to diffuse a portion of its vapour through the gases. A plate being introduced appeared at first to act a little, but after sixty-one hours the diminution was very small. Upon putting the same plate into a pure mixture of oxygen and hydrogen, it acted at once and powerfully, having apparently suffered no diminution of its force.

651. A little vapour of ether being mixed with the oxygen and hydrogen retarded the action of the plate, but did not prevent it altogether. A little of the vapour of the condensed oil-gas liquor[1] retarded the action still more, but not nearly so much as an equal volume of olefiant gas would have done. In both these cases it was the original oxygen and hydrogen which combined together, the ether and the oil-gas vapour remaining unaffected, and in both cases the plates retained the power of acting on fresh oxygen and hydrogen.

652. Spongy platina was then used in place of the plates, and jets of hydrogen mingled with the different gases thrown against it in

[1] *Philosophical Transactions*, 1825, p. 440.

air. The results were exactly of the same kind, although presented occasionally in a more imposing form. Thus, mixtures of one volume of olefiant gas or carbonic oxide with three of hydrogen could not heat the spongy platina when the experiments were commenced at common temperatures; but a mixture of equal volumes of nitrogen and hydrogen acted very well, causing ignition. With carbonic acid the results were still more striking. A mixture of three volumes of that gas with one of hydrogen caused *ignition* of the platina, yet that mixture would not continue to burn from the jet when attempts were made to light it by a taper. A mixture even of *seven* volumes of carbonic acid and *one* of hydrogen will thus cause the ignition of cold spongy platina, and yet, as if to supply a contrast, than which none can be greater, *it cannot burn at a taper*, but causes the extinction of the latter. On the other hand, the mixtures of carbonic oxide or olefiant gas, which can do nothing with the platina, are *inflamed* by the taper, burning well.

653. Hydrogen mingled with the vapour of ether or oil-gas liquor causes the ignition of the spongy platina. The mixture with oil-gas burns with a flame far brighter than that of the mixture of hydrogen and olefiant gas already referred to, so that it would appear that the retarding action of the hydrocarbons is not at all in proportion merely to the quantity of carbon present.

654. In connexion with these interferences, I must state, that hydrogen itself, prepared from steam passed over ignited iron, was found when mingled with oxygen to resist the action of platina. It had stood over water seven days, and had lost all fetid smell; but a jet of it would not cause the ignition of spongy platina, commencing at common temperatures; nor would it combine with oxygen in a tube either under the influence of a prepared plate or of spongy platina. A mixture of one volume of this gas with three of pure hydrogen, and the due proportion of oxygen, was not affected by plates after fifty hours. I am inclined to refer the effect to carbonic oxide present in the gas, but have not had time to verify the suspicion. The power of the plates was not destroyed (640, 646).

655. Such are the general facts of these remarkable interferences. Whether the effect produced by such small quantities of certain gases depends upon any direct action which they may exert upon the particles of oxygen and hydrogen, by which the latter are rendered less inclined to combine, or whether it depends upon their modifying the action of the plate temporarily (for they produce no real change on it), by investing it through the agency of a stronger attraction than that of the hydrogen, or otherwise, remains to be decided by more extended experiments.

656. The theory of action which I have given for the original phenomena appears to me quite sufficient to account for all the effects by reference to known properties, and dispenses with the assumption of any new power of matter. I have pursued this subject at some length, as one of great consequence, because I am convinced that the superficial actions of matter, whether between two bodies, or of one piece of the same body, and the actions of particles not directly or strongly in combination, are becoming daily more and more important to our theories of chemical as well as mechanical philosophy.[1] In all ordinary cases of combustion it is evident that an action of the kind considered, occurring upon the surface of the carbon in the fire, and also in the bright part of a flame, must have great influence over the combinations there taking place.

657. The condition of elasticity upon the exterior of the gaseous or vaporous mass already referred to (626, 627), must be connected directly with the action of solid bodies, as nuclei, on vapours, causing condensation upon them in preference to any condensation in the vapours themselves; and in the well-known effect of nuclei on solutions a similar condition may have existence (623), for an analogy in condition exists between the parts of a body in solution, and those of a body in the vaporous or gaseous state. This thought leads us to the consideration of what are the respective conditions at the surfaces of contact of two portions of the same substance at the same temperature, one in the solid or liquid, and the other in the vaporous state; as, for instance,

[1] As a curious illustration of the influence of mechanical forces over chemical affinity, I will quote the refusal of certain substances to effloresce when their surfaces are perfect, which yield immediately upon the surface being broken. If crystals of carbonate of soda, or phosphate of soda, or sulphate of soda, having no part of their surfaces broken, be preserved from external violence, they will not effloresce. I have thus retained crystals of carbonate of soda perfectly transparent and unchanged from September 1827 to January 1833; and crystals of sulphate of soda from May 1832 to the present time, November 1833. If any part of the surface were scratched or broken, then efflorescence began at that part, and covered the whole. The crystals were merely placed in evaporating basins and covered with paper.

steam and water. It would seem that the particles of vapour next to the particles of liquid are in a different relation to the latter to what they would be with respect to any other liquid or solid substance; as, for instance, mercury or platina, if they were made to replace the water, i.e., if the view of independent action which I have taken (626, 627) as a consequence of Dalton's principles, be correct. It would also seem that the mutual relation of similar particles, and the indifference of dissimilar particles which Dalton has established as a matter of fact amongst gases and vapours, extends to a certain degree amongst solids and fluids, that is, when they are in relation by contact with vapours, either of their own substance or of other bodies. But though I view these points as of great importance with respect to the relations existing between different substances and their physical constitution in the solid, liquid, or gaseous state, I have not sufficiently considered them to venture any strong opinions or statements here.[1]

658. There are numerous well-known cases, in which substances, such as oxygen and hydrogen, act readily in their *nascent* state, and produce chemical changes which they are not able to effect if once they have assumed the gaseous condition. Such instances are very common at the poles of the voltaic pile, and are, I think, easily accounted for, if it be considered that at the moment of separation of any such particle it is entirely surrounded by other particles of a *different* kind with which it is in close contact, and has not yet assumed those relations and conditions which it has in its fully developed state, and which it can only assume by association with other particles of its own kind. For, at the moment, its elasticity is absent, and it is in the same relation to particles with which it is in contact, and for which it has an affinity, as the particles of oxygen and hydrogen are to each other on the surface of clean platina (626, 627).

659. The singular effects of retardation produced by very small quantities of some gases, and not by large quantities of others (640, 645, 652), if dependent upon any relation of the added gas to the surface of the solid, will then probably be found immediately connected with the curious phenomena which are presented by different gases when passing through narrow tubes at low pressures, which I observed many years ago;[2] and this action of surfaces must, I think, influence the highly interesting phenomena of the diffusion of gases, at least in the form in which it has been experimented upon by Mr. Graham in 1829 and 1831,[3] and also by Dr. Mitchell of Philadelphia[4] in 1830. It seems very probable that if such a substance as spongy platina were used, another law for the diffusion of gases under the circumstances would come out than that obtained by the use of plaster of Paris.

660. I intended to have followed this section by one on the secondary piles of Ritter, and the peculiar properties of the poles of the pile, or of metals through which electricity has passed, which have been observed by Ritter, Van Marum, Yelin, De la Rive, Marianini, Berzelius, and others. It appears to me that all these phenomena bear a satisfactory explanation on known principles, connected with the investigation just terminated, and do not require the assumption of any new state or new property. But as the experiments advanced, especially those of Marianini, require very careful repetition and examination, the necessity of pursuing the subject of electro-chemical decomposition obliges me for a time to defer the researches to which I have just referred.

Royal Institution, November 30, 1833

[1] In reference to this paragraph and also 626, see a correction by Dr. C. Henry, in his valuable paper on this curious subject. *Philosophical Magazine*, 1835, Vol. VI, p. 365.—*Dec.* 1838.

[2] *Quarterly Journal of Science*, 1819, Vol. VII, p. 106.

[3] *Quarterly Journal of Science*, Vol. XXVIII, p. 74, and *Edinburgh Transactions*, 1831.

[4] *Journal of the Royal Institution* for 1831, p. 101.

SEVENTH SERIES

§ 11. *On Electro-chemical Decomposition, continued*[1] ¶ iv. *On Some General Conditions of Electro-chemical Decomposition* ¶ v. *On a New Measurer of Volta-electricity* ¶ vi. *On the Primary or Secondary Character of the Bodies Evolved at the Electrodes* ¶ vii. *On the Definite Nature and Extent of Electro-chemical Decompositions* § 13. *On the Absolute Quantity of Electricity Associated with the Particles or Atoms of Matter*

RECEIVED JANUARY 9, READ JANUARY 23, FEBRUARY 6 AND 13, 1834

Preliminary

661. THE theory which I believe to be a true expression of the facts of electro-chemical decomposition, and which I have therefore detailed in a former series of these *Researches*, is so much at variance with those previously advanced, that I find the greatest difficulty in stating results, as I think, correctly, whilst limited to the use of terms which are current with a certain accepted meaning. Of this kind is the term *pole*, with its prefixes of positive and negative, and the attached ideas of attraction and repulsion. The general phraseology is that the positive pole *attracts* oxygen, acids, &c., or more cautiously, that it *determines* their evolution upon its surface; and that the negative pole acts in an equal manner upon hydrogen, combustibles, metals, and bases. According to my view, the determining force is *not* at the poles, but *within* the body under decomposition; and the oxygen and acids are rendered at the *negative* extremity of that body, whilst hydrogen, metals, &c., are evolved at the *positive* extremity (518, 524).

662. To avoid, therefore, confusion and circumlocution, and for the sake of greater precision of expression than I can otherwise obtain, I have deliberately considered the subject with two friends, and with their assistance and concurrence in framing them, I purpose henceforward using certain other terms, which I will now define. The *poles*, as they are usually called, are only the doors or ways by which the electric current passes into and out of the decomposing body (556); and they of course, when in contact with that body, are the limits of its extent in the direction of the current. The

term has been generally applied to the metal surfaces in contact with the decomposing substance; but whether philosophers generally would also apply it to the surfaces of air (465, 471) and water (493), against which I have effected electro-chemical decomposition, is subject to doubt. In place of the term pole, I propose using that of *electrode*,[2] and I mean thereby that substance, or rather surface, whether of air, water, metal, or any other body, which bounds the extent of the decomposing matter in the direction of the electric current.

663. The surfaces at which, according to common phraseology, the electric current enters and leaves a decomposing body, are most important places of action, and require to be distinguished apart from the poles, with which they are mostly, and the electrodes, with which they are always, in contact. Wishing for a natural standard of electric direction to which I might refer these, expressive of their difference and at the same time free from all theory, I have thought it might be found in the earth. If the magnetism of the earth be due to electric currents passing round it, the latter must be in a constant direction, which, according to present usage of speech, would be from east to west, or, which will strengthen this help to the memory, that in which the sun appears to move. If in any case of electro-decomposition we consider the decomposing body as placed so that the current passing through it shall be in the same direction, and parallel to that supposed to exist in the earth, then the surfaces at which the electricity is passing into and out of the substance would have an invariable reference, and exhibit constantly the same relations of

[1] Refer to the note after 1047, Series VIII.—*Dec.* 1838.

[2] ἤλεκτρον, and ὁδὸς 'a way.'

361

powers. Upon this notion we purpose calling that towards the east the *anode*,[1] and that towards the west the *cathode*;[2] and whatever changes may take place in our views of the nature of electricity and electrical action, as they must affect the *natural standard* referred to, in the same direction, and to an equal amount with any decomposing substances to which these terms may at any time be applied, there seems no reason to expect that they will lead to confusion, or tend in any way to support false views. The *anode* is therefore that surface at which the electric current, according to our present expression, enters: it is the *negative* extremity of the decomposing body; is where oxygen, chlorine, acids, &c., are evolved; and is against or opposite the positive electrode. The *cathode* is that surface at which the current leaves the decomposing body, and is its *positive* extremity; the combustible bodies, metals, alkalies, and bases, are evolved there, and it is in contact with the negative electrode.

664. I shall have occasion in these *Researches*, also, to class bodies together according to certain relations derived from their electrical actions (822); and wishing to express those relations without at the same time involving the expression of any hypothetical views, I intend using the following names and terms. Many bodies are decomposed directly by the electric current, their elements being set free; these I propose to call *electrolytes*.[3] Water, therefore, is an electrolyte. The bodies which, like nitric or sulphuric acids, are decomposed in a secondary manner (752, 757), are not included under this term. Then for *electro-chemically decomposed*, I shall often use the term *electrolyzed*, derived in the same way, and implying that the body spoken of is separated into its components under the influence of electricity: it is analogous in its sense and sound to *analyze*, which is derived in a similar manner. The term *electrolytical* will be understood at once: muriatic acid is electrolytical, boracic acid is not.

665. Finally, I require a term to express those bodies which can pass to the *electrodes*, or, as they are usually called, the poles. Substances are frequently spoken of as being *electro-negative*, or *electro-positive*, according as they go under the supposed influence of a direct attraction to the positive or negative pole. But these

terms are much too significant for the use to which I should have to put them; for though the meanings are perhaps right, they are only hypothetical, and may be wrong; and then, through a very imperceptible, but still very dangerous, because continual, influence, they do great injury to science, by contracting and limiting the habitual views of those engaged in pursuing it. I propose to distinguish such bodies by calling those *anions*[4] which go to the *anode* of the decomposing body; and those passing to the *cathode*, *cations*;[5] and when I have occasion to speak of these together, I shall call them *ions*. Thus the chloride of lead is an *electrolyte*, and when *electrolyzed* evolves the two *ions*, chlorine and lead, the former being an *anion*, and the latter a *cation*.

666. These terms being once well-defined, will, I hope, in their use enable me to avoid much periphrasis and ambiguity of expression. I do not mean to press them into service more frequently than will be required, for I am fully aware that names are one thing and science another.

667. It will be well understood that I am giving no opinion respecting the nature of the electric current now, beyond what I have done on former occasions (283, 517); and that though I speak of the current as proceeding from the parts which are positive to those which are negative (663), it is merely in accordance with the conventional, though in some degree tacit, agreement entered into by scientific men, that they may have a constant, certain, and definite means of referring to the direction of the forces of that current.[6]

¶ iv. *On Some General Conditions of Electro-chemical Decomposition*

669. From the period when electro-chemical decomposition was first effected to the present time, it has been a remark, that those elements which, in the ordinary phenomena of chemical affinity, were the most directly opposed to each other, and combined with the greatest attractive force, were those which were the most readily evolved at the opposite extremities of the decomposing bodies (549).

670. If this result was evident when water was supposed to be essential to, and was pres-

---

[1] ἄνω 'upwards' and ὁδὸς 'a way;' the way which the sun rises.

[2] κατά 'downwards'; and ὁδὸς 'a way'; the way which the sun sets.

[3] ἤλεκτρον, and λύω, *solvo*. N. Electrolyte, V. Electrolyze.

[4] ἀνιὼν 'that which goes up.' (Neuter participle.)

[5] κατιὼν 'that which goes down.'

[6] Since this paper was read, I have changed some of the terms which were first proposed, that I might employ only such as were at the same time simple in their nature, clear in their reference, and free from hypothesis.

ent in, almost every case of such decomposition (472), it is far more evident now that it has been shown and proved that water is not necessarily concerned in the phenomena (474), and that other bodies much surpass it in some of the effects supposed to be peculiar to that substance.

671. Water, from its constitution and the nature of its elements, and from its frequent presence in cases of electrolytic action, has hitherto stood foremost in this respect. Though a compound formed by very powerful affinity, it yields up its elements under the influence of a very feeble electric current; and it is doubtful whether a case of electrolyzation can occur, where, being present, it is not resolved into its first principles.

672. The various oxides, chlorides, iodides, and salts, which I have shown are decomposable by the electric current when in the liquid state, under the same general law with water (402), illustrate in an equally striking manner the activity, in such decompositions, of elements directly and powerfully opposed to each other by their chemical relations.

673. On the other hand, bodies dependent on weak affinities very rarely give way. Take, for instance, glasses: many of those formed of silica, lime, alkali, and oxide of lead, may be considered as little more than solutions of substances one in another.[1] If bottle-glass be fused, and subjected to the voltaic pile, it does not appear to be at all decomposed (408). If flint glass, which contains substances more directly opposed, be operated upon, it suffers some decomposition; and if borate of lead glass, which is a definite chemical compound, be experimented with, it readily yields up its elements (408).

674. But the result which is found to be so striking in the instances quoted is not at all borne out by reference to other cases where a similar consequence might have been expected. It may be said, that my own theory of electro-chemical decomposition would lead to the expectation that all compound bodies should give way under the influence of the electric current with a facility proportionate to the strength of the affinity by which their elements, either proximate or ultimate, are combined. I am not sure that that follows as a consequence of the theory; but if the objection is supposed to be one presented by the facts, I have no doubt it will be removed when we obtain a more intimate acquaintance with, and precise idea of, the nature of chemical affinity and the mode of action of an electric current over it (518, 524): besides which, it is just as directly opposed to any other theory of electro-chemical decomposition as the one I have propounded; for if it be admitted, as is generally the case, that the more directly bodies are opposed to each other in their attractive forces, the more powerfully do they combine, then the objection applies with equal force to any of the theories of electrolyzation which have been considered, and is an addition to those which I have taken against them.

675. Amongst powerful compounds which are not decomposed, boracic acids stand prominent (408). Then again, the iodide of sulphur, and the chlorides of sulphur, phosphorus, and carbon, are not decomposable under common circumstances, though their elements are of a nature which would lead to a contrary expectation. Chloride of antimony (402, 690), the hydro-carbons, acetic acid, ammonia, and many other bodies undecomposable by the voltaic pile, would seem to be formed by an affinity sufficiently strong to indicate that the elements were so far contrasted in their nature as to sanction the expectation that the pile would separate them, especially as in some cases of mere solution (530, 544), where the affinity must by comparison be very weak, separation takes place.[2]

676. It must not be forgotten, however, that much of this difficulty, and perhaps the whole, may depend upon the absence of conducting power, which, preventing the transmission of the current, prevents of course the effects due to it. All known compounds being non-conductors when solid, but conductors when liquid, are decomposed, with *perhaps* the single exception at present known of periodide of mercury (679, 691);[3] and even water itself, which so easily yields up its elements when the current passes, if rendered quite pure, scarcely suffers change, because it then becomes a very bad conductor.

677. If it should hereafter be proved that the want of decomposition in those cases where, from chemical considerations, it might be so strongly expected (669, 672, 674), is due to the absence or deficiency of conducting power, it would also at the same time be proved that decomposition *depends* upon conduction, and not the latter upon the former (413); and in water

---

[1] *Philosophical Transactions*, 1830, p. 49.

[2] With regard to solution, I have met with some reasons for supposing that it will probably disappear as a cause of transference, and intend resuming the consideration at a convenient opportunity.

[3] See now, 1340, 1341.—*Dec.* 1838.

this seems to be very nearly decided. On the other hand, the conclusion is almost irresistible that in electrolytes the power of transmitting the electricity across the substance is *dependent* upon their capability of suffering decomposition; taking place only whilst they are decomposing, and being proportionate to the quantity of elements separated (821). I may not, however, stop to discuss this point experimentally at present.

678. When a compound contains such elements as are known to pass towards the opposite extremities of the voltaic pile, still the proportions in which they are present appear to be intimately connected with capability in the compound of suffering or resisting decomposition. Thus, the protochloride of tin readily conducts, and is decomposed (402), but the perchloride neither conducts nor is decomposed (406). The protiodide of tin is decomposed when fluid (402); the periodide is not (405). The periodide of mercury when fused is not decomposed (691), even though it does conduct. I was unable to contrast it with the protiodide, the latter being converted into mercury and periodide by heat.

679. These important differences induced me to look more closely to certain binary compounds, with a view of ascertaining whether a *law* regulating the *decomposability* according to some *relation of the proportionals or equivalents* of the elements, could be discovered. The *proto* compounds only, amongst those just referred to, were decomposable; and on referring to the substances quoted to illustrate the force and generality of the law of conduction and decomposition which I discovered (402), it will be found that all the oxides, chlorides, and iodides subject to it, except the chloride of antimony and the periodide of mercury (to which may now perhaps be added corrosive sublimate), are also decomposable, whilst many *per* compounds of the same elements, not subject to the law, were not so (405, 406).

680. The substances which appeared to form the strongest exceptions to this general result were such bodies as the sulphuric, phosphoric, nitric, arsenic, and other acids.

681. On experimenting with sulphuric acid, I found no reason to believe that it was by itself a conductor of, or decomposable by, electricity, although I had previously been of that opinion (552). When very strong it is a much worse conductor than if diluted. [1]If then subjected to the action of a powerful battery, oxy-

[1] De la Rive.

gen appears at the *anode*, or positive electrode, although much is absorbed (728), and hydrogen and sulphur appear at the *cathode*, or negative electrode. Now the hydrogen has with me always been pure, not sulphuretted, and has been deficient in proportion to the sulphur present, so that it is evident that when decomposition occurred water must have been decomposed. I endeavoured to make the experiment with anhydrous sulphuric acid; and it appeared to me that, when fused, such acid was not a conductor, nor decomposed; but I had not enough of the dry acid in my possession to allow me to decide the point satisfactorily. My belief is, that when sulphur appears during the action of the pile on sulphuric acid, it is the result of a secondary action, and that the acid itself is not electrolyzable (757).

682. Phosphoric acid is, I believe, also in the same condition; but I have found it impossible to decide the point, because of the difficulty of operating on fused anhydrous phosphoric acid. Phosphoric acid which has once obtained water cannot be deprived of it by heat alone. When heated, the hydrated acid volatilizes. Upon subjecting phosphoric acid, fused upon the ring end of a wire (401), to the action of the voltaic apparatus, it conducted, and was decomposed; but gas, which I believe to be hydrogen, was always evolved at the negative electrode, and the wire was not affected as would have happened had phosphorus been separated. Gas was also evolved at the positive electrode. From all the facts, I conclude it was the water and not the acid which was decomposed.

683. *Arsenic acid.* This substance conducted, and was decomposed; but it contained water, and I was unable at the time to press the investigation so as to ascertain whether a fusible anhydrous arsenic acid could be obtained. It forms, therefore, at present no exception to the general result.

684. Nitrous acid, obtained by distilling nitrate of lead, and keeping it in contact with strong sulphuric acid, was found to conduct and decompose slowly. But on examination there were strong reasons for believing that water was present, and that the decomposition and conduction depended upon it. I endeavoured to prepare a perfectly anhydrous portion, but could not spare the time required to procure an unexceptionable result.

685. Nitric acid is a substance which I believe is not decomposed directly by the electric current. As I want the facts in illustration of

the distinction existing between primary and secondary decomposition, I will merely refer to them in this place (752).

686. That these mineral acids should confer facility of conduction and decomposition on water, is no proof that they are competent to favour and suffer these actions in themselves. Boracic acid does the same thing, though not decomposable. M. de la Rive has pointed out that chlorine has this power also; but being to us an elementary substance, it cannot be due to its capability of suffering decomposition.

687. *Chloride of sulphur* does not conduct, nor is it decomposed. It consists of single proportionals of its elements, but is not on that account an exception to the rule (679), which does not affirm that *all* compounds of single proportionals of elements are decomposable, but that such as are decomposable are so constituted.

688. *Protochloride of phosphorus* does not conduct nor become decomposed.

689. *Protochloride of carbon* does not conduct nor suffer decomposition. In association with this substance, I submitted the *hydro-chloride of carbon* from olefiant gas and chlorine to the action of the electric current; but it also refused to conduct or yield up its elements.

690. With regard to the exceptions (679), upon closer examination some of them disappear. Chloride of antimony (a compound of one proportional of antimony and one and a half of chlorine) of recent preparation was put into a tube (Pl. VI, *Fig 13*) (789), and submitted when fused to the action of the current, the positive electrode being of plumbago. No electricity passed, and no appearance of decomposition was visible at first; but when the positive and negative electrodes were brought very near each other in the chloride, then a feeble action occurred and a feeble current passed. The effect altogether was so small (although quite amenable to the law before given [394]), and so unlike the decomposition and conduction occurring in all the other cases, that I attribute it to the presence of a minute quantity of water (for which this and many other chlorides have strong attractions, producing hydrated chlorides), or perhaps of a true protochloride consisting of single proportionals (695, 796).

691. *Periodide of mercury* being examined in the same manner, was found most distinctly to insulate whilst solid, but conduct when fluid, according to the law of *liquido-conduction* (402); but there was no appearance of decomposition.

No iodine appeared at the *anode*, nor mercury or other substance at the *cathode*. The case is, therefore, no exception to the rule, that only compounds of single proportionals are decomposable; but it is an exception, and I think the only one, to the statement, that all bodies subject to the law of liquido-conduction are decomposable. I incline, however, to believe that a portion of protiodide of mercury is retained dissolved in the periodide, and that to its slow decomposition the feeble conducting power is due. Periodide would be formed, as a secondary result, at the *anode;* and the mercury at the *cathode* would also form, as a secondary result, protiodide. Both these bodies would mingle with the fluid mass, and thus no final separation appear, notwithstanding the continued decomposition.

692. When *perchloride of mercury* was subjected to the voltaic current, it did not conduct in the solid state, but it did conduct when fluid. I think, also, that in the latter case it was decomposed; but there are many interfering circumstances which require examination before a positive conclusion can be drawn.[1]

693. When the ordinary protoxide of antimony is subjected to the voltaic current in a fused state, it also is decomposed, although the effect from other causes soon ceases (402, 801). This oxide consists of one proportional of antimony and one and a half of oxygen, and is therefore an exception to the general law assumed. But in working with this oxide and the chloride, I observed facts which lead me to doubt whether the compounds usually called the protoxide and the protochloride do not often contain other compounds, consisting of single proportions, which are the true *proto* compounds, and which, in the case of the oxide, might give rise to the decomposition above described.

694. The ordinary sulphuret of antimony is considered as being the compound with the smallest quantity of sulphur, and analogous in its proportions to the ordinary protoxide. But I find that if it be fused with metallic antimony, a new sulphuret is formed, containing much more of the metal than the former, and separating distinctly, when fused, both from the pure metal on the one hand, and the ordinary gray sulphuret on the other. In some rough experiments, the metal thus taken up by the ordinary sulphuret of antimony was equal to half the proportion of that previously in the sul-

---

[1] With regard to perchloride and periodide of mercury, see now 1340, 1341.—*Dec.* 1838.

phuret, in which case the new sulphuret would consist of *single* proportionals.

695. When this new sulphuret was dissolved in muriatic acid, although a little antimony separated, yet it appeared to me that a true protochloride, consisting of *single* proportionals, was formed, and from that by alkalies, &c., a true protoxide, consisting also of *single* proportionals, was obtainable. But I could not stop to ascertain this matter strictly by analysis.

696. I believe, however, that there is such an oxide; that it is often present in variable proportions in what is commonly called protoxide, throwing uncertainty upon the results of its analysis, and causing the electrolytic decomposition above described.[1]

697. Upon the whole, it appears probable that all those binary compounds of elementary bodies which are capable of being electrolyzed when fluid, but not whilst solid, according to the law of liquido-conduction (394), consist of single proportionals of their elementary principles: and it may be because of their departure from this simplicity of composition, that boracic acid, ammonia, perchlorides, periodides, and many other direct compounds of elements, are indecomposable.

698. With regard to salts and combinations of compound bodies, the same simple relation does not appear to hold good. I could not decide this by bisulphates of the alkalies, for as long as the second proportion of acid remained, water was retained with it. The fused salts conducted, and were decomposed; but hydrogen always appeared at the negative electrode.

699. A biphosphate of soda was prepared by heating, and ultimately fusing, the ammonia-phosphate of soda. In this case the fused bisalt conducted, and was decomposed; but a little gas appeared at the negative electrode; and though I believe the salt itself was electrolyzed, I am not quite satisfied that water was entirely absent.

700. Then a biborate of soda was prepared; and this, I think, is an unobjectionable case. The salt, when fused, conducted, and was decomposed, and gas appeared at both electrodes: even when the boracic acid was increased to three proportionals, the same effect took place.

701. Hence this class of compound combinations does not seem to be subject to the same simple law as the former class of binary combinations. Whether we may find reason to consider them as mere solutions of the compound of single proportionals in the excess of acid, is a matter which, with some apparent exceptions occurring amongst the sulphurets, must be left for decision by future examination.

702. In any investigation of these points, great care must be taken to exclude water; for if present, secondary effects are so frequently produced as often seemingly to indicate an electro-decomposition of substances, when no true result of the kind has occurred (742, &c.).

703. It is evident that all the cases in which decomposition *does not occur, may* depend upon the want of conduction (677, 413); but that does not at all lessen the interest excited by seeing the great difference of effect due to a change, not in the nature of the elements, but merely in their proportions; especially in any attempt which may be made to elucidate and expound the beautiful theory put forth by Sir Humphry Davy,[2] and illustrated by Berzelius and other eminent philosophers, that ordinary chemical affinity is a mere result of the electrical attractions of the particles of matter.

¶ v. *On a New Measurer of Volta-electricity*

704. I have already said, when engaged in reducing common and voltaic electricity to one standard of measurement (377), and again when introducing my theory of electro-chemical decomposition (504, 505, 510), that the chemical decomposing action of a current *is constant for a constant quantity of electricity,* notwithstanding the greatest variations in its sources, in its intensity, in the size of the *electrodes* used, in the nature of the conductors (or non-conductors [307]) through which it is passed, or in other circumstances. The conclusive proofs of the truth of these statements shall be given almost immediately (783, &c.).

705. I endeavoured upon this law to construct an instrument which should measure out the electricity passing through it, and which, being interposed in the course of the current used in any particular experiment, should serve at pleasure, either as a *comparative standard* of effect, or as a *positive measurer* of this subtile agent.

706. There is no substance better fitted, under ordinary circumstances, to be the indicating body in such an instrument than water; for it is decomposed with facility when rendered a better conductor by the addition of acids or

---

[1] In relation to this and the three preceding paragraphs, and also 801, see Berzelius's correction of the nature of the supposed new sulphuret and oxide, *Phil. Mag.,* 1836, Vol. VIII, 476: and for the probable explanation of the effects obtained with the protoxide, refer to 1340, 1341.—*Dec.* 1838.

[2] *Philosophical Transactions,* 1807, pp. 32, 39; also 1826, pp. 387, 389.

salts; its elements may in numerous cases be obtained and collected without any embarrassment from secondary action, and, being gaseous, they are in the best physical condition for separation and measurement. Water, therefore, acidulated by sulphuric acid, is the substance I shall generally refer to, although it may become expedient in peculiar cases or forms of experiment to use other bodies (843).

707. The first precaution needful in the construction of the instrument was to avoid the recombination of the evolved gases, an effect which the positive electrode has been found so capable of producing (571). For this purpose various forms of decomposing apparatus were used. The first consisted of straight tubes, each containing a plate and wire of platina soldered together by gold, and fixed hermetically in the glass at the closed extremity of the tube (Pl. VI, *Fig. 5*). The tubes were about eight inches long, 0.7 of an inch in diameter, and graduated. The platina plates were about an inch long, as wide as the tubes would permit, and adjusted as near to the mouths of the tubes as was consistent with the safe collection of the gases evolved. In certain cases, where it was required to evolve the elements upon as small a surface as possible, the metallic extremity, instead of being a plate, consisted of the wire bent into the form of a ring (Pl. VI, *Fig. 6*). When these tubes were used as measurers, they were filled with the dilute sulphuric acid, inverted in a basin of the same liquid (Pl. VI, *Fig. 7*), and placed in an inclined position, with their mouths near to each other, that as little decomposing matter should intervene as possible; and also, in such a direction that the platina plates should be in vertical planes (720).

708. Another form of apparatus is that delineated (Pl. VI, *Fig. 8*). The tube is bent in the middle; one end is closed; in that end is fixed a wire and plate, *a*, proceeding so far downwards, that, when in the position figured, it shall be as near to the angle as possible, consistently with the collection, at the closed extremity of the tube, of all the gas evolved against it. The plane of this plate is also perpendicular (720). The other metallic termination, *b*, is introduced at the time decomposition is to be effected, being brought as near the angle as possible, without causing any gas to pass from it towards the closed end of the instrument. The gas evolved against it is allowed to escape.

709. The third form of apparatus contains both electrodes in the same tube; the trans-

mission, therefore, of the electricity, and the consequent decomposition, is far more rapid than in the separate tubes. The resulting gas is the sum of the portions evolved at the two electrodes, and the instrument is better adapted than either of the former as a measurer of the quantity of voltaic electricity transmitted in ordinary cases. It consists of a straight tube (Pl. VI, *Fig. 9*), closed at the upper extremity, and graduated, through the sides of which pass platina wires (being fused into the glass), which are connected with two plates within. The tube is fitted by grinding into one mouth of a double-necked bottle. If the latter be one-half or two-thirds full of the dilute sulphuric acid (706), it will, upon inclination of the whole, flow into the tube and fill it. When an electric current is passed through the instrument, the gases evolved against the plates collect in the upper portion of the tube, and are not subject to the recombining power of the platina.

710. Another form of the instrument is given at Pl. VI, *Fig. 10*.

711. A fifth form is delineated (Pl. VI, *Fig. 11*). This I have found exceedingly useful in experiments continued in succession for days together, and where large quantities of indicating gas were to be collected. It is fixed on a weighted foot, and has the form of a small retort containing the two electrodes: the neck is narrow, and sufficiently long to deliver gas issuing from it into a jar placed in a small pneumatic trough. The electrode chamber, sealed hermetically at the part held in the stand, is five inches in length, and 0.6 of an inch in diameter; the neck about nine inches in length, and 0.4 of an inch in diameter internally. The figure will fully indicate the construction.

712. It can hardly be requisite to remark, that in the arrangement of any of these forms of apparatus, they, and the wires connecting them with the substance, which is collaterally subjected to the action of the same electric current, should be so far insulated as to ensure a certainty that all the electricity which passes through the one shall also be transmitted through the other.

713. Next to the precaution of collecting the gases, if mingled, out of contact with the platinum, was the necessity of testing the law of a *definite electrolytic* action, upon water at least, under all varieties of condition; that, with a conviction of its certainty, might also be obtained a knowledge of those interfering circum-

stances which would require to be practically guarded against.

714. The first point investigated was the influence or indifference of extensive variations in the size of the electrodes, for which purpose instruments like those last described (709, 710, 711) were used. One of these had plates 0.7 of an inch wide, and nearly four inches long; another had plates only 0.5 of an inch wide, and 0.8 of an inch long; a third had wires 0.02 of an inch in diameter, and three inches long; and a fourth, similar wires only half an inch in length. Yet when these were filled with dilute sulphuric acid, and, being placed in succession, had one common current of electricity passed through them, very nearly the same quantity of gas was evolved in all. The difference was sometimes in favour of one and sometimes on the side of another; but the general result was that the largest quantity of gases was evolved at the smallest electrodes, namely, those consisting merely of platina wires.

715. Experiments of a similar kind were made with the single-plate, straight tubes (707), and also with the curved tubes (708), with similar consequences; and when these, with the former tubes, were arranged together in various ways, the result, as to the equality of action of large and small metallic surfaces when delivering and receiving the same current of electricity, was constantly the same. As an illustration, the following numbers are given. An instrument with two wires evolved 74.3 volumes of mixed gases; another with plates 73.25 volumes; whilst the sum of the oxygen and hydrogen in two separate tubes amounted to 73.65 volumes. In another experiment the volumes were 55.3, 55.3, and 54.4.

716. But it was observed in these experiments, that in single-plate tubes (707) more hydrogen was evolved at the negative electrode than was proportionate to the oxygen at the positive electrode; and generally, also, more than was proportionate to the oxygen and hydrogen in a double-plate tube. Upon more minutely examining these effects, I was led to refer them, and also the differences between wires and plates (714), to the solubility of the gases evolved, especially at the positive electrode.

717. When the positive and negative electrodes are equal in surface, the bubbles which rise from them in dilute sulphuric acid are always different in character. Those from the positive plate are exceedingly small, and separate instantly from every part of the surface of the metal, in consequence of its perfect clean-

liness (633); whilst in the liquid they give it a hazy appearance, from their number and minuteness; are easily carried down by currents, and therefore not only present far greater surface of contact with the liquid than larger bubbles would do, but are retained a much longer time in mixture with it. But the bubbles at the negative surface, though they constitute twice the volume of the gas at the positive electrode, are nevertheless very inferior in number. They do not rise so universally from every part of the surface, but seem to be evolved at different points; and though so much larger, they appear to cling to the metal, separating with difficulty from it, and when separated, instantly rising to the top of the liquid. If, therefore, oxygen and hydrogen had equal solubility in, or powers of combining with, water under similar circumstances, still under the present conditions the oxygen would be far the most liable to solution; but when to these is added its well-known power of forming a compound with water, it is no longer surprising that such a compound should be produced in small quantities at the positive electrode; and indeed the bleaching power which some philosophers have observed in a solution at this electrode, when chlorine and similar bodies have been carefully excluded, is probably due to the formation there, in this manner, of oxy-water.

718. That more gas was collected from the wires than from the plates, I attribute to the circumstance, that as equal quantities were evolved in equal times, the bubbles at the wires having been more rapidly produced, in relation to any part of the surface, must have been much larger; have been therefore in contact with the fluid by a much smaller surface, and for a much shorter time than those at the plates; hence less solution and a greater amount collected.

719. There was also another effect produced, especially by the use of large electrodes, which was both a consequence and a proof of the solution of part of the gas evolved there. The collected gas, when examined, was found to contain small portions of nitrogen. This I attribute to the presence of air dissolved in the acid used for decomposition. It is a well-known fact, that when bubbles of a gas but slightly soluble in water or solutions pass through them, the portion of this gas which is dissolved displaces a portion of that previously in union with the liquid: and so, in the decompositions under consideration, as the oxygen dissolves, it displaces a part of the air, or at least of the nitrogen, previously united to the acid; and

this effect takes place *most extensively* with large plates, because the gas evolved at them is in the most favourable condition for solution.

720. With the intention of avoiding this solubility of the gases as much as possible, I arranged the decomposing plates in a vertical position (707, 708), that the bubbles might quickly escape upwards, and that the downward currents in the fluid should not meet ascending currents of gas. This precaution I found to assist greatly in producing constant results, and especially in experiments to be hereafter referred to, in which other liquids than dilute sulphuric acid, as for instance solution of potash, were used.

721. The irregularities in the indications of the measurer proposed, arising from the solubility just referred to, are but small, and may be very nearly corrected by comparing the results of two or three experiments. They may also be almost entirely avoided by selecting that solution which is found to favour them in the least degree (728); and still further by collecting the hydrogen only, and using that as the indicating gas; for being much less soluble than oxygen, being evolved with twice the rapidity and in larger bubbles (717), it can be collected more perfectly and in greater purity.

722. From the foregoing and many other experiments, it results that *variation in the size of the electrodes causes no variation in the chemical action of a given quantity of electricity upon water*.

723. The next point in regard to which the principle of constant electro-chemical action was tested, was *variation of intensity*. In the first place, the preceding experiments were repeated, using batteries of an *equal* number of plates, *strongly* and *weakly* charged; but the results were alike. They were then repeated, using batteries sometimes containing forty, and at other times only five pairs of plates; but the results were still the same. *Variations therefore in the intensity*, caused by difference in the strength of charge, or in the number of alternations used, *produced no difference as to the equal action of large and small electrodes*.

724. Still these results did not prove that variation in the intensity of the current was not accompanied by a corresponding variation in the electro-chemical effects, since the actions at *all* the surfaces might have increased or diminished together. The deficiency in the evidence is, however, completely supplied by the former experiments on different-sized electrodes; for with variation in the size of these, a

variation in the intensity must have occurred. The intensity of an electric current traversing conductors alike in their nature, quality, and length, is probably as the quantity of electricity passing through a given sectional area perpendicular to the current, divided by the time (360, *note*); and therefore when large plates were contrasted with wires separated by an equal length of the same decomposing conductor (714), whilst one current of electricity passed through both arrangements, that electricity must have been in a very different state, as to *tension*, between the plates and between the wires; yet the chemical results were the same.

725. The difference in intensity, under the circumstances described, may be easily shown practically, by arranging two decomposing apparatus as in Pl. VI, *Fig. 12* where the same fluid is subjected to the decomposing power of the same current of electricity, passing in the vessel A between large platina plates, and in the vessel B between small wires. If a third decomposing apparatus, such as that delineated Pl. VI, *Fig. 11* (711), be connected with the wires at *a b*, Pl. VI, *Fig. 12*, it will serve sufficiently well, by the degree of decomposition occurring in it, to indicate the relative state of the two plates as to intensity; and if it then be applied in the same way, as a test of the state of the wires at *a' b'*, it will, by the increase of decomposition within, show how much greater the intensity is there than at the former points. The connexions of P and N with the voltaic battery are of course to be continued during the whole time.

726. A third form of experiment, in which difference of intensity was obtained, for the purpose of testing the principle of equal chemical action, was to arrange three volta-electrometers, so that after the electric current had passed through one, it should divide into two parts, each of which should traverse one of the remaining instruments, and should then reunite. The sum of the decomposition in the two latter vessels was always equal to the decomposition in the former vessel. But the *intensity* of the divided current could not be the same as that it had in its original state; and therefore *variation of intensity has no influence on the results if the quantity of electricity remain the same*. The experiment, in fact, resolves itself simply into an increase in the size of the electrodes (725).

727. The *third point*, in respect to which the principle of equal electro-chemical action on

water was tested, was *variation of the strength of the solution used*. In order to render the water a conductor, sulphuric acid had been added to it (707); and it did not seem unlikely that this substance, with many others, might render the water more subject to decomposition, the electricity remaining the same in quantity. But such did not prove to be the case. Diluted sulphuric acid, of different strengths, was introduced into different decomposing apparatus, and submitted simultaneously to the action of the same electric current (714). Slight differences occurred, as before, sometimes in one direction, sometimes in another; but the final result was, that *exactly the same quantity of water was decomposed in all the solutions by the same quantity of electricity*, though the sulphuric acid in some was seventy-fold what it was in others. The strengths used were of specific gravity 1.495, and downwards.

728. When an acid having a specific gravity of about 1.336 was employed, the results were most uniform, and the oxygen and hydrogen (716) most constantly in the right proportion to each other. Such an acid gave more gas than one much weaker acted upon by the same current, apparently because it had less solvent power. If the acid were very strong, then a remarkable disappearance of oxygen took place; thus, one made by mixing two measures of strong oil of vitriol with one of water, gave forty-two volumes of hydrogen, but only twelve of oxygen. The hydrogen was very nearly the same with that evolved from acid of the specific gravity 1.232. I have not yet had time to examine minutely the circumstances attending the disappearance of the oxygen in this case, but imagine it is due to the formation of oxywater, which Thénard has shown is favoured by the presence of acid.

729. Although not necessary for the practical use of the instrument I am describing, yet as connected with the important point of constant electro-chemical action upon water, I now investigated the effects produced by an electric current passing through aqueous solutions of acids, salts, and compounds, exceedingly different from each other in their nature, and found them to yield astonishingly uniform results. But many of them which are connected with a secondary action will be more usefully described hereafter (778).

730. When solutions of caustic potassa or soda, or sulphate of magnesia, or sulphate of soda, were acted upon by the electric current,

just as much oxygen and hydrogen was evolved from them as from the diluted sulphuric acid, with which they were compared. When a solution of ammonia, rendered a better conductor by sulphate of ammonia (554), or a solution of subcarbonate of potassa was experimented with, the *hydrogen* evolved was in the same quantity as that set free from the diluted sulphuric acid with which they were compared. Hence *changes in the nature of the solution do not alter the constancy of electrolytic action upon water*.

731. I have already said, respecting large and small electrodes, that change of order caused no change in the general effect (715). The same was the case with different solutions, or with different intensities; and however the circumstances of an experiment might be varied, the results came forth exceedingly consistent, and proved that the electro-chemical action was still the same.

732. I consider the foregoing investigation as sufficient to prove the very extraordinary and important principle with respect to WATER, *that when subjected to the influence of the electric current, a quantity of it is decomposed exactly proportionate to the quantity of electricity which has passed*, notwithstanding the thousand variations in the conditions and circumstances under which it may at the time be placed; and further, that when the interference of certain secondary effects (742, &c.), together with the solution or recombination of the gas and the evolution of air, are guarded against, *the products of the decomposition may be collected with such accuracy, as to afford a very excellent and valuable measurer of the electricity concerned in their evolution*.

733. The forms of instrument which I have given, Pl. VI, *Figs. 9, 10, 11* (709, 710, 711), are probably those which will be found most useful, as they indicate the quantity of electricity by the largest volume of gases, and cause the least obstruction to the passage of the current. The fluid which my present experience leads me to prefer is a solution of sulphuric acid of specific gravity about 1.336, or from that to 1.25; but it is very essential that there should be no organic substance, nor any vegetable acid, nor other body, which, by being liable to the action of the oxygen or hydrogen evolved at the electrodes (773, &c.), shall diminish their quantity, or add other gases to them.

734. In many cases when the instrument is used as a *comparative standard*, or even as *a*

measurer, it may be desirable to collect the hydrogen only, as being less liable to absorption or disappearance in other ways than the oxygen; whilst at the same time its volume is so large, as to render it a good and sensible indicator. In such cases the first and second form of apparatus have been used, Pl. VI, *Figs. 7, 8* (707, 708). The indications obtained were very constant, the variations being much smaller than in those forms of apparatus collecting both gases; and they can also be procured when solutions are used in comparative experiments, which, yielding no oxygen or only secondary results of its action, can give no indications if the educts at both electrodes be collected. Such is the case when solutions of ammonia, muriatic acid, chlorides, iodides, acetates or other vegetable salts, &c., are employed.

735. In a few cases, as where solutions of metallic salts liable to reduction at the negative electrode are acted upon, the oxygen may be advantageously used as the measuring substance. This is the case, for instance, with sulphate of copper.

736. There are therefore two general forms of the instrument which I submit as a measurer of electricity; one, in which both the gases of the water decomposed are collected (709, 710, 711); and the other, in which a single gas, as the hydrogen only, is used (707, 708). When referred to as a *comparative instrument*, (a use I shall now make of it very extensively), it will not often require particular precaution in the observation; but when used as an *absolute measurer*, it will be needful that the barometric pressure and the temperature be taken into account, and that the graduation of the instruments should be to one scale; the hundredths and smaller divisions of a cubical inch are quite fit for this purpose, and the hundredth may be very conveniently taken as indicating a DE-GREE of electricity.

737. It can scarcely be needful to point out further than has been done how this instrument is to be used. It is to be introduced into the course of the electric current, the action of which is to be exerted anywhere else, and if 60° or 70° of electricity are to be measured out, either in one or several portions, the current, whether strong or weak, is to be continued until the gas in the tube occupies that number of divisions or hundredths of a cubical inch. Or if a quantity competent to produce a certain effect is to be measured, the effect is to be obtained, and then the indication read off. In exact experiments it is necessary to correct the volume of gas for changes in temperature and pressure, and especially for moisture.[1] For the latter object the volta-electrometer (Pl. VI, *Fig. 11*) is most accurate, as its gas can be measured over water, whilst the others retain it over acid or saline solutions.

738. I have not hesitated to apply the term *degree* (736), in analogy with the use made of it with respect to another most important imponderable agent, namely, heat; and as the definite expansion of air, water, mercury, &c., is there made use of to measure heat, so the equally definite evolution of gases is here turned to a similar use for electricity.

739. The instrument offers the only *actual measurer* of voltaic electricity which we at present possess. For without being at all affected by variations in time or intensity, or alterations in the current itself, of any kind, or from any cause, or even of intermissions of action, it takes note with accuracy of the quantity of electricity which has passed through it, and reveals that quantity by inspection; I have therefore named it a VOLTA-ELECTROMETER.

740. Another mode of measuring volta-electricity may be adopted with advantage in many cases, dependent on the quantities of metals or other substances evolved either as primary or as secondary results; but I refrain from enlarging on this use of the products, until the principles on which their constancy depends have been fully established (791, 843).

741. By the aid of this instrument I have been able to establish the definite character of electro-chemical action in its most general sense; and I am persuaded it will become of the utmost use in the extensions of the science which these views afford. I do not pretend to have made its detail perfect, but to have demonstrated the truth of the principle, and the utility of the application.[2]

¶ vi. *On the Primary or Secondary Character of the Bodies Evolved at the Electrodes*

742. Before the *volta-electrometer* could be employed in determining, as a *general law*, the constancy of electro-decomposition, it became necessary to examine a distinction, already recognised among scientific men, relative to the

---

[1] For a simple table of correction for moisture, I may take the liberty of referring to my *Chemical Manipulation*, edition of 1830, p. 376.
[2] As early as the year 1811, Messrs. Gay-Lussac and Thénard employed chemical decomposition as a measure of the electricity of the voltaic pile. See *Recherches Physico-chymiques*, p. 12. The principles and precautions by which it becomes an exact measure were of course not then known.—*Dec.* 1838.

products of that action, namely, their primary or secondary character; and, if possible, by some general rule or principle, to decide when they were of the one or the other kind. It will appear hereafter that great mistakes respecting electro-chemical action and its consequences have arisen from confounding these two classes of results together.

743. When a substance under decomposition yields at the electrodes those bodies uncombined and unaltered which the electric current has separated, then they may be considered as primary results, even though themselves compounds. Thus the oxygen and hydrogen from water are primary results; and so also are the acid and alkali (themselves compound bodies) evolved from sulphate of soda. But when the substances separated by the current are changed at the electrodes before their appearance, then they give rise to secondary results, although in many cases the bodies evolved are elementary.

744. These secondary results occur in two ways, being sometimes due to the mutual action of the evolved substance and the matter of the electrode, and sometimes to its action upon the substances contained in the body itself under decomposition. Thus, when carbon is made the positive electrode in dilute sulphuric acid, carbonic oxide and carbonic acid occasionally appear there instead of oxygen; for the latter, acting upon the matter of the electrode, produces these secondary results. Or if the positive electrode, in a solution of nitrate or acetate of lead, be platina, then peroxide of lead appears there, equally a secondary result with the former, but now depending upon an action of the oxygen on a substance in the solution. Again, when ammonia is decomposed by platina electrodes, nitrogen appears at the anode;[1] but though an elementary body, it is a secondary result in this case, being derived from the chemical action of the oxygen electrically evolved there, upon the ammonia in the surrounding solution (554). In the same manner when aqueous solutions of metallic salts are decomposed by the current, the metals evolved at the cathode, though elements, are always secondary results, and not immediate consequences of the decomposing power of the electric current.

745. Many of these secondary results are extremely valuable; for instance, all the interesting compounds which M. Becquerel has obtained by feeble electric currents are of this nature; but they are essentially chemical, and

[1] Annales de Chimie, 1804, Vol. LI, p. 167.

must, in the theory of electrolytic action, be carefully distinguished from those which are directly due to the action of the electric current.

746. The nature of the substances evolved will often lead to a correct judgement of their primary or secondary character, but is not sufficient alone to establish that point. Thus, nitrogen is said to be attracted sometimes by the positive and sometimes by the negative electrode, according to the bodies with which it may be combined (554, 555), and it is on such occasions evidently viewed as a primary result;[2] but I think I shall show, that, when it appears at the positive electrode, or rather at the anode, it is a secondary result (748). Thus, also, Sir Humphry Davy[3] and with him the great body of chemical philosophers (including myself), have given the appearance of copper, lead, tin, silver, gold, &c., at the negative electrode, when their aqueous solutions were acted upon by the voltaic current, as proofs that the metals, as a class, were attracted to that surface; thus assuming the metal, in each case, to be a primary result. These, however, I expect to prove, are all secondary results; the mere consequence of chemical action, and no proofs either of the attraction or of the law announced respecting their places.[4]

747. But when we take to our assistance the law of constant electro-chemical action already proved with regard to water (732), and which I hope to extend satisfactorily to all bodies (821), and consider the quantities as well as the nature of the substances set free, a generally accurate judgement of the primary or secondary character of the results may be formed: and this important point, so essential to the theory of electrolyzation, since it decides what are the particles directly under the influence of the current, (distinguishing them from such as are not affected), and what are the results to be expected, may be established with such degree of certainty as to remove innumerable ambiguities and doubtful considerations from this branch of the science.

748. Let us apply these principles to the case of ammonia, and the supposed determination of nitrogen to one or the other electrode (554,

[2] Annales de Chimie, 1804, Vol. LI, p. 172.
[3] Elements of Chemical Philosophy, pp. 144, 161.
[4] It is remarkable that up to 1804 it was the received opinion that the metals were reduced by the nascent hydrogen. At that date the general opinion was reversed by Hisinger and Berzelius (Annales de Chimie, 1804, Vol. LI, p. 174), who stated that the metals were evolved directly by the electricity: in which opinion it appears, from that time, Davy coincided (Philosophical Transactions, 1826, p. 388.)

555). A pure strong solution of ammonia is as bad a conductor, and therefore as little liable to electrolyzation, as pure water; but when sulphate of ammonia is dissolved in it, the whole becomes a conductor; nitrogen *almost* and occasionally *quite* pure is evolved at the *anode*, and hydrogen at the *cathode*; the ratio of the volume of the former to that of the latter varying, but being as 1 to about 3 or 4. This result would seem at first to imply that the electric current had decomposed ammonia, and that the nitrogen had been determined towards the positive electrode. But when the electricity used was measured out by the volta-electrometer (707, 736), it was found that the hydrogen obtained was exactly in the proportion which would have been supplied by decomposed water, whilst the nitrogen had no certain or constant relation whatever. When, upon multiplying experiments, it was found that, by using a stronger or weaker solution, or a more or less powerful battery, the gas evolved at the *anode* was a mixture of oxygen and nitrogen, varying both in proportion and absolute quantity, whilst the hydrogen at the *cathode* remained constant, no doubt could be entertained that the nitrogen at the *anode* was a secondary result, depending upon the chemical action of the nascent oxygen, determined to that surface by the electric current, upon the ammonia in solution. It was the water, therefore, which was electrolyzed, not the ammonia. Further, the experiment gives no real indication of the tendency of the element nitrogen to either one electrode or the other; nor do I know of any experiment with nitric acid, or other compounds of nitrogen, which shows the tendency of this element, under the influence of the electric current, to pass in either direction along its course.

749. As another illustration of secondary results, the effects on a solution of acetate of potassa may be quoted. When a very strong solution was used, more gas was evolved at the *anode* than at the *cathode*, in the proportion of 4 to 3 nearly: that from the *anode* was a mixture of carbonic oxide and carbonic acid; that from the *cathode* pure hydrogen. When a much weaker solution was used, less gas was evolved at the *anode* than at the *cathode*; and it now contained carburetted hydrogen, as well as carbonic oxide and carbonic acid. This result of carburetted hydrogen at the positive electrode has a very anomalous appearance, if considered as an immediate consequence of the decomposing power of the current. It, however, as well as the carbonic oxide and acid, is only a *secondary result*; for it is the water alone which suffers electro-decomposition, and it is the oxygen eliminated at the *anode* which, reacting on the acetic acid, in the midst of which it is evolved, produces those substances that finally appear there. This is fully proved by experiments with the volta-electrometer (707); for then the hydrogen evolved from the acetate at the *cathode* is always found to be definite, being exactly proportionate to the electricity which has passed through the solution, and, in quantity, the same as the hydrogen evolved in the volta-electrometer itself. The appearance of the carbon in combination with the hydrogen at the positive electrode, and its non-appearance at the negative electrode, are in curious contrast with the results which might have been expected from the law usually accepted respecting the final places of the elements.

750. If the salt in solution be an acetate of lead, then the results at both electrodes are secondary, and cannot be used to estimate or express the amount of electro-chemical action, except by a circuitous process (843). In place of oxygen or even the gases already described (749), peroxide of lead now appears at the positive, and lead itself at the negative electrode. When other metallic solutions are used, containing, for instance, peroxides, as that of copper, combined with this or any other decomposable acid, still more complicated results will be obtained; which, viewed as direct results of the electro-chemical action, will, in their proportions, present nothing but confusion; but will appear perfectly harmonious and simple if they be considered as secondary results, and will accord in their proportions with the oxygen and hydrogen evolved from water by the action of a definite quantity of electricity.

751. I have experimented upon many bodies, with a view to determine whether the results were primary or secondary. I have been surprised to find how many of them, in ordinary cases, are of the latter class, and how frequently water is the only body electrolyzed in instances where other substances have been supposed to give way. Some of these results I will give in as few words as possible.

752. *Nitric acid.* When very strong, it conducted well, and yielded oxygen at the positive electrode. No gas appeared at the negative electrode; but nitrous acid, and apparently nitric oxide, were formed there, which, dissolving, rendered the acid yellow or red, and at last even effervescent, from the spontaneous sepa-

ration of nitric oxide. Upon diluting the acid with its bulk or more of water, gas appeared at the negative electrode. Its quantity could be varied by variations, either in the strength of the acid or of the voltaic current: for that acid from which no gas separated at the *cathode*, with a weak voltaic battery, did evolve gas there with a stronger; and that battery which evolved no gas there with a strong acid, did cause its evolution with an acid more dilute. The gas at the *anode* was always oxygen; that at the *cathode* hydrogen. When the quantity of products was examined by the volta-electrometer (707), the oxygen, whether from strong or weak acid, proved to be in the same proportion as from water. When the acid was diluted to specific gravity 1.24, or less, the hydrogen also proved to be the same in quantity as from water. Hence I conclude that the nitric acid does not undergo electrolyzation, but the water only; that the oxygen at the *anode* is always a primary result, but that the products at the *cathode* are often secondary, and due to the reaction of the hydrogen upon the nitric acid.

753. *Nitre.* A solution of this salt yields very variable results, according as one or other form of tube is used, or as the electrodes are large or small. Sometimes the whole of the hydrogen of the water decomposed may be obtained at the negative electrode; at other times, only a part of it, because of the ready formation of secondary results. The solution is a very excellent conductor of electricity.

754. *Nitrate of ammonia,* in aqueous solution, gives rise to secondary results very varied and uncertain in their proportions.

755. *Sulphurous acid.* Pure liquid sulphurous acid does not conduct nor suffer decomposition by the voltaic current,[1] but, when dissolved in water, the solution acquires conducting power, and is decomposed, yielding oxygen at the *anode*, and hydrogen and sulphur at the *cathode*.

756. A solution containing sulphuric acid in addition to the sulphurous acid, was a better conductor. It gave very little gas at either electrode: that at the *anode* was oxygen, that at the *cathode* pure hydrogen. From the *cathode* also rose a white turbid stream, consisting of diffused sulphur, which soon rendered the whole solution milky. The volumes of gases were in no regular proportion to the quantities evolved from water in the voltameter. I conclude that the sulphurous acid was not at all affected by

the electric current in any of these cases, and that the water present was the only body electro-chemically decomposed; that, at the *anode*, the oxygen from the water converted the sulphurous acid into sulphuric acid, and, at the *cathode*, the hydrogen electrically evolved decomposed the sulphurous acid, combining with its oxygen, and setting its sulphur free. I conclude that the sulphur at the negative electrode was only a secondary result; and, in fact, no part of it was found combined with the small portion of hydrogen which escaped when weak solutions of sulphurous acid were used.

757. *Sulphuric acid.* I have already given my reasons for concluding that sulphuric acid is not electrolyzable, i.e., not decomposable directly by the electric current, but occasionally suffering by a secondary action at the *cathode* from the hydrogen evolved there (681). In the year 1800, Davy considered the sulphur from sulphuric acid as the result of the action of the nascent hydrogen.[2] In 1804, Hisinger and Berzelius stated that it was the direct result of the action of the voltaic pile,[3] an opinion which from that time Davy seems to have adopted, and which has since been commonly received by all. The change of my own opinion requires that I should correct what I have already said of the decomposition of sulphuric acid in a former series of these *Researches* (552): I do not now think that the appearance of the sulphur at the negative electrode is an immediate consequence of electrolytic action.

758. *Muriatic acid.* A strong solution gave hydrogen at the negative electrode, and chlorine only at the positive electrode; of the latter, a part acted on the platina and a part was dissolved. A minute bubble of gas remained; it was not oxygen, but probably air previously held in solution.

759. It was an important matter to determine whether the chlorine was a primary result, or only a secondary product, due to the action of the oxygen evolved from water at the *anode* upon the muriatic acid; i.e., whether the muriatic acid was electrolyzable, and if so, whether the decomposition was *definite*.

760. The muriatic acid was gradually diluted. One part with six of water gave only chlorine at the *anode*. One part with eight of water gave only chlorine; with nine of water, a little oxygen appeared with the chlorine: but the occurrence or non-occurrence of oxygen at these

---

[1] See also De la Rive, *Bibliothèque Universelle*, Vol. XL, p. 205; or *Quarterly Journal of Science*, Vol. XXVII, p. 407.

[2] *Nicholson's Quarterly Journal*, Vol. IV, pp. 280, 281.

[3] *Annales de Chimie*, 1804, Vol. LI, p. 173.

strengths depended, in part, on the strength of the voltaic battery used. With fifteen parts of water, a little oxygen, with much chlorine, was evolved at the *anode*. As the solution was now becoming a bad conductor of electricity, sulphuric acid was added to it: this caused more ready decomposition, but did not sensibly alter the proportion of chlorine and oxygen.

761. The muriatic acid was now diluted with 100 times its volume of dilute sulphuric acid. It still gave a large proportion of chlorine at the *anode*, mingled with oxygen; and the result was the same, whether a voltaic battery of 40 pairs of plates or one containing only 5 pairs were used. With acid of this strength, the oxygen evolved at the *anode* was to the hydrogen at the *cathode*, in volume, as 17 is to 64; and therefore the chlorine would have been 30 volumes, had it not been dissolved by the fluid.

762. Next with respect to the quantity of elements evolved. On using the volta-electrometer, it was found that, whether the strongest or the weakest muriatic acid were used, whether chlorine alone or chlorine mingled with oxygen appeared at the *anode*, still the hydrogen evolved at the *cathode* was a constant quantity, i.e., exactly the same as the hydrogen which the *same quantity of electricity* could evolve from water.

763. This constancy does not decide whether the muriatic acid is electrolyzed or not, although it proves that, if so, it must be in definite proportions to the quantity of electricity used. Other considerations may, however, be allowed to decide the point. The analogy between chlorine and oxygen, in their relations to hydrogen, is so strong, as to lead almost to the certainty that, when combined with that element, they would perform similar parts in the process of electro-decomposition. They both unite with it in single proportional or equivalent quantities; and the number of proportionals appearing to have an intimate and important relation to the decomposability of a body (697), those in muriatic acid, as well as in water, are the most favourable, or those perhaps even necessary, to decomposition. In other binary compounds of chlorine also, where nothing equivocal depending on the simultaneous presence of it and oxygen is involved, the chlorine is directly eliminated at the *anode* by the electric current. Such is the case with the chloride of lead (395), which may be justly compared with protoxide of lead (402), and stands in the same relation to it as muriatic acid to water. The chlorides of potassium, sodium, barium,

&c., are in the same relation to the protoxides of the same metals and present the same results under the influence of the electric current (402).

764. From all the experiments, combined with these considerations, I conclude that muriatic acid is decomposed by the direct influence of the electric current, and that the quantities evolved are, and therefore the chemical action is, *definite for a definite quantity of electricity*. For though I have not collected and measured the chlorine, in its separate state, at the *anode* there can exist no doubt as to its being proportional to the hydrogen at the *cathode*; and the results are therefore sufficient to establish the general law of *constant electro-chemical action* in the case of muriatic acid.

765. In the dilute acid (761), I conclude that a part of the water is electro-chemically decomposed, giving origin to the oxygen, which appears mingled with the chlorine at the *anode*. The oxygen *may* be viewed as a secondary result; but I incline to believe that it is not so; for, if it were, it might be expected in largest proportion from the stronger acid, whereas the reverse is the fact. This consideration, with others, also leads me to conclude that muriatic acid is more easily decomposed by the electric current than water; since, even when diluted with eight or nine times its quantity of the latter fluid, it alone gives way, the water remaining unaffected.

766. *Chlorides.* On using solutions of chlorides in water—for instance, the chlorides of sodium or calcium—there was evolution of chlorine only at the positive electrode, and of hydrogen, with the oxide of the base, as soda or lime, at the negative electrode. The process of decomposition may be viewed as proceeding in two or three ways, all terminating in the same results. Perhaps the simplest is to consider the chloride as the substance electrolyzed, its chlorine being determined to and evolved at the *anode*, and its metal passing to the *cathode*, where, finding no more chlorine, it acts upon the water, producing hydrogen and an oxide as secondary results. As the discussion would detain me from more important matter, and is not of immediate consequence, I shall defer it for the present. It is, however, of *great consequence* to state, that, on using the volta-electrometer, the hydrogen in both cases was definite; and if the results do not prove the definite decomposition of chlorides (which shall be proved elsewhere, 789, 794, 814), they are not in the slightest degree opposed to such a conclusion, and do support the *general law*.

767. *Hydriodic acid.* A solution of hydriodic acid was affected exactly in the same manner as muriatic acid. When strong, hydrogen was evolved at the negative electrode, in definite proportion to the quantity of electricity which had passed, i.e., in the same proportion as was evolved by the same current from water; and iodine without any oxygen was evolved at the positive electrode. But when diluted, small quantities of oxygen appeared with the iodine at the *anode*, the proportion of hydrogen at the *cathode* remaining undisturbed.

768. I believe the decomposition of the hydriodic acid in this case to be direct, for the reasons already given respecting muriatic acid (763, 764).

769. *Iodides.* A solution of iodide of potassium being subjected to the voltaic current, iodine appeared at the positive electrode (without any oxygen), and hydrogen with free alkali at the negative electrode. The same observations as to the mode of decomposition are applicable here as were made in relation to the chlorides when in solution (766).

770. *Hydro-fluoric acid and fluorides.* Solution of hydrofluoric acid did not appear to be decomposed under the influence of the electric current: it was the water which gave way apparently. The fused fluorides were electrolyzed (417); but having during these actions obtained *fluorine* in the separate state, I think it better to refer to a future series of these *Researches*, in which I purpose giving a fuller account of the results than would be consistent with propriety here.[1]

771. *Hydro-cyanic acid* in solution conducts very badly. The definite proportion of hydrogen (equal to that from water) was set free at the *cathode*, whilst at the *anode* a small quantity of oxygen was evolved and apparently a solution of cyanogen formed. The action altogether corresponded with that on a dilute muriatic or hydriodic acid. When the hydro-cyanic acid was made a better conductor by sulphuric acid, the same results occurred.

Cyanides. With a solution of the cyanide of potassium, the result was precisely the same as with a chloride or iodide. No oxygen was evolved at the positive electrode, but a brown solution formed there. For the reasons given when speaking of the chlorides (766), and because a fused cyanide of potassium evolves cyanogen at the positive electrode,[2] I incline to believe that the cyanide in solution is *directly* decomposed.

772. *Ferro-cyanic acid* and the *ferro-cyanides*, as also *sulpho-cyanic acid* and the *sulpho-cyanides*, presented results corresponding with those just described (771).

773. *Acetic acid.* Glacial acetic acid, when fused (405), is not decomposed by, nor does it conduct, electricity. On adding a little water to it, still there were no signs of action; on adding more water, it acted slowly and about as pure water would do. Dilute sulphuric acid was added to it in order to make it a better conductor; then the definite proportion of hydrogen was evolved at the *cathode*, and a mixture of oxygen in very deficient quantity, with carbonic acid, and a little carbonic oxide, at the *anode*. Hence it appears that acetic acid is not electrolyzable, but that a portion of it is decomposed by the oxygen evolved at the *anode*, producing secondary results, varying with the strength of the acid, the intensity of the current, and other circumstances.

774. *Acetates.* One of these has been referred to already, as affording only secondary results relative to the acetic acid (749). With many of the metallic acetates the results at both electrodes are secondary (746, 750).

Acetate of soda fused and anhydrous is directly decomposed, being, as I believe, a true electrolyte, and evolving soda and acetic acid at the *cathode* and *anode*. These however have no sensible duration, but are immediately resolved into other substances; charcoal, sodiuretted hydrogen, &c., being set free at the former, and, as far as I could judge under the circumstances, acetic acid mingled with carbonic oxide, carbonic acid, &c., at the latter.

775. *Tartaric acid.* Pure solution of tartaric acid is almost as bad a conductor as pure water. On adding sulphuric acid, it conducted well, the results at the positive electrode being primary or secondary in different proportions, according to variations in the strength of the acid and the power of the electric current (752). Alkaline tartrates gave a large proportion of secondary results at the positive electrode. The hydrogen at the negative electrode remained constant unless certain triple metallic salts were used.

776. Solutions, of salts containing other vegetable acids, as the benzoates; of sugar, gum,

---

[1] I have not obtained fluorine: my expectations, amounting to conviction, passed away one by one when subjected to rigorous examination; some very singular results were obtained; and to one of these I refer at 1340.—*Dec.* 1838.

[2] It is a very remarkable thing to see carbon and nitrogen in this case determined powerfully towards the positive surface of the voltaic battery; but it is perfectly in harmony with the theory of electro-chemical decomposition which I have advanced.

&c., dissolved in dilute sulphuric acid; of resin, albumen, &c., dissolved in alkalies, were in turn submitted to the electrolytic power of the voltaic current. In all these cases, secondary results to a greater or smaller extent were produced at the positive electrode.

777. In concluding this division of these *Researches*, it cannot but occur to the mind that the final result of the action of the electric current upon substances, placed between the electrodes, instead of being simple may be very complicated. There are two modes by which these substances may be decomposed, either by the direct force of the electric current, or by the action of bodies which that current may evolve. There are also two modes by which new compounds may be formed, i.e., by combination of the evolving substances whilst in their nascent state (658), directly with the matter of the electrode; or else their combination with those bodies, which being contained in, or associated with, the body suffering decomposition, are necessarily present at the *anode* and *cathode*. The complexity is rendered still greater by the circumstance that two or more of these actions may occur simultaneously, and also in variable proportions to each other. But it may in a great measure be resolved by attention to the principles already laid down (747).

778. When *aqueous* solutions of bodies are used, secondary results are exceedingly frequent. Even when the water is not present in large quantity, but is merely that of combination, still secondary results often ensue: for instance, it is very possible that in Sir Humphry Davy's decomposition of the hydrates of potassa and soda, a part of the potassium produced was the result of a secondary action. Hence, also, a frequent cause for the disappearance of the oxygen and hydrogen which would otherwise be evolved: and when hydrogen does *not* appear at the *cathode* in an *aqueous solution*, it perhaps always indicates that a secondary action has taken place there. No exception to this rule has as yet occurred to my observation.

779. Secondary actions are *not confined to aqueous solutions*, or cases where water is present. For instance, various chlorides acted upon, when fused (402), by platina electrodes, have the chlorine determined electrically to the *anode*. In many cases, as with the chlorides of lead, potassium, barium, &c., the chlorine acts on the platina and forms a compound with it, which dissolves; but when protochloride of tin is used, the chlorine at the *anode* does not act upon the platina, but upon the chloride al-

ready there, forming a perchloride which rises in vapour (790, 804). These are, therefore, instances of secondary actions of both kinds, produced in bodies containing no water.

780. The production of boron from fused borax (402, 417) is also a case of secondary action; for boracic acid is not decomposable by electricity (408), and it was the sodium evolved at the *cathode* which, reacting on the boracic acid around it, took oxygen from it and set boron free in the experiments formerly described.

781. Secondary actions have already, in the hands of M. Becquerel, produced many interesting results in the formation of compounds; some of them new, others imitations of those occurring naturally.[1] It is probable they may prove equally interesting in an opposite direction, i.e., as affording cases of analytic decomposition. Much information regarding the composition, and perhaps even the arrangement, of the particles of such bodies as the vegetable acids and alkalies, and organic compounds generally, will probably be obtained by submitting them to the action of nascent oxygen, hydrogen, chlorine, &c., at the electrodes; and the action seems the more promising, because of the thorough command which we possess over attendant circumstances, such as the strength of the current, the size of the electrodes, the nature of the decomposing conductor, its strength, &c., all of which may be expected to have their corresponding influence upon the final result.

782. It is to me a great satisfaction that the extreme variety of secondary results has presented nothing opposed to the doctrine of a constant and definite electro-chemical action, to the particular consideration of which I shall now proceed.

¶ vii. *On the Definite Nature and Extent of Electro-chemical Decompositions*

783. In the Third Series of these *Researches*, after proving the identity of electricities derived from different sources, and showing, by actual measurement, the extraordinary quantity of electricity evolved by a very feeble voltaic arrangement (371, 376), I announced a law, derived from experiment, which seemed to me of the utmost importance to the science of electricity in general, and that branch of it denominated *electro-chemistry* in particular. The law was expressed thus: *The chemical power of a current of electricity is in direct proportion to the absolute quantity of electricity which passes* (377).

[1] *Annales de Chimie*, Vol. XXXV, p. 113.

784. In the further progress of the successive investigations, I have had frequent occasion to refer to the same law, sometimes in circumstances offering powerful corroboration of its truth (456, 504, 505); and the present series already supplies numerous new cases in which it holds good (704, 722, 726, 732). It is now my object to consider this great principle more closely, and to develop some of the consequences to which it leads. That the evidence for it may be the more distinct and applicable, I shall quote cases of decomposition subject to as few interferences from secondary results as possible, effected upon bodies very simple, yet very definite in their nature.

785. In the first place, I consider the law as so fully established with respect to the decomposition of *water*, and under so many circumstances which might be supposed, if anything could, to exert an influence over it, that I may be excused entering into further detail respecting that substance, or even summing up the results here (732). I refer, therefore, to the whole of the subdivision of this series of *Researches* which contains the account of the *volta-electrometer* (704, &c.).

786. In the next place, I also consider the law as established with respect to *muriatic acid* by the experiments and reasoning already advanced, when speaking of that substance, in the subdivision respecting primary and secondary results (758, &c.).

787. I consider the law as established also with regard to *hydriodic acid* by the experiments and considerations already advanced in the preceding division of this series of *Researches* (767, 768).

788. Without speaking with the same confidence, yet from the experiments described, and many others not described, relating to hydrofluoric, hydro-cyanic, ferro-cyanic, and sulpho-cyanic acids (770, 771, 772), and from the close analogy which holds between these bodies and the hydracids of chlorine, iodine, bromine, &c., I consider these also as coming under subjection to the law, and assisting to prove its truth.

789. In the preceding cases, except the first, the water is believed to be inactive; but to avoid any ambiguity arising from its presence, I sought for substances from which it should be absent altogether; and, taking advantage of the law of conduction already developed (380, &c.), I soon found abundance, amongst which *protochloride of tin* was first subjected to decomposition in the following manner. A piece of platina wire had one extremity coiled up in-

to a small knob, and, having been carefully weighed, was sealed hermetically into a piece of bottle-glass tube, so that the knob should be at the bottom of the tube within (Pl. VI, *Fig. 13*). The tube was suspended by a piece of platina wire, so that the heat of a spirit-lamp could be applied to it. Recently fused protochloride of tin was introduced in sufficient quantity to occupy, when melted, about one-half of the tube; the wire of the tube was connected with a volta-electrometer (711), which was itself connected with the negative end of a voltaic battery; and a platina wire connected with the positive end of the same battery was dipped into the fused chloride in the tube; being however so bent, that it could not by any shake of the hand or apparatus touch the negative electrode at the bottom of the vessel. The whole arrangement is delineated in Pl. VI, *Fig. 14*.

790. Under these circumstances the chloride of tin was decomposed: the chlorine evolved at the positive electrode formed bichloride of tin (779), which passed away in fumes, and the tin evolved at the negative electrode combined with the platina, forming an alloy, fusible at the temperature to which the tube was subjected, and therefore never occasioning metallic communication through the decomposing chloride. When the experiment had been continued so long as to yield a reasonable quantity of gas in the volta-electrometer, the battery connexion was broken, the positive electrode removed, and the tube and remaining chloride allowed to cool. When cold, the tube was broken open, the rest of the chloride and the glass being easily separable from the platina wire and its button of alloy. The latter when washed was then reweighed, and the increase gave the weight of the tin reduced.

791. I will give the particular results of one experiment, in illustration of the mode adopted in this and others, the results of which I shall have occasion to quote. The negative electrode weighed at first 20 grains; after the experiment, it, with its button of alloy, weighed 23.2 grains. The tin evolved by the electric current at the *cathode* weighed therefore 3.2 grains. The quantity of oxygen and hydrogen collected in the volta-electrometer = 3.85 cubic inches. As 100 cubic inches of oxygen and hydrogen, in the proportions to form water, may be considered as weighing 12.92 grains, the 3.85 cubic inches would weigh 0.49742 of a grain; that being, therefore, the weight of water decomposed by the same electric current as was able to decompose such weight of protochloride of

tin as could yield 3.2 grains of metal. Now 0.49742 : 3.2 :: 9, the equivalent of water is to 57.9, which should therefore be the equivalent of tin, if the experiment had been made without error, and if the electro-chemical decomposition *is in this case also definite*. In some chemical works 58 is given as the chemical equivalent of tin, in others 57.9. Both are so near to the result of the experiment, and the experiment itself is so subject to slight causes of variation (as from the absorption of gas in the volta-electrometer [716], &c.), that the numbers leave little doubt of the applicability of the *law of definite action* in this and all similar cases of electro-decomposition.

792. It is not often I have obtained an accordance in numbers so near as that I have just quoted. Four experiments were made on the protochloride of tin, the quantities of gas evolved in the volta-electrometer being from 2.05 to 10.29 cubic inches. The average of the four experiments gave 58.53 as the electro-chemical equivalent for tin.

793. The chloride remaining after the experiment was pure protochloride of tin; and no one can doubt for a moment that the equivalent of chlorine had been evolved at the *anode*, and, having formed bichloride of tin as a secondary result, had passed away.

794. *Chloride of lead* was experimented upon in a manner exactly similar, except that a change was made in the nature of the positive electrode; for as the chlorine evolved at the *anode* forms no perchloride of lead, but acts directly upon the platina, it produces, if that metal be used, a solution of chloride of platina in the chloride of lead; in consequence of which a portion of platina can pass to the *cathode*, and would then produce a vitiated result. I therefore sought for, and found in plumbago, another substance, which could be used safely as the positive electrode in such bodies as chlorides, iodides, &c. The chlorine or iodine does not act upon it, but is evolved in the free state; and the plumbago has no reaction, under the circumstances, upon the fused chloride or iodide in which it is plunged. Even if a few particles of plumbago should separate by the heat or the mechanical action of the evolved gas, they can do no harm in the chloride.

795. The mean of three experiments gave the number of 100.85 as the equivalent for lead. The chemical equivalent is 103.5. The deficiency in my experiments I attribute to the solution of part of the gas (716) in the volta-electrometer; but the results leave no doubt on

my mind that both the lead and the chlorine are, in this case, evolved in *definite quantities* by the action of a given quantity of electricity (814, &c.).

796. *Chloride of antimony.* It was in endeavouring to obtain the electro-chemical equivalent of antimony from the chloride, that I found reasons for the statement I have made respecting the presence of water in it in an earlier part of these *Researches* (690, 693, &c.).

797. I endeavoured to experiment upon the *oxide of lead* obtained by fusion and ignition of the nitrate in a platina crucible, but found great difficulty, from the high temperature required for perfect fusion, and the powerful fluxing qualities of the substance. Green-glass tubes repeatedly failed. I at last fused the oxide in a small porcelain crucible, heated fully in a charcoal fire; and, as it was essential that the evolution of the lead at the *cathode* should take place beneath the surface, the negative electrode was guarded by a green-glass tube, fused around it in such a manner as to expose only the knob of platina at the lower end (Pl. VI, *Fig. 15*), so that it could be plunged beneath the surface, and thus exclude contact of air or oxygen with the lead reduced there. A platina wire was employed for the positive electrode, that metal not being subject to any action from the oxygen evolved against it. The arrangement is given in Pl. VI, *Fig. 16*.

798. In an experiment of this kind the equivalent for the lead came out 93.17, which is very much too small. This, I believe, was because of the small interval between the positive and negative electrodes in the oxide of lead; so that it was not unlikely that some of the froth and bubbles formed by the oxygen at the *anode* should occasionally even touch the lead reduced at the *cathode*, and re-oxidize it. When I endeavoured to correct this by having more litharge, the greater heat required to keep it all fluid caused a quicker action on the crucible, which was soon eaten through, and the experiment stopped.

799. In one experiment of this kind I used borate of lead (408, 673). It evolves lead, under the influence of the electric current, at the *anode*, and oxygen at the *cathode*; and as the boracic acid is not either directly (408) or incidentally decomposed during the operation, I expected a result dependent on the oxide of lead. The borate is not so violent a flux as the oxide, but it requires a higher temperature to make it quite liquid; and if not very hot, the bubbles of oxygen cling to the positive elec-

trode, and retard the transfer of electricity. The number for lead came out 101.29, which is so near to 103.5 as to show that the action of the current had been definite.

800. *Oxide of bismuth*. I found this substance required too high a temperature, and acted too powerfully as a flux, to allow of any experiment being made on it, without the application of more time and care than I could give at present.

801. The ordinary *protoxide of antimony*, which consists of one proportional of metal and one and a half of oxygen, was subjected to the action of the electric current in a green-glass tube (789), surrounded by a jacket of platina foil, and heated in a charcoal fire. The decomposition began and proceeded very well at first, apparently indicating, according to the general law (679, 697), that this substance was one containing such elements and in such proportions as made it amenable to the power of the electric current. This effect I have already given reasons for supposing may be due to the presence of a true protoxide, consisting of single proportionals (696, 693). The action soon diminished, and finally ceased, because of the formation of a higher oxide of the metal at the positive electrode. This compound, which was probably the peroxide, being infusible and insoluble in the protoxide, formed a crystalline crust around the positive electrode; and thus insulating it, prevented the transmission of the electricity. Whether if it had been fusible and still immiscible, it would have decomposed, is doubtful, because of its departure from the required composition (697). It was a very natural secondary product at the positive electrode (779). On opening the tube it was found that a little antimony had been separated at the negative electrode; but the quantity was too small to allow of any quantitative result being obtained.[1]

802. *Iodide of lead*. This substance can be experimented with in tubes heated by a spirit-lamp (789); but I obtained no good results from it, whether I used positive electrodes of platina or plumbago. In two experiments the numbers for the lead came out only 75.46 and 73.45, instead of 103.5. This I attribute to the formation of a periodide at the positive electrode, which, dissolving in the mass of liquid iodide, came in contact with the lead evolved at the negative electrode, and dissolved part of it, becoming itself again protiodide. Such a periodide does exist; and it is very rarely that

[1] This paragraph is subject to the corrective note now appended to paragraph 696.—*Dec.* 1838.

the iodide of lead formed by precipitation, and well-washed, can be fused without evolving much iodine, from the presence of this percompound; nor does crystallization from its hot aqueous solution free it from this substance. Even when a little of the protiodide and iodine are merely rubbed together in a mortar, a portion of the periodide is formed. And though it is decomposed by being fused and heated to dull redness for a few minutes, and the whole reduced to protiodide, yet that is not at all opposed to the possibility, that a little of that which is formed in great excess of iodine at the *anode*, should be carried by the rapid currents in the liquid into contact with the *cathode*.

803. This view of the result was strengthened by a third experiment, where the space between the electrodes was increased to one-third of an inch; for now the interfering effects were much diminished, and the number of the lead came out 89.04; and it was fully confirmed by the results obtained in the cases of *transfer* to be immediately described (818).

The experiments on iodide of lead therefore offer no exception to the *general law* under consideration, but on the contrary may, from general considerations, be admitted as included in it.

804. *Protiodide of tin*. This substance, when fused (402), conducts and is decomposed by the electric current, tin is evolved at the *anode*, and periodide of tin as a secondary result (779, 790) at the *cathode*. The temperature required for its fusion is too high to allow of the production of any results fit for weighing.

805. *Iodide of potassium* was subjected to electrolytic action in a tube, like that in Pl. VI, *Fig. 13* (789). The negative electrode was a globule of lead, and I hoped in this way to retain the potassium, and obtain results that could be weighed and compared with the volta-electrometer indication; but the difficulties dependent upon the high temperature required, the action upon the glass, the fusibility of the platina induced by the presence of the lead, and other circumstances, prevented me from procuring such results. The iodide was decomposed with the evolution of iodine at the *anode*, and of potassium at the *cathode*, as in former cases.

806. In some of these experiments several substances were placed in succession, and decomposed simultaneously by the same electric current: thus, protochloride of tin, chloride of lead, and water, were thus acted on at once. It is needless to say that the results were com-

parable, the tin, lead, chlorine, oxygen, and hydrogen evolved being *definite in quantity* and electro-chemical equivalents to each other.

807. Let us turn to another kind of proof of the *definite chemical action of electricity*. If any circumstances could be supposed to exert an influence over the quantity of the matters evolved during electrolytic action, one would expect them to be persent when electrodes of different substances, and possessing very different chemical affinities for such matters, were used. Platina has no power in dilute sulphuric acid of combining with the oxygen at the *anode*, though the latter be evolved in the nascent state against it. Copper, on the other hand, immediately unites with the oxygen, as the electric current sets it free from the hydrogen; and zinc is not only able to combine with it, but can, without any help from the electricity, abstract it directly from the water, at the same time setting torrents of hydrogen free. Yet in cases where these three substances were used as the positive electrodes in three similar portions of the same dilute sulphuric acid, specific gravity 1.336, precisely the same quantity of water was decomposed by the electric current, and precisely the same quantity of hydrogen set free at the *cathodes* of the three solutions.

808. The experiment was made thus. Portions of the dilute sulphuric acid were put into three basins. Three volta-electrometer tubes, of the form, Pl. VI, *Figs.* 5, 7, were filled with the same acid, and one inverted in each basin (707). A zinc plate, connected with the positive end of a voltaic battery, was dipped into the first basin, forming the positive electrode there, the hydrogen, which was abundantly evolved from it by the direct action of the acid, being allowed to escape. A copper plate, which dipped into the acid of the second basin, was connected with the negative electrode of the *first* basin; and a platina plate, which dipped into the acid of the third basin, was connected with the negative electrode of the *second* basin. The negative electrode of the third basin was connected with a volta-electrometer (711), and that with the negative end of the voltaic battery.

809. Immediately that the circuit was complete, the *electro-chemical action* commenced in all the vessels. The hydrogen still rose in, apparently, undiminished quantities from the positive zinc electrode in the first basin. No oxygen was evolved at the positive copper elec-

trode in the second basin, but a sulphate of copper was formed there; whilst in the third basin the positive platina electrode evolved pure oxygen gas, and was itself unaffected. But in *all* the basins the hydrogen liberated at the *negative* platina electrodes was the *same in quantity*, and the same with the volume of hydrogen evolved in the volta-electrometer, showing that in all the vessels the current had decomposed an equal quantity of water. In this trying case, therefore, the *chemical action of electricity* proved to be *perfectly definite*.

810. A similar experiment was made with muriatic acid diluted with its bulk of water. The three positive electrodes were zinc, silver, and platina; the first being able to separate and combine with the chlorine *without* the aid of the current; the second combining with the chlorine only after the current had set it free; and the third rejecting almost the whole of it. The three negative electrodes were, as before, platina plates fixed within glass tubes. In this experiment, as in the former, the quantity of hydrogen evolved at the *cathodes* was the same for all, and the same as the hydrogen evolved in the volta-electrometer. I have already given my reasons for believing that in these experiments it is the muriatic acid which is directly decomposed by the electricity (764); and the results prove that the quantities so decomposed are *perfectly definite* and proportionate to the quantity of electricity which has passed.

811. In this experiment the chloride of silver formed in the second basin retarded the passage of the current of electricity, by virtue of the law of conduction before described (394), so that it had to be cleaned off four or five times during the course of the experiment; but this caused no difference between the results of that vessel and the others.

812. Charcoal was used as the positive electrode in both sulphuric and muriatic acids (808, 810); but this change produced no variation of the results. A zinc positive electrode, in sulphate of soda or solution of common salt, gave the same constancy of operation.

813. Experiments of a similar kind were then made with bodies altogether in a different state, i.e., with *fused* chlorides, iodides, &c. I have already described an experiment with fused chloride of silver, in which the electrodes were of metallic silver, the one rendered negative becoming increased and lengthened by the addition of metal, whilst the other was dissolved and eaten away by its abstraction. This experiment was repeated, two weighed pieces of sil-

ver wire being used as the electrodes, and a volta-electrometer included in the circuit. Great care was taken to withdraw the negative electrodes so regularly and steadily that the crystals of reduced silver should not form a *metallic* communication beneath the surface of the fused chloride. On concluding the experiment the positive electrode was re-weighed, and its loss ascertained. The mixture of chloride of silver, and metal, withdrawn in successive portions at the negative electrode, was digested in solution of ammonia, to remove the chloride, and the metallic silver remaining also weighed: it was the reduction at the *cathode*, and exactly equalled the solution at the *anode*; and each portion was as nearly as possible the equivalent to the water decomposed in the volta-electrometer.

814. The infusible condition of the silver at the temperature used, and the length and ramifying character of its crystals, render the above experiment difficult to perform, and uncertain in its results. I therefore wrought with chloride of lead, using a green-glass tube, formed as in Pl. VI, *Fig. 17*. A weighed platina wire was fused into the bottom of a small tube, as before described (789). The tube was then bent to an angle, at about half an inch distance from he closed end; and the part between the angle and the extremity being softened, was forced upward, as in the figure, so as to form a bridge, or rather separation, producing two little depressions or basins *a*, *b*, within the tube. This arrangement was suspended by a platina wire, as before, so that the heat of a spirit-lamp could be applied to it, such inclination being given to it as would allow all air to escape during the fusion of the chloride of lead. A positive electrode was then provided, by bending up the end of a platina wire into a knot, and fusing about twenty grains of metallic lead on to it, in a small closed tube of glass, which was afterwards broken away. Being so furnished, the wire with its lead was weighed, and the weight recorded.

815. Chloride of lead was now introduced into the tube, and carefully fused. The leaded electrode was also introduced; after which the metal, at its extremity, soon melted. In this state of things the tube was filled up to *c* with melted chloride of lead; the end of the electrode to be rendered negative was in the basin *b*, and the electrode of melted lead was retained in the basin *a*, and, by connexion with the proper conducting wire of a voltaic battery, was rendered positive. A volta-electrometer was included in the circuit.

816. Immediately upon the completion of the communication with the voltaic battery, the current passed, and decomposition proceeded. No chlorine was evolved at the positive electrode; but as the fused chloride was transparent, a button of alloy could be observed gradually forming and increasing in size at *b*, whilst the lead at *a* could also be seen gradually to diminish. After a time, the experiment was stopped; the tube allowed to cool, and broken open; the wires, with their buttons, cleaned and weighed; and their change in weight compared with the indication of the volta-electrometer.

817. In this experiment the positive electrode had lost just as much lead as the negative one had gained (795), and the loss and gain were very nearly the equivalents of the water decomposed in the volta-electrometer, giving for lead the number 101.5. It is therefore evident, in this instance, that causing a *strong affinity*, or *no affinity*, for the substance evolved at the *anode*, to be active during the experiment (807), produces no variation in the definite action of the electric current.

818. A similar experiment was then made with iodide of lead, and in this manner all confusion from the formation of a periodide avoided (803). No iodine was evolved during the whole action, and finally the loss of lead at the *anode* was the same as the gain at the *cathode*, the equivalent number, by comparison with the result in the volta-electrometer, being 103.5.

819. Then protochloride of tin was subjected to the electric current in the same manner, using of course, a tin positive electrode. No bichloride of tin was now formed (779, 790). On examining the two electrodes, the positive had lost precisely as much as the negative had gained; and by comparison with the volta-electrometer, the number for tin came out 59.

820. It is quite necessary in these and similar experiments to examine the interior of the bulbs of alloy at the ends of the conducting wires; for occasionally, and especially with those which have been positive, they are cavernous, and contain portions of the chloride or iodide used, which must be removed before the final weight is ascertained. This is more usually the case with lead than tin.

821. All these facts combine into, I think, an irresistible mass of evidence, proving the truth of the important proposition which I at first laid down, namely, *that the chemical power of a current of electricity is in direct proportion to the absolute quantity of electricity which passes* (377,

783). They prove, too, that this is not merely true with one substance, as water, but generally with all electrolytic bodies; and, further, that the results obtained with any *one substance* do not merely agree amongst themselves, but also with those obtained from *other substances*, the whole combining together into *one series of definite electro-chemical actions* (505). I do not mean to say that no exceptions will appear: perhaps some may arise, especially amongst substances existing only by weak affinity; but I do not expect that any will seriously disturb the result announced. If, in the well-considered, well-examined, and, I may surely say, well-ascertained doctrines of the definite nature of ordinary chemical affinity, such exceptions occur, as they do in abundance, yet, without being allowed to disturb our minds as to the general conclusion, they ought also to be allowed if they should present themselves at this, the opening of a new view of electro-chemical action; not being held up as obstructions to those who may be engaged in rendering that view more and more perfect, but laid aside for a while, in hopes that their perfect and consistent explanation will ultimately appear.

822. The doctrine of *definite electro-chemical action* just laid down, and, I believe, established, leads to some new views of the relations and classifications of bodies associated with or subject to this action. Some of these I shall proceed to consider.

823. In the first place, compound bodies may be separated into two great classes, namely, those which are decomposable by the electric current, and those which are not: of the latter, some are conductors, others non-conductors, of voltaic electricity.[1] The former do not depend for their decomposability upon the nature of their elements only; for, of the same two elements, bodies may be formed, of which one shall belong to one class and another to the other class; but probably on the proportions also (697). It is further remarkable, that with very few, if any, exceptions (414, 691), these decomposable bodies are exactly those governed by the remarkable law of conduction I have before described (394); for that law does not extend to the many compound fusible substances that are excluded from this class. I propose to call bodies of this, the decomposable class, *electrolytes* (664).

[1] I mean here by *voltaic electricity*, merely electricity from a most abundant source, but having very small intensity.

824. Then, again, the substances into which these divide, under the influence of the electric current, form an exceedingly important general class. They are combining bodies; are directly associated with the fundamental parts of the doctrine of chemical affinity; and have each a definite proportion, in which they are always evolved during electrolytic action. I have proposed to call these bodies generally *ions*, or particularly *anions* and *cations*, according as they appear at the *anode* or *cathode* (665); and the numbers representing the proportions in which they are evolved *electro-chemical equivalents*. Thus hydrogen, oxygen, chlorine, iodine, lead, tin are *ions*; the three former are *anions*, the two metals are *cations*, and 1, 8, 36, 125, 104, 58, are their *electro-chemical equivalents* nearly.

825. A summary of certain points already ascertained respecting *electrolytes*, *ions*, and *electro-chemical equivalents*, may be given in the following general form of propositions, without, I hope, including any serious error.

826. i. A single *ion*, i.e., one not in combination with another, will have no tendency to pass to either of the electrodes, and will be perfectly indifferent to the passing current, unless it be itself a compound of more elementary *ions*, and so subject to actual decomposition. Upon this fact is founded much of the proof adduced in favour of the new theory of electrochemical decomposition, which I put forth in a former series of these *Researches* (518, &c.).

827. ii. If one *ion* be combined in right proportions (697) with another strongly opposed to it in its ordinary chemical relations, i.e., if an *anion* be combined with a *cation*, then both will travel, the one to the *anode*, the other to the *cathode*, of the decomposing body (530, 542, 547).

828. iii. If, therefore, an *ion* pass towards one of the electrodes, another *ion* must also be passing simultaneously to the other electrode, although, from secondary action, it may not make its appearance (743).

829. iv. A body decomposable directly by the electric current, i.e., an *electrolyte*, must consist of two *ions*, and must also render them up during the act of decomposition.

830. v. There is but one *electrolyte* composed of the same two elementary *ions*; at least such appears to be the fact (697), dependent upon a law, that *only single electro-chemical equivalents of elementary ions can go to the electrodes, and not multiples*.

831. vi. A body not decomposable when alone, as boracic acid, is not directly decomposable by the electric current when in combination (780). It may act as an *ion* going wholly to the *anode* or *cathode*, but does not yield up its elements, except occasionally by a secondary action. Perhaps it is superfluous for me to point out that this proposition has *no relation* to such cases as that of water, which, by the presence of other bodies, is rendered a better conductor of electricity, and *therefore* is more freely decomposed.

832. vii. The nature of the substance of which the electrode is formed, provided it be a conductor, causes no difference in the electro-decomposition, either in kind or degree (807, 813): but it seriously influences, by secondary action (744), the state in which the *ions* finally appear. Advantage may be taken of this principle in combining and collecting such *ions* as, if evolved in their free state, would be unmanageable.[1]

833. viii. A substance which, being used as the electrode, can combine with the *ion* evolved against it, is also, I believe, an *ion*, and combines, in such cases, in the quantity represented by its *electro-chemical equivalent*. All the experiments I have made agree with this view; and it seems to me, at present, to result as a necessary consequence. Whether, in the secondary actions that take place, where the *ion* acts, not upon the matter of the electrode, but on that which is around it in the liquid (744), the same consequence follows, will require more extended investigation to determine.

834. ix. Compound *ions* are not necessarily composed of electro-chemical equivalents of simple *ions*. For instance, sulphuric acid, boracic acid, phosphoric acid, are *ions*, but not *electrolytes*, i.e., not composed of electro-chemical equivalents of simple *ions*.

835. x. Electro-chemical equivalents are always consistent; i.e., the same number which represents the equivalent of a substance A when it is separating from a substance B, will also represent A when separating from a third substance C. Thus, 8 is the electrochemical equivalent of oxygen, whether separating from hydrogen, or tin, or lead; and 103.5 is the electro-chemical equivalent of lead, whether separating from oxygen, or chlorine, or iodine.

836. xi. Electro-chemical equivalents coincide, and are the same with ordinary chemical equivalents.

837. By means of experiment and the preceding propositions, a knowledge of *ions* and their electro-chemical equivalents may be obtained in various ways.

838. In the first place, they may be determined directly, as has been done with hydrogen, oxygen, lead, and tin, in the numerous experiments already quoted.

839. In the next place, from propositions ii and iii, may be deduced the knowledge of many other *ions*, and also their equivalents. When chloride of lead was decomposed, platina being used for both electrodes (395), there could remain no more doubt that chlorine was passing to the *anode*, although it combined with the platina there, than when the positive electrode, being of plumbago (794), allowed its evolution in the free state; neither could there, in either case, remain any doubt that for every 103.5 parts of lead evolved at the *cathode*, 36 parts of chlorine were evolved at the *anode*, for the remaining chloride of lead was unchanged. So also, when in a metallic solution one volume of oxygen, or a secondary compound containing that proportion, appeared at the *anode*, no doubt could arise that hydrogen, equivalent to two volumes, had been determined to the *cathode*, although, by a secondary action, it had been employed in reducing oxides of lead, copper, or other metals, to the metallic state. In this manner, then, we learn from the experiments already described in these *Researches*, that chlorine, iodine, bromine, fluorine, calcium, potassium, strontium, magnesium, manganese, &c., are *ions*, and that their *electrochemical equivalents* are the same as their *ordinary chemical equivalents*.

840. Propositions iv and v extend our means of gaining information. For if a body of known chemical composition is found to be decomposable, and the nature of the substance evolved as a primary or even a secondary result (743, 777) at one of the electrodes, be ascertained, the electro-chemical equivalent of that body may be deduced from the known constant composition of the substance evolved. Thus, when fused protiodide of tin is decomposed by the voltaic current (804), the conclusion may be drawn, that both the iodine and tin are *ions*,

---

[1] It will often happen that the electrodes used may be of such a nature as, with the fluid in which they are immersed, to produce an electric current, either according with or opposing that of the voltaic arrangement used, and in this way, or by direct chemical action, may sadly disturb the results. Still, in the midst of all these confusing effects, the electric current, which actually passes in any direction through the body suffering decomposition, will produce its own definite electrolytic action.

and that the proportions in which they combine in the fused compound express their electro-chemical equivalents. Again, with respect to the fused iodide of potassium (805), it is an electrolyte; and the chemical equivalents will also be the electro-chemical equivalents.

811. If proposition viii sustain extensive experimental investigation, then it will not only help to confirm the results obtained by the use of the other propositions, but will give abundant original information of its own.

842. In many instances, the *secondary results* obtained by the action of the evolved *ion* on the substances present in the surrounding liquid or solution, will give the electro-chemical equivalent. Thus, in the solution of acetate of lead, and, as far as I have gone, in other proto-salts subjected to the reducing action of the nascent hydrogen at the *cathode*, the metal precipitated has been in the same quantity as if it had been a primary product (provided no free hydrogen escaped there), and therefore gave accurately the number representing its electro-chemical equivalent.

843. Upon this principle it is that secondary results may occasionally be used as measurers of the volta-electric current (706, 740); but there are not many metallic solutions that answer this purpose well: for unless the metal is easily precipitated, hydrogen will be evolved at the *cathode* and vitiate the result. If a soluble peroxide is formed at the *anode*, or if the precipitated metal crystallize across the solution and touch the positive electrode, similar vitiated results are obtained. I expect to find in some salts, as the acetates of mercury and zinc, solutions favourable for this use.

844. After the first experimental investigations to establish the definite chemical action of electricity, I have not hesitated to apply the more strict results of chemical analysis to correct the numbers obtained as electrolytic results. This, it is evident, may be done in a great number of cases, without using too much liberty towards the due severity of scientific research. The series of numbers representing electro-chemical equivalents must, like those expressing the ordinary equivalents of chemically acting bodies, remain subject to the continual correction of experiment and sound reasoning.

845. I give the following brief table of *ions* and their electro-chemical equivalents, rather as a specimen of a first attempt than as anything that can supply the want which must very quickly be felt, of a full and complete tab-

ular account of this class of bodies. Looking forward to such a table as of extreme utility (if well-constructed) in developing the intimate relation of ordinary chemical affinity to electrical actions, and identifying the two, not to the imagination merely, but to the conviction of the senses and a sound judgement, I may be allowed to express a hope, that the endeavour will always be to make it a table of *real*, and not *hypothetical*, electro-chemical equivalents; for we shall else overrun the facts, and lose all sight and consciousness of the knowledge lying directly in our path.

846. The equivalent numbers do not profess to be exact, and are taken almost entirely from the chemical results of other philosophers in whom I could repose more confidence, as to these points, than in myself.

847. TABLE OF IONS

Anions

Oxygen	8	Phosphoric acid	35.7
Chlorine	35.5	Carbonic acid	22
Iodine	126	Boracic acid	24
Bromine	78.3	Acetic acid	51
Fluorine	18.7	Tartaric acid	66
Cyanogen	26	Citric acid	58
Sulphuric acid	40	Oxalic acid	36
Selenic acid	64	Sulphur (?)	16
Nitric acid	54	Selenium (?)	
Chloric acid	75.5	Sulpho-cyanogen	

Cations

Hydrogen	1	Mercury	200
Potassium	39.2	Silver	108
Sodium	23.3	Platina	98.6?
Lithium	10	Gold	(?)
Barium	68.7		
Strontium	43.8	Ammonia	17
Calcium	20.5	Potassa	47.2
Magnesium	12.7	Soda	31.3
Manganese	27.7	Lithia	18
Zinc	32.5	Baryta	76.7
Tin	57.9	Strontia	51.8
Lead	103.5	Lime	28.5
Iron	28	Magnesia	20.7
Copper	31.6	Alumina	(?)
Cadmium	55.8	Protoxides generally.	
Cerium	46	Quinia	171.6
Cobalt	29.5	Cinchona	160
Nickel	29.5	Morphia	290
Antimony	64.6?	Vegeto-alkalies general-	
Bismuth	71	ly.	

848. This table might be further arranged into groups of such substances as either act with, or replace, each other. Thus, for instance, acids and bases act in relation to each other: but they do not act in association with oxygen, hydrogen, or elementary substances. There is indeed little or no doubt that, when the electrical relations of the particles of matter come

to be closely examined, this division must be made. The simple substances, with cyanogen, sulpho-cyanogen, and one or two other compound bodies, will probably form the first group; and the acids and bases, with such analogous compounds as may prove to be *ions*, the second group. Whether these will include all *ions*, or whether a third class of more complicated results will be required, must be decided by future experiments.

849. It is *probable* that all our present elementary bodies are *ions*, but that is not as yet certain. There are some, such as carbon, phosphorus, nitrogen, silicon, boron, aluminium, the right of which to the title of *ion* it is desirable to decide as soon as possible. There are also many compound bodies, and amongst them alumina and silica, which it is desirable to class immediately by unexceptionable experiments. It is also *possible*, that all combinable bodies, compound as well as simple, may enter into the class of *ions*; but at present it does not seem to me probable. Still the experimental evidence I have is so small in proportion to what must gradually accumulate around, and bear upon, this point, that I am afraid to give a strong opinion upon it.

850. I think I cannot deceive myself in considering the doctrine of definite electro-chemical action as of the utmost importance. It touches by its facts more directly and closely than any former fact, or set of facts, have done, upon the beautiful idea, that ordinary chemical affinity is a mere consequence of the electrical attractions of the particles of different kinds of matter; and it will probably lead us to the means by which we may enlighten that which is at present so obscure, and either fully demonstrate the truth of the idea, or develop that which ought to replace it.

851. A very valuable use of electro-chemical equivalents will be to decide, in cases of doubt, what is the true chemical equivalent, or definite proportional, or atomic number of a body; for I have such conviction that the power which governs electro-decomposition and ordinary chemical attractions is the same; and such confidence in the overruling influence of those natural laws which render the former definite, as to feel no hesitation in believing that the latter must submit to them also. Such being the case, I can have no doubt that, assuming hydrogen as 1, and dismissing small fractions for the simplicity of expression, the equivalent number or atomic weight of oxygen is 8, of chlorine 36, of bromine 78.4, of lead 103.5, of tin 59, &c.,

notwithstanding that a very high authority doubles several of these numbers.

§ 13. *On the Absolute Quantity of Electricity Associated with the Particles or Atoms of Matter*

852. The theory of definite electrolytical or electro-chemical action appears to me to touch immediately upon the *absolute quantity* of electricity or electric power belonging to different bodies. It is impossible, perhaps, to speak on this point without committing oneself beyond what present facts will sustain; and yet it is equally impossible, and perhaps would be impolitic, not to reason upon the subject. Although we know nothing of what an atom is, yet we cannot resist forming some idea of a small particle, which represents it to the mind; and though we are in equal, if not greater, ignorance of electricity, so as to be unable to say whether it is a particular matter or matters, or mere motion of ordinary matter, or some third kind of power or agent, yet there is an immensity of facts which justify us in believing that the atoms of matter are in some way endowed or associated with electrical powers, to which they owe their most striking qualities, and amongst them their mutual chemical affinity. As soon as we perceive, through the teaching of Dalton, that chemical powers are, however varied the circumstances in which they are exerted, definite for each body, we learn to estimate the relative degree of force which resides in such bodies: and when upon that knowledge comes the fact, that the electricity, which we appear to be capable of loosening from its habitation for a while, and conveying from place to place, *whilst it retains its chemical force*, can be measured out, and being so measured is found to be *as definite in its action* as any of *those portions* which, remaining associated with the particles of matter, give them their *chemical relation*; we seem to have found the link which connects the proportion of that we have evolved to the proportion of that belonging to the particles in their natural state.

853. Now it is wonderful to observe how small a quantity of a compound body is decomposed by a certain portion of electricity. Let us, for instance, consider this and a few other points in relation to water. *One grain* of water, acidulated to facilitate conduction, will require an electric current to be continued for three minutes and three-quarters of time to effect its decomposition, which current must be powerful enough to retain a platina wire $\frac{1}{104}$ of

an inch in thickness,[1] red-hot, in the air during the whole time; and if interrupted anywhere by charcoal points, will produce a very brilliant and constant star of light. If attention be paid to the instantaneous discharge of electricity of tension, as illustrated in the beautiful experiments of Mr. Wheatstone,[2] and to what I have said elsewhere on the relation of common and voltaic electricity (371, 375), it will not be too much to say that this necessary quantity of electricity is equal to a very powerful flash of lightning. Yet we have it under perfect command; can evolve, direct, and employ it at pleasure; and when it has performed its full work of electrolyzation, it has only separated the elements of *a single grain of water.*

854. On the other hand, the relation between the conduction of the electricity and the decomposition of the water is so close, that one cannot take place without the other. If the water is altered only in that small degree which consists in its having the solid instead of the fluid state, the conduction is stopped, and the decomposition is stopped with it. Whether the conduction be considered as depending upon the decomposition, or not (413, 703), still the relation of the two functions is equally intimate and inseparable.

855. Considering this close and twofold relation, namely, that without decomposition, transmission of electricity does not occur; and, that for a given definite quantity of electricity passed, an equally definite and constant quantity of water or other matter is decomposed; considering also that the agent, which is electricity, is simply employed in overcoming electrical powers in the body subjected to its action; it seems a probable, and almost a natural consequence, that the quantity which passes

is the *equivalent* of, and therefore equal to, that of the particles separated; i.e., that if the electrical power which holds the elements of a grain of water in combination, or which makes a grain of oxygen and hydrogen in the right proportions unite into water when they are made to combine, could be thrown into the condition of *a current*, it would exactly equal the current required for the separation of that grain of water into its elements again.

856. This view of the subject gives an almost overwhelming idea of the extraordinary quantity or degree of electric power which naturally belongs to the particles of matter; but it is not inconsistent in the slightest degree with the facts which can be brought to bear on this point. To illustrate this I must say a few words on the voltaic pile.[3]

857. Intending hereafter to apply the results given in this and the preceding series of *Researches* to a close investigation of the source of electricity in the voltaic instrument, I have refrained from forming any decided opinion on the subject; and without at all meaning to dismiss metallic contact, or the contact of dissimilar substances, being conductors, but not metallic, as if they had nothing to do with the origin of the current, I still am fully of opinion with Davy, that it is at least continued by chemical action, and that the supply constituting the current is almost entirely from that source.

858. Those bodies which, being interposed between the metals of the voltaic pile, render it active, *are all of them electrolytes* (476); and it cannot but press upon the attention of every one engaged in considering this subject, that in those bodies (so essential to the pile) decomposition and the transmission of a current are so intimately connected, that one cannot happen without the other. This I have shown abundantly in water, and numerous other cases (402, 476). If, then, a voltaic trough have its extremities connected by a body capable of being decomposed, as water, we shall have a continuous current through the apparatus; and whilst it remains in this state we may look at the part where the acid is acting upon the plates, and that where the current is acting upon the water, as the reciprocals of each other. In both

---

[1] I have not stated the length of wire used, because I find by experiment, as would be expected in theory, that it is indifferent. The same quantity of electricity which, passed in a given time, can heat an inch of platina wire of a certain diameter red-hot, can also heat a hundred, a thousand, or any length of the same wire to the same degree, provided the cooling circumstances are the same for every part in all cases. This I have proved by the volta-electrometer. I found that whether half an inch or eight inches were retained at one constant temperature of dull redness, equal quantities of water were decomposed in equal times. When the half-inch was used, only the centre portion of wire was ignited. A fine wire may even be used as a rough but ready regulator of a voltaic current; for if it be made part of the circuit, and the larger wires communicating with it be shifted nearer to or farther apart, so as to keep the portion of wire in the circuit sensibly at the same temperature, the current passing through it will be nearly uniform.

[2] *Literary Gazette,* 1833, March 1 and 8. *Philosophical Magazine,* 1833, p. 204. *L'Institut,* 1833, p. 261.

[3] By the term *voltaic pile,* I mean such apparatus or arrangement of metals as up to this time have been called so, and which contain water, brine, acids, or other aqueous solutions or decomposable substances (476), between their plates. Other kinds of electric apparatus may be hereafter invented, and I hope to construct some not belonging to the class of instruments discovered by Volta.

parts we have the two conditions *inseparable in such bodies as these*, namely, the passing of a current, and decomposition; and this is as true of the cells in the battery as of the water cell; for no voltaic battery has as yet been constructed in which the chemical action is only that of combination: *decomposition is always included*, and is, I believe, an essential chemical part.

859. But the difference in the two parts of the connected battery, that is, the decomposition or experimental cell, and the acting cells, is simply this. In the former we urge the current through, but it, apparently of necessity, is accompanied by decomposition: in the latter we cause decompositions by ordinary chemical actions (which are, however, themselves electrical), and, as a consequence, have the electrical current; and as the decomposition dependent upon the current is definite in the former case, so is the current associated with the decomposition also definite in the latter (862, &c.).

860. Let us apply this in support of what I have surmised respecting the enormous electric power of each particle or atom of matter (856). I showed in a former series of these *Researches* on the relation by measure of common and voltaic electricity, that two wires, one of platina and one of zinc, each one-eighteenth of an inch in diameter, placed five-sixteenths of an inch apart, and immersed to the depth of five-eighths of an inch in acid, consisting of one drop of oil of vitriol and four ounces of distilled water at a temperature of about 60° Fahr., and connected at the other extremities by a copper wire eighteen feet long, and one-eighteenth of an inch in thickness, yielded as much electricity in little more than three seconds of time as a Leyden battery charged by thirty turns of a very large and powerful plate electric machine in full action (371). This quantity, though sufficient if passed at once through the head of a rat or cat to have killed it, as by a flash of lightning, was evolved by the mutual action of so small a portion of the zinc wire and water in contact with it, that the loss of weight sustained by either would be inappreciable by our most delicate instruments; and as to the water which could be decomposed by that current, it must have been insensible in quantity, for no trace of hydrogen appeared upon the surface of the platina during those three seconds.

861. What an enormous quantity of electricity, therefore, is required for the decomposition of a single grain of water! We have already seen that it must be in quantity sufficient to sustain a platina wire $\frac{1}{104}$ of an inch in thickness, red-hot, in contact with the air, for three minutes and three quarters (853), a quantity which is almost infinitely greater than that which could be evolved by the little standard voltaic arrangement to which I have just referred (860, 371). I have endeavoured to make a comparison by the loss of weight of such a wire in a given time in such an acid, according to a principle and experiment to be almost immediately described (862); but the proportion is so high that I am almost afraid to mention it. It would appear that 800,000 such charges of the Leyden battery as I have referred to above, would be necessary to supply electricity sufficient to decompose a single grain of water; or, if I am right, to equal the quantity of electricity which is naturally associated with the elements of that grain of water, endowing them with their mutual chemical affinity.

862. In further proof of this high electric condition of the particles of matter, and the *identity as to quantity of that belonging to them with that necessary for their separation*, I will describe an experiment of great simplicity but extreme beauty, when viewed in relation to the evolution of an electric current and its decomposing powers.

863. A dilute sulphuric acid, made by adding about one part by measure of oil of vitriol to thirty parts of water, will act energetically upon a piece of zinc plate in its ordinary and simple state: but, as Mr. Sturgeon has shown,[1] not at all, or scarcely so, if the surface of the metal has in the first instance been amalgamated; yet the amalgamated zinc will act powerfully with platina as an electromotor, hydrogen being evolved on the surface of the latter metal, as the zinc is oxidized and dissolved. The amalgamation is best effected by sprinkling a few drops of mercury upon the surface of the zinc, the latter being moistened with the dilute acid, and rubbing with the fingers or tow so as to extend the liquid metal over the whole of the surface. Any mercury in excess, forming liquid drops upon the zinc, should be wiped off.[2]

864. Two plates of zinc thus amalgamated were dried and accurately weighed; one, which we will call A, weighed 163.1 grains; the other, to be called B, weighed 148.3 grains. They were

[1] *Recent Experimental Researches*, &c., 1830, p. 74, &c.

[2] The experiment may be made with pure zinc, which, as chemists well know, is but slightly acted upon by dilute sulphuric acid in comparison with ordinary zinc, which during the action is subject to an infinity of voltaic actions. See De la Rive on this subject, *Bibliothèque Universelle*, 1830, p. 391.

about five inches long, and 0.4 of an inch wide. An earthenware pneumatic trough was filled with dilute sulphuric acid, of the strength just described (863), and a gas jar, also filled with the acid, inverted in it.[1] A plate of platina of nearly the same length, but about three times as wide as the zinc plates, was put up into this jar. The zinc plate A was also introduced into the jar, and brought in contact with the platina, and at the same moment the plate B was put into the acid of the trough, but out of contact with other metallic matter.

865. Strong action immediately occurred in the jar upon the contact of the zinc and platina plates. Hydrogen gas rose from the platina, and was collected in the jar, but no hydrogen or other gas rose from *either* zinc plate. In about ten or twelve minutes, sufficient hydrogen having been collected, the experiment was stopped; during its progress a few small bubbles had appeared upon plate B, but none upon plate A. The plates were washed in distilled water, dried, and reweighed. Plate B weighed 148.3 grains, as before, having lost nothing by the direct chemical action of the acid. Plate A weighed 154.65 grains, 8.45 grains of it having been oxidized and dissolved during the experiment.

866. The hydrogen gas was next transferred to a water-trough and measured; it amounted to 12.5 cubic inches, the temperature being 52°, and the barometer 29.2 inches. This quantity, corrected for temperature, pressure, and moisture, becomes 12.15453 cubic inches of dry hydrogen at mean temperature and pressure; which, increased by one half for the oxygen that must have gone to the *anode*, i.e., to the zinc, gives 18.232 cubic inches as the quantity of oxygen and hydrogen evolved from the water decomposed by the electric current. According to the estimate of the weight of the mixed gas before adopted (791), this volume is equal to 2.3535544 grains, which therefore is the weight of water decomposed; and this quantity is to 8.45, the quantity of zinc oxidized, as 9 is to 32.31. Now taking 9 as the equivalent number of water, the number 32.5 is given as the equivalent number of zinc; a coincidence sufficiently near to show, what indeed could not but happen, that for an equivalent of zinc oxidized an equivalent of water must be decomposed.[2]

[1] The acid was left during a night with a small piece of unamalgamated zinc in it, for the purpose of evolving such air as might be inclined to separate, and bringing the whole into a constant state.
[2] The experiment was repeated several times with the same results.

867. But let us observe *how* the water is decomposed. It is electrolyzed, i.e., is decomposed voltaically, and not in the ordinary manner (as to appearance) of chemical decompositions; for the oxygen appears at the *anode* and the hydrogen at the *cathode* of the body under decomposition, and these were in many parts of the experiment above an inch asunder. Again, the ordinary chemical affinity was not enough under the circumstances to effect the decomposition of the water, as was abundantly proved by the inaction on plate B; the voltaic current was essential. And to prevent any idea that the chemical affinity was almost sufficient to decompose the water, and that a smaller current of electricity might, under the circumstances, cause the hydrogen to pass to the *cathode*, I need only refer to the results which I have given (807, 813) to show that the chemical action at the electrodes has not the slightest influence over the *quantities* of water or other substances decomposed between them, but that they are entirely dependent upon the quantity of electricity which passes.

868. What, then, follows as a necessary consequence of the whole experiment? Why, this: that the chemical action upon 32.31 parts, or one equivalent of zinc, in this simple voltaic circle, was able to evolve such quantity of electricity in the form of a current, as, passing through water, should decompose 9 parts, or one equivalent of that substance: and considering the definite relations of electricity as developed in the preceding parts of the present paper, the results prove that the quantity of electricity which, being naturally associated with the particles of matter, gives them their combining power, is able, when thrown into a current, to separate those particles from their state of combination; or, in other words, that *the electricity which decomposes, and that which is evolved by the decomposition of, a certain quantity of matter, are alike.*

869. The harmony which this theory of the definite evolution and the equivalent definite action of electricity introduces into the associated theories of definite proportions and electro-chemical affinity, is very great. According to it, the equivalent weights of bodies are simply those quantities of them which contain equal quantities of electricity, or have naturally equal electric powers; it being the ELECTRICITY which *determines* the equivalent number, *because* it determines the combining force. Or, if we adopt the atomic theory or phraseology, then the atoms of bodies which are equivalents

to each other in their ordinary chemical action have equal quantities of electricity naturally associated with them. But I must confess I am jealous of the term *atom*; for though it is very easy to talk of atoms, it is very difficult to form a clear idea of their nature, especially when compound bodies are under consideration.

870. I cannot refrain from recalling here the beautiful idea put forth, I believe, by Berzelius (703) in his development of his views of the electro-chemical theory of affinity, that the heat and light evolved during cases of powerful combination are the consequence of the electric discharge which is at the moment taking place. The idea is in perfect accordance with the view I have taken of the *quantity* of electricity associated with the particles of matter.

871. In this exposition of the law of the definite action of electricity, and its corresponding definite proportion in the particles of bodies, I do not pretend to have brought, as yet, every case of chemical or electro-chemical action under its dominion. There are numerous considerations of a theoretical nature, especially respecting the compound particles of matter and the resulting electrical forces which they ought to possess, which I hope will gradually receive their development; and there are numerous experimental cases, as, for instance, those of compounds formed by weak affinities, the simultaneous decomposition of water and salts, &c., which still require investigation. But whatever the results on these and numerous other points may be, I do not believe that the facts which I have advanced, or even the general laws deduced from them, will suffer any serious change; and they are of sufficient importance to justify their publication, though much may yet remain imperfect or undone. Indeed, it is the great beauty of our science, CHEMISTRY, that advancement in it, whether in a degree great or small, instead of exhausting the subjects of research, opens the doors to further and more abundant knowledge, overflowing with beauty and utility, to those who will be at the easy personal pains of undertaking its experimental investigation.

872. The definite production of electricity (868) in association with its definite action proves, I think, that the current of electricity in the voltaic pile is sustained by chemical decomposition, or rather by chemical action, and not by contact only. But here, as elsewhere (857), I beg to reserve my opinion as to the real action of contact, not having yet been able to make up my mind as to whether it is an exciting cause of the current, or merely necessary to allow of the conduction of electricity, otherwise generated, from one metal to the other.

873. But admitting that chemical action is the source of electricity, what an infinitely small fraction of that which is active do we obtain and employ in our voltaic batteries! Zinc and platina wires, one-eighteenth of an inch in diameter and about half an inch long, dipped into dilute sulphuric acid, so weak that it is not sensibly sour to the tongue, or scarcely to our most delicate test-papers, will evolve more electricity in one-twentieth of a minute (860) than any man would willingly allow to pass through his body at once. The chemical action of a grain of water upon four grains of zinc can evolve electricity equal in quantity to that of a powerful thunder-storm (868, 861). Nor is it merely true that the quantity is active; it can be directed and made to perform its full equivalent duty (867, &c.). Is there not, then, great reason to hope and believe that, by a closer *experimental* investigation of the principles which govern the development and action of this subtile agent, we shall be able to increase the power of our batteries, or invent new instruments which shall a thousandfold surpass in energy those which we at present possess?

874. Here for a while I must leave the consideration of the *definite chemical action of electricity*. But before I dismiss this series of experimental *Researches*, I would call to mind that, in a former series, I showed the current of electricity was also *definite in its magnetic action* (216, 366, 367, 376, 377); and, though this result was not pursued to any extent, I have no doubt that the success which has attended the development of the chemical effects is not more than would accompany an investigation of the magnetic phenomena.

Royal Institution, December 31, 1833

EIGHTH SERIES

§ 14. *On the Electricity of the Voltaic Pile; its Source, Quantity, Intensity, and General Characters* ¶ i. *On Simple Voltaic Circles* ¶ ii. *On the Intensity Necessary for Electrolyzation* ¶ iii. *On Associated Voltaic Circles, or the Voltaic Battery* ¶ iv. *On the Resistance of an Electrolyte to Electrolytic Action and on Interpositions* ¶ v. *General Remarks on the Active Voltaic Battery*

RECEIVED APRIL 7, READ JUNE 5, 1834

¶ i. *On Simple Voltaic Circles*

875. THE great question of the source of electricity, in the voltaic pile has engaged the attention of so many eminent philosophers, that a man of liberal mind and able to appreciate their powers would probably conclude, although he might not have studied the question, that the truth was somewhere revealed. But if in pursuance of this impression he were induced to enter upon the work of collating results and conclusions, he would find such contradictory evidence, such equilibrium of opinion, such variation and combination of theory, as would leave him in complete doubt respecting what he should accept as the true interpretation of nature: he would be forced to take upon himself the labour of repeating and examining the facts, and then use his own judgement on them in preference to that of others.

876. This state of the subject must, to those who have made up their minds on the matter, be my apology for entering upon its investigation. The views I have taken of the definite action of electricity in decomposing bodies (783), and the identity of the power so used with the power to be overcome (855), founded not on a mere opinion or general notion, but on facts which, being altogether new, were to my mind precise and conclusive, gave me, as I conceived, the power of examining the question with advantages not before possessed by any, and which might compensate, on my part, for the superior clearness and extent of intellect on theirs. Such are the considerations which have induced me to suppose I might help in deciding the question, and be able to render assistance in that great service of removing *doubtful knowledge*. Such knowledge is the early morning light of every advancing science, and is essential to its development; but the man who is engaged in dispelling that which is deceptive in it, and revealing more clearly that which is true, is as useful in his place, and as necessary to the general progress of the science, as he who first broke through the intellectual darkness, and opened a path into knowledge before unknown to man.

877. The identity of the force constituting the voltaic current or electrolytic agent, with that which holds the elements of electrolytes together (855), or in other words with chemical affinity, seemed to indicate that the electricity of the pile itself was merely a mode of exertion, or exhibition, or existence of *true chemical action*, or rather of its cause; and I have consequently already said that I agree with those who believe that the *supply* of electricity is due to chemical powers (857).

878. But the great question of whether it is originally due to metallic contact or to chemical action, i.e., whether it is the first or the second which *originates* and determines the current, was to me still doubtful; and the beautiful and simple experiment with amalgamated zinc and platina, which I have described minutely as to its results (863, &c.), did not decide the point; for in that experiment the chemical action does not take place without the contact of the metals, and the metallic contact is inefficient without the chemical action. Hence either might be looked upon as the *determining* cause of the current.

879. I thought it essential to decide this question by the simplest possible forms of apparatus and experiment, that no fallacy might be inadvertently admitted. The well-known difficulty of effecting decomposition by a single pair of plates, except in the fluid exciting them into action (863), seemed to throw insurmountable obstruction in the way of such experi-

391

PLATE VII

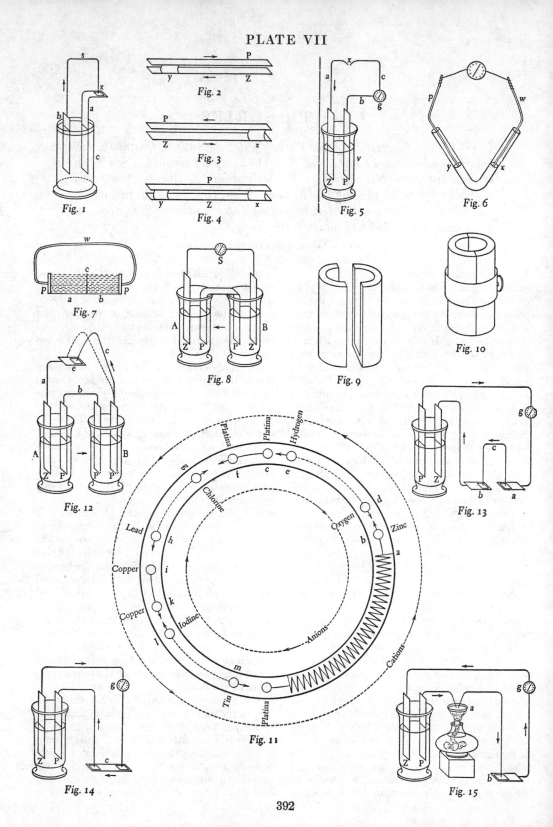

Fig. 1

Fig. 2

Fig. 3

Fig. 4

Fig. 5

Fig. 6

Fig. 7

Fig. 8

Fig. 9

Fig. 10

Fig. 11

Fig. 12

Fig. 13

Fig. 14

Fig. 15

ments; but I remembered the easy decomposability of the solution of iodide of potassium (316), and seeing no theoretical reason, if metallic contact was not *essential*, why true electro-decomposition should not be obtained without it, even in a single circuit, I persevered and succeeded.

880. A plate of zinc, about eight inches long and half an inch wide, was cleaned and bent in the middle to a right angle, (Pl. VII, *Fig. 1 a*). A plate of platina, about three inches long and half an inch wide, was fastened to a platina wire, and the latter bent as in the figure, *b*. These two pieces of metal were arranged together as delineated, but as yet without the vessel *c*, and its contents, which consisted of dilute sulphuric acid mingled with a little nitric acid. At *x* a piece of folded bibulous paper, moistened in a solution of iodide of potassium, was placed on the zinc, and was pressed upon by the end of the platina wire. When under these circumstances the plates were dipped into the acid of the vessel *c*, there was an immediate effect at *x*, the iodide being decomposed, and iodine appearing at the *anode* (663), i.e., against the end of the platina wire.

881. As long as the lower ends of the plates remained in the acid the electric current continued, and the decomposition proceeded at *x*. On removing the end of the wire from place to place on the paper, the effect was evidently very powerful; and on placing a piece of turmeric paper between the white paper and zinc, both papers being moistened with the solution of iodide of potassium, alkali was evolved at the *cathode* (663) against the zinc, in proportion to the evolution of iodine at the *anode*. Hence the decomposition was perfectly polar, and decidedly dependent upon a current of electricity passing from the zinc through the acid to the platina in the vessel *c*, and back from the platina through the solution to the zinc at the paper *x*.

882. That the decomposition at *x* was a true electrolytic action, due to a current determined by the state of things in the vessel *c*, and not dependent upon any mere direct chemical action of the zinc and platina on the iodide, or even upon any *current* which the solution of iodide might by its action on those metals tend to form at *x*, was shown, in the first place, by removing the vessel *c* and its acid from the plates, when all decomposition at *x* ceased, and in the next by connecting the metals, either in or out of the acid, together, when decomposition of the iodide at *x* occurred, but in a *reverse*

order; for now alkali appeared against the end of the platina wire, and the iodine passed to the zinc, the current being the contrary of what it was in the former instance, and produced directly by the difference of action of the solution in the paper on the two metals. The iodine of course *combined* with the zinc.

883. When this experiment was made with pieces of zinc amalgamated over the whole surface (863), the results were obtained with equal facility and in the same direction, even when only dilute sulphuric acid was contained in the vessel *c* (Pl. VII, *Fig. 1*). Whichsoever end of the zinc was immersed in the acid, still the effects were the same: so that if, for a moment, the mercury might be supposed to supply the metallic contact, the inversion of the amalgamated piece destroys that objection. The use of *unamalgamated zinc* (880) removes all possibility of doubt.[1]

884. When, in pursuance of other views (930), the vessel *c* was made to contain a solution of caustic potash in place of acid, still the same results occurred. Decomposition of the iodide was effected freely, though there was no metallic contact of dissimilar metals, and the current of electricity was in the *same direction* as when acid was used at the place of excitement.

885. Even a solution of common salt in the glass *c* could produce all these effects.

886. Having made a galvanometer with platina wires, and introduced it into the course of the current between the platina plate and the place of decomposition *x*, it was affected, giving indications of currents in the same direction as those shown to exist by the chemical action.

887. If we consider these results generally, they lead to very important conclusions. In the first place, they prove, in the most decisive manner, that *metallic contact is not necessary for the production of the voltaic current*. In the

---

[1] The following is a more striking mode of making the above elementary experiment. Prepare a plate of zinc, ten or twelve inches long and two inches wide, and clean it thoroughly: provide also two discs of clean platina, about one inch and a half in diameter: — dip three or four folds of bibulous paper into a strong solution of iodide of potassium, place them on the clean zinc at one end of the plate, and put on them one of the platina discs: finally dip similar folds of paper or a piece of linen cloth into a mixture of equal parts nitric acid and water, and place it at the other end of the zinc plate with the second platina disc upon it. In this state of things no change at the solution of the iodide will be perceptible; but if the two discs be connected by a platina (or any other) wire for a second or two, and then that over the iodide be raised, it will be found that the *whole* of the surface beneath is deeply stained with *evolved iodine.* —*Dec.* 1838.

next place, they show a most extraordinary mutual relation of the chemical affinities of the fluid which *excites* the current, and the fluid which is *decomposed* by it.

888. For the purpose of simplifying the consideration, let us take the experiment with amalgamated zinc. The metal so prepared exhibits no effect until the current can pass: it at the same time introduces no new action, but merely removes an influence which is extraneous to those belonging either to the production or the effect of the electric current under investigation (1000); an influence also which, when present, tends only to confuse the results.

889. Let two plates, one of amalgamated zinc and the other of platina, be placed parallel to each other (Pl. VII, *Fig. 2*), and introduce a drop of dilute sulphuric acid, *y*, between them at one end: there will be no sensible chemical action at that spot unless the two plates are connected somewhere else, as at P Z, by a body capable of conducting electricity. If that body be a metal or certain forms of carbon, then the current passes, and, as it circulates through the fluid at *y*, decomposition ensues.

890. Then remove the acid from *y*, and introduce a drop of the solution of iodide of potassium at *x* (Pl. VII, *Fig. 3*). Exactly the same set of effects occur, except that when the metallic communication is made at P Z, the electric current is in the opposite direction to what it was before, as is indicated by the arrows, which show the courses of the currents (667).

891. Now *both* the solutions used are conductors, but the conduction in them is essentially connected with decomposition (858) in a certain constant order, and therefore the appearance of the elements in certain places *shows* in what direction a current has passed when the solutions are thus employed. Moreover, we find that when they are used at opposite ends of the plates, as in the last two experiments (889, 890), metallic contact being allowed at the other extremities, the currents are in opposite directions. We have evidently, therefore, the power of opposing the actions of the two fluids simultaneously to each other at the opposite ends of the plates, using each one as a conductor for the discharge of the current of electricity, which the other tends to generate; in fact, substituting them for metallic contact, and combining both experiments into one (Pl. VII, *Fig. 4*). Under these circumstances, there is an opposition of forces: the fluid, which brings into play the stronger set of chemical affinities for the zinc, (being the dilute acid), overcomes

the force of the other, and determines the formation and direction of the electric current; not merely making that current pass through the weaker liquid, but actually reversing the tendency which the elements of the latter have in relation to the zinc and platina if not thus counteracted, and forcing them in the contrary direction to that they are inclined to follow, that its own current may have free course. If the dominant action at *y* be removed by making metallic contact there, then the liquid at *x* resumes its power; or if the metals be not brought into contact at *y*, but the affinities of the solution there weakened, whilst those active at *x* are strengthened, then the latter gains the ascendency, and the decompositions are produced in a contrary order.

892. Before drawing a *final* conclusion from this mutual dependence and state of the chemical affinities of two distant portions of acting fluids (916), I will proceed to examine more minutely the various circumstances under which the re-action of the body suffering decomposition is rendered evident upon the action of the body, also undergoing decomposition, which produces the voltaic current.

893. The use of *metallic contact* in a single pair of plates, and the cause of its great superiority above contact made by other kinds of matter, become now very evident. When an amalgamated zinc plate is dipped into dilute sulphuric acid, the force of chemical affinity exerted between the metal and the fluid is not sufficiently powerful to cause sensible action at the surfaces of contact, and occasion the decomposition of water by the oxidation of the metal, although it *is* sufficient to produce such a condition of the electricity (or the power upon which chemical affinity depends) as would produce a current if there were a path open for it (916, 956); and that current would complete the conditions necessary, under the circumstances, for the decomposition of the water.

894. Now the presence of a piece of platina touching both the zinc and the fluid to be decomposed, opens the path required for the electricity. Its *direct communication* with the zinc is effectual, far beyond any communication made between it and that metal (i.e., between the platina and zinc), by means of decomposable conducting bodies, or, in other words, *electrolytes*, as in the experiment already described (891); because, when *they* are used, the chemical affinities between them and the zinc produce a contrary and opposing action to that which is influential in the dilute sulphuric acid;

or if that action be but small, still the affinity of their component parts for each other has to be overcome, for they cannot conduct without suffering decomposition; and this decomposition is found *experimentally* to react back upon the forces which in the acid tend to produce the current (904, 910, &c.), and in numerous cases entirely to neutralize them. Where direct contact of the zinc and platina occurs, these obstructing forces are not brought into action, and therefore the production and the circulation of the electric current and the concomitant action of decomposition are then highly favoured.

895. It is evident, however, that one of these opposing actions may be dismissed, and yet an electrolyte be used for the purpose of completing the circuit between the zinc and platina immersed separately into the dilute acid; for if, in Pl. VII, *Fig. 1*, the platina wire be retained in metallic contact with the zinc plate *a*, at *x*, and a division of the platina be made elsewhere, as at *s*, then the solution of iodide placed there, being in contact with platina at both surfaces, exerts no chemical affinities for that metal; or if it does, they are equal on both sides. Its power, therefore, of forming a current in opposition to that dependent upon the action of the acid in the vessel *c*, is removed, and only its resistance to decomposition remains as the obstacle to be overcome by the affinities exerted in the dilute sulphuric acid.

896. This becomes the condition of a single pair of active plates where *metallic contact* is allowed. In such cases, only one set of opposing affinities are to be overcome by those which are dominant in the vessel *c*; whereas, when metallic contact is not allowed, two sets of opposing affinities must be conquered (894).

897. It has been considered a difficult, and by some an impossible thing, to decompose bodies by the current from a single pair of plates, even when it was so powerful as to heat bars of metal red-hot, as in the case of Hare's calorimeter, arranged as a single voltaic circuit, or of Wollaston's powerful single pair of metals. This difficulty has arisen altogether from the antagonism of the chemical affinity engaged in producing the current with the chemical affinity to be overcome, and depends entirely upon their relative intensity; for when the sum of forces in one has a certain degree of superiority over the sum of forces in the other, the former gain the ascendency, determine the current, and overcome the latter so as to make the substance exerting them yield up its elements in

perfect accordance, both as to direction and quantity, with the course of those which are exerting the most intense and dominant action.

898. Water has generally been the substance, the decomposition of which has been sought for as a chemical test of the passage of an electric current. But I now began to perceive a reason for its failure, and for a fact which I had observed long before (315, 316) with regard to the iodide of potassium, namely, that bodies would differ in facility of decomposition by a given electric current, according to the condition and intensity of their ordinary chemical affinities. This reason appeared in their *reaction upon the affinities* tending to cause the current: and it appeared probable, that many substances might be found which could be decomposed by the current of a single pair of zinc and platina plates immersed in dilute sulphuric acid, although water resisted its action. I soon found this to be the case, and as the experiments offer new and beautiful proofs of the direct relation and opposition of the chemical affinities concerned in producing and in resisting the stream of electricity, I shall briefly describe them.

899. The arrangement of the apparatus was as in Pl. VII, *Fig. 5*. The vessel *v* contained dilute sulphuric acid; Z and P are the zinc and platina plates; *a*, *b*, and *c* are platina wires; the decompositions were effected at *x*, and occasionally, indeed generally, a galvanometer was introduced into the circuit at *g*: its place only is here given, the circle at *g* having no reference to the size of the instrument. Various arrangements were made at *x*, according to the kind of decomposition to be effected. If a drop of liquid was to be acted upon, the two ends were merely dipped into it; if a solution contained in the pores of paper was to be decomposed, one of the extremities was connected with a platina plate supporting the paper, whilst the other extremity rested on the paper, *e* (Pl. VII, *Fig. 12*): or sometimes, as with sulphate of soda, a plate of platina sustained two portions of paper, one of the ends of the wires resting upon each piece, *c* (Pl. VII, *Fig. 14*). The darts represent the direction of the electric current (667).

900. Solution of *iodide of potassium*, in moistened paper, being placed at the interruption of the circuit at *x*, was readily decomposed. Iodine was evolved at the *anode*, and alkali at the *cathode*, of the decomposing body.

901. *Protochloride of tin*, when fused and placed at *x*, was also readily decomposed, yielding perchloride of tin at the *anode* (779), and tin at the *cathode*.

902. Fused chloride of silver, placed at x, was also easily decomposed; chlorine was evolved at the *anode*, and brilliant metallic silver, either in films upon the surface of the liquid, or in crystals beneath, evolved at the *cathode*.

903. Water acidulated with sulphuric acid, solution of muriatic acid, solution of sulphate of soda, fused nitre, and the fused chloride and iodide of lead were not decomposed by this single pair of plates, excited only by dilute sulphuric acid.

904. These experiments give abundant proofs that a single pair of plates can electrolyze bodies and separate their elements. They also show in a beautiful manner the direct relation and opposition of the chemical affinities concerned at the two points of action. In those cases where the sum of the opposing affinities at x was sufficiently beneath the sum of the acting affinities in v, decomposition took place; but in those cases where they rose higher, decomposition was effectually resisted and the current ceased to pass (891).

905. It is however, evident, that the sum of acting affinities in v may be increased by using other fluids than dilute sulphuric acid, in which latter case, as I believe it is merely the affinity of the zinc for the oxygen already combined with hydrogen in the water that is exerted in producing the electric current (919): and when the affinities are so increased, the view I am supporting leads to the conclusion that bodies which resisted in the preceding experiments would then be decomposed, because of the increased difference between their affinities and the acting affinities thus exalted. This expectation was fully confirmed in the following manner.

906. A little nitric acid was added to the liquid in the vessel v, so as to make a mixture which I shall call diluted nitro-sulphuric acid. On repeating the experiments with this mixture, all the substances before decomposed again gave way, and much more readily. But, besides that, many which before resisted electrolyzation, now yielded up their elements. Thus, solution of sulphate of soda, acted upon in the interstices of litmus and turmeric paper, yielded acid at the *anode* and alkali at the *cathode*; solution of muriatic acid tinged by indigo yielded chlorine at the *anode* and hydrogen at the *cathode;* solution of nitrate of silver yielded silver at the *cathode*. Again, fused nitre and the fused iodide and chloride of lead were decomposable by the current of this single pair of plates, though they were not by the former (903).

907. A solution of acetate of lead was ap-parently not decomposed by this pair, nor did water acidulated by sulphuric acid seem at first to give way (973).

908. The increase of intensity or power of the current produced by a simple voltaic circle, with the increase of the force of the chemical action at the exciting place, is here sufficiently evident. But in order to place it in a clearer point of view, and to show that the decomposing effect was not at all dependent, in the latter cases, upon the mere capability of evolving *more* electricity, experiments were made in which the quantity evolved could be increased without variation in the intensity of the exciting cause. Thus the experiments in which dilute sulphuric acid was used (899) were repeated, using large plates of zinc and platina in the acid; but still those bodies which resisted decomposition before, resisted it also under these new circumstances. Then again, where nitro-sulphuric acid was used (906), mere wires of platina and zinc were immersed in the exciting acid; yet, notwithstanding this change, those bodies were now decomposed which resisted any current tending to be formed by the dilute sulphuric acid. For instance, muriatic acid could not be decomposed by a single pair of plates when immersed in dilute sulphuric acid; nor did making the solution of sulphuric acid strong, nor enlarging the size of the zinc and platina plates immersed in it, increase the power; but if to a weak sulphuric acid a very little nitric acid was added, then the electricity evolved had power to decompose the muriatic acid, evolving chlorine at the *anode* and hydrogen at the *cathode*, even when mere wires of metals were used. This mode of increasing the intensity of the electric current, as it excludes the effect dependent upon many pairs of plates, or even the effect of making any one acid stronger or weaker, is at once referable to the condition and force of the chemical affinities which are brought into action, and may, both in principle and practice, be considered as perfectly distinct from any other mode.

909. The direct reference which is thus experimentally made in the simple voltaic circle of the *intensity* of the electric current to the *intensity* of the chemical action going on at the place where the existence and direction of the current is determined, leads to the conclusion that by using selected bodies, as fused chlorides, salts, solutions of acids, &c., which may act upon the metals employed with different degrees of chemical force; and using also met-

als in association with platina, or with each other, which shall differ in the degree of chemical action exerted between them and the exciting fluid or electrolyte, we shall be able to obtain a series of comparatively constant effects due to electric currents of different intensities, which will serve to assist in the construction of a scale competent to supply the means of determining relative degrees of intensity with accuracy in future researches.[1]

910. I have already expressed the view which I take of the decomposition in the experimental place, as being the direct consequence of the superior exertion at some other spot of the same kind of power as that to be overcome, and therefore as the result of an antagonism of forces of the *same* nature (891, 904). Those at the place of decomposition have a reaction upon, and a power over, the exerting or determining set proportionate to what is needful to overcome their own power; and hence a curious result of *resistance* offered by decompositions to the original determining force, and consequently to the current. This is well shown in the cases where such bodies as chloride of lead, iodide of lead, and water would not decompose with the current produced by a single pair of zinc and platina plates in sulphuric acid (903), although they would with a current of higher intensity produced by stronger chemical powers. In such cases no sensible portion of the current passes (967); the action is stopped; and I am now of opinion that in the case of the law of conduction which I described in the fourth series of these *Researches* (413), the bodies which are electrolytes in the fluid state cease to be such in the solid form, because the attractions of the particles by which they are retained in combination and in their relative position, are then too powerful for the electric current.[2] The particles retain their places; and as decomposition is prevented, the transmission of the electricity is prevented also; and although a battery of many plates may be used, yet if it be of that perfect kind which allows of no extraneous or indirect action (1000), the whole of the affinities concerned in the activity of that battery are at the same time also suspended and counteracted.

911. But referring to the *resistance* of each single case of decomposition, it would appear that as these differ in force according to the af-

finities by which the elements in the substance tend to retain their places, they also would supply cases constituting a series of degrees by which to measure the initial intensities of simple voltaic or other currents of electricity, and which, combined with the scale of intensities determined by different degrees of *acting force* (909), would probably include a sufficient set of differences to meet almost every important case where a reference to intensity would be required.

912. According to the experiments I have already had occasion to make, I find that the following bodies are electrolytic in the order in which I have placed them, those which are first being decomposed by the current of lowest intensity. These currents were always from a single pair of plates, and may be considered as elementary *voltaic forces*.

> Iodide of potassium (solution)
> Chloride of silver (fused)
> Protochloride of tin (fused)
> Chloride of lead (fused)
> Iodide of lead (fused)
> Muriatic acid (solution)
> Water, acidulated with sulphuric acid

913. It is essential that, in all endeavours to obtain the relative electrolytic intensity necessary for the decomposition of different bodies, attention should be paid to the nature of the electrodes and the other bodies present which may favour secondary actions (986). If in electro-decomposition one of the elements separated has an affinity for the electrode, or for bodies present in the surrounding fluid, then the affinity resisting decomposition is in part balanced by such power, and the true place of the electrolyte in a table of the above kind is not obtained: thus, chlorine combines with a positive platina electrode freely, but iodine scarcely at all, and therefore I believe it is that the fused chlorides stand first in the preceding table. Again, if in the decomposition of water not merely sulphuric but also a little nitric acid be present, then the water is more freely decomposed, for the hydrogen at the *cathode* is not ultimately expelled, but finds oxygen in the nitric acid, with which it can combine to produce a secondary result; the affinities opposing decomposition are in this way diminished, and the elements of the water can then be separated by a current of lower intensity.

914. Advantage may be taken of this principle to interpolate more minute degrees into the scale of initial intensities already referred to (909, 911) than is there spoken of; for by combining the force of a current *constant* in its inten-

---

[1] In relation to this difference and its probable cause, see considerations on inductive polarization, 1354, &c.—*Dec.* 1838.

[2] Refer onwards to 1705.—*Dec.* 1838.

sity, with the use of electrodes consisting of matter, having more or less affinity for the elements evolved from the decomposing electrolyte, various intermediate degrees may be obtained.

915. Returning to the consideration of the source of electricity (878, &c.), there is another proof of the most perfect kind that metallic contact has nothing to do with the *production* of electricity in the voltaic circuit, and further, that electricity is only another mode of the exertion of chemical forces. It is, the production of the *electric spark* before any contact of metals is made, and by the exertion of *pure and unmixed chemical forces*. The experiment, which will be described further on (956), consists in obtaining the spark upon making contact between a plate of zinc and a plate of copper plunged into dilute sulphuric acid. In order to make the arrangement as elementary as possible, mercurial surfaces were dismissed, and the contact made by a copper wire connected with the copper plate, and then brought to touch a clean part of the zinc plate. The electric spark appeared, and it must of necessity have existed and passed *before the zinc and the copper were in contact.*

916. In order to render more distinct the principles which I have been endeavouring to establish, I will restate them in their simplest form, according to my present belief. The electricity of the voltaic pile (856 *note*) is not dependent either in its origin or its continuance upon the contact of the metals with each other (880, 915). It is entirely due to chemical action (882), and is proportionate in its intensity to the intensity of the affinities concerned in its production (908); and in its quantity to the quantity of matter which has been chemically active during its evolution (869). This definite production is again one of the strongest proofs that the electricity is of chemical origin.

917. As *volta-electro-generation* is a case of mere chemical action, so *volta-electro-decomposition* is simply a case of the preponderance of one set of chemical affinities more powerful in their nature, over another set which are less powerful: and if the instance of two opposing sets of such forces (891) be considered, and their mutual relation and dependence borne in mind, there appears no necessity for using, in respect to such cases, any other term than chemical affinity (though that of electricity may be very convenient), or supposing any new agent to be concerned in producing the re-

sults; for we may consider that the powers at the two places of action are in direct communion and balanced against each other through the medium of the metals (891), Pl. VII, *Fig. 4*, in a manner analogous to that in which mechanical forces are balanced against each other by the intervention of the lever (1031).

918. All the facts show us that that power commonly called chemical affinity, can be communicated to a distance through the metals and certain forms of carbon; that the electric current is only another form of the forces of chemical affinity; that its power is in proportion to the chemical affinities producing it; that when it is deficient in force it may be helped by calling in chemical aid, the want in the former being made up by an equivalent of the latter; that, in other words, *the forces termed chemical affinity and electricity are one and the same.*

919. When the circumstances connected with the production of electricity in the ordinary voltaic circuit are examined and compared, it appears that the source of that agent, always meaning the electricity which circulates and completes the current in the voltaic apparatus, and gives that apparatus power and character (947, 996), exists in the chemical action which takes place directly between the metal and the body with which it combines, and not at all in the subsequent action of the substance so produced with the acid present.[1] Thus, when zinc, platina, and dilute sulphuric acid are used, it is the union of the zinc with the oxygen of the water which determines the current; and though the acid is essential to the removal of the oxide so formed, in order that another portion of zinc may act on another portion of water, it does not, by combination with that oxide, produce any sensible portion of the current of electricity which circulates; for the quantity of electricity is dependent upon the quantity of zinc oxidized, and in definite proportion to it: its intensity is in proportion to the intensity of the chemical affinity of the zinc for the oxygen under the circumstances, and is scarcely, if at all, affected by the use of either strong or weak acid (908).

920. Again, if zinc, platina, and muriatic acid are used, the electricity appears to be dependent upon the affinity of the zinc for the chlorine, and to be circulated in exact proportion to the number of particles of zinc and chlorine which unite, being in fact an equivalent to them.

[1] Wollaston, *Philosophical Transactions*, 1801, p. 427

921. But in considering this oxidation, or other direct action upon the METAL itself, as the cause and source of the electric current, it is of the utmost importance to observe that the oxygen or other body must be in a peculiar condition, namely, in the state of *combination*; and not only so, but limited still further to such a state of combination and in such proportions as will constitute an *electrolyte* (823). A pair of zinc and platina plates cannot be so arranged in oxygen gas as to produce a current of electricity, or act as a voltaic circle, even though the temperature may be raised so high as to cause oxidation of the zinc far more rapidly than if the pair of plates were plunged into dilute sulphuric acid; for the oxygen is not part of an electrolyte, and cannot therefore conduct the forces onwards by decomposition, or even as metals do by itself. Or if its gaseous state embarrass the minds of some, then liquid chlorine may be taken. It does not excite a current of electricity through the two plates by combining with the zinc, for its particles cannot transfer the electricity active at the point of combination across to the platina. It is not a conductor of itself, like the metals; nor is it an electrolyte, so as to be capable of conduction during decomposition, and hence there is simple chemical action at the spot, and no electric current.[1]

922. It might at first be supposed that a conducting body not electrolytic might answer as the third substance between the zinc and the platina; and it is true that we have some such capable of exerting chemical action upon the metals. They must, however, be chosen from the metals themselves, for there are no bodies of this kind except those substances and charcoal. To decide the matter by experiment, I made the following arrangement. Melted tin was put into a glass tube bent into the form of the letter V (Pl. VII, *Fig. 6*), so as to fill the half of each limb, and two pieces of thick platina wire, *p*, *w*, inserted, so as to have their ends immersed some depth in the tin: the whole was then allowed to cool, and the ends *p* and *w* connected with a delicate galvanometer. The part of the tube at *x* was now reheated, whilst

[1] I do not mean to affirm that no traces of electricity ever appear in such cases. What I mean is, that no electricity is evolved in any way, due or related to the causes which excite voltaic electricity, or proportionate to them. That which does appear occasionally is the smallest possible fraction of that which the acting matter could produce if arranged so as to act voltaically, probably not the one hundred thousandth, or even the millionth part, and is very probably altogether different in its source.

the portion *y* was retained cool. The galvanometer was immediately influenced by the thermo-electric current produced. The heat was steadily increased at *x*, until at last the tin and platina combined there; an effect which is known to take place with strong chemical action and high ignition; but not the slightest additional effect occurred at the galvanometer. No other deflection than that due to the thermo-electric current was observable the whole time. Hence, though a conductor, and one capable of exerting chemical action on the tin, was used, yet, not being an *electrolyte*, not the slightest effect of an electrical current could be observed (947).

923. From this it seems apparent that the peculiar character and condition of an electrolyte is *essential* in one part of the voltaic circuit; and its nature being considered, good reasons appear why it and it alone should be effectual. An electrolyte is always a compound body: it can conduct, but only whilst decomposing. Its conduction depends upon its decomposition and the *transmission of its particles* in directions parallel to the current; and so intimate is this connexion, that if their transition be stopped, the current is stopped also; if their course be changed, its course and direction change with them; if they proceed in one direction, it has no power to proceed in any other than a direction invariably dependent on them. The particles of an electrolytic body are all so mutually connected, are in such relation with each other through their whole extent in the direction of the current, that if the last is not disposed of, the first is not at liberty to take up its place in the new combination which the powerful affinity of the most active metal tends to produce; and then the current itself is stopped; for the dependencies of the current and the decomposition are so mutual, that whichsoever be originally determined, i.e., the motion of the particles or the motion of the current, the other is invariable in its concomitant production and its relation to it.

924. Consider, then, water as an electrolyte and also as an oxidizing body. The attraction of the zinc for the oxygen is greater, under the circumstances, than that of the oxygen for the hydrogen; but in combining with it, it tends to throw into circulation a current of electricity in a certain direction. This direction is consistent (as is found by innumerable experiments) with the transfer of the hydrogen from the zinc towards the platina, and the transfer in the opposite direction of fresh oxygen from the platina towards the zinc; so that the current

can pass in that one line, and, whilst it passes, can consist with and favour the renewal of the conditions upon the surface of the zinc, which at first determined both the combination and circulation. Hence the continuance of the action there, and the continuation of the current. It therefore appears quite as essential that there should be an electrolyte in the circuit, in order that the action may be transferred forward, in a *certain constant direction*, as that there should be an oxidizing or other body capable of acting directly on the metal; and it also appears to be essential that these two should merge into one, or that the principle directly active on the metal by chemical action should be one of the *ions* of the electrolyte used. Whether the voltaic arrangement be excited by solution of acids, or alkalies, or sulphurets, or by fused substances (476), this principle has always hitherto, as far as I am aware, been an *anion* (943); and I anticipate, from a consideration of the principles of electric action, that it must of necessity be one of that class of bodies.

925. If the action of the sulphuric acid used in the voltaic circuit be considered, it will be found incompetent to produce any sensible portion of the electricity of the current by its combination with the oxide formed, for this simple reason, it is deficient in a most essential condition; it forms no part of an electrolyte, nor is it in relation with any other body present in the solution which will permit of the mutual transfer of the particles and the consequent transfer of the electricity. It is true that, as the plane at which the acid is dissolving the oxide of zinc formed by the action of the water is in contact with the metal zinc, there seems no difficulty in considering how the oxide there could communicate an electrical state, proportionate to its own chemical action on the acid, to the metal, which is a conductor, without decomposition. But on the side of the acid there is no substance to complete the circuit: the water, as water, cannot conduct it, or at least only so small a proportion that it is merely an incidental and almost inappreciable effect (970); and it cannot conduct it as an electrolyte, because an electrolyte conducts in consequence of the *mutual* relation and action of its particles; and neither of the elements of the water, nor even the water itself, as far as we can perceive, are *ions* with respect to the sulphuric acid (848).[1]

926. This view of the secondary character of the sulphuric acid as an agent in the production of the voltaic current, is further confirmed by the fact that the current generated and transmitted is directly and exactly proportional to the quantity of water decomposed and the quantity of zinc oxidized (868, 991), and is the same as that required to decompose the same quantity of water. As, therefore, the decomposition of the water shows that the electricity has passed by its means, there remains no other electricity to be accounted for or to be referred to any action other than that of the zinc and the water on each other.

927. The general case (for it includes the former one [924]), of acids and bases, may theoretically be stated in the following manner. Let *a* (Pl. VII, *Fig.* 7), be supposed to be a dry oxacid, and *b* a dry base, in contact at *c*, and in electric communication at their extremities by plates of platina *p p*, and a platina wire *w*. If this acid and base were fluid, and combination took place at *c*, with an affinity ever so vigorous, and capable of originating an electric current, the current could not circulate in any important degree; because, according to the experimental results, neither *a* nor *b* could conduct without being decomposed, for they are either electrolytes or else insulators, under all circumstances, except to very feeble and unimportant currents (970, 986). Now the affinities at *c* are not such as tend to cause the *elements* either of *a* or *b* to separate, but only such as would make the two bodies combine together as a whole; the point of action is, therefore, insulated, the action itself local (921, 947), and no current can be formed.

928. If the acid and base be dissolved in water, then it is possible that a small portion of the electricity due to chemical action may be conducted by the water without decomposition (966, 984); but the quantity will be so small as to be utterly disproportionate to that due to the equivalents of chemical force; will be merely incidental; and, as it does not involve the essential principles of the voltaic pile, it forms no part of the phenomena at present under investigation.[2]

929. If for the oxacid a hydracid be substituted (927)—as one analogous to the muriatic,

[1] It will be seen that I here agree with Sir Humphry Davy, who has experimentally supported the opinion that acids and alkalies in combining do not produce any current of electricity. *Philosophical Transactions*, 1826, p. 398.

[2] It will I trust be fully understood that in these investigations I am not professing to take an account of every small, incidental, or barely possible effect, dependent upon slight disturbances of the electric fluid during chemical action, but am seeking to distinguish and identify those actions on which the power of the voltaic battery essentially depends.

for instance—then the state of things changes altogether, and a current due to the chemical action of the acid on the base is possible. But now both the bodies act as electrolytes, for it is only one principle of each which combine mutually—as, for instance, the chlorine with the metal—and the hydrogen of the acid and the oxygen of the base are ready to traverse with the chlorine of the acid and the metal of the base in conformity with the current and according to the general principles already so fully laid down.

930. This view of the oxidation of the metal, or other *direct* chemical action upon it, being the sole cause of the production of the electric current in the ordinary voltaic pile, is supported by the effects which take place when alkaline or sulphuretted solutions (931, 943) are used for the electrolytic conductor instead of dilute sulphuric acid. It was in elucidation of this point that the experiments without metallic contact, and with solution of alkali as the exciting fluid, already referred to (884), were made.

931. Advantage was then taken of the more favourable condition offered, when metallic contact is allowed (895), and the experiments upon the decomposition of bodies by a single pair of plates (899) were repeated, solution of caustic potassa being employed in the vessel *v* (Pl. VII, *Fig. 5*), in place of dilute sulphuric acid. All the effects occurred as before: the galvanometer was deflected; the decompositions of the solutions of iodide of potassium, nitrate of silver, muriatic acid, and sulphate of soda ensued at *x*; and the places where the evolved principles appeared, as well as the deflection of the galvanometer, indicated a current in the *same direction* as when acid was in the vessel *v*; i.e., from the zinc through the solution to the platina, and back by the galvanometer and substance suffering decomposition to the zinc.

932. The similarity in the action of either dilute sulphuric acid or potassa goes indeed far beyond this, even to the proof of identity in *quantity* as well as in *direction* of the electricity produced. If a plate of amalgamated zinc be put into a solution of potassa, it is not sensibly acted upon; but if touched in the solution by a plate of platina, hydrogen is evolved on the surface of the latter metal, and the zinc is oxidized exactly as when immersed in dilute sulphuric acid (863). I accordingly repeated the experiment before described with weighed plates of zinc (864, &c.), using however solu-

tion of potassa instead of dilute sulphuric acid. Although the time required was much longer than when acid was used, amounting to three hours for the oxidizement of 7.55 grains of zinc, still I found that the hydrogen evolved at the platina plate was the equivalent of the metal oxidized at the surface of the zinc. Hence the whole of the reasoning which was applicable in the former instance applies also here, the current being in the same direction, and its decomposing effect in the same degree, as if acid instead of alkali had been used (868).

933. The proof, therefore, appears to me complete that the combination of the acid with the oxide, in the former experiment, had nothing to do with the production of the electric current; for the same current is here produced when the action of the acid is absent, and the reverse action of an alkali is present. I think it cannot be supposed for a moment that the alkali acted chemically as an acid to the oxide formed; on the contrary, our general chemical knowledge leads to the conclusion that the ordinary metallic oxides act rather as acids to the alkalies; yet that kind of action would tend to give a reverse current in the present case, if any were due to the union of the oxide of the exciting metal with the body which combines with it. But instead of any variation of this sort, the direction of the electricity was constant, and its quantity also directly proportional to the water decomposed, or the zinc oxidized. There are reasons for believing that acids and alkalies, when in contact with metals upon which they cannot act directly, still have a power of influencing their attractions for oxygen (941); but all the effects in these experiments prove, I think, that it is the oxidation of the metal necessarily dependent upon, and associated as it is with, the electrolyzation of the water (921, 923) that produces the current; and that the acid or alkali merely acts as solvents, and by removing the oxidized zinc, allows other portions to decompose fresh water, and so continues the evolution or determination of the current.

934. The experiments were then varied by using solution of ammonia instead of solution of potassa; and as it, when pure, is like water, a bad conductor (554), it was occasionally improved in that power by adding sulphate of ammonia to it. But in all the cases the results were the same as before; decompositions of the same kind were effected, and the electric current producing these was in the same direction as in the experiments just described.

935. In order to put the equal and similar action of acid and alkali to stronger proof, arrangements were made as in Pl. VII, *Fig. 8*; the glass vessel A contained dilute sulphuric acid, the corresponding glass vessel B solution of potassa, P P was a plate of platina dipping into both solutions, and Z Z two plates of amalgamated zinc connected with a delicate galvanometer. When these were plunged at the same time into the two vessels, there was generally a first feeble effect, and that in favour of the alkali, i.e., the electric current tended to pass through the vessels in the direction of the arrow, being the reverse direction of that which the acid in A would have produced alone: but the effect instantly ceased, and the action of the plates in the vessels was so equal, that, being contrary because of the contrary position of the plates, no permanent current resulted.

936. Occasionally a zinc plate was substituted for the plate P P, and platina plates for the plates Z Z; but this caused no difference in the results: nor did a further change of the middle plate to copper produce any alteration.

937. As the opposition of electro-motive pairs of plates produces results other than those due to the mere difference of their independent actions (1011, 1045), I devised another form of apparatus, in which the action of acid and alkali might be more directly compared. A cylindrical glass cup, about two inches deep within, an inch in internal diameter, and at least a quarter of an inch in thickness, was cut down the middle into halves (Pl. VII, *Fig. 9*). A broad brass ring, larger in diameter than the cup, was supplied with a screw at one side; so that when the two halves of the cup were within the ring, and the screw was made to press tightly against the glass, the cup held any fluid put into it. Bibulous paper of different degrees of permeability was then cut into pieces of such a size as to be easily introduced between the loosened halves of the cup, and served, when the latter were tightened again, to form a porous division down the middle of the cup, sufficient to keep any two fluids on opposite sides of the paper from mingling, except very slowly, and yet allowing them to act freely as one *electrolyte*. The two spaces thus produced I will call the cells A and B (Pl. VII, *Fig. 10*). This instrument I have found of most general application in the investigation of the relation of fluids and metals amongst themselves and to each other. By combining its use with that of the galvanometer, it is easy to ascertain the relation of one metal with two fluids, or of two metals with one fluid, or of two metals and two fluids upon each other.

938. Dilute sulphuric acid, sp. gr. 1.25, was put into the cell A, and a strong solution of caustic potassa into the cell B; they mingled slowly through the paper, and at last a thick crust of sulphate of potassa formed on the side of the paper next to the alkali. A plate of clean platina was put into each cell and connected with a delicate galvanometer, but no electric current could be observed. Hence the *contact* of acid with one platina plate, and alkali with the other, was unable to produce a current: nor was the combination of the acid with the alkali more effectual (925).

939. When one of the platina plates was removed and a zinc plate substituted, either amalgamated or not, a strong electric current was produced. But, whether the zinc were in the acid whilst the platina was in the alkali, or whether the reverse order were chosen, the electric current was always from the zinc through the electrolyte to the platina, and back through the galvanometer to the zinc, the current seeming to be strongest when the zinc was in the alkali and the platina in the acid.

940. In these experiments, therefore, the acid seems to have no power over the alkali, but to be rather inferior to it in force. Hence there is no reason to suppose that the combination of the oxide formed with the acid around it has any direct influence in producing the electricity evolved, the whole of which appears to be due to the oxidation of the metal (919).

941. The alkali, in fact, is superior to the acid in bringing a metal into what is called the positive state; for if plates of the same metal, as zinc, tin, lead, or copper, be used both in the acid or alkali, the electric current is from the alkali across the cell to the acid, and back through the galvanometer to the alkali, as Sir Humphry Davy formerly stated.[1] This current is so powerful, that if amalgamated zinc, or tin, or lead be used, the metal in the acid evolves hydrogen the moment it is placed in communication with that in the alkali, not from any direct action of the acid upon it, for if the contact be broken the action ceases, but because it is powerfully negative with regard to the metal in the alkali.

942. The superiority of alkali is further proved by this, that if zinc and tin be used, or tin and lead, whichsoever metal is put into the alkali becomes positive, that in the acid being

[1] *Elements of Chemical Philosophy*, p. 149; or *Philosophical Transactions*, 1826, p. 403.

negative. Whichsoever is in the alkali is oxidized, whilst that in the acid remains in the metallic state, as far as the electric current is concerned.

943. When sulphuretted solutions are used (930) in illustration of the assertion, that it is the chemical action of the metal and one of the *ions* of the associated electrolyte that produces all the electricity of the voltaic circuit, the proofs are still the same. Thus, as Sir Humphry Davy[1] has shown, if iron and copper be plunged into dilute acid, the current is from the iron through the liquid to the copper; in solution of potassa it is in the same direction, but in solution of sulphuret of potassa it is reversed. In the two first cases it is oxygen which combines with the iron, in the latter sulphur which combines with the copper, that produces the electric current; but both of these are *ions*, existing as such in the electrolyte, which is at the same moment suffering decomposition; and, what is more, both of these are *anions*, for they leave the electrolytes at their *anodes*, and act just as chlorine, iodine, or any other *anion* would act which might have been previously chosen as that which should be used to throw the voltaic circle into activity.

944. The following experiments complete the series of proofs of the origin of the electricity in the voltaic pile. A fluid amalgam of potassium, containing not more than a hundredth of that metal, was put into pure water, and connected through the galvanometer with a plate of platina in the same water. There was immediately an electric current from the amalgam through the electrolyte to the platina. This must have been due to the oxidation only of the metal, for there was neither acid nor alkali to combine with, or in any way act on, the body produced.

945. Again, a plate of clean lead and a plate of platina were put into *pure* water. There was immediately a powerful current produced from the lead through the fluid to the platina: it was even intense enough to decompose solution of the iodide of potassium when introduced into the circuit in the form of apparatus already described (880) (Pl. VII, *Fig.* 1). Here no action of acid or alkali on the oxide formed from the lead could supply the electricity: it was due solely to the oxidation of the metal.

946. There is no point in electrical science which seems to me of more importance than the state of the metals and the electrolytic con-

[1] *Elements of Chemical Philosophy*, p. 148.

ductor in a simple voltaic circuit *before and at* the moment when metallic contact is first completed. If clearly understood, I feel no doubt it would supply us with a direct key to the laws under which the great variety of voltaic excitements, direct and incidental, occur, and open out new fields of research for our investigation.[2]

947. We seem to have the power of deciding to a certain extent in numerous cases of chemical affinity, (as of zinc with the oxygen of water, &c., &c.) which of *two modes of action of the attractive power* shall be exerted (996). In the one mode we can transfer the power onwards, and make it produce elsewhere its equivalent of action (867, 917); in the other, it is not transferred, but exerted wholly at the spot. The first is the case of volta-electric excitation, the other ordinary chemical affinity: but both are chemical actions and due to one force or principle.

948. The general circumstances of the former mode occur in all instances of voltaic currents, but may be considered as in their perfect condition, and then free from those of the second mode, in some only of the cases; as in those of plates of zinc and platina in solution of potassa, or of amalgamated zinc and platina in dilute sulphuric acid.

949. Assuming it sufficiently proved, by the preceding experiments and considerations, that the electro-motive action depends, when zinc, platina, and dilute sulphuric acid are used, upon the mutual affinity of the metal zinc and the oxygen of the water (921, 924), it would appear that the metal, when alone, has not power enough, under the circumstances, to take the oxygen and expel the hydrogen from the water; for, in fact, no such action takes place. But it would also appear that it has power so far to act, by its attraction for the oxygen of the particles in contact with it, as to place the similar forces already active between these and the other particles of oxygen and the particles of hydrogen in the water, in a peculiar state of tension or polarity, and probably also at the same time to throw those of its own particles which are in contact with the water into a similar but opposed state. Whilst this state is retained, no further change occurs; but when it is relieved, by completion of the circuit, in which case the forces determined in opposite directions, with respect to the zinc and the electrolyte, are found exactly competent to neutralize

[2] In connexion with this part of the subject refer now to Series XI, 1164, Series XII, 1343–1358, and Series XIII, 1621. &c.—*Dec.* 1838.

each other, then a series of decompositions and recompositions takes place amongst the particles of oxygen and hydrogen constituting the water, between the place of contact with the platina and the place where the zinc is active; these intervening particles being evidently in close dependence upon and relation to each other. The zinc forms a direct compound with those particles of oxygen which were, previously, in divided relation to both it and the hydrogen: the oxide is removed by the acid, and a fresh surface of zinc is presented to the water, to renew and repeat the action.

950. Practically, the state of tension is best relieved by dipping a metal which has less attraction for oxygen than the zinc, into the dilute acid, and making it also touch the zinc. The force of chemical affinity, which has been influenced or polarized in the particles of the water by the dominant attraction of the zinc for the oxygen, is then transferred, in a most extraordinary manner, through the two metals, so as to re-enter upon the circuit in the electrolytic conductor, which, unlike the metals in that respect, cannot convey or transfer it without suffering decomposition; or rather, probably, it is exactly balanced and neutralized by the force which at the same moment completes the combination of the zinc with the oxygen of the water. The forces, in fact, of the two particles which are acting towards each other, and which are therefore in opposite directions, are the origin of the two opposite forces, or directions of force, in the current. They are of necessity equivalent to each other. Being transferred forward in contrary directions, they produce what is called the voltaic current: and it seems to me impossible to resist the idea that it must be preceded by a *state of tension* in the fluid, and between the fluid and the zinc; the *first consequence* of the affinity of the zinc for the oxygen of the water.

951. I have sought carefully for indications of a state of tension in the electrolytic conductor; and conceiving that it might produce something like structure, either before or during its discharge, I endeavoured to make this evident by polarized light. A glass cell, seven inches long, one inch and a half wide, and six inches deep, had two sets of platina electrodes adapted to it, one set for the ends, and the other for the sides. Those for the *sides* were seven inches long by three inches high, and when in the cell were separated by a little frame of wood covered with calico; so that when made active by connexion with a battery upon any solution in the

cell, the bubbles of gas rising from them did not obscure the central parts of the liquid.

952. A saturated solution of sulphate of soda was put into the cell, and the electrodes connected with a battery of 150 pairs of 4-inch plates: the current of electricity was conducted across the cell so freely that the discharge was as good as if a wire had been used. A ray of polarized light was then transmitted through this solution, directly across the course of the electric current, and examined by an analysing plate; but though it penetrated seven inches of solution thus subject to the action of the electricity, and though contact was sometimes made, sometimes broken, and occasionally reversed during the observations, not the slightest trace of action on the ray could be perceived.

953. The large electrodes were then removed, and others introduced which fitted the *ends* of the cell. In each a slit was cut, so as to allow the light to pass. The course of the polarized ray was now parallel to the current, or in the direction of its axis (517); but still no effect, under any circumstances of contact or disunion, could be perceived upon it.

954. A strong solution of nitrate of lead was employed instead of the sulphate of soda, but no effects could be detected.

955. Thinking it possible that the discharge of the electric forces by the successive decompositions and recompositions of the particles of the electrolyte might neutralize and therefore destroy any effect which the first state of tension could by possibility produce, I took a substance which, being an excellent electrolyte when fluid, was a perfect insulator when solid, namely, borate of lead, in the form of a glass plate, and connecting the sides and the edges of this mass with the metallic plates, sometimes in contact with the poles of a voltaic battery, and sometimes even with the electric machine, for the advantage of the much higher intensity then obtained, I passed a polarized ray across it in various directions, as before, but could not obtain the slightest appearance of action upon the light. Hence I conclude that notwithstanding the new and extraordinary state which must be assumed by an electrolyte, either during decomposition (when a most enormous quantity of electricity must be traversing it), or in the state of tension which is assumed as preceding decomposition, and which might be supposed to be retained in the solid form of the electrolyte, still it has no power of affecting a polarized ray of light; for no kind of structure or

tension can in this way be rendered evident.

956. There is, however, one beautiful experimental proof of a state of tension acquired by the metals and the electrolyte before the electric current is produced, and *before contact* of the different metals is made (915); in fact, at that moment when chemical forces only are efficient as a cause of action. I took a voltaic apparatus, consisting of a single pair of large plates, namely, a cylinder of amalgamated zinc, and a double cylinder of copper. These were put into a jar containing dilute sulphuric acid,[1] and could at pleasure be placed in metallic communication by a copper wire adjusted so as to dip at the extremities into two cups of mercury connected with the two plates.

957. Being thus arranged, there was no chemical action whilst the plates were not connected. On *making* the connexion a spark was obtained,[2] and the solution was immediately decomposed. On breaking it, the usual spark was obtained, and the decomposition ceased. In this case it is evident that the first spark must have occurred before metallic contact was made, for it passed through an interval of air; and also that it must have tended to pass before the electrolytic action began; for the latter could not take place until the current passed, and the current could not pass before the spark appeared. Hence I think there is sufficient proof, that as it is the zinc and water which by their mutual action produce the electricity of this apparatus, so these, by their first contact with each other, were placed in a state of powerful tension (951), which, though it could not produce the actual decomposition of the water, was able to make a spark of electricity pass between the zinc and a fit discharger as soon as the interval was rendered sufficiently small. The experiment demonstrates the direct production of the electric spark from pure chemical forces.

958. There are a few circumstances connected with the production of this spark by a single pair of plates, which should be known, to ensure success to the experiment.[3] When the

amalgamated surfaces of contact are quite clean and dry, the spark, on making contact, is quite as brilliant as on breaking it, if not even more so. When a film of oxide or dirt was present at either mercurial surface, then the first spark was often feeble, and often failed, the breaking spark, however, continuing very constant and bright. When a little water was put over the mercury, the spark was greatly diminished in brilliancy, but very regular both on making and breaking contact. When the contact was made between clean platina, the spark was also very small, but regular both ways. The true electric spark is, in fact, very small, and when surfaces of mercury are used, it is the combustion of the metal which produces the greater part of the light. The circumstances connected with the burning of the mercury are most favourable on breaking contact; for the act of separation exposes clean surfaces of metal, whereas, on making contact, a thin film of oxide, or soiling matter, often interferes. Hence the origin of the general opinion that it is only when the contact is broken that the spark passes.

959. With reference to the other set of cases, namely, those of local action (947) in which chemical affinity being exerted causes no transference of the power to a distance where no electric current is produced, it is evident that forces of the most intense kind must be active, and in some way balanced in their activity, during such combinations; these forces being directed so immediately and exclusively towards each other, that no signs of the powerful electric current they can produce become apparent, although the same final state of things is obtained as if that current had passed. It was Berzelius, I believe, who considered the heat and light evolved in cases of combustion as the consequences of this mode of exertion of the electric powers of the combining particles. But it will require a much more exact and extensive knowledge of the nature of electricity, and the manner in which it is associated with the atoms of matter, before we can understand accurately the action of this power in thus causing their union, or comprehend the nature of the great difference which it presents in the two modes of action just distinguished. We may imagine, but such imaginations must for the time be classed with the great mass of *doubtful knowledge* (876) which we ought rather to strive to diminish than to increase; for the very extensive contradictions of this knowledge

---

[1] When nitro-sulphuric acid is used, the spark is more powerful, but local chemical action can then commence, and proceed without requiring metallic contact.

[2] It has been universally supposed that no spark is produced on making the contact between a single pair of plates. I was led to expect one from the considerations already advanced in this paper. The wire of communication should be short; for with a long wire, circumstances strongly affecting the spark are introduced.

[3] See in relation to precautions respecting a spark, 1074.—*Dec.* 1838.

by itself shows that but a small portion of it can ultimately prove true.[1]

960. Of the two modes of action in which chemical affinity is exerted, it is important to remark that that which produces the electric current is as *definite* as that which causes ordinary chemical combination; so that in examining the *production* or *evolution* of electricity in cases of combination or decomposition, it will be necessary, not merely to observe certain effects dependent upon a current of electricity, but also their *quantity*: and though it may often happen that the forces concerned in any particular case of chemical action may be partly exerted in one mode and partly in the other, it is only those which are efficient in producing the current that have any relation to voltaic action. Thus, in the combination of oxygen and hydrogen to produce water, electric powers to a most enormous amount are for the time active (861, 873); but any mode of examining the flame which they form during energetic combination, which has as yet been devised, has given but the feeblest traces. These therefore may not, cannot, be taken as evidences of the nature of the action; but are merely incidental results, incomparably small in relation to the forces concerned, and supplying no information of the way in which the particles are active on each other, or in which their forces are finally arranged.

961. That such cases of chemical action produce no *current of electricity*, is perfectly consistent with what we know of the voltaic apparatus, in which it is essential that one of the combining elements shall form part of, or be in direct relation with, an electrolytic conductor (921, 923). That such cases produce no *free electricity of tension*, and that when they are converted into cases of voltaic action they produce a current in which the opposite forces are so equal as to neutralize each other, prove the equality of the forces in the opposed acting particles of matter, and therefore the equality of electric power in those quantities of matter which are called *electro-chemical equivalents* (824). Hence another proof of the definite nature of electro-chemical action (783, &c.), and that chemical affinity and electricity are forms of the same power (917, &c.).

962. The direct reference of the effects produced by the voltaic pile at the place of experimental decomposition to the chemical affinities active at the place of excitation (891, 917), gives a very simple and natural view of the

[1] Refer to 1738, etc. Series XIV.—*Dec.* 1838.

cause why the bodies (or *ions*) evolved pass in certain directions; for it is only when they pass in those directions that their forces can consist with and compensate (in direction at least) the superior forces which are dominant at the place where the action of the whole is determined. If, for instance, in a voltaic circuit, the activity of which is determined by the attraction of zinc for the oxygen of water, the zinc move from right to left, then any other *cation* included in the circuit, being part of an electrolyte, or forming part of it at the moment, will also move from right to left: and as the oxygen of the water, by its natural affinity for the zinc, moves from left to right, so any other body of the same class with it (i.e., any other *anion*), under its government for the time, will move from left to right.

963. This I may illustrate by reference to Pl. VII, *Fig. 11*, the double circle of which may represent a complete voltaic circuit, the direction of its forces being determined by supposing for a moment the zinc b and the platina c as representing plates of those metals acting upon water, d, e, and other substances, but having their energy exalted so as to effect several decompositions by the use of a battery at a (989). This supposition may be allowed, because the action in the battery will only consist of repetitions of what would take place between b and c, if they really constituted but a single pair. The zinc b, and the oxygen d, by their mutual affinity, tend to unite; but as the oxygen is already in association with the hydrogen e, and has its inherent chemical or electric powers neutralized for the time by those of the latter, the hydrogen e must leave the oxygen d, and advance in the direction of the arrow head, or else the zinc b cannot move in the same direction to unite to the oxygen d, nor the oxygen d move in the contrary direction to unite to the zinc b, the relation of the *similar* forces of b and e, in contrary directions, to the *opposite* forces of d being the preventive. As the hydrogen e advances, it, on coming against the platina c, f, which forms a part of the circuit, communicates its electric or chemical forces through it to the next electrolyte in the circuit, fused chloride of lead, g, h, where the chlorine must move in conformity with the direction of the oxygen at d, for it has to compensate the forces disturbed in its part of the circuit by the superior influence of those between the oxygen and zinc at d, b, aided as they are by those of the battery a; and for a similar reason the lead must move in the direction pointed out by the

arrow head, that it may be in right relation to the first moving body of its own class, namely, the zinc *b*. If copper intervene in the circuit from *i* to *k*, it acts as the platina did before; and if another electrolyte, as the iodide of tin, occur at *l, m,* then the iodine *l,* being an *anion,* must move in conformity with the exciting *anion,* namely, the oxygen *d,* and the *cation* tin *m* move in correspondence with the other *cations b, e,* and *h,* that the chemical forces may be in equilibrium as to their direction and quantity throughout the circuit. Should it so happen that the anions in their circulation can combine with the metals at the *anodes* of the respective electrolytes, as would be the case at the platina *f* and the copper *k,* then those bodies becoming parts of electrolytes, under the influence of the current, immediately travel; but considering their relation to the zinc *b,* it is evidently impossible that they can travel in any other direction than what will accord with its course, and therefore can never tend to pass otherwise than *from* the anode and *to* the cathode.

964. In such a circle as that delineated, therefore, all the known *anions* may be grouped within, and all the *cations* without. If any number of them enter as *ions* into the constitution of *electrolytes,* and, forming one circuit, are simultaneously subject to one common current, the anions must move in accordance with each other in one direction, and the cations in the other. Nay, more than that, equivalent portions of these bodies must so advance in opposite directions: for the advance of every 32.5 parts of the zinc *b* must be accompanied by a motion in the opposite direction of 8 parts of oxygen at *d,* of 36 parts of chlorine at *g,* of 126 parts of iodine at *l;* and in the same direction by electro-chemical equivalents of hydrogen, lead, copper and tin, at *e, h, k,* and *m.*

965. If the present paper be accepted as a correct expression of facts, it will still only prove a confirmation of certain general views put forth by Sir Humphry Davy in his Bakerian Lecture for 1806,[1] and revised and re-stated by him in another Bakerian Lecture, on electrical and chemical changes, for the year 1826.[2] His general statement is, that *chemical and electrical attractions were produced by the same cause, acting in one case on particles, in the other on masses, of matter; and that the same property, under different modifications, was the cause of all*

the phenomena exhibited by different voltaic combinations.[3] This statement I believe to be true; but in admitting and supporting it, I must guard myself from being supposed to assent to all that is associated with it in the two papers referred to, or as admitting the experiments which are there quoted as decided proofs of the truth of the principle. Had I thought them so, there would have been no occasion for this investigation. It may be supposed by some that I ought to go through these papers, distinguishing what I admit from what I reject, and giving good experimental or philosophical reasons for the judgment in both cases. But then I should be equally bound to review, for the same purpose, all that has been written both for and against the necessity of metallic contact—for and against the origin of voltaic electricity in chemical action—a duty which I may not undertake in the present paper.[4]

¶ ii. *On the Intensity Necessary for Electrolyzation*

966. It became requisite, for the comprehension of many of the conditions attending voltaic action, to determine positively, if possible, whether electrolytes could resist the action of an electric current when beneath a certain intensity? whether the intensity at which the current ceased to act would be the same for all bodies? and also whether the electrolytes thus resisting decomposition would conduct the electric current as a metal does, after they cease to conduct as electrolytes, or would act as perfect insulators?

967. It was evident from the experiments described (904, 906) that different bodies were decomposed with very different facilities, and apparently that they required for their decomposition currents of different intensities, resisting some, but giving way to others. But it was needful, by very careful and express experiments, to determine whether a current could really pass through and yet not decompose an electrolyte (910).

[1] *Philosophical Transactions,* 1807.
[2] *Ibid.,* 1826, p. 383.
[3] *Ibid.,* 1826, p. 389.
[4] I at one time intended to introduce here, in the form of a note, a table of reference to the papers of the different philosophers who have referred the origin of the electricity in the voltaic pile to contact or to chemical action, or to both; but on the publication of the first volume of M. Becquerel's highly important and valuable *Traité de l'Electricité et du Magnétisme,* I thought it far better to refer to that work for these references, and the views held by the authors quoted. See pages 86, 91, 104, 110, 112, 117, 118, 120, 151, 152, 224, 227, 228, 232, 233, 252, 255, 257, 258, 290, &c.—July 3rd, 1834.

968. An arrangement (Pl. VII, *Fig. 12*) was made, in which two glass vessels contained the same dilute sulphuric acid, sp. gr. 1.25. The plate *z* was amalgamated zinc, in connexion, by a platina wire *a*, with the platina plate *e*; *b* was a platina wire connecting the two platina plates P P'; *c* was a platina wire connected with the platina plate P''. On the plate *e* was placed a piece of paper moistened in solution of iodide of potassium: the wire *c* was so curved that its end could be made to rest at pleasure on this paper, and show, by the evolution of iodine there, whether a current was passing; or, being placed in the dotted position, it formed a direct communication with the platina plate *e*, and the electricity could pass without causing decomposition. The object was to produce a current by the action of the acid on the amalgamated zinc in the first vessel A; to pass it through the acid in the second vessel B by platina electrodes, that its power of decomposing water might, if existing, be observed; and to verify the existence of the current at pleasure, by decomposition at *e*, without involving the continual obstruction to the current which would arise from making the decomposition there constant. The experiment, being arranged, was examined and the existence of a current ascertained by the decomposition at *e*; the whole was then left with the end of the wire *c* resting on the plate *e*, so as to form a constant metallic communication there.

969. After several hours, the end of the wire *c* was replaced on the test-paper at *e*: decomposition occurred, and *the proof* of a passing current was therefore complete. The current was very feeble compared to what it had been at the beginning of the experiment, because of a peculiar state acquired by the metal surfaces in the second vessel, which caused them to oppose the passing current by a force which they possess under these circumstances (1040). Still it was proved, by the decomposition, that this state of the plates in the second vessel was not able entirely to stop the current determined in the first, and that was all that was needful to be ascertained in the present inquiry.

970. This apparatus was examined from time to time, and an electric current always found circulating through it, until twelve days had elapsed, during which the water in the second vessel had been constantly subject to its action. Notwithstanding this lengthened period, not the slightest appearance of a bubble upon either of the plates in that vessel occurred. From the results of the experiment, I conclude

that a current *had* passed, but of so low an intensity as to fall beneath that degree at which the elements of water, unaided by any secondary force resulting from the capability of combination with the matter of the electrodes, or of the liquid surrounding them, separated from each other.

971. It may be supposed, that the oxygen and hydrogen had been evolved in such small quantities as to have entirely dissolved in the water, and finally to have escaped at the surface, or to have reunited into water. That the hydrogen can be so dissolved was shown in the first vessel; for after several days minute bubbles of gas gradually appeared upon a glass rod, inserted to retain the zinc and platina apart, and also upon the platina plate itself, and these were hydrogen. They resulted principally in this way: notwithstanding the amalgamation of the zinc, the acid exerted a little direct action upon it, so that a small stream of hydrogen bubbles was continually rising from its surface; a little of this hydrogen gradually dissolved in the dilute acid, and was in part set free against the surfaces of the rod and the plate, according to the well-known action of such solid bodies in solutions of gases (623, &c.).

972. But if the gases had been evolved in the second vessel by the decomposition of water, and had tended to dissolve, still there would have been every reason to expect that a few bubbles should have appeared on the electrodes, especially on the negative one, if it were only because of its action as a nucleus on the solution supposed to be formed; but none appeared even after twelve days.

973. When a few drops only of nitric acid were added to the vessel A (Pl. VII, *Fig. 12*), then the results were altogether different. In less than five minutes bubbles of gas appeared on the plates P' and P'' in the second vessel. To prove that this was the effect of the electric current (which by trial at *e* was found at the same time to be passing), the connexion at *e* was broken, the plates P' P'' cleared from bubbles and left in the acid of the vessel B, for fifteen minutes: during that time no bubbles appeared upon them; but on restoring the communication at *e*, a minute did not elapse before gas appeared in bubbles upon the plates. The proof, therefore, is most full and complete, that the current excited by dilute sulphuric acid with a little nitric acid in vessel A, has intensity enough to overcome the chemical affinity exerted between the oxygen and hydrogen of the water in the vessel B, whilst that excited

by dilute sulphuric acid alone has *not* sufficient intensity.

974. On using a strong solution of caustic potassa in the vessel A, to excite the current, it was found by the decomposing effects at *e*, that the current passed. But it had not intensity enough to decompose the water in the vessel B; for though left for fourteen days, during the whole of which time the current was found to be passing, still not the slightest appearance of gas appeared on the plates P' P'', nor any other signs of the water having suffered decomposition.

975. Sulphate of soda in solution was then experimented with, for the purpose of ascertaining with respect to it, whether a certain electrolytic intensity was also required for its decomposition in this state, in analogy with the result established with regard to water (974). The apparatus was arranged as in Pl. VII, *Fig. 13*; P and Z are the platina and zinc plates dipping into a solution of common salt; *a* and *b* are platina plates connected by wires of platina (except in the galvanometer *g*) with P and Z; *c* is a connecting wire of platina, the ends of which can be made to rest either on the plates *a*, *b*, or on the papers moistened in solutions which are placed upon them; so that the passage of the current without decomposition, or with one or two decompositions, was under ready command, as far as arrangement was concerned. In order to change the *anodes* and *cathodes* at the places of decomposition, the form of apparatus (Pl. VII, *Fig. 14*) was occasionally adopted. Here only one platina plate, *c*, was used; both pieces of paper on which decomposition was to be effected were placed upon it, the wires from P and Z resting upon these pieces of paper, or upon the plate *c*, according as the current with or without decomposition of the solutions was required.

976. On placing solution of iodide of potassium in paper at one of the decomposing localities, and solution of sulphate of soda at the other, so that the electric current should pass through both at once, the solution of iodide was slowly decomposed, yielding iodine at the *anode* and alkali at the *cathode*; but the solution of sulphate of soda exhibited no signs of decomposition, neither acid nor alkali being evolved from it. On placing the wires so that the iodide alone was subject to the action of the current (900), it was quickly and powerfully decomposed; but on arranging them so that the sulphate of soda alone was subject to action, it still refused to yield up its elements.

Finally, the apparatus was so arranged under a wet bell-glass, that it could be left for twelve hours, the current passing during the whole time through a solution of sulphate of soda, retained in its place by only two thicknesses of bibulous litmus and turmeric paper. At the end of that time it was ascertained by the decomposition of iodide of potassium at the second place of action, that the current was passing and had passed for the twelve hours, and yet no trace of acid or alkali from the sulphate of soda appeared.

977. From these experiments it may, I think, be concluded, that a solution of sulphate of soda can conduct a current of electricity, which is unable to decompose the neutral salt present; that this salt in the state of solution, like water, requires a certain electrolytic intensity for its decomposition; and that the necessary intensity is much higher for this substance than for the iodide of potassium in a similar state of solution.

978. I then experimented on bodies rendered decomposable by fusion, and first on *chloride of lead*. The current was excited by dilute sulphuric acid without any nitric acid between zinc and platina plates (Pl. VII, *Fig. 15*), and was then made to traverse a little chloride of lead fused upon glass at *a*, a paper moistened in solution of iodide of potassium at *b*, and a galvanometer at *g*. The metallic terminations at *a* and *b* were of platina. Being thus arranged, the decomposition at *b* and the deflection at *g* showed that an electric current was passing, but there was no appearance of decomposition at *a*, not even after a *metallic* communication at *b* was established. The experiment was repeated several times, and I am led to conclude that in this case the current has not intensity sufficient to cause the decomposition of the chloride of lead; and further, that, like water (974), fused chloride of lead can conduct an electric current having an intensity below that required to effect decomposition.

979. *Chloride of silver* was then placed at *a*, *Fig. 15*, instead of chloride of lead. There was a very ready decomposition of the solution of iodide of potassium at *b*, and when metallic contact was made there, very considerable deflection of the galvanometer needle at *g*. Platina also appeared to be dissolved at the anode of the fused chloride at *a*, and there was every appearance of a decomposition having been effected there.

980. A further proof of decomposition was obtained in the following manner. The platina

wires in the fused chloride at a were brought very near together (metallic contact having been established at b), and left so; the deflection at the galvanometer indicated the passage of a current, feeble in its force, but constant. After a minute or two, however, the needle would suddenly be violently affected, and indicate a current as strong as if metallic contact had taken place at a. This I actually found to be the case, for the silver reduced by the action of the current crystallized in long delicate spiculæ, and these at last completed the metallic communication; and at the same time that they transmitted a more powerful current than the fused chloride, they proved that electrochemical decomposition of that chloride had been going on. Hence it appears, that the current excited by dilute sulphuric acid between zinc and platina, has an intensity above that required to electrolyze the fused chloride of silver when placed between platina electrodes, although it has not intensity enough to decompose chloride of lead under the same circumstances.

981. A drop of *water* placed at a instead of the fused chlorides, showed as in the former case (970), that it could conduct a current unable to decompose it, for decomposition of the solution of iodide at b occurred after some time. But its conducting power was much below that of the fused chloride of lead (978).

982. Fused *nitre* at a conducted much better than water: I was unable to decide with certainty whether it was electrolyzed, but I incline to think not, for there was no discoloration against the platina at the *cathode*. If sulpho-nitric acid had been used in the exciting vessel, both the nitre and the chloride of lead would have suffered decomposition like the water (906).

983. The results thus obtained of conduction without decomposition, and the necessity of a certain electrolytic intensity for the separation of the *ions* of different electrolytes, are immediately connected with the experiments and results given in § 10 of the Fourth Series of these *Researches* (418, 423, 444, 449). But it will require a more exact knowledge of the nature of intensity, both as regards the first origin of the electric current, and also the manner in which it may be reduced, or lowered by the intervention of longer or shorter portions of bad conductors, whether decomposable or not, before their relation can be minutely and fully understood.

984. In the case of water, the experiments I have as yet made, appear to show that, when the electric current is reduced in intensity below the point required for decomposition, then the degree of conduction is the same whether sulphuric acid, or any other of the many bodies which can affect its transferring power as an electrolyte, are present or not. Or, in other words, that the necessary electrolytic intensity for water is the same whether it be pure, or rendered a better conductor by the addition of these substances; and that for currents of less intensity than this, the water, whether pure or acidulated, has equal conducting power. An apparatus (Pl. VII, *Fig. 12*), was arranged with dilute sulphuric acid in the vessel A, and pure distilled water in the vessel B. By the decomposition at e, it appeared as if water was a *better* conductor than dilute sulphuric acid for a current of such low intensity as to cause no decomposition. I am inclined, however, to attribute this apparent superiority of water to variations in that peculiar condition of the platina electrodes which is referred to farther on in this Series (1040), and which is assumed, as far as I can judge, to a greater degree in dilute sulphuric acid than in pure water. The power therefore, of acids, alkalies, salts, and other bodies in solution, to increase conducting power, appears to hold good only in those cases where the electrolyte subject to the current suffers decomposition, and loses all influence when the current transmitted has too low an intensity to affect chemical change. It is probable that the ordinary conducting power of an electrolyte in the solid state (419) is the same as that which it possesses in the fluid state for currents, the tension of which is beneath the due electrolytic intensity.

985. Currents of electricity, produced by less than eight or ten series of voltaic elements, can be reduced to that intensity at which water can conduct them without suffering decomposition, by causing them to pass through three or four vessels in which water shall be successively interposed between platina surfaces. The principles of interference upon which this effect depends, will be described hereafter (1009, 1018), but the effect may be useful in obtaining currents of standard intensity, and is probably applicable to batteries of any number of pairs of plates.

986. As there appears every reason to expect that all electrolytes will be found subject to the law which requires an electric current of a certain intensity for their decomposition, but that they will differ from each other in the degree of intensity required, it will be desirable

hereafter to arrange them in a table, in the order of their electrolytic intensities. Investigations on this point must, however, be very much extended and include many more bodies than have been here mentioned before such a table can be constructed. It will be especially needful in such experiments, to describe the nature of the electrodes used, or, if possible, to select such as, like platina or plumbago in certain cases, shall have no power of assisting the separation of the *ions* to be evolved (913).

987. Of the two modes in which bodies can transmit the electric forces, namely, that which is so characteristically exhibited by the metals, and usually called conduction, and that in which it is accompanied by decomposition, the first appears common to all bodies, although it occurs with almost infinite degrees of difference; the second is at present distinctive of the electrolytes. It is, however, just possible that it may hereafter be extended to the metals; for their power of conducting without decomposition may, perhaps justly, be ascribed to their requiring a very high electrolytic intensity for their decomposition.

987½. The establishment of the principle that a certain electrolytic intensity is necessary before decomposition can be effected, is of great importance to all those considerations which arise regarding the probable effects of weak currents, such for instance as those produced by natural thermo-electricity, or natural voltaic arrangements in the earth. For to produce an effect of decomposition or of combination, a current must not only exist, but have a certain intensity before it can overcome the quiescent affinities opposed to it, otherwise it will be conducted, producing no permanent chemical effects. On the other hand, the principles are also now evident by which an opposing action can be so weakened, by the juxtaposition of bodies not having quite affinity enough to cause direct action between them (913), that a very weak current shall be able to raise the sum of actions sufficiently high, and cause chemical changes to occur.

988. In concluding this division *on the intensity necessary for electrolyzation*, I cannot resist pointing out the following remarkable conclusion in relation to intensity generally. It would appear that when a voltaic current is produced, having a certain intensity, dependent upon the strength of the chemical affinities by which that current is excited (916), it can decompose a particular electrolyte without relation to the quantity of electricity passed, the *intensity* deciding whether the electrolyte shall give way or not. If that conclusion be confirmed, then we may arrange circumstances so that the *same quantity* of electricity may pass in the *same time*, in at the *same surface*, into the *same decomposing body in the same state*, and yet, differing in intensity, will *decompose in one case and in the other not:* for taking a source of too low an intensity to decompose, and ascertaining the quantity passed in a given time, it is easy to take another source having a sufficient intensity, and reducing the quantity of electricity from it by the intervention of bad conductors to the same proportion as the former current, and then all the conditions will be fulfilled which are required to produce the result described.

¶ iii. *On Associated Voltaic Circles, or the Voltaic Battery*

989. Passing from the consideration of single circles (875, &c.) to their association in the voltaic battery, it is a very evident consequence that if matters are so arranged that two sets of affinities, in place of being opposed to each other as in Pl. VII, *Figs. 1, 4* (880, 891), are made to act in conformity, then, instead of either interfering with the other, it will rather assist it. This is simply the case of two voltaic pairs of metals arranged so as to form one circuit. In such arrangements the activity of the whole is known to be increased, and when ten, or a hundred, or any larger number of such alternations are placed in conformable association with each other, the power of the whole becomes proportionably exalted, and we obtain that magnificent instrument of philosophic research, the *voltaic battery*.

990. But it is evident from the principles of definite action already laid down that the *quantity* of electricity in the current cannot be increased with the increase of the *quantity of metal* oxidized and dissolved at each new place of chemical action. A single pair of zinc and platina plates throws as much electricity into the form of a current, by the oxidation of 32.5 grains of the zinc (868) as would be circulated by the same alteration of a thousand times that quantity, or nearly five pounds of metal oxidized at the surface of the zinc plates of a thousand pairs placed in regular battery order. For it is evident, that the electricity which passes across the acid from the zinc to the platina in the first cell, and which has been associated with, or even evolved by, the decomposition of a definite portion of water in that cell, cannot

pass from the zinc to the platina across the acid in the second cell, without the decomposition of the same quantity of water there, and the oxidation of the same quantity of zinc by it (924, 949). The same result recurs in every other cell; the electro-chemical equivalent of water must be decomposed in each, before the current can pass through it; for the quantity of electricity passed and the quantity of electrolyte decomposed, *must* be the equivalents of each other. The action in each cell, therefore, is not to increase the quantity set in motion in any one cell, but to aid in urging forward that quantity, the passing of which is consistent with the oxidation of its own zinc; and in this way it exalts that peculiar property of the current which we endeavour to express by the term *intensity*, without increasing the *quantity* beyond that which is proportionate to the quantity of zinc oxidized in any single cell of the series.

991. To prove this, I arranged ten pairs of amalgamated zinc and platina plates with dilute sulphuric acid in the form of a battery. On completing the circuit, all the pairs acted and evolved gas at the surfaces of the platina. This was collected and found to be alike in quantity for each plate; and the quantity of hydrogen evolved at any one platina plate was in the same proportion to the quantity of metal dissolved from any one zinc plate, as was given in the experiment with a single pair (864, &c.). It was therefore certain, that, just as much electricity and no more had passed through the series of ten pair of plates as had passed through, or would have been put into motion by, any single pair, notwithstanding that ten times the quantity of zinc had been consumed.

992. This truth has been proved also long ago in another way, by the action of the evolved current on a magnetic needle; the deflecting power of one pair of plates in a battery being equal to the deflecting power of the whole, provided the wires used be sufficiently large to carry the current of the single pair freely; but the *cause* of this equality of action could not be understood whilst the definite action and evolution of electricity (783, 869) remained unknown.

993. The superior decomposing power of a battery over a single pair of plates is rendered evident in two ways. Electrolytes held together by an affinity so strong as to resist the action of the current from a single pair, yield up their elements to the current excited by many pairs; and that body which is decomposed by

the action of one or of few pairs of metals, &c., is resolved into its *ions* the more readily as it is acted upon by electricity urged forward by many alternations.

994. Both these effects are, I think, easily understood. Whatever *intensity* may be, (and that must of course depend upon the nature of electricity, whether it consist of a fluid or fluids, or of vibrations of an ether, or any other kind or condition of matter), there seems to be no difficulty in comprehending that the *degree* of intensity at which a current of electricity is evolved by a first voltaic element shall be increased when that current is subjected to the action of a second voltaic element, acting in conformity and possessing equal powers with the first: and as the decompositions are merely opposed actions, but exactly of the same kind as those which generate the current (917), it seems to be a natural consequence, that the affinity which can resist the force of a single decomposing action may be unable to oppose the energies of many decomposing actions, operating conjointly, as in the voltaic battery.

995. That a body which can give way to a current of feeble intensity should give way more freely to one of stronger force, and yet involve no contradiction to the law of definite electrolytic action, is perfectly consistent. All the facts and also the theory I have ventured to put forth tend to show that the act of decomposition opposes a certain force to the passage of the electric current; and, that this obstruction should be overcome more or less readily, in proportion to the greater or less intensity of the decomposing current, is in perfect consistency with all our notions of the electric agent.

996. I have elsewhere (947) distinguished the chemical action of zinc and dilute sulphuric acid into two portions; that which, acting effectually on the zinc, evolves hydrogen at once upon its surface, and that which, producing an arrangement of the chemical forces throughout the electrolyte present (in this case water), tends to take oxygen from it, but cannot do so unless the electric current consequent thereon can have free passage, and the hydrogen be delivered elsewhere than against the zinc. The electric current depends altogether upon the second of these; but when the current can pass, by favouring the electrolytic action it tends to diminish the former and increase the latter portion.

997. It is evident, therefore, that when ordinary zinc is used in a voltaic arrangement, there is an enormous waste of that power which

it is the object to throw into the form of an electric current; a consequence which is put in its strongest point of view when it is considered that three ounces and a half of zinc, properly oxidized, can circulate enough electricity to decompose nearly one ounce of water, and cause the evolution of about 2400 cubic inches of hydrogen gas. This loss of power not only takes place during the time the electrodes of the battery are in communication, being then proportionate to the quantity of hydrogen evolved against the surface of any one of the zinc plates, but includes also *all* the chemical action which goes on when the extremities of the pile are not in communication.

998. This loss is far greater with ordinary zinc than with the pure metal, as M. De la Rive has shown.[1] The cause is, that when ordinary zinc is acted upon by dilute sulphuric acid, portions of copper, lead, cadmium, or other metals which it may contain, are set free upon its surface; and these, being in contact with the zinc, form small but very active voltaic circles, which cause great destruction of the zinc and evolution of hydrogen, apparently upon the zinc surface, but really upon the surface of these incidental metals. In the same proportion as they serve to discharge or convey the electricity back to the zinc, do they diminish its power of producing an electric current which shall extend to a greater distance across the acid, and be discharged only through the copper or platina plate which is associated with it for the purpose of forming a voltaic apparatus.

999. All these evils are removed by the employment of an amalgam of zinc in the manner recommended by Mr. Kemp,[2] or the use of the amalgamated zinc plates of Mr. Sturgeon (863), who has himself suggested and objected to their application in galvanic batteries; for he says, "Were it not on account of the brittleness and other inconveniences occasioned by the incorporation of the mercury with the zinc, amalgamation of the zinc surfaces in galvanic batteries would become an important improvement; for the metal would last much longer, and remain bright for a considerable time, even for several successive hours; essential considerations in the employment of this apparatus."[3]

[1] *Quarterly Journal of Science*, 1831, p. 388; or *Bibliothèque Universelle*, 1830, p. 391.
[2] *Jameson's Edinburgh Journal*, October 1828.
[3] *Recent Experimental Researches*, p. 42, &c. Mr. Sturgeon is of course unaware of the definite production of electricity by chemical action, and is in fact quoting the experiment as the strongest argument *against* the chemical theory of galvanism.

1000. Zinc so prepared, even though impure, does not sensibly decompose the water of dilute sulphuric acid, but still has such affinity for the oxygen, that the moment a metal which, like copper or platina, has little or no affinity, touches it in the acid, action ensues, and a powerful and abundant electric current is produced. It is probable that the mercury acts by bringing the surface, in consequence of its fluidity, into one uniform condition, and preventing those differences in character between one spot and another which are necessary for the formation of the minute voltaic circuits referred to (998). If any difference does exist at the first moment, with regard to the proportion of zinc and mercury, at one spot on the *surface*, as compared with another, that spot having the least mercury is first acted on, and, by solution of the zinc, is soon placed in the same condition as the other parts, and the whole plate rendered superficially uniform. One part cannot, therefore, act as a discharger to another; and hence *all* the chemical power upon the water at its surface is in that equable condition (949), which, though it tends to produce an electric current through the liquid to another plate of metal which can act as a discharger (950), presents no irregularities by which any one part, having weaker affinities for oxygen, can act as a discharger to another. Two excellent and important consequences follow upon this state of the metal. The first is, that the *full equivalent* of electricity is obtained for the oxidation of a certain quantity of zinc; the second, that a battery constructed with the zinc so prepared, and charged with dilute sulphuric acid, is active only whilst the electrodes are connected, and ceases to act or be acted upon by the acid the instant the communication is broken.

1001. I have had a small battery of ten pairs of plates thus constructed, and am convinced that arrangements of this kind will be very important, especially in the development and illustration of the philosophical principles of the instrument. The metals I have used are amalgamated zinc and platina, connected together by being soldered to platina wires, the whole apparatus having the form of the *couronne des tasses*. The liquid used was dilute sulphuric acid of sp. gr. 1.25. No action took place upon the metals except when the electrodes were in communication, and then the action upon the zinc was only in proportion to the decomposition in the experimental cell; for when the current was retarded there, it was retarded also in the battery, and no waste of the powers of the metal was incurred.

1002. In consequence of this circumstance, the acid in the cells remained active for a very much longer time than usual. In fact, time did not tend to lower it in any sensible degree: for whilst the metal was preserved to be acted upon at the proper moment, the acid also was preserved almost at its first strength. Hence a constancy of action far beyond what can be obtained by the use of common zinc.

1003. Another excellent consequence was the renewal, during the interval of rest, between two experiments of the first and most efficient state. When an amalgamated zinc and a platina plate, immersed in dilute sulphuric acid, are first connected, the current is very powerful, but instantly sinks very much in force, and in some cases actually falls to only an eighth or a tenth of that first produced (1036). This is due to the acid which is in contact with the zinc becoming neutralized by the oxide formed; the continued quick oxidation of the metal being thus prevented. With ordinary zinc, the evolution of gas at its surface tends to mingle all the liquid together, and thus bring fresh acid against the metal, by which the oxide formed there can be removed. With the amalgamated zinc battery, at every cessation of the current, the saline solution against the zinc is gradually diffused amongst the rest of the liquid; and upon the renewal of contact at the electrodes, the zinc plates are found most favourably circumstanced for the production of a ready and powerful current.

1004. It might at first be imagined that amalgamated zinc would be much inferior in force to common zinc, because of the lowering of its energy, which the mercury might be supposed to occasion over the whole of its surface; but this is not the case. When the electric currents of two pairs of platina and zinc plates were opposed, the difference being that one of the zincs was amalgamated and the other not, the current from the amalgamated zinc was most powerful, although no gas was evolved against it, and much was evolved at the surface of the unamalgamated metal. Again, as Davy has shown,[1] if amalgamated and unamalgamated zinc be put in contact, and dipped into dilute sulphuric acid, or other exciting fluids, the former is positive to the latter, i.e., the current passes from the amalgamated zinc, through the fluid, to the unprepared zinc. This he accounts for by supposing that "there is not any inher-

[1] *Philosophical Transactions*, 1826, p. 405.

ent and specific property in each metal which gives it the electrical character, but that it depends upon its peculiar state—on that form of aggregation which fits it for chemical change."

1005. The superiority of the amalgamated zinc is not, however, due to any such cause, but is a very simple consequence of the state of the fluid in contact with it; for as the unprepared zinc acts directly and alone upon the fluid, whilst that which is amalgamated does not, the former (by the oxide it produces) quickly neutralizes the acid in contact with its surface, so that the progress of oxidation is retarded, whilst at the surface of the amalgamated zinc, any oxide formed is instantly removed by the free acid present, and the clean metallic surface is always ready to act with full energy upon the water. Hence its superiority (1037).

1006. The progress of improvement in the voltaic battery and its applications, is evidently in the contrary direction at present to what it was a few years ago; for in place of increasing the number of plates, the strength of acid, and the extent altogether of the instrument, the change is rather towards its first state of simplicity, but with a far more intimate knowledge and application of the principles which govern its force and action. Effects of decomposition can now be obtained with ten pairs of plates (417), which required five hundred or a thousand pairs for their production in the first instance. The capability of decomposing fused chlorides, iodides, and other compounds, according to the law before established (380, &c.), and the opportunity of collecting certain of the products, without any loss, by the use of apparatus of the nature of those already described (789, 814, &c.), render it probable that the voltaic battery may become a useful and even economical manufacturing instrument; for theory evidently indicates that an equivalent of a rare substance may be obtained at the expense of three or four equivalents of a very common body, namely, zinc: and practice seems thus far to justify the expectation. In this point of view I think it very likely that plates of platina or silver may be used instead of plates of copper with advantage, and that then the evil arising occasionally from solution of the copper, and its precipitation on the zinc (by which the electromotive power of the zinc is so much injured) will be avoided (1047).

¶ iv. *On the Resistance of an Electrolyte to Electrolytic Action, and on Interpositions*

1007. I have already illustrated, in the simplest possible form of experiment (891, 910), the resistance established at the place of decomposition to the force active at the exciting place. I purpose examining the effects of this resistance more generally; but it is rather with reference to their practical interference with the action and phenomena of the voltaic battery, than with any intention at this time to offer a strict and philosophical account of their nature. Their general and principal cause is the resistance of the chemical affinities to be overcome; but there are numerous other circumstances which have a joint influence with these forces (1034, 1040, &c.), each of which would require a minute examination before a correct account of the whole could be given.

1008. As it will be convenient to describe the experiments in a form different to that in which they were made, both forms shall first be explained. Plates of platina, copper, zinc, and other metals, about three quarters of an inch wide and three inches long, were associated together in pairs by means of platina wires to which they were soldered (Pl. VIII, *Fig. 1*), the plates of one pair being either alike or different, as might be required. These were arranged in glasses, *Fig. 2*, so as to form Volta's crown of cups. The acid or fluid in the cups never covered the whole of any plate; and occasionally small glass rods were put into the cups, between the plates, to prevent their contact. Single plates were used to terminate the series and complete the connexion with a galvanometer, or with a decomposing apparatus (899, 968, &c.), or both. Now if Pl. VIII, *Fig. 3*, be examined and compared with *Fig. 4*, the latter may be admitted as representing the former in its simplest condition; for the cups I, II, and III of the former, with their contents, are represented by the cells I, II, and III of the latter, and the metal plates Z and P of the former by the similar plates represented Z and P in the latter. The only difference, in fact, between the apparatus, *Fig. 3*, and the trough represented *Fig. 4*, is that twice the quantity of surface of contact between the metal and acid is allowed in the first to what would occur in the second.

1009. When the extreme plates of the arrangement just described (Pl. VIII, *Fig. 3*), are connected metallically through the galvanometer *g*, then the whole represents a battery consisting of two pairs of zinc and platina plates urging a current forward, which has, however, to decompose water unassisted by any direct chemical affinity before it can be transmitted across the cell III, and therefore before it can circulate. This decomposition of water, which is opposed to the passage of the current, may, as a matter of convenience, be considered as taking place either against the surfaces of the two platina plates which constitute the electrodes in the cell III, or against the two surfaces of that platina plate which separates the cells II and III, *Fig. 4*, from each other. It is evident that if that plate were away, the battery would consist of two pairs of plates and two cells, arranged in the most favourable position for the production of a current. The platina plate therefore, which being introduced as at *x*, has oxygen evolved at one surface and hydrogen at the other (that is, if the decomposing current passes), may be considered as the cause of any obstruction arising from the decomposition of water by the electrolytic action of the current; and I have usually called it the interposed plate.

1010. In order to simplify the conditions, dilute sulphuric acid was first used in all the cells, and platina for the interposed plates; for then the initial intensity of the current which tends to be formed is constant, being due to the power which zinc has of decomposing water; and the opposing force of decomposition is also constant, the elements of the water being unassisted in their separation at the interposed plates by any affinity or secondary action at the electrodes (744), arising either from the nature of the plate itself or the surrounding fluid.

1011. When only one voltaic pair of zinc and platina plates was used, the current of electricity was entirely stopped to all practical purposes by interposing one platina plate (Pl. VIII, *Fig. 5*), i.e., by requiring of the current that it should decompose water, and evolve both its elements, before it should pass. This consequence is in perfect accordance with the views before given (910, 917, 973). For as the whole result depends upon the opposition of forces at the places of electric excitement and electro-decomposition, and as water is the substance to be decomposed at both before the current can move, it is not to be expected that the zinc should have such powerful attraction for the oxygen, as not only to be able to take it from its associated hydrogen, but leave such a surplus of force as, passing to the second place of decomposition, should be there able to effect a second separation of the elements of water. Such an effect would require that the force of attraction between zinc and oxygen should un-

PLATE VIII

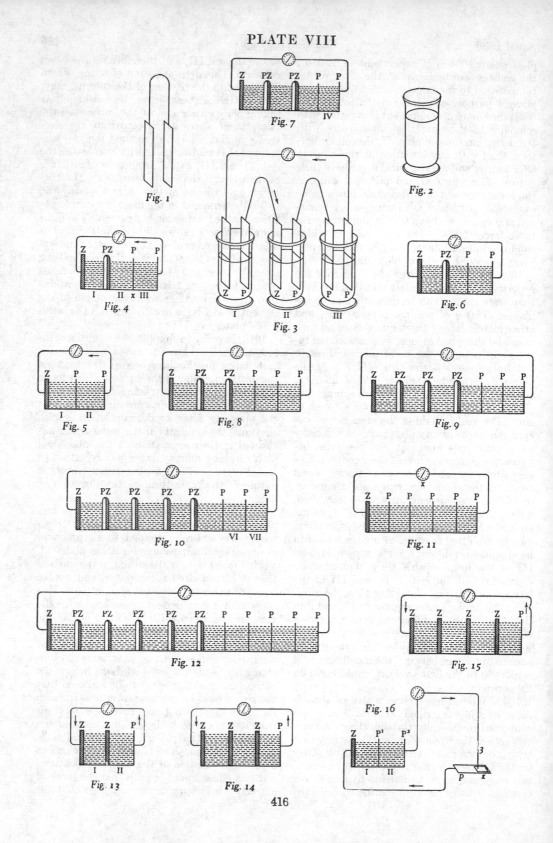

Fig. 1

Fig. 2

Fig. 3

Fig. 4

Fig. 5

Fig. 6

Fig. 7

Fig. 8

Fig. 9

Fig. 10

Fig. 11

Fig. 12

Fig. 13

Fig. 14

Fig. 15

Fig. 16

der the circumstances be *at least* twice as great as the force of attraction between the oxygen and hydrogen.

1012. When two pairs of zinc and platina exciting plates were used, the current was also practically stopped by one interposed platina plate (Pl. VIII, *Fig. 6*). There was a very feeble effect of a current at first, but it ceased almost immediately. It will be referred to, with many other similar effects, hereafter (1017).

1013. Three pairs of zinc and platina plates (Pl. VIII, *Fig. 7*), were able to produce a current which could pass an interposed platina plate, and effect the electrolyzation of water in cell IV. The current was evident, both by the continued deflection of the galvanometer, and the production of bubbles of oxygen and hydrogen at the electrodes in cell IV. Hence the accumulated surplus force of three plates of zinc, which are active in decomposing water, is more than equal, when added together, to the force with which oxygen and hydrogen are combined in water, and is sufficient to cause the separation of these elements from each other.

1014. The three pairs of zinc and platina plates were now opposed by two intervening platina plates (Pl. VIII, *Fig. 8*). In this case the current was stopped.

1015. Four pairs of zinc and platina plates were also neutralized by two interposed platina plates, *Fig. 9*.

1016. Five pairs of zinc and platina, with two interposed platina plates, *Fig. 10*, gave a feeble current; there was permanent deflection at the galvanometer, and decomposition in the cells VI and VII. But the current was very feeble; very much less than when all the intermediate plates were removed and the two extreme ones only retained: for when they were placed six inches asunder in one cell, they gave a powerful current. Hence five exciting pairs, with two interposed obstructing plates, do not give a current at all comparable to that of a single unobstructed pair.

1017. I have already said that a *very feeble current* passed when the series included one interposed platina and two pairs of zinc and platina plates (1012). A similarly feeble current passed in every case, and even when only one exciting pair and four intervening platina plates were used (Pl. VIII, *Fig. 11*), a current passed which could be detected at *x*, both by chemical action on the solution of iodide of potassium, and by the galvanometer. This current I believe to be due to electricity reduced in intensity below the point requisite for the

decomposition of water (970, 984); for water can conduct electricity of such low intensity by the same kind of power which it possesses in common with metals and charcoal, though it cannot conduct electricity of higher intensity without suffering decomposition, and then opposing a new force consequent thereon. With an electric current of, or under this intensity, it is probable that increasing the number of interposed platina plates would not involve an increased difficulty of conduction.

1018. In order to obtain an idea of the additional interfering power of each added platina plate, six voltaic pairs and four intervening platinas were arranged as in Pl. VIII, *Fig. 12*; a very feeble current then passed (985, 1017). When one of the platinas was removed so that three intervened, a current somewhat stronger passed. With two intervening platinas a still stronger current passed; and with only one intervening platina a very fair current was obtained. But the effect of the successive plates, taken in the order of their interposition, was very different, as might be expected; for the first retarded the current more powerfully than the second, and the second more than the third.

1019. In these experiments both amalgamated and unamalgamated zinc were used, but the results generally were the same.

1020. The effects of retardation just described were altered altogether when changes were made in the *nature of the liquid* used between the plates, either in what may be called the *exciting* or the *retarding* cells. Thus, retaining the exciting force the same, by still using pure dilute sulphuric acid for that purpose, if a little nitric acid were added to the liquid in the *retarding* cells, then the transmission of the current was very much facilitated. For instance, in the experiment with one pair of exciting plates and one intervening plate (1011) (Pl. VIII, *Fig. 5*), when a few drops of nitric acid were added to the contents of cell II, then the current of electricity passed with considerable strength (though it soon fell from other causes [1036, 1040]), and the same increased effect was produced by the nitric acid when many interposed plates were used.

1021. This seems to be a consequence of the diminution of the difficulty of decomposing water when its hydrogen, instead of being absolutely expelled, as in the former cases, is transferred to the oxygen of the nitric acid, producing a secondary result at the *cathode* (752); for in accordance with the chemical views of the electric current and its action already advanced (913), the water, instead of opposing a resistance to decomposition equal to the full amount of the force of mutual attraction between its oxygen and hydrogen, has that force counteracted in part, and therefore diminished by the attraction of the hydrogen at the *cathode* for the oxygen of the nitric acid which surrounds it, and with which it ultimately combines instead of being evolved in its free state.

1022. When a little nitric acid was put into the exciting cells, then again the circumstances favouring the transmission of the current were strengthened, for the *intensity* of the current itself was increased by the addition (906). When therefore a little nitric acid was added to both the *exciting* and the *retarding* cells, the current of electricity passed with very considerable freedom.

1023. When dilute muriatic acid was used, it produced and transmitted a current more easily than pure dilute sulphuric acid, but not so readily as dilute nitric acid. As muriatic acid appears to be decomposed more freely than water (765), and as the affinity of zinc for chlorine is very powerful, it might be expected to produce a current more intense than that from the use of dilute sulphuric acid; and also to transmit it more freely by undergoing decomposition at a lower intensity (912).

1024. In relation to the effect of these interpositions, it is necessary to state that they do not appear to be at all dependent upon the size of the electrodes, or their distance from each other in the acid, except that when a current *can pass*, changes in these facilitate or retard its passage. For on repeating the experiment with one intervening and one pair of exciting plates (1011), Pl. VIII, *Fig. 5*, and in place of the interposed plate P using sometimes a mere wire, and sometimes very large plates (1008), and also changing the terminal exciting plates Z and P, so that they were sometimes wires only and at others of great size, still the results were the same as those already obtained.

1025. In illustration of the effect of distance, an experiment like that described with two exciting pairs and one intervening plate (1012), Pl. VIII, *Fig. 6*, was arranged so that the distance between the plates in the third cell could be increased to six or eight inches, or diminished to the thickness of a piece of intervening bibulous paper. Still the result was the same in both cases, the effect not being sensibly greater, when the plates were merely separated by the paper, than when a great way apart; so that the principal opposition to the current in this case does not depend upon the *quantity* of intervening electrolytic conductor, but on the *relation of its elements to the intensity of the current*, or to the chemical nature of the electrodes and the surrounding fluids.

1026. When the acid was sulphuric acid, *increasing its strength* in any of the cells caused no change in the effects; it did not produce a more intense current in the exciting cells (908), or cause the current produced to traverse the decomposing cells more freely. But if to very weak sulphuric acid a few drops of nitric acid were added, then either one or other of those effects could be produced; and, as might be expected in a case like this, where the exciting or conducting action bore a *direct* reference to the acid itself, increasing the strength of this (the nitric acid) also increased its powers.

1027. The *nature of the interposed plate* was now varied to show its relation to the phenomena either of excitation or retardation, and amalgamated zinc was first substituted for platina. On employing one voltaic pair and one interposed zinc plate (Pl. VIII, *Fig. 13*), there was as powerful a current, apparently, as if the interposed zinc plate was away. Hydrogen was evolved against P in cell II, and against the side of the second zinc in cell I; but no gas appeared against the side of the zinc in cell II, nor against the zinc in cell I.

1028. On interposing two amalgamated zinc plates (Pl. VIII, *Fig. 14*), instead of one, there was still a powerful current, but interference had taken place. On using three intermediate zinc plates, *Fig. 15*, there was still further retardation, though a good current of electricity passed.

1029. Considering the retardation as due to the inaction of the amalgamated zinc upon the dilute acid, in consequence of the slight though general effect of diminished chemical power produced by the mercury on the surface, and viewing this inaction as the circumstance which rendered it necessary that each plate should have its tendency to decompose water assisted slightly by the electric current, it was expected that plates of the metal in the unamalgamated state would probably not require such assistance, and would offer no sensible impediment to the passing of the current. This expectation was fully realized in the use of two and three interposed unamalgamated plates. The electric current passed through them as freely as if there had been no such plates in the way. They offered no obstacle, because they could decompose water without the current; and the latter had only to give direction to a part of the forces, which would have been active whether it had passed or not.

1030. Interposed plates of copper were then employed. These seemed at first to occasion no obstruction, but after a few minutes the current almost entirely ceased. This effect appears due to the surfaces taking up that peculiar condition (1040) by which they tend to produce a reverse current; for when one or more of the plates were turned round, which could easily be effected with the *couronne des tasses* form of experiment (Pl. VIII, *Fig. 3*), then the current was powerfully renewed for a few moments, and then again ceased. Plates of platina and copper, arranged as a voltaic pile with dilute sulphuric acid, could not form a voltaic trough competent to act for more than a few minutes, because of this peculiar counteracting effect.

1031. All these effects of retardation, exhibited by decomposition against surfaces for which the evolved elements have more or less affinity, or are altogether deficient in attraction, show generally, though beautifully, the chemical relations and source of the current, and also the balanced state of the affinities at the places of excitation and decomposition. In this way they add to the mass of evidence in favour of the identity of the two; for they demonstrate, as it were, the antagonism of the *chemical powers* at the electromotive part with the *chemical powers* at the interposed parts; they show that the first are *producing* electric effects, and the second *opposing* them; they bring the two into direct relation; they prove that either can determine the other, thus making what appears to be cause and effect convertible, and thereby demonstrating that both chemical and electrical action are merely two exhibitions of one single agent or power (916, &c.).

1032. It is quite evident that as water and other electrolytes can conduct electricity without suffering decomposition (986), when the electricity is of sufficiently low intensity, it may not be asserted as absolutely true in all cases that whenever electricity passes through an electrolyte it produces a definite effect of decomposition. But the quantity of electricity which can pass in a given time through an electrolyte without causing decomposition, is so small as to bear no comparison to that required in a case of very moderate decomposition, and with electricity above the intensity required for electrolyzation, I have found no sensible departure as yet from the law of *definite elec-*

trolytic action developed in the preceding series of these *Researches* (783, &c.).

1033. I cannot dismiss this division of the present paper without making a reference to the important experiments of M. Aug. De la Rive on the effects of interposed plates.[1] As I have had occasion to consider such plates merely as giving rise to new decompositions, and in that way only causing obstruction to the passage of the electric current, I was freed from the necessity of considering the peculiar effects described by that philosopher. I was the more willing to avoid for the present touching upon these, as I must at the same time have entered into the views of Sir Humphry Davy upon the same subject,[2] and also those of Marianini[3] and Ritter,[4] which are connected with it.

¶ v. *General Remarks on the Active Voltaic Battery*

1034. When the ordinary voltaic battery is brought into action, its very activity produces certain effects, which react upon it, and cause serious deterioration of its power. These render it an exceedingly inconstant instrument as to the *quantity* of effect which it is capable of producing. They are already, in part, known and understood; but as their importance, and that of certain other coincident results, will be more evident by reference to the principles and experiments already stated and described, I have thought it would be useful, in this investigation of the voltaic pile, to notice them briefly here.

1035. When the battery is in action, it causes such substances to be formed and arranged in contact with the plates as very much weaken its power, or even tend to produce a counter current. They are considered by Sir Humphry Davy as sufficient to account for the phenomena of Ritter's secondary piles, and also for the effects observed by M. A. De la Rive with interposed platina plates.[5]

1036. I have already referred to this consequence (1003), as capable, in some cases, of lowering the force of the current to one-eighth or one-tenth of what it was at the first moment, and have met with instances in which its interference was very great. In an experiment in which one voltaic pair and one interposed platina plate were used with dilute sulphuric acid in the cells (Pl. VIII, *Fig. 16*), the wires of

---

[1] *Annales de Chimie*, Vol. XXVIII, p. 190; and *Mémoires de Génève.*
[2] *Philosophical Transactions*, 1826, p. 413.
[3] *Annales de Chimie*, Vol. XXXIII, pp. 117, 119, &c.
[4] *Journal de Physique*, Vol. LVII, pp. 349, 350.
[5] *Philosophical Transactions*, 1826, p. 413.

communication were so arranged, that the end of that marked 3 could be placed at pleasure upon paper moistened in the solution of iodide of potassium at x, or directly upon the platina plate there. If, after an interval during which the circuit had not been complete, the wire 3 were placed upon the paper, there was evidence of a current, decomposition ensued, and the galvanometer was affected. If the wire 3 were made to touch the metal of p, a comparatively strong sudden current was produced, affecting the galvanometer, but lasting only for a moment; the effect at the galvanometer ceased, and if the wire 3 were placed on the paper at x, no signs of decomposition occurred. On raising the wire 3, and breaking the circuit altogether for a while, the apparatus resumed its first power, requiring, however, from five to ten minutes for this purpose; and then, as before, on making contact between 3 and p, there was again a momentary current, and immediately all the effects apparently ceased.

1037. This effect I was ultimately able to refer to the state of the film of fluid in contact with the zinc plate in cell i. The acid of that film is instantly neutralized by the oxide formed; the oxidation of the zinc cannot, of course, go on with the same facility as before; and the chemical action being thus interrupted, the voltaic action diminishes with it. The time of the rest was required for the diffusion of the liquid, and its replacement by other acid. From the serious influence of this cause in experiments with single pairs of plates of different metals, in which I was at one time engaged, and the extreme care required to avoid it, I cannot help feeling a strong suspicion that it interferes more frequently and extensively than experimenters are aware of, and therefore direct their attention to it.

1038. In considering the effect in delicate experiments of this source of irregularity of action in the voltaic apparatus, it must be remembered that it is only that very small portion of matter which is directly in contact with the oxidizable metal which has to be considered with reference to the change of its nature; and this portion is not very readily displaced from its position upon the surface of the metal (582, 605), especially if that metal be rough and irregular. In illustration of this effect, I will quote a remarkable experiment. A burnished platina plate (569) was put into hot strong sulphuric acid for an instant only: it was then put into distilled water, moved about

in it, taken out, and wiped dry: it was put into a second portion of distilled water, moved about in it, and again wiped: it was put into a third portion of distilled water, in which it was moved about for nearly eight seconds; it was then, without wiping, put into a fourth portion of distilled water, where it was allowed to remain five minutes. The two latter portions of water were then tested for sulphuric acid; the third gave no sensible appearance of that substance, but the fourth gave indications which were not merely evident, but abundant for the circumstances under which it had been introduced. The result sufficiently shows with what difficulty that portion of the substance which is in *contact* with the metal leaves it; and as the contact of the fluid formed against the plate in the voltaic circuit must be as intimate and as perfect as possible, it is easy to see how quickly and greatly it must vary from the general fluid in the cells, and how influential in diminishing the force of the battery this effect must be.

1039. In the ordinary voltaic pile, the influence of this effect will occur in all variety of degrees. The extremities of a trough of twenty pairs of plates of Wollaston's construction were connected with the volta-electrometer, Pl. VI, *Fig. 11* (711), of the Seventh Series of these *Researches*, and after five minutes the number of bubbles of gas issuing from the extremity of the tube, in consequence of the decomposition of the water, noted. Without moving the plates, the acid between the copper and zinc was agitated by the introduction of a feather. The bubbles were immediately evolved more rapidly, above twice the number being produced in the same portion of time as before. In this instance it is very evident that agitation by a feather must have been a very imperfect mode of restoring the acid in the cells against the plates towards its first equal condition; and yet imperfect as the means were, they more than doubled the power of the battery. The *first effect* of a battery which is known to be so superior to the degree of action which the battery can sustain, is almost entirely due to the favourable condition of the acid in contact with the plates.

1040. A *second* cause of diminution in the force of the voltaic battery, consequent upon its own action, is that extraordinary state of the surfaces of the metals (969) which was first described, I believe, by Ritter,[1] to which he refers the powers of his secondary piles, and which

[1] *Journal de Physique,* LVII, p. 349.

has been so well experimented upon by Marianini, and also by A. De la Rive. If the apparatus, Pl. VIII, *Fig. 16* (1036), be left in action for an hour or two, with the wire 3 in contact with the plate *p*, so as to allow a free passage for the current, then, though the contact be broken for ten or twelve minutes, still, upon its renewal, only a feeble current will pass, not at all equal in force to what might be expected. Further, if P[1] and P[2] be connected by a metal wire, a powerful momentary current will pass from P[2] to P[1] through the acid, and therefore in the reverse direction to that produced by the action of the zinc in the arrangement; and after this has happened, the general current can pass through the whole of the system as at first, but by its passage again restores the plates P[2] and P[1] into the former opposing condition. This, generally, is the fact described by Ritter, Marianini, and De la Rive. It has great opposing influence on the action of a pile, especially if the latter consist of but a small number of alternations, and has to pass its current through many interpositions. It varies with the solution in which the interposed plates are immersed, with the intensity of the current, the strength of the pile, the time of action, and especially with accidental discharges of the plates by inadvertent contacts or reversions of the plates during experiments, and must be carefully watched in every endeavour to trace the source, strength, and variations of the voltaic current. Its effect was avoided in the experiments already described (1036, &c.), by making contact between the plates P[1] and P[2] before the effect dependent upon the state of the solution in contact with the zinc plate was observed, and by other precautions.

1041. When an apparatus like Pl. VIII, *Fig. 11* (1017) with several platina plates was used, being connected with a battery able to force a current through them, the power which they acquired, of producing a reversed current, was very considerable.

1042. *Weak and exhausted charges* should never be used at the same time with *strong and fresh ones* in the different cells of a trough, or the different troughs of a battery: the fluid in all the cells should be alike, else the plates in the weaker cells, in place of assisting, retard the passage of the electricity generated in, and transmitted across, the stronger cells. Each zinc plate so circumstanced has to be assisted in decomposing power before the whole current can pass between it and the liquid. So that, if in a battery of fifty pairs of plates, ten of the cells contain a weaker charge than the others, it is as if ten decomposing plates were opposed to the transit of the current of forty pairs of generating plates (1031). Hence a serious loss of force, and hence the reason why, if the ten pairs of plates were removed, the remaining forty pairs would be much more powerful than the whole fifty.

1043. Five similar troughs, of ten pairs of plates each, were prepared, four of them with a good uniform charge of acid, and the fifth with the partially neutralized acid of a used battery. Being arranged in right order, and connected with a volta-electrometer (711), the whole fifty pairs of plates yielded 1.1 cubic inch of oxygen and hydrogen in one minute: but on moving one of the connecting wires so that only the four well-charged troughs should be included in the circuit, they produced with the same volta-electrometer 8.4 cubical inches of gas in the same time. Nearly seven-eighths of the power of the four troughs had been lost, therefore, by their association with the fifth trough.

1044. The same battery of fifty pairs of plates, after being thus used, was connected with a volta-electrometer (711), so that by quickly shifting the wires of communication, the current of the whole of the battery, or of any portion of it, could be made to pass through the instrument for given portions of time in succession. The whole of the battery evolved 0.9 of a cubic inch of oxygen and hydrogen in half a minute; the forty plates evolved 4.6 cubic inches in the same time; the whole then evolved 1 cubic inch in the half-minute, the ten weakly charged evolved 0.4 of a cubic inch in the time given: and finally the whole evolved 1.15 cubic inch in the standard time. The order of the observations was that given: the results sufficiently show the extremely injurious effect produced by the mixture of strong and weak charges in the same battery.[1]

1045. In the same manner associations of *strong and weak* pairs of plates should be carefully avoided. A pair of copper and platina plates arranged in *accordance* with a pair of zinc and platina plates in dilute sulphuric acid, were found to stop the action of the latter, or even of two pairs of the latter, as effectually almost as an interposed plate of platina (1011), or as if the copper itself had been platina. It, in fact, became an interposed decomposing

---

[1] The gradual increase in the action of the whole fifty pairs of plates was due to the elevation of temperature in the weakly charged trough by the passage of the current, in consequence of which the exciting energies of the fluid within were increased.

plate, and therefore a retarding instead of an assisting pair.

1046. The *reversal*, by accident or otherwise, of the plates in a battery has an exceedingly injurious effect. It is not merely the counteraction of the current which the reversed plates can produce, but their effect also in retarding even as indifferent plates, and requiring decomposition to be effected upon their surface, in *accordance* with the course of the current, before the latter can pass. They oppose the current, therefore, in the first place, as interposed platina plates would do (1011—1018); and to this they add a force of opposition as counter-voltaic plates. I find that, in a series of four pairs of zinc and platina plates in dilute sulphuric acid, if one pair be reversed, it very nearly neutralizes the power of the whole.

1047. There are many other causes of reaction, retardation, and irregularity in the voltaic battery. Amongst them is the not unusual one of precipitation of copper upon the zinc in the cells, the injurious effect of which has before been adverted to (1006). But their interest is not perhaps sufficient to justify any increase of the length of this paper, which is rather intended to be an investigation of the theory of the voltaic pile than a particular account of its practical application.[1]

Note. Many of the views and experiments in this series of my *Experimental Researches* will be seen at once to be corrections and extensions of the theory of electro-chemical decomposition, given in the fifth and seventh series of these *Researches*. The expressions I would now alter are those which concern the independence of the evolved elements in relation to the poles or electrodes, and the reference of their evolution to powers entirely internal (524, 537, 661). The present paper fully shows my present views; and I would refer to paragraphs 891, 904, 910, 917, 918, 947, 963, 1007, 1031, &c., as stating what they are. I hope this note will be considered as sufficient in the way of correction at present; for I would rather defer revising the whole theory of electro-chemical decomposition until I can obtain clearer views of the way in which the power under consideration can appear at one time as associated with particles giving them their chemical attraction, and at another as free electricity (493, 957).—M. F.

Royal Institution, March 31, 1834

[1] For further practical results relating to these points of the philosophy of the voltaic battery, see Series X, § 17, 1160–1163.—*Dec.* 1838.

NINTH SERIES

§ 15. *On the Influence by Induction of an Electric Current on itself:— and on the Inductive Action of Electric Currents Generally*

Received December 18, 1834, Read January 29, 1835

1048. THE following investigations relate to a very remarkable inductive action of electric currents, or of the different parts of the same current (74), and indicate an immediate connexion between such inductive action and the direct transmission of electricity through conducting bodies, or even that exhibited in the form of a spark.

1049. The inquiry arose out of a fact communicated to me by Mr. Jenkin, which is as follows. If an ordinary wire of short length be used as the medium of communication between the two plates of an electromotor consisting of a single pair of metals, no management will enable the experimenter to obtain an electric shock from this wire; but if the wire which surrounds an electro-magnet be used, a shock is felt each time the contact with the electromotor is broken, provided the ends of the wire be grasped one in each hand.

1050. Another effect is observed at the same time, which has long been known to philosophers, namely, that a bright electric spark occurs at the place of disjunction.

1051. A brief account of these results, with some of a corresponding character which I had observed in using long wires, was published in the *Philosophical Magazine* for 1834;[1] and I added to them some observations on their nature. Further investigations led me to perceive the inaccuracy of my first notions, and ended in identifying these effects with the phenomena of induction which I had been fortunate enough to develop in the First Series of these *Experimental Researches* (1—59).[2] Notwithstanding

[1] Vol. V, pp. 349, 444.
[2] *Philosophical Transactions*, 1832, p. 126.

this identity, the extension and the peculiarity of the views respecting electric currents which the results supply lead me to believe that they will be found worthy of the attention of the Royal Society.

1052. The *electromotor* used consisted of a cylinder of zinc introduced between the two parts of a double cylinder of copper, and preserved from metallic contact in the usual way by corks. The zinc cylinder was eight inches high and four inches in diameter. Both it and the copper cylinder were supplied with stiff wires, surmounted by cups containing mercury; and it was at these cups that the contacts of wires, helices, or electro-magnets, used to complete the circuit, were made or broken. These cups I will call G and E throughout the rest of this paper (1079).

1053. Certain *helices* were constructed, some of which it will be necessary to describe. A pasteboard tube had four copper wires, one twenty-fourth of an inch in thickness, wound round it, each forming a helix in the same direction from end to end: the convolutions of each wire were separated by string, and the superposed helices prevented from touching by intervening calico. The lengths of the wires forming the helices were 48, 49.5, 48, and 45 feet. The first and third wires were united together so as to form one consistent helix of 96 feet in length; and the second and fourth wires were similarly united to form a second helix, closely interwoven with the first, and 94.5 feet in length. These helices may be distinguished by the numbers i and ii. They were carefully examined by a powerful current of electricity, and a galvanometer, and found to have no communication with each other.

1054. Another helix was constructed upon a similar pasteboard tube, two lengths of the same copper wire being used, each forty-six feet long. These were united into one consistent helix of ninety-two feet, which therefore was nearly equal in value to either of the former helices, but was not in close inductive association with them. It may be distinguished by the number iii.

1055. A fourth helix was constructed of very thick copper wire, being one-fifth of an inch in diameter; the length of wire used was seventy-nine feet, independent of the straight terminal portions.

1056. The principal *electro-magnet* employed consisted of a cylindrical bar of soft iron twenty-five inches long, and one inch and three-quarters in diameter, bent into a ring, so that the ends nearly touched, and surrounded by three coils of thick copper wire, the similar ends of which were fastened together; each of these terminations was soldered to a copper rod, serving as a conducting continuation of the wire. Hence any electric current sent through the rods was divided in the helices surrounding the ring, into three parts, all of which, however, moved in the same direction. The three wires may therefore be considered as representing one wire, of thrice the thickness of the wire really used.

1057. Other electro-magnets could be made at pleasure by introducing a soft iron rod into any of the helices described (1053, &c.).

1058. The *galvanometer* which I had occasion to use was rough in its construction, having but one magnetic needle, and not at all delicate in its indications.

1059. The effects to be considered *depend on the conductor* employed to complete the communication between the zinc and copper plates of the electromotor; and I shall have to consider this conductor under four different forms: as the helix of an electro-magnet (1056); as an ordinary helix (1053, &c.); as a *long* extended wire, having its course such that the parts can exert little or no mutual influence; and as a *short* wire. In all cases the conductor was of copper.

1060. The peculiar effects are best shown by the *electromagnet* (1056). When it was used to complete the communication at the electromotor, there was no sensible spark on *making* contact, but on *breaking* contact there was a very large and bright spark, with considerable combustion of the mercury. Then, again, with respect to the shock: if the hands were moistened in salt and water, and good contact between them and the wires retained, no shock could be felt upon *making* contact at the electromotor, but a powerful one on *breaking* contact.

1061. When the *helix* i or iii (1053, &c.) was used as the connecting conductor, there was also a good spark on breaking contact, but none (sensibly) on making contact. On trying to obtain the shock from these helices, I could not succeed at first. By joining the similar ends of i and ii so as to make the two helices equivalent to one helix, having wire of double thickness, I could just obtain the sensation. Using the helix of thick wire (1055) the shock was distinctly obtained. On placing the tongue between two plates of silver connected by wires with the parts which the hands had heretofore touched (1064), there was a powerful shock on *breaking* contact, but none on *making* contact.

1062. The power of producing these phenomena exists therefore in the simple helix, as in the electro-magnet, although by no means in the same high degree.

1063. On putting a bar of soft iron into the helix, it became an electro-magnet (1057), and its power was instantly and greatly raised. On putting a bar of copper into the helix, no change was produced, the action being that of the helix alone. The two helices i and ii, made into one helix of twofold length of wire, produced a greater effect than either i or ii alone.

1064. On descending from the helix to the mere *long wire*, the following effects were obtained. A copper wire, 0.18 of an inch in diameter, and 132 feet in length, was laid out upon the floor of the laboratory, and used as the connecting conductor (1059): it gave no sensible spark on making contact, but produced a bright one on breaking contact, yet not so bright as that from the helix (1061). On endeavouring to obtain the electric shock at the moment contact was broken, I could not succeed so as to make it pass through the hands; but by using two silver plates fastened by small wires to the extremity of the principal wire used, and introducing the tongue between those plates, I succeeded in obtaining powerful shocks upon the tongue and gums, and could easily convulse a flounder, an eel, or a frog. None of these effects could be obtained directly from the electromotor, i.e., when the tongue, frog, or fish was in a similar, and therefore comparative manner, interposed in the course of the communication between the zinc and copper plates, separated everywhere else by the acid used to excite the combination, or by air. The bright spark and the shock, produced only on breaking contact, are therefore effects of the same kind as those produced in a higher degree by the helix, and in a still higher degree by the electro-magnet.

1065. In order to compare an extended wire with a helix, the helix i, containing ninety-six feet, and ninety-six feet of the same-sized wire lying on the floor of the laboratory, were used alternately as conductors: the former gave a much brighter spark at the moment of disjunction than the latter. Again, twenty-eight feet of copper wire were made up into a helix, and being used gave a good spark on disjunction at the electromotor; being then suddenly pulled out and again employed, it gave a much smaller spark than before, although nothing

but its spiral arrangement had been changed.

1066. As the superiority of a helix over a wire is important to the philosophy of the effect, I took particular pains to ascertain the fact with certainty. A wire of copper sixty-seven feet long was bent in the middle so as to form a double termination which could be communicated with the electromotor; one of the halves of this wire was made into a helix and the other remained in its extended condition. When these were used alternately as the connecting wire, the helix half gave by much the strongest spark. It even gave a stronger spark than when it and the extended wire were used conjointly as a double conductor.

1067. When a *short wire* is used, *all* these effects disappear. If it be only two or three inches long, a spark can scarcely be perceived on breaking the junction. If it be ten or twelve inches long and moderately thick, a small spark may be more easily obtained. As the length is increased, the spark becomes proportionately brighter, until from extreme length the resistance offered by the metal as a conductor begins to interfere with the principal result.

1068. The effect of elongation was well shown thus: 114 feet of copper wire, one-eighteenth of an inch in diameter, were extended on the floor and used as a conductor; it remained cold, but gave a bright spark on breaking contact. Being crossed so that the two terminations were in contact near the extremities, it was again used as a conductor, only twelve inches now being included in the circuit: the wire became very hot from the greater quantity of electricity passing through it, and yet the spark on breaking contact was scarcely visible. The experiment was repeated with a wire one-ninth of an inch in diameter and thirty-six feet long with the same results.

1069. That the effects, and also the action, in all these forms of the experiment are identical, is evident from the manner in which the former can be gradually raised from that produced by the shortest wire to that of the most powerful electro-magnet: and this capability of examining what will happen by the most powerful apparatus, and then experimenting for the same results, or reasoning from them, with the weaker arrangements, is of great advantage in making out the true principles of the phenomena.

1070. The action is evidently dependent upon the wire which serves as a conductor; for it varies as that wire varies in its length or arrangement. The shortest wire may be considered as exhibiting the full effect of spark or shock which the electromotor can produce by its own direct power: all the additional force which the arrangements described can excite being due to some affection of the current, either permanent or momentary, in the wire itself. That it is a *momentary* effect, produced only at the instant of breaking contact, will be fully proved (1089, 1100).

1071. No change takes place in the quantity or intensity of the current during the time the latter is *continued*, from the moment after contact is made, up to that previous to disunion, except what depends upon the increased obstruction offered to the passage of the electricity by a long wire as compared to a short wire. To ascertain this point with regard to *quantity*, the helix i (1053) and the galvanometer (1058) were both made parts of the metallic circuit used to connect the plates of a small electromotor, and the deflection at the galvanometer was observed; then a soft iron core was put into the helix, and as soon as the momentary effect was over, and the needle had become stationary, it was again observed, and found to stand exactly at the same division as before. Thus the quantity passing through the wire when the current was continued was the same either with or without the soft iron, although the peculiar effects occurring at the moment of disjunction were very different in degree under such variation of circumstances.

1072. That the quality of *intensity* belonging to the constant current did not vary with the circumstances favouring the peculiar results under consideration, so as to yield an explanation of those results, was ascertained in the following manner. The current excited by an electromotor was passed through short wires, and its intensity tried by subjecting different substances to its electrolyzing power (912, 966, &c.); it was then passed through the wires of the powerful electro-magnet (1056), and again examined with respect to its intensity by the same means and found unchanged. Again, the constancy of the *quantity* passed in the above experiment (1071) adds further proof that the intensity could not have varied; for had it been increased upon the introduction of the soft iron, there is every reason to believe that the quantity passed in a given time would also have increased.

1073. The fact is, that under many variations of the experiments, the permanent current *loses* in force as the effects upon breaking contact become *exalted*. This is abundantly evident in the comparative experiments with long and short wires (1068); and is still more strikingly shown by the following variation. Solder an inch or two in length of fine platina wire (about one-hundredth of an inch in diameter) on to one end of the long communicating wire, and also a similar length of the same platina wire on to one end of the short communication; then, in comparing the effects of these two communications, make and break contact between the platina terminations and the mercury of the cup G or E (1079). When the short wire is used, the platina will be *ignited by the constant current*, because of the quantity of electricity, but the spark on breaking contact will be hardly visible; on using the longer communicating wire, which by obstructing will diminish the current, the platina will remain cold whilst the current passes, but give a bright spark at the moment it ceases: thus the strange result is obtained of a diminished spark and shock from the strong current, and increased effects from the weak one. Hence the spark and shock at the moment of disjunction, although resulting from great intensity and quantity of the current *at that moment*, are no direct indicators or measurers of the intensity or quantity of the constant current previously passing, and by which they are ultimately produced.

1074. It is highly important in using the spark as an indication, by its relative brightness, of these effects, to bear in mind certain circumstances connected with its production and appearance (958). An ordinary electric spark is understood to be the bright appearance of electricity passing suddenly through an interval of air, or other badly conducting matter. A voltaic spark is sometimes of the same nature, but, generally, is due to the ignition and even combustion of a minute portion of a good conductor; and that is especially the case when the electromotor consists of but one or few pairs of plates. This can be very well observed if either or both of the metallic surfaces intended to touch be solid and pointed. The moment they come in contact the current passes; it heats, ignites, and even burns the touching points, and the appearance is as if the spark passed on making contact, whereas it is only a case of ignition by the current, contact being previously made, and is perfectly analogous to the ignition of a fine platina wire connecting the extremities of a voltaic battery.

1075. When mercury constitutes one or both of the surfaces used, the brightness of the spark is greatly increased. But as this effect is due to the action on, and probable combustion of, the metal, such sparks must only be compared with other sparks also taken from mercurial surfaces, and not with such as may be taken, for instance, between surfaces of platina or gold, for then the appearances are far less bright, though the same quantity of electricity be passed. It is not at all unlikely that the commonly occurring circumstance of combustion may affect even the duration of the light; and that sparks taken between mercury, copper, or other combustible bodies, will continue for a period sensibly longer than those passing between platina or gold.

1076. When the end of a short clean copper wire, attached to one plate of an electromotor, is brought down carefully upon a surface of mercury connected with the other plate, a spark, almost continuous, can be obtained. This I refer to a succession of effects of the following nature: first, contact—then ignition of the touching points—recession of the mercury from the mechanical results of the heat produced at the place of contact, and the electromagnetic condition of the parts at the moment[1] —breaking of the contact and the production of the peculiar intense effect dependent thereon—renewal of the contact by the returning surface of the undulating mercury—and then a repetition of the same series of effects, and that with such rapidity as to present the appearance of a continued discharge. If a long wire or an electro-magnet be used as the connecting conductor instead of a short wire, a similar appearance may be produced by tapping the vessel containing the mercury and making it vibrate; but the sparks do not usually follow each other so rapidly as to produce an apparently continuous spark, because of the time required, when the long wire or electro-magnet is used, both for the full development of the current (1101, 1106) and for its complete cessation.

1077. Returning to the phenomena in question, the first thought that arises in the mind is that the electricity circulates with something like *momentum or inertia* in the wire, and that thus a long wire produces effects at the instant the current is stopped, which a short wire cannot produce. Such an explanation is, however, at once set aside by the fact that the same length of wire produces the effects in very different degrees, according as it is simply extended, or made into a helix, or forms the cir-

cuit of an electro-magnet (1069). The experiments to be adduced (1089) will still more strikingly show that the idea of momentum cannot apply.

1078. The bright spark at the electromotor, and the shock in the arms, appeared evidently to be due to *one* current in the long wire, divided into two parts by the double channel afforded through the body and through the electromotor; for that the spark was evolved at the place of disjunction with the electromotor, not by any direct action of the latter, but by a force immediately exerted in the wire of communication, seemed to be without doubt (1070). It followed, therefore, that by using a better conductor in place of the human body, the *whole* of this extra current might be made to pass at that place: and thus be separated from that which the electromotor could produce by its immediate action, and its *direction* be examined apart from any interference of the original and originating current. This was found to be true; for on connecting the ends of the principal wire together by a cross-wire two or three feet in length, applied just where the hands had felt the shock, the whole of the extra current passed by the new channel, and then no better spark than one producible by a short wire was obtained on disjunction at the electromotor.

1079. The *current* thus separated was examined by galvanometers and decomposing apparatus introduced into the course of this wire. I will always speak of it as the current in the cross-wire or wires, so that no mistake, as to its place or origin, may occur. In the wood-cut, Z and C represent the zinc and copper plates of the electromotor; G and E the cups of mercury

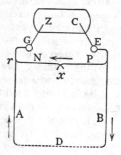

where contact is made or broken (1052); A and B the terminations of D, the long wire, the helix or the electro-magnet, used to complete the circuit; N and P are the cross-wires, which can either be brought into contact at *x*, or else have a galvanometer (1058) or an electrolyzing apparatus (312, 316) interposed there.

The production of the *shock* from the current in the cross-wire, whether D was a long extended wire, or a helix, or an electro-magnet, has been already described (1060, 1061, 1064).

1080. The *spark* of the cross-wire current could be produced at *x* in the following manner: D was made an electro-magnet; the metallic extremities at x were held close together, or rubbed lightly against each other, whilst contact was broken at G or E. When the communication was perfect at x, little or no spark appeared at G or E. When the condition of vicinity at x was favourable for the result required, a bright spark would pass there at the moment of disjunction, *none* occurring at G and E: this spark was the luminous passage of the extra current through the cross-wires. When there was no contact or passage of current at x, then the spark appeared at G or E, the extra current forcing its way through the electromotor itself. The same results were obtained by the use of the helix or the extended wire at D in place of the electro-magnet.

1081. On introducing a fine platina wire at x, and employing the electro-magnet at D, no visible effects occurred as long as contact was continued; but on breaking contact at G or E, the fine wire was instantly ignited and fused. A longer or thicker wire could be so adjusted at x as to show ignition, without fusion, every time the contact was broken at G or E.

1082. It is rather difficult to obtain this effect with helices or wires, and for very simple reasons: with the helices i, ii, or iii, there was such retardation of the electric current, from the length of wire used, that a full inch of platina wire one-fiftieth of an inch in diameter could be retained ignited at the cross-wires during the *continuance of contact*, by the portion of electricity passing through it. Hence it was impossible to distinguish the particular effects at the moments of making or breaking contact from this constant effect. On using the thick wire helix (1055), the same results ensued.

1083. Proceeding upon the known fact that electric currents of great quantity but low intensity, though able to ignite thick wires, cannot produce that effect upon thin ones, I used a very fine platina wire at x, reducing its diameter until a spark appeared at G or E, when contact was broken there. A quarter of an inch of such wire might be introduced at x without being ignited by the *continuance* of contact at G or E; but when contact was broken at either place, this wire became red-hot: proving, by this method, the production of the induced current at that moment.

1084. *Chemical decomposition* was next effected by the cross-wire current, an electro-magnet being used at D, and a decomposing apparatus, with solution of iodide of potassium in paper (1079), employed at x. The con-

ducting power of the connecting system A B D was sufficient to carry all the primary current, and consequently no chemical action took place at x during the *continuance* of contact at G and E; but when contact was broken, there was instantly decomposition at x. The iodine appeared against the wire N, and not against the wire P; thus demonstrating that the current through the cross-wires, when contact was broken, was in the *reverse direction* to that marked by the arrow, or that which the electromotor would have sent through it.

1085. In this experiment a bright spark occurs at the place of disjunction, indicating that only a small part of the extra current passed the apparatus at x, because of the small conducting power of the latter.

1086. I found it difficult to obtain the chemical effects with the simple helices and wires, in consequence of the diminished inductive power of these arrangements, and because of the passage of a strong constant current at x whenever a very active electromotor was used (1082).

1087. The most instructive set of results was obtained, however, when the *galvanometer* was introduced at x. Using an electro-magnet at D, and continuing contact, a current was then indicated by the deflection, proceeding from P to N, in the direction of the arrow; the cross-wire serving to carry one part of the electricity excited by the electromotor, and that part of the arrangement marked A B D, the other and far greater part, as indicated by the arrows. The magnetic needle was then forced back, by pins applied upon opposite sides of its two extremities, to its natural position when uninfluenced by a current; after which, contact being *broken* at G or E, it was deflected strongly in the opposite direction; thus showing, in accordance with the chemical effects (1084), that the extra current followed a course in the cross-wires *contrary* to that indicated by the arrow, i.e., contrary to the one produced by the direct action of the electromotor.[1]

1088. With the *helix* only (1061), these effects could scarcely be observed, in consequence of the smaller inductive force of this arrangement, the opposed action from induction in the galvanometer wire itself, the mechanical condition and tension of the needle from the effect

---

[1] It was ascertained experimentally, that if a strong current was passed through the galvanometer only, and the needle restrained in one direction as above in its natural position, when the current was stopped, no vibration of the needle in the opposite direction took place.

of blocking (1087) whilst the current due to continuance of contact was passing round it; and because of other causes. With the *extended wire* (1064) all these circumstances had still greater influence, and therefore allowed less chance of success.

1089. These experiments, establishing as they did, by the quantity, intensity, and even direction, a distinction between the primary or generating current and the extra current, led me to conclude that the latter was identical with the induced current described (6, 26, 74) in the first series of these *Researches*; and this opinion I was soon able to bring to proof, and at the same times obtained not the partial (1078) but entire separation of one current from the other.

1090. The double helix (1053) was arranged so that it should form the connecting wire between the plates of the electromotor, ii being out of the current, and its ends unconnected. In this condition i acted very well, and gave a good spark at the time and place of disjunction. The opposite ends of ii were then connected together so as to form an endless wire, i remaining unchanged: but now *no spark*, or one scarcely sensible, could be obtained from the latter at the place of disjunction. Then, again, the ends of ii were held so nearly together that any current running round that helix should be rendered visible as a spark: and in this manner a spark was obtained from ii when the junction of i with the electromotor was broken, in place of appearing at the disjoined extremity of i itself.

1091. By introducing a galvanometer or decomposing apparatus into the circuit formed by the helix ii, I could easily obtain the deflections and decomposition occasioned by the induced current due to the breaking contact at helix i, or even to that occasioned by making contact of that helix with the electromotor; the results in both cases indicating the contrary directions of the two induced currents thus produced (26).

1092. All these effects, except those of decomposition, were reproduced by two extended long wires, not having the form of helices, but placed close to each other; and thus it was proved that the *extra current* could be removed from the wire carrying the original current to a neighbouring wire, and was at the same time identified, in direction and every other respect, with the currents producible by induction (1089). The case, therefore, of the bright spark and shock on disjunction may now be stated thus: if a current be established in a wire, and

another wire, forming a complete circuit, be placed parallel to the first, at the moment the current in the first is stopped it induces a current in the *same* direction in the second, the first exhibiting then but a feeble spark; but if the second wire be away, disjunction of the first wire induces a current in itself in the same direction, producing a strong spark. The strong spark in the single long wire or helix, at the moment of disjunction, is therefore the equivalent of the current which would be produced in a neighbouring wire if such second current were permitted.

1093. Viewing the phenomena as the results of the induction of electrical currents, many of the principles of action, in the former experiments, become far more evident and precise. Thus the different effects of short wires, long wires, helices, and electro-magnets (1069) may be comprehended. If the inductive action of a wire a foot long upon a collateral wire also a foot in length be observed, it will be found very small; but if the same current be sent through a wire fifty feet long, it will induce in a neighbouring wire of fifty feet a far more powerful current at the moment of making or breaking contact, each successive foot of wire adding to the sum of action; and by parity of reasoning, a similar effect should take place when the conducting wire is also that in which the induced current is formed (74): hence the reason why a long wire gives a brighter spark on breaking contact than a short one (1068), although it carries much less electricity.

1094. If the long wire be made into a helix, it will then be still more effective in producing sparks and shocks on breaking contact; for by the mutual inductive action of the convolutions each aids its neighbour, and will be aided in turn, and the sum of effect will be very greatly increased.

1095. If an electro-magnet be employed, the effect will be still more highly exalted; because the iron, magnetized by the power of the continuing current, will lose its magnetism at the moment the current ceases to pass, and in so doing will tend to produce an electric current in the wire around it (37, 38), in conformity with that which the cessation of current in the helix itself also tends to produce.

1096. By applying the laws of the induction of electric currents formerly developed (6, &c.), various new conditions of the experiments could be devised, which by their results should serve as tests of the accuracy of the view just given. Thus, if a long wire be doubled, so that the current in the two halves shall have opposite actions, it ought not to give a sensible spark at the moment of disjunction: and this proved to be the case, for a wire forty feet long, covered with silk, being doubled and tied closely together to within four inches of the extremities, when used in that state, gave scarcely a perceptible spark; but being opened out and the parts separated, it gave a very good one. The two helices i and ii being joined at their similar ends, and then used at their other extremities to connect the plates of the electromotor, thus constituted one long helix, of which one half was opposed in direction to the other half: under these circumstances it gave scarcely a sensible spark, even when the soft iron core was within, although containing nearly two hundred feet of wire. When it was made into one consistent helix of the same length of wire it gave a very bright spark.

1007. Similar proofs can be drawn from the mutual inductive action of two separate currents (1110); and it is important for the general principles that the consistent action of two such currents should be established. Thus, two currents going in the same direction should, if simultaneously stopped, aid each other by their relative influence; or if proceeding in contrary directions, should oppose each other under similar circumstances. I endeavoured at first to obtain two currents from two different electromotors, and passing them through the helices i and ii, tried to effect the disjunctions mechanically at the same moment. But in this I could not succeed: one was always separated before the other, and in that case produced little or no spark, its inductive power being employed in throwing a current round the remaining complete circuit (1090): the current which was stopped last always gave a bright spark. If it were ever to become needful to ascertain whether two junctions were accurately broken at the same moment, these sparks would afford a test for the purpose, having an infinitesimal degree of perfection.

1098. I was able to prove the points by other expedients. Two short thick wires were selected to serve as terminations, by which contact could be made or broken with the electromotor. The compound helix, consisting of i and ii (1053), was adjusted so that the extremities of the two helices could be placed in communication with the two terminal wires, in such a manner that the current moving through the thick wires should be divided into two equal portions in the two helices, these portions travelling, according to the mode of connexion, either in the same direction or in contrary directions at pleasure. In this manner two streams could be obtained, both of which could be stopped simultaneously, because the disjunction could be broken at G or F by removing a single wire. When the helices were in contrary directions, there was scarcely a sensible spark at the place of disjunction; but when they were in accordance there was a very bright one.

1099. The helix i was now used constantly, being sometimes associated, as above, with helix ii in an according direction, and sometimes with helix iii, which was placed at a little distance. The association i and ii, which presented two currents able to affect each other by induction, because of their vicinity, gave a brighter spark than the association i and iii, where the two streams could not exert their mutual influence; but the difference was not so great as I expected.

1100. Thus all the phenomena tend to prove that the effects are due to an inductive action, occurring at the moment when the principal current is stopped. I at one time thought they were due to an action continued during the *whole time* of the current, and expected that a steel magnet would have an influence according to its position in the helix, comparable to that of a soft iron bar, in assisting the effect. This, however, is not the case; for hard steel, or a magnet in the helix, is not so effectual as soft iron; nor does it make any difference how the magnet is placed in the helix, and for very simple reasons, namely, that the effect does not depend upon a permanent state of the core, but a *change of state*; and that the magnet or hard steel cannot sink through such a difference of state as soft iron, at the moment contact ceases, and therefore cannot produce an equal effect in generating a current of electricity by induction (34, 37).

1101. As an electric current acts by induction with equal energy at the moment of its commencement as at the moment of its cessation (10, 26), but in a contrary direction, the reference of the effects under examination to an inductive action would lead to the conclusion that corresponding effects of an opposite nature must occur in a long wire, a helix, or an electro-magnet, every time that *contact is made* with the electromotor. These effects will tend to establish a resistance for the first moment in the long conductor, producing a result equivalent to the reverse of a shock or a spark. Now it is very difficult to devise means fit for the recognition of such negative results; but as it is probable that some positive effect is produced at the time, if we knew what to expect, I think the few facts bearing upon this subject with which I am acquainted are worth recording.

1102. The electro-magnet was arranged with an electrolyzing apparatus at x, as before described (1084), except that the intensity of the chemical action at the electromotor was increased until the electric current was just able to produce the feeblest signs of decomposition whilst contact was continued at G and E (1079) (the iodine of course appearing against the end of the cross-wire P); the wire N was also separated from A at r, so that contact there could be made or broken at pleasure. Under these circumstances the following set of actions was repeated several times: contact was broken at r, then broken at G, next made at r, and lastly renewed at G; thus any current from N to P due to *breaking* of contact was avoided, but any additional force to the current from P to N due to *making* contact could be observed. In this way it was found that a much greater decomposing effect (causing the evolution of iodine against P) could be obtained by a few completions of contact than by the current which could pass in a much longer time if the contact was *continued*. This I attribute to the act of induction in the wire A B D at the moment of contact rendering that wire a worse conductor, or rather retarding the passage of the electricity through it for the instant, and so throwing a greater quantity of the electricity which the electromotor could produce through the cross-wire passage N P. The instant the induction ceased, A B D resumed its full power of carrying a constant current of electricity, and could have it highly increased, as we know by the former experiments (1060) by the opposite inductive action brought into activity at the moment contact at Z or C was *broken*.

1103. A galvanometer was then introduced at x, and the deflection of the needle noted whilst contact was continued at G and E: the needle was then blocked as before in one direction (1087), so that it should not return when the current ceased, but remain in the position in which the current could retain it. Contact at G or E was broken, producing of course no visible effect; it was then renewed, and the needle was instantly deflected, passing from the blocking pins to a position still farther from its natural place than that which the constant current

could give, and thus showing, by the temporary excess of current in this cross communication, the temporary retardation in the circuit A B D.

1104. On adjusting a platina wire at x (1081) so that it should not be ignited by the current passing through it whilst contact at G and E was *continued*, and yet become red-hot by a current somewhat more powerful, I was readily able to produce its ignition upon *making contact*, and again upon *breaking contact*. Thus the momentary retardation in A B D on making contact was again shown by this result, as well also as the opposite result upon breaking contact. The two ignitions of the wire at x were of course produced by electric currents moving in opposite directions.

1105. Using the *helix* only, I could not obtain distinct deflections at x, due to the extra effect on making contact, for the reasons already mentioned (1088). By using a very fine platina wire there (1083), I did succeed in obtaining the igniting effect for making contact in the same manner, though by no means to the same degree, as with the electro-magnet (1104).

1106. We may also consider and estimate the effect on *making contact*, by transferring the force of induction from the wire carrying the original current to a lateral wire, as in the cases described (1090); and we then are sure, both by the chemical and galvanometrical results (1091), that the forces upon making and breaking contact, like action and reaction, are equal in their strength but contrary in their direction. If, therefore, the effect on making contact resolves itself into a mere retardation of the current at the first moment of its existence, it must be, in its degree, equivalent to the high exaltation of that same current at the moment contact is broken.

1107. Thus the case, under the circumstances, is that the intensity and quantity of electricity moving in a current are smaller when the current commences or is increased, and greater when it diminishes or ceases, than they would be if the inductive action occurring at these moments did not take place; or than they are in the original current wire if the inductive action be transferred from that wire to a collateral one (1090).

1108. From the facility of transference to neighbouring wires, and from the effects generally, the inductive forces appear to be lateral, i.e., exerted in a direction perpendicular to the direction of the originating and produced currents: and they also appear to be accurately represented by the magnetic curves, and closely related to, if not identical with, magnetic forces.

1109. There can be no doubt that the current in one part of a wire can act by induction upon other parts of the *same* wire which are lateral to the first, i.e., in the same vertical section (74), or in the parts which are more or less oblique to it (1112), just as it can act in producing a current in a neighbouring wire or in a neighbouring coil of the same wire. It is this which gives the appearance of the current acting upon itself: but all the experiments and all analogy tend to show that the elements (if I may so say) of the currents do not act upon themselves, and so cause the effect in question, but produce it by exciting currents in conducting matter which is lateral to them.

1110. It is possible that some of the expressions I have used may seem to imply that the inductive action is essentially the action of one current upon another, or of one element of a current upon another element of the same current. To avoid any such conclusion I must explain more distinctly my meaning. If an endless wire be taken, we have the means of generating a current in it which shall run round the circuit without adding any electricity to what was previously in the wire. As far as we can judge, the electricity which appears as a current is the same as that which before was quiescent in the wire; and though we cannot as yet point out the essential condition of difference of the electricity at such times, we can easily recognize the two states. Now when a current acts by induction upon conducting matter lateral to it, it probably acts upon the electricity in that conducting matter whether it be in the form of a current or quiescent, in the one case increasing or diminishing the current according to its direction, in the other producing a current, and the *amount* of the inductive action is probably the same in both cases. Hence, to say that the action of induction depended upon the mutual relation of two or more currents would, according to the restricted sense in which the term current is understood at present (283, 517, 667) be an error.

1111. Several of the effects, as, for instances, those with helices (1066), with according or counter currents (1097, 1098), and those on the production of lateral currents (1090), appeared to indicate that a current could produce an effect of induction in a neighbouring wire more readily than in its own carrying wire, in which

case it might be expected that some variation of result would be produced if a bundle of wires were used as a conductor instead of a single wire. In consequence the following experiments were made. A copper wire one twenty-third of an inch in diameter was cut into lengths of five feet each, and six of these being laid side by side in one bundle, had their opposite extremities soldered to two terminal pieces of copper. This arrangement could be used as a discharging wire, but the general current could be divided into six parallel streams, which might be brought close together, or, by the separation of the wires, be taken more or less out of each other's influence. A somewhat brighter spark was, I think, obtained on breaking contact when the six wires were close together than when held asunder.

1112. Another bundle, containing twenty of these wires, was eighteen feet long: the terminal pieces were one-fifth of an inch in diameter, and each six inches long. This was compared with nineteen feet in length of copper wire one-fifth of an inch in diameter. The bundle gave a smaller spark on breaking contact than the latter, even when its strands were held together by string: when they were separated, it gave a still smaller spark. Upon the whole, however, the diminution of effect was not such as I expected: and I doubt whether the results can be considered as any proof of the truth of the supposition which gave rise to them.

1113. The inductive force by which two elements of one current (1109, 1110) act upon each other appears to diminish as the line joining them becomes oblique to the direction of the current and to vanish entirely when it is parallel. I am led by some results to suspect that it then even passes into the repulsive force noticed by Ampère,[1] which is the cause of the elevations in mercury described by Sir Humphry Davy,[2] and which again is probably directly connected with the quality of intensity.

1114. Notwithstanding that the effects appear only at the making and breaking of contact (the current remaining unaffected, seemingly, in the interval), I cannot resist the impression that there is some connected and correspondent effect produced by this lateral action of the elements of the electric stream during the time of its continuance (60, 242). An action of this kind, in fact, is evident in the magnetic relations of the parts of the current. But admitting (as we may do for the moment)

---

[1] *Recueil d'Observations Electro-Dynamiques*, p. 285.
[2] *Philosophical Transactions*, 1823, p. 155.

the magnetic forces to constitute the power which produces such striking and different results at the commencement and termination of a current, still there appears to be a link in the chain of effects, a wheel in the physical mechanism of the action, as yet unrecognised. If we endeavour to consider electricity and magnetism as the results of two forces of a physical agent, or a peculiar condition of matter, exerted in determinate directions perpendicular to each other, then, it appears to me, that we must consider these two states or forces as convertible into each other in a greater or smaller degree; i.e., that an element of an electric current has not a determinate electric force and a determinate magnetic force constantly existing in the same ratio, but that the two forces are, to a certain degree, convertible by a process or change of condition at present unknown to us. How else can a current of a given intensity and quantity be able, by its direct action, to sustain a state which, when allowed to react, (at the cessation of the original current) shall produce a second current, having an intensity and quantity far greater than the generating one? This cannot result from a direct reaction of the electric force; and if it result from a change of electrical into magnetic force, and a reconversion back again, it will show that they differ in something more than mere direction, as regards *that agent* in the conducting wire which constitutes their immediate cause.

1115. With reference to the appearance, at different times, of the contrary effects produced by the making and breaking contact, and their separation by an intermediate and indifferent state, this separation is probably more apparent than real. If the conduction of electricity be effected by vibrations (283), or by any other mode in which opposite forces are successively and rapidly excited and neutralized, then we might expect a peculiar and contrary development of force at the commencement and termination of the periods during which the conducting action should last (somewhat in analogy with the colours produced at the outside of an imperfectly developed solar spectrum): and the intermediate actions, although not sensible in the same way, may be very important and, for instance, perhaps constitute the very essence of conductibility. It is by views and reasons such as these, which seem to me connected with the fundamental laws and facts of electrical science, that I have been induced to

enter, more minutely than I otherwise should have done, into the experimental examination of the phenomena described in this paper.

1116. Before concluding, I may briefly remark that on using a voltaic battery of fifty pairs of plates instead of a single pair (1052), the effects were exactly of the same kind. The spark on making contact, for the reasons before given, was very small (1101, 1107); that on breaking contact, very excellent and brilliant. The *continuous* discharge did not seem altered in character, whether a short wire or the powerful electro-magnet were used as a connecting discharger.

1117. The effects produced at the commencement and end of a current (which are separated by an interval of time when that current is supplied from a voltaic apparatus) must occur at the same moment when a common electric discharge is passed through a long wire. Whether, if happening accurately at the same moment, they would entirely neutralize each other, or whether they would not still give some definite peculiarity to the discharge, is a matter remaining to be examined; but it is very probable that the peculiar character and pungency of sparks drawn from a long wire depend in part upon the increased intensity given at the termination of the discharge by the inductive action then occurring.

1118. In the wire of the helix of magneto-electric machines (as, for instance, in Mr. Saxton's beautiful arrangement), an important influence of these principles of action is evidently shown. From the construction of the apparatus the current is permitted to move in a complete metallic circuit of great length during the first instants of its formation: it gradually rises in strength, and is then suddenly stopped by the breaking of the metallic circuit; and thus great intensity is given *by induction* to the electricity, which at that moment passes (1060, 1064). This intensity is not only shown by the brilliancy of the spark and the strength of the shock, but also by the necessity which has been experienced of well-insulating the convolutions of the helix, in which the current is formed: and it gives to the current a force at these moments very far above that which the apparatus could produce if the principle which forms the subject of this paper were not called into play.

Royal Institution, December 8, 1834

TENTH SERIES

§ 16. *On an Improved Form of the Voltaic Battery* § 17. *Some Practical Results Respecting the Construction and Use of the Voltaic Battery*

RECEIVED JUNE 16, READ JUNE 18, 1835

1119. I HAVE lately had occasion to examine the voltaic trough practically, with a view to improvements in its construction and use; and though I do not pretend that the results have anything like the importance which attaches to the discovery of a new law or principle, I still think they are valuable, and may therefore, if briefly told, and in connexion with former papers, be worthy the approbation of the Royal Society.

§ 16. *On an Improved Form of the Voltaic Battery*

1120. In a simple voltaic circuit (and the same is true of the battery) the chemical forces which, during their activity, give power to the instrument, are generally divided into two portions; one of these is exerted locally, whilst the other is transferred round the circle (947, 996); the latter constitutes the electric current of the instrument, whilst the former is altogether lost or wasted. The ratio of these two portions of power may be varied to a great extent by the influence of circumstances: thus, in a battery not closed, *all* the action is local; in one of the ordinary construction, *much* is in circulation when the extremities are in communication: and in the perfect one, which I have described (1001), *all* the chemical power circulates and becomes electricity. By referring to the quantity of zinc dissolved from the plates (865, 1126), and the quantity of decomposition effected in the volta-electrometer (711, 1126) or elsewhere, the proportions of the local and transferred actions under any particular circumstances can be ascertained, and the efficacy of the voltaic arrangement, or the waste of chemical power at its zinc plates, be accurately determined.

1121. If a voltaic battery were constructed of zinc and platina, the latter metal surrounding the former, as in the double copper arrangement, and the whole being excited by dilute sulphuric acid, then no insulating divisions of glass, porcelain or air would be required between the contiguous platina surfaces; and,

provided these did not touch metallically, the same acid which, being between the zinc and platina, would excite the battery into powerful action, would, between the two surfaces of platina, produce no discharge of the electricity, nor cause any diminution of the power of the trough. This is a necessary consequence of the resistance to the passage of the current which I have shown occurs at the place of decomposition (1007, 1011); for that resistance is fully able to stop the current, and therefore acts as insulation to the electricity of the contiguous plates, inasmuch as the current which tends to pass between them never has a higher intensity than that due to the action of a single pair.

1122. If the metal surrounding the zinc be copper (1045), and if the acid be nitro-sulphuric acid (1020), then a slight discharge between the two contiguous coppers does take place, provided there be no other channel open by which the forces may circulate; but when such a channel is permitted, the return or back discharge of which I speak is exceedingly diminished, in accordance with the principles laid down in the Eighth Series of these *Researches*.

1123. Guided by these principles I was led to the construction of a voltaic trough, in which the coppers, passing round both surfaces of the zincs, as in Wollaston's construction, should not be separated from each other except by an intervening thickness of paper, or in some other way, so as to prevent metallic contact, and should thus constitute an instrument compact, powerful, economical, and easy of use. On examining, however, what had been done before, I found that the new trough was in all essential respects the same as that invented and described by Dr. Hare, Professor in the University of Pennsylvania, to whom I have great pleasure in referring it.

1124. Dr. Hare has fully described his trough.[1]

---

[1] *Philosophical Magazine*, 1824, Vol. LXIII, p. 241; or *Silliman's Journal*, Vol. VII. See also a previous paper by Dr. Hare, *Annals of Philosophy*, 1821, Vol. I, p. 329, in which he speaks of the nonnecessity of insulation between the coppers.

In it the contiguous copper plates are separated by thin veneers of wood, and the acid is poured on to, or off, the plates by a quarter revolution of an axis, to which both the trough containing the plates, and another trough to collect and hold the liquid, are fixed. This arrangement I have found the most convenient of any, and have therefore adopted it. My zinc plates were cut from rolled metal, and when soldered to the copper plates had the form delineated, *Fig. 1*. These were then bent over a

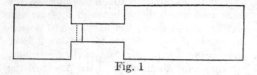

Fig. 1

gauge into the form *Fig. 2*, and when packed in the wooden box constructed to receive them, were arranged as in *Fig. 3*,[1] little plugs of cork

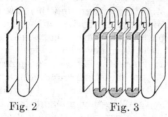

Fig. 2   Fig. 3

being used to keep the zinc plates from touching the copper plates, and a single or double thickness of cartridge paper being interposed between the contiguous surfaces of copper to prevent them from coming in contact. Such was the facility afforded by this arrangement, that a trough of forty pairs of plates could be unpacked in five minutes, and repacked again in half an hour; and the whole series was not more than fifteen inches in length.

1125. This trough, of forty pairs of plates three inches square, was compared, as to the ignition of a platina wire, the discharge between points of charcoal, the shock on the human frame, &c., with forty pairs of four-inch plates having double coppers, and used in porcelain troughs divided into insulating cells, the strength of the acid employed to excite both being the same. In all these effects the former appeared quite equal to the latter. On comparing a second trough of the new construction, containing twenty pairs of four-inch plates, with twenty pairs of four-inch plates in porcelain troughs, excited by acid of the same strength,

the new trough appeared to surpass the old one in producing these effects, especially in the ignition of wire.

1126. In these experiments the new trough diminished in its energy much more rapidly than the one on the old construction, and this was a necessary consequence of the smaller quantity of acid used to excite it, which in the case of the forty pairs of new construction was only one-seventh part of that used for the forty pairs in the porcelain troughs. To compare, therefore, both forms of the voltaic trough in their decomposing powers, and to obtain accurate data as to their relative values, experiments of the following kind were made. The troughs were charged with a known quantity of acid of a known strength; the electric current was passed through a volta-electrometer (711) having electrodes 4 inches long and 2.3 inches in width, so as to oppose as little obstruction as possible to the current; the gases evolved were collected and measured, and gave the quantity of water decomposed. Then the whole of the charge used was mixed together, and a known part of it analysed, by being precipitated and boiled with excess of carbonate of soda, and the precipitate well-washed, dried, ignited, and weighed. In this way the quantity of metal oxidized and dissolved by the acid was ascertained; and the part removed from each zinc plate, or from all the plates, could be estimated and compared with the water decomposed in the volta-electrometer. To bring these to one standard of comparison, I have reduced the results so as to express the loss at the plates in equivalents of zinc for the equivalent of water decomposed at the volta-electrometer: I have taken the equivalent number of water as 9, and of zinc as 32.5, and have considered 100 cubic inches of the mixed oxygen and hydrogen, as they were collected over a pneumatic trough, to result from the decomposition of 12.68 grains of water.

1127. The acids used in these experiments were three: sulphuric, nitric, and muriatic. The sulphuric acid was strong oil of vitriol; one cubical inch of it was equivalent to 486 grains of marble. The nitric acid was very nearly pure; one cubical inch dissolved 150 grains of marble. The muriatic acid was also nearly pure, and one cubical inch dissolved 108 grains of marble. These were always mixed with water by volumes, the standard of volume being a cubical inch.

1128. An acid was prepared consisting of 200 parts water, 4½ parts sulphuric acid, and 4

---

[1] The papers between the coppers are, for the sake of distinctness, omitted in the figure.

parts nitric acid; and with this both my trough containing forty pairs of three-inch plates, and four porcelain troughs, arranged in succession, each containing ten pairs of plates with double coppers four inches square, were charged. These two batteries were then used in succession, and the action of each was allowed to continue for twenty or thirty minutes, until the charge was nearly exhausted, the connexion with the volta-electrometer being carefully preserved during the whole time, and the acid in the troughs occasionally mixed together. In this way the former trough acted so well, that for each equivalent of water decomposed in the volta-electrometer only from 2 to 2.5 equivalents of zinc were dissolved from each plate. In four experiments the average was 2.21 equivalents for each plate, or 88.4 for the whole battery. In the experiments with the porcelain troughs, the equivalents of consumption at each plate were 3.54, or 141.6 for the whole battery. In a perfect voltaic battery of forty pairs of plates (991, 1001) the consumption would have been one equivalent for each zinc plate, or forty for the whole.

1129. Similar experiments were made with two voltaic batteries, one containing twenty pairs of four-inch plates, arranged as I have described (1124), and the other twenty pairs of four-inch plates in porcelain troughs. The average of five experiments with the former was a consumption of 3.7 equivalents of zinc from each plate, or 74 from the whole: the average of three experiments with the latter was 5.5 equivalents from each plate, or 110 from the whole: to obtain this conclusion two experiments were struck out, which were much against the porcelain troughs, and in which some unknown deteriorating influence was supposed to be accidentally active. In all the experiments, care was taken not to compare *new* and *old* plates together, as that would have introduced serious errors into the conclusions (1146).

1130. When ten pairs of the new arrangement were used, the consumption of zinc at each plate was 6.76 equivalents, or 67.6 for the whole. With ten pairs of the common construction, in a porcelain trough, the zinc oxidized was, upon an average, 15.5 equivalents for each plate, or 155 for the entire trough.

1131. No doubt, therefore, can remain of the equality or even the great superiority of this form of voltaic battery over the best previously in use, namely, that with double coppers, in which the cells are insulated. The insulation of the coppers may therefore be dispensed with; and it is that circumstance which principally permits of such other alterations in the construction of the trough as gives it its practical advantages.

1132. The advantages of this form of trough are very numerous and great. i. It is exceedingly compact, for 100 pairs of plates need not occupy a trough of more than three feet in length. ii. By Dr. Hare's plan of making the trough turn upon copper pivots which rest upon copper bearings, the latter afford *fixed* terminations; and these I have found it very convenient to connect with two cups of mercury, fastened in the front of the stand of the instrument. These fixed terminations give the great advantage of arranging an apparatus to be used in connexion with the battery *before* the latter is put into action. iii. The trough is put into readiness for use in an instant, a single jug of dilute acid being sufficient for the charge of 100 pairs of four-inch plates. iv. On making the trough pass through a quarter of a revolution, it becomes active, and the great advantage is obtained of procuring for the experiment the effect of the *first contact* of the zinc and acid, which is twice or sometimes even thrice that which the battery can produce a minute or two after (1036, 1150). v. When the experiment is completed, the acid can be at once poured from between the plates, so that the battery is never left to waste during an unconnected state of its extremities; the acid is not unnecessarily exhausted; the zinc is not uselessly consumed; and, besides avoiding these evils, the charge is mixed and rendered uniform, which produces a great and good result (1039); and, upon proceeding to a second experiment, the important effect of *first contact* is again obtained. vi. The saving of zinc is very great. It is not merely that, whilst in action, the zinc performs more voltaic duty (1128, 1129), but *all* the destruction which takes place with the ordinary forms of battery between the experiments is prevented. This saving is of such extent, that I estimate the zinc in the new form of battery to be thrice as effective as that in the ordinary form. vii. The importance of this saving of metal is not merely that the value of the zinc is saved, but that the battery is much lighter and more manageable; and also that the surfaces of the zinc and copper plates may be brought much nearer to each other when the battery is constructed, and remain so until it is worn out: the latter is a very important advantage (1148). viii. Again, as, in consequence of the saving, thinner plates will perform the duty of thick ones, rolled zinc may be used: and I have found rolled zinc superior to cast zinc in action; a superiority which I incline to attribute to its greater purity (1144). ix. Another advantage is obtained in the economy of the acid used, which is proportionate to the diminution of the zinc dissolved. x. The acid also is more easily exhausted, and is in such small quantity that there is never any occasion to return an old charge into use. The acid of old charges whilst out of use, often dissolves portions of copper from the black *flocculi* usually mingled with it, which are derived from the zinc; now any portion of copper in solution in the charge does great harm, because, by the *local* action of the acid and zinc, it tends to precipitate upon the latter, and diminish its voltaic efficacy (1145). xi. By using a due mixture of nitric and sulphuric acid for the charge (1139), no gas is evolved from the troughs; so that a battery of several hundred pairs of plates may, without inconvenience, be close to the experimenter. xii. If, during a series of experiments, the acid becomes exhausted, it can be withdrawn, and replaced by other acid with the utmost facility; and after the experiments are concluded, the great advantage of easily washing the plates is at command. And it appears to me that in place of making, under different circumstances, mutual sacrifices of comfort, power, and economy, to obtain a desired end, all are at once obtained by Dr. Hare's form of trough.

1133. But there are some disadvantages which I have not yet had time to overcome, though I trust they will finally be conquered. One is the extreme difficulty of making a wooden trough constantly water-tight under the alternations of wet and dry to which the voltaic instrument is subject. To remedy this evil, Mr. Newman is now engaged in obtaining porcelain troughs. The other disadvantage is a precipitation of copper on the zinc plates. It appears to me to depend mainly on the circumstance that the papers between the coppers retain acid when the trough is emptied; and that this acid slowly acting on the copper, forms a salt, which gradually mingles with the next charge, and is reduced on the zinc plate by the local action (1120): the power of the whole battery is then reduced. I expect that by using slips of glass or wood to separate the coppers at their edges, their contact can be sufficiently prevented, and the space between them be left so open that the acid of a charge can be poured and washed out, and so be removed from *every part* of the trough when the experiments in which the latter is used are completed.

1134. The actual superiority of the troughs which I have constructed on this plan, I believe to depend, first and principally, on the closer approximation of the zinc and copper surfaces; in my troughs they are only one-tenth of an inch apart (1148); and, next, on the superior quality of the rolled zinc above the cast zinc used in the construction of the ordinary pile. It cannot be that insulation between the contiguous coppers is a disadvantage, but I do not find that it is any advantage; for when, with both the forty pairs of three-inch plates and the twenty pairs of four-inch plates, I used papers well-soaked in wax,[1] these being so large that when folded at the edges they wrapped over each other, so as to make cells as insulating as those of the porcelain troughs, still no sensible advantage in the chemical action was obtained.

1135. As, upon principle, there must be a discharge of part of the electricity from the edges of the zinc and copper plates at the sides of the trough, I should prefer, and intend having, troughs constructed with a plate or plates of crown glass at the sides of the trough: the bottom will need none, though to glaze that and the ends would be no disadvantage. The plates need not be fastened in, but only set in their places; nor need they be in large single pieces.

§ 17. *Some Practical Results Respecting the Construction and Use of the Voltaic Battery* (1034 &c.)

1136. The electro-chemical philosopher is well acquainted with some practical results obtained from the voltaic battery by MM. Gay-Lussac and Thenard, and given in the first forty-five pages of their *Recherches Physico-Chimiques*. Although the following results are generally of the same nature, yet the advancement made in this branch of science of late years, the knowledge of the definite action of electricity, and the more accurate and philosophical mode of estimating the results by the equivalents of zinc consumed, will be their sufficient justification.

1137. *Nature and strength of the acid.* My battery of forty pairs of three-inch plates was charged with acid consisting of 200 parts water and 9 oil of vitriol. Each plate lost, in the average of the experiments, 4.66 equivalents of zinc for the equivalent of water decomposed in the volta-electrometer, or the whole battery

[1] A single paper thus prepared could insulate the electricity of a trough of forty pairs of plates.

186.4 equivalents of zinc. Being charged with a mixture of 200 water and 16 of the muriatic acid, each plate lost 3.8 equivalents of zinc for the water decomposed, or the whole battery 152 equivalents of zinc. Being charged with a mixture of 200 water and 8 nitric acid, each plate lost 1.85 equivalents of zinc for one equivalent of water decomposed, or the whole battery 74.16 equivalents of zinc. The sulphuric and muriatic acids evolved much hydrogen at the plates in the trough; the nitric acid no gas whatever. The relative strengths of the original acids have already been given (1127); but a difference in that respect makes no important difference in the results when thus expressed by equivalents (1140).

1138. Thus nitric acid proves to be the best for this purpose; its superiority appears to depend upon its favouring the electrolyzation of the liquid in the cells of the trough upon the principles already explained (905, 973, 1022), and consequently favouring the transmission of the electricity, and therefore the production of transferable power (1120).

1139. The addition of nitric acid might, consequently, be expected to improve sulphuric and muriatic acids. Accordingly, when the same trough was charged with a mixture of 200 water, 9 oil of vitriol, and 4 nitric acid, the consumption of zinc was at each plate 2.786, and for the whole battery 111.5, equivalents. When the charge was 200 water, 9 oil of vitriol, and 8 nitric acid, the loss per plate was 2.26, or for the whole battery 90.4 equivalents. When the trough was charged with a mixture of 200 water, 16 muriatic acid, and 6 nitric acid, the loss per plate was 2.11, or for the whole battery 84.4 equivalents. Similar results were obtained with my battery of twenty pairs of four-inch plates (1129). Hence it is evident that the nitric acid was of great service when mingled with the sulphuric acid; and the charge generally used after this time for ordinary experiments consisted of 200 water, 4½ oil of vitriol, and 4 nitric acid.

1140. It is not to be supposed that the different strengths of the acids produced the differences above; for within certain limits I found the electrolytic effects to be nearly as the strengths of the acids, so as to leave the expression of force, when given in equivalents, almost constant. Thus, when the trough was charged with a mixture of 200 water and 8 nitric acid, each plate lost 1.854 equivalent of zinc. When the charge was 200 water and 16 nitric acid, the loss per plate was 1.82 equiva-

lent. When it was 200 water and 32 nitric acid, the loss was 2.1 equivalents. The differences here are not greater than happen from unavoidable irregularities, depending on other causes than the strength of acid.

1141. Again, when a charge consisting of 200 water, 4½ oil of vitriol, and 4 nitric acid was used, each zinc plate lost 2.16 equivalents; when the charge with the same battery was 200 water, 9 oil of vitriol, and 8 nitric acid, each zinc plate lost 2.26 equivalents.

1142. I need hardly say that no copper is dissolved during the regular action of the voltaic trough. I have found that much ammonia is formed in the cells when nitric acid, either pure or mixed with sulphuric acid, is used. It is produced in part as a secondary result at the cathodes (663) of the different portions of fluid constituting the necessary electrolyte, in the cells.

1143. *Uniformity of the charge.* This is a most important point, as I have already shown experimentally (1042, &c.). Hence one great advantage of Dr. Hare's mechanical arrangement of his trough.

1144. *Purity of the zinc.* If pure zinc could be obtained, it would be very advantageous in the construction of the voltaic apparatus (998). Most zincs, when put into dilute sulphuric acid, leave more or less of an insoluble matter upon the surface in the form of a crust, which contains various metals, as copper, lead, zinc, iron, cadmium, &c., in the metallic state. Such particles, by discharging part of the transferable power, render it, as to the whole battery, local; and so diminish the effect. As an indication connected with the more or less perfect action of the battery, I may mention that no gas ought to rise from the zinc plates. The more gas which is generated upon these surfaces, the greater is the local action and the less the transferable force. The investing crust is also inconvenient, by preventing the displacement and renewal of the charge upon the surface of the zinc. Such zinc as, dissolving in the cleanest manner in a dilute acid, dissolves also the slowest, is the best; zinc which contains much copper should especially be avoided. I have generally found rolled Liege or Mosselman's zinc the purest; and to the circumstance of having used such zinc in its construction attribute in part the advantage of the new battery (1134).

1145. *Foulness of the zinc plates.* After use, the plates of a battery should be cleaned from the metallic powder upon their surfaces, especially if they are employed to obtain the laws of action of the battery itself. This precaution was always attended to with the porcelain trough batteries in the experiments described (1125, &c.). If a few foul plates are mingled with many clean ones, they make the action in the different cells irregular, and the transferable power is accordingly diminished, whilst the local and wasted power is increased. No old charge containing copper should be used to excite a battery.

1146. *New and old plates.* I have found voltaic batteries far more powerful when the plates were new than when they have been used two or three times; so that a new and a used battery cannot be compared together, or even a battery with itself on the first and after times of use. My trough of twenty pairs of four-inch plates, charged with acid consisting of 200 water, $4\frac{1}{2}$ oil of vitriol, and 4 nitric acid, lost, upon the first time of being used, 2.32 equivalents per plate. When used after the fourth time with the same charge, the loss was from 3.26 to 4.47 equivalents per plate; the average being 3.7 equivalents. The first time the forty pair of plates (1124) were used, the loss at each plate was only 1.65 equivalent; but afterwards it became 2.16, 2.17, 2.52. The first time twenty pair of four-inch plates in porcelain troughs were used, they lost, per plate, only 3.7 equivalents; but after that, the loss was 5.25, 5.36, 5.9 equivalents. Yet in all these cases the zincs had been well-cleaned from adhering copper, &c., before each trial of power.

1147. With the rolled zinc the fall in force soon appeared to become constant, i.e., to proceed no further. But with the cast zinc plates belonging to the porcelain troughs, it appeared to continue, until at last, with the same charge, each plate lost above twice as much zinc for a given amount of action as at first. These troughs were, however, so irregular that I could not always determine the circumstances affecting the amount of electrolytic action.

1148. *Vicinity of the copper and zinc.* The importance of this point in the construction of voltaic arrangements, and the greater power, as to immediate action, which is obtained when the zinc and copper surfaces are near to each other than when removed farther apart, are well known. I find that the power is not only greater on the instant, but also that the sum of transferable power, in relation to the whole sum of chemical action at the plates, is much increased. The cause of this gain is very evident. Whatever tends to retard the circulation of the transferable force (i.e., the electricity) diminishes the proportion of such force, and

increases the proportion of that which is local (996, 1120). Now the liquid in the cells possesses this retarding power, and therefore acts injuriously, in greater or less proportion, according to the quantity of it between the zinc and copper plates, i.e., according to the distances between their surfaces. A trough, therefore, in which the plates are only half the distance asunder at which they are placed in another, will produce more transferable, and less local, force than the latter; and thus, because the electrolyte in the cells can transmit the current more readily, both the intensity and quantity of electricity is increased for a given consumption of zinc. To this circumstance mainly I attribute the superiority of the trough I have described (1134).

1149. The superiority of *double coppers* over single plates also depends in part upon diminishing the resistance offered by the electrolyte between the metals. For, in fact, with double coppers the sectional area of the interposed acid becomes nearly double that with single coppers, and therefore it more freely transfers the electricity. Double coppers are, however, effective, mainly because they virtually double the acting surface of the zinc, or nearly so; for in a trough with single copper plates and the usual construction of cells, that surface of zinc which is not opposed to a copper surface is thrown almost entirely out of voltaic action, yet the acid continues to act upon it and the metal is dissolved, producing very little more than local effect (947, 996). But when by doubling the copper, that metal is opposed to the second surface of the zinc plate, then a great part of the action upon the latter is converted into transferable force, and thus the power of the trough as to quantity of electricity is highly exalted.

1150. *First immersion of the plates.* The great effect produced at the first immersion of the plates (apart from their being new or used [1146]) I have attributed elsewhere to the unchanged condition of the acid in contact with the zinc plate (1003, 1037): as the acid becomes neutralized, its exciting power is proportionably diminished. Hare's form of trough secures much advantage of this kind, by mingling the liquid, and bringing what may be considered as a fresh surface of acid against the plates every time it is used immediately after a rest.

1151. *Number of plates.*[1] The most advantageous number of plates in a battery used for chemical decomposition depends almost en-

[1] Gay-Lussac and Thenard, *Recherches Physico-Chimiques*, Vol. I, p. 29.

tirely upon the resistance to be overcome at the place of action; but whatever that resistance may be, there is a certain number which is more economical than either a greater or a less. Ten pairs of four-inch plates in a porcelain trough of the ordinary construction, acting in the volta electrometer (1126) upon dilute sulphuric acid of spec. grav. 1.314, gave an average consumption of 15.4 equivalents per plate, or 154 equivalents on the whole. Twenty pairs of the same plates, with the same acid, gave only a consumption of 5.5 per plate, or 110 equivalents upon the whole. When forty pairs of the same plates were used, the consumption was 3.54 equivalents per plate, or 141.6 upon the whole battery. Thus the consumption of zinc arranged as *twenty* plates was more advantageous than if arranged either as *ten* or as *forty*.

1152. Again, ten pairs of my four-inch plates (1129) lost 6.76 each, or the whole ten 67.6 equivalent of zinc, in effecting decomposition; whilst twenty pairs of the same plates, excited by the same acid, lost 3.7 equivalents each, or on the whole 74 equivalents. In other comparative experiments of numbers, ten pairs of the three inch-plates (1125) lost 3.725, or 37.25 equivalents upon the whole; whilst twenty pairs lost 2.53 each, or 50.6 in all; and forty pairs lost on an average 2.21, or 88.4 altogether. In both these cases, therefore, increase of numbers had not been advantageous as to the effective production of *transferable chemical power* from the *whole quantity of chemical force* active at the surfaces of excitation (1120).

1153. But if I had used a weaker acid or a worse conductor in the volta-electrometer, then the number of plates which would produce the most advantageous effect would have risen; or if I had used a better conductor than that really employed in the volta-electrometer, I might have reduced the number even to one; as, for instance, when a thick wire is used to complete the circuit (865, &c.). And the cause of these variations is very evident, when it is considered that each successive plate in the voltaic apparatus does not add anything to the *quantity* of transferable power or electricity which the first plate can put into motion, provided a good conductor be present, but tends only to exalt the *intensity* of that quantity, so as to make it more able to overcome the obstruction of bad conductors (994, 1158).

1154. *Large or small plates.*[1] The advantageous use of large or small plates for electroly-

zations will evidently depend upon the facility with which the transferable power of electricity can pass. If in a particular case the most effectual number of plates is known (1151), then the addition of more zinc would be most advantageously made in increasing the *size* of the plates, and not their *number*. At the same time, large increase in the size of the plates would raise in a small degree the most favourable number.

1155. Large and small plates should not be used together in the same battery: the small ones occasion a loss of the power of the large ones, unless they be excited by an acid proportionably more powerful; for with a certain acid they cannot transmit the same portion of electricity in a given time which the same acid can evolve by action on the larger plates.

1156. *Simultaneous decompositions.* When the number of plates in a battery much surpasses the most favourable proportion (1151—1153), two or more decompositions may be effected simultaneously with advantage. Thus my forty pairs of plates (1124) produced in one voltaelectrometer 22.8 cubic inches of gas. Being recharged exactly in the same manner, they produced in each of two volta-electrometers 21 cubical inches. In the first experiment the whole consumption of zinc was 88.4 equivalents, and in the second only 48.28 equivalents, for the whole of the water decomposed in both volta-electrometers.

1157. But when the twenty pairs of four-inch plates (1129) were tried in a similar manner, the results were in the opposite direction. With one volta-electrometer 52 cubic inches of gas were obtained; with two, only 14.6 cubic inches from each. The quantity of charge was not the same in both cases, though it was of the same strength, but on rendering the results comparative by reducing them to equivalents (1126), it was found that the consumption of metal in the first case was 74, and in the second case 97, equivalents for the *whole* of the water decomposed. These results of course depend upon the same circumstances of retardation, &c., which have been referred to in speaking of the proper number of plates (1151).

1158. That the *transferring*, or, as it is usually called, *conducting*, *power* of an electrolyte which is to be decomposed, or other interposed body, should be rendered as good as possible,[2] is very evident (1020, 1120). With a perfectly good conductor and a good battery, nearly all

[1] Gay-Lussac and Thenard, *Recherches Physico-Chimiques*, Vol. I, p. 29.

[2] Gay-Lussac and Thenard, *Recherches Physico-Chimiques*, Vol. I, pp. 13, 15, 22.

the electricity is passed, i.e., *nearly all* the chemical power becomes transferable, even with a single pair of plates (867). With an interposed non-conductor none of the chemical power becomes transferable. With an imperfect conductor more or less of the chemical power becomes transferable as the circumstances favouring the transfer of forces across the imperfect conductor are exalted or diminished: these circumstances are actual increase or improvement of the conducting power, enlargement of the electrodes, approximation of the electrodes, and increased intensity of the passing current.

1159. The introduction of common spring water in place of one of the volta-electrometers used with twenty pairs of four-inch plates (1156) caused such obstruction as not to allow one-fifteenth of the transferable force to pass which would have circulated without it. Thus fourteen-fifteenths of the available force of the battery were destroyed, being converted into local force (which was rendered evident by the evolution of gas from the zincs), and yet the platina electrodes in the water were three inches long, nearly an inch wide, and not a quarter of an inch apart.

1160. These points, i.e., the increase of conducting power, the enlargement of the electrodes, and their approximation, should be especially attended to in *volta-electrometers*. The principles upon which their utility depend are so evident that there can be no occasion for further development of them here.

Royal Institution, October 11, 1834

ELEVENTH SERIES

§ 18. *On Induction* ¶ i. *Induction an Action of Contiguous Particles* ¶ ii. *On the Absolute Charge of Matter* ¶ iii. *Electrometer and Inductive Apparatus Employed* ¶ iv. *Induction in Curved Lines* ¶ v. *On Specific Induction, or Specific Inductive Capacity* ¶ vi. *General Results as to Induction*

RECEIVED NOVEMBER 30, READ DECEMBER 21, 1837

¶ i. *Induction an Action of Contiguous Particles*

1161. THE science of electricity is in that state in which every part of it requires experimental investigation; not merely for the discovery of new effects, but what is just now of far more importance, the development of the means by which the old effects are produced, and the consequent more accurate determination of the first principles of action of the most extraordinary and universal power in nature: and to those philosophers who pursue the inquiry zealously yet cautiously, combining experiment with analogy, suspicious of their preconceived notions, paying more respect to a fact than a theory, not too hasty to generalize, and above all things, willing at every step to cross-examine their own opinions, both by reasoning and experiment, no branch of knowledge can afford so fine and ready a field for discovery as this. Such is most abundantly shown to be the case by the progress which electricity has made in the last thirty years: chemistry and magnetism have successively acknowledged its over-ruling influence: and it is probable that every effect depending upon the powers of inorganic matter, and perhaps most of those related to vegetable and animal life, will ultimately be found subordinate to it.

1162. Amongst the actions of different kinds into which electricity has conventionally been subdivided, there is, I think, none which excels, or even equals in importance, that called *induction*. It is of the most general influence in electrical phenomena, appearing to be concerned in every one of them, and has in reality the character of a first, essential, and fundamental principle. Its comprehension is so important that I think we cannot proceed much further in the investigation of the laws of electricity without a more thorough understanding of its nature: how otherwise can we hope to comprehend the harmony and even unity of action which doubtless governs electrical excitement by friction, by chemical means, by heat, by magnetic influence, by evaporation, and even by the living being?

1163. In the long-continued course of experimental inquiry in which I have been engaged, this general result has pressed upon me constantly, namely, the necessity of admitting two forces, or two forms or directions of a force (516, 517), combined with the impossibility of separating these two forces (or electricities) from each other, either in the phenomena of statical electricity or those of the current. In association with this, the impossibility under any circumstances, as yet, of absolutely charging matter of any kind with one or the other electricity only, dwelt on my mind, and made me wish and search for a clearer view than any that I was acquainted with, of the way in which electrical powers and the particles of matter are related; especially in inductive actions, upon which almost all others appeared to rest.

1164. When I discovered the general fact that electrolytes refused to yield their elements to a current when in the solid state, though they gave them forth freely if in the liquid condition (380, 394, 402), I thought I saw an opening to the elucidation of inductive action, and the possible subjugation of many dissimilar phenomena to one law. For let the electrolyte be water, a plate of ice being coated with platina foil on its two surfaces, and these coatings connected with any continued source of the two electrical powers, the ice will charge like a Leyden arrangement, presenting a case of common induction, but no current will pass. If the ice be liquefied, the induction will fall to a certain degree, because a current can now pass; but its passing is dependent upon a *peculiar molecular arrangement* of the particles consistent with the transfer of the elements of the electrolyte in opposite directions, the degree of discharge and the quantity of elements evolved being exactly proportioned to each other (377, 783). Whether the charging of the metallic coating be effected by a powerful electrical machine, a strong and large voltaic battery, or a single pair of plates, makes no difference in the principle, but only in the degree of action (360). Common induction takes place in each case if the electrolyte be solid, or if fluid, chemical action and decomposition ensue, provided opposing actions do not interfere; and it is of high importance occasionally thus to compare effects in their extreme degrees, for the purpose of enabling us to comprehend the nature of an action in its weak state, which may be only sufficiently evident to us in its stronger condition (451). As, therefore, in the electrolytic action, *induction* appeared to be the *first* step, and *decomposition* the *second* (the power of separating these steps from each other by giving the solid or fluid condition to the electrolyte being in our hands); as the induction

was the same in its nature as that through air, glass, wax, &c., produced by any of the ordinary means; and as the whole effect in the electrolyte appeared to be an action of the particles thrown into a peculiar or polarized state, I was led to suspect that common induction itself was in all cases an *action of contiguous particles*,[1] and that electrical action at a distance (i.e., ordinary inductive action) never occurred except through the influence of the intervening matter.

1165. The respect which I entertain towards the names of Epinus, Cavendish, Poisson, and other most eminent men, all of whose theories I believe consider induction as an action at a distance and in straight lines, long indisposed me to the view I have just stated; and though I always watched for opportunities to prove the opposite opinion, and made such experiments occasionally as seemed to bear directly on the point, as, for instance, the examination of electrolytes, solid and fluid, whilst under induction by polarized light (951, 955), it is only of late, and by degrees, that the extreme generality of the subject has urged me still further to extend my experiments and publish my view. At present I believe ordinary induction in all cases to be an action of contiguous particles consisting in a species of polarity, instead of being an action of either particles or masses at sensible distances; and if this be true, the distinction and establishment of such a truth must be of the greatest consequence to our further progress in the investigation of the nature of electric forces. The linked condition of electrical induction with chemical decomposition; of voltaic excitement with chemical action; the transfer of elements in an electrolyte; the original cause of excitement in all cases; the nature and relation of conduction and insulation; of the direct and lateral or transverse action constituting electricity and magnetism; with many other things more or less incomprehensible at present, would all be affected by it, and perhaps receive a full explication in their reduction under one general law.

1166. I searched for an unexceptionable test of my view, not merely in the accordance of known facts with it, but in the consequences which would flow from it if true; especially in

---

[1] The word *contiguous* is perhaps not the best that might have been used here and elsewhere; for as particles do not touch each other it is not strictly correct. I was induced to employ it, because in its common acceptation it enabled me to state the theory plainly and with facility. By contiguous particles I mean those which are next.—*Dec.* 1838.

those which would not be consistent with the theory of action at a distance. Such a consequence seemed to me to present itself in the direction in which inductive action could be exerted. If in straight lines only, though not perhaps decisive, it would be against my view; but if in curved lines also, that would be a natural result of the action of contiguous particles, but, as I think, utterly incompatible with action at a distance, as assumed by the received theories, which, according to every fact and analogy we are acquainted with, is always in straight lines.

1167. Again, if induction be an action of contiguous particles, and also the first step in the process of electrolyzation (949, 1164), there seemed reason to expect some particular relation of it to the different kinds of matter through which it would be exerted, or something equivalent to a *specific electric induction* for different bodies, which, if it existed, would unequivocally prove the dependence of induction on the particles; and though this, in the theory of Poisson and others, haᵉ never been supposed to be the case, I was soon led to doubt the received opinion, and have taken great pains in subjecting this point to close experimental examination.

1168. Another ever-present question on my mind has been, whether electricity has an actual and independent existence as a fluid or fluids, or was a mere power of matter, like what we conceive of the attraction of gravitation. If determined either way it would be an enormous advance in our knowledge; and as having the most direct and influential bearing on my notions, I have always sought for experiments which would in any way tend to elucidate that great inquiry. It was in attempts to prove the existence of electricity separate from matter, by giving an independent charge of either positive or negative power only, to some one substance, and the utter failure of all such attempts, whatever substance was used or whatever means of exciting or *evolving* electricity were employed, that first drove me to look upon induction as an action of the particles of matter, each having *both* forces developed in it in exactly equal amount. It is this circumstance, in connexion with others, which makes me desirous of placing the remarks on absolute charge first, in the order of proof and argument, which I am about to adduce in favour of my view, that electric induction is an action of the contiguous particles of the insulating medium or *dielectric*.[1]

¶ ii. *On the Absolute Charge of Matter*

1169. Can matter, either conducting or nonconducting, be charged with one electric force independently of the other, in any degree, either in a sensible or latent state?

1170. The beautiful experiments of Coulomb upon the equality of action of *conductors*, whatever their substance, and the residence of *all* the electricity upon their surfaces,[2] are sufficient, if properly viewed, to prove that *conductors cannot be bodily charged*; and as yet no means of communicating electricity to a conductor so as to place its particles in relation to one electricity, and not at the same time to the other in exactly equal amount, has been discovered.

1171. With regard to electrics or non-conductors, the conclusion does not at first seem so clear. They may easily be electrified bodily, either by communication (1247) or excitement; but being so charged, every case in succession, when examined, came out to be a case of induction, and not of absolute charge. Thus, glass within conductors could easily have parts not in contact with the conductor brought into an excited state; but it was always found that a portion of the inner surface of the conductor was in an opposite and equivalent state, or that another part of the glass itself was in an equally opposite state, an *inductive* charge and not an *absolute* charge having been acquired.

1172. Well-purified oil of turpentine, which I find to be an excellent liquid insulator for most purposes, was put into a metallic vessel, and, being insulated, an endeavour was made to charge its particles, sometimes by contact of the metal with the electrical machine, and at others by a wire dipping into the fluid within; but whatever the mode of communication, no electricity of one kind only was retained by the arrangement, except what appeared on the exterior surface of the metal, that portion being present there only by an inductive action through the air to the surrounding conductors. When the oil of turpentine was confined in glass vessels, there were at first some appearances as if the fluid did receive an absolute charge of electricity from the charging wire, but these were quickly reduced to cases of common induction jointly through the fluid, the glass, and the surrounding air.

1173. I carried these experiments on with air to a very great extent. I had a chamber built, being a cube of twelve feet. A slight cu-

---

[1] I use the word *dielectric* to express that substance through or across which the electric forces are acting. —*Dec.* 1838.

[2] *Mémoires de l'Académie*, 1786, pp. 67, 69, 72; 1787, p. 452.

bical wooden frame was constructed, and copper wire passed along and across it in various directions, so as to make the sides a large network, and then all was covered in with paper, placed in close connexion with the wires, and supplied in every direction with bands of tin foil, that the whole might be brought into good metallic communication, and rendered a free conductor in every part. This chamber was insulated in the lecture-room of the Royal Institution; a glass tube about six feet in length was passed through its side, leaving about four feet within and two feet on the outside, and through this a wire passed from the large electrical machine (290) to the air within. By working the machine, the air in this chamber could be brought into what is considered a highly electrified state (being, in fact, the same state as that of the air of a room in which a powerful machine is in operation), and at the same time the outside of the insulated cube was everywhere strongly charged. But putting the chamber in communication with the perfect discharging train described in a former series (292), and working the machine so as to bring the air within to its utmost degree of charge if I quickly cut off the connexion with the machine, and at the same moment or instantly after insulated the cube, the air within had not the least power to communicate a further charge to it. If any portion of the air was electrified, as glass or other insulators may be charged (1171), it was accompanied by a corresponding opposite action *within* the cube, the whole effect being merely a case of induction. Every attempt to charge air bodily and independently with the least portion of either electricity failed.

1174. I put a delicate gold-leaf electrometer within the cube, and then charged the whole by an *outside* communication, very strongly, for some time together; but neither during the charge or after the discharge did the electrometer or air within show the least signs of electricity. I charged and discharged the whole arrangement in various ways, but in no case could I obtain the least indication of an absolute charge; or of one by induction in which the electricity of one kind had the smallest superiority in quantity over the other. I went into the cube and lived in it, and using lighted candles, electrometers, and all other tests of electrical states, I could not find the least influence upon them, or indication of anything particular given by them, though all the time the outside of the cube was powerfully charged, and large sparks and brushes were darting off from every

part of its outer surface. The conclusion I have come to is that non-conductors, as well as conductors, have never yet had an absolute and independent charge of one electricity communicated to them, and that to all appearance such a state of matter is impossible.

1175. There is another view of this question which may be taken under the supposition of the existence of an electric fluid or fluids. It may be impossible to have one fluid or state in a free condition without its producing by induction the other, and yet possible to have cases in which an isolated portion of matter in one condition being uncharged shall, by a change of state, evolve one electricity or the other: and though such evolved electricity might immediately induce the opposite state in its neighbourhood, yet the mere evolution of one electricity without the other in the *first instance*, would be a very important fact in the theories which assume a fluid or fluids; these theories as I understand them assigning not the slightest reason why such an effect should not occur.

1176. But on searching for such cases I cannot find one. Evolution by friction, as is well known, gives both powers in equal proportion. So does evolution by chemical action, notwithstanding the great diversity of bodies which may be employed, and the enormous quantity of electricity which can in this manner be evolved (371, 376, 861, 868, 961). The more promising cases of change of state, whether by evaporation, fusion, or the reverse processes, still give both forms of the power in *equal* proportion; and the cases of splitting of mica and other crystals, the breaking of sulphur, &c., are subject to the same law of limitation.

1177. As far as experiment has proceeded, it appears, therefore, impossible either to evolve or make disappear one electric force without equal and corresponding change in the other. It is also equally impossible experimentally to charge a portion of matter with one electric force independently of the other. Charge always implies *induction*, for it can in no instance be effected without; and also the presence of the *two* forms of power, equally at the moment of the development and afterwards. There is no *absolute* charge of matter with one fluid; no latency of a single electricity. This though a negative result is an exceedingly important one, being probably the consequence of a natural impossibility, which will become clear to us when we understand the true condition and theory of the electric power.

1178. The preceding considerations already point to the following conclusions: bodies cannot be charged absolutely, but only relatively, and by a principle which is the same with that of *induction*. All *charge* is sustained by induction. All phenomena of *intensity* include the principle of induction. All *excitation* is dependent on or directly related to induction. All *currents* involve previous intensity and therefore previous induction. INDUCTION appears to be the essential function both of the first development and the consequent phenomena of electricity.

¶ iii. *Electrometer and Inductive Apparatus Employed*

1179. Leaving for a time the further consideration of the preceding facts until they can be collated with other results bearing directly on the great question of the nature of induction, I will now describe the apparatus I have had occasion to use; and in proportion to the importance of the principles sought to be established is the necessity of doing this so clearly, as to leave no doubt of the results behind.

1180. *Electrometer*. The measuring instrument I have employed has been the torsion balance electrometer of Coulomb, constructed, generally, according to his directions,[1] but with certain variations and additions, which I will briefly describe. The lower part was a glass cylinder eight inches in height and eight inches in diameter; the tube for the torsion thread was seventeen inches in length. The torsion thread itself was not of metal, but glass, according to the excellent suggestion of the late Dr. Ritchie.[2] It was twenty inches in length, and of such tenuity that when the shellac lever and attached ball, &c., were connected with it, they made about ten vibrations in a minute. It would bear torsion through four revolutions or 1440°, and yet, when released, return accurately to its position; probably it would have borne considerably more than this without injury. The repelled ball was of pith, gilt, and was 0.3 of an inch in diameter. The horizontal stem or lever supporting it was of shellac, according to Coulomb's direction, the arm carrying the ball being 2.4 inches long, and the other only 1.2 inches: to this was attached the vane, also described by Coulomb, which I found to answer admirably its purpose of quickly destroying vibrations. That the inductive action within the electrometer might be uniform in all positions

[1] *Mémoires de l'Académie*, 1785, p. 570.
[2] *Philosophical Transactions*, 1830.

of the repelled ball and in all states of the apparatus, two bands of tinfoil, about an inch wide each, were attached to the inner surface of the glass cylinder, going entirely round it, at the distance of 0.4 of an inch from each other, and at such a height that the intermediate clear surface was in the same horizontal plane with the lever and ball. These bands were connected with each other and with the earth, and, being perfect conductors, always exerted a uniform influence on the electrified balls within, which the glass surface, from its irregularity of condition at different times, I found, did not. For the purpose of keeping the air within the electrometer in a constant state as to dryness, a glass dish, of such size as to enter easily within the cylinder, had a layer of fused potash placed within it, and this being covered with a disc of fine wire-gauze to render its inductive action uniform at all parts, was placed within the instrument at the bottom and left there.

1181. The movable ball used to take and measure the portion of electricity under examination, and which may be called the *repelling*, or the *carrier*, ball, was of soft alder wood, well and smoothly gilt. It was attached to a fine shellac stem, and introduced through a hole into the electrometer according to Coulomb's method: the stem was fixed at its upper end in a block or vice, supported on three short feet; and on the surface of the glass cover above was a plate of lead with stops on it, so that when the carrier ball was adjusted in its right position, with the vice above bearing at the same time against these stops, it was perfectly easy to bring away the carrier-ball and restore it to its place again very accurately, without any loss of time.

1182. It is quite necessary to attend to certain precautions respecting these balls. If of pith alone they are bad; for when very dry, that substance is so imperfect a conductor that it neither receives nor gives a charge freely, and so, after contact with a charged conductor, it is liable to be in an uncertain condition. Again, it is difficult to turn pith so smooth as to leave the ball, even when gilt, so free from irregularities of form, as to retain its charge undiminished for a considerable length of time. When, therefore, the balls are finally prepared and gilt they should be examined; and being electrified, unless they can hold their charge with very little diminution for a considerable time, and yet be discharged instantly and perfectly by the touch of an uninsulated conductor, they should be dismissed.

1183. It is, perhaps, unnecessary to refer to the graduation of the instrument, further than to explain how the observations were made. On a circle or ring of paper on the outside of the glass cylinder, fixed so as to cover the internal lower ring of tinfoil, were marked four points corresponding to angles of 90°; four other points exactly corresponding to these points being marked on the upper ring of tinfoil within. By these and the adjusting screws on which the whole instrument stands, the glass torsion thread could be brought accurately into the centre of the instrument and of the graduations on it. From one of the four points on the exterior of the cylinder a graduation of 90° was set off, and a corresponding graduation was placed upon the upper tinfoil on the opposite side of the cylinder within; and a dot being marked on that point of the surface of the repelled ball nearest to the side of the electrometer, it was easy, by observing the line which this dot made with the lines of the two graduations just referred to, to ascertain accurately the position of the ball. The upper end of the glass thread was attached, as in Coulomb's original electrometer, to an index, which had its appropriate graduated circle, upon which the degree of torsion was ultimately to be read off.

1184. After the levelling of the instrument and adjustment of the glass thread, the blocks which determine the place of the *carrier ball* are to be regulated (1181) so that, when the carrier arrangement is placed against them, the centre of the ball may be in the radius of the instrument corresponding to 0° on the lower graduation or that on the side of the electrometer, and at the same level and distance from the centre as the *repelled ball* on the suspended torsion lever. Then the torsion index is to be turned until the ball connected with it (the repelled ball) is accurately at 30°, and finally the graduated arc belonging to the torsion index is to be adjusted so as to bring 0° upon it to the index. This state of the instrument was adopted as that which gave the most direct expression of the experimental results, and in the form having fewest variable errors; the angular distance of 30° being always retained as the standard distance to which the balls were in every case to be brought, and the whole of the torsion being read off at once on the graduated circle above. Under these circumstances the distance of the balls from each other was not merely the same in degree, but their position in the instrument, and in relation to every part of it, was actually the same every time that a measurement was made; so that all irregularities arising from slight difference of form and action in the instrument and the bodies around were avoided. The only difference which could occur in the position of anything within, consisted in the deflexion of the torsion thread from a vertical position, more or less, according to the force of repulsion of the balls; but this was so slight as to cause no interfering difference in the symmetry of form within the instrument, and gave no error in the amount of torsion force indicated on the graduation above.

1185. Although the constant angular distance of 30° between the centres of the balls was adopted, and found abundantly sensible, for all ordinary purposes, yet the facility of rendering the instrument far more sensible by diminishing this distance was at perfect command; the results at different distances being very easily compared with each other either by experiment, or, as they are inversely as the squares of the distances, by calculation.

1186. The Coulomb balance electrometer requires experience to be understood; but I think it a very valuable instrument in the hands of those who will take pains by practice and attention to learn the precautions needful in its use. Its insulating condition varies with circumstances, and should be examined before it is employed in experiments. In an ordinary and fair condition, when the balls were so electrified as to give a repulsive torsion force of 400° at the standard distance of 30°, it took nearly four hours to sink to 50° at the same distance; the average loss from 400° to 300° being at the rate of 2.7° per minute, from 300° to 200° of 1.7° per minute, from 200° to 100° of 1.3° per minute, and from 100° to 50° of 0.87° per minute. As a complete measurement by the instrument may be made in much less than a minute, the amount of loss in that time is but small, and can easily be taken into account.

1187. *The inductive apparatus.* My object was to examine inductive action carefully when taking place through different media, for which purpose it was necessary to subject these media to it in exactly similar circumstances, and in such quantities as should suffice to eliminate any variations they might present. The requisites of the apparatus to be constructed were, therefore, that the inducing surfaces of the conductors should have a constant form and state, and be at a constant distance from each other; and that either solids, fluids, or

PLATE IX

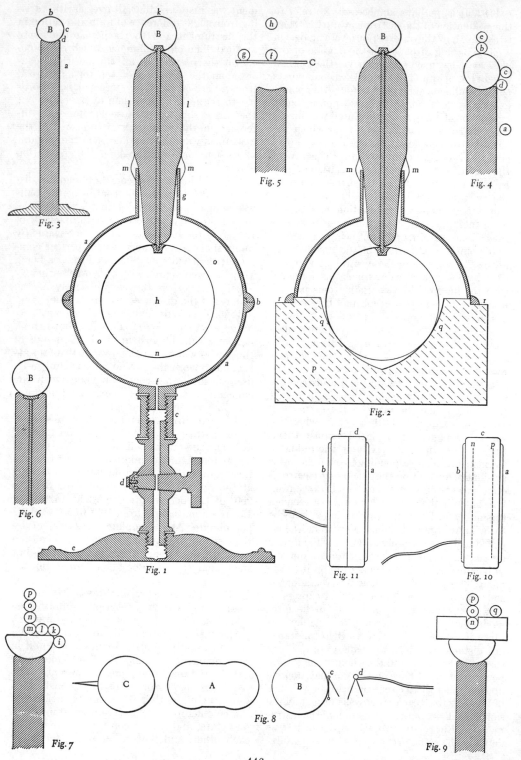

Fig. 3

Fig. 5

Fig. 4

Fig. 6

Fig. 2

Fig. 1

Fig. 11

Fig. 10

Fig. 7

Fig. 8

Fig. 9

gases might be placed and retained between these surfaces with readiness and certainty, and for any length of time.

1188. The apparatus used may be described in general terms as consisting of two metallic spheres of unequal diameter, placed, the smaller within the larger, and concentric with it; the interval between the two being the space through which the induction was to take place. A section of it is given (Pl. IX, *Fig. 1*) on a scale of one-half: *a, a* are the two halves of a brass sphere, with an air-tight joint at *b*, like that of the Magdeburg hemispheres, made perfectly flush and smooth inside so as to present no irregularity; *c* is a connecting piece by which the apparatus is joined to a good stop-cock *d*, which is itself attached either to the metallic foot *e*, or to an air-pump. The aperture within the hemisphere at *f* is very small: *g* is a brass collar fitted to the upper hemisphere, through which the shellac support of the inner ball and its stem passes; *h* is the inner ball, also of brass; it screws on to a brass stem *i*, terminated above by a brass ball B; *l, l* is a mass of shellac, moulded carefully on to *i*, and serving both to support and insulate it and its balls *h*, B. The shellac stem *l* is fitted into the socket *g*, by a little ordinary resinous cement, more fusible than shellac, applied at *m m* in such a way as to give sufficient strength and render the apparatus air-tight there, yet leave as much as possible of the lower part of the shellac stem untouched, as an insulation between the ball *h* and the surrounding sphere *a, a*. The ball *h* has a small aperture at *n*, so that when the apparatus is exhausted of one gas and filled with another, the ball *h* may itself also be exhausted and filled, that no variation of the gas in the interval *o* may occur during the course of an experiment.

1189. It will be unnecessary to give the dimensions of all the parts, since the drawing is to a scale of one-half: the inner ball has a diameter of 2.33 inches, and the surrounding sphere an internal diameter of 3.57 inches. Hence the width of the intervening space, through which the induction is to take place, is 0.62 of an inch; and the extent of this place or plate, i.e. the surface of a medium sphere, may be taken as twenty-seven square inches, a quantity considered as sufficiently large for the comparison of different substances. Great care was taken in finishing well the inducing surfaces of the ball *h* and sphere *a, a*: and no varnish or lacquer was applied to them, or to any part of the metal of the apparatus.

1190. The attachment and adjustment of the shellac stem was a matter requiring considerable care, especially as, in consequence of its cracking, it had frequently to be renewed. The best lac was chosen and applied to the wire *i*, so as to be in good contact with it everywhere, and in perfect continuity throughout its own mass. It was not smaller than is given by scale in the drawing, for when less it frequently cracked within a few hours after it was cold. I think that very slow cooling or annealing improved its quality in this respect. The collar *g* was made as thin as could be, that the lac might be as wide there as possible. In order that at every re-attachment of the stem to the upper hemisphere the ball *h* might have the same relative position, a gauge *p* (Pl. IX, *Fig. 2*) was made of wood, and this being applied to the ball and hemisphere whilst the cement at *m* was still soft, the bearings of the ball at *q q*, and the hemisphere at *r r*, were forced home, and the whole left until cold. Thus all difficulty in the adjustment of the ball in the sphere was avoided.

1191. I had occasion at first to attach the stem to the socket by other means, as a band of paper or a plugging of white silk thread; but these were very inferior to the cement, interfering much with the insulating power of the apparatus.

1192. The retentive power of this apparatus was, when in good condition, better than that of the electrometer (1186), i.e., the proportion of loss of power was less. Thus when the apparatus was electrified, and also the balls in the electrometer, to such a degree, that after the inner ball had been in contact with the top *k* of the ball of the apparatus, it caused a repulsion indicated by 600° of torsion force, then in falling from 600° to 400° the average loss was 8.6° per minute; from 400° to 300° the average loss was 2.6° per minute; from 300° to 200° it was 1.7° per minute; from 200° to 170° it was 1° per minute. This was after the apparatus had been charged for a short time; at the first instant of charging there is an apparent loss of electricity, which can only be comprehended hereafter (1207, 1250).

1193. When the apparatus loses its insulating power suddenly, it is almost always from a crack near to or within the brass socket. These cracks are usually transverse to the stem. If they occur at the part attached by common cement to the socket, the air cannot enter, and thus constituting vacua, they conduct away the electricity and lower the charge, as fast almost as if a piece of metal had been introduced there. Occasionally stems in this state, being taken out and cleared from the common cement, may, by the careful application of the heat of a spirit-lamp, be so far softened and melted as to restore the perfect continuity of the parts; but if that does not succeed in replacing things in a good condition, the remedy is a new shellac stem.

1194. The apparatus when in order could easily be exhausted of air and filled with any given gas; but when that gas was acid or alkaline, it could not properly be removed by the air-pump, and yet required to be perfectly cleared away. In such cases the apparatus was opened and emptied of gas; and with respect to the inner ball h, it was washed out two or three times with distilled water introduced at the screw-hole, and then being heated above 212°, air was blown through to render the interior perfectly dry.

1195. The inductive apparatus described is evidently a Leyden phial, with the advantage, however, of having the *dielectric* or insulating medium changed at pleasure. The balls h and B, with the connecting wire i, constitute the charged conductor, upon the surface of which all the electric force is resident by virtue of induction (1178). Now though the largest portion of this induction is between the ball h and the surrounding sphere $a\,a$, yet the wire i and the ball B determine a part of the induction from their surfaces towards the external surrounding conductors. Still, as all things in that respect remain the same, whilst the medium within at $o\,o$, may be varied, any changes exhibited by the whole apparatus will in such cases depend upon the variations made in the interior; and these were the changes I was in search of, the negation or establishment of such differences being the great object of my inquiry. I considered that these differences, if they existed, would be most distinctly set forth by having two apparatuses of the kind described, precisely similar in every respect; and then, *different insulating media* being within, to charge one and measure it, and after dividing the charge with the other, to observe what the ultimate conditions of both were. If insulating media really had any specific differences in favouring or opposing inductive action through them, such differences, I conceived, could not fail of being developed by such a process.

1196. I will wind up this description of the apparatuses, and explain the precautions necessary to their use, by describing the form and order of the experiments made to prove their equality when both contained common air. In order to facilitate reference I will distinguish the two by the terms *app. i* and *app. ii.*

1197. The electrometer is first to be adjusted and examined (1184), and the app. i and ii are to be perfectly discharged. A Leyden phial is to be charged to such a degree that it would give a spark of about one-sixteenth or one-twentieth of an inch in length between two balls of half an inch diameter; and the carrier ball of the electrometer being charged by this phial is to be introduced into the electrometer, and the lever ball brought by the motion of the torsion index against it; the charge is thus divided between the balls, and repulsion ensues. It is useful then to bring the repelled ball to the standard distance of 30° by the motion of the torsion index, and observe the force in degrees required for this purpose; this force will in future experiments be called *repulsion of the balls.*

1198. One of the inductive apparatus, as, for instance, app. i, is now to be charged from the Leyden phial, the latter being in the state it was in when used to charge the balls; the carrier ball is to be brought into contact with the top of its upper ball k (Pl. IX, *Fig. 1*), then introduced into the electrometer, and the repulsive force (at the distance of 30°) measured. Again, the carrier should be applied to the app. i and the measurement repeated; the apparatus i and ii are then to be joined, so as to *divide* the charge, and afterwards the force of each measured by the carrier ball, applied as before, and the results carefully noted. After this both i and ii are to be discharged; then app. ii charged, measured, divided with app. i, and the force of each again measured and noted. If in each case the half charges of app. i and ii are equal, and are together equal to the whole charge before division, then it may be considered as proved that the two apparatuses are precisely equal in power, and fit to be used in cases of comparison between different insulating media or *dielectrics.*

1199. But the *precautions* necessary to obtain accurate results are numerous. The apparatuses i and ii must always be placed on a thoroughly uninsulating medium. A mahogany table, for instance, is far from satisfactory in this respect, and therefore a sheet of tinfoil, connected with an extensive discharging train (292), is what I have used. They must be so placed also as not to be too near each other, and yet equally exposed to the inductive influence of surrounding objects; and these objects, again, should not be disturbed in their position during an experiment, or else variations of induction upon the external ball B of the apparatus may occur, and so errors be introduced into the results. The carrier ball, when receiving its portion of electricity from the apparatus, should always be applied at the same part of the ball, as, for instance, the summit k, and always in the same way; variable induction from the vicinity of the head, hands, &c., being avoided, and the ball after contact being withdrawn upwards in a regular and constant manner.

1200. As the stem had occasionally to be changed (1190), and the change might occasion slight variations in the position of the ball within, I made such a variation purposely, to the amount of an eighth of an inch (which is far more than ever could occur in practice), but did not find that it sensibly altered the relation of the apparatus, or its inductive condition *as a whole*. Another trial of the apparatuses was made as to the effect of dampness in the air, one being filled with very dry air, and the other with air from over water. Though this produced no change in the result, except an occasional tendency to more rapid dissipation, yet the precaution was always taken when working with gases (1290) to dry them perfectly.

1201. It is essential that the interior of the apparatus should be perfectly free from *dust or small loose particles*, for these very rapidly lower the charge and interfere on occasions when their presence and action would hardly be expected. To breathe on the interior of the apparatus and wipe it out quietly with a clean silk handkerchief, is an effectual way of removing them; but then the intrusion of other particles should be carefully guarded against, and a dusty atmosphere should for this and several other reasons be avoided.

1202. The shellac stem requires occasionally to be well-wiped, to remove, in the first instance, the film of wax and adhering matter which is upon it; and afterwards to displace dirt and dust which will gradually attach to it in the course of experiments. I have found much to depend upon this precaution, and a silk handkerchief is the best wiper.

1203. But wiping and some other circumstances tend to give a charge to the surface of the shellac stem. This should be removed, for,

if allowed to remain, it very seriously affects the degree of charge given to the carrier ball by the apparatus (1232). This condition of the stem is best observed by discharging the apparatus, applying the carrier ball to the stem, touching it with the finger, insulating and removing it, and examining whether it has received any charge (by induction) from the stem; if it has, the stem itself is in a charged state. The best method of removing the charge I have found to be, to cover the finger with a single fold of a silk handkerchief, and breathing on the stem, to wipe it immediately after with the finger; the ball B and its connected wire, &c., being at the same time *uninsulated*: the wiping place of the silk must not be changed; it then becomes sufficiently damp not to excite the stem, and is yet dry enough to leave it in a clean and excellent insulating condition. If the air be dusty, it will be found that a single charge of the apparatus will bring on an electric state of the outside of the stem, in consequence of the carrying power of the particles of dust; whereas in the morning, and in a room which has been left quiet, several experiments can be made in succession without the stem assuming the least degree of charge.

1204. Experiments should not be made by candle or lamp light except with much care, for flames have great and yet unsteady powers of affecting and dissipating electrical charges.

1205. As a final observation on the state of the apparatuses, they should retain their charges well and uniformly, and alike for both, and at the same time allow of a perfect and instantaneous discharge, giving afterwards no charge to the carrier ball, whatever part of the ball B it may be applied to (1218).

1206. With respect to the balance electrometer, all the precautions that need be mentioned are, that the carrier ball is to be preserved during the first part of an experiment in its electrified state, the loss of electricity which would follow upon its discharge being avoided; and that in introducing it into the electrometer through the hole in the glass plate above, care should be taken that it do not touch, or even come near to, the edge of the glass.

1207. When the whole charge in one apparatus is divided between the two, the gradual fall, apparently from dissipation, in the apparatus which has *received* the half charge is greater than in the one *originally* charged. This is due to a peculiar effect to be described hereafter (1250, 1251), the interfering influence of which may be avoided to a great extent by going through the steps of the process regularly and quickly; therefore, after the original charge has been measured, in app. i for instance, i and ii are to be symmetrically joined by their balls B, the carrier touching one of these balls at the same time; it is first to be removed, and then the apparatus separated from each other; app. ii is next quickly to be measured by the carrier, then app. i; lastly, ii is to be discharged, and the discharged carrier applied to it to ascertain whether any residual effect is present (1205), and app. i being discharged is also to be examined in the same manner and for the same purpose.

1208. The following is an example of the division of a charge by the two apparatuses, air being the dielectric in both of them. The observations are set down one under the other in the order in which they were taken, the left-hand numbers representing the observations made on app. i, and the right-hand numbers those on app. ii. App. i is that which was originally charged, and after two measurements, the charge was divided with app. ii.

App. i	App. ii	
Balls 160°		
	———	0°
254°	———	
250	———	
divided and instantly taken		
	———122	
124	———	
1	———	after being discharged
	———	2 after being discharged

1209. Without endeavouring to allow for the loss which must have been gradually going on during the time of the experiment, let us observe the results of the numbers as they stand. As 1° remained in app. i in an undischargeable state, 249° may be taken as the utmost amount of the transferable or divisible charge, the half of which is 124°.5. As app. ii was free of charge in the first instance, and immediately after the division was found with 122°, this amount *at least* may be taken as what it had received. On the other hand 124° minus 1°, or 123°, may be taken as the half of the transferable charge retained by app. i. Now these do not differ much from each other, or from 124°.5, the half of the full amount of transferable charge; and when the gradual loss of charge evident in the difference between 254° and 250° of app. i is also taken into account, there is every reason to admit the result as showing an equal division of charge, *unattended by any disappearance of power except that due to dissipation.*

1210. I will give another result, in which

app. ii was first charged, and where the residual action of that apparatus was greater than in the former case.

App. i	App. ii	
Balls 150°		
	———152°	
	———148	
divided and instantly taken		
70°	———	
	——— 78	
	———	5 immediately after discharge
0	———	immediately after discharge

1211. The transferable charge being 148°−5°, its half is 71°.5, which is not far removed from 70°, the half charge of i; or from 73°, the half charge of ii: these half charges again making up the sum of 143°, or just the amount of the whole transferable charge. Considering the errors of experiment, therefore, these results may again be received as showing that the apparatus were equal in inductive capacity, or in their powers of receiving charges.

1212. The experiments were repeated with charges of negative electricity with the same general results.

1213. That I might be sure of the sensibility and action of the apparatus, I made such a change in one as ought upon principle to increase its inductive force, i.e., I put a metallic lining into the lower hemisphere of app. i, so as to diminish the thickness of the intervening air in that part, from 0.62 to 0.435 of an inch: this lining was carefully shaped and rounded so that it should not present a sudden projection within at its edge, but a gradual transition from the reduced interval in the lower part of the sphere to the larger one in the upper.

1214. This change immediately caused app. i to produce effects indicating that it had a greater aptness or capacity for induction than app. ii. Thus, when a transferable charge in app. ii of 469° was divided with app. i, the former retained a charge of 225°, whilst the latter showed one of 227°, i.e. the former had lost 244° in communicating 227° to the latter; on the other hand, when app. i had a transferable charge in it of 381° divided by contact with app. ii, it lost 181° only, whilst it gave to app. ii as many as 194:—the sum of the divided forces being in the first instance *less*, and in the second instance *greater* than the original undivided charge. These results are the more striking, as only one-half of the interior of app. i was modified, and they show that the instruments are capable of bringing out differences in inductive force from amongst the errors of experiment, when these differences are much less than that produced by the alteration made in the present instance.

¶ iv. *Induction in Curved Lines*

1215. Amongst those results deduced from the molecular view of induction (1166), which, being of a peculiar nature, are the best tests of the truth or error of the theory, the expected action in curved lines is, I think, the most important at present; for, if shown to take place in an unexceptionable manner, I do not see how the old theory of action at a distance and in straight lines can stand, or how the conclusion that ordinary induction is an action of contiguous particles can be resisted.

1216. There are many forms of old experiments which might be quoted as favourable to, and consistent with the view I have adopted. Such are most cases of electro-chemical decomposition, electrical brushes, auras, sparks, &c.; but as these might be considered equivocal evidence, inasmuch as they include a current and discharge (though they have long been to me indications of prior molecular action [1230]), I endeavoured to devise such experiments for first proofs as should not include transfer, but relate altogether to the pure simple inductive action of statical electricity.

1217. It was also of importance to make these experiments in the simplest possible manner, using not more than one insulating medium or dielectric at a time, lest differences of slow conduction should produce effects which might erroneously be supposed to result from induction in curved lines. It will be unnecessary to describe the steps of the investigation minutely; I will at once proceed to the simplest mode of proving the facts, first in air and then in other insulating media.

1218. A cylinder of solid shellac, 0.9 of an inch in diameter and seven inches in length, was fixed upright in a wooden foot (Pl. IX, *Fig. 3*): it was made concave or cupped at its upper extremity so that a brass ball or other small arrangement could stand upon it. The upper half of the stem having been excited *negatively* by friction with warm flannel, a brass ball, B, 1 inch in diameter, was placed on the top, and then the whole arrangement examined by the carrier ball and Coulomb's electrometer (1180, &c.). For this purpose the balls of the electrometer were charged *positively* to about 360°, and then the carrier being applied to various parts of the ball B, the two were uninsulated whilst in contact or in position, then

insulated,[1] separated, and the charge of the carrier examined as to its nature and force. Its electricity was always positive, and its force at the different positions *a*, *b*, *c*, *d*, &c. (Pl. IX, *Figs. 3* and *4*) observed in succession, was as follows:

at *a*	above 1000°
b it was	149
c	270
d	512
b	130

1219. To comprehend the full force of these results, it must first be understood, that all the charges of the ball B and the carrier are charges by induction, from the action of the excited surface of the shellac cylinder; for whatever electricity the ball B received by *communication* from the shellac, either in the first instance or afterwards, was removed by the uninsulating contacts, only that due to induction remaining; and this is shown by the charges taken from the ball in this its uninsulated state being always positive, or of the contrary character to the electricity of the shellac. In the next place, the charges at *a*, *c*, and *d* were of such a nature as might be expected from an inductive action in straight lines, but that obtained at *b* is *not so*: it is clearly a charge by induction, but *induction* in *a curved line*; for the carrier ball whilst applied to *b*, and after its removal to a distance of six inches or more from B, could not, in consequence of the size of B, be connected by a straight line with any part of the excited and inducing shellac.

1220. To suppose that the upper part of the *uninsulated* ball B, should in some way be retained in an electrified state by that portion of the surface of the ball which is in sight of the shellac, would be in opposition to what we know already of the subject. Electricity is retained upon the surface of conductors only by induction (1178); and though some persons may not be prepared as yet to admit this with respect to insulated conductors, all will as regards uninsulated conductors like the ball B; and to decide the matter we have only to place the carrier ball at *e* (Pl. IX, *Fig. 4*), so that it shall not come in contact with B, uninsulate it by a metallic rod descending perpendicularly, insulate it, remove it, and examine its state; it

---

[1] It can hardly be necessary for me to say here that whatever general state the carrier ball acquired in any place where it was uninsulated and then insulated, it retained on removal from that place, notwithstanding that it might pass through other places that would have given to it, if uninsulated, a different condition.

will be found charged with the same kind of electricity as, and even to a *higher degree* (1224) than, if it had been in contact with the summit of B.

1221. To suppose, again, that induction acts in some way *through or across* the metal of the ball, is negatived by the simplest considerations; but a fact in proof will be better. If instead of the ball B a small disc of metal be used, the carrier may be charged at, or above the middle of its upper surface: but if the plate be enlarged to about 1½ or 2 inches in diameter, C (Pl. IX, *Fig. 5*), then no charge will be given to the carrier at *f*, though when applied nearer to the edge at *g*, or even *above the middle* at *h*, a charge will be obtained; and this is true though the plate may be a mere thin film of gold-leaf. Hence it is clear that the induction is not *through* the metal, but through the surrounding air or *dielectric*, and that in curved lines.

1222. I had another arrangement, in which a wire passing downwards through the middle of the shellac cylinder to the earth, was connected with the ball B (Pl. IX, *Fig. 6*) so as to keep it in a constantly uninsulated state. This was a very convenient form of apparatus, and the results with it were the same as those just described.

1223. In another case the ball B was supported by a shellac stem, independently of the excited cylinder of shellac, and at half an inch distance from it; but the effects were the same. Then the brass ball of a charged Leyden jar was used in place of the excited shellac to produce induction; but this caused no alteration of the phenomena. Both positive and negative inducing charges were tried with the same general results. Finally, the arrangement was inverted in the air for the purpose of removing every possible objection to the conclusions, but they came out exactly the same.

1224. Some results obtained with a brass hemisphere instead of the ball B were exceedingly interesting. It was 1.36 of an inch in diameter (Pl. IX, *Fig. 7*), and being placed on the top of the excited shellac cylinder, the carrier ball was applied, as in the former experiments (1218), at the respective positions delineated in the figure. At *i* the force was 112°, at *k* 108°, at *l* 65°, at *m* 35°; the inductive force gradually diminishing, as might have been expected, to this point. But on raising the carrier to the position *n*, the charge increased to 87°; and on raising it still higher to *o*, the charge still further increased to 105°: at a higher point

still, *p*, the charge taken was smaller in amount, being 98°, and continued to diminish for more elevated positions. Here the induction fairly turned a corner. Nothing, in fact, can better show both the curved lines or courses of the inductive action, disturbed as they are from their rectilineal form by the shape, position, and condition of the metallic hemisphere; and also a *lateral tension*, so to speak, of these lines on one another: all depending, as I conceive, on induction being an action of the contiguous particles of the dielectric, which being thrown into a state of polarity and tension, are in mutual relation by their forces in all directions.

1225. As another proof that the whole of these actions were inductive I may state a result which was exactly what might be expected, namely, that if uninsulated conducting matter was brought round and near to the excited shellac stem, then the inductive force was directed towards it, and could not be found on the top of the hemisphere. Removing this matter the lines of force resumed their former direction. The experiment affords proofs of the lateral tension of these lines, and supplies a warning to remove such matter in repeating the above investigation.

1226. After these results on curved inductive action in air I extended the experiments to other gases, using first carbonic acid and then hydrogen: the phenomena were precisely those already described. In these experiments I found that if the gases were confined in vessels they required to be very large, for whether of glass or earthenware. the conducting power of such materials is so great that the induction of the excited shellac cylinder towards them is as much as if they were metal; and if the vessels be small, so great a portion of the inductive force is determined towards them that the lateral tension or mutual repulsion of the lines of force before spoken of (1224), by which their inflexion is caused, is so much relieved in other directions, that no inductive charge will be given to the carrier ball in the positions *k, l, m, n, o, p* (Pl. IX, *Fig. 7*). A very good mode of making the experiment is to let large currents of the gases ascend or descend through the air, and carry on the experiments in these currents.

1227. These experiments were then varied by the substitution of a liquid dielectric, namely, *oil of turpentine*, in place of air and gases. A dish of thin glass well-covered with a film of shellac (1272), which was found by trial to insulate well, had some highly rectified oil of turpentine put into it to the depth of half an inch, and being then placed upon the top of the brass hemisphere (*Fig. 7*), observations were made with the carrier ball as before (1224). The results were the same, and the circumstance of some of the positions being within the fluid and some without, made no sensible difference.

1228. Lastly, I used a few solid dielectrics for the same purpose, and with the same results. These were shellac, sulphur, fused and cast borate of lead, flint glass well-covered with a film of lac, and spermaceti. The following was the form of experiment with sulphur, and all were of the same kind. A square plate of the substance, two inches in extent and 0.6 of an inch in thickness, was cast with a small hole or depression in the middle of one surface to receive the carrier ball. This was placed upon the surface of the metal hemisphere (Pl. IX, *Fig. 9*) arranged on the excited lac as in former cases, and observations were made at *n*, *o*, *p*, and *q*. Great care was required in these experiments to free the sulphur or other solid substance from any charge it might previously have received. This was done by breathing and wiping (1203), and the substance being found free from all electrical excitement, was then used in the experiment; after which it was removed and again examined, to ascertain that it had received no charge, but had acted really as a dielectric. With all these precautions the results were the same: and it is thus very satisfactory to obtain the curved inductive action through *solid bodies*, as any possible effect from the translation of charged particles in fluids or gases, which some persons might imagine to be the case, is here entirely negatived.

1229. In these experiments with solid dielectrics, the degree of charge assumed by the carrier ball at the situations *n*, *o*, *p* (Pl. IX, *Fig. 9*), was decidedly greater than that given to the ball at the same places when air only intervened between it and the metal hemisphere. This effect is consistent with what will hereafter be found to be the respective relations of these bodies, as to their power of facilitating induction through them (1269, 1273, 1277).

1230. I might quote *many* other forms of experiment, some old and some new, in which induction in curved or contorted lines takes place, but think it unnecessary after the preceding results; I shall therefore mention but two. If a conductor A (Pl. IX, *Fig. 8*) be electrified, and an insulated metallic ball B, or even a plate, provided the edges be not too thin, be held before it, a small electrometer at *c* or at *d*, unin-

sulated, will give signs of electricity, opposite in its nature to that of A, and therefore caused by induction, although the influencing and influenced bodies cannot be joined by a right line passing through the air. Or if, the electrometers being removed, a point be fixed at the back of the ball in its uninsulated state as at C, this point will become luminous and discharge the conductor A. The latter experiment is described by Nicholson,[1] who, however, reasons erroneously upon it. As to its introduction here, though it is a case of discharge, the discharge is preceded by induction, and that induction must be in curved lines.

1231. As argument against the received theory of induction and in favour of that which I have ventured to put forth, I cannot see how the preceding results can be avoided. The effects are clearly inductive effects produced by electricity, not in currents but in its statical state, and this induction is exerted in lines of force which, though in many experiments they may be straight, are here curved more or less according to circumstances. I use the term *line of inductive force* merely as a temporary conventional mode of expressing the direction of the power in cases of induction; and in the experiments with the hemisphere (1224), it is curious to see how, when certain lines have terminated on the under surface and edge of the metal, those which were before lateral to them *expand and open out from each other*, some bending round and terminating their action on the upper surface of the hemisphere, and others meeting, as it were, above in their progress outwards, uniting their forces to give an increased charge to the carrier ball, at an *increased distance* from the source of power, and influencing each other so as to cause a second flexure in the contrary direction from the first one. All this appears to me to prove that the whole action is one of contiguous particles, related to each other, not merely in the lines which they may be conceived to form through the dielectric, between the *inductric* and the *inducteous* surfaces (1483), but in other lateral directions also. It is this which gives an effect equivalent to a lateral repulsion or expansion in the lines of force I have spoken of, and enables induction to turn a corner (1304). The power, instead of being like that of gravity, which causes particles to act on each other through straight lines, whatever other particles may be between them, is more analogous to that of a series of

[1] *Encyclopædia Britannica* [7th edition], Vol. VI, p. 504.

magnetic needles, or to the condition of the particles considered as forming the whole of a straight or a curved magnet. So that in whatever way I view it, and with great suspicion of the influence of favourite notions over myself, I cannot perceive how the ordinary theory applied to explain induction can be a correct representation of that great natural principle of electrical action.

1232. I have had occasion in describing the precautions necessary in the use of the inductive apparatus, to refer to one founded on induction in curved lines (1203); and after the experiments already described, it will easily be seen how great an influence the shellac stem may exert upon the charge of the carrier ball when applied to the apparatus (1218), unless that precaution be attended to.

1233. I think it expedient, next in the course of these experimental researches, to describe some effects due to *conduction*, obtained with such bodies as glass, lac, sulphur, &c., which had not been anticipated. Being understood, they will make us acquainted with certain precautions necessary in investigating the great question of specific inductive capacity.

1234. One of the inductive apparatus already described (1187, &c.) had a hemispherical cup of shellac introduced which being in the interval between the inner ball and the lower hemisphere, nearly occupied the space there; consequently when the apparatus was charged, the lac was the dielectric or insulating medium through which the induction took place in that part. When this apparatus was first charged with electricity (1198) up to a certain intensity, as 400°, measured by the Coulomb's electrometer (1180), it sank much faster from that degree than if it had been previously charged to a higher point, and had gradually fallen to 400°; or than it would do if the charge were, by a second application, raised up again to 400°; all other things remaining the same. Again, if after having been charged for some time, as fifteen or twenty minutes, it was suddenly and perfectly discharged, even the stem having all electricity removed from it (1203), then the apparatus being left to itself, would gradually recover a charge, which in nine or ten minutes would rise up to 50° or 60°, and in one instance to 80°.

1235. The electricity, which in these cases returned from an apparently latent to a sensible state, was always of the same kind as that which had been given by the charge. The return took place at both the inducing surfaces; for if after the perfect discharge of the apparatus the whole was insulated, as the inner ball resumed a positive state the outer sphere acquired a negative condition.

1236. This effect was at once distinguished from that produced by the excited stem acting in curved lines of induction (1203, 1232), by the circumstance that all the returned electricity could be perfectly and instantly discharged. It appeared to depend upon the shellac within, and to be, in some way, due to electricity evolved from it in consequence of a previous condition into which it had been brought by the charge of the metallic coatings or balls.

1237. To examine this state more accurately, the apparatus, with the hemispherical cup of shellac in it, was charged for about forty-five minutes to above 600° with positive electricity at the balls *h* and B. (*Fig. 104*) above and within. It was then discharged, opened, the shellac taken out, and its state examined; this was done by bringing the carrier ball near the shellac, uninsulating it, insulating it, and then observing what charge it had acquired. As it would be a charge by induction, the state of the ball would indicate the opposite state of electricity in that surface of the shellac which had produced it. At first the lac appeared quite free from any charge; but gradually its two surfaces assumed opposite states of electricity, the concave surface, which had been next the inner and positive ball, assuming a positive state, and the convex surface, which had been in contact with the negative coating, acquiring a negative state; these states gradually increased in intensity for some time.

1238. As the return action was evidently greatest instantly after the discharge, I again put the apparatus together, and charged it for fifteen minutes as before, the inner ball positively. I then discharged it, instantly removing the upper hemisphere with the interior ball, and, leaving the shellac cup in the lower uninsulated hemisphere, examined its inner surface by the carrier ball as before (1237). In this way I found the surface of the shellac actually *negative*, or in the reverse state to the ball which had been in it; this state quickly disappeared, and was succeeded by a positive condition, gradually increasing in intensity for some time, in the same manner as before. The first negative condition of the surface opposite the positive charging ball is a natural consequence of the state of things, the charging ball being in contact with the shellac only in a few points. It does not interfere with the general result and peculiar state now under consideration, except that it assists in illustrating in a very marked manner the ultimate assumption by the surfaces of the shellac of an electrified condition, similar to that of the metallic surfaces opposed to or against them.

1239. *Glass* was then examined with respect to its power of assuming this peculiar state. I had a thick flint-glass hemispherical cup formed, which would fit easily into the space *o* of the lower hemisphere (1188, 1189); it had been heated and varnished with a solution of shellac in alcohol, for the purpose of destroying the conducting power of the vitreous surface (1254). Being then well-warmed and experimented with, I found it could also assume the *same state*, but not apparently to the same degree, the return action amounting in different cases to quantities from 6° to 18°.

1240. *Spermaceti* experimented with in the same manner gave striking results. When the original charge had been sustained for fifteen or twenty minutes at about 500°, the return charge was equal to 95° or 100°, and was about fourteen minutes arriving at the maximum effect. A charge continued for not more than two or three seconds was here succeeded by a return charge of 50° or 60°. The observations formerly made (1234) held good with this substance. Spermaceti, though it will insulate a low charge for some time, is a better conductor than shellac, glass, and sulphur; and this conducting power is connected with the readiness with which it exhibits the particular effect under consideration.

1241. *Sulphur.* I was anxious to obtain the amount of effect with this substance, first, because it is an excellent insulator, and in that respect would illustrate the relation of the effect to the degree of conducting power possessed by the dielectric (1247); and in the next place, that I might obtain that body giving the smallest degree of the effect now under consideration for the investigation of the question of specific inductive capacity (1277).

1242. With a good hemispherical cup of sulphur cast solid and sound, I obtained the return charge, but only to an amount of 17° or 18°. Thus glass and sulphur, which are bodily very bad conductors of electricity, and indeed almost perfect insulators, gave very little of this return charge.

1243. I tried the same experiment having *air* only in the inductive apparatus. After a continued high charge for some time I could obtain a little effect of return action, but it was ultimately traced to the shellac of the stem.

1244. I sought to produce something like this state with one electric power and without induction; for upon the theory of an electric fluid or fluids, that did not seem impossible, and then I should have obtained an absolute charge (1169, 1177), or something equivalent to it. In this I could not succeed. I excited the outside of a cylinder of shellac very highly for some time, and then quickly discharging it (1203), waited and watched whether any return charge would appear, but such was not the case. This is another fact in favour of the inseparability of the two electric forces (1177), and another argument for the view that induction and its concomitant phenomena depend upon a polarity of the particles of matter.

1245. Although inclined at first to refer these effects to a peculiar masked condition of a certain portion of the forces, I think I have since correctly traced them to known principles of electrical action. The effects appear to be due to an actual penetration of the charge to some distance within the electric, at each of its two surfaces, by what we call *conduction*; so that, to use the ordinary phrase, the electric forces sustaining the induction are not upon the metallic surfaces only, but upon and within the dielectric also, extending to a greater or smaller depth from the metal linings. Let *c* (Pl. IX, *Fig. 10*) be the section of a plate of any dielectric, *a* and *b* being the metallic coatings; let *b* be uninsulated, and *a* be charged positively; after ten or fifteen minutes, if *a* and *b* be discharged, insulated, and immediately examined, no electricity will appear in them; but in a short time, upon a second examination, they will appear charged in the same way, though not to the same degree, as they were at first. Now suppose that a portion of the positive force has, under the coercing influence of all the forces concerned, penetrated the dielectric and taken up its place at the line *p*, a corresponding portion of the negative force having also assumed its position at the line *n*; that in fact the electric at these two parts has become charged positive and negative; then it is clear that the induction of these two forces will be much greater one towards the other, and less in an external direction, now that they are at the small distance *n p* from each other, than when they were at the larger interval *a b*. Then let *a* and *b* be discharged; the discharge destroys or neutralizes all external induction, and the coatings are therefore found by the carrier ball unelectrified; but it also removes almost the whole of the forces by which the electric charge was driven into the dielectric, and though probably a part of that charge goes forward in its passage and terminates in what we call discharge, the greater portion returns on its course to the surfaces of c, and consequently to the conductors a and b, and constitutes the recharge observed.

1246. The following is the experiment on which I rest for the truth of this view. Two plates of spermaceti, d and f (Pl. IX, *Fig. 11*), were put together to form the dielectric, a and b being the metallic coatings of this compound plate, as before. The system was charged, then discharged, insulated, examined, and found to give no indications of electricity to the carrier ball. The plates d and f were then separated from each other, and instantly a with d was found in a positive state, and b with f in a negative state, nearly all the electricity being in the linings a and b. Hence it is clear that, of the forces sought for, the positive was in one-half of the compound plate and the negative in the other half; for when removed bodily with the plates from each other's inductive influence, they appeared in separate places, and resumed of necessity their power of acting by induction on the electricity of surrounding bodies. Had the effect depended upon a peculiar relation of the contiguous particles of matter only, then each half-plate, d and f, should have shown positive force on one surface and negative on the other.

1247. Thus it would appear that the best solid insulators, such as shellac, glass, and sulphur, have conductive properties to such an extent, that electricity can penetrate them bodily, though always subject to the overruling condition of induction (1178). As to the depth to which the forces penetrate in this form of charge of the particles, theoretically, it should be throughout the mass, for what the charge of the metal does for the portion of dielectric next to it should be done by the charged dielectric for the portion next beyond it again; but probably in the best insulators the sensible charge is to a very small depth only in the dielectric, for otherwise more would disappear in the first instance whilst the original charge is sustained, less time would be required for the assumption of the particular state, and more electricity would re-appear as return charge.

1248. The condition of *time* required for this penetration of the charge is important, both as respects the general relation of the cases to conduction, and also the removal of an objection that might otherwise properly be raised to

certain results respecting specific inductive capacities, hereafter to be given (1269, 1277).

1249. It is the assumption for a time of this charged state of the glass between the coatings in the Leyden jar, which gives origin to a well-known phenomenon, usually referred to the diffusion of electricity over the uncoated portion of the glass, namely, the *residual charge*. The extent of charge which can spontaneously be recovered by a large battery, after perfect uninsulation of both surfaces, is very considerable, and by far the largest portion of this is due to the return of electricity in the manner described. A plate of shellac six inches square, and half an inch thick, or a similar plate of spermaceti an inch thick, being coated on the sides with tinfoil as a Leyden arrangement, will show this effect exceedingly well.

1250. The peculiar condition of dielectrics which has now been described, is evidently capable of producing an effect interfering with the results and conclusions drawn from the use of the two inductive apparatus, when shellac, glass, &c., is used in one or both of them (1192, 1207), for upon dividing the charge in such cases according to the method described (1198, 1207), it is evident that the apparatus just receiving its half charge must fall faster in its tension than the other. For suppose app. i first charged, and app. ii used to divide with it; though both may actually lose alike, yet app. i, which has been diminished one-half, will be sustained by a certain degree of return action or charge (1234), whilst app. ii will sink the more rapidly from the coming on of the particular state. I have endeavoured to avoid this interference by performing the whole process of comparison as quickly as possible, and taking the force of app. ii immediately after the division, before any sensible diminution of the tension arising from the assumption of the peculiar state could be produced; and I have assumed that as about three minutes pass between the first charge of app. i and the division, and three minutes between the division and discharge, when the force of the non-transferable electricity is measured, the contrary tendencies for those periods would keep that apparatus in a moderately steady and uniform condition for the latter portion of time.

1251. The particular action described occurs in the shellac of the stems, as well as in the *dielectric* used within the apparatuses. It therefore constitutes a cause by which the outside of the stems may in some operations become charged with electricity, independent of the action of dust or carrying particles (1203).

¶v. *On Specific Induction, or Specific Inductive Capacity*

1252. I now proceed to examine the great question of specific inductive capacity, i.e., whether different dielectric bodies actually do possess any influence over the degree of induction which takes place through them. If any such difference should exist, it appeared to me not only of high importance in the further comprehension of the laws and results of induction, but an additional and very powerful argument for the theory I have ventured to put forth, that the whole depends upon a molecular action, in contradistinction to one at sensible distances.

The question may be stated thus: suppose A an electrified plate of metal suspended in the air, and B and C two exactly similar plates, placed parallel to and on each side of A at equal distances and uninsulated; A will then induce equally towards B and C. If in this position of the plates some other dielectric than air, as shellac, be introduced between A and C, will the induction between them remain the same? Will the relation of C and B to A be unaltered, notwithstanding the difference of the dielectrics interposed between them?[1]

1253. As far as I recollect, it is assumed that no change will occur under such variation of circumstances, and that the relations of B and C to A depend entirely upon their distance. I only remember one experimental illustration of the question, and that is by Coulomb,[2] in which he shows that a wire surrounded by shellac took exactly the same quantity of electricity from a charged body as the same wire in air. The experiment offered to me no proof of the truth of the supposition: for it is not the mere films of dielectric substances surrounding the charged body which have to be examined and compared, but the *whole mass* between that body and the surrounding conductors at which the induction terminates. Charge depends upon induction (1171, 1178); and if induction is related to the particles of the surrounding dielectric, then it is related to *all* the particles of that dielectric inclosed by the surrounding conductors, and not merely to the few situated next to the charged body. Whether

the difference I sought for existed or not, I soon found reason to doubt the conclusion that might be drawn from Coulomb's result; and therefore had the apparatus made, which, with its use, has been already described (1187, &c.), and which appears to me well-suited for the investigation of the question.

1254. Glass, and many bodies which might at first be considered as very fit to test the principle, proved exceedingly unfit for that purpose. Glass, principally in consequence of the alkali it contains, however well-warmed and dried it may be, has a certain degree of conducting power upon its surface, dependent upon the moisture of the atmosphere, which renders it unfit for a test experiment. Resin, wax, naphtha, oil of turpentine, and many other substances were in turn rejected, because of a slight degree of conducting power possessed by them; and ultimately shellac and sulphur were chosen, after many experiments, as the dielectrics best fitted for the investigation. No difficulty can arise in perceiving how the possession of a feeble degree of conducting power tends to make a body produce effects, which would seem to indicate that it had a greater capability of allowing induction through it than another body perfect in its insulation. This source of error has been that which I have found most difficult to obviate in the proving experiments.

1255. *Induction through shellac.* As a preparatory experiment, I first ascertained generally that when a part of the surface of a thick plate of shellac was excited or charged, there was no sensible difference in the character of the induction sustained by that charged part, whether exerted through the air in the one direction, or through the shellac of the plate in the other; provided the second surface of the plate had not, by contact with conductors, the action of dust, or any other means, become charged (1203). Its solid condition enabled it to retain the excited particles in a permanent position, but that appeared to be all; for these particles acted just as freely through the shellac on one side as through the air on the other. The same general experiment was made by attaching a disc of tinfoil to one side of the shellac plate, and electrifying it, and the results were the same. Scarcely any other solid substance than shellac and sulphur, and no liquid substance that I have tried, will bear this examination. Glass in its ordinary state utterly fails; yet it was essentially necessary to obtain this

---

[1] Refer for the practical illustration of this statement to the supplementary note commencing 1307, &c.—*Dec.* 1838.

[2] *Mémoires de l'Académie,* 1787, pp. 452, 453.

prior degree of perfection in the dielectric used, before any further progress could be made in the principal investigation.

1256. *Shellac and air* were compared in the first place. For this purpose a thick hemispherical cup of shellac was introduced into the lower hemisphere of one of the inductive apparatus (1187, &c.), so as nearly to fill the lower half of the space *o, o* (Pl. IX, *Fig. 1*) between it and the inner ball; and then charges were divided in the manner already described (1198, 1207), each apparatus being used in turn to receive the first charge before its division by the other. As the apparatuses were known to have equal inductive power when air was in both (1209, 1211), any differences resulting from the introduction of the shellac would show a peculiar action in it, and if unequivocally referable to a specific inductive influence, would establish the point sought to be sustained. I have already referred to the precautions necessary in making the experiments (1199, &c.); and with respect to the error which might be introduced by the assumption of the peculiar state, it was guarded against, as far as possible, in the first place, by operating quickly (1248); and, afterwards, by using that dielectric as glass or sulphur, which assumed the peculiar state most slowly, and in the least degree (1239, 1241).

1257. The shellac hemisphere was put into app. i, and app. ii left filled with air. The results of an experiment in which the charge through air was divided and reduced by the shellac app. were as follows:

App. i. Lac   App. ii. Air
Balls 255°

0° _____	
_____	304°
_____	297
Charge divided	
113 _____	
_____	121
0 _____	after being discharged
_____	7 after being discharged

1258. Here 297°, minus 7°, or 290°, may be taken as the divisible charge of app. ii (the 7° being fixed stem action [1203, 1232]), of which 145° is the half. The lac app. i gave 113° as the power or tension it had acquired after division; and the air app. ii gave 121°, minus 7°, or 114°, as the force it possessed from what it retained of the divisible charge of 290°. These two numbers should evidently be alike, and they are very nearly so, indeed far within the errors of experiment and observation. But these numbers differ very much from 145°, or the force which the half charge would have had if app. i

had contained air instead of shellac; and it appears that whilst in the division the induction through the air has lost 176° of force, that through the lac has only gained 113°.

1259. If this difference be assumed as depending entirely on the greater facility possessed by shellac of allowing or causing inductive action through its substance than that possessed by air, then this capacity for electric induction would be inversely as the respective loss and gain indicated above; and assuming the capacity of the air apparatus as 1, that of the shellac apparatus would be $\frac{176}{113}$ or 1.55.

1260. This extraordinary difference was so unexpected in its amount, as to excite the greatest suspicion of the general accuracy of the experiment, though the perfect discharge of app. i after the division, showed that the 113° had been taken and given up readily. It was evident that, if it really existed, it ought to produce corresponding effects in the reverse order; and that when induction through shellac was converted into induction through air, the force or tension of the whole ought to be *increased*. The app. i was therefore charged in the first place, and its force divided with app. ii. The following were the results:

App. i. Lac   App. ii. Air

_____	0°
215° _____	
204 _____	
Charge divided	
_____	118
118 _____	
_____	0 after being discharged
0 _____	after being discharged

1261. Here 204° must be the utmost of the divisible charge. The app. i and app. ii present 118° as their respective forces; both now much *above* the half of the first force, or 102°, whereas in the former case they were below it. The lac app. i has lost only 86°, yet it has given to the air app. ii 118°, so that the lac still appears much to surpass the air, the capacity of the lac app. i to the air app. ii being as 1.37 to 1.

1262. The difference of 1.55 and 1.37 as the expression of the capacity for the induction of shellac seems considerable, but is in reality very admissible under the circumstances, for both are in error in *contrary directions*. Thus in the last experiment the charge fell from 215° to 204° by the joint effects of dissipation and absorption (1192, 1250), during the time which elapsed in the electrometer operations, between the applications of the carrier ball required to give those two results. Nearly an equal time must have elapsed between the application of the carrier which gave the 204° result, and the division of the charge between the two apparatus; and as the fall in force progressively decreases in amount (1192), if in this case it be taken at 6° only, it will reduce the whole transferable charge at the time of division to 198° instead of 204°; this diminishes the loss of the shellac charge to 80° instead of 86°; and then the expression of specific capacity for it is increased, and, instead of 1.37, is 1.47 times that of air.

1263. Applying the same correction to the former experiment in which air was *first* charged, the result is of the *contrary* kind. No shellac hemisphere was then in the apparatus, and therefore the loss would be principally from dissipation, and not from absorption: hence it would be nearer to the degree of loss shown by the numbers 304° and 297°, and being assumed as 6° would reduce the divisible charge to 284°. In that case the air would have lost 170°, and communicated only 113° to the shellac; and the relative specific capacity of the latter would appear to be 1.50, which is very little indeed removed from 1.47, the expression given by the second experiment when corrected in the same way.

1264. The shellac was then removed from app. i and put into app. ii and the experiments of division again made. I give the results, because I think the importance of the point justifies and even requires them.

App. i. Air　　App. ii. Lac
Balls 200°
　　　　_____　　0°
286°　　_____
283
Charge divided
　　　　_____ 110
109　　_____
　　　　_____　0.25 after discharge
Trace　　　　after discharge

Here app. i retained 109°, having lost 174° in communicating 110° to app. ii; and the capacity of the air app. is to the lac app., therefore, as 1 to 1.58. If the divided charge be corrected for an assumed loss of only 3°, being the amount of previous loss in the same time, it will make the capacity of the shellac app. 1.55 only.

1265. Then app. ii was charged, and the charge divided thus:

App. i. Air　　App. ii. Lac
0°　　_____
　　　　_____ 256°
　　　　_____ 251
Charge divided
146　　_____
　　　　_____ 149
a little _____　after discharge
　　　_____　a little after discharge

Here app. i acquired a charge of 146°, while app. ii lost only 102° in communicating that amount of force; the capacities being, therefore, to each other as 1 to 1.43. If the whole transferable charge be corrected for a loss of 4° previous to division, it gives the expression of 1.49 for the capacity of the shellac apparatus.

1266. These four expressions of 1.47, 1.50, 1.55, and 1.49 for the power of the shellac apparatus, through the different variations of the experiment, are very near to each other; the average is close upon 1.5, which may hereafter be used as the expression of the result. It is a very important result; and, showing for this particular piece of shellac a decided superiority over air in allowing or causing the act of induction, it proved the growing necessity of a more close and rigid examination of the whole question.

1267. The shellac was of the best quality, and had been carefully selected and cleaned; but as the action of any conducting particles in it would tend, virtually, to diminish the quantity or thickness of the dielectric used, and produce effects as if the two inducing surfaces of the conductors in that apparatus were nearer together than in the one with air only, I prepared another shellac hemisphere, of which the material had been dissolved in strong spirit of wine, the solution filtered, and then carefully evaporated. This is not an easy operation, for it is difficult to drive off the last portions of alcohol without injuring the lac by the heat applied; and unless they be dissipated, the substance left conducts too well to be used in these experiments. I prepared two hemispheres this way, one of them unexceptionable; and with it I repeated the former experiments with all precautions. The results were exactly of the same kind; the following expressions for the capacity of the shellac apparatus, whether it were app. i or ii, being given directly by the experiments, 1.46, 1.50, 1.52, 1.51; the average of these and several others being very nearly 1.5.

1268. As a final check upon the general conclusion, I then actually brought the surfaces of the air apparatus, corresponding to the place of the shellac in its apparatus, nearer together, by putting a metallic lining into the lower hemisphere of the one not containing the lac (1213). The distance of the metal surface from the carrier ball was in this way diminished from 0.62 of an inch to 0.435 of an inch, whilst the interval occupied by the lac in the other apparatus remained 0.62 of an inch as before. Notwithstanding this change, the lac apparatus showed its former superiority; and whether it or the air apparatus was charged first, the capacity of the lac apparatus to the air apparatus was by the experimental results as 1.45 to 1.

1269. From all the experiments I have made, and their constant results, I cannot resist the conclusion that shellac does exhibit a case of *specific inductive capacity*. I have tried to check the trials in every way, and if not remove, at least estimate, every source of error. That the final result is not due to common conduction is shown by the capability of the apparatus to retain the communicated charge; that it is not due to the conductive power of inclosed small particles, by which they could acquire a polarized condition as conductors, is shown by the effects of the shellac purified by alcohol; and, that it is not due to any influence of the charged state, formerly described (1250), first absorbing and then evolving electricity, is indicated by the *instantaneous* assumption and discharge of those portions of the power which are concerned in the phenomena, that instantaneous effect occurring in these cases, as in all others of ordinary induction, by charged conductors. The latter argument is the more striking in the case where the air apparatus is employed to divide the charge with the lac apparatus, for it obtains its portion of electricity in an *instant*, and yet is charged far above the *mean*.

1270. Admitting for the present the general fact sought to be proved; then 1.5, though it expresses the capacity of the apparatus containing the hemisphere of shellac, by no means expresses the relation of lac to air. The lac only occupies one-half of the space *o*, *o*, of the apparatus containing it, through which the induction is sustained; the rest is filled with air, as in the other apparatus; and if the effect of the two upper halves of the globes be abstracted, then the comparison of the shellac powers in the lower half of the one, with the power of the air in the lower half of the other, will be as 2.1; and even this must be less than the truth, for the induction of the upper part of the apparatus, i.e., of the wire and ball B (Pl. IX, *Fig. 1*) to external objects, must be the same in both, and considerably diminish the difference dependent upon, and really producible by, the influence of the shellac within.

1271. *Glass.* I next worked with glass as the dielectric. It involved the possibility of conduction on its surface, but it excluded the idea of conducting particles within its substance (1267) other than those of its own mass. Besides

this it does not assume the charged state (1239) so readily, or to such an extent, as shellac.

1272. A thin hemispherical cup of glass being made hot was covered with a coat of shellac dissolved in alcohol, and after being dried for many hours in a hot place, was put into the apparatus and experimented with. It exhibited effects so slight, that, though they were in the direction indicating a superiority of glass over air, they were allowed to pass as possible errors of experiment; and the glass was considered as producing no sensible effect.

1273. I then procured a thick hemispherical flint glass cup resembling that of shellac (1239), but not filling up the space *o*, *o*, so well. Its average thickness was 0.4 of an inch, there being an additional thickness of air, averaging 0.22 of an inch, to make up the whole space of 0.62 of an inch between the inductive metallic surfaces. It was covered with a film of shellac as the former was (1272), and being made very warm, was introduced into the apparatus, also warmed, and experiments made with it as in the former instances (1257, &c.). The general results were the same as with shellac, i.e., glass surpassed air in its power of favouring induction through it. The two best results as respected the state of the apparatus for retention of charge, &c., gave, when the air apparatus was charged first 1.336, and when the glass apparatus was charged first 1.45, as the specific inductive capacity for glass, both being without correction. The average of nine results, four with the glass apparatus first charged, and five with the air apparatus first charged, gave 1.38 as the power of the glass apparatus; 1.22 and 1.46 being the minimum and maximum numbers with all the errors of experiment upon them. In all the experiments the glass apparatus took up its inductive charge instantly, and lost it as readily (1269); and during the short time of each experiment, acquired the peculiar state in a small degree only, so that the influence of this state, and also of conduction upon the results, must have been small.

1274. Allowing specific inductive capacity to be proved and active in this case, and 1.38 as the expression for the glass apparatus, then the specific inductive capacity of flint glass will be above 1.76, not forgetting that this expression is for a piece of glass of such thickness as to occupy not quite two-thirds of the space through which the induction is sustained (1253, 1273).

1275. *Sulphur.* The same hemisphere of this substance was used in app. ii as was formerly referred to (1242). The experiments were well made, i.e. the sulphur itself was free from charge both before and after each experiment, and no action from the stem appeared (1203, 1232), so that no correction was required on that account. The following are the results when the air apparatus was first charged and divided:

App. i. Air　App. ii. Sulphur
Balls 280°

0°_____	
_____	0°
438 _____	
434 _____	
Charge divided	
_____	162
164 _____	
_____	160
162 _____	
_____	0 after discharge
0 _____	after discharge

Here app. i retained 164°, having lost 270° in communicating 162° to app. ii, and the capacity of the air apparatus is to that of the sulphur apparatus as 1 to 1.66.

1276. Then the sulphur apparatus was charged first, thus:

_____	0°
0°_____	
_____	395
_____	388
Charge divided	
237 _____	
_____	238
0 _____	after discharge
_____	0 after discharge

Here app. ii retained 238°, and gave up 150° in communicating a charge of 237° to app. i, and the capacity of the air apparatus is to that of the sulphur apparatus as 1 to 1.58. These results are very near to each other, and we may take the mean 1.62 as representing the specific inductive capacity of the sulphur apparatus; in which case the specific inductive capacity of sulphur itself as compared to air = 1 (1270) will be about or above 2.24.

1277. This result with sulphur I consider as one of the most unexceptionable. The substance when fused was perfectly clear, pellucid, and free from particles of dirt (1267), so that no interference of small conducting bodies confused the result. The substance when solid is an excellent insulator, and by experiment was found to take up, with great slowness, that state (1241, 1242) which alone seemed likely to disturb the conclusion. The experiments themselves, also, were free from any need of correc-

tion. Yet notwithstanding these circumstances, so favourable to the exclusion of error, the result is a higher specific inductive capacity for sulphur than for any other body as yet tried; and though this may in part be due to the sulphur being in a better shape, i.e., filling up more completely the space *o, o,* (Pl. X, *Fig. 1*) than the cups of shellac and glass, still I feel satisfied that the experiments altogether fully prove the existence of a difference between dielectrics as to their power of favouring an inductive action through them; which difference may, for the present, be expressed by the term *specific inductive capacity*.

1278. Having thus established the point in the most favourable cases that I could anticipate, I proceeded to examine other bodies amongst solids, liquids, and gases. These results I shall give with all convenient brevity.

1279. *Spermaceti.* A good hemisphere of spermaceti being tried as to conducting power whilst its two surfaces were still in contact with the tinfoil moulds used in forming it, was found to conduct sensibly even whilst warm. On removing it from the moulds and using it in one of the apparatuses, it gave results indicating a specific inductive capacity between 1.3 and 1.6 for the apparatus containing it. But as the only mode of operation was to charge the air apparatus, and then after a quick contact with the spermaceti apparatus, ascertain what was left in the former (1281), no great confidence can be placed in the results. They are not in opposition to the general conclusion, but cannot be brought forward as argument in favour of it.

1280. I endeavoured to find some liquids which would insulate well, and could be obtained in sufficient quantity for these experiments. Oil of turpentine, native naphtha rectified, and the condensed oil gas fluid, appeared by common experiments to promise best as to insulation. Being left in contact with fused carbonate of potassa, chloride of lime, and quick lime for some days and then filtered, they were found much injured in insulating power; but after distillation acquired their best state, though even then they proved to be conductors when extensive metallic contact was made with them.

1281. *Oil of turpentine rectified.* I filled the lower half of app. i with the fluid: and as it would not hold a charge sufficiently to enable me first to measure and then divide it, I charged app. ii containing air, and dividing its charge with app. i by a quick contact, measured that remaining in app. ii: for, theoretically, if a quick contact would divide up to equal tension between the two apparatuses, yet without sensible loss from the conducting power of app. i; and app. ii were left charged to a degree of tension above half the original charge, it would indicate that oil of turpentine had less specific inductive capacity than air; or, if left charged below that mean state of tension, it would imply that the fluid had the greater inductive capacity. In an experiment of this kind, app. ii gave as its charge 390° before division with app. i, and 175° afterwards, which is less than the half of 390°. Again, being at 175° before division, it was 79° after, which is also less than half the divided charge. Being at 79°, it was a third time divided, and then fell to 36°, less than the half of 79°. Such are the best results I could obtain; they are not inconsistent with the belief that oil of turpentine has a greater specific capacity than air, but they do not prove the fact, since the disappearance of more than half the charge may be due to the conducting power merely of the fluid.

1282. *Naphtha.* This liquid gave results similar in their nature and direction to those with oil of turpentine.

1283. A most interesting class of substances, in relation to specific inductive capacity, now came under review, namely, the gases or aeriform bodies. These are so peculiarly constituted, and are bound together by so many striking physical and chemical relations, that I expected some remarkable results from them: air in various states was selected for the first experiments.

1284. *Air, rare and dense.* Some experiments of division (1208) seemed to show that dense and rare air were alike in the property under examination. A simple and better process was to attach one of the apparatuses to an airpump, to charge it, and then examine the tension of the charge when the air within was more or less rarefied. Under these circumstances it was found, that commencing with a certain charge, that charge did not change in its tension or force as the air was rarefied, until the rarefaction was such that *discharge* across the space o, o (Pl. IX, *Fig. 1*) occurred. This discharge was proportionate to the rarefaction; but having taken place, and lowered the tension to a certain degree, that degree was not at all affected by restoring the pressure and density of the air to their first quantities.

Inches of Mercury

Thus at a pressure of	30	the charge was	88°
Again	30	the charge was	88
Again	30	the charge was	87
Reduced to	14	the charge was	87
Raised again to	30	the charge was	86
Being now reduced to	3.4	the charge fell to	81
Raised again to	30	the charge was still	81

1285. The charges were low in these experiments, first that they might not pass off at low pressure, and next that little loss by dissipation might occur. I now reduced them still lower, that I might rarefy further, and for this purpose in the following experiment used a measuring interval in the electrometer of only 15° (1185). The pressure of air within the apparatus being reduced to 1.9 inches of mercury, the charge was found to be 29°; then letting in air till the pressure was 30 inches, the charge was still 29°.

1286. These experiments were repeated with pure oxygen with the same consequences.

1287. This result of *no variation* in the electric tension being produced by variation in the density or pressure of the air, agrees perfectly with those obtained by Mr. Harris,[1] and described in his beautiful and important investigations contained in the *Philosophical Transactions*; namely that induction is the same in rare and dense air, and that the divergence of an electrometer under such variations of the air continues the same, provided no electricity pass away from it. The effect is one entirely independent of that power which dense air has of causing a higher charge to be *retained* upon the surface of conductors in it than can be retained by the same conductors in rare air; a point I propose considering hereafter.

1288. I then compared *hot and cold air* together, by raising the temperature of one of the inductive apparatus as high as it could be without injury, and then dividing charges between it and the other apparatus containing cold air. The temperatures were about 50° and 200°. Still the power or capacity appeared to be unchanged; and when I endeavoured to vary the experiment, by charging a cold apparatus and then warming it by a spirit lamp, I could obtain no proof that the inductive capacity underwent any alteration.

1289. I compared *damp and dry air* together, but could find no difference in the results.

1290. *Gases.* A very long series of experiments

[1] *Philosophical Transactions*, 1834, pp. 223, 224. 237, 244.

was then undertaken for the purpose of comparing *different gases* one with another. They were all found to insulate well, except such as acted on the shellac of the supporting stem; these were chlorine, ammonia, and muriatic acid. They were all dried by appropriate means before being introduced into the apparatus. It would have been sufficient to have compared each with air; but, in consequence of the striking result which came out, namely, that *all had the same power of* or *capacity for*, sustaining induction through them (which perhaps might have been expected after it was found that no variation of density or pressure produced any effect), I was induced to compare them, experimentally, two and two in various ways, that no difference might escape me, and that the sameness of result might stand in full opposition to the contrast of property, composition, and condition which the gases themselves presented.

1291. The experiments were made upon the following pairs of gases.

1. Nitrogen and	Oxygen
2. Oxygen	Air
3. Hydrogen	Air
4. Muriatic acid gas	Air
5. Oxygen	Hydrogen
6. Oxygen	Carbonic acid
7. Oxygen	Olefiant gas
8. Oxygen	Nitrous gas
9. Oxygen	Sulphurous acid
10. Oxygen	Ammonia
11. Hydrogen	Carbonic acid
12. Hydrogen	Olefiant gas
13. Hydrogen	Sulphurous acid
14. Hydrogen	Fluo-silicic acid
15. Hydrogen	Ammonia
16. Hydrogen	Arseniuretted hydrogen
17. Hydrogen	Sulphuretted hydrogen
18. Nitrogen	Olefiant gas
19. Nitrogen	Nitrous gas
20. Nitrogen	Nitrous oxide
21. Nitrogen	Ammonia
22. Carbonic oxide	Carbonic acid
23. Carbonic oxide	Olefiant gas
24. Nitrous oxide	Nitrous gas
25. Ammonia	Sulphurous acid

1292. Notwithstanding the striking contrasts of all kinds which these gases present of property, of density, whether simple or compound, anions or cathions (665), of high or low pressure (1284, 1286), hot or cold (1288), not the least difference in their capacity to favour or admit electrical induction through them could be perceived. Considering the point established that in all these gases induction takes place by an action of contiguous particles, this is the

more important, and adds one to the many striking relations which hold between bodies having the gaseous condition and form. Another equally important electrical relation, which will be examined in the next paper,[1] is that which the different gases have to each other at the *same pressure* of causing the retention of the *same or different degrees of charge* upon conductors in them. These two results appear to bear importantly upon the subject of electrochemical excitation and decomposition; for as *all* these phenomena, different as they seem to be, must depend upon the electrical forces of the particles of matter, the very distance at which they seem to stand from each other will do much, if properly considered, to illustrate the principle by which they are held in one common bond, and subject, as they must be, to one common law.

1293. It is just possible that the gases may differ from each other in their specific inductive capacity, and yet by quantities so small as not to be distinguished in the apparatus I have used. It must be remembered, however, that in the gaseous experiments the gases occupy all the space *o o* (Pl. IX, *Fig. 1*), between the inner and the outer ball, except the small portion filled by the stem; and the results, therefore, are twice as delicate as those with solid dielectrics.

1294. The insulation was good in all the experiments recorded, except Nos. 10, 15, 21, and 25, being those in which ammonia was compared with other gases. When shellac is put into ammoniacal gas its surface gradually acquires conducting power, and in this way the lac part of the stem within was so altered, that the ammonia apparatus could not retain a charge with sufficient steadiness to allow of division. In these experiments, therefore, the other apparatus was charged; its charge measured and divided with the ammonia apparatus by a quick contact, and what remained untaken away by the division again measured (1281). It was so nearly one-half of the original charge, as to authorize, with this reservation, the insertion of ammoniacal gas amongst the other gases, as having equal power with them.

¶vi. *General Results as to Induction*

1295. Thus *induction* appears to be essentially an action of contiguous particles, through the intermediation of which the electric force, originating or appearing at a certain place, is propagated to or sustained at a distance, ap-

[1] See in relation to this point 1382, &c.—*Dec.* 1838.

pearing there as a force of the same kind exactly equal in amount, but opposite in its direction and tendencies (1164). Induction requires no sensible thickness in the conductors which may be used to limit its extent; an uninsulated leaf of gold may be made very highly positive on one surface, and as highly negative on the other, without the least interference of the two states whilst the inductions continue. Nor is it affected by the nature of the limiting conductors, provided time be allowed, in the case of those which conduct slowly, for them to assume their final state (1170).

1296. But with regard to the *dielectrics* or insulating media, matters are very different (1167). Their thickness has an immediate and important influence on the degree of induction. As to their quality, though all gases and vapours are alike, whatever their state; yet amongst solid bodies, and between them and gases, there are differences which prove the existence of *specific inductive capacities*, these differences being in some cases very great.

1297. The direct inductive force, which may be conceived to be exerted in lines between the two limiting and charged conducting surfaces, is accompanied by a lateral or transverse force equivalent to a dilatation or repulsion of these representative lines (1224); or the attractive force which exists amongst the particles of the dielectric in the direction of the induction is accompanied by a repulsive or a diverging force in the transverse direction (1304).

1298. Induction appears to consist in a certain polarized state of the particles, into which they are thrown by the electrified body sustaining the action, the particles assuming positive and negative points or parts, which are symmetrically arranged with respect to each other and the inducting surfaces or particles.[1] The state must be a forced one, for it is originated and sustained only by force, and sinks to the normal or quiescent state when that force is removed. It can be *continued* only in insulators by the same portion of electricity, because they only can retain this state of the particles (1304).

1299. The principle of induction is of the utmost generality in electric action. It constitutes charge in every ordinary case, and probably in every case; it appears to be the cause of

all excitement, and to precede every current. The degree to which the particles are affected in this their forced state, before discharge of one kind or another supervenes, appears to constitute what we call *intensity*.

1300. When a Leyden jar is *charged*, the particles of the glass are forced into this polarized and constrained condition by the electricity of the charging apparatus. *Discharge* is the return of these particles to their natural state from their state of tension, whenever the two electric forces are allowed to be disposed of in some other direction.

1301. All charge of conductors is on their surface, because being essentially inductive, it is there only that the medium capable of sustaining the necessary inductive state begins. If the conductors are hollow and contain air or any other dielectric, still no *charge* can appear upon that internal surface, because the dielectric there cannot assume the polarized state throughout, in consequence of the opposing actions in different directions.

1302. The known influence of *form* is perfectly consistent with the corpuscular view of induction set forth. An electrified cylinder is more affected by the influence of the surrounding conductors (which complete the condition of charge) at the ends than at the middle, because the ends are exposed to a greater sum of inductive forces than the middle; and a point is brought to a higher condition than a ball, because by relation to the conductors around, more inductive force terminates on its surface than on an equal surface of the ball with which it is compared. Here too, especially, can be perceived the influence of the lateral or transverse force (1297), which, being a power of the nature of or equivalent to repulsion, causes such a disposition of the lines of inductive force in their course across the dielectric, that they must accumulate upon the point, the end of the cylinder, or any projecting part.

1303. The influence of *distance* is also in harmony with the same view. There is perhaps no distance so great that induction cannot take place through it:[2] but with the same constraining force (1298) it takes place the more easily, according as the extent of dielectric through which it is exerted is lessened. And as it is as-

[1] The theory of induction which I am stating does not pretend to decide whether electricity be a fluid or fluids, or a mere power or condition of recognized matter. That is a question which I may be induced to consider in the next or following series of these researches.

[2] I have traced it experimentally from a ball placed in the middle of the large cube formerly described (1173) to the sides of the cube six feet distant, and also from the same ball placed in the middle of our large lecture-room to the walls of the room at twenty-six feet distance, the charge sustained upon the ball in these cases being solely due to induction through these distances.

sumed by the theory that the particles of the dielectric, though tending to remain in a normal state, are thrown into a forced condition during the induction; so it would seem to follow that the fewer there are of these intervening particles opposing their tendency to the assumption of the new state, the greater degree of change will they suffer, i.e., the higher will be the condition they assume, and the larger the amount of inductive action exerted through them.

1304. I have used the phrases *lines of inductive force* and *curved lines* of force (1231, 1297, 1298, 1302) in a general sense only, just as we speak of the lines of magnetic force. The lines are imaginary, and the force in any part of them is of course the resultant of compound forces, every molecule being related to every other molecule in *all* directions by the tension and reaction of those which are contiguous. The transverse force is merely this relation considered in a direction oblique to the lines of inductive force, and at present I mean no more than that by the phrase. With respect to the term *polarity* also, I mean at present only a disposition of force by which the same molecule acquires opposite powers on different parts. The particular way in which this disposition is made will come into consideration hereafter, and probably varies in different bodies, and so produces variety of electrical relation.[1] All I am anxious about at present is, that a more particular meaning should not be attached to the expressions used than I contemplate. Further inquiry, I trust, will enable us by degrees to restrict the sense more and more, and so render the explanation of electrical phenomena day by day more and more definite.

1305. As a test of the probable accuracy of my views, I have throughout this experimental examination compared them with the conclusions drawn by M. Poisson from his beautiful mathematical inquiries.[2] I am quite unfit to form a judgment of these admirable papers; but as far as I can perceive, the theory I have set forth and the results I have obtained are not in opposition to such of those conclusions as represent the final disposition and state of the forces in the limited number of cases he has considered. His theory assumes a very different mode of action in induction to that which I have ventured to support, and would probably find its mathematical test in the endeavour to apply it to cases of induction in curved lines.

To my feeling it is insufficient in accounting for the retention of electricity upon the surface of conductors by the pressure of the air, an effect which I hope to show is simple and consistent according to the present view;[3] and it does not touch voltaic electricity, or in any way associate it and what is called ordinary electricity under one common principle.

I have also looked with some anxiety to the results which that indefatigable philosopher Harris has obtained in his investigation of the laws of induction,[4] knowing that they were experimental, and having a full conviction of their exactness; but I am happy in perceiving no collision at present between them and the views I have taken.

1306. Finally, I beg to say that I put forth my particular view with doubt and fear, lest it should not bear the test of general examination, for unless true it will only embarrass the progress of electrical science. It has long been on my mind, but I hesitated to publish it until the increasing persuasion of its accordance with all known facts, and the manner in which it linked together effects apparently very different in kind, urged me to write the present paper. I as yet see no inconsistency between it and nature, but, on the contrary, think I perceive much new light thrown by it on her operations; and my next papers will be devoted to a review of the phenomena of conduction, electrolyzation, current, magnetism, retention, discharge, and some other points, with an application of the theory to these effects, and an examination of it by them.

Royal Institution, November 16, 1837

Supplementary Note to Experimental Researches in Electricity, Eleventh Series
RECEIVED MARCH 29, 1838

1307. I have recently put into an experimental form that general statement of the question of *specific inductive capacity* which is given at No. 1252 of Series XI, and the result is such as to lead me to hope the Council of the Royal Society will authorize its addition to the paper in the form of a supplementary note. Three circular brass plates, about five inches in diameter, were mounted side by side upon insulating pillars; the middle one, A, was a fixture, but the outer plates B and C were moveable on slides, so that all three could be brought with their sides almost into contact, or separated to

---

[1] See now 1685, &c.—*Dec.* 1838.
[2] *Mémoires de l'Institut*, 1811, Vol. XII, the first page 1, and the second paging 163.

[3] Refer to 1377, 1378, 1379, 1398.—*Dec.* 1838.
[4] *Philosophical Transactions*, 1834, p. 213.

any required distance. Two gold leaves were suspended in a glass jar from insulated wires; one of the outer plates B was connected with one of the gold leaves, and the other outer plate with the other leaf. The outer plates B and C were adjusted at the distance of an inch and a quarter from the middle plate A, and the gold leaves were fixed at two inches apart; A was then slightly charged with electricity, and the plates B and C, with their gold leaves, thrown out of insulation *at the same time*, and then left insulated. In this state of things A was charged positive inductrically, and B and C negative inducteously; the same dielectric, air, being in the two intervals, and the gold leaves hanging, of course, parallel to each other in a relatively unelectrified state.

1308. A plate of shellac three-quarters of an inch in thickness, and four inches square, suspended by clean white silk thread, was very carefully deprived of all charge (1203) (so that it produced no effect on the gold leaves if A were uncharged) and then introduced between plates A and B; the electric relation of the three plates was immediately altered, and the gold leaves attracted each other. On removing the shellac this attraction ceased; on introducing it between A and C it was renewed; on removing it the attraction again ceased; and the shellac when examined by a delicate Coulomb electrometer was still without charge.

1309. As A was positive, B and C were of course negative; but as the specific inductive capacity of shellac is about twice that of air (1270), it was expected that when the lac was introduced between A and B, A would induce more towards B than towards C; that therefore B would become more negative than before towards A, and consequently, because of its insulated condition, be positive externally, as at its back or at the gold leaves; whilst C would be less negative towards A, and therefore negative outwards or at the gold leaves. This was found to be the case; for on whichever side of A the shellac was introduced the external plate at that side was positive, and the external plate on the other side negative towards each other, and also to uninsulated external bodies.

1310. On employing a plate of sulphur instead of shellac, the same results were obtained; consistent with the conclusions drawn regarding the high specific inductive capacity of that body already given (1276).

1311. These effects of specific inductive capacity can be exalted in various ways, and it is this capability which makes the great value of the apparatus. Thus I introduced the shellac between A and B, and then for a moment connected B and C, uninsulated them, and finally left them in the insulated state; the gold leaves were of course hanging parallel to each other. On removing the shellac the gold leaves attracted each other; on introducing the shellac between A and C this attraction was *increased* (as had been anticipated from theory), and the leaves came together, though not more than four inches long, and hanging three inches apart.

1312. By simply bringing the gold leaves nearer to each other I was able to show the difference of specific inductive capacity when only thin plates of shellac were used, the rest of the dielectric space being filled with air. By bringing B and C nearer to A another great increase of sensibility was made. By enlarging the size of the plates still further power was gained. By diminishing the extent of the wires, &c., connected with the gold leaves, another improvement resulted. So that in fact the gold leaves became, in this manner, as delicate a test of *specific inductive action* as they are, in Bennet's and Singer's electrometers, of ordinary electrical charge.

1313. It is evident that by making the three plates the sides of cells, with proper precautions as regards insulation, &c., this apparatus may be used in the examination of gases, with far more effect than the former apparatus (1187, 1290), and may, perhaps, bring out differences which have as yet escaped me (1292, 1293).

1314. It is also evident that two metal plates are quite sufficient to form the instrument; the state of the single inducteous plate when the dielectric is changed, being examined either by bringing a body excited in a known manner towards its gold leaves, or, what I think will be better, employing a carrier ball in place of the leaf, and examining that ball by the Coulomb electrometer (1180). The inductive and inducteous surfaces may even be balls; the latter being itself the carrier ball of the Coulomb's electrometer (1181, 1229).

1315. To increase the effect, a small condenser may be used with great advantage. Thus if, when two inducteous plates are used, a little condenser were put in the place of the gold leaves, I have no doubt the three principal plates might be reduced to an inch or even half an inch in diameter. Even the gold leaves act to each other for the time as the plates of a condenser. If only two plates were used, by the proper application of the condenser the same reduction might take place. This expectation is fully justified by an effect already observed and described (1229).

1316. In that case the application of the instrument to very extensive research is evident. Comparatively small masses of dielectrics could be examined, as diamonds and crystals. An expectation, that the specific inductive capacity of crystals will vary in different directions, according as the lines of inductive force (1304) are parallel to, or in other positions in relation to the axes of the crystals, can be

tested:[1] I purpose that these and many other thoughts which arise respecting specific inductive action and the polarity of the particles of dielectric matter, shall be put to the proof as soon as I can find time.

1317. Hoping that this apparatus will form an instrument of considerable use, I beg to propose for it (at the suggestion of a friend) the name of *differential inductometer*.

Royal Institution, March 29, 1838

[1] Refer for this investigation to 1689—1698.— *Dec.* 1838.

TWELFTH SERIES

§ 18. *On Induction (continued)* ¶ vii. *Conduction, or Conductive Discharge* ¶ viii. *Electrolytic Discharge* ¶ ix. *Disruptive Discharge —Insulation—Spark—Brush—Difference of Discharge at the Positive and Negative Surfaces of Conductors*

RECEIVED JANUARY 11, READ FEBRUARY 8, 1838

1318. I PROCEED now, according to my promise, to examine, by the great facts of electrical science, that theory of induction which I have ventured to put forth (1165, 1295, &c.). The principle of induction is so universal that it pervades all electrical phenomena; but the general case which I purpose at present to go into consists of insulation traced into and terminating with discharge, with the accompanying effects. This case includes the various *modes* of discharge, and also the condition and characters of a current; the elements of magnetic action being amongst the latter. I shall necessarily have occasion to speak theoretically, and even hypothetically; and though these papers profess to be experimental researches, I hope that, considering the facts and investigations contained in the last series in support of the particular view advanced, I shall not be considered as taking too much liberty on the present occasion, or as departing too far from the character which they ought to have, especially as I shall use every opportunity which presents itself of returning to that strong test of truth, *experiment*.

1319. Induction has as yet been considered in these papers only in cases of insulation; opposed to insulation is *discharge*. The action or effect which may be expressed by the general term *discharge*, may take place, as far as we are aware at present, in several modes. Thus,

that which is called simply *conduction* involves no chemical action, and apparently no displacement of the particles concerned. A second mode may be called *electrolytic discharge*; in it chemical action does occur, and particles must, to a certain degree, be displaced. A third mode, namely, that by sparks or brushes, may, because of its violent displacement of the particles of the *dielectric* in its course, be called the *disruptive discharge*; and a fourth may, perhaps, be conveniently distinguished for a time by the words *convection*, or *carrying discharge*, being that in which discharge is effected either by the carrying power of solid particles, or those of gases and liquids. Hereafter, perhaps, all these modes may appear as the result of one common principle, but at present they require to be considered apart; and I will now speak of the *first* mode, for amongst all the forms of discharge, that which we express by the term *conduction* appears the most simple and the most directly in contrast with insulation.

¶vii. *Conduction, or Conductive Discharge*

1320. Though assumed to be essentially different, yet neither Cavendish nor Poisson attempt to explain by, or even state in, their theories, what the essential difference between insulation and conduction is. Nor have I anything, perhaps, to offer in this respect, *except* that, according to my view of induction, insulation and conduction depend upon the same molecular action of the dielectrics concerned; are only extreme degrees of *one common condition* or effect; and in any sufficient mathematical theory of electricity must be taken as cases of the same kind. Hence the importance of the endeavour to show the connection between them under my theory of the electrical relations of contiguous particles.

1321. Though the action of the insulating dielectric in the charged Leyden jar, and that of the wire in discharging it, may seem very different, they may be associated by numerous intermediate links, which carry us on from one to the other, leaving, I think, no necessary connection unsupplied. We may observe some of these in succession for information respecting the whole case.

1322. Spermaceti has been examined and found to be a dielectric, through which induction can take place (1240, 1246), its specific inductive capacity being about or above 1.8 (1279), and the inductive action has been considered in it, as in all other substances, an action of contiguous particles.

1323. But spermaceti is also a *conductor*, though in so low a degree that we can trace the process of conduction, as it were, step by step through the mass (1247); and even when the electric force has travelled through it to a certain distance, we can, by removing the coercitive (which is at the same time the inductive) force, cause it to return upon its path and reappear in its first place (1245, 1246). Here induction appears to be a necessary preliminary to conduction. It of itself brings the contiguous particles of the dielectric into a certain condition, which, if retained by them, constitutes *insulation*, but if lowered by the communication of power from one particle to another, constitutes *conduction*.

1324. If *glass* or *shellac* be the substances under consideration, the same capabilities of suffering either induction or conduction through them appear (1233, 1239, 1247), but not in the same degree. The conduction almost disappears (1239, 1242); the induction therefore is sustained, i.e., the polarized state into which the inductive force has brought the contiguous particles is retained, there being little discharge action between them, and therefore the *insulation* continues. But, what discharge there is, appears to be consequent upon that condition of the particles into which the induction throws them; and thus it is that ordinary insulation and conduction are closely associated together

or rather are extreme cases of one common condition.

1325. In ice or water we have a better conductor than spermaceti, and the phenomena of induction and insulation therefore rapidly disappear, because conduction quickly follows upon the assumption of the inductive state. But let a plate of cold ice have metallic coatings on its sides, and connect one of these with a good electrical machine in work, and the other with the ground, and it then becomes easy to observe the phenomena of induction through the ice, by the electrical tension which can be obtained and continued on both the coatings (419, 426). For although that portion of power which at one moment gave the inductive condition to the particles is at the next lowered by the consequent discharge due to the conductive act, it is succeeded by another portion of force from the machine to restore the inductive state. If the ice be converted into water the same succession of actions can be just as easily proved, provided the water be distilled, and (if the machine be not powerful enough) a voltaic battery be employed.

1326. All these considerations impress my mind strongly with the conviction, that insulation and ordinary conduction cannot be properly separated when we are examining into their nature; that is, into the general law or laws under which their phenomena are produced. They appear to me to consist in an action of contiguous particles dependent on the forces developed in electrical excitement; these forces bring the particles into a state of tension or polarity, which constitutes both *induction* and *insulation*; and being in this state, the continuous particles have a power or capability of communicating their forces one to the other, by which they are lowered, and discharge occurs. Every body appears to discharge (444, 987); but the possession of this capability in a *greater or smaller degree* in different bodies, makes them better or worse conductors, worse or better insulators; and both *induction* and *conduction* appear to be the same in their principle and action (1320), except that in the latter an effect common to both is raised to the highest degree, whereas in the former it occurs in the best cases, in only an almost insensible quantity.

1327. That in our attempts to penetrate into the nature of electrical action, and to deduce laws more general than those we are at present acquainted with, we should endeavour to bring apparently opposite effects to stand side by side in harmonious arrangement, is an opinion of long standing, and sanctioned by the ablest philosophers. I hope, therefore, I may be excused the attempt to look at the highest cases of conduction as analogous to, or even the same in kind with, those of induction and insulation.

1328. If we consider the slight penetration of sulphur (1241, 1242) or shellac (1234) by electricity, or the feebler insulation sustained by spermaceti (1240, 1279), as essential consequences and indications of their *conducting* power, then may we look on the resistance of metallic wires to the passage of electricity through them as *insulating* power. Of the numerous well-known cases fitted to show this resistance in what are called the perfect conductors, the experiments of Professor Wheatstone best serve my present purpose, since they were carried to such an extent as to show that *time* entered as an element into the conditions of conduction[1] even in metals. When discharge was made through a copper wire 2640 feet in length, and ¼th of an inch in diameter, so that the luminous sparks at each end of the wire, and at the middle, could be observed in the same place, the latter was found to be sensibly behind the two former in time, they being by the conditions of the experiment simultaneous. Hence a proof of retardation; and what reason can be given why this retardation should not be of the same kind as that in spermaceti, or in lac, or sulphur? But as, in them, retardation is insulation, and insulation is induction, why should we refuse the same relation to the same exhibitions of force in the metals?

1329. We learn from the experiment that if *time* be allowed the retardation is gradually overcome; and the same thing obtains for the spermaceti, the lac, and glass (1248); give but time in proportion to the retardation, and the latter is at last vanquished. But if that be the case, and all the results are alike in kind, the only difference being in the length of time, why should we refuse to metals the previous inductive action, which is admitted to occur in the other bodies? The diminution of *time* is no negation of the action; nor is the lower degree of tension requisite to cause the forces to traverse the metal, as compared to that necessary in the cases of water, spermaceti, or lac. These differences would only point to the conclusion, that in metals the particles under induction can transfer their forces when at a lower degree of tension or polarity, and with greater facility than in the instances of the other bodies.

[1] *Philosophical Transactions*, 1834, p. 583.

1330. Let us look at Mr. Wheatstone's beautiful experiment in another point of view. If, leaving the arrangement at the middle and two ends of the long copper wire unaltered, we remove the two intervening portions and replace them by wires of iron or platina, we shall have a much greater retardation of the middle spark than before. If, removing the iron, we were to substitute for it only five or six feet of water in a cylinder of the same diameter as the metal, we should have still greater retardation. If from water we passed to spermaceti, either directly or by gradual steps through other bodies (even though we might vastly enlarge the bulk, for the purpose of evading the occurrence of a spark elsewhere [1331] than at the three proper intervals), we should have still greater retardation, until at last we might arrive, by degrees so small as to be inseparable from each other, at actual and permanent insulation. What, then, is to separate the principle of these two extremes, perfect conduction and perfect insulation, from each other; since the moment we leave in the smallest degree perfection at either extremity, we involve the element of perfection at the opposite end? Especially too, as we have not in nature the case of perfection either at one extremity or the other, either of insulation or conduction.

1331. Again, to return to this beautiful experiment in the various forms which may be given to it: the forces are not all in the wire (after they have left the Leyden jar) during the whole time (1328) occupied by the discharge; they are disposed in part through the surrounding dielectric under the well-known form of induction; and if that dielectric be air, induction takes place from the wire through the air to surrounding conductors, until the ends of the wire are electrically related through its length, and discharge has occurred, i.e., for the *time* during which the middle spark is retarded beyond the others. This is well shown by the old experiment, in which a long wire is so bent that two parts (Pl. X, *Fig.* 1), *a*, *b*, near its extremities shall approach within a short distance, as a quarter of an inch, of each other in the air. If the discharge of a Leyden jar, charged to a sufficient degree, be sent through such a wire, by far the largest portion of the electricity will pass as a spark across the air at the interval, and not by the metal. Does not the middle part of the wire, therefore, act here as an insulating medium, though it be of metal? and is not the spark through the air an indication of the tension (simultaneous with *in-*

PLATE X

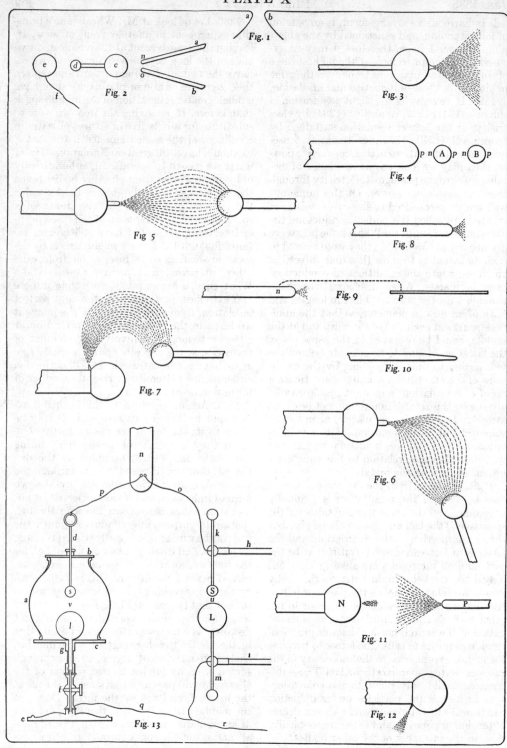

Fig. 1

Fig. 2

Fig. 3

Fig. 4

Fig 5

Fig. 8

Fig. 9

Fig. 7

Fig. 10

Fig. 6

Fig. 11

Fig. 12

Fig. 13

duction) of the electricity in the ends of this single wire? Why should not the wire and the air both be regarded as dielectrics; and the action at its commencement, and whilst there is tension, as an inductive action? If it acts through the contorted lines of the wire, so it also does in curved and contorted lines through air (1219, 1224, 1231), and other insulating dielectrics (1228); and we can apparently go so far in the analogy, whilst limiting the case to the inductive action only, as to show that amongst insulating dielectrics some lead away the lines of force from others (1229), as the wire will do from worse conductors, though in it the principal effect is no doubt due to the ready discharge between the particles whilst in a low state of tension. The retardation is for the time insulation; and it seems to me we may just as fairly compare the air at the interval *a*, *b* (*Fig. 1*) and the wire in the circuit, as two bodies of the same kind and acting upon the same principles, as far as the first inductive phenomena are concerned, notwithstanding the different forms of discharge which ultimately follow,[1] as we may compare, according to Coulomb's investigations,[2] *different lengths* of different insulating bodies required to produce the same amount of insulating effect.

1332. This comparison is still more striking when we take into consideration the experiment of Mr. Harris, in which he stretched a fine wire across a glass globe, the air within being rarefied.[3] On sending a charge through the joint arrangement of metal and rare air, as much, if not more, electricity passed by the latter as by the former. In the air, rarefied as it was, there can be no doubt the discharge was preceded by induction (1284); and to my mind all the circumstances indicate that the same was the case with the metal; that, in fact, both substances are dielectrics, exhibiting the same effects in consequence of the action of the same causes, the only variation being one of degree in the different substances employed.

1333. Judging on these principles, velocity of discharge through the *same wire* may be varied greatly by attending to the circumstances which cause variations of discharge through spermaceti or sulphur. Thus, for instance, it must vary with the tension or intensity of the first urging force (1234, 1240), which tension is charge and induction. So if the two ends of

the wire, in Professor Wheatstone's experiment, were immediately connected with two large insulated metallic surfaces exposed to the air, so that the primary act of induction, after making the contact for discharge, might be in part removed from the internal portion of the wire at the first instant, and disposed for the moment on its surface jointly with the air and surrounding conductors, then I venture to anticipate that the middle spark would be more retarded than before; and if these two plates were the inner and outer coating of a large jar or a Leyden battery, then the retardation of that spark would be still greater.

1334. Cavendish was perhaps the first to show distinctly that discharge was not always by one channel,[4] but, if several are present, by many at once. We may make these different channels of different bodies, and by proportioning their thicknesses and lengths, may include such substances as air, lac, spermaceti, water, protoxide of iron, iron and silver, and by *one* discharge make each convey its proportion of the electric force. Perhaps the air ought to be excepted, as its discharge by conduction is questionable at present (1336); but the others may all be limited in their mode of discharge to pure conduction. Yet several of them suffer previous induction, precisely like the induction through the air, it being a necessary preliminary to their discharging action. How can we therefore separate any one of these bodies from the others, as to the *principles and mode* of insulating and conducting, except by mere degree? All seem to me to be dielectrics acting alike, and under the same common laws.

1335. I might draw another argument in favour of the general sameness, in nature and action, of good and bad conductors (and all the bodies I refer to are conductors more or less), from the perfect equipoise in action of very different bodies when opposed to each other in magneto-electric inductive action, as formerly described (213), but am anxious to be as brief as is consistent with the clear examination of the probable truth of my views.

1336. With regard to the possession by the gases of any conducting power of the simple kind now under consideration, the question is a very difficult one to determine at present. Experiments seem to indicate that they do insulate certain low degrees of tension perfectly, and that the effects which may have appeared to be occasioned by *conduction* have been the result of the carrying power of the charged

[1] These will be examined hereafter (1348, &c.).
[2] *Mémoires de l' Académie*, 1785, p. 612; or *Encyclopædia Britannica* [7th edition], First Supplement, Vol. I, p. 611.
[3] *Philosophical Transactions*, 1834, p. 242.

[4] *Philosophical Transactions*, 1776, p. 197.

particles, either of the air or of dust, in it. It is equally certain, however, that with higher degrees of tension or charge the particles discharge to one another, and that is conduction. If the gases possess the power of insulating a certain low degree of tension continuously and perfectly, such a result may be due to their peculiar physical state, and the condition of separation under which their particles are placed. But in that, or in any case, we must not forget the fine experiments of Cagniard de la Tour,[1] in which he has shown that liquids and their vapours can be made to pass gradually into each other, to the entire removal of any marked distinction of the two states. Thus, hot dry steam and cold water pass by insensible gradations into each other; yet the one is amongst the gases as an insulator and the other a comparatively good conductor. As to conducting power, therefore, the transition from metals even up to gases is gradual; substances make but one series in this respect, and the various cases must come under one condition and law (444). The specific differences of bodies as to conducting power only serves to strengthen the general argument, that conduction, like insulation, is a result of induction, and is an action of contiguous particles.

1337. I might go on now to consider induction and its concomitant, *conduction*, through mixed dielectrics, as, for instance, when a charged body, instead of acting across air to a distant uninsulated conductor, acts jointly through it and an interposed insulated conductor. In such a case, the air and the conducting body are the mixed dielectrics; and the latter assumes a polarized condition as a mass, like that which my theory assumes *each particle* of the air to possess at the same time (1679). But I fear to be tedious in the present condition of the subject, and hasten to the consideration of other matter.

1338. To sum up, in some degree, what has been said, I look upon the first effect of an excited body upon neighbouring matters to be the production of a polarized state of their particles, which constitutes *induction*; and this arises from its action upon the particles in immediate contact with it, which again act upon those contiguous to them, and thus the forces are transferred to a distance. If the induction remain undiminished, then perfect insulation is the consequence; and the higher the polarized condition which the particles can acquire

or maintain, the higher is the intensity which may be given to the acting forces. If, on the contrary, the contiguous particles, upon acquiring the polarized state, have the power to communicate their forces, then conduction occurs, and the tension is lowered, conduction being a distinct act of discharge between neighbouring particles. The lower the state of tension at which this discharge between the particles of a body takes place, the better conductor is that body. In this view, insulators may be said to be bodies whose particles can retain the polarized state; whilst conductors are those whose particles cannot be permanently polarized. If I be right in my view of induction, then I consider the reduction of these two effects (which have been so long held distinct) to an action of contiguous particles obedient to one common law, as a very important result; and, on the other hand, the identity of character which the two acquire when viewed by the theory (1326), is additional presumptive proof in favour of the correctness of the latter.

1339. That heat has great influence over simple conduction is well known (445), its effect being, in some cases, almost an entire change of the characters of the body (432, 1340). Harris has, however, shown that it in no respect affects gaseous bodies, or at least air;[2] and Davy has taught us that, as a class, metals have their conducting power *diminished* by it.[3]

1340. I formerly described a substance, sulphuret of silver, whose conducting power was increased by heat (433, 437, 438); and I have since then met with another as strongly affected in the same way: this is fluoride of lead. When a piece of that substance, which had been fused and cooled, was introduced into the circuit of a voltaic battery, it stopped the current. Being heated, it acquired conducting powers before it was visibly red-hot in daylight; and even sparks could be taken against it whilst still solid. The current alone then raised its temperature (as in the case of sulphuret of silver) until it fused, after which it seemed to conduct as well as the metallic vessel containing it; for whether the wire used to complete the circuit touched the fused fluoride only, or was in contact with the platina on which it was supported, no sensible difference in the force of the current was observed. During all the time there was scarcely a trace of decomposing

[1] *Annales de Chimie*, XXI, pp. 127, 178; or *Quarterly Journal of Science*, XV, 145.

[2] *Philosophical Transactions*, 1834, p. 230.
[3] *Ibid.*, 1821, p. 431.

action of the fluoride, and what did occur seemed referable to the air and moisture of the atmosphere, and not to electrolytic action.

1341. I have now very little doubt that periodide of mercury (414, 448, 691) is a case of the same kind, and also corrosive sublimate (692). I am also inclined to think, since making the above experiments, that the anomalous action of the protoxide of antimony, formerly observed and described (693, 801), may be referred in part to the same cause.

1342. I have no intention at present of going into the particular relation of heat and electricity, but we may hope hereafter to discover by experiment the law which probably holds together all the above effects with those of the *evolution* and the *disappearance* of heat by the current, and the striking and beautiful results of thermo-electricity, in one common bond.

¶ viii. *Electrolytic Discharge*

1343. I have already expressed in a former paper (1164), the view by which I hope to associate ordinary induction and electrolyzation. Under that view, the discharge of electric forces by electrolyzation is rather an effect superadded, in a certain class of bodies, to those already described as constituting induction and insulation, than one independent of and distinct from these phenomena.

1344. Electrolytes, as respects their insulating and conducting forces, belong to the general category of bodies (1320, 1334); and if they are in the solid state (as nearly all can assume that state), they retain their place, presenting then no new phenomenon (426, &c.); or if one occur, being in so small a proportion as to be almost unimportant. When liquefied, they also belong to the same list whilst the electric intensity is below a certain degree; but at a given intensity (910, 912, 1007), fixed for each, and very low in all known cases, they play a new part, causing discharge in proportion (783) to the development of certain chemical effects of combination and decomposition; and at this point, move out from the general class of insulators and conductors, to form a distinct one by themselves. The former phenomena have been considered (1320, 1338); it is the latter which have now to be revised, and used as a test of the proposed theory of induction.

1345. The theory assumes, that the particles of the dielectric (now an electrolyte) are in the first instance brought, by ordinary inductive action, into a polarized state, and raised to a certain degree of tension or intensity before discharge commences; the inductive state being, in fact, a *necessary preliminary* to discharge. By taking advantage of those circumstances which bear upon the point, it is not difficult to increase the tension indicative of this state of induction, and so make the state itself more evident. Thus, if distilled water be employed, and a long narrow portion of it placed between the electrodes of a powerful voltaic battery, we have at once indications of the intensity which can be sustained at these electrodes by the inductive action through the water as a dielectric, for sparks may be obtained, gold leaves diverged, and Leyden bottles charged at their wires. The water is in the condition of the spermaceti (1322, 1323), a bad conductor and a bad insulator; but what it does insulate is by virtue of inductive action, and that induction is the preparation for and precursor of discharge (1338).

1346. The induction and tension which appear at the limits of the portion of water in the direction of the current are only the sums of the induction and tension of the contiguous particles between those limits; and the limitation of the inductive tension, to a certain degree shows (time entering in each case as an important element of the result), that when the particles have acquired a certain relative state, *discharge*, or a transfer of forces equivalent to ordinary conduction, takes place.

1347. In the inductive condition assumed by water before discharge comes on, the particles polarized are the particles of the *water*, that being the dielectric used;[1] but the discharge between particle and particle is not, as before, a mere interchange of their powers or forces at the polar parts, but an actual separation of them into their two elementary particles, the oxygen travelling in one direction, and carrying with it its amount of the force it had acquired during the polarization, and the hydrogen doing the same thing in the other direction, until they each meet the next approaching particle, which is in the same electrical state with that they have left, and by association of their forces with it, produce what constitutes discharge. This part of the action may be regarded as a carrying one (1319, 1572, 1622), performed by the constituent particles of the dielectric. The latter is always a compound body (664, 823); and by those who have considered the subject and are acquainted with the philosophical view of transfer which was first put forth by Grotthuss,[2] its particles may

---

[1] See 1699—1708.—*Dec.* 1838.

[2] *Annales de Chimie*, LVIII, 60; and LXIII, 20.

easily be compared to a series of metallic conductors under inductive action, which, whilst in that state, are divisible into these elementary moveable halves.

1348. Electrolytic discharge depends, of necessity, upon the non-conduction of the dielectric as a whole, and there are two steps or acts in the process: first a polarization of the molecules of the substance and then a lowering of the forces by the separation, advance in opposite directions, and recombination of the elements of the molecules, these being, as it were, the halves of the originally polarized conductors or particles.

1349. These views of the decomposition of electrolytes and the consequent effect of discharge, which, as to the particular case, are the same with those of Grotthuss (481) and Davy (482), though they differ from those of Biot (487), De la Rive (490), and others, seem to me to be fully in accordance not merely with the theory I have given of induction generally (1165), but with all the known *facts* of common induction, conduction, and electrolytic discharge; and in that respect help to confirm in my mind the truth of the theory set forth. The new mode of discharge which electrolyzation presents must surely be an evidence of the *action of contiguous particles*; and as this appears to depend directly upon a previous inductive state, which is the same with common induction, it greatly strengthens the argument which refers induction in all cases to an action of contiguous particles also (1295, &c.).

1350. As an illustration of the condition of the polarized particles in a dielectric under induction, I may describe an experiment. Put into a glass vessel some clear rectified oil of turpentine, and introduce two wires passing through glass tubes where they coincide with the surface of the fluid, and terminating either in balls or points. Cut some very clean dry white silk into small particles, and put these also into the liquid: then electrify one of the wires by an ordinary machine and discharge by the other. The silk will immediately gather from all parts of the liquid, and form a band of particles reaching from wire to wire, and if touched by a glass rod will show considerable tenacity; yet the moment the supply of electricity ceases, the band will fall away and disappear by the dispersion of its parts. The *conduction* by the silk is in this case very small; and after the best examination I could give to the effects, the impression on my mind is, that the adhesion of the whole is due to the polarity

which each filament acquires, exactly as the particles of iron between the poles of a horseshoe magnet are held together in one mass by a similar disposition of forces. The particles of silk therefore represent to me the condition of the molecules of the dielectric itself, which I assume to be polar, just as that of the silk is. In all cases of conductive discharge the contiguous polarized particles of the body are able to effect a neutralization of their forces with greater or less facility, as the silk does also in a very slight degree. Further we are not able to carry the parallel, except in imagination; but if we could divide each particle of silk into two halves, and let each half travel until it met and united with the next half in an opposite state, it would then exert its carrying power (1347), and so far represent electrolytic discharge.

1351. Admitting that electrolytic discharge is a consequence of previous induction, then how evidently do its numerous cases point to induction in curved lines (521, 1216), and to the divergence or lateral action of the lines of inductive force (1231), and so strengthen that part of the general argument in the former paper! If two balls of platina, forming the electrodes of a voltaic battery, are put into a large vessel of dilute sulphuric acid, the whole of the surfaces are covered with the respective gases in beautifully regulated proportions, and the mind has no difficulty in conceiving the direction of the curved lines of discharge, and even the intensity of force of the different lines, by the quantity of gas evolved upon the different parts of the surface. From this condition of the lines of inductive force arise the general effects of diffusion; the appearance of the anions or cathions round the edges and on the farther side of the electrodes when in the form of plates; and the manner in which the current or discharge will follow all the forms of the electrolyte, however contorted. Hence, also, the effects which Nobili has so well examined and described[1] in his papers on the distribution of currents in conducting masses. All these effects indicate the curved direction of the currents or discharges which occur in and through the dielectrics, and these are in every case *preceded* by equivalent inductive actions of the contiguous particles.

1352. Hence also the advantage, when the exciting forces are weak or require assistance, of enlarging the mass of the electrolyte; of increasing the size of the electrodes; of making the coppers surround the zincs: all is in har-

[1] *Bibliothèque Universelle*, 1835, LIX, 263, 416.

mony with the view of induction which I am endeavouring to examine; I do not perceive as yet one fact against it.

1353. There are many points of *electrolytic discharge* which ultimately will require to be very closely considered, though I can but slightly touch upon them. It is not that, as far as I have investigated them, they present any contradiction to the view taken (for I have carefully, though unsuccessfully, sought for such cases), but simply want of time as yet to pursue the inquiry, which prevents me from entering upon them here.

1354. One point is, that different electrolytes or dielectrics require different initial intensities for their decomposition (912). This may depend upon the degree of polarization which the particles require before electrolytic discharge commences. It is in direct relation to the chemical affinity of the substances concerned; and will probably be found to have a relation or analogy to the specific inductive capacity of different bodies (1252, 1296). It thus promises to assist in causing the great truths of those extensive sciences, which are occupied in considering the forces of the particles of matter, to fall into much closer order and arrangement than they have heretofore presented.

1355. Another point is the facilitation of electrolytic conducting power or discharge by the addition of substances to the dielectric employed. This effect is strikingly shown where water is the body whose qualities are improved, but, as yet, no general law governing all the phenomena has been detected. Thus some acids, as the sulphuric, phosphoric, oxalic, and nitric, increase the power of water enormously; whilst others, as the tartaric and citric acids, give but little power; and others, again, as the acetic and boracic acids, do not produce a change sensible to the voltameter (739). Ammonia produces no effect, but its carbonate does. The caustic alkalies and their carbonates produce a fair effect. Sulphate of soda, nitre (753), and many soluble salts produce much effect. Percyanide of mercury and corrosive sublimate produce no effect; nor does iodine, gum, or sugar, the test being a voltameter. In many cases the added substance is acted on either directly or indirectly, and then the phenomena are more complicated; such substances are muriatic acid (758), the soluble protochlorides (766), and iodides (769), nitric acid (752), &c. In other cases the substance added is not, when alone, subject to or a conductor of the

powers of the voltaic battery, and yet both gives and receives power when associated with water. M. de la Rive has pointed this result out in sulphurous acid,[1] iodine and bromine;[2] the chloride of arsenic produces the same effect. A far more striking case, however, is presented by that very influential body, sulphuric acid (681): and probably phosphoric acid also is in the same peculiar relation.

1356. It would seem in the cases of those bodies which suffer no change themselves, as sulphuric acid (and perhaps in all), that they affect water in its conducting power only as an electrolyte; for whether little or much improved, the decomposition is proportionate to the quantity of electricity passing (727, 730), and the transfer is therefore due to electrolytic discharge. This is in accordance with the fact already stated as regards water (984), that the conducting power is not improved for electricity of force below the electrolytic intensity of the substance acting as the dielectric; but both facts (and some others) are against the opinion which I formerly gave, that the power of salts, &c. might depend upon their assumption of the liquid state by solution in the water employed (410). It occurs to me that the effect may perhaps be related to, and have its explanation in differences of specific inductive capacities.

1357. I have described in the last paper, cases, where shellac was rendered a conductor by absorption of ammonia (1294). The same effect happens with muriatic acid; yet both these substances, when gaseous, are non-conductors; and the ammonia, also when in strong solution (748). Mr. Harris has mentioned instances[3] in which the conducting power of metals is seriously altered by a very little alloy. These may have no relation to the former cases, but nevertheless should not be overlooked in the general investigation which the whole question requires.

1358. Nothing is perhaps more striking in that class of dielectrics which we call electrolytes, than the extraordinary and almost complete suspension of their peculiar mode of effecting discharge when they are rendered *solid* (380, &c.), even though the intensity of the induction acting through them may be increased

[1] *Quarterly Journal,* XXVII, 407; or *Bibliothèque Universelle,* XL, 205. Kemp says sulphurous acid is a very good conductor, *Quarterly Journal,* 1831, p. 613.
[2] *Quarterly Journal,* XXIV, 465; or *Annales de Chimie,* XXXV, 161.
[3] *Philosophical Transactions,* 1827, p. 22.

a hundredfold or more (419). It not only establishes a very general relation between the physical properties of these bodies and electricity acting by induction through them, but draws both their physical and chemical relations so near together, as to make us hope we shall shortly arrive at the full comprehension of the influence they mutually possess over each other.

¶ ix. *Disruptive Discharge and Insulation*

1359. The next form of discharge has been distinguished by the adjective *disruptive* (1319), as it in every case displaces more or less the particles amongst and across which it suddenly breaks. I include under it, discharge in the form of sparks, brushes, and glow (1405), but exclude the cases of currents of air, fluids, &c., which, though frequently accompanying the former, are essentially distinct in their nature.

1360. The conditions requisite for the production of an electric spark in its simplest form are well-known. An insulating dielectric must be interposed between two conducting surfaces in opposite states of electricity, and then if the actions be continually increased in strength, or otherwise favoured, either by exalting the electric state of the two conductors, or bringing them nearer to each other, or diminishing the density of the dielectric, a *spark* at last appears, and the two forces are for the time annihilated, for *discharge* has occurred.

1361. The conductors (which may be considered as the termini of the inductive action) are in ordinary cases most generally metals, whilst the dielectrics usually employed are common air and glass. In my view of induction, however, every dielectric becomes of importance, for as the results are considered essentially dependent on these bodies, it was to be expected that differences of action never before suspected would be evident upon close examination, and so at once give fresh confirmation of the theory, and open new doors of discovery into the extensive and varied fields of our science. This hope was especially entertained with respect to the gases, because of their high degree of insulation, their uniformity in physical condition, and great difference in chemical properties.

1362. All the effects prior to the discharge are inductive; and the degree of tension which it is necessary to attain before the spark passes is therefore, in the examination I am now making of the new view of induction, a very important point. It is the limit of the influence which the dielectric exerts in resisting discharge; it is a measure, consequently, of the conservative power of the dielectric, which in its turn may be considered as becoming a measure, and therefore a representative of the intensity of the electric forces in activity.

1363. Many philosophers have examined the circumstances of this limiting action in air, but, as far as I know, none has come near Mr. Harris as to the accuracy with, and the extent to, which he has carried on his investigations.[1] Some of his results I must very briefly notice, premising that they are all obtained with the use of air as the *dielectric* between the conducting surfaces.

1364. First as to the *distance* between the two balls used, or in other words, the *thickness* of the dielectric across which the induction was sustained. The quantity of electricity, measured by a unit jar, or otherwise on the same principle with the unit jar, in the charged or inductive ball, necessary to produce spark discharge, was found to vary exactly with the distance between the balls, or between the discharging points, and that under very varied and exact forms of experiment.[2]

1365. Then with respect to variation in the *pressure* or *density* of the air. The quantities of electricity required to produce discharge across a *constant* interval varied exactly with variations of the density; the quantity of electricity and density of the air being in the same simple ratio. Or, if the quantity was retained the same, whilst the interval and density of the air were varied, then these were found in the inverse simple ratio of each other, the same quantity passing across twice the distance with air rarefied to one-half.[3]

1366. It must be remembered that these effects take place without any variation of the *inductive* force by condensation or rarefaction of the air. That force remains the same in air,[4] and in all gases (1284, 1292), whatever their rarefaction may be.

1367. Variation of the *temperature* of the air produced no variation of the quantity of electricity required to cause discharge across a given interval.[5]

Such are the general results, which I have occasion for at present, obtained by Mr. Harris, and they appear to me to be unexceptionable.

[1] *Philosophical Transactions*, 1834, p. 225.
[2] *Ibid.*, p. 225.
[3] *Ibid.*, p. 229.
[4] *Ibid.*, pp. 237, 244.
[5] *Ibid.*, p. 230.

1368. In the theory of induction founded upon a molecular action of the dielectric, we have to look to the state of that body principally for the cause and determination of the above effects. Whilst the induction continues, it is assumed that the particles of the dielectric are in a certain polarized state, the tension of this state rising higher in each particle as the induction is raised to a higher degree, either by approximation of the inducing surfaces, variation of form, increase of the original force, or other means; until at last, the tension of the particles having reached the utmost degree which they can sustain without subversion of the whole arrangement, discharge immediately after takes place.

1369. The theory does not assume, however, that *all* the particles of the dielectric subject to the inductive action are affected to the same amount, or acquire the same tension. What has been called the lateral action of the lines of inductive force (1231, 1297), and the diverging and occasionally curved form of these lines, is against such a notion. The idea is, that any section taken through the dielectric across the lines of inductive force, and including *all of them*, would be equal, in the sum of the forces, to the sum of the forces in any other section; and that, therefore, the whole amount of tension for each such section would be the same.

1370. Discharge probably occurs, not when all the particles have attained to a certain degree of tension, but when that particle which is most affected has been exalted to the subverting or turning point (1410). For though *all* particles in the line of induction resist charge, and are associated in their actions so as to give a sum of resisting force, yet when any one is brought up to the overturning point, *all* must give way in the case of a spark between ball and ball. The breaking down of that one must of necessity cause the whole barrier to be overturned, for it was at its utmost degree of resistance when it possessed the aiding power of that one particle, in addition to the power of the rest, and the power of that one is now lost. Hence *tension* or *intensity*[1] may, according to the theory, be considered as represented by the particular condition of the particles, or the amount in them of forced variation from their normal state (1298, 1368).

1371. The whole effect produced by a charged conductor on a distant conductor, insulated or not, is by my theory assumed to be due to an action propagated from particle to particle of the intervening and insulating dielectric, all the particles being considered as thrown for the time into a forced condition, from which they endeavour to return to their normal or natural state. The theory, therefore, seems to supply an easy explanation of the influence of *distance* in affecting induction (1303, 1364). As the distance is diminished induction increases; for there are then fewer particles in the line of inductive force to oppose their united resistance to the assumption of the forced or polarized state, and *vice versa*. Again, as the distance diminishes, discharge across happens with a lower charge of electricity; for if, as in Harris' experiments (1364), the interval be diminished to one-half, then half the electricity required to discharge across the first interval is sufficient to strike across the second; and it is evident, also, that at that time there are only half the number of interposed molecules uniting their forces to resist the discharge.

1372. The effect of enlarging the conducting surfaces which are opposed to each other in the act of induction, is, if the electricity be limited in its supply, to lower the intensity of action; and this follows as a very natural consequence from the increased area of the dielectric across which the induction is effected. For by diffusing the inductive action, which at first was exerted through one square inch of sectional area of the dielectric, over two or three square inches of such area, twice or three times the number of molecules of the dielectric are brought into the polarized condition, and employed in sustaining the inductive action, and consequently the tension belonging to the smaller number on which the limited force was originally accumulated, must fall in a proportionate degree.

1373. For the same reason diminishing these opposing surfaces must increase the intensity, and the effect will increase until the surfaces become points. But in this case, the tension of the particles of the dielectric next the points is higher than that of particles midway, because of the lateral action and consequent bulging, as it were, of the lines of inductive force at the middle distance (1369).

1374. The more exalted effects of induction on a point *p*, or any small surface, as the rounded end of a rod, when it is opposed to a large surface, as that of a ball or plate, rather than to another point or end, the distance being in both cases the same, fall into harmonious rela-

[1] See Harris on proposed particular meaning of these terms, *Philosophical Transactions*, 1834, p. 222.

tion with my theory (1302). For in the latter case, the small surface *p* is affected only by those particles which are brought into the inductive condition by the equally small surface of the opposed conductor, whereas when that is a ball or plate the lines of inductive force from the latter are concentrated, as it were, upon the end *p*. Now though the molecules of the dielectric against the large surface may have a much lower state of tension than those against the corresponding smaller surface, yet they are also far more numerous, and, as the lines of inductive force converge towards a point, are able to communicate to the particles contained in any cross section (1369) nearer the small surface an amount of tension equal to their own, and consequently much higher for each individual particle; so that, at the surface of the smaller conductor, the tension of a particle rises much, and if that conductor were to terminate in a point, the tension would rise to an infinite degree, except that it is limited, as before (1368), by discharge. The nature of the discharge from small surfaces and points under induction will be resumed hereafter (1425, &c.).

1375. *Rarefaction* of the air does not alter the *intensity* of inductive action (1284, 1287); nor is there any reason, as far as I can perceive, why it should. If the quantity of electricity and the distance remain the same, and the air be rarefied one-half, then, though one-half of the particles of the dielectric are removed, the other half assume a double degree of tension in their polarity, and therefore the inductive forces are balanced, and the result remains unaltered as long as the induction and insulation are sustained. But the case of *discharge* is very different; for as there are only half the number of dielectric particles in the rarefied atmosphere, so these are brought up to the discharging intensity by half the former quantity of electricity; discharge, therefore, ensues, and such a consequence of the theory is in perfect accordance with Mr. Harris' results (1365).

1376. The *increase* of electricity required to cause discharge over the same distance, when the pressure of the air or its density is increased, flows in a similar manner, and on the same principle (1375), from the molecular theory.

1377. Here I think my view of induction has a decided advantage over others, especially over that which refers the retention of electricity on the surface of conductors in air to the *pressure of the atmosphere* (1305). The latter is the view which, being adopted by Poisson

and Biot,[1] is also, I believe, that generally received; and it associates two such dissimilar things, as the ponderous air and the subtile and even hypothetical fluid or fluids of electricity, by gross mechanical relations; by the bonds of mere static pressure. My theory, on the contrary, sets out at once by connecting the electric forces with the particles of matter; it derives all its proofs, and even its origin in the first instance, from experiment; and then, without any further assumption, seems to offer at once a full explanation of these and many other singular, peculiar, and, I think, heretofore unconnected effects.

1378. An important assisting experimental argument may here be adduced, derived from the difference of specific inductive capacity of different dielectrics (1269, 1274, 1278). Consider an insulated sphere electrified positively and placed in the centre of another and larger sphere uninsulated, a uniform dielectric, as air, intervening. The case is really that of my apparatus (1187), and also, in effect, that of any ball electrified in a room and removed to some distance from irregularly-formed conductors. Whilst things remain in this state the electricity is distributed (so to speak) uniformly over the surface of the electrified sphere. But introduce such a dielectric as sulphur or lac, into the space between the two conductors on one side only, or opposite one part of the inner sphere, and immediately the electricity on the latter is diffused unequally (1229, 1270, 1309), although the form of the conducting surfaces, their distances, and the *pressure* of the atmosphere remain perfectly unchanged.

1379. Fusinieri took a different view from that of Poisson, Biot, and others, of the reason why rarefaction of air caused easy diffusion of electricity. He considered the effect as due to the removal of the *obstacle* which the air presented to the expansion of the substances from which the electricity passed.[2] But platina balls show the phenomena *in vacuo* as well as volatile metals and other substances; besides which, when the rarefaction is very considerable, the electricity passes with scarcely any resistance, and the production of no sensible heat; so that I think Fusinieri's view of the matter is likely to gain but few assents.

1380. I have no need to remark upon the discharging or collecting power of flame or hot air. I believe, with Harris, that the mere heat

[1] *Encyclopædia Britannica* [7th edition], Supplement, Vol. IV, Article *Electricity*, pp. 76, 81, &c.
[2] *Bib. Univ.*, 1831, XLVIII, 375.

does nothing (1367), the rarefaction only being influential. The effect of rarefaction has been already considered generally (1375); and that caused by the heat of a burning light, with the pointed form of the wick, and the carrying power of the carbonaceous particles which for the time are associated with it, are fully sufficient to account for all the effects.

1381. We have now arrived at the important question, how will the inductive tension requisite for insulation and disruptive discharge be sustained in gases, which, having the same physical state and also the *same pressure* and the *same temperature* as *air*, differ from it in specific gravity, in chemical qualities, and it may be in peculiar relations, which not being as yet recognized, are purely electrical (1361)?

1382. Into this question I can enter now only as far as is essential for the present argument, namely, that insulation and inductive tension do not depend merely upon the charged conductors employed, but also, and essentially, upon the interposed dielectric, in consequence of the molecular action of its particles (1292).

1383. A glass vessel *a* (Pl. X, *Fig. 13*) was ground at the top and bottom so as to be closed by two ground brass plates, *b* and *c*; *b* carried a stuffing-box, with a sliding rod *d* terminated by a brass ball *s* below, and a ring above. The lower plate was connected with a foot, stopcock, and socket, *e*, *f* and *g*; and also with a brass ball *l*, which by means of a stem attached to it and entering the socket *g*, could be fixed at various heights. The metallic parts of this apparatus were not varnished, but the glass was well-covered with a coat of shellac previously dissolved in alcohol. On exhausting the vessel at the air-pump it could be filled with any other gas than air, and, in such cases, the gas so passed in was dried whilst entering by fused chloride of calcium.

1384. The other part of the apparatus consisted of two insulating pillars, *h* and *i*, to which were fixed two brass balls, and through these passed two sliding rods, *k* and *m*, terminated at each end by brass balls; *n* is the end of an insulated conductor, which could be rendered either positive or negative from an electrical machine; *o* and *p* are wires connecting it with the two parts previously described, and *q* is a wire which, connecting the two opposite sides of the collateral arrangements, also communicates with a good discharging train *r* (292).

1385. It is evident that with the discharge from the machine electricity may pass either between *s* and *l*, or S and L. The regulation adopted in the first experiments was to keep *s* and *l* with their distance *unchanged*, but to introduce first one gas and then another into the vessel *a*, and then balance the discharge at the one place against that at the other; for by making the interval at *u* sufficiently small, all the discharge would pass there, or making it sufficiently large it would all occur at the interval *v* in the receiver. On principle it seemed evident, that in this way the varying interval *u* might be taken as a measure, or rather indication of the resistance to discharge through the gas at the constant interval *v*. The following are the constant dimensions.

Ball *s*	0.93 of an inch
Ball S	0.96 of an inch
Ball *l*	2.02 of an inch
Ball L	1.95 of an inch
Interval *v*	0.62 of an inch

1386. On proceeding to experiment it was found that when air or any gas was in the receiver *a*, the interval *u* was not a fixed one; it might be altered through a certain range of distance, and yet sparks pass either there or at *v* in the receiver. The extremes were therefore noted, i.e. the greatest distance short of that at which the discharge *always* took place at *v* in the gas, and the least distance short of that at which it *always* took place at *u* in the air. Thus, with air in the receiver, the extremes at *u* were 0.56 and 0.79 of an inch, the range of 0.23 between these distances including intervals at which sparks passed occasionally either at one place or the other.

1387. The small balls *s* and S could be rendered either positive or negative from the machine, and as gases were expected and were found to differ from each other in relation to this change (1399), the results obtained under these differences of charge were also noted.

1388. The following is a table of results; the gas named is that in the vessel *a*. The smallest, greatest, and mean interval at *u* in air is expressed in parts of an inch, the interval *v* being constantly 0.62 of an inch.

	Smallest	Greatest	Mean
Air, *s* and S, pos.	0.60	0.79	0.695
Air, *s* and S, neg.	0.59	0.68	0.635
Oxygen, *s* and S, pos.	0.41	0.60	0.505
Oxygen, *s* and S, neg.	0.50	0.52	0.510
Nitrogen, *s* and S, pos.	0.55	0.68	0.615
Nitrogen, *s* and S, neg.	0.59	0.70	0.645

(*Continued on next page*)

(*Continued*)

	Small-est	Great-est	Mean
Hydrogen, *s* and S, pos.	0.30	0.44	0.370
Hydrogen, *s* and S, neg.	0.25	0.30	0.275
Carbonic acid, *s* and S, pos.	0.56	0.72	0.640
Carbonic acid, *s* and S, neg.	0.58	0.60	0.590
Olefiant gas, *s* and S, pos.	0.64	0.86	0.750
Olefiant gas, *s* and S, neg.	0.69	0.77	0.730
Coal gas, *s* and S, pos.	0.37	0.61	0.490
Coal gas, *s* and S, neg.	0.47	0.58	0.525
Muriatic acid gas, *s* and S, pos.	0.89	1.32	1.105
Muriatic acid gas, *s* and S, neg.	0.67	0.75	0.720

1389. The above results were all obtained at one time. On other occasions other experiments were made, which gave generally the same results as to order, though not as to numbers. Thus:

Hydrogen, *s* and S, pos.	0.23	0.57	0.400
Carbonic acid, *s* and S, pos.	0.51	1.05	0.780
Olefiant gas, *s* and S, pos.	0.66	1.27	0.965

I did not notice the difference of the barometer on the days of experiment.[1]

1390. One would have expected only two distances, one for each interval, for which the discharge might happen either at one or the other; and that the least alteration of either would immediately cause one to predominate constantly over the other. But that under common circumstances is not the case. With air in the receiver, the variation amounted to 0.2 of an inch nearly on the smaller interval of 0.6, and with muriatic acid gas, the variation was above 0.4 on the smaller interval of 0.9. Why is it that when a fixed interval (the one in the receiver) will pass a spark that cannot go across 0.6 of air at one time, it will immediately after, and apparently under exactly similar circumstances, not pass a spark that can go across 0.8 of air?

1391. It is probable that part of this variation will be traced to particles of dust in the air drawn into and about the circuit (1568). I believe also that part depends upon a variable charged condition of the surface of the glass vessel *a*. That the whole of the effect is not traceable to the influence of circumstances in the vessel *a*, may be deduced from the fact, that when sparks occur between balls in free air they frequently are not straight, and often pass otherwise than by the shortest distance. These variations in air itself, and at different parts of the very same balls, show the presence and influence of circumstances which are calculated to produce effects of the kind now under consideration.

[1] Similar experiments in different gases are described at 1507, 1508.—*Dec.* 1838.

1392. When a spark had passed at either interval, then, generally, more tended to appear at the *same* interval, as if a preparation had been made for the passing of the latter sparks. So also on continuing to work the machine quickly the sparks generally followed at the same place. This effect is probably due in part to the warmth of the air heated by the preceding spark, in part to dust, and I suspect in part to something unperceived as yet in the circumstances of discharge.

1393. A very remarkable difference, which is *constant* in its direction, occurs when the electricity communicated to the balls *s* and S is changed from positive to negative, or in the contrary direction. It is that the range of variation is always greater when the small balls are positive than when they are negative. This is exhibited in the following table, drawn from the former experiments.

	Pos.	Neg.
In Air the range was	0.19	0.09
Oxygen	0.19	0.02
Nitrogen	0.13	0.11
Hydrogen	0.14	0.05
Carbonic acid	0.16	0.02
Olefiant gas	0.22	0.08
Coal gas	0.24	0.12
Muriatic acid	0.43	0.08

I have no doubt these numbers require considerable correction, but the general result is striking, and the differences in several cases very great.

1394. Though, in consequence of the variation of the striking distance (1386), the interval in air fails to be a measure, as yet, of the insulating or resisting power of the gas in the vessel, yet we may for present purposes take the mean interval as representing in some degree that power. On examining these mean intervals as they are given in the third column (1388), it will be very evident, that gases, when employed as dielectrics, have peculiar electrical relations to insulation, and therefore to induction, very distinct from such as might be supposed to depend upon their mere physical qualities of specific gravity or pressure.

1395. First, it is clear that at the *same pressure* they are not alike, the difference being as great as 37 and 110. When the small balls are charged positively, and with the same surfaces and the same pressure, muriatic acid gas has three times the insulating or restraining power (1362) of hydrogen gas, and nearly twice that of oxygen, nitrogen, or air.

1396. Yet it is evident that the difference is not due to specific gravity, for though hydrogen is the lowest, and therefore lower than oxygen, oxygen is much beneath nitrogen, or olefiant gas; and carbonic acid gas, though considerably heavier than olefiant gas or muriatic acid gas, is lower than either. Oxygen as a heavy, and olefiant as a light gas, are in strong contrast with each other; and if we may reason of olefiant gas from Harris' results with air (1365), then it might be rarefied to two-thirds its usual density, or to a specific gravity of 9.3 (hydrogen being 1), and having neither the same density nor pressure as oxygen, would have equal insulating powers with it, or equal tendency to resist discharge.

1397. Experiments have already been described (1291, 1292) which show that the gases are sensibly alike in their inductive capacity. This result is not in contradiction with the existence of great differences in their restraining power. The same point has been observed already in regard to dense and rare air (1375).

1398. Hence arises a new argument proving that it cannot be mere pressure of the atmosphere which prevents or governs discharge (1377, 1378), but a specific electric quality or relation of the gaseous medium. Hence also additional argument for the theory of molecular inductive action.

1399. Other specific differences amongst the gases may be drawn from the preceding series of experiments, rough and hasty as they are. Thus the positive and negative series of mean intervals do not give the same differences. It has been already noticed that the negative numbers are lower than the positive (1393), but, besides that, the *order* of the positive and negative results is not the same. Thus, on comparing the mean numbers (which represent for the present insulating tension), it appears that in air, hydrogen, carbonic acid, olefiant gas and muriatic acid, the tension rose higher when the smaller ball was made positive than when rendered negative, whilst in oxygen, nitrogen, and coal gas, the reverse was the case. Now though the numbers cannot be trusted as exact, and though air, oxygen, and nitrogen should probably be on the same side, yet some of the results, as, for instance, those with muriatic acid, fully show a peculiar relation and difference amongst gases in this respect. This was further proved by making the interval in air 0.8 of an inch whilst muriatic acid gas was in the vessel *a*; for on charging the small balls

s and S positively, *all* the discharge took place through the *air*; but on charging them negatively, *all* the discharge took place through the *muriatic acid gas*.

1400. So also, when the conductor *n* was connected *only* with the muriatic acid gas apparatus, it was found that the discharge was more facile when the small ball *s* was negative than when positive; for in the latter case, much of the electricity passed off as brush discharge through the air from the connecting wire *p*; but in the former case, it all seemed to go through the muriatic acid.

1401. The consideration, however, of positive and negative discharge across air and other gases will be resumed in the further part of this, or in the next paper (1465, 1525).

1402. Here for the present I must leave this part of the subject, which had for its object only to observe how far gases agreed or differed as to their power of retaining a charge on bodies acting by induction through them. All the results conspire to show that induction is an action of contiguous molecules (1295, &c.); but besides confirming this, the first principle placed for proof in the present inquiry, they greatly assist in developing the specific properties of each gaseous dielectric, at the same time showing that further and extensive experimental investigation is necessary, and holding out the promise of new discovery as the reward of the labour required.

1403. When we pass from the consideration of dielectrics like the gases to that of bodies having the liquid and solid condition, then our reasonings in the present state of the subject assume much more of the character of mere supposition. Still I do not perceive anything adverse to the theory, in the phenomena which such bodies present. If we take three insulating dielectrics, as air, oil of turpentine, and shellac, and use the same balls or conductors at the same intervals in these three substances, increasing the intensity of the induction until discharge take place, we shall find that it must be raised much higher in the fluid than for the gas, and higher still in the solid than for the fluid. Nor is this inconsistent with the theory; for with the liquid, though its molecules are free to move almost as easily as those of the gas, there are many more particles introduced into the given interval; and such is also the case when the solid body is employed. Besides that with the solid, the cohesive force of the body used will produce some effect; for though the production of the polarized states in the particle of a solid may not be obstructed, but, on the contrary, may in some cases be even favoured (1164, 1344) by its solidity or other circumstances, yet solidity may well exert an influence on the point of final subversion (just as it prevents discharge in an electrolyte), and so enable inductive intensity to rise to a much higher degree.

1404. In the cases of solids and liquids too, bodies may, and most probably do, possess specific differences as to their ability of assuming the polarized state, and also as to the extent to which that polarity must rise before discharge occurs. An analogous difference exists in the specific inductive capacities already pointed out in a few substances (1278) in the last paper. Such a difference might even account for the various degrees of insulating and conducting power possessed by different bodies, and, if it should be found to exist, would add further strength to the argument in favour of the molecular theory of inductive action.

1405. Having considered these various cases of sustained insulation in non-conducting dielectrics up to the highest point which they can attain, we find that they terminate at last in *disruptive discharge*; the peculiar condition of the molecules of the dielectric which was necessary to the continuous induction, being equally essential to the occurrence of that effect which closes all the phenomena. This discharge is not only in its appearance and condition different to the former modes by which the lowering of the powers was effected (1320, 1343), but, whilst really the same in principle, varies much from itself in certain characters, and thus presents us with the forms of *spark*, *brush*, and *glow* (1359). I will first consider *the spark*, limiting it for the present to the case of discharge between two oppositely electrified conducting surfaces.

The Electric Spark or Flash

1406. The *spark* is consequent upon a discharge or lowering of the polarized inductive state of many dielectric particles, by a particular action of a few of the particles occupying a very small and limited space; all the previously polarized particles returning to their first or normal condition in the inverse order in which they left it, and uniting their powers meanwhile to produce, or rather to continue (1417—1436) the discharge effect in the place where the subversion of force first occurred. My impression is that the few particles situated where

discharge occurs are nor merely pushed apart, but assume a peculiar state, a highly exalted condition for the time, i.e., have thrown upon them all the surrounding forces in succession, and rising up to a proportionate intensity of condition, perhaps equal to that of chemically combining atoms, discharge the powers, possibly in the same manner as they do theirs, by some operation at present unknown to us; and so the end of the whole. The ultimate effect is exactly as if a metallic wire had been put into the place of the discharging particles; and it does not seem impossible that the principles of action in both cases, may, hereafter, prove to be the same.

1407. The *path of the spark*, or of the discharge, depends on the degree of tension acquired by the particles in the line of discharge, circumstances, which in every common case are very evident and by the theory easy to understand, rendering it higher in them than in their neighbours, and, by exalting them first to the requisite condition, causing them to determine the course of the discharge. Hence the selection of the path, and the solution of the wonder which Harris has so well described[1] as existing under the old theory. All is prepared amongst the molecules beforehand, by the prior induction, for the path either of the electric spark or of lightning itself.

1408. The same difficulty is expressed as a principle by Nobili for voltaic electricity, almost in Mr. Harris's words, namely,[2] "electricity directs itself towards the point where it can most easily discharge itself," and the results of this as a principle he has well wrought out for the case of voltaic currents. But the *solution* of the difficulty, or the proximate cause of the effects, is the same; induction brings the particles up to or towards a certain degree of tension (1370); and by those which first attain it, is the discharge first and most efficiently performed.

1409. The *moment* of discharge is probably determined by that molecule of the dielectric which, from the circumstances, has its tension most quickly raised up to the maximum intensity. In all cases where the discharge passes from conductor to conductor this molecule must be on the surface of one of them; but when it passes between a conductor and a non-conductor, it is, perhaps, not always so (1453). When this particle has acquired its maximum tension, then the whole barrier of resistance is

[1] *Nautical Magazine*, 1834, p. 229.
[2] *Bibliothèque Universelle*, 1835, LIX, 275.

broken down in the line or lines of inductive action originating at it, and disruptive discharge occurs (1370): and such an inference, drawn as it is from the theory, seems to me in accordance with Mr. Harris' facts and conclusions respecting the resistance of the atmosphere, namely, that it is not really greater at any one discharging distance than another.[1]

1410. It seems probable that the tension of a particle of the same dielectric, as air, which is requisite to produce discharge, is a *constant quantity*, whatever the shape of the part of the conductor with which it is in contact, whether ball or point; whatever the thickness or depth of dielectric throughout which induction is exerted; perhaps, even, whatever the state, as to rarefaction or condensation of the dielectric; and whatever the nature of the conductor, good or bad, with which the particle is for the moment associated. In saying so much, I do not mean to exclude small differences which may be caused by the reaction of neighbouring particles on the deciding particle, and indeed, it is evident that the intensity required in a particle must be related to the condition of those which are contiguous. But if the expectation should be found to approximate to truth, what a generality of character it presents! and, in the definiteness of the power possessed by a particular molecule, may we not hope to find an immediate relation to the force which, being electrical, is equally definite and constitutes chemical affinity?

1411. Theoretically it would seem that, at the moment of discharge by the spark in one line of inductive force, not merely would all the other lines throw their forces into this one (1406), but the lateral effect, equivalent to a repulsion of these lines (1224, 1297), would be relieved and, perhaps, followed by a contrary action, amounting to a collapse or attraction of these parts. Having long sought for some transverse force in statical electricity, which should be the equivalent to magnetism or the transverse force of current electricity, and conceiving that it might be connected with the transverse action of the lines of inductive force already described (1297), I was desirous, by various experiments, of bringing out the effect of such a force, and making it tell upon the phenomena of electro-magnetism and magneto-electricity.[2]

1412. Amongst other results, I expected and sought for the mutual affection, or even the lateral coalition of two similar sparks, if they could be obtained simultaneously side by side, and sufficiently near to each other. For this purpose, two similar Leyden jars were supplied with rods of copper projecting from their balls in a horizontal direction, the rods being about 0.2 of an inch thick, and rounded at the ends. The jars were placed upon a sheet of tinfoil, and so adjusted that their rods, *a* and *b*, were near together, in the position represented in plan (Pl. X, *Fig. 2*): *c* and *d* were two brass balls connected by a brass rod and insulated: *e* was also a brass ball connected, by a wire, with the ground and with the tinfoil upon which the Leyden jars were placed. By laying an insulated metal rod across from *a* to *b*, charging the jars, and removing the rod, both the jars could be brought up to the same intensity of charge (1370). Then, making the ball *e* approach the ball *d*, at the moment the spark passed there, two sparks passed between the rods *n*, *o*, and the ball *c*; and as far as the eye could judge, or the conditions determine, they were simultaneous.

1413. Under these circumstances two modes of discharge took place; either each end had its own particular spark to the ball, or else one end only was associated by a spark with the ball, but was at the same time related to the other end by a spark between the two.

1414. When the ball *c* was about an inch in diameter, the ends *n* and *o*, about half an inch from it, and about 0.4 of an inch from each other, the two sparks to the ball could be obtained. When for the purpose of bringing the sparks nearer together, the ends, *n* and *o*, were brought closer to each other, then, unless very carefully adjusted, only one end had a spark with the ball, the other having a spark to it; and the least variation of position would cause either *n* or *o* to be the end which, giving the direct spark to the ball, was also the one through, or by means of which, the other discharged its electricity.

1415. On making the ball *c* smaller, I found that then it was needful to make the interval between the ends *n* and *o* larger in proportion to the distance between them and the ball *c*. On making *c* larger, I found I could diminish the interval, and so bring the two simultaneous separate sparks closer together, until, at last, the distance between them was not more at the widest part than 0.6 of their whole length.

[1] *Philosophical Transactions*, 1834, pp. 227, 229.
[2] See further investigations of this subject, 1658–1666, 1709–1735.—*Dec.* 1838.

1416. Numerous sparks were then passed and carefully observed. They were very rarely straight, but either curved or bent irregularly. In the average of cases they were, I think, decidedly convex towards each other; perhaps two-thirds presented more or less of this effect, the rest bulging more or less outwards. I was never able, however, to obtain sparks which, separately leaving the ends of the wires n and o, conjoined into one spark before they reached or communicated with the ball c. At present, therefore, though I think I saw a tendency in the sparks to unite, I cannot assert it as a fact.

1417. But there is one very interesting effect here, analogous to, and it may be in part the same with, that I was searching for: I mean the increased facility of discharge where the spark passes. For instance, in the cases where one end, as n, discharged the electricity of both ends to the ball c (Pl. XII, Fig. 2), the electricity of the other end o, had to pass through an interval of air 1.5 times as great as that which it might have taken, by its direct passage between the end and the ball itself. In such cases, the eye could not distinguish, even by the use of Wheatstone's means,[1] that the spark from the end n, which contained both portions of electricity, was a double spark. It could not have consisted of two sparks taking separate courses, for such an effect would have been visible to the eye; but it is just possible, that the spark of the first end n and its jar, passing at the smallest interval of time before that of the other o, had heated and expanded the air in its course, and made it so much more favourable to discharge, that the electricity of the end o preferred leaping across to it and taking a very circuitous route, rather than the more direct one to the ball. It must, however, be remarked, in answer to this supposition, that the one spark between d and e would, by its influence, tend to produce simultaneous discharges at n and o, and certainly did so, when no preponderance was given to one wire over the other; as to the previous inductive effect (1414).

1418. The fact, however, is that disruptive discharge is favourable to itself. It is at the outset a case of tottering equilibrium: and if time be an element in discharge, in however minute a proportion (1436), then the commencement of the act at any point favours its continuance and increase there, and portions of power will be discharged by a

course which they would not otherwise have taken.

1419. The mere heating and expansion of the air itself by the first portion of electricity which passes, must have a great influence in producing this result.

1420. As to the result itself, we see its effect in every electric spark; for it is not the whole quantity which passes that determines the discharge, but merely that small portion of force which brings the deciding molecule (1370) up to its maximum tension; then, when its forces are subverted and discharge begins, all the rest passes by the same course, from the influence of the favouring circumstances just referred to; and whether it be the electricity on a square inch, or a thousand square inches of charged glass, the discharge is complete. Hereafter we shall find the influence of this effect in the formation of brushes (1435); and it is not impossible that we may trace it producing the jagged spark and the forked lightning.

1421. The characters of the electric spark in *different gases* vary, and the variation *may* be due simply to the effect of the heat evolved at the moment. But it may also be due to that specific relation of the particles and the electric forces which I have assumed as the basis of a theory of induction; the facts do not oppose such a view; and in that view the variation strengthens the argument for molecular action, as it would seem to show the influence of the latter in every part of the electrical effect (1423, 1454).

1422. The appearances of the sparks in different gases have often been observed and recorded,[2] but I think it not out of place to notice briefly the following results; they were obtained with balls of brass (platina surfaces would have been better), and at common pressures. In *air*, the sparks have that intense light and bluish colour which are so well known, and often have faint or dark parts in their course, when the quantity of electricity passing is not great. In *nitrogen*, they are very beautiful, having the same general appearance as in air, but have decidedly more colour of a bluish or purple character, and I thought were remarkably sonorous. In *oxygen*, the sparks were whiter than in air or nitrogen, and I think not so brilliant. In *hydrogen*, they had a very fine crimson colour, not due to its rarity, for the character

---

[1] *Philosophical Transactions*, 1834, pp. 584, 585.

[2] See Van Marum's description of the Teylerian machine, Vol. I, p. 112, and Vol. II, p. 196; also *Encyclopædia Britannica* [7th edition], Vol. VI, Article *Electricity*, pp. 505, 507.

passed away as the atmosphere was rarefied (1459).[1] Very little sound was produced in this gas; but that is a consequence of its physical condition.[2] In *carbonic acid gas*, the colour was similar to that of the spark in air, but with a little green in it: the sparks were remarkably irregular in form, more so than in common air: they could also, under similar circumstances as to size of ball, &c., be obtained much longer than in air, the gas showing a singular readiness to cause the discharge in the form of spark. In *muriatic acid gas*, the spark was nearly white: it was always bright throughout, never presenting those dark parts which happen in air, nitrogen, and some other gases. The gas was dry, and during the whole experiment the surface of the glass globe within remained quite dry and bright. In *coal gas*, the spark was sometimes green, sometimes red, and occasionally one part was green and another red: black parts also occur very suddenly in the line of the spark, i.e., they are not connected by any dull part with bright portions, but the two seem to join directly one with the other.

1423. These varieties of character impress my mind with a feeling, that they are due to a direct relation of the electric powers to the particles of the dielectric through which the discharge occurs, and are not the mere results of a casual ignition or a secondary kind of action of the electricity, upon the particles which it finds in its course and thrusts aside in its passage (1454).

1424. The spark may be obtained in media which are far denser than air, as in oil of turpentine, olive oil, resin, glass, &c.: it may also be obtained in bodies which being denser likewise approximate to the condition of conductors, as spermaceti, water, &c. But in these cases, nothing occurs which, as far as I can perceive, is at all hostile to the general views I have endeavoured to advocate.

The Electric Brush

1425. The *brush* is the next form of disruptive discharge which I shall consider. There are many ways of obtaining it, or rather of exalting its characters; and all these ways illustrate the principles upon which it is produced. If an insulated conductor, connected with the positive conductor of an electrical machine, have a metal rod 0.3 of an inch in diameter projecting from it outwards from the machine, and term-

inating by a rounded end or a small ball, it will generally give good brushes; or, if the machine be not in good action, then many ways of assisting the formation of the brush can be resorted to; thus, the hand or any *large* conducting surface may be approached towards the termination to increase inductive force (1374): or the termination may be smaller and of badly conducting matter, as wood: or sparks may be taken between the prime conductor of the machine and the secondary conductor to which the termination giving brushes belongs: or, which gives to the brushes exceedingly fine characters and great magnitude, the air around the termination may be rarefied more or less, either by heat or the air-pump; the former favourable circumstances being also continued.

1426. The brush when obtained by a powerful machine on a ball about 0.7 of an inch in diameter, at the end of a long brass rod attached to the positive prime conductor, had the general appearance as to form represented in Pl. X, *Fig. 3*: a short conical bright part or root appeared at the middle part of the ball projecting directly from it, which at a little distance from the ball. broke out suddenly into a wide brush of pale ramifications having a quivering motion, and being accompanied at the same time with a low dull chattering sound.

1427. At first the brush seems continuous, but Professor Wheatstone has shown that the whole phenomenon consists of successive intermitting discharges.[3] If the eye be passed rapidly, not by a motion of the head, but of the eyeball itself, across the direction of the brush, by first looking steadfastly about 10° or 15° above, and then instantly as much below it, the general brush will be resolved into a number of individual brushes, standing in a row upon the line which the eye passed over; each elementary brush being the result of a single discharge, and the space between them representing both the time during which the eye was passing over that space, and that which elapsed between one discharge and another.

1428. The single brushes could easily be separated to eight or ten times their own width, but were not at the same time extended, i.e., they did not become more indefinite in shape, but, on the contrary, less so, each being more distinct in form, ramification, and character, because of its separation from the others, in its effects upon the eye. Each, therefore, was instantaneous in its existence (1436). Each had the conical root complete (1426).

---

[1] Van Marum says they are about four times as large in hydrogen as in air, Vol. I, p. 122.

[2] Leslie, *Cambridge Phil. Transactions*. 267.

[3] *Philosophical Transactions*, 1834, p. 586.

1429. On using a smaller ball, the general brush was smaller, and the sound, though weaker, more continuous. On resolving the brush into its elementary parts, as before, these were found to occur at much shorter intervals of time than in the former case, but still the discharge was intermitting.

1430. Employing a wire with a round end, the brush was still smaller, but, as before, separable into successive discharges. The sound, though feebler, was higher in pitch, being a distinct musical note.

1431. The sound is, in fact due to the recurrence of the noise of each separate discharge, and these, happening at intervals nearly equal under ordinary circumstances, cause a definite note to be heard, which, rising in pitch with the increased rapidity and regularity of the intermitting discharges, gives a ready and accurate measure of the intervals, and so may be used in any case when the discharge is heard, even though the appearances may not be seen, to determine the element of *time*. So when, by bringing the hand towards a projecting rod or ball, the pitch of the tone produced by a brushy discharge increases, the effect informs us that we have increased the induction (1374), and by that means increased the rapidity of the alternations of charge and discharge.

1432. By using wires with finer terminations, smaller brushes were obtained, until they could hardly be distinguished as brushes; but as long as *sound* was heard, the discharge could be ascertained by the eye to be intermitting; and when the sound ceased, the light became *continuous* as a glow (1359, 1405, 1526—1543).

1433. To those not accustomed to use the eye in the manner I have described, or, in cases where the recurrence is too quick for any unassisted eye, the beautiful revolving mirror of Professor Wheatstone[1] will be useful for such developments of condition as those mentioned above. Another excellent process is to produce the brush or other luminous phenomenon on the end of a rod held in the hand opposite to a charged positive or negative conductor, and then move the rod rapidly from side to side whilst the eye remains still. The successive discharges occur of course in different places, and the state of things before, at, and after a single coruscation or brush can be exceedingly well separated.

1434. The *brush* is in reality a discharge between a bad or a non-conductor and either a conductor or another non-conductor. Under

[1] *Philosophical Transactions*, 1834, pp. 584, 585.

common circumstances, the brush is a discharge between a conductor and air, and I conceive it to take place in something like the following manner. When the end of an electrified rod projects into the middle of a room, induction takes place between it and the walls of the room, across the dielectric, air; and the lines of inductive force accumulate upon the end in greater quantity than elsewhere, or the particles of air at the end of the rod are more highly polarized than those at any other part of the rod, for the reasons already given (1374). The particles of air situated in sections across these lines of force are least polarized in the sections towards the walls and most polarized in those nearer to the end of the wires (1369): thus, it may well happen, that a particle at the end of the wire is at a tension that will immediately terminate in discharge, whilst in those even only a few inches off, the tension is still beneath that point. But suppose the rod to be charged positively, a particle of air A (Pl. X, *Fig. 4*), next it, being polarized, and having of course its negative force directed towards the rod and its positive force outwards; the instant that discharge takes place between the positive force of the particle of the rod opposite the air and the negative force of the particle of air towards the rod, the whole particle of air becomes positively electrified; and when, the next instant, the discharged part of the rod resumes its positive state by conduction from the surface of metal behind, it not only acts on the particles beyond A, by throwing A into a polarized state again, but A itself, because of its charged state, exerts a distinct inductive act toward these further particles, and the tension is consequently so much exalted between A and B, that discharge takes place there also, as well as again between the metal and A.

1435. In addition to this effect, it has been shown that, the act of discharge having once commenced, the whole operation, like a case of unstable equilibrium, is hastened to a conclusion (1370, 1418), the rest of the act being facilitated in its occurrence, and other electricity than that which caused the first necessary tension hurrying to the spot. When, therefore, disruptive discharge has once commenced at the root of a brush, the electric force which has been accumulating in the conductor attached to the rod finds a more ready discharge there than elsewhere, and will at once follow the course marked out as it were for it, thus leaving the conductor in a partially discharged state, and the air about the end of the wire in a charged condition; and the time necessary for restoring the full charge of the conductor, and the dispersion of the charged air in a greater or smaller degree, by the joint forces of repulsion from the conductor and attraction towards the walls of the room, to which its inductive action is directed, is just that time which forms the interval between brush and brush (1420, 1427, 1431, 1447).

1436. The words of this description are long, but there is nothing in the act or the forces on which it depends to prevent the discharge being *instantaneous,* as far as we can estimate and measure it. The consideration of *time* is, however, important in several points of view (1418), and in reference to disruptive discharge, it seemed from theory far more probable that it might be detected in a brush than in a spark; for in a brush, the particles in the line through which the discharge passes are in very different states as to intensity, and the discharge is already complete in its act at the root of the brush, before the particles at the extremity of the ramifications have yet attained their maximum intensity.

1437. I consider *brush* discharge as probably a successive effect in this way. Discharge begins at the root (1426, 1553), and, extending itself in succession to all parts of the single brush, continues to go on at the root and the previously formed parts until the whole brush is complete; then, by the fall in intensity and power at the conductor, it ceases at once in all parts, to be renewed, when that power has risen again to a sufficient degree. But in a *spark,* the particles in the line of discharge being, from the circumstances, nearly alike in their intensity of polarization, suffer discharge so nearly at the same moment as to make the time quite insensible to us.

1438. Mr. Wheatstone has already made experiments which fully illustrate this point. He found that the brush generally had a sensible duration, but that with his highest capabilities he could not detect any such effect in the spark.[1] I repeated his experiment on the brush, though with more imperfect means, to ascertain whether I could distinguish a longer duration in the stem or root of the brush than in the extremities, and the appearances were such as to make me think an effect of this kind was produced.

1439. That the discharge breaks into several ramifications, and by them passes through portions of air alike, or nearly alike, as to polarization and the degree of tension the particles

[1] *Philosophical Transactions,* 1836, pp. 586, 590.

there have acquired, is a very natural result of the previous state of things, and rather to be expected than that the discharge should continue to go straight out into space in a single line amongst those particles which, being at a distance from the end of the rod, are in a lower state of tension than those which are near: and whilst we cannot but conclude, that those parts where the branches of a single brush appear, are more favourably circumstanced for discharge than the darker parts between the ramifications, we may also conclude, that in those parts where the light of concomitant discharge is equal, there the circumstances are nearly equal also. The single successive brushes are by no means of the same particular shape even when they are observed without displacement of the rod or surrounding objects (1427, 1433), and the successive discharges may be considered as taking place into the mass of air around, through different roads at each brush, according as minute circumstances, such as dust, &c. (1391, 1392), may have favoured the course by one set of particles rather than another.

1440. Brush discharge does not essentially require any current of the medium in which the brush appears: the current almost always occurs, but is a consequence of the brush, and will be considered hereafter (1562—1610). On holding a blunt point positively charged towards uninsulated water, a star or glow appeared on the point, a current of air passed from it, and the surface of the water was depressed; but on bringing the point so near that sonorous brushes passed, then the current of air instantly ceased, and the surface of the water became level.

1441. The discharge by a brush is not to all the particles of air that are near the electrified conductor from which the brush issues; only those parts where the ramifications pass are electrified: the air in the central dark parts between them receives no charge, and, in fact, at the time of discharge, has its electric and inductive tension considerably lowered. For consider *Fig.* 128 to represent a single positive brush; the induction before the discharge is from the end of the rod outwards, in diverging lines towards the distant conductors, as the walls of the room, &c., and a particle at *a* has polarity of a certain degree of tension, and tends with a certain force to become charged; but at the moment of discharge, the air in the ramifications *b* and *d,* acquiring also a positive state, opposes its influence to that of the positive conductor on *a,* and the tension of the particle at *a* is therefore diminished rather than increased. The charged particles at *b* and *d* are now inductive bodies, but their lines of inductive action are still outwards towards the walls of the room; the direction of the polarity and the tendency of other particles to charge from these, being governed by, or in conformity with, these lines of force.

1442. The particles that are charged are probably very highly charged, but, the medium being a non-conductor, they cannot communicate that state to their neighbours. They travel, therefore, under the influence of the repulsive and attractive forces, from the charged conductor towards the nearest uninsulated conductor, or the nearest body in a different state to themselves, just as charged particles of dust would travel, and are then discharged; each particle acting, in its course, as a centre of inductive force upon any bodies near which it may come. The travelling of these charged particles when they are numerous, causes wind and currents, but these will come into consideration under *carrying discharge* (1319, 1562, &c.).

1443. When air is said to be electrified, and it frequently assumes this state near electrical machines, it consists, according to my view, of a mixture of electrified and unelectrified particles, the latter being in very large proportion to the former. When we gather electricity from air, by a flame or by wires, it is either by the actual discharge of these particles, or by effects dependent on their inductive action, a case of either kind being producible at pleasure. That the law of equality between the two forces or forms of force in inductive action is as strictly preserved in these as in other cases, is fully shown by the fact, formerly stated (1173, 1174), that, however strongly air in a vessel might be charged positively, there was an exactly equal amount of negative force on the inner surface of the vessel itself, for no residual portion of either the one or the other electricity could be obtained.

1444. I have nowhere said, nor does it follow, that the air is charged only where the luminous brush appears. The charging may extend beyond those parts which are visible, i.e., particles to the right or left of the lines of light may receive electricity, the parts which are luminous being so only because much electricity is passing by them to other parts (1437); just as in a spark discharge the light is greater as more electricity passes, though it has no necessary relation to the quantity required to commence discharge (1370, 1420). Hence the form we see in a brush may by no means represent the whole quantity of air electrified; for an invisible portion, clothing the invisible form to a certain depth, may, at the same time, receive its charge (1552).

1445. Several effects which I have met with in muriatic acid gas tend to make me believe that that gaseous body allows of a dark discharge. At the same time, it is quite clear from theory, that in some gases, the reverse of this may occur, i.e., that the charging of the air may not extend even so far as the light. We do not know as yet enough of the electric light to be able to state on what it depends, and it is very possible that, when electricity bursts forth into air, all the particles of which are in a state of tension, light may be evolved by such as, being very near to, are not of, those which actually receive a charge at the time.

1446. The farther a brush extends in a gas, the farther no doubt is the charge or discharge carried forward; but this may vary between different gases, and yet the intensity required for the first moment of discharge not vary in the same, but in some other proportion. Thus with respect to nitrogen and muriatic acid gases, the former, as far as my experiments have proceeded, produces far finer and larger brushes than the latter (1458, 1462), but the intensity required to commence discharge is much higher for the muriatic acid than the nitrogen (1395). Here again, therefore, as in many other qualities, specific differences are presented by different gaseous dielectrics, and so prove the special relation of the latter to the act and the phenomena of induction.

1447. To sum up these considerations respecting the character and condition of the brush, I may state that it is a spark to air; a diffusion of electric force to matter, not by conduction, but disruptive discharge, a dilute spark which, passing to very badly conducting matter, frequently discharges but a small portion of the power stored up in the conductor; for as the air charged reacts on the conductor, whilst the conductor, by loss of electricity, sinks in its force (1435), the discharge quickly ceases, until by the dispersion of the charged air and the renewal of the excited conditions of the conductor, circumstances have risen up to their first effective condition, again to cause discharge, and again to fall and rise.

1448. The brush and spark gradually pass into one another. Making a small ball positive by a good electrical machine with a large prime conductor, and approaching a large uninsulated discharging ball towards it, very beautiful variations from the spark to the brush may be obtained. The drawings of long and powerful sparks, given by Van Marum,[1] Harris and others,[2] also indicate the same phenomena. As far as I have observed, whenever the spark has been brushy in air of common pressures, the whole of the electricity has not been discharged, but only portions of it, more or less according to circumstances; whereas, whenever the effect has been a distinct spark throughout the whole of its course, the discharge has been perfect, provided no interruption had been made to it elsewhere, in the discharging circuit, than where the spark occurred.

1449. When an electrical brush from an inch to six inches in length or more is issuing into free air, it has the form given (Pl. X, *Fig. 3*). But if the hand, a ball, or any knobbed conductor be brought near, the extremities of the coruscations turn towards it and each other, and the whole assumes various forms according to circumstances, as in Pl. X, *Figs. 5, 6*, and *7*. The influence of the circumstances in each case is easily traced, and I might describe it here, but that I should be ashamed to occupy the time of the Society in things so evident. But how beautifully does the curvature of the ramifications illustrate the curved form of the lines of inductive force existing previous to the discharge! for the former are consequences of the latter, and take their course, in each discharge, where the previous inductive tension had been raised to the proper degree. They represent these curves just as well as iron filings represent magnetic curves, the visible effects in both cases being the consequences of the action of the forces in *the places where* the effects appear. The phenomena, therefore, constitute additional and powerful testimony (1216, 1230) to that already given in favour both of induction through dielectrics in curved lines (1231), and of the lateral relation of these lines, by an effect equivalent to a repulsion producing divergence, or, as in the cases figured, the bulging form.

1450. In reference to the theory of molecular inductive action, I may also add, the proof deducible from the long brushy ramifying spark which may be obtained between a small ball on the positive conductor of an electrical machine, and a larger one at a distance (1448,

[1] Description of the Teylerian machine, Vol. I, pp. 28, 32; Vol. II, p. 226, &c.
[2] *Philosophical Transactions*, 1834, p. 243.

1504). What a fine illustration that spark affords of the previous condition of *all* the particles of the dielectric between the surfaces of discharge, and how unlike the appearances are to any which would be deduced from the theory which assumes inductive action to be action at a distance, in straight lines only; and charge, as being electricity retained upon the surface of conductors by the mere pressure of the atmosphere!

1451. When the brush is obtained in rarefied air, the appearances vary greatly, according to circumstances, and are exceedingly beautiful. Sometimes a brush may be formed of only six or seven branches, these being broad and highly luminous, of a purple colour, and in some parts an inch or more apart: by a spark discharge at the prime conductor (1455) single brushes may be obtained at pleasure. Discharge in the form of a brush is favoured by rarefaction of the air, in the same manner and for the same reason as discharge in the form of a spark (1375); but in every case there is previous induction and charge through the dielectric, and polarity of its particles (1437), the induction being, as in any other instance, alternately raised by the machine and lowered by the discharge. In certain experiments the rarefaction was increased to the utmost degree, and the opposed conducting surfaces brought as near together as possible without producing glow (1529): the brushes then contracted in their lateral dimensions, and recurred so rapidly as to form an apparently continuous arc of light from metal to metal. Still the discharge could be observed to intermit (1427), so that even under these high conditions, induction preceded each single brush, and the tense polarized condition of the contiguous particles was a necessary preparation for the discharge itself.

1452. The brush form of disruptive discharge may be obtained not only in air and gases, but also in much denser media. I procured it in *oil of turpentine* from the end of a wire going through a glass tube into the fluid contained in a metal vessel. The brush was small and very difficult to obtain; the ramifications were simple, and stretched out from each other, diverging very much. The light was exceedingly feeble, a perfectly dark room being required for its observation. When a few solid particles, as of dust or silk, were in the liquid, the brush was produced with much greater facility.

1453. The running together or coalescence of different lines of discharge (1412) is very beautifully shown in the brush in air. This point may present a little difficulty to those who are not accustomed to see in every discharge an equal exertion of power in opposite directions, a positive brush being considered by such (perhaps in consequence of the common phrase *direction of a current*) as indicating a breaking forth in different directions of the original force, rather than a tendency to convergence and union in one line of passage. But the ordinary case of the brush may be compared, for its illustration, with that in which, by holding the knuckle opposite to highly excited glass, a discharge occurs, the ramifications of a brush then leading from the glass and converging into a spark on the knuckle. Though a difficult experiment to make, it is possible to obtain discharge between highly excited shellac and the excited glass of a machine: when the discharge passes, it is, from the nature of the charged bodies, brush at each end and spark in the middle, beautifully illustrating that tendency of discharge to facilitate like action, which I have described in a former page (1418).

1454. The brush has *specific characters* in different gases, indicating a relation to the particles of these bodies even in a stronger degree than the spark (1422, 1423). This effect is in strong contrast with the non-variation caused by the use of different substances as *conductors* from which the brushes are to originate. Thus, using such bodies as wood, card, charcoal, nitre, citric acid, oxalic acid, oxide of lead, chloride of lead, carbonate of potassa, *potassa fusa*, strong solution of potash, oil of vitriol, sulphur, sulphuret of antimony, and hæmatite, no variation in the character of the brushes was obtained, except that (dependent upon their effect as better or worse conductors) of causing discharge with more or less readiness and quickness from the machine.[1]

1455. The following are a few of the effects I observed in different gases at the positively charged surfaces, and with atmospheres varying in their pressure. The general effect of rarefaction was the same for all the gases: at first, sparks passed; these gradually were converted into brushes, which became larger and more distinct in their ramifications, until, upon further rarefaction, the latter began to collapse and draw in upon each other, till they formed a stream across from conductor to conductor:

[1] Exception must, of course, be made of those cases where the root of the brush, becoming a spark, causes a little diffusion or even decomposition of the matter there, and so gains more or less of a particular colour at that part.

then a few lateral streams shot out towards the glass of the vessel from the conductors; these became thick and soft in appearance, and were succeeded by the full constant glow which covered the discharging wire. The phenomena varied with the size of the vessel (1477), the degree of rarefaction, and the discharge of electricity from the machine. When the latter was in successive sparks, they were most beautiful, the effect of a spark from a small machine being equal to, and often surpassing, that produced by the *constant* discharge of a far more powerful one.

1456. *Air.* Fine positive brushes are easily obtained in air at common pressures, and possess the well-known purplish light. When the air is rarefied, the ramifications are very long, filling the globe (1477); the light is greatly increased, and is of a beautiful purple colour, with an occasional rose tint in it.

1457. *Oxygen.* At common pressures, the brush is very close and compressed, and of a dull whitish colour. In rarefied oxygen, the form and appearance are better, the colour somewhat purplish, but all the characters very poor compared to those in air.

1458. *Nitrogen* gives brushes with great facility at the positive surface, far beyond any other gas I have tried: they are almost always fine in form, light, and colour, and in rarefied nitrogen are magnificent. They surpass the discharges in any other gas as to the quantity of light evolved.

1459. *Hydrogen*, at common pressures, gave a better brush than oxygen, but did not equal nitrogen; the colour was greenish gray. In rarefied hydrogen, the ramifications were very fine in form and distinctness, but pale in colour, with a soft and velvety appearance, and not at all equal to those in nitrogen. In the rarest state of the gas, the colour of the light was a pale gray green.

1460. *Coal gas.* The brushes were rather difficult to produce, the contrast with nitrogen being great in this respect. They were short and strong, generally of a greenish colour, and possessing much of the spark character: for, occurring on both the positive and negative terminations, often when there was a dark interval of some length between the two brushes, still the quick, sharp sound of the spark was produced, as if the discharge had been sudden through this gas, and partaking, in that respect, of the character of a spark. In rare coal gas, the brush forms were better, but the light very poor and the colour gray.

1461. *Carbonic acid gas* produces a very poor brush at common pressures, as regards either size, light, or colour; and this is probably connected with the tendency which this gas has to discharge the electricity as a spark (1422). In rarefied carbonic acid, the brush is better in form, but weak as to light, being of a dull greenish or purplish hue, varying with the pressure and other circumstances.

1462. *Muriatic acid gas.* It is very difficult to obtain the brush in this gas at common pressures. On gradually increasing the distance of the rounded ends, the sparks suddenly ceased when the interval was about an inch, and the discharge, which was still through the gas in the globe, was silent and dark. Occasionally a very short brush could for a few moments be obtained, but it quickly disappeared. Even when the intermitting spark current (1455) from the machine was used, still I could only with difficulty obtain a brush, and that very short, though I used rods with rounded terminations (about 0.25 of an inch in diameter) which had before given them most freely in air and nitrogen. During the time of this difficulty with the muriatic gas, magnificent brushes were passing off from different parts of the machine into the surrounding air. On rarefying the gas, the formation of the brush was facilitated, but it was generally of a low squat form, very poor in light, and very similar on both the positive and negative surfaces. On rarefying the gas still more, a few large ramifications were obtained of a pale bluish colour, utterly unlike those in nitrogen.

1463. In all the gases, the different forms of disruptive discharge may be linked together and gradually traced from one extreme to the other, i.e. from the spark to the glow (1405, 1526), or, it may be, to a still further condition to be called dark discharge (1544–1560); but it is, nevertheless, very surprising to see what a specific character each keeps whilst under the predominance of the general law. Thus, in muriatic acid, the brush is very difficult to obtain, and there comes in its place almost a dark discharge, partaking of the readiness of the spark action. Moreover, in muriatic acid, I have *never* observed the spark with any dark interval in it. In nitrogen, the spark readily changes its character into that of brush. In carbonic acid gas, there seems to be a facility to occasion spark discharge, whilst yet that gas is unlike nitrogen in the facility of the latter to form brushes, and unlike muriatic acid in its own fa-

cility to continue the spark. These differences add further force, first to the observations already made respecting the spark in various gases (1422, 1423), and then, to the proofs deducible from it, of the relation of the electrical forces to the particles of matter.

1464. The peculiar characters of nitrogen in relation to the electric discharge (1422, 1458) must, evidently, have an important influence over the form and even the occurrence of lightning. Being that gas which most readily produces coruscations, and, by them, extends discharge to a greater distance than any other gas tried, it is also that which constitutes four-fifths of our atmosphere; and as, in atmospheric electrical phenomena, one, and sometimes both the inductive forces are resident on the particles of the air, which, though probably affected as to conducting power by the aqueous particles in it, cannot be considered as a good conductor; so the peculiar power possessed by nitrogen, to originate and effect discharge in the form of a brush or of ramifications, has probably, an important relation to its electrical service in nature, as it most seriously affects the character and condition of the discharge when made. The whole subject of discharge from and through gases is of great interest, and, if only in reference to atmospheric electricity, deserves extensive and close experimental investigation.

Difference of Discharge at the Positive and Negative Conducting Surfaces

1465. I have avoided speaking of this well-known phenomenon more than was quite necessary, that I might bring together here what I have to say on the subject. When the brush discharge is observed in air at the positive and negative surfaces, there is a very remarkable difference, the true and full comprehension of which would, no doubt, be of the utmost importance to the physics of electricity; it would throw great light on our present subject, i.e., the molecular action of dielectrics under induction, and its consequences; and seems very open to, and accessible by, experimental inquiry.

1466. The difference in question used to be expressed in former times by saying that a point charged positively gave brushes into the air, whilst the same point charged negatively gave a star. This is true only of bad conductors, or of metallic conductors charged intermittingly, or otherwise controlled by collateral induction. If metallic points project *freely* into the air, the positive and negative light upon them differ very little in appearance, and the difference can be observed only upon close examination.

1467. The effect varies exceedingly under different circumstances, but, as we must set out from some position, may perhaps be stated thus: if a metallic wire with a rounded termination in free air be used to produce the brushy discharge, then the brushes obtained when the wire is charged negatively are very poor and small, by comparison with those produced when the charge is positive. Or if a large metal ball connected with the electrical machine be charged *positively*, and a fine uninsulated point be gradually brought towards it, a star appears on the point when at a considerable distance, which, though it becomes brighter, does not change its form of a star until it is close up to the ball: whereas, if the ball be charged negatively, the point at a considerable distance has a star on it as before; but when brought nearer (in my case to the distance of $1\frac{1}{2}$ inch), a brush formed on it, extending to the negative ball; and when still nearer, (at $\frac{1}{8}$ of an inch distance), the brush ceased, and bright sparks passed. These variations, I believe, include the whole series of differences, and they seem to show at once, that the negative surface tends to retain its discharging character unchanged, whilst the positive surface, under similar circumstances, permits of great variation.

1468. There are several points in the character of the negative discharge to air which it is important to observe. A metal rod, 0.3 of an inch in diameter, with a rounded end projecting into the air, was charged negatively, and gave a short noisy brush (Pl. X, *Fig. 8*). It was ascertained both by sight (1427, 1433) and sound (1431) that the successive discharges were very rapid in their recurrence, being seven or eight times more numerous in the same period, than those produced when the rod was charged positively to an equal degree. When the rod was positive, it was easy, by working the machine a little quicker, to replace the brush by a glow (1405, 1463), but when it was negative no efforts could produce this change. Even by bringing the hand opposite the wire, the only effect was to increase the number of brush discharges in a given period, raising at the same time the sound to a higher pitch.

1469. A point opposite the negative brush exhibited a star, and as it was approximated caused the size and sound of the negative brush to diminish, and, at last, to cease, leaving the negative end silent and dark, yet effective as to discharge.

1470. When the round end of a smaller wire (Pl. X, *Fig. 9*) was advanced towards the negative brush, it (becoming positive by induction) exhibited the quiet glow at 8 inches distance, the negative brush continuing. When nearer, the pitch of the sound of the negative brush rose, indicating quicker intermittences (1431); still nearer, the positive end threw off ramifications and distinct brushes; at the same time, the negative brush contracted in its lateral directions and collected together, giving a peculiar narrow longish brush, in shape like a hair pencil, the two brushes existing at once, but very different in their form and appearance, and especially in the more rapid recurrence of the negative discharges than of the positive. On using a smaller positive wire for the same experiment, the glow first appeared on it, and then the brush, the negative brush being affected at the same time; and the two at one distance became exceedingly alike in appearance, and the sounds, I thought, were in unison; at all events they were in harmony, so that the intermissions of discharge were either isochronous, or a simple ratio existed between the intervals. With a higher action of the machine, the wires being retained unaltered, the negative surface became dark and silent, and a glow appeared on the positive one. A still higher action changed the latter into a spark. Finer positive wires gave other variations of these effects, the description of which I must not allow myself to go into here.

1471. A thinner rod was now connected with the negative conductor in place of the larger one (1468), its termination being gradually diminished to a blunt point, as in Pl. X, *Fig. 10*; and it was beautiful to observe that, notwithstanding the variation of the brush, the same general order of effects was produced. The end gave a small sonorous negative brush, which the approach of the hand or a large conducting surface did not alter, until it was so near as to produce a spark. A fine point opposite to it was luminous at á distance; being nearer it did not destroy the light and sound of the negative brush, but only tended to have a brush produced on itself, which, at a still less distance, passed into a spark joining the two surfaces.

1472. When the distinct negative and positive brushes are produced simultaneously in relation to each other in air, the former almost always has a contracted form, as in Pl. X, *Fig. 11*, very much indeed resembling the figure which the positive brush itself has when influenced by the lateral vicinity of positive parts acting by induction. Thus a brush issuing from a point in the re-entering angle of a positive conductor has the same compressed form (Pl. X, *Fig. 12*).

1473. The character of the negative brush is not affected by the chemical nature of the substances of the conductors (1454), but only by their possession of the conducting power in a greater or smaller degree.

1474. Rarefaction of common air about a negative ball or blunt point facilitated the development of the negative brush, the effect being, I think, greater than on a positive brush, though great on both. Extensive ramifications could be obtained from a ball or end electrified negatively to the plate of the air-pump on which the jar containing it stood.

1475. A very important variation of the relative forms and conditions of the positive and negative brush takes place on varying the dielectric in which they are produced. The difference is so very great that it points to a specific relation of this form of discharge to the particular gas in which it takes place, and opposes the idea that gases are but obstructions to the discharge, acting one like another and merely in proportion to their pressure (1377).

1476. In *air*, the superiority of the positive brush is well known (1467, 1472). In *nitrogen*, it is as great or even greater than in air (1458). In *hydrogen*, the positive brush loses a part of its superiority, not being so good as in nitrogen or air; whilst the negative brush does not seem injured (1459). In *oxygen*, the positive brush is compressed and poor (1457); whilst the negative did not become less: the two were so alike that the eye frequently could not tell one from the other, and this similarity continued when the oxygen was gradually rarefied. In *coal gas*, the brushes are difficult of production as com-

pared to nitrogen (1460), and the positive not much superior to the negative in its character, either at common or low pressures. In *carbonic acid gas*, this approximation of character also occurred. In *muriatic acid gas*, the positive brush was very little better than the negative, and both difficult to produce (1462) as compared with the facility in nitrogen or air.

1477. These experiments were made with rods of brass about a quarter of an inch thick having rounded ends, these being opposed in a glass globe 7 inches in diameter, containing the gas to be experimented with. The electric machine was used to communicate directly, sometimes the positive, and sometimes the negative state, to the rod in connection with it.

1478. Thus we see that, notwithstanding there is a general difference in favour of the superiority of the positive brush over the negative, that difference is at its maximum in nitrogen and air; whilst in carbonic acid, muriatic acid, coal gas, and oxygen, it diminishes, and at last almost disappears. So that in this particular effect, as in all others yet examined, the evidence is in favour of that view which refers the results to a direct relation of the electric forces with the molecules of the matter concerned in the action (1421, 1423, 1463). Even when special phenomena arise under the operation of the general law, the theory adopted seems fully competent to meet the case.

1479. Before I proceed further in tracing the probable cause of the difference between the positive and negative brush discharge, I wish to know the results of a few experiments which are in course of preparation: and thinking this Series of *Researches* long enough, I shall here close it with the expectation of being able in a few weeks to renew the inquiry, and entirely redeem my pledge (1306).

Royal Institution, Dec. 23, 1837

THIRTEENTH SERIES

§ 18. *On Induction (continued)* ¶ ix. *Disruptive Discharge (continued)—Peculiarities of Positive and Negative Discharge either as Spark or Brush—Glow Discharge—Dark Discharge* ¶ x. *Convection, or Carrying Discharge* ¶ xi. *Relation of a Vacuum to Electrical Phenomena* § 19. *Nature of the Electrical Current*

RECEIVED FEBRUARY 22, READ MARCH 15, 1838

¶ ix. *Disruptive Discharge (continued)*

1480. LET us now direct our attention to the general difference of the positive and negative disruptive discharge, with the object of tracing, as far as possible, the cause of that difference, and whether it depends on the charged conductors principally, or on the interposed dielectric; and as it appears to be great in air and nitrogen (1476), let us observe the phenomena in air first.

1481. The general case is best understood by a reference to surfaces of considerable size rather than to points, which involve (as a secondary effect) the formation of currents (1562). My investigation, therefore, was carried on with balls and terminations of different diameters, and the following are some of the principal results.

1482. If two balls of very different dimensions, as for instance one-half an inch, and the other three inches in diameter, be arranged at the ends of rods so that either can be electrified by a machine and made to discharge by sparks to the other, which is at the same time uninsulated; then, as is well known, far longer sparks are obtained when the small ball is positive and the large ball negative, than when the small ball is negative and the large ball positive. In the former case, the sparks are 10 or 12 inches in length; in the latter, an inch or an inch and a half only.

1483. But previous to the description of further experiments, I will mention two words, for which with many others I am indebted to a friend, and which I think it would be expedient to introduce and use. It is important in ordinary inductive action, to distinguish at which charged surface the induction originates and is sustained: i.e., if two or more metallic balls, or other masses of matter, are in inductive relation, to express which are charged originally, and which are brought by them into the opposite electrical condition. I propose to call those bodies which are originally charged, *inductric* bodies; and those which assume the opposite state, in consequence of the induction, *inducteous* bodies. This distinction is not needful because there is any difference between the sums of the *inductric* and the *inducteous* forces; but principally because, when a ball A is inductric, it not merely brings a ball B, which is opposite to it, into an inducteous state, but also many other surrounding conductors, though some of them may be a considerable distance off, and the consequence is, that the balls do not bear the same precise relation to each other when, first one, and then the other, is made the inductric ball; though, in each case, the *same ball* be made to assume the *same state.*

1484. Another liberty which I may also occasionally take in language I will explain and limit. It is that of calling a particular spark or brush, *positive* or *negative*, according as it may be considered as *originating* at a positive or a negative surface. We speak of the brush as positive or negative when it shoots out from surfaces previously in those states; and the experiments of Mr. Wheatstone go to prove that it *really begins* at the charged surface, and from thence extends into the air (1437, 1438) or other dielectric. According to my view, *sparks* also originate or are determined at one particular spot (1370), namely, that where the tension first rises up to the maximum degree; and when this can be determined, as in the simultaneous use of large and small balls, in which case the discharge begins or is determined by the latter, I would call that discharge which passes *at once*, a positive spark, if it was at the positive surface that the maximum intensity was first obtained; or a negative spark, if that necessary intensity was first obtained at the negative surface.

1485. An apparatus was arranged, as in Pl. XI, *Fig. 2*: A and B were brass balls of very different diameters attached to metal rods, moving through sockets on insulating pillars, so that the distance between the balls could be varied at pleasure. The large ball A, 2 inches in diameter, was connected with an insulated brass conductor, which could be rendered positive or negative directly from a cylinder machine: the small ball B, 0.25 of an inch in diameter, was connected with a discharging train (292) and perfectly uninsulated. The brass rods sustaining the balls were 0.2 of an inch in thickness.

1486. When the large ball was *positive* and inductric (1483), negative sparks occurred until the interval was 0.49 of an inch; then mixed brush and spark between that and 0.51; and from 0.52 and upwards, negative brush alone. When the large ball was made *negative* and inductric, then positive spark alone occurred until the interval was as great as 1.15 inches; spark and brush from that up to 1.55; and to have the positive brush alone, it required an interval of at least 1.65 inches.

1487. The balls A and B were now changed for each other. Then making the small ball B inductric *positively*, the positive sparks alone continued only up to 0.67; spark and brush occurred from 0.68 up to 0.72; and positive brush alone from 0.74 and upwards. Rendering the small ball B inductric and *negative*, negative sparks alone occurred up to 0.40; then spark and brush at 0.42; whilst from 0.44 and upwards the noisy negative brush alone took place.

1488. We thus find a great difference as the balls are rendered inductric or inducteous; the small ball rendered *positive* inducteously giving a spark nearly twice as long as that produced when it was charged positive inductrically, and a corresponding difference, though not, under the circumstances, to the same extent, was manifest, when it was rendered *negative*.[1]

1489. Other results are, that the small ball rendered positive gives a much longer spark than when it is rendered negative, and that the small ball rendered negative gives a brush more readily than when positive, in relation to the effect produced by increasing the distance between the two balls.

1490. When the interval was below 0.4 of an inch, so that the small ball should give sparks,

whether positive or negative, I could not observe that there was any constant difference, either in their ready occurrence or the number which passed in a given time. But when the interval was such that the small ball when negative gave a brush, then the discharges from it, as separate negative brushes, were far more numerous than the corresponding discharges from it when rendered positive, whether those positive discharges were as sparks or brushes.

1491. It is, therefore, evident that, when a ball is discharging electricity in the form of brushes, the brushes are far more numerous, and each contains or carries off far less electric force when the electricity so discharged is negative, than when it is positive.

1492. In all such experiments as those described, the point of change from spark to brush is very much governed by the working state of the electrical machine and the size of the conductor connected with the discharging ball. If the machine be in strong action and the conductor large, so that much power is accumulated quickly for each discharge, then the interval is greater at which the sparks are replaced by brushes; but the general effect is the same.[2]

1493. These results, though indicative of very striking and peculiar relations of the electric force or forces, do not show the relative degrees of charge which the small ball acquires before discharge occurs, i.e., they do not tell whether it acquires a higher condition in the negative, or in the positive state, immediately preceding that discharge. To illustrate this important point I arranged two places of discharge as represented, Pl. XI, *Fig. 3*. A and D are brass balls 2 inches in diameter, B and C are smaller brass balls 0.25 of an inch in diameter; the forks L and R supporting them were of brass wire 0.2 of an inch in diameter: the space between the large and small ball on the same fork was 5 inches, that the two places of discharge *n* and *o* might be sufficiently removed from each other's influence. The fork L was connected with a projecting cylindrical conductor, which could be rendered positive or negative at pleasure, by an electrical machine, and the fork R was attached to another conductor, but thrown into an uninsulated state by connection with a discharging train (292). The two intervals or places of discharge *n* and *o* could be varied at pleasure, their extent being measured by the occasional introduction of a diagonal scale. It is evident that, as the balls

---

[1] For similar experiments on different gases, see 1518.—*Dec.* 1838.

[2] For similar experiments in different gases, see 1510–1517.—*Dec.* 1838.

PLATE XI

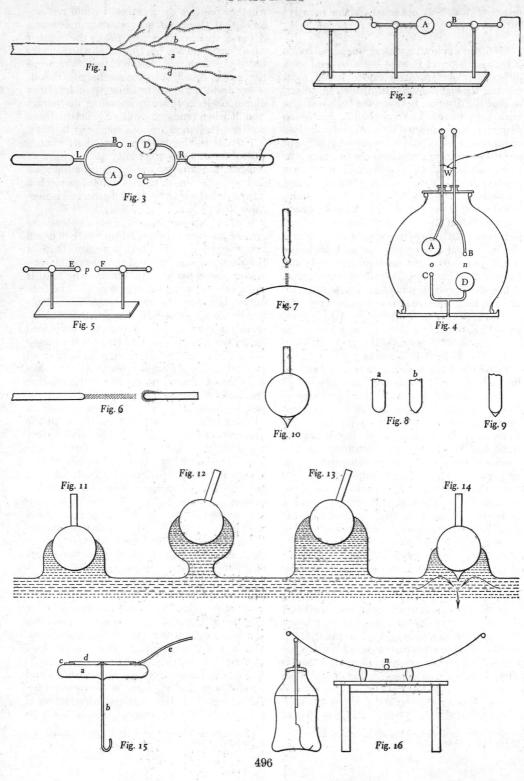

Fig. 1

Fig. 2

Fig. 3

Fig. 5

Fig. 7

Fig. 4

Fig. 6

Fig. 10

Fig. 8

Fig. 9

Fig. 11

Fig. 12

Fig. 13

Fig. 14

Fig. 15

Fig. 16

A and B connected with the same conductor are always charged at once, and that discharge may take place to either of the balls connected with the discharging train, the intervals of discharge *n* and *o* may be properly compared to each other, as respects the influence of large and small balls when charged positively and negatively in air.

1494. When the intervals *n* and *o* were each made = 0.9 of an inch, and the balls A and B inductric *positively*, the discharge was all at *n* from the small ball of the conductor to the large ball of the discharging train, and mostly by positive brush, though once by a spark. When the balls A and B were made inductric *negatively*, the discharge was still from the same small ball, at *n*, by a constant negative brush.

1495. I diminished the intervals *n* and *o* to 0.6 of an inch. When A and B were inductric *positively*, all the discharge was at *n* as a positive brush: when A and B were inductric *negatively*, still all the discharge was at *n*, as a negative brush.

1496. The facility of discharge at the positive and negative small balls, therefore, did not appear to be very different. If a difference had existed, there were always two small balls, one in each state, that the discharge might happen at that most favourable to the effect. The only difference was that one was in the inductric, and the other in the inducteous state, but whichsoever happened for the time to be in that state, whether positive or negative, had the advantage.

1497. To counteract this interfering influence, I made the interval *n* = 0.79 and interval *o* = 0.58 of an inch. Then, when the balls A and B were *inductive positive*, the discharge was about equal at both intervals. When, on the other hand, the balls A and B were inductric *negative*, there was discharge, still at both, but most at *n*, as if the small ball *negative* could discharge a little easier than the same ball *positive*.

1498. The small balls and terminations used in these and similar experiments may very correctly be compared, in their action, to the same balls and ends when electrified in free air at a much greater distance from conductors, than they were in those cases from each other. In the first place, the discharge, even when as a spark is, according to my view, determined, and, so to speak, begins at a spot on the surface of the small ball (1374), occurring when the intensity there has risen up to a certain maximum degree (1370); this determination of discharge at a particular spot first, being easily

traced from the spark into the brush, by increasing the distance, so as, at last, even to render the time evident which is necessary for the production of the effect (1436, 1438). In the next place, the large balls which I have used might be replaced by larger balls at a still greater distance, and so, by successive degrees, may be considered as passing into the sides of the rooms; these being under general circumstances the inducteous bodies, whilst the small ball rendered either positive or negative is the inductric body.

1499. But, as has long been recognised, the small ball is only a blunt end, and, electrically speaking, a point only a small ball; so that when a point or blunt end is throwing out its brushes into the air, it is acting exactly as the small balls have acted in the experiments already described, and by virtue of the same properties and relations.

1500. It may very properly be said with respect to the experiments, that the large negative ball is as essential to the discharge as the small positive ball, and also that the large negative ball shows as much superiority over the large positive ball (which is inefficient in causing a spark from its opposed small negative ball) as the small positive ball does over the small negative ball; and probably when we understand the real cause of the difference, and refer it rather to the condition of the particles of the dielectric than to the sizes of the conducting balls, we may find much importance in such an observation. But for the present, and whilst engaged in investigating the point, we may admit, what is the fact, that the forces are of higher intensity at the surfaces of the smaller balls than at those of the larger (1372, 1374); that the former, therefore, determine the discharge, by first rising up to that exalted condition which is necessary for it; and that, whether brought to this condition by induction towards the walls of a room or the large balls I have used, these may fairly be compared one with the other in their influence and actions.

1501. The conclusions I arrive at are: first, that when two equal small conducting surfaces equally placed in air are electrified, one positively and the other negatively, that which is negative can discharge to the air at a tension a little lower than that required for the positive ball: second, that when discharge does take place, much more passes at each time from the positive than from the negative surface (1491). The last conclusion is very abundantly proved by the optical analysis of the positive and negative brushes already described (1468), the latter set of discharges being found to recur five or six times oftener than the former.[1]

1502. If, now, a small ball be made to give brushes or brushy sparks by a powerful machine, we can, in some measure, understand and relate the difference perceived when it is rendered positive or negative. It is known to give when positive a much larger and more powerful spark than when negative, and with greater facility (1482): in fact, the spark, although it takes away so much more electricity at once, commences at a tension higher only in a small degree, if at all. On the other hand, if rendered negative, though discharge may commence at a lower degree, it continues but for a very short period, very little electricity passing away each time. These circumstances are directly related; for the extent to which the positive spark can reach, and the size and extent of the positive brush, are consequences of the capability which exists of much electricity passing off at one discharge from the positive surface (1468, 1501).

1503. But to refer these effects only to the form and size of the conductor, would, according to my notion of induction, be a very imperfect mode of viewing the whole question (1523, 1600). I apprehend that the effects are due altogether to the mode in which the particles of the interposed dielectric polarize, and I have already given some experimental indications of the differences presented by different electrics in this respect (1475, 1476). The modes of polarization, as I shall have occasion hereafter to show, may be very diverse in different dielectrics. With respect to common air, what seems to be the consequence of a superiority in the positive force at the surface of the small ball, may be due to the more exalted condition of the negative polarity of the particles of air, or of the nitrogen in it (the negative part being, perhaps, more compressed, whilst the positive part is more diffuse, or *vice versa* [1687, &c.]); for such a condition could determine certain effects at the positive ball which would not take place to the same degree at the negative ball, just as well as if the positive ball had possessed some special and independent power of its own.

1504. The opinion, that the effects are more likely to be dependent upon the dielectric than

the ball, is supported by the character of the two discharges. If a small positive ball be throwing off brushes with ramifications ten inches long, how can the ball affect that part of a ramification which is five inches from it? Yet the portion beyond that place has the same character as that preceding it, and no doubt has that character impressed by the same general principle and law. Looking upon the action of the contiguous particles of a dielectric as fully proved, I see, in such a ramification, a propagation of discharge from particle to particle, each doing for the one next it what was done for it by the preceding particle, and what was done for the first particle by the charged metal against which it was situated.

1505. With respect to the general condition and relations of the positive and negative brushes in dense or rare air, or in other media and gases, if they are produced at different times and places they are of course independent of each other. But when they are produced from opposed ends or balls at the same time, in the same vessel of gas (1470, 1477), they are frequently related; and circumstances may be so arranged that they shall be isochronous, occurring in equal numbers in equal times; or shall occur in multiples, i.e., with two or three negatives to one positive; or shall alternate, or be quite irregular. All these variations I have witnessed; and when it is considered that the air in the vessel, and also the glass of the vessel, can take a momentary charge, it is easy to comprehend their general nature and cause.

1506. Similar experiments to those in air (1485, 1493) were made in different gases, the results of which I will describe as briefly as possible. The apparatus is represented Pl. XI, *Fig. 4*, consisting of a bell-glass eleven inches in diameter at the widest part, and ten and a half inches high up to the bottom of the neck. The balls are lettered, as in Pl. XI, *Fig. 3*, and are in the same relation to each other; but A and B were on separate sliding wires, which, however, were generally joined by a cross wire, *w*, above, and that connected with the brass conductor, which received its positive or negative charge from the machine. The rods of A and B were graduated at the part moving through the stuffing-box, so that the application of a diagonal scale applied there told what was the distance between these balls and those beneath them. As to the position of the balls in the jar, and their relation to each other, C and D were three and a quarter inches apart, their

[1] A very excellent mode of examining the relation of small positive and negative surfaces would be by the use of drops of gum water, solutions, or other liquids. See onwards (1581, 1593).

height above the pump plate five inches, and the distance between any of the balls and the glass of the jar one inch and three-quarters at least, and generally more. The balls A and D were two inches in diameter, as before (1493); the balls B and C only 0.15 of an inch in diameter.

Another apparatus was occasionally used in connection with that just described, being an open discharger (Pl. XI, *Fig. 5*), by which a comparison of the discharge in air and that in gases could be obtained. The balls E and F, each 0.6 of an inch in diameter, were connected with sliding rods and other balls, and were insulated. When used for comparison, the brass conductor was associated at the same time with the balls A and B of *Figure 4* and ball E of this apparatus (*Fig. 5*); whilst the balls C, D and F were connected with the discharging train.

1507. I will first tabulate the results as to the *restraining power* of the gases over discharge. The balls A and C (*Fig. 4*) were thrown out of action by distance, and the effects at B and D, or the interval *n* in the gas, compared with those at the interval *p* in the air, between E and F (*Fig. 5*). The table sufficiently explains itself. It will be understood that all discharge was in the air, when the interval there was less than that expressed in the first or third columns of figures; and all the discharge in the gas, when the interval in air was greater than that in the second or fourth column of figures. At intermediate distances the discharge was occasionally at both places, i.e., sometimes in the air, sometimes in the gas.

	Interval *p* in parts of an inch			
Constant interval *n* between B and D = 1 inch	When the small ball B was inductric and *positive* the discharge was all at *p* in the air before	at *n* in the gas after	When the small ball B was inductric and *negative* the discharge was all at *p* in the air before	at *n* in the gas after
	p =	*p* =	*p* =	*p* =
In Air	0.40	0.50	0.28	0.33
In Nitrogen	0.30	0.65	0.31	0.40
In Oxygen	0.33	0.52	0.27	0.30
In Hydrogen	0.20	0.40	0.22	0.24
In Coal gas	0.20	0.90	0.20	0.27
In Carbonic acid	0.64	1.30	0.30	0.45

1508. These results are the same generally, as far as they go, as those of the like nature in the last series (1388), and confirm the conclusion that different gases restrain discharge in very different proportions. They are probably not so good as the former ones, for the glass jar not being varnished acted irregularly, sometimes taking a certain degree of charge as a non-conductor, and at other times acting as a

conductor in the conveyance and derangement of that charge. Another cause of difference in the ratios is, no doubt, the relative sizes of the discharge balls in air; in the former case they were of very different size, here they were alike.

1509. In future experiments intended to have the character of accuracy, the influence of these circumstances ought to be ascertained, and, above all things, the gases themselves ought to be contained in vessels of metal, and not of glass.

1510. The next set of results are those obtained when the intervals *n* and *o* (Pl. XI, *Fig. 4*) were made equal to each other, and relate to the greater facility of discharge at the small ball, when rendered positive or negative (1493).

1511. In *air*, with the intervals = 0.4 of an inch, A and B being inductric and positive, discharge was nearly equal at *n* and *o*; when A and B were inductric and negative, the discharge was mostly at *n* by negative brush. When the intervals were = 0.8 of an inch, with A and B inductric positively, all discharge was at *n* by positive brush; with A and B inductric negatively, all the discharge was at *n* by a negative brush. It is doubtful, therefore from these results, whether the negative ball has any greater facility than the positive.

1512. *Nitrogen.* Intervals *n* and *o* = 0.4 of an inch: A, B inductric positive, discharge at both intervals, most at *n*, by positive sparks; A, B inductric negative, discharge equal at *n* and *o*. The intervals made −0.8 of an inch: A, B inductric positive, discharge all at *n* by positive brush; A, B inductric negative, discharge most at *o* by positive brush. In this gas, therefore, though the difference is not decisive, it would seem that the positive small ball caused the most ready discharge.

1513. *Oxygen.* Intervals *n* and *o* −0.4 of an inch: A, B inductric positive, discharge nearly equal; inductric negative, discharge mostly at *n* by negative brush. Made the intervals = 0.8 of an inch: A, B inductric positive, discharge both at *n* and *o*; inductric negative, discharge all at *o* by negative brush. So here the negative small ball seems to give the most ready discharge.

1514. *Hydrogen.* Intervals *n* and *o* = 0.4 of an inch: A, B inductric positive, discharge nearly equal: inductric negative, discharge mostly at *o*. Intervals = 0.8 of an inch: A and B inductric positive, discharge mostly at *n*, as positive brush; inductric negative, discharge mostly at *o*, as positive brush. Here the positive discharge seems most facile.

1515. *Coal gas.* n and o = 0.4 of an inch: A, B inductric positive, discharge nearly all at o by negative spark: A, B inductric negative, discharge nearly all at n by negative spark. Intervals = 0.8 of an inch, and A, B inductric positive, discharge mostly at o by negative brush: A, B inductric negative, discharge all at n by negative brush. Here the negative discharge most facile.

1516. *Carbonic acid gas.* n and o = 0.4 of an inch: A, B inductric positive, discharge nearly all at o, or negative: A, B inductric negative, discharge nearly all at n, or negative. Intervals = 0.8 of an inch: A, B inductric positive, discharge mostly at o, or negative: A, B inductric negative, discharge all at n, or negative. In this case the negative had a decided advantage in facility of discharge.

1517. Thus, if we may trust this form of experiment, the negative small ball has a decided advantage in facilitating disruptive discharge over the positive small ball in some gases, as in carbonic acid gas and coal gas (1399), whilst in others that conclusion seems more doubtful; and in others, again, there seems a probability that the positive small ball may be superior. All these results were obtained at very nearly the same pressure of the atmosphere.

1518. I made some experiments in these gases whilst in the air jar (Pl. XI, *Fig. 4*), as to the change from spark to brush, analogous to those in the open air already described (1486, 1487). I will give, in a table, the results as to when brush began to appear mingled with the spark; but the after results were so varied, and the nature of the discharge in different gases so different, that to insert the results obtained without further investigation, would be of little use. At intervals less than those expressed the discharge was always by spark.

	Discharge between balls B and D		Discharge between balls A and C	
	Small ball B inductric *pos.*	Small ball B inductric *neg.*	Large ball A inductric *pos.*	Large ball A inductric *neg.*
Air	0.55	0.30	0.40	0.75
Nitrogen	0.30	0.40	0.52	0.41
Oxygen	0.70	0.30	0.45	0.82
Hydrogen	0.20	0.10		
Coal gas	0.13	0.30	0.30	0.14
Carbonic acid	0.82	0.43	1.60	above 1.80; had not space.

1519. It is to be understood that sparks occurred at much higher intervals than these; the table only expresses that distance beneath which all discharge was as spark. Some curious relations of the different gases to discharge are already discernible, but it would be useless to consider them until illustrated by further experiments.

1520. I ought not to omit noticing here, that Professor Belli of Milan has published a very valuable set of experiments on the relative dissipation of positive and negative electricity in the air;[1] he finds the latter far more ready, in this respect, than the former.

1521. I made some experiments of a similar kind, but with sustained high charges; the results were less striking than those of Signore Belli, and I did not consider them as satisfactory. I may be allowed to mention, in connexion with the subject, an interfering effect which embarrassed me for a long time. When I threw positive electricity from a given point into the air, a certain intensity was indicated by an electrometer on the conductor connected with the point, but as the operation continued this intensity rose several degrees; then making the conductor negative with the same point attached to it, and all other things remaining the same, a certain degree of tension was observed in the first instance, which also gradually rose as the operation proceeded. Returning the conductor to the positive state, the tension was at first low, but rose as before; and so also when again made negative.

1522. This result appeared to indicate that the point which had been giving off one electricity was, by that, more fitted for a short time to give off the other. But on closer examination I found the whole depended upon the inductive reaction of that air, which being charged by the point, and gradually increasing in quantity before it, as the positive or negative issue was continued, diverted and removed a part of the inductive action of the surrounding wall, and thus apparently affected the powers of the point, whilst really it was the dielectric itself that was causing the change of tension.

1523. The results connected with the different conditions of positive and negative discharge will have a far greater influence on the philosophy of electrical science than we at present imagine, especially if, as I believe, they depend on the peculiarity and degree of polarized

[1] *Bibliothèque Universelle*, 1836, September, p. 152.

condition which the molecules of the dielectrics concerned acquire (1503, 1600). Thus, for instance, the relation of our atmosphere and the earth within it, to the occurrence of spark or brush, must be especial and not accidental (1464). It would not else consist with other meteorological phenomena, also of course dependent on the special properties of the air, and which being themselves in harmony the most perfect with the functions of animal and vegetable life, are yet restricted in their actions, not by loose regulations, but by laws the most precise.

1524. Even in the passage through air of the voltaic current we see the peculiarities of positive and negative discharge at the two charcoal points; and if these discharges are made to take place simultaneously to mercury, the distinction is still more remarkable, both as to the sound and the quantity of vapour produced.

1525. It seems very possible that the remarkable difference recently observed and described by my friend Professor Daniell,[1] namely that when a zinc and a copper ball, the same in size, were placed respectively in copper and zinc spheres, also the same in size, and excited by electrolytes or dielectrics of the same strength and nature, the zinc ball far surpassed the zinc sphere in action, may also be connected with these phenomena; for it is not difficult to conceive how the polarity of the particles shall be affected by the circumstance of the positive surface, namely the zinc, being the larger or the smaller of the two inclosing the electrolyte. It is even possible, that with different electrolytes or dielectrics the ratio may be considerably varied, or in some cases even inverted.

Glow Discharge

1526. That form of disruptive discharge which appears as a *glow* (1359, 1405), is very peculiar and beautiful: it seems to depend on a quick and almost continuous charging of the air close to, and in contact with, the conductor.

1527. *Diminution of the charging surface* will produce it. Thus, when a rod 0.3 of an inch in diameter, with a rounded termination, was rendered positive in free air, it gave fine brushes from the extremity, but occasionally these disappeared, and a quiet phosphorescent continuous glow took their place, covering the whole of the end of the wire, and extending a very small distance from the metal into the air. With a rod 0.2 of an inch in diameter the glow was more readily produced. With still smaller rods,

[1] *Philosophical Transactions*, 1838, p. 47.

and also with blunt conical points, it occurred still more readily; and with a fine point I could not obtain the brush in free air, but only this glow. The positive glow and the positive star are, in fact, the same.

1528. *Increase of power in the machine* tends to produce the glow; for rounded terminations which will give only brushes when the machine is in weak action, will readily give the glow when it is in good order.

1529. *Rarefaction of the air* wonderfully favours the glow phenomena. A brass ball, two and a half inches in diameter, being made positively inductric in an air-pump receiver, became covered with glow over an area of two inches in diameter, when the pressure was reduced to 4.4 inches of mercury. By a little adjustment the ball could be covered all over with this light. Using a brass ball 1.25 inches in diameter, and making it inducteously positive by an inductric negative point, the phenomena, at high degrees of rarefaction, were exceedingly beautiful. The glow came over the positive ball, and gradually increased in brightness, until it was at last very luminous; and it also stood up like a low flame, half an inch or more in height. On touching the sides of the glass jar this lambent flame was affected, assumed a ring form, like a crown on the top of the ball, appeared flexible, and revolved with a comparatively slow motion, i.e., about four or five times in a second. This ring-shape and revolution are beautifully connected with the mechanical currents (1576) taking place within the receiver. These glows in rarefied air are often highly exalted in beauty by a spark discharge at the conductor (1551, *note*).

1530. To obtain a *negative glow* in air at common pressures is difficult. I did not procure it on the rod 0.3 of an inch in diameter by my machine, nor on much smaller rods; and it is questionable as yet, whether, even on fine points, what is called the negative star is a very reduced and minute, but still intermitting brush, or a glow similar to that obtained on a positive point.

1531. In rarefied air the negative glow can easily be obtained. If the rounded ends of two metal rods, about 0.2 of an inch in diameter, are introduced into a globe or jar (the air within being rarefied), and being opposite to each other, are about four inches apart, the glow can be obtained on both rods, covering not only the ends, but an inch or two of the part behind. On using *balls* in the air-pump jar, and adjusting the distance and exhaustion, the negative ball could be covered with glow, whether it were the inductric or the inducteous surface.

1532. When rods are used it is necessary to be aware that, if placed concentrically in the jar or globe, the light on one rod is often reflected by the sides of the vessel on to the other rod, and makes it apparently luminous, when really it is not so. This effect may be detected by shifting the eye at the time of observation, or avoided by using blackened rods.

1533. It is curious to observe the relation of *glow*, *brush*, and *spark* to each other, as produced by positive or negative surfaces; thus, beginning with spark discharge, it passes into brush much sooner when the surface at which the discharge commences (1484) is negative, than it does when positive; but proceeding onwards in the order of change, we find that the positive brush passes into *glow* long before the negative brush does. So that, though each presents the three conditions in the same general order, the series are not precisely the same. It is probable, that, when these points are minutely examined, as they must be shortly, we shall find that each different gas or dielectric presents its own peculiar results, dependent upon the mode in which its particles assume polar electric condition.

1534. The glow occurs in all gases in which I have looked for it. These are air, nitrogen, oxygen, hydrogen, coal gas, carbonic acid, muriatic acid, sulphurous acid and ammonia. I thought also that I obtained it in oil of turpentine, but if so it was very dull and small.

1535. The glow is always accompanied by a wind proceeding either directly out from the glowing part, or directly towards it; the former being the most general case. This takes place even when the glow occurs upon a ball of considerable size: and if matters be so arranged that the ready and regular access of air to a part exhibiting the glow be interfered with or prevented, the glow then disappears.

1536. I have never been able to analyse or separate the glow into visible elementary intermitting discharges (1427, 1433), nor to obtain the other evidence of intermitting action, namely an audible sound (1431). The want of success, as respects trials made by ocular means, may depend upon the large size of the glow preventing the separation of the visible images: and, indeed, if it does intermit, it is not likely that all parts intermit at once with a simultaneous regularity.

1537. All the effects tend to show, that *glow* is due to a continuous charge or discharge of air; in the former case being accompanied by a current from, and in the latter by one to, the place of the glow. As the surrounding air comes up to the charged conductor, on attaining that spot at which the tension of the particles is raised to the sufficient degree (1370, 1410). it becomes charged, and then moves off, by the joint action of the forces to which it is subject; and, at the same time that it makes way for other particles to come and be charged in turn, actually helps to form that current by which they are brought into the necessary position. Thus, through the regularity of the forces, a constant and quiet result is produced; and that result is, the charging of successive portions of air, the production of a current, and of a continuous glow.

1538. I have frequently been able to make the termination of a rod, which, when left to itself, would produce a brush, produce in preference a glow, simply by aiding the formation of a current of air at its extremity; and, on the other hand, it is not at all difficult to convert the glow into brushes, by affecting the current of air (1574, 1579) or the inductive action near it.

1539. The transition from glow, on the one hand, to brush and spark, on the other, and, therefore, their connexion, may be established in various ways. Those circumstances which tend to facilitate the charge of the air by the excited conductor, and also those which tend to keep the tension at the same degree notwithstanding the discharge, assist in producing the glow; whereas those which tend to resist the charge of the air or other dielectric, and those which favour the accumulation of electric force prior to discharge, which, sinking by that act, has to be exalted before the tension can again acquire the requisite degree, favour intermitting discharge, and, therefore, the production of brush or spark. Thus, rarefaction of the air, the removal of large conducting surfaces from the neighbourhood of the glowing termination, the presentation of a sharp point towards it, help to sustain or produce the glow: but the condensation of the air, the presentation of the hand or other large surface, the gradual approximation of a discharging ball, tend to convert the glow into brush or even spark. All these circumstances may be traced and reduced, in a manner easily comprehensible, to their relative power of assisting to produce, either a *continuous* discharge to the air, which gives the glow; or an *interrupted* one, which produces the brush, and, in a more exalted condition, the spark.

1540. The rounded end of a brass rod, 0.3 of an inch in diameter, was covered with a positive glow by the working of an electrical machine: on stopping the machine, so that the charge of the connected conductor should fall, the glow changed for a moment into brushes just before the discharge ceased altogether, illustrating the necessity for a certain high continuous charge, for a certain sized termination. Working the machine so that the intensity should be just low enough to give continual brushes from the end in free air, the approach of a fine point changed these brushes into a glow. Working the machine so that the termination presented a continual glow in free air, the gradual approach of the hand caused the glow to contract at the very end of the wire, then to throw out a luminous point, which, becoming a foot stalk (1426), finally produced brushes with large ramifications. All these results are in accordance with what is stated above (1539).

1541. Greasing the end of a rounded wire will immediately make it produce brushes instead of glow. A ball having a blunt point which can be made to project more or less beyond its surface, at pleasure, can be made to produce every gradation from glow, through brush, to spark.

1542. It is also very interesting and instructive to trace the transition from spark to glow, through the intermediate condition of stream, between ends in a vessel containing air more or less rarefied; but I fear to be prolix.

1543. All the effects show, that the glow is in its nature exactly the same as the luminous part of a brush or ramification, namely a charging of air; the only difference being, that the glow has a continuous appearance from the constant renewal of the same action in the same place, whereas the ramification is due to a momentary, independent and intermitting action of the same kind.

Dark Discharge.

1544. I will now notice a very remarkable circumstance in the luminous discharge accompanied by negative glow, which may, perhaps, be correctly traced hereafter into discharges of much higher intensity. Two brass rods, 0.3 of an inch in diameter, entering a glass globe on opposite sides, had their ends brought into contact, and the air about them very much rarefied. A discharge of electricity from the machine was then made through them, and whilst that was continued the ends were separated from each other. At the moment of separation a continuous glow came over the end of the negative rod, the positive termination remaining quite dark. As the distance was increased, a purple stream or haze appeared on the end of the positive rod, and proceeded directly outwards towards the negative rod; elongating as the interval was enlarged, but never joining the negative glow, there being always a short dark space between. This space, of about $\frac{1}{16}$th or $\frac{1}{20}$th of an inch, was apparently invariable in its extent and its position, relative to the negative rod; nor did the negative glow vary. Whether the negative end where inductric or inducteous, the same effect was produced. It was strange to see the positive purple haze diminish or lengthen as the ends were separated, and yet this dark space and the negative glow remain unaltered (Pl. XI, *Fig. 6*).

1545. Two balls were then used in a large air-pump receiver, and the air rarefied. The usual transitions in the character of the discharge took place; but whenever the luminous stream, which appears after the spark and the brush have ceased, was itself changed into glow at the balls, the dark space occurred, and that whether the one or the other ball was made inductric, or positive, or negative.

1546. Sometimes when the negative ball was large, the machine in powerful action, and the rarefaction high, the ball would be covered over half its surface with glow, and then, upon a hasty observation, would seem to exhibit no dark space: but this was a deception, arising from the overlapping of the convex termination of the negative glow and the concave termination of the positive stream. More careful observation and experiment have convinced me, that when the negative glow occurs, it never visibly touches the luminous part of the positive discharge, but that the dark space is always there.

1547. This singular separation of the positive and negative discharge, as far as concerns their luminous character, under circumstances which one would have thought very favourable to their coalescence, is probably connected with their differences when in the form of brush, and is perhaps even dependent on the same cause. Further, there is every likelihood that the dark parts which occur in feeble sparks are also connected with these phenomena.[1] To understand them would be very important, for it is quite clear that in many of the experiments, indeed in all that I have quoted, discharge is

---

[1] See Professor Johnson's experiments. *Silliman's Journal*, XXV, p. 57.

taking place across the dark part of the dielectric to an extent quite equal to what occurs in the luminous part. This difference in the result would seem to imply a distinction in the modes by which the two electric forces are brought into equilibrium in the respective parts; and looking upon all the phenomena as giving additional proofs, that it is to the condition of the particles of the dielectric we must refer for the principles of induction and discharge, so it would be of great importance if we could know accurately in what the difference of action in the dark and the luminous parts consisted.

1548. The dark discharge through air (1552), which in the case mentioned is very evident (1544), leads to the inquiry, whether the particles of air are generally capable of effecting discharge from one to another without becoming luminous; and the inquiry is important, because it is connected with that degree of tension which is necessary to originate discharge (1368, 1370). Discharge between *air and conductors* without luminous appearances are very common; and non-luminous discharges by carrying currents of air and other fluids (1562, 1595) are also common enough: but these are not cases in point, for they are not discharges between insulating particles.

1549. An arrangement was made for discharge between two balls (1485) (Pl. XI, *Fig. 2*) but, in place of connecting the inducteous ball directly with the discharging train, it was put in communication with the inside coating of a Leyden jar, and the discharging train with the outside coating. Then working the machine, it was found that whenever sonorous and luminous discharge occurred at the balls A B, the jar became charged; but that when these did not occur, the jar acquired no charge: and such was the case when small rounded terminations were used in place of the balls, and also in whatever manner they were arranged. Under these circumstances, therefore, discharge even between the air and conductors was always luminous.

1550. But in other cases, the phenomena are such as to make it almost certain that dark discharge can take place across air. If the rounded end of a metal rod, 0.15 of an inch in diameter, be made to give a good negative brush, the approach of a smaller end or a blunt point opposite to it will, at a certain distance, cause a diminution of the brush, and a glow will appear on the positive inducteous wire, accompanied by a current of air passing from it. Now, as the air is being charged both at the positive and negative surfaces, it seems a reasonable conclusion, that the charged portions meet somewhere in the interval, and there discharge to each other, without producing any luminous phenomena. It is possible, however, that the air electrified positively at the glowing end may travel on towards the negative surface, and actually form that atmosphere into which the visible negative brushes dart, in which case dark discharge need not, of necessity, occur. But I incline to the former opinion, and think, that the diminution in size of the negative brush, as the positive glow comes on to the end of the opposed wire, is in favour of that view.

1551. Using rarefied air as the dielectric, it is very easy to obtain luminous phenomena as brushes, or glow, upon both conducting balls or terminations, whilst the interval is dark, and that, when the action is so momentary that I think we cannot consider currents as effecting discharge across the dark part. Thus if two balls, about an inch in diameter, and 4 or more inches apart, have the air rarefied about them, and are then interposed in the course of discharge, an interrupted or spark current being produced at the machine,[1] each termination may be made to show luminous phenomena, whilst more or less of the interval is quite dark. The discharge will pass as suddenly as a retarded spark (295, 334), i.e., in an interval of time almost inappreciably small, and in such a case, I think it must have passed across the dark part as true disruptive discharge, and not by convection.

1552. Hence I conclude that dark disruptive discharge may occur (1547, 1550); and also, that, in the luminous brush, the visible ramifications may not show the full extent of the disruptive discharge (1444, 1452), but that each may have a dark outside, enveloping, as it were, every part through which the discharge extends. It is probable, even, that there are such things as dark discharges analogous in form to the brush and the spark, but not luminous in any part (1445).

1553. The occurrence of dark discharge in any case shows at how low a tension disruptive discharge may occur (1548), and indicates that the light of the ultimate brush or spark is in no relation to the intensity required (1368, 1370). So to speak, the discharge begins in darkness, and the light is a mere consequence of the

---

[1] By spark current I mean one passing in a series of spark between the conductor of the machine and the apparatus: by a continuous current one that passes through metallic conductors, and in that respect without interruption at the same place.

quantity which, after discharge has commenced, flows to that spot and there finds its most facile passage (1418, 1435). As an illustration of the growth generally of discharge, I may remark that, in the experiments on the transition in oxygen of the discharge from spark to brush (1518), every spark was immediately preceded by a short brush.

1554. The phenomena relative to dark discharge in other gases, though differing in certain characters from those in air, confirm the conclusions drawn above. The two rounded terminations (1544) (Pl. XI, *Fig. 6*), were placed in *muriatic acid gas* (1445, 1463) at the pressure of 6.5 inches of mercury, and a continuous machine current of electricity sent through the apparatus: bright sparks occurred until the interval was about or above an inch, when they were replaced by squat brushy intermitting glows upon both terminations, with a dark part between. When the current at the machine was in spark, then each spark caused a discharge across the muriatic acid gas, which, with a certain interval, was bright; with a larger interval, was straight across and flamy, like a very exhausted and sudden, but not a dense sharp spark; and with a still larger interval, produced a feeble brush on the inductric positive end, and a glow on the inducteous negative end, the dark part being between (1544); and at such times, the spark at the conductor, instead of being sudden and sonorous, was dull and quiet (334).

1555. On introducing more muriatic acid gas, until the pressure was 29.97 inches, the same terminations gave bright sparks within at small distances; but when they were about an inch or more apart, the discharge was generally with very small brushes and glow, and frequently with no light at all, though electricity had passed through the gas. Whenever the bright spark did pass through the muriatic acid gas at this pressure, it was bright throughout, presenting no dark or dull space.

1556. In *coal gas*, at common pressures, when the distance was about an inch, the discharge was accompanied by short brushes on the ends, and a dark interval of half an inch or more between them, notwithstanding the discharge had the sharp quick sound of a dull spark, and could not have depended in the dark part on *convection* (1562).

1557. This gas presents several curious points in relation to the bright and dark parts of spark discharge. When bright sparks passed between the rod ends 0.3 of an inch in diameter (1544),

very sudden dark parts would occur next to the brightest portions of the spark. Again, with these ends and also with balls (1422), the bright sparks would be sometimes red, sometimes green, and occasionally green and red in different parts of the same spark. Again, in the experiments described (1518), at certain intervals a very peculiar pale, dull, yet sudden discharge would pass, which, though apparently weak, was very direct in its course, and accompanied by a sharp snapping noise, as if quick in its occurrence.

1558. *Hydrogen* frequently gave peculiar sparks, one part being bright red, whilst the other was a dull pale gray, or else the whole spark was dull and peculiar.

1559. *Nitrogen* presented a very remarkable discharge, between two balls of the respective diameters of 0.15 and 2 inches (1506, 1518), the smaller one being rendered negative either directly or inducteously. The peculiar discharge occurs at intervals between 0.42 and 0.68, and even at 1.4 inches when the large ball was inductric positively; it consisted of a little brushy part on the small negative ball, then a dark space, and lastly a dull straight line on the large positive ball (Pl. XI, *Fig. 7*). The position of the dark space was very constant, and is probably in direct relation to the dark space described when negative glow was produced (1544). When by any circumstance a bright spark was determined, the contrast with the peculiar spark described was very striking; for it always had a faint purple part, but the place of this part was constantly near the positive ball.

1560. Thus dark discharge appears to be decidedly established. But its establishment is accompanied by proofs that it occurs in different degrees and modes in different gases. Hence then another specific action, added to the many (1296, 1398, 1399, 1423, 1454, 1503) by which the electrical relations of insulating dielectrics are distinguished and established, and another argument in favour of that molecular theory of induction, which is at present under examination.[1]

1561. What I have had to say regarding disruptive discharge has extended to some length, but I hope will be excused in consequence of the importance of the subject. Before concluding my remarks, I will again intimate in the form

[1] I cannot resist referring here by a note to Biot's philosophical view of the nature of the light of the electric discharge, *Annales de Chimie*, LIII, p. 321.

of a query, whether we have not reason to consider the tension or retention and after discharge in air or other insulating dielectrics, as the same thing with retardation and discharge in a metal wire, differing only, but almost infinitely, in degree (1334, 1336). In other words, can we not, by a gradual chain of association, carry up discharge from its occurrence in air, through spermaceti and water, to solutions, and then on to chlorides, oxides and metals, without any essential change in its character; and, at the same time, connecting the insensible conduction of air, through muriatic acid gas and the dark discharge, with the better conduction of spermaceti, water, and the all but perfect conduction of the metals, associate the phenomena at both extremes? and may it not be, that the retardation and ignition of a wire are effects exactly correspondent in their nature to the retention of charge and spark in air? If so, here again the two extremes in property amongst dielectrics will be found to be in intimate relation, the whole difference probably depending upon the mode and degree in which their particles polarize under the influence of inductive actions (1338, 1603, 1610).

¶ x. *Convection, or Carrying Discharge*

1562. The last kind of discharge which I have to consider is that effected by the motion of charged particles from place to place. It is apparently very different in its nature to any of the former modes of discharge (1319), but, as the result is the same, may be of great importance in illustrating, not merely the nature of discharge itself, but also of what we call the electric current. It often, as before observed, in cases of brush and glow (1440, 1535), joins its effect to that of disruptive discharge, to complete the act of neutralization amongst the electric forces.

1563. The particles which being charged, then travel, may be either of insulating or conducting matter, large or small. The consideration in the first place of a large particle of conducting matter may perhaps help our conceptions.

1564. A copper boiler 3 feet in diameter was insulated and electrified, but so feebly that dissipation by brushes or disruptive discharge did not occur at its edges or projecting parts in a sensible degree. A brass ball, 2 inches in diameter, suspended by a clean white silk thread, was brought towards it, and it was found that, if the ball was held for a second or two near any part of the charged surface of the boiler, at such distance (two inches more or less) as not

to receive any direct charge from it, it became itself charged, although insulated the whole time; and its electricity was the *reverse* of that of the boiler.

1565. This effect was the strongest opposite the edges and projecting parts of the boiler, and weaker opposite the sides, or those extended portions of the surface which, according to Coulomb's results, have the weakest charge. It was very strong opposite a rod projecting a little way from the boiler. It occurred when the copper was charged negatively as well as positively: it was produced also with small balls down to 0.2 of an inch and less in diameter, and also with smaller charged conductors than the copper. It is, indeed, hardly possible in some cases to carry an insulated ball within an inch or two of a charged plane or convex surface without its receiving a charge of the contrary kind to that of the surface.

1566. This effect is one of induction between the bodies, not of communication. The ball, when related to the positive charged surface by the intervening dielectric, has its opposite sides brought into contrary states, that side towards the boiler being negative and the outer side positive. More inductric action is directed towards it than would have passed across the same place if the ball had not been there, for several reasons; amongst others, because, being a conductor, the resistance of the particles of the dielectric, which otherwise would have been there, is removed (1298); and also, because the reacting positive surface of the ball being projected farther out from the boiler than when there is no introduction of conducting matter, is more free therefore to act through the rest of the dielectric towards surrounding conductors, and so favours the exaltation of that inductric polarity which is directed in its course. It is, as to the exaltation of force upon its outer surface beyond that upon the inductric surface of the boiler, as if the latter were itself protuberant in that direction. Thus it acquires a state like, but higher than, that of the surface of the boiler which causes it; and sufficiently exalted to discharge at its positive surface to the air, or to affect small particles, as it is itself affected by the boiler, and they flying to it, take a charge and pass off; and so the ball, as a whole, is brought into the contrary inducteous state. The consequence is, that, if free to move, its tendency, under the influence of all the forces, to approach the boiler is increased, whilst it at the same time becomes more and more exalted in its condition, both of polarity and charge, until, at a certain distance, discharge takes place, it acquires the same state as the boiler, is repelled, and passing to that conductor most favourably circumstanced to discharge it, there resumes its first indifferent condition.

1567. It seems to me, that the manner in which inductric bodies affect uncharged floating or moveable conductors near them, is very frequently of this nature, and generally so when it ends in a carrying operation (1562, 1602). The manner in which, whilst the dominant inductric body cannot give off its electricity to the air, the inducteous body *can* effect the discharge of the same kind of force, is curious, and, in the case of elongated or irregularly shaped conductors, such as filaments or particles of dust, the effect will often be very ready, and the consequent attraction immediate.

1568. The effect described is also probably influential in causing those variations in spark discharge referred to in the last series (1386, 1390, 1391): for if a particle of dust were drawn towards the axis of induction between the balls, it would tend, whilst at some distance from that axis, to commence discharge at itself, in the manner described (1566), and that commencement might so far facilitate the act (1417, 1420) as to make the complete discharge, as spark, pass through the particle, though it might not be the shortest course from ball to ball. So also, with equal balls at equal distances, as in the experiments of comparison already described (1493, 1506), a particle being between one pair of balls would cause discharge there in preference; or even if a particle were between each, difference of size or shape would give one for the time a predominance over the other.

1569. The power of particles of dust to carry off electricity in cases of high tension is well known, and I have already mentioned some instances of the kind in the use of the inductive apparatus (1201). The general operation is very well shown by large light objects, as the toy called the electrical spider; or, if smaller ones are wanted for philosophical investigation, by the smoke of a glowing green wax taper, which, presenting a successive stream of such particles, makes their course visible.

1570. On using oil of turpentine as the dielectric, the action and course of small conducting carrying particles in it can be well observed. A few short pieces of thread will supply the place of carriers, and their progressive action is exceedingly interesting.

1571. A very striking effect was produced on oil of turpentine, which, whether it was due to the carrying power of the particles in it, or to any other action of them, is perhaps as yet doubtful. A portion of that fluid in a glass vessel had a large uninsulated silver dish at the bottom, and an electrified metal rod with a round termination dipping into it at the top. The insulation was very good, and the attraction and other phenomena striking. The rod end, with a drop of gum water attached to it, was then electrified in the fluid; the gum water soon spun off in fine threads, and was quickly dissipated through the oil of turpentine. By the time that four drops had in this way been commingled with a pint of the dielectric, the latter had lost by far the greatest portion of its insulating power; no sparks could be obtained in the fluid; and all the phenomena dependent upon insulation had sunk to a low degree. The fluid was very slightly turbid. Upon being filtered through paper only, it resumed its first clearness, and now insulated as well as before. The water, therefore, was merely diffused through the oil of turpentine, not combined with or dissolved in it: but whether the minute particles acted as carriers, or whether they were not rather gathered together in the line of highest inductive tension (1350), and there, being drawn into elongated forms by the electric forces, combined their effects to produce a band of matter having considerable conducting power, as compared with the oil of turpentine, is as yet questionable.

1572. The analogy between the action of solid conducting carrying particles and that of the charged particles of fluid insulating substances, acting as dielectrics, is very evident and simple; but in the latter case the result is, necessarily, currents in the mobile media. Particles are brought by inductric action into a polar state; and the latter after rising to a certain tension (1370), is followed by the communication of a part of the force originally on the conductor; the particles consequently become charged, and then, under the joint influence of the repellent and attractive forces, are urged towards a discharging place, or to that spot where these inductric forces are most easily compensated by the contrary inducteous forces.

1573. Why a point should be so exceedingly favourable to the production of currents in a fluid insulating dielectric, as air, is very evident. It is at the extremity of the point that the intensity necessary to charge the air is first acquired (1374); it is from thence that the charged particle recedes; and the mechanical force which it impresses on the air to form a current is in every way favoured by the shape and position of the rod, of which the point forms the termination. At the same time, the point, having become the origin of an active mechanical force, does, by the very act of causing that force, namely, by discharge, prevent any other part of the rod from acquiring the same necessary condition, and so preserves and sustains its own predominance.

1574. The very varied and beautiful phenomena produced by sheltering or enclosing the point, illustrate the production of the current exceedingly well, and justify the same conclusions; it being remembered that in such cases the effect upon the discharge is of two kinds. For the current may be interfered with by stopping the access of fresh uncharged air, or retarding the removal of that which has been charged, as when a point is electrified in a tube of insulating matter closed at one extremity; or the *electric condition* of the point itself may be altered by the relation of other parts in its neighbourhood, also rendered electric, as when the point is in a metal tube, by the metal itself, or when it is in the glass tube, by a similar action of the charged parts of the glass, or even by the surrounding air which has been charged, and which cannot escape.

1575. Whenever it is intended to observe such inductive phenomena in a fluid dielectric as have a direct relation to, and dependence upon, the fluidity of the medium, such, for instance, as discharge from points, or attractions and repulsions, &c., then the mass of the fluid should be great, and in such proportion to the distance between the inductric and inducteous surfaces as to include all the *lines of inductive force* (1369) between them; otherwise, the effects of currents, attraction, &c., which are the resultants of all these forces, cannot be obtained. The phenomena which occur in the open air, or in the middle of a globe filled with oil of turpentine, will not take place in the same media if confined in tubes of glass, shellac, sulphur, or other such substances, though they be excellent insulating dielectrics; nor can they be expected: for in such cases, the polar forces, instead of being all dispersed amongst fluid particles which tend to move under their influence, are now associated in many parts with particles that, notwithstanding their tendency to motion, are constrained by their solidity to remain quiescent.

1576. The varied circumstances under which, with conductors differently formed and constituted, currents can occur, all illustrate the same simplicity of production. A *ball*, if the intensity be raised sufficiently on its surface, and that intensity be greatest on a part consistent with the production of a current of air up to and off from it, will produce the effect like a point (1537); such is the case whenever the glow occurs upon a ball, the current being essential to that phenomenon. If as large a sphere as can well be employed with the production of glow be used, the glow will appear at the place where the current leaves the ball, and that will be the part directly opposite to the connection of the ball and rod which supports it; but by increasing the tension elsewhere, so as to raise it above the tension upon that spot, which can easily be effected inductively, then the place of the glow and the direction of the current will also change, and pass to that spot which for the time is most favourable for their production (1591).

1577. For instance, approaching the hand towards the ball will tend to cause brush (1539), but by increasing the supply of electricity the condition of glow may be preserved; then on moving the hand about from side to side the position of the glow will very evidently move with it.

1578. A point brought towards a glowing ball would at twelve or fourteen inches distance make the glow break into brush, but when still nearer, glow was reproduced, probably dependent upon the discharge of wind or air passing from the point to the ball, and this glow was very obedient to the motion of the point, following it in every direction.

1579. Even a current of wind could affect the place of the glow; for a varnished glass tube being directed sideways towards the ball, air was sometimes blown through it at the ball and sometimes not. In the former case, the place of the glow was changed a little, as if it were blown away by the current, and this is just the result which might have been anticipated. All these effects illustrate beautifully the general causes and relations, both of the glow and the current of air accompanying it (1574).

1580. Flame facilitates the production of a current in the dielectric surrounding it. Thus, if a ball which would not occasion a current in the air have a flame, whether large or small, formed on its surface, the current is produced with the greatest ease; but not the least difficulty can occur in comprehending the effective action of the flame in this case, if its relation, as part of the surrounding dielectric, to the electrified ball, be but for a moment considered (1375, 1380).

1581. Conducting fluid terminations, instead of rigid points, illustrate in a very beautiful manner the formation of the currents, with their effects and influence in exalting the conditions under which they were commenced. Let the rounded end of a brass rod, 0.3 of an inch or thereabouts in diameter, point downwards in free air; let it be amalgamated, and have a drop of mercury suspended from it; and then let it be powerfully electrized. The mercury will present the phenomenon of *glow*; a current of air will rush along the rod, and set off from the mercury directly downwards; and the form of the metallic drop will be slightly affected, the convexity at a small part near the middle and lower part becoming greater, whilst it diminishes all round at places a little removed from this spot. The change is from the form of *a* (Pl. XI, *Fig. 8*) to that of *b*, and is due almost, if not entirely, to the mechanical force of the current of air sweeping over its surface.

1582. As a comparative observation, let it be noticed, that a ball gradually brought towards it converts the glow into brushes, and ultimately sparks pass from the most projecting part of the mercury. A point does the same, but at much smaller distances.

1583. Take next a drop of strong solution of muriate of lime; being electrified, a part will probably be dissipated, but a considerable portion, if the electricity be not too powerful, will remain, forming a conical drop (Pl. XI, *Fig. 9*), accompanied by a strong current. If glow be produced, the drop will be smooth on the surface. If a short low brush is formed, a minute tremulous motion of the liquid will be visible; but both effects coincide with the principal one to be observed, namely the regular and successive charge of air, the formation of a wind or current, and the form given by that current to the fluid drop. If a discharge ball be gradually brought toward the cone, sparks will at last pass, and these will be from the apex of the cone to the approached ball, indicating a considerable degree of conducting power in this fluid.

1584. With a drop of water, the effects were of the same kind, and were best obtained when a portion of gum water or of syrup hung from a ball (Pl. XI, *Fig. 10*). When the machine was worked slowly, a fine large quiet conical drop, with concave lateral outline, and a small rounded end, was produced, on which the glow appeared, whilst a steady wind issued, in a direction from the point of the cone, of sufficient force to depress the surface of uninsulated water held opposite to the termination. When the machine was worked more rapidly some of the water was driven off; the smaller pointed portion left was roughish on the surface, and the sound of successive brush discharges was heard. With still more electricity, more water was dispersed; that which remained was elongated and contracted, with an alternating motion; a stronger brush discharge was heard, and the vibrations of the water and the successive discharges of the individual brushes were simultaneous. When water from beneath was brought towards the drop, it did not indicate the same regular strong contracted current of air as before; and when the distance was such that sparks passed, the water beneath was *attracted* rather than driven away, and the current of air *ceased*.

1585. When the discharging ball was brought near the drop in its first quiet glowing state (1582), it converted that glow into brushes, and caused the vibrating motion of the drop. When still nearer, sparks passed, but they were always from the metal of the rod, over the surface of the water, to the point, and then across the air to the ball. This is a natural consequence of the deficient conducting power of the fluid (1584, 1585).

1586. Why the drop vibrated, changing its form between the periods of discharging brushes, so as to be more or less acute at particular instants, to be most acute when the brush issued forth, and to be isochronous in its action, and how the quiet glowing liquid drop, on assuming the conical form, facilitated, as it were, the first action, are points, as to theory, so evident, that I will not stop to speak of them. The principal thing to observe at present is, the formation of the carrying current of air, and the manner in which it exhibits its existence and influence by giving form to the drop.

1587. That the drop, when of water, or a better conductor than water, is formed into a cone principally by the current of air, is shown amongst other ways (1594) thus. A sharp point being held opposite the conical drop, the latter soon lost its pointed form; was retracted and became round; the current of air from it ceased, and was replaced by one from the point beneath, which, if the latter were held near enough to the drop, actually blew it aside, and rendered it concave in form.

1588. It is hardly necessary to say what happened with still worse conductors than water, as oil, or oil of turpentine; the fluid itself was then spun out into threads and carried off, not only because the air rushing over its surface helped to sweep it away, but also because its insulating particles assumed the same charged state as the particles of air, and, not being able to discharge to them in a much greater degree than the air particles themselves could do, were carried off by the same causes which urged these in their course. A similar effect with melted sealing-wax on a metal point forms an old and well-known experiment.

1589. A drop of gum water in the exhausted receiver of the air-pump was not sensibly affected in its form when electrified. When air was let in, it began to show change of shape when the pressure was ten inches of mercury. At the pressure of fourteen or fifteen inches the change was more sensible, and as the air increased in density the effects increased, until they were the same as those in the open atmosphere. The diminished effect in the rare air I refer to the relative diminished energy of its current; that diminution depending, in the first place, on the lower electric condition of the electrified ball in the rarefied medium, and in the next, on the attenuated condition of the dielectric, the cohesive force of water in relation to rarefied air being something like that of mercury to dense air (1581), whilst that of water in dense air may be compared to that of mercury in oil of turpentine (1597).

1590. When a ball is covered with a thick conducting fluid, as treacle or syrup, it is easy by inductive action to determine the wind from almost any part of it (1577); the experiment, which before was of rather difficult performance, being rendered facile in consequence of the fluid enabling that part, which at first was feeble in its action, to rise into an exalted condition by assuming a pointed form.

1591. To produce the current, the electric intensity must rise and continue at *one spot*, namely at the origin of the current, higher than elsewhere, and then, air having a uniform and ready access, the current is produced. If no current be allowed (1574), then discharge may take place by brush or spark. But whether it be by brush or spark, or wind, it seems very probable that the initial intensity or tension at which a particle of a given gaseous dielectric charges, or commences discharge, is, under the conditions before expressed, always the same (1410).

1592. It is not supposed that all the air which enters into motion is electrified; on the contrary, much that is not charged is carried on into the stream. The part which is really charged may be but a small proportion of that which is ultimately set in motion (1442).

1593. When a drop of gum water (1584) is made *negative*, it presents a larger cone than when made positive; less of the fluid is thrown off, and yet, when a ball is approached, sparks can hardly be obtained, so pointed is the cone, and so free the discharge. A point held opposite to it did not cause the retraction of the cone to such an extent as when it was positive. All the effects are so different from those presented by the positive cone that I have no doubt such drops would present a very instructive method of investigating the difference of positive and negative discharge in air and other dielectrics (1480, 1501).

1594. That I may not be misunderstood (1587), I must observe here that I do not consider the cones produced as the result *only* of the current of air or other insulating dielectric over their surface. When the drop is of badly conducting matter, a part of the effect is due to the electrified state of the particles, and this part constitutes almost the whole when the matter is melted sealing-wax, oil of turpentine, and similar insulating bodies (1588). But even when the drop is of good conducting matter, as water, solutions, or mercury, though the effect above spoken of will then be insensible (1607), still it is not the mere current of air or other dielectric which produces all the change of form; for a part is due to those attractive forces by which the charged drop, if free to move, would travel along the line of strongest induction, and not being free to move, has its form elongated until the *sum* of the different forces tending to produce this form is balanced by the cohesive attraction of the fluid. The effect of the attractive forces are well shown when treacle, gum water, or syrup is used; for the long threads which spin out, at the same time that they form the axes of the currents of air, which may still be considered as determined at their points, are like flexible conductors, and shew by their directions in what way the attractive forces draw them.

1595. When the phenomena of currents are observed in dense insulating dielectrics, they present us with extraordinary degrees of mechanical force. Thus, if a pint of well-rectified and filtered (1571) oil of turpentine be put into a glass vessel, and two wires be dipped into it in different places, one leading to the electrical machine, and the other to the discharging train, on working the machine the fluid will be thrown into violent motion throughout its whole mass, whilst at the same time it will rise two, three or four inches up the machine wire, and dart off in jets from it into the air.

1596. If very clean uninsulated mercury be at the bottom of the fluid, and the wire from the machine be terminated either by a ball or a point, and also pass through a glass tube extending both above and below the surface of the oil of turpentine, the currents can be better observed, and will be seen to rush down the wire, proceeding directly from it towards the mercury, and there, diverging in all directions, will ripple its surface strongly, and mounting up at the sides of the vessel, will return to re-enter upon their course.

1597. A drop of mercury being suspended from an amalgamated brass ball, preserved its form almost unchanged in air (1581); but when immersed in the oil of turpentine it became very pointed, and even particles of the metal could be spun out and carried off by the currents of the dielectric. The form of the liquid metal was just like that of the syrup in air (1584), the point of the cone being quite as fine, though not so long. By bringing a sharp uninsulated point towards it, it could also be effected in the same manner as the syrup drop in air (1587), though not so readily, because of the density and limited quantity of the dielectric.

1598. If the mercury at the bottom of the fluid be connected with the electrical machine, whilst a rod is held in the hand terminating in a ball three quarters of an inch, less or more, in diameter, and the ball be dipped into the electrified fluid, very striking appearances ensue. When the ball is raised again so as to be at a level nearly out of the fluid, large portions of the latter will seem to cling to it (Pl. XI, *Fig. 11*). If it be raised higher, a column of the oil of turpentine will still connect it with that in the basin below (*Fig. 12*). If the machine be excited into more powerful action, this will become more bulky, and may then also be raised higher, assuming the form (*Fig. 13*); and all the time that these effects continue, currents and counter-currents, sometimes running very close together, may be observed in the raised column of fluid.

1599. It is very difficult to decide by sight the direction of the currents in such experiments as these. If particles of silk are introduced they cling about the conductors; but using drops of water and mercury, the course of the fluid dielectric seems well indicated. Thus, if a drop of water be placed at the end of a rod (1571) over the uninsulated mercury, it is soon swept away in particles streaming downwards towards the mercury. If another drop be placed on the mercury beneath the end of the rod, it is quickly dispersed in all directions in the form of streaming particles, the attractive forces drawing it into elongated portions, and the currents carrying them away. If a drop of mercury be hung from a ball used to raise a column of the fluid (1598), then the shape of the drop seems to show currents travelling in the fluid in the direction indicated by the arrows (Pl. XI, *Fig. 14*).

1600. A very remarkable effect is produced on these phenomena, connected with positive and negative charge and discharge, namely that a ball charged positively raises a much higher and larger column of the oil of turpentine than when charged negatively. There can be no doubt that this is connected with the difference of positive and negative action already spoken of (1480, 1525), and tends much to strengthen the idea that such difference is referable to the particles of the dielectric rather than to the charged conductors, and is dependent upon the mode in which these particles polarize (1503, 1523).

1601. Whenever currents travel in insulating dielectrics they really effect discharge; and it is important to observe, though a very natural result, that it is indifferent which way the current or particles travel, as with reversed direction their state is reversed. The change is easily made, either in air or oil of turpentine, between two opposed rods, for an insulated ball being placed in connexion with either rod and brought near its extremity, will cause the current to set towards it from the opposite end.

1602. The two currents often occur at once, as when both terminations present brushes, and frequently when they exhibit the glow (1531). In such cases, the charged particles, or many of them, meet and mutually discharge each other (1548, 1612). If a smoking wax taper be held at the end of an insulating rod towards a charged prime conductor, it will very often happen that two currents will form, and be rendered visible by its vapour, one passing as a fine filament of smoky particles directly to the charged conductor, and the other passing as directly from the same taper wick outwards, and from the conductor: the principles of inductric action and charge, which were referred to in considering the relation of a carrier ball and a conductor (1566), being here also called into play.

1603. The general analogy and, I think I may say, identity of action found to exist as to insulation and conduction (1338, 1561) when bodies, the best and the worst in the classes of insulators or conductors, were compared, led me to believe that the phenomena of *convection* in badly conducting media were not without their parallel amongst the best conductors, such even as the metals. Upon consideration, the cones produced by Davy[1] in fluid metals, as mercury and tin, seemed to be cases in point, and probably also the elongation of the metallic medium through which a current of electricity was passing, described by Ampere (1113);[2] for it is not difficult to conceive, that the diminution of convective effect, consequent upon the high conducting power of the metallic media used in these experiments, might be fully compensated for by the enormous quantity of electricity passing. In fact, it is impossible not to expect *some* effect, whether sensible or not, of the kind in question, when such a current is passing through a fluid offering a sensible resistance to the passage of the electricity, and, thereby, giving proof of a certain degree of insulating power (1328).

1604. I endeavoured to connect the convective currents in air, oil of turpentine, &c., and those in metals, by intermediate eases, but found this not easy to do. On taking bodies, for instance, which, like water, acids, solutions, fused salts or chlorides, &c., have intermediate conducting powers, the minute quantity of electricity which the common machine can supply (371, 861) is exhausted instantly, so that the cause of the phenomenon is kept either very low in intensity, or the instant of time during which the effect lasts is so small that one cannot hope to observe the result sought for. If a voltaic battery be used, these bodies are all electrolytes, and the evolution of gas, or the production of other changes, interferes and prevents observation of the effect required.

1605. There are, nevertheless, some experiments which illustrate the connection. Two platina wires, forming the electrodes of a powerful voltaic battery, were placed side by side, near each other, in distilled water hermetically

sealed up in a strong glass tube, some minute vegetable fibres being present in the water. When, from the evolution of gas and the consequent increased pressure, the bubbles formed on the electrodes were so small as to produce but feebly ascending currents, then it could be observed that the filaments present were attracted and repelled between the two wires, as they would have been between two oppositely charged surfaces in air or oil of turpentine, moving so quickly as to displace and disturb the bubbles and the currents which these tended to form. Now I think it cannot be doubted that under similar circumstances, and with an abundant supply of electricity, of sufficient tension also, convective currents might have been formed; the attractions and repulsions of the filaments were, in fact, the elements of such currents (1572), and therefore water, though almost infinitely above air or oil of turpentine as a conductor, is a medium in which similar currents can take place.

1606. I had an apparatus made (Pl. XI, *Fig. 15*) in which *a* is a plate of shellac, *b* a fine platina wire passing through it, and having only the section of the wire exposed above; *c* a ring of bibulous paper resting on the shellac, and *d* distilled water retained by the paper in its place, and just sufficient in quantity to cover the end of the wire *b*; another wire, *e*, touched a piece of tinfoil lying in the water, and was also connected with a discharging train; in this way it was easy, by rendering *b* either positive or negative, to send a current of electricity by its extremity into the fluid, and so away by the wire *e*.

1607. On connecting *b* with the conductor of a powerful electrical machine, not the least disturbance of the level of the fluid over the end of the wire during the working of the machine could be observed; but at the same time there was not the smallest indication of electrical charge about the conductor of the machine, so complete was the discharge. I conclude that the quantity of electricity passed in a *given time* had been too small, when compared with the conducting power of the fluid to produce the desired effect.

1608. I then charged a large Leyden battery (291), and discharged it through the wire *b*, interposing, however, a wet thread, two feet long, to prevent a spark in the water, and to reduce what would else have been a sudden violent discharge into one of more moderate character, enduring for a sensible length of time (334). I now did obtain a very brief ele-

---

[1] *Philosophical Transactions*, 1823, p. 155.
[2] *Bibliothèque Universelle*, XXI, 47.

vation of the water over the end of the wire; and though a few minute bubbles of gas were at the same time formed there, so as to prevent me from asserting that the effect was unequivocally the same as that obtained by DAVY in the metals, yet, according to my best judgement, it was partly, and I believe principally, of that nature.

1609. I employed a voltaic battery of 100 pair of four-inch plates for experiments of a similar nature with electrolytes. In these cases the shellac was cupped, and the wire *b* 0.2 of an inch in diameter. Sometimes I used a positive amalgamated zinc wire in contact with dilute sulphuric acid; at others, a negative copper wire in a solution of sulphate of copper; but, because of the evolution of gas, the precipitation of copper, &c., I was not able to obtain decided results. It is but right to mention, that when I made use of mercury, endeavouring to repeat DAVY'S experiment, the battery of 100 pair was not sufficient to produce the elevations.[1]

1610. The latter experiments (1609) may therefore be considered as failing to give the hoped-for proof, but I have much confidence in the former (1605, 1608), and in the considerations (1603) connected with them. If I have rightly viewed them, and we may be allowed to compare the currents at points and surfaces in such extremely different bodies as air and the metals, and admit that they are effects of the *same* kind, differing only in degree and in proportion to the insulating or conducting power of the dielectric used, what great additional argument we obtain in favour of that theory, which in the phenomena of insulation and conduction also, as in these, would link *the same* apparently dissimilar substances together (1336, 1561); and how completely the general view, which refers all the phenomena to the direct action of the molecules of matter, seems to embrace the various isolated phenomena as they successively come under consideration!

1611. The connection of this convective or carrying effect, which depends upon a certain degree of insulation, with conduction; i.e., the occurrence of both in so many of the substances referred to, as, for instance, the metals, water, air, &c., would lead to many very curious the-

oretical generalizations, which I must not indulge in here. One point, however, I shall venture to refer to. Conduction appears to be essentially an action of contiguous particles, and the considerations just stated, together with others formerly expressed (1326, 1336, &c.), lead to the conclusion, that all bodies conduct, and by the same process, air as well as metals; the only difference being in the necessary degree of force or tension between the particles which must exist before the act of conduction or transfer from one particle to another can take place.

1612. The question then arises, what is this limiting condition which separates, as it were, conduction and insulation from each other? Does it consist in a difference between the two contiguous particles, or the contiguous poles of these particles, in the nature and amount of positive and negative force, no communication or discharge occurring unless that difference rises up to a certain degree, variable for different bodies, but always the same for the same body? Or is it true that, however small the difference between two such particles, if *time* be allowed, equalization of force will take place, even with the particles of such bodies as air, sulphur or lac? In the first case, insulating power in any particular body would be proportionate to the degree of the assumed necessary difference of force; in the second, to the *time* required to equalize equal degrees of difference in different bodies. With regard to airs, one is almost led to expect a permanent difference of force; but in all other bodies, time seems to be quite sufficient to ensure, ultimately, complete conduction. The difference in the modes by which insulation may be sustained, or conduction effected, is not a mere fanciful point, but one of great importance, as being essentially connected with the molecular theory of induction, and the manner in which the particles of bodies assume and retain their polarized state.

¶ xi. *Relation of a Vacuum to Electrical Phenomena*

1613. It would seem strange, if a theory which refers all the phenomena of insulation and conduction, i.e., all electrical phenomena, to the action of contiguous particles, were to omit to notice the assumed possible case of a *vacuum*. Admitting that a vacuum can be produced, it would be a very curious matter indeed to know what its relation to electrical phenomena would be; and as shellac and metal are directly opposed to each other, whether a

[1] In the experiments at the Royal Institution, Sir H. Davy used, I think, 500 or 600 pairs of plates. Those at the London Institution were made with the apparatus of Mr. Pepys (consisting of an enormous single pair of plates), described in the *Philosophical Transactions* for 1823, p. 187.

vacuum would be opposed to them both, and allow neither of induction or conduction across it. Mr. Morgan[1] has said that a vacuum does not conduct. Sir H. Davy concluded from his investigations, that as perfect a vacuum as could be made[2] did conduct, but does not consider the prepared spaces which he used as absolute vacua. In such experiments I think I have observed the luminous discharge to be principally on the inner surface of the glass; and it does not appear at all unlikely that, if the vacuum refused to conduct, still the surface of glass next it might carry on that action.

1614. At one time, when I thought inductive force was exerted in right lines, I hoped to illustrate this important question by making experiments on induction with metallic mirrors (used only as conducting vessels) exposed towards a very clear sky at night time, and of such concavity that nothing but the firmament could be visible from the lowest part of the concave n (Pl. XI, *Fig. 16*). Such mirrors, when electrified, as by connection with a Leyden jar, and examined by a carrier ball, readily gave electricity at the lowest part of their concavity if in a room; but I was in hopes of finding that, circumstanced as before stated, they would give little or none at the same spot, if the atmosphere above really terminated in a vacuum. I was disappointed in the conclusion, for I obtained as much electricity there as before; but on discovering the action of induction in curved lines (1231), found a full and satisfactory explanation of the result.

1615. My theory, as far as I have ventured it, does not pretend to decide upon the consequences of a vacuum. It is not at present limited sufficiently, or rendered precise enough, either by experiments relating to spaces void of matter, or those of other kinds, to indicate what would happen in the vacuum case. I have only as yet endeavoured to establish, what all the facts seem to prove, that when electrical phenomena, as those of induction, conduction, insulation and discharge occur, they depend on, and are produced by the action of *contiguous* particles of matter, the next existing particle being considered as the contiguous one; and I have further assumed, that these particles are polarized; that each exhibits the two forces, or the force in two directions (1295, 1298); and that they act at a distance, only by acting on the *contiguous* and intermediate particles.

1616. But assuming that a perfect vacuum

were to intervene in the course of the lines of inductive action (1304), it does not follow from this theory, that the particles on opposite sides of such a vacuum could not act on each other. Suppose it possible for a positively electrified particle to be in the centre of a vacuum an inch in diameter, nothing in my present views forbids that the particle should act at the distance of half an inch on all the particles forming the inner superficies of the bounding sphere, and with a force consistent with the well-known law of the squares of the distance. But suppose the sphere of an inch were full of insulating matter, the electrified particle would not then, according to my notion, act directly on the distant particles, but on those in immediate association with it, employing *all* its power in polarizing them; producing in them negative force equal in amount to its own positive force and directed towards the latter, and positive force of equal amount directed outwards and acting in the same manner upon the layer of particles next in succession. So that ultimately, those particles in the surface of a sphere of half an inch radius, which were acted on *directly* when that sphere was a vacuum, will now be acted on *indirectly* as respects the central particle or source of action, i.e., they will be polarized in the same way, and with the same amount of force.

§ 19. *Nature of the Electrical Current*

1617. The word *current* is so expressive in common language that when applied in the consideration of electrical phenomena we can hardly divest it sufficiently of its meaning, or prevent our minds from being prejudiced by it (283, 511). I shall use it in its common electrical sense, namely to express generally a certain condition and relation of electrical forces supposed to be in progression.

1618. A current is produced both by excitement and discharge; and whatsoever the variation of the two general causes may be, the effect remains the same. Thus excitement may occur in many ways, as by friction, chemical action, influence of heat, change of condition, induction, &c.; and discharge has the forms of conduction, electrolyzation, disruptive discharge, and convection; yet the current connected with these actions, when it occurs, appears in all cases to be the same. This constancy in the character of the current, notwithstanding the particular and great variations which may be made in the mode of its occurrence, is exceedingly striking and important; and its in-

[1] *Philosophical Transactions*, 1785, p. 272.
[2] *Ibid.*, 1822, p. 64.

vestigation and development promise to supply the most open and advantageous road to a true and intimate understanding of the nature of electrical forces.

1619. As yet the phenomena of the current have presented nothing in opposition to the view I have taken of the nature of induction as an action of contiguous particles. I have endeavoured to divest myself of prejudices and to look for contradictions, but I have not perceived any in conductive, electrolytic, convective, or disruptive discharge.

1620. Looking at the current as a *cause*, it exerts very extraordinary and diverse powers, not only in its course and on the bodies in which it exists, but collaterally, as in inductive or magnetic phenomena.

1621. *Electrolytic action.* One of its direct actions is the exertion of pure chemical force, this being a result which has now been examined to a considerable extent. The effect is found to be *constant* and *definite* for the quantity of electric force discharged (783, &c.); and beyond that, the *intensity* required is in relation to the intensity of the affinity or forces to be overcome (904, 906, 911). The current and its consequences are here proportionate; the one may be employed to represent the other; no part of the effect of either is lost or gained; so that the case is a strict one, and yet it is the very case which most strikingly illustrates the doctrine that induction is an action of contiguous particles (1164, 1343).

1622. The process of electrolytic discharge appears to me to be in close analogy, and perhaps in its nature identical with another process of discharge, which at first seems very different from it, I mean *convection* (1347, 1572). In the latter case the particles may travel for yards across a chamber; they may produce strong winds in the air, so as to move machinery; and in fluids, as oil of turpentine, may even shake the hand, and carry heavy metallic bodies about;[1] and yet I do not see that the force, either in kind or action, is at all different to that by which a particle of hydrogen leaves one particle of oxygen to go to another, or by which a particle of oxygen travels in the contrary direction.

[1] If a metallic vessel three or four inches deep, containing oil of turpentine, be insulated and electrified, and a rod with a ball (an inch or more in diameter) at the end have the ball immersed in the fluid whilst the end is held in the hand, the mechanical force generated when the ball is moved to and from the sides of the vessel will soon be evident to the experimenter.

1623. Travelling particles of the air can effect chemical changes just as well as the contact of a fixed platina electrode, or that of a combining electrode, or the ions of a decomposing electrolyte (453, 471); and in the experiment formerly described, where eight places of decomposition were rendered active by one current (469), and where charged particles of air in motion were the only electrical means of connecting these parts of the current, it seems to me that the action of the particles of the electrolyte and of the air were essentially the same. A particle of air was rendered positive; it travelled in a certain determinate direction, and coming to an electrolyte, communicated its powers; an equal amount of positive force was accordingly acquired by another particle (the hydrogen), and the latter, so charged, travelled as the former did, and in the same direction, until it came to another particle, and transferred its power and motion, making that other particle active. Now, though the particle of air travelled over a visible and occasionally a large space, whilst the particle of the electrolyte moved over an exceedingly small one; though the air particle might be oxygen, nitrogen, or hydrogen, receiving its charge from force of high intensity, whilst the electrolytic particle of hydrogen had a natural aptness to receive the positive condition with extreme facility; though the air particle might be charged with very little electricity at a very high intensity by one process, whilst the hydrogen particle might be charged with much electricity at a very low intensity by another process; these are not differences of kind, as relates to the final discharging action of these particles, but only of degree; not essential differences which make things unlike, but such differences as give to things, similar in their nature, that great variety which fits them for their office in the system of the universe.

1624. So when a particle of air, or of dust in it, electrified at a negative point, moves on through the influence of the inductive forces (1572) to the next positive surface, and after discharge passes away, it seems to me to represent exactly that particle of oxygen which, having been rendered negative in the electrolyte, is urged by the same disposition of inductive forces, and going to the positive platina electrode, is there discharged, and then passes away, as the air or dust did before it.

1625. *Heat* is another direct effect of the *current* upon substances in which it occurs, and it becomes a very important question, as to the relation of the electric and heating forces, whether the latter is always definite in amount.[1] There are many cases, even amongst bodies which conduct without change, that at present are irreconcileable with the assumption that it is;[2] but there are also many which indicate that, when proper limitations are applied, the heat produced is definite. Harris has shown this for a given length of current in a metallic wire, using common electricity;[3] and De la Rive has proved the same point for voltaic electricity by his beautiful application of Breguet's thermometer.[4]

1626. When the production of heat is observed in electrolytes under decomposition, the results are still more complicated. But important steps have been taken in the investigation of this branch of the subject by De la Rive[5] and others; and it is more than probable that, when the right limitations are applied, constant and definite results will here also be obtained.

1627. It is a most important part of the character of the current, and essentially connected with its very nature, that it is always the same. The two forces are everywhere in it. There is never one current of force or one fluid only. Any one part of the current may, as respects the presence of the two forces there, be considered as precisely the same with any other part; and the numerous experiments which imply their possible separation, as well as the theoretical expressions which, being used daily, assume it, are, I think, in contradiction with facts (511, &c.). It appears to me to be as impossible to assume a current of positive or a current of negative force alone, or of the two at once with any predominance of one over the other, as it is to give an absolute charge to matter (516, 1169, 1177).

1628. The establishment of this truth, if, as I think, it be a truth, or on the other hand the disproof of it, is of the greatest consequence. If, as a first principle, we can establish that the centres of the two forces, or elements of force, never can be separated to any sensible distance, or at all events not farther than the space between two contiguous particles (1615), or if we can establish the contrary conclusion, how much more clear is our view of what lies before us, and how much less embarrassed the ground over which we have to pass in attaining to it, than if we remain halting between two opinions! And if, with that feeling, we rigidly test every experiment which bears upon the point, as far as our prejudices will let us (1161), instead of permitting them with a theoretical expression to pass too easily away, are we not much more likely to attain the real truth, and from that proceed with safety to what is at present unknown?

1629. I say these things, not, I hope, to advance a particular view, but to draw the strict attention of those who are able to investigate and judge of the matter, to what must be a turning point in the theory of electricity; to a separation of two roads, one only of which can be right: and I hope I may be allowed to go a little further into the facts which have driven me to the view I have just given.

1630. When a wire in the voltaic circuit is heated, the temperature frequently rises first, or most at one end. If this effect be due to any relation of positive or negative as respects the current, it would be exceedingly important. I therefore examined several such cases; but when, keeping the contacts of the wire and its position to neighbouring things unchanged, I altered the direction of the current, I found that the effect remained unaltered, showing that it depended, not upon the direction of the current, but on other circumstances. So there is here no evidence of a difference between one part of the circuit and another.

1631. The same point, i.e., uniformity in every part, may be illustrated by what may be considered as the inexhaustible nature of the current when producing particular effects; for these effects depend upon transfer only, and do not consume the power. Thus a current which will heat one inch of platina wire will heat a hundred inches (853, note). If a current be sustained in a constant state, it will decompose the fluid in one voltameter only, or in twenty others if they be placed in the circuit, in each to an amount equal to that in the single one.

1632. Again, in cases of disruptive discharge, as in the spark, there is frequently a dark part (1422) which, by Professor Johnson, has been called the neutral point;[6] and this has given rise to the use of expressions implying that

---

[1] See De la Rive's Researches, *Bib. Universelle*, 1829, XL, p. 40.

[2] Amongst others, Davy, *Philosophical Transactions*, 1821, p. 438. Pelletier's important results, *Annales de Chimie*, 1834, LVI, p. 371 and Becquerel's non-heating current, *Bib. Universelle*, 1835, LX, 218.

[3] *Philosophical Transactions*, 1824, pp. 225, 228.

[4] *Annales de Chimie*, 1836, LXII, 177.

[5] *Bib. Universelle*, 1829, XL, 49; and Ritchie, *Phil. Trans.* 1832, p. 296.

[6] *Silliman's Journal*, 1834, XXV, p. 57.

there are two electricities existing separately, which, passing to that spot, there combine and neutralize each other.[1] But if such expressions are understood as correctly indicating that positive electricity alone is moving between the positive ball and that spot, and negative electricity only between the negative ball and that spot, then what strange conditions these parts must be in; conditions, which to my mind are every way unlike those which really occur! In such a case, one part of a current would consist of positive electricity only, and that moving in one direction; another part would consist of negative electricity only, and that moving in the other direction; and a third part would consist of an accumulation of the two electricities, not moving in either direction, but mixing up together, and being in a relation to each other utterly unlike any relation which could be supposed to exist in the two former portions of the discharge. This does not seem to me to be natural. In a current, whatever form the discharge may take, or whatever part of the circuit or current is referred to, as much positive force as is there exerted in one direction, so much negative force is there exerted in the other. If it were not so we should have bodies electrified, not merely positive and negative, but on occasions in a most extraordinary manner, one being charged with five, ten, or twenty times as much of both positive and negative electricity in equal quantities as another. At present, however, there is no known fact indicating such states.

1633. Even in cases of convection, or carrying discharge, the statement that the current is everywhere the same must in effect be true (1627); for how, otherwise, could the results formerly described occur? When currents of air constituted the mode of discharge between the portions of paper moistened with iodide of potassium or sulphate of soda (465, 469), decomposition occurred; and I have since ascertained that, whether a current of positive air issued from a spot, or one of negative air passed towards it, the effect of the evolution of iodine or of acid was the same, whilst the reversed currents produced alkali. So also in the magnetic experiments (307) whether the discharge was effected by the introduction of a wire, or the occurrence of a spark, or the passage of convective currents either one way or the other (depending on the electrified state of the particles), the result was the same, being in all cases dependent upon the perfect current.

[1] Thomson on *Heat and Electricity*, p. 471.

1634. Hence, the section of a current compared with other sections of the same current must be a constant quantity, if the actions exerted be of the same kind; or if of different kinds, then the forms under which the effects are produced are equivalent to each other, and experimentally convertible at pleasure. It is in sections, therefore, we must look for identity of electrical force, even to the sections of sparks and carrying actions, as well as those of wires and electrolytes.

1635. In illustration of the utility and importance of establishing that which may be the true principle, I will refer to a few cases. The doctrine of unipolarity, as formerly stated, and I think generally understood,[2] is evidently inconsistent with my view of a current (1627); and the later singular phenomena of poles and flames described by Erman and others[3] partake of the same inconsistency of character. If a unipolar body could exist, i.e., one that could conduct the one electricity and not the other, what very new characters we should have a right to expect in the currents of single electricities passing through them, and how greatly ought they to differ, not only from the common current which is supposed to have both electricities travelling in opposite directions in equal amount at the same time, but also from each other! The facts, which are excellent, have, however, gradually been more correctly explained by Becquerel,[4] Andrews[5] and others; and I understand that Professor Ohms[6] has perfected the work, in his close examination of all the phenomena; and after showing that similar phenomena can take place with good conductors, proves that with soap, &c., many of the effects are the mere consequences of the bodies evolved by electrolytic action.

[2] Erman, *Annales de Chimie*, 1807, LXI, p. 115. Davy's *Elements*, p. 168. Biot, *Encyclopædia Britannica* [7th edition], Supp. IV, p. 444. Becquerel, *Traité*, 1, p. 167. De la Rive, *Bib. Univ.*, 1837, VII, 392.
[3] Erman, *Annales de Chimie*, 1824, XXV, 278. Becquerel, *Ibid.*, XXXVI, p. 329.
[4] Becquerel, *Annales de Chimie*, 1831, XLVI, p. 283.
[5] Andrews, *Philosophical Magazine*, 1836, IX, 182.
[6] Schweigger's *Jahrbuch der Chimie*, &c. 1830. Heft 8. Not understanding German, it is with extreme regret I confess I have not access, and cannot do justice, to the many most valuable papers in experimental electricity published in that language. I take this opportunity also of stating another circumstance which occasions me great trouble, and, as I find by experience, may make me seemingly regardless of the labours of others:—it is a gradual loss of memory for some years past; and now, often when I read a memoir, I remember that I have seen it before, and would have rejoiced if at the right time I could have recollected and referred to it in the progress of my own papers.—M. F.

1636. I conclude, therefore, that the *facts* upon which the doctrine of unipolarity was founded are not adverse to that unity and indivisibility of character which I have stated the current to possess, any more than the phenomena of the pile itself (which might well bear comparison with those of unipolar bodies), are opposed to it. Probably the effects which have been called effects of unipolarity, and the peculiar differences of the positive and negative surface when discharging into air, gases, or other dielectrics (1480, 1525) which have been already referred to, may have considerable relation to each other.[1]

1637. M. de la Rive has recently described a peculiar and remarkable effect of heat on a current when passing between electrodes and a fluid.[2] It is, that if platina electrodes dip into acidulated water, no change is produced in the passing current by making the positive electrode hotter or colder; whereas making the negative electrode hotter increased the deflexion of a galvanometer affected by the current, from 12° to 30° and even 45°, whilst making it colder diminished the current in the same high proportions.

1638. That one electrode should have this striking relation to heat whilst the other remained absolutely without, seem to me as incompatible with what I conceived to be the character of a current as unipolarity (1627, 1635), and it was therefore with some anxiety that I repeated the experiment. The electrodes which I used were platina; the electrolyte, water containing about one sixth of sulphuric acid by weight: the voltaic battery consisted of two pairs of amalgamated zinc and platina plates in dilute sulphuric acid, and the galvanometer in the circuit was one with two needles, and gave when the arrangement was complete a deflexion of 10° or 12°.

1639. Under these circumstances heating either electrode increased the current; heating both produced still more effect. When both were heated, if either were cooled, the effect on the current fell in proportion. The proportion of effect due to heating this or that electrode varied, but on the whole heating the negative seemed to favour the passage of the current somewhat more than heating the positive. Whether the application of heat were by a flame applied underneath, or one directed by a

blowpipe from above, or by a hot iron or coal, the effect was the same.

1640. Having thus removed the difficulty out of the way of my views regarding a current, I did not pursue this curious experiment further. It is probable, that the difference between my results and those of M. de la Rive may depend upon the relative values of the currents used; for I employed only a weak one resulting from two pairs of plates two inches long and half an inch wide, whilst M. de la Rive used four pairs of plates of sixteen square inches in surface.

1641. Electric discharges in the atmosphere in the form of balls of fire have occasionally been described. Such phenomena appear to me to be incompatible with all that we know of electricity and its modes of discharge. As *time* is an element in the effect (1418, 1436) it is possible perhaps that an electric discharge might really pass as a ball from place to place; but as everything shows that its velocity must be almost infinite, and the time of its duration exceedingly small, it is impossible that the eye should perceive it as anything else than a line of light. That phenomena of balls of fire may appear in the atmosphere, I do not mean to deny; but that they have anything to do with the discharge of ordinary electricity, or are at all related to lightning or atmospheric electricity, is much more than doubtful.

1642. All these considerations, and many others, help to confirm the conclusion, drawn over and over again, that the current is an indivisible thing; an axis of power, in every part of which both electric forces are present in equal amount[3] (517, 1627). With conduction and electrolyzation, and even discharge by spark, such a view will harmonize without hurting any of our preconceived notions; but as relates to convection, a more startling result appears, which must therefore be considered.

1643. If two balls A and B be electrified in opposite states and held within each other's influence, the moment they move towards each other, a current, or those effects which are understood by the word current, will be produced. Whether A move towards B, or B move in the opposite direction towards A, a current, and in both cases having the same *direction*, will re-

---

[1] See also Hare in *Silliman's Journal*, 1833, XXIV, 246.

[2] *Bibliothèque Universelle*, 1837, VII, 388.

[3] I am glad to refer here to the results obtained by Mr. Christie with magneto-electricity, *Philosophical Transactions*, 1833, p. 113, note. As regards the current in a wire, they confirm everything that I am contending for.

sult. If A and B move from each other, then a *current* in the opposite direction, or equivalent effects, will be produced.

1644. Or, as charge exists only by induction (1178, 1299), and a body when electrified is necessarily in relation to other bodies in the opposite state; so, if a ball be electrified positively in the middle of a room and be then moved in any direction, effects will be produced, as if a *current* in the same direction (to use the conventional mode of expression) had existed: or, if the ball be negatively electrified, and then moved, effects as if a current in a direction contrary to that of the motion had been formed, will be produced.

1645. I am saying of a single particle or of two what I have before said, in effect, of many (1633). If the former account of currents be true, then that just stated must be a necessary result. And, though the statement may seem startling at first, it is to be considered that, according to my theory of induction, the charged conductor or particle is related to the distant conductor in the opposite state, or that which terminates the extent of the induction, by all the intermediate particles (1165, 1295), these becoming polarized exactly as the particles of a solid electrolyte do when interposed between the two electrodes. Hence the conclusion regarding the unity and identity of the current in the case of convection, jointly with the former cases, is not so strange as it might at first appear.

1646. There is a very remarkable phenomenon or effect of the electrolytic discharge, first pointed out, I believe, by Mr. Porrett, of the accumulation of fluid under decomposing action in the current on one side of an interposed diaphragm.[1] It is a mechanical result; and as the liquid passes from the positive towards the negative electrode in all the known cases, it seems to establish a relation to the polar condition of the dielectric in which the current exists (1164, 1525). It has not as yet been sufficiently investigated by experiment; for De la Rive says,[2] it requires that the water should be a bad conductor, as, for instance, distilled water, the effect not happening with strong solutions; whereas, Dutrochet says[3] the contrary is the case, and that, the effect is not directly due to the electric current.

1647. Becquerel, in his *Traité de l'Electricité*, has brought together the considerations

which arise for and against the opinion that the effect generally is an electric effect.[4] Though I have no decisive fact to quote at present, I cannot refrain from venturing an opinion, that the effect is analogous both to combination and convection (1623), being a case of carrying due to the relation of the diaphragm and the fluid in contact with it, through which the electric discharge is jointly effected; and further, that the peculiar relation of positive and negative small and large surfaces already referred to (1482, 1503, 1525), may be the direct cause of the fluid and the diaphragm travelling in contrary but determinate directions. A very valuable experiment has been made by M. Becquerel with particles of clay,[5] which will probably bear importantly on this point.

1648. *As long as* the terms *current* and *electro-dynamic* are used to express those relations of the electric forces in which progression of either fluids or effects are supposed to occur (283), *so long* will the idea of velocity be associated with them; and this will, perhaps, be more especially the case if the hypothesis of a fluid or fluids be adopted.

1649. Hence has arisen the desire of estimating this velocity either directly or by some effect dependent on it; and amongst the endeavours to do this correctly, may be mentioned especially those of Dr. Watson[6] in 1748, and of Professor Wheatstone[7] in 1834; the electricity in the early trials being supposed to travel from end to end of the arrangement, but in the later investigations a distinction occasionally appearing to be made between the transmission of the effect and of the supposed fluid by the motion of whose particles that effect is produced.

1650. Electrolytic action has a remarkable bearing upon this question of the velocity of the current, especially as connected with the theory of an electric fluid or fluids. In it there is an evident transfer of power with the transfer of each particle of the anion or cathion present, to the next particles of the cathion or anion; and as the amount of power is definite, we have in this way a means of localizing as it were the force, identifying it by the particle and dealing it out in successive portions, which leads, I think, to very striking results.

1651. Suppose, for instance, that water is undergoing decomposition by the powers of a

[1] *Annals of Philosophy*, 1816, VIII, p. 75.
[2] *Annales de Chimie*, 1835, XXVIII, p. 196.
[3] *Annales de Chimie*, 1832, XLIX, p. 423.

[4] Vol. IV, p. 192, 197.
[5] *Traité de l'Electricité*, I, p. 285.
[6] *Philosophical Transactions*, 1748.
[7] *Ibid.*, 1834, p. 583.

voltaic battery. Each particle of hydrogen as it moves one way, or of oxygen as it moves in the other direction, will transfer a certain amount of electrical force associated with it in the form of chemical affinity (822, 852, 918) onwards through a distance, which is equal to that through which the particle itself has moved. This transfer will be accompanied by a corresponding movement in the electrical forces throughout every part of the circuit formed (1627, 1634), and its effects may be estimated, as, for instance, by the heating of a wire (853) at any particular section of the current however distant. If the water be a cube of an inch in the side, the electrodes touching, each by a surface of one square inch, and being an inch apart, then, by the time that a tenth of it, or 25.25 grains, is decomposed, the particles of oxygen and hydrogen throughout the mass may be considered as having moved relatively to each other in opposite directions, to the amount of the tenth of an inch; i.e., that two particles at first in combination will after the motion be the tenth of an inch apart. Other motions which occur in the fluid will not at all interfere with this result; for they have no power of accelerating or retarding the electric discharge, and possess in fact no relation to it.

1652. The quantity of electricity in 25.25 grains of water is, according to an estimate of the force which I formerly made (861), equal to above 24 millions of charges of a large Leyden battery; or it would have kept any length of a platina wire $\frac{1}{104}$ of an inch in diameter red-hot for an hour and a half (853). This result, though given only as an approximation, I have seen no reason as yet to alter, and it is confirmed generally by the experiments and results of M. Pouillet.[1] According to Mr. Wheatstone's experiments, the influence or effects of the current would appear at a distance of 576,000 miles in a second.[2] We have, therefore, in this view of the matter, on the one hand, an enormous quantity of power equal to a most destructive thunder-storm appearing instantly at the distance of 576,000 miles from its source, and on the other, a quiet effect, in producing which the power had taken an hour and a half to travel through the tenth of an inch: yet these are the equivalents to each other, being effects observed at the sections of one and the same current (1634).

1653. It is time that I should call attention to the lateral or transverse forces of the *cur-*

rent. The great things which have been achieved by Oersted, Arago, Ampère, Davy, De la Rive, and others, and the high degree of simplification which has been introduced into their arrangement by the theory of Ampère, have not only done their full service in advancing most rapidly this branch of knowledge, but have secured to it such attention that there is no necessity for urging on its pursuit. I refer of course to magnetic action and its relations; but though this is the only recognised lateral action of the current, there is great reason for believing that others exist and would by their discovery reward a close search for them (951).

1654. The magnetic or transverse action of the current seems to be in a most extraordinary degree independent of those variations or modes of action which it presents directly in its course; it consequently is of the more value to us, as it gives us a higher relation of the power than any that might have varied with each mode of discharge. This discharge, whether it be by conduction through a wire with infinite velocity (1652), or by electrolyzation with its corresponding and exceeding slow motion (1651), or by spark, and probably even by convection, produces a transverse magnetic action always the same in kind and direction.

1655. It has been shown by several experimenters that whilst the discharge is of the *same kind* the amount of lateral or magnetic force is very constant (216, 366, 367, 368, 376). But when we wish to compare discharge of different kinds, for the important purpose of ascertaining whether the same amount of current will in its *different forms* produce the same amount of transverse action, we find the data very imperfect. Davy noticed that when the electric current was passing through an aqueous solution it affected a magnetic needle,[3] and Dr. Ritchie says, that the current in the electrolyte is as magnetic as that in a metallic wire,[4] and has caused water to revolve round a magnet as a wire carrying the current would revolve.

1656. Disruptive discharge produces its magnetic effects: a strong spark, passed transversely to a steel needle, will magnetise it as well as if the electricity of the spark were conducted by a metallic wire occupying the line of discharge; and Sir H. Davy has shown that the discharge of a voltaic battery *in vacuo* is affected and has motion given to it by approximated magnets.[5]

---

[1] Becquerel, *Traité de l'Electricité*, V, p. 278.
[2] *Philosophical Transactions*, 1834, p. 589.

[3] *Philosophical Transactions*, 1821, p. 426.
[4] *Ibid.*, 1832, p. 294.
[5] *Ibid.*, p. 427.

1657. Thus the three very different modes of discharge, namely, conduction, electrolyzation, and disruptive discharge, agree in producing the important transverse phenomenon of magnetism. Whether convection or carrying discharge will produce the same phenomenon has not been determined, and the few experiments I have as yet had time to make do not enable me to answer in the affirmative.

1658. Having arrived at this point in the consideration of the current and in the endeavour to apply its phenomena as tests of the truth or fallacy of the theory of induction which I have ventured to set forth, I am now very much tempted to indulge in a few speculations respecting its lateral action and its possible connection with the transverse condition of the lines of ordinary induction (1165, 1304).[1] I have long sought and still seek for an effect or condition which shall be to statical electricity what magnetic force is to current electricity (1411); for as the lines of discharge are associated with a certain transverse effect, so it appeared to me impossible but that the lines of tension or of inductive action, which of necessity precede that discharge, should also have their correspondent transverse condition or effect (951).

1659. According to the beautiful theory of Ampère, the transverse force of a current may be represented by its attraction for a similar current and its repulsion of a contrary current. May not then the equivalent transverse force of static electricity be represented by that lateral tension or repulsion which the lines of inductive action appear to possess (1304)? Then again, when current or discharge occurs between two bodies, previously under inductrical relations to each other, the lines of inductive force will weaken and fade away, and, as their lateral repulsive tension diminishes, will contract and ultimately disappear in the line of discharge. May not this be an effect identical with the attractions of similar currents? i.e., may not the passage of static electricity into current electricity, and that of the lateral tension of the lines of inductive force into the lateral attraction of lines of similar discharge, have the same relation and dependences, and run parallel to each other?

1660. The phenomena of induction amongst currents which I had the good fortune to discover some years ago (6, &c., 1048) may per-

chance here form a connecting link in the series of effects. When a current is first formed, it tends to produce a current in the contrary direction in all the matter around it; and if that matter have conducting properties and be fitly circumstanced, such a current is produced. On the contrary, when the original current is stopped, one in the same direction tends to form all around it, and, in conducting matter properly arranged, will be excited.

1661. Now though we perceive the effects only in that portion of matter which, being in the neighbourhood, has conducting properties, yet hypothetically it is probable, that the non-conducting matter has also its relations to, and is affected by, the disturbing cause, though we have not yet discovered them. Again and again the relation of conductors and non-conductors has been shown to be one not of opposition in kind, but only of degree (1334, 1603); and, therefore, for this, as well as for other reasons, it is probable, that what will affect a conductor will affect an insulator also; producing perhaps what may deserve the term of the electrotonic state (60, 242, 1114).

1662. It is the feeling of the necessity of some lateral connection between the lines of electric force (1114); of some link in the chain of effects as yet unrecognised, that urges me to the expression of these speculations. The same feeling has led me to make many experiments on the introduction of insulating dielectrics having different inductive capacities (1270, 1277) between magnetic poles and wires carrying currents, so as to pass across the lines of magnetic force. I have employed such bodies both at rest and in motion, without, as yet, being able to detect any influence produced by them; but I do by no means consider the experiments as sufficiently delicate, and intend, very shortly, to render them more decisive.[2]

1663. I think the hypothetical question may at present be put thus: can such considerations as those already generally expressed (1658) account for the transverse effects of electrical currents? are two such currents in relation to each other merely by the inductive condition of the particles of matter between them, or are they in relation by some higher quality and condition (1654), which, acting at a distance and not by the intermediate particles, has, like the force of gravity, no relation to them?

1664. If the latter be the case, then, when electricity is acting upon and in matter, its direct and its transverse action are essen-

[1] Refer for further investigations to 1709—1736. —*Dec.* 1838.

[2] See onwards 1711—1726.—*Dec.* 1838.

tially different in their nature; for the former, if I am correct, will depend upon the contiguous particles, and the latter will not. As I have said before, this may be so, and I incline to that view at present; but I am desirous of suggesting considerations why it may not, that the question may be thoroughly sifted.

1665. The transverse power has a character of polarity impressed upon it. In the simplest forms it appears as attraction or repulsion, according as the currents are in the same or different directions: in the current and the magnet it takes up the condition of tangential forces; and in magnets and their particles produces poles. Since the experiments have been made which have persuaded me that the polar forces of electricity, as in induction and electrolytic action (1298, 1343), show effects at a distance only by means of the polarized contiguous and intervening particles, I have been led to expect that *all polar forces* act in the same general manner; and the other kinds of phenomena which one can bring to bear upon the subject seem fitted to strengthen that expectation. Thus in crystallizations the effect is transmitted from particle to particle; and in this manner, in acetic acid or freezing water a crystal a few inches or even a couple of feet in length will form in less than a second, but progressively and by a transmission of power from particle to particle. And, as far as I remember, no case of polar action, or partaking of polar action, except the one under discussion, can be found which does not act by contiguous

particles.[1] It is apparently of the nature of polar forces that such should be the case, for the one force either finds or developes the contrary force near to it, and has, therefore, no occasion to seek for it at a distance.

1666. But leaving these hypothetical notions respecting the nature of the lateral action out of sight, and returning to the direct effects, I think that the phenomena examined and reasoning employed in this and the two preceding papers tend to confirm the view first taken (1164), namely that ordinary inductive action and the effects dependent upon it are due to an action of the contiguous particles of the dielectric interposed between the charged surfaces or parts which constitute, as it were, the terminations of the effect. The great point of distinction and power (if it have any) in the theory is, the making the dieletric of essential and specific importance, instead of leaving it as it were a mere accidental circumstance or the simple representative of space, having no more influence over the phenomena than the space occupied by it. I have still certain other results and views respecting the nature of the electrical forces and excitation, which are connected with the present theory; and, unless upon further consideration they sink in my estimation, I shall very shortly put them into form as another series of these electrical researches.

Royal Institution, February 14, 1838

---

[1] I mean by contiguous particles those which are next to each other, not that there is *no* space between them. See (1616).

FOURTEENTH SERIES

§ 20. *Nature of the Electric Force or Forces*   § 21. *Relation of the Electric and Magnetic Forces*   § 22. *Note on Electrical Excitation*

RECEIVED JUNE 21, 1838, READ JUNE 21, 1838

§ 20. *Nature of the Electric Force or Forces*

1667. THE theory of induction set forth and illustrated in the three preceding series of experimental researches does not assume anything new as to the nature of the electric force or forces, but only as to their distribution. The effects may depend upon the association of one electric fluid with the particles of matter, as in the theory of Franklin, Epinus, Cavendish, and Mossotti; or they may depend upon the association of two electric fluids, as in the the-

ory of Dufay and Poisson; or they may not depend upon anything which can properly be called the electric fluid, but on vibrations or other affections of the matter in which they appear. The theory is unaffected by such differences in the mode of viewing the nature of the forces; and though it professes to perform the important office of stating *how* the powers are arranged (at least in inductive phenomena), it does not, as far as I can yet perceive, supply a single experiment which can be considered as a distinguishing test of the truth of any one of these various views.

1668. But, to ascertain how the forces are arranged, to trace them in their various relations to the particles of matter, to determine their general laws, and also the specific differences which occur under these laws, is as important as, if not more so than, to know whether the forces reside in a fluid or not; and with the hope of assisting in this research, I shall offer some further developments, theoretical and experimental, of the conditions under which I suppose the particles of matter are placed when exhibiting inductive phenomena.

1669. The theory assumes that all the *particles*, whether of insulating or conducting matter, are as wholes conductors.

1670. That not being polar in their normal state, they can become so by the influence of neighbouring charged particles, the polar state being developed at the instant, exactly as in an insulated conducting *mass* consisting of many particles.

1671. That the particles when polarized are in a forced state, and tend to return to their normal or natural condition.

1672. That being as wholes conductors, they can readily be charged, either *bodily* or *polarly*.

1673. That particles which being contiguous[1] are also in the line of inductive action can communicate or transfer their polar forces one to another *more* or *less* readily.

1674. That those doing so less readily require the polar forces to be raised to a higher degree before this transference or communication takes place.

1675. That the *ready* communication of forces between contiguous particles constitutes *conduction*, and the *difficult* communication *insulation*; conductors and insulators being bodies whose particles naturally possess the property of communicating their respective forces easily or with difficulty; having these differences just as they have differences of any other natural property.

1676. That ordinary induction is the effect resulting from the action of matter charged with excited or free electricity upon insulating matter, tending to produce in it an equal amount of the contrary state.

1677. That it can do this only by polarizing the particles contiguous to it, which perform the same office to the next, and these again to those beyond; and that thus the action is propagated from the excited body to the next conducting mass, and there renders the contrary force evident in consequence of the effect of communication which supervenes in the conducting mass upon the polarization of the particles of that body (1675).

1678. That therefore induction can only take place through or across insulators; that induction is insulation, it being the necessary consequence of the state of the particles and the mode in which the influence of electrical forces is transferred or transmitted through or across such insulating media.

1679. The particles of an insulating dielectric whilst under induction may be compared to a series of small magnetic needles, or more correctly still to a series of small insulated conductors. If the space round a charged globe were filled with a mixture of an insulating dielectric, as oil of turpentine or air, and small globular conductors, as shot, the latter being at a little distance from each other so as to be insulated, then these would in their condition and action exactly resemble what I consider to be the condition and action of the particles of the insulating dielectric itself (1337). If the globe were charged, these little conductors would all be polar; if the globe were discharged, they would all return to their normal state, to be polarized again upon the recharging of the globe. The state developed by induction through such particles on a mass of conducting matter at a distance would be of the contrary kind, and exactly equal in amount to the force in the inductric globe. There would be a lateral diffusion of force (1224, 1297), because each polarized sphere would be in an active or tense relation to all those contiguous to it, just as one magnet can affect two or more magnetic needles near it, and these again a still greater number beyond them. Hence would result the production of curved lines of inductive force if the inducteous body in such a mixed dielectric were an uninsulated metallic ball (1219, &c.) or other properly shaped mass. Such curved lines are the consequences of the two electric forces arranged as I have assumed them to be: and, that the inductive force can be directed in such curved lines is the strongest proof of the presence of the two powers and the polar condition of the dielectric particles.

1680. I think it is evident that, in the case stated, action at a distance can only result through an action of the contiguous conducting particles. There is no reason why the inductive body should polarize or affect *distant* conductors

---

[1] See note to 1164.—*Dec.* 1838.

and leave those *near* it, namely the particles of the dielectric, unaffected: and everything in the form of fact and experiment with conducting masses or particles of a sensible size contradicts such a supposition.

1681. A striking character of the electric power is that it is limited and exclusive, and that the two forces being always present are exactly equal in amount. The forces are related in one of two ways, either as in the natural normal condition of an uncharged insulated conductor; or as in the charged state, the latter being a case of induction.

1682. Cases of induction are easily arranged so that the two forces being limited in their direction shall present no phenomena or indications external to the apparatus employed. Thus, if a Leyden jar, having its external coating a little higher than the internal, be charged and then its charging ball and rod removed, such jar will present no electrical appearances so long as its outside is uninsulated. The two forces which may be said to be in the coatings, or in the particles of the dielectric contiguous to them, are entirely engaged to each other by induction through the glass; and a carrier ball (1181) applied either to the inside or outside of the jar will show no signs of electricity. But if the jar be insulated, and the charging ball and rod, in an uncharged state and suspended by an insulating thread of white silk, be restored to their place, then the part projecting above the jar will give electrical indications and charge the carrier, and at the same time the *outside* coating of the jar will be found in the opposite state and inductric towards external surrounding objects.

1683. These are simple consequences of the theory. Whilst the charge of the inner coating could induce only through the glass towards the outer coating, and the latter contained no more of the contrary force than was equivalent to it, no induction external to the jar could be perceived; but when the inner coating was extended by the rod and ball so that it could induce through the air towards external objects, then the tension of the polarized glass molecules would, by their tendency to return to the normal state, fall a little, and a portion of the charge passing to the surface of this new part of the inner conductor, would produce inductive action through the air towards distant objects, whilst at the same time a part of the force in the outer coating previously directed inwards would now be at liberty, and indeed be constrained to induct outwards through the air, producing in that outer coating what is sometimes called, though I think very improperly, free charge. If a small Leyden jar be converted into that form of apparatus usually known by the name of the electric well, it will illustrate this action very completely.

1684. The terms *free charge* and *dissimulated electricity* convey therefore erroneous notions if they are meant to imply any difference as to the mode or kind of action. The charge upon an insulated conductor in the middle of a room is in the same relation to the walls of that room as the charge upon the inner coating of a Leyden jar is to the outer coating of the same jar. The one is not more *free* or more *dissimulated* than the other; and when sometimes we make electricity appear where it was not evident before, as upon the outside of a charged jar, when, after insulating it, we touch the inner coating, it is only because we divert more or less of the inductive force from one direction into another; for not the slightest change is in such circumstances impressed upon the character or action of the force.

1685. Having given this general theoretical view, I will now notice particular points relating to the nature of the assumed electric polarity of the insulating dielectric particles.

1686. The polar state may be considered in common induction as a forced state, the particles tending to return to their normal condition. It may probably be raised to a very high degree by approximation of the inductric and inducteous bodies or by other circumstances; and the phenomena of electrolyzation (861, 1652, 1706) seem to imply that the quantity of power which can thus be accumulated on a single particle is enormous. Hereafter we may be able to compare corpuscular forces, as those of gravity, cohesion, electricity, and chemical affinity, and in some way or other from their effects deduce their relative equivalents; at present we are not able to do so, but there seems no reason to doubt that their electrical, which are at the same time their chemical forces (891, 918), will be by far the most energetic.

1687. I do not consider the powers when developed by the polarization as limited to two distinct points or spots on the surface of each particle to be considered as the poles of an axis, but as resident on large portions of that surface, as they are upon the surface of a conductor of sensible size when it is thrown into a polar state. But it is very probable, notwithstanding, that the particles of different bodies may present specific differences in this respect, the powers not being equally diffused though equal in quantity; other circumstances also, as form and quality, giving to each a peculiar polar relation. It is perhaps to the existence of some such differences as these that we may attribute the specific actions of the different dielectrics in relation to discharge (1394, 1508). Thus with respect to oxygen and nitrogen singular contrasts were presented when spark and brush discharge were made to take place in these gases, as may be seen by reference to the table in paragraph 1518 of the Thirteenth Series; for with nitrogen, when the small negative or the large positive ball was rendered inductric, the effects corresponded with those which in oxygen were produced when the small positive or the large negative ball was rendered inductric.

1688. In such solid bodies as glass, lac, sulphur, &c., the particles appear to be able to become polarized in all directions, for a mass when experimented upon so as to ascertain its inductive capacity in three or more directions (1690), gives no indication of a difference. Now as the particles are fixed in the mass, and as the direction of the induction through them must change with its change relative to the mass, the constant effect indicates that they can be polarized electrically in any direction. This accords with the view already taken of each particle as a whole being a conductor (1669), and, as an experimental fact, helps to confirm that view.

1689. But though particles may thus be polarized in *any* direction under the influence of powers which are probably of extreme energy (1686), it does not follow that each particle may not tend to polarize to a greater degree, or with more facility, in one direction than another; or that different kinds may not have specific differences in this respect, as they have differences of conducting and other powers (1296, 1326, 1395). I sought with great anxiety for a relation of this nature; and selecting crystalline bodies as those in which all the particles are symmetrically placed, and therefore best fitted to indicate any result which might depend upon variation of the direction of the forces to the direction of the particles in which they were developed, experimented very carefully with them. I was the more strongly stimulated to this inquiry by the beautiful electrical condition of the crystalline bodies tourmaline and boracite, and hoped also to discover a relation between electric polarity and that of crystallization, or even of cohesion itself (1316).

My experiments have not established any connexion of the kind sought for. But as I think it of equal importance to shew either that there is or is not such a relation, I shall briefly describe the results.

1690. The form of experiment was as follows. A brass ball 0.73 of an inch in diameter, fixed at the end of a horizontal brass rod, and that at the end of a brass cylinder, was by means of the latter connected with a large Leyden battery (291) by perfect metallic communications, the object being to keep that ball, by its connexion with the charged battery in an electrified state, very nearly uniform, for half an hour at a time. This was the inductric ball. The inducteous ball was the carrier of the torsion electrometer (1229, 1314); and the dielectric between them was a cube cut from a crystal, so that two of its faces should be perpendicular to the optical axis, whilst the other four were parallel to it. A small projecting piece of shellac was fixed on the inductric ball at that part opposite to the attachment of the brass rod, for the purpose of preventing actual contact between the ball and the crystal cube. A coat of shellac was also attached to that side of the carrier ball which was to be towards the cube, being also that side which was farthest from

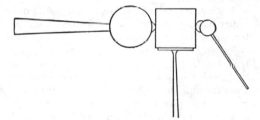

the repelled ball in the electrometer when placed in its position in that instrument. The cube was covered with a thin coat of shellac dissolved in alcohol, to prevent the deposition of damp upon its surface from the air. It was supported upon a small table of shellac fixed on the top of a stem of the same substance, the latter being of sufficient strength to sustain the cube, and yet flexible enough from its length to act as a spring, and allow the cube to bear, when in its place, against the shellac on the inductric ball.

1691. Thus it was easy to bring the inducteous ball always to the same distance from the inductric ball, and to uninsulate and insulate it again in its place; and then, after measuring the force in the electrometer (1181), to return it to its place opposite to the inductric ball for a second observation. Or it was easy by revolving the stand which supported the cube to bring four of its faces in succession towards the inductric ball, and so observe the force when the lines of inductive action (1304) coincided with, or were transverse to, the direction of the optical axis of the crystal. Generally from twenty to twenty-eight observations were made in succession upon the four vertical faces of a cube, and then an average expression of the inductive force was obtained, and compared with similar averages obtained at other times, every precaution being taken to secure accurate results.

1692. The first cube used was of *rock crystal*; it was 0.7 of an inch in the side. It presented a remarkable and constant difference, the average of not less than 197 observations, giving 100 for the specific inductive capacity in the direction coinciding with the optical axis of the cube, whilst 93.59 and 93.31 were the expressions for the two transverse directions.

1693. But with a second cube of rock crystal corresponding results were not obtained. It was 0.77 of an inch in the side. The average of many experiments gave 100 for the specific inductive capacity coinciding with the direction of the optical axis, and 98.6 and 99.92 for the two other directions.

1694. Lord Ashley, whom I have found ever ready to advance the cause of science, obtained for me the loan of three globes of rock crystal belonging to Her Grace the Duchess of Sutherland for the purposes of this investigation. Two had such fissures as to render them unfit for the experiments (1193, 1698). The third which was very superior, gave me no indications of any difference in the inductive force for different directions.

1695. I then used cubes of Iceland spar. One 0.5 of an inch in diameter gave 100 for the axial direction, and 98.66 and 95.74 for the two cross directions. The other, 0.8 of an inch in the side, gave 100 for the axial direction, whilst 101.73 and 101.86 were the numbers for the cross direction.

1696. Besides these differences there were others, which I do not think it needful to state, since the main point is not confirmed. For though the experiments with the first cube raised great expectation, they have not been generalized by those which followed. I have no doubt of the results as to that cube, but they cannot as yet be referred to crystallization. There are in the cube some faintly coloured layers parallel to the optical axis, and the matter which colours them may have an influence; but then the layers are also nearly parallel to a cross direction, and if at all influential should shew some effect in that direction also, which they did not.

1697. In some of the experiments one half or one part of a cube showed a superiority to another part, and this I could not trace to any charge the different parts had received. It was found that the varnishing of the cubes prevented any communication of charge to them, except (in a few experiments) a small degree of the negative state, or that which was contrary to the state of the inductric ball (1564, 1566).

1698. I think it right to say that, as far as I could perceive, the insulating character of the cubes used was perfect, or at least so nearly perfect, as to bear a comparison with shellac, glass, &c. (1255). As to the cause of the differences, other than regular crystalline structure, there may be several. Thus minute fissures in the crystal insensible to the eye may be so disposed as to produce a sensible electrical difference (1193). Or the crystallization may be irregular; or the substance may not be quite pure; and if we consider how minute a quantity of matter will alter greatly the conducting power of water, it will seem not unlikely that a little extraneous matter diffused through the whole or part of a cube, may produce effects sufficient to account for all the irregularities of action that have been observed.

1699. An important inquiry regarding the electrical polarity of the particles of an insulating dielectric, is, whether it be the molecules of the particular substance acted on, or the component or ultimate particles, which thus act the part of insulated conducting polarizing portions (1669).

1700. The conclusion I have arrived at is, that it is the molecules of the substance which polarize as wholes (1347); and that however complicated the composition of a body may be, all those particles or atoms which are held together by chemical affinity to form one molecule of the resulting body act as one conducting mass or particle when inductive phenomena and polarization are produced in the substance of which it is a part.

1701. This conclusion is founded on several considerations. Thus if we observe the insulating and conducting power of elements when they are used as dielectrics, we find some, as sulphur, phosphorus, chlorine, iodine, &c., whose particles insulate, and therefore polarize in a high degree; whereas others, as the metals, give scarcely any indication of possessing a sensible proportion of this power (1328), their particles freely conducting one to another. Yet when these enter into combination they form substances having no direct relation apparently, in this respect, to their elements; for water, sulphuric acid, and such compounds formed of insulating elements, conduct by comparison freely; whilst oxide of lead, flint glass, borate of lead, and other metallic compounds containing very high proportions of conducting matter, insulate excellently well. Taking oxide of lead therefore as the illustration, I conceive that it is not the particles of oxygen and lead which polarize separately under the act of induction, but the molecules of oxide of lead which exhibit this effect, all the elements of one particle of the resulting body, being held together as parts of one conducting individual by the bonds of chemical affinity; which is but another term for electrical force (918).

1702. In bodies which are electrolytes we have still further reason for believing in such a state of things. Thus when water, chloride of tin, iodide of lead, &c., in the solid state are between the electrodes of the voltaic battery, their particles polarize as those of any other insulating dielectric do (1164); but when the liquid state is conferred on these substances, the polarized particles divide, the two halves, each in a highly charged state, travelling onwards until they meet other particles in an opposite and equally charged state, with which they combine, to the neutralization of their chemical, i.e., their electrical forces, and the reproduction of compound particles, which can again polarize as wholes, and again divide to repeat the same series of actions (1347).

1703. But though electrolytic particles polarize as wholes, it would appear very evident that in them it is not a matter of entire indifference *how* the particle polarizes (1689), since, when free to move (380, &c.) the polarities are ultimately distributed in reference to the elements; and sums of force equivalent to the polarities, and very definite in kind and amount, separate, as it were, from each other, and travel onwards with the elementary particles. And though I do not pretend to know what an atom is, or how it is associated or endowed with electrical force, or how this force is arranged in the cases of combination and decomposition, yet the strong belief I have in the electrical polarity of particles when under inductive action, and the bearing of such an opinion on the gen-

eral effects of induction, whether ordinary or electrolytic, will be my excuse, I trust, for a few hypothetical considerations.

1704. In electrolyzation it appears that the polarized particles would (because of the gradual change which has been induced upon the chemical, i.e., the electrical forces of their elements [918]) rather divide than discharge to each other without division (1348); for if their division, i.e., their decomposition and recombination, be prevented by giving them the solid state, then they will insulate electricity perhaps a hundred fold more intense than that necessary for their electrolyzation (419, &c.). Hence the tension necessary for direct conduction in such bodies appears to be much higher than that for decomposition (419, 1164, 1344).

1705. The remarkable stoppage of electrolytic conduction by solidification (380, 1358), is quite consistent with these views of the dependence of that process on the polarity which is common to all insulating matter when under induction, though attended by such peculiar electro-chemical results in the case of electrolytes. Thus it may be expected that the first effect of induction is so to polarize and arrange the particles of water that the positive or hydrogen pole of each shall be from the positive electrode and towards the negative electrode, whilst the negative or oxygen pole of each shall be in the contrary direction; and thus when the oxygen and hydrogen of a particle of water have separated, passing to and combining with other hydrogen and oxygen particles, unless these new particles of water could turn round they could not take up that position necessary for their successful electrolytic polarization. Now solidification, by fixing the water particles and preventing them from assuming that essential preliminary position, prevents also their electrolysis (413); and so the transfer of forces in that manner being prevented (1347, 1703), the substance acts as an ordinary insulating dielectric (for it is evident by former experiments [419, 1704] that the insulating tension is higher than the electrolytic tension), induction through it rises to a higher degree, and the polar condition of the molecules as wholes, though greatly exalted, is still securely maintained.

1706. When decomposition happens in a fluid electrolyte, I do not suppose that all the molecules in the same sectional plane (1634) part with and transfer their electrified particles or elements at once. Probably the *discharge force* for that plane is summed up on one or a few particles, which decomposing, travelling and recombining, restore the balance of forces, much as in the case of spark disruptive discharge (1406); for as those molecules resulting from particles which have just transferred power must by their position (1705) be less favourably circumstanced than others, so there must be some which are most favourably disposed, and these, by giving way first, will for the time lower the tension and produce discharge.

1707. In former investigations of the action of electricity (821, &c.) it was shown, from many satisfactory cases, that the quantity of electric power transferred onwards was in proportion to and was definite for a given quantity of matter moving as anion or cathion onwards in the electrolytic line of action; and there was strong reason to believe that each of the particles of matter then dealt with, had associated with it a definite amount of electrical force, constituting its force of chemical affinity, the chemical equivalents and the electro-chemical equivalents being the same (836). It was also found with few, and I may now perhaps say with no exceptions (1341), that only those compounds containing elements in single proportions could exhibit the characters and phenomena of electrolytes (697); oxides, chlorides, and other bodies containing more than one proportion of the electro-negative element refusing to decompose under the influence of the electric current.

1708. Probable reasons for these conditions and limitations arise out of the molecular theory of induction. Thus when a liquid dielectric, as chloride of tin, consists of molecules, each composed of a single particle of each of the elements, then as these can convey equivalent opposite forces by their separation in opposite directions, both decomposition and transfer can result. But when the molecules, as in the bichloride of tin, consist of one particle or atom of one element, and two of the other, then the simplicity with which the particles may be supposed to be arranged and to act, is destroyed. And, though it may be conceived that when the molecules of bichloride of tin are polarized as wholes by the induction across them, the positive polar force might accumulate on the one particle of tin whilst the negative polar force accumulated on the two particles of chlorine associated with it, and that these might respectively travel right and left to unite with other two of chlorine and one of tin, in analogy with what happens in cases of compounds consisting of single proportions, yet this is not altogether so evident or probable. For when a particle of tin combines with two of chlorine, it is difficult to conceive that there should not be some relation of the three in the resulting molecule analogous to fixed position, the one particle of metal being perhaps symmetrically placed in relation to the two of chlorine: and, it is not difficult to conceive of such particles that they could not assume that position dependent both on their polarity and the relation of their elements, which appears to be the first step in the process of electrolyzation (1345, 1705).

§ 21. *Relation of the Electric and Magnetic Forces*

1709. I have already ventured a few speculations respecting the probable relation of magnetism, as the transverse force of the current, to the divergent or transverse force of the lines of inductive action belonging to static electricity (1658, &c.).

1710. In the further consideration of this subject it appeared to me to be of the utmost importance to ascertain, if possible, whether this lateral action which we call magnetism, or sometimes the induction of electrical currents (26, 1048, &c.), is extended to a distance *by the action of the intermediate particles* in analogy with the induction of static electricity, or the various effects, such as conduction, discharge, &c., which are dependent on that induction; or, whether its influence at a distance is altogether independent of such intermediate particles (1662.).

1711. I arranged two magneto-electric helices with iron cores end to end, but with an interval of an inch and three-quarters between them, in which interval was placed the end or pole of a bar magnet. It is evident, that on moving the magnetic pole from one core towards the other, a current would tend to form in both helices, in the one because of the lowering, and in the other because of the strengthening of the magnetism induced in the respective soft iron cores. The helices were connected together, and also with a galvanometer, so that these two currents should coincide in direction, and tend by their joint force to deflect the needle of the instrument. The whole arrangement was so effective and delicate, that moving the magnetic pole about the eighth of an inch to and fro two or three times, in periods equal to those required for the vibrations of the galvanometer needle, was sufficient to cause considerable vibration in the latter; thus showing readily the consequence of strengthening the influence of the magnet on the one core and helix, and diminishing it on the other.

1712. Then without disturbing the distances of the magnet and cores, plates of substances were interposed. Thus calling the two cores A and B, a plate of shellac was introduced between the magnetic pole and A for the time occupied by the needle in swinging one way; then it was withdrawn for the time occupied in the return swing; introduced again for another equal portion of time; withdrawn for another portion, and so on eight or nine times; but not the least effect was observed on the needle. In other cases the plate was alternated, i.e., it was introduced between the magnet and A for one period of time, withdrawn and introduced between the magnet and B for the second period, withdrawn and restored to its first place for the third period, and so on, but with no effect on the needle.

1713. In these experiments *shellac* in plates 0.9 of an inch in thickness, *sulphur* in a plate 0.9 of an inch in thickness, and *copper* in a plate 0.7 of an inch in thickness were used without any effect. And I conclude that bodies, contrasted by the extremes of conducting and insulating power, and opposed to each other as strongly as metals, air, and sulphur, show no difference with respect to magnetic forces when placed in their lines of action, at least under the circumstances described.

1714. With a plate of iron, or even a small piece of that metal, as the head of a nail, a very different effect was produced, for then the galvanometer immediately showed its sensibility, and the perfection of the general arrangement.

1715. I arranged matters so that a plate of *copper* 0.2 of an inch in thickness, and ten inches in diameter, should have the part near the edge interposed between the magnet and the core, in which situation it was first rotated rapidly, and then held quiescent alternately, for periods according with that required for the swinging of the needle; but not the least effect upon the galvanometer was produced.

1716. A plate of shellac 0.6 of an inch in thickness was applied in the same manner, but whether rotating or not it produced no effect.

1717. Occasionally the plane of rotation was directly across the magnetic curve: at other times it was made as oblique as possible; the direction of the rotation being also changed in different experiments, but not the least effect was produced.

1718. I now removed the helices with their soft iron cores, and replaced them by two *flat* helices wound upon cardboard, each containing forty-two feet of silked copper wire, and having no associated iron. Otherwise the arrangement was as before, and exceedingly sensible; for a very slight motion of the magnet between the helices produced an abundant vibration of the galvanometer needle.

1719. The introduction of plates of shellac, sulphur, or copper into the intervals between the magnet and these helices (1713), produced not the least effect, whether the former were quiescent or in rapid revolution (1715). So here no evidence of the influence of the intermediate particles could be obtained (1710).

1720. The magnet was then removed and replaced by a flat helix, corresponding to the two former, the three being parallel to each other. The middle helix was so arranged that a voltaic current could be sent through it at pleasure. The former galvanometer was removed, and one with a double coil employed, one of the lateral helices being connected with one coil, and the other helix with the other coil, in such manner that when a voltaic current was sent through the middle helix its inductive action (26) on the lateral helices should cause currents in them, having contrary directions in the coils of the galvanometer. By a little adjustment of the distances these induced currents were rendered exactly equal, and the galvanometer needle remained stationary notwithstanding their frequent production in the instrument. I will call the middle coil C, and the external coils A and B.

1721. A plate of copper 0.7 of an inch thick and six inches square, was placed between coils C and B, their respective distances remaining unchanged; and then a voltaic current from twenty pairs of 4-inch plates was sent through the coil C, and intermitted, in periods fitted to produce an effect on the galvanometer (1712), if any difference had been produced in the effect of C on A and B. But notwithstanding the presence of air in one interval and copper in the other, the inductive effect was exactly alike on the two coils, and as if air had occupied both intervals. So that notwithstanding the facility with which any induced currents might form in the thick copper plate, the coil outside of it was just as much affected by the central helix C as if no such conductor as the copper had been there (65).

1722. Then, for the copper plate was substituted one of sulphur 0.9 of an inch thick; still the results were exactly the same, i.e., there was no action at the galvanometer.

1723. Thus it appears that when a voltaic current in one wire is exerting its inductive action to produce a contrary or a similar current in a neighbouring wire, according as the primary current is commencing or ceasing, it makes not the least difference whether the intervening space is occupied by such insulating bodies as air, sulphur and shellac, or such conducting bodies as copper, and the other non-magnetic metals.

1724. A correspondent effect was obtained with the like forces when resident in a magnet thus. A single flat helix (1718) was connected with a galvanometer, and a magnetic pole placed near to it; then by moving the magnet to and from the helix, or the helix to and from the magnet, currents were produced indicated by the galvanometer.

1725. The thick copper plate (1721) was afterwards interposed between the magnetic pole and the helix; nevertheless on moving these to and fro, effects exactly the same in direction and amount, were obtained as if the copper had not been there. So also on introducing a plate of sulphur into the interval, not the least influence on the currents produced by motion of the magnet or coils could be obtained.

1726. These results, with many others which I have not thought it needful to describe, would lead to the conclusion that (judging by the *amount* of effect produced at a distance by forces transverse to the electric current, i.e., magnetic forces), the intervening matter, and therefore the intervening particles, have nothing to do with the phenomena; or in other words, that though the inductive force of static electricity is transmitted to a distance by the action of the intermediate particles (1164, 1666), the transverse inductive force of currents, which can also act at a distance, is not transmitted by the intermediate particles in a similar way.

1727. It is however very evident that such a conclusion cannot be considered as proved. Thus when the metal copper is between the pole and the helix (1715, 1719, 1725) or between the two helices (1721) we know that its particles are affected, and can by proper arrangements make their peculiar state for the time very evident by the production of either electrical or magnetical effects. It seems impossible to consider this effect on the particles of the intervening matter as independent of that produced by the inductric coil or magnet C, on the inducteous coil or core A (1715, 1721); for since the inducteous body is equally affected by the inductric body whether these intervening and affected particles of copper are present or not (1723, 1725), such a supposition would imply that the particles so affected had no reaction back on the original inductric forces. The more reasonable conclusion, as it appears to me, is, to consider these affected particles as efficient in continuing the action onwards from the inductric to the inducteous body, and by this very communication producing the effect of *no loss* of induced power at the latter.

1728. But then it may be asked what is the relation of the particles of insulating bodies, such as air, sulphur, or lac, when *they* intervene in the line of magnetic action? The answer to this is at present merely conjectural. I have long thought there must be a particular condition of such bodies corresponding to the state which causes currents in metals and other conductors (26, 53, 191, 201, 213); and considering that the bodies are insulators one would expect that state to be one of tension. I have by rotating non-conducting bodies near magnetic poles and poles near them, and also by causing powerful electric currents to be suddenly formed and to cease around and about insulators in various directions, endeavoured to make some such state sensible, but have not succeeded. Nevertheless, as any such state must be of exceedingly low intensity, because of the feeble intensity of the currents which are used to induce it, it may well be that the state may exist, and may be discoverable by some more experimentalist, though I have not been able to make it sensible.

1729. It appears to me possible, therefore, and even probable, that magnetic action may be communicated to a distance by the action of the intervening particles, in a manner having a relation to the way in which the inductive forces of static electricity are transferred to a distance (1677); the intervening particles assuming for the time more or less of a peculiar condition, which (though with a very imperfect idea) I have several times expressed by the term *electro-tonic state* (60, 242, 1114, 1661). I hope it will not be understood that I hold the settled opinion that such is the case. I would rather in fact have proved the contrary, namely, that magnetic forces are quite independent of the matter intervening between the inductric and the inducteous bodies; but I cannot get over the difficulty presented by such substances as copper, silver, lead, gold, carbon, and even aqueous solutions (201, 213), which though they are known to assume a peculiar state whilst intervening between the bodies acting and acted upon (1727), no more interfere with the final result than those which have as yet had no peculiarity of condition discovered in them.

1730. A remark important to the whole of this investigation ought to be made here. Although I think the galvanometer used as I have described it (1711, 1720) is quite sufficient to prove that the final amount of action on each of the two coils or the two cores A and B (1713, 1719) is equal, yet there is an effect which *may* be consequent on the difference of action of two interposed bodies which it would not show. As time enters as an element into these actions[1] (125), it is very possible that the induced actions on the helices or cores A, B, though they rise to the same degree when air and copper, or air and lac are contrasted as intervening substances, do not do so in the same time; and yet, because of the length of time occupied by a vibration of the needle, this difference may not be visible, both effects rising to their maximum in periods so short as to make no sensible portion of that required for a vibration of the needle, and so exert no visible influence upon it.

1731. If the lateral or transverse force of electrical currents, or what appears to be the same thing, magnetic power, could be proved to be influential at a distance independently of the intervening contiguous particles, then, as it appears to me, a real distinction of a high and important kind, would be established between the natures of these two forces (1654, 1664). I do not mean that the powers are independent of each other and might be rendered separately active, on the contrary they are probably essentially associated (1654), but it by no means follows that they are of the same nature. In common statical induction, in conduction, and in electrolyzation, the forces at the opposite extremities of the particles which coincide with the lines of action and have commonly been distinguished by the term electric, are polar, and in the cases of contiguous particles act only to insensible distances; whilst those which are transverse to the direction of these lines, and are called magnetic, are circumferential, act at a distance, and if not through the mediation of the intervening particles, have their relations to ordinary matter entirely unlike those of the electrical forces with which they are associated.

[1] See *Annales de Chimie*, 1833, Vol. LI, pp. 422, 428.

1732. To decide this question of the identity or distinction of the two kinds of power, and establish their true relation, would be exceedingly important. The question seems fully within the reach of experiment, and offers a high reward to him who will attempt its settlement.

1733. I have already expressed a hope of finding an effect or condition which shall be to statical electricity what magnetic force is to current electricity (1658). If I could have proved to my own satisfaction that magnetic forces extended their influence to a distance by the conjoined action of the intervening particles in a manner analogous to that of electrical forces, then I should have thought that the natural tension of the lines of inductive action (1659), or that state so often hinted at as the electro-tonic state (1661, 1662), was this related condition of statical electricity.

1734. It may be said that the state of *no lateral action* is to static or inductive force the equivalent of *magnetism* to current force; but that can only be upon the view that electric and magnetic action are in their nature essentially different (1664). If they are the same power, the whole difference in the results being the consequence of the difference of *direction*, then the normal or *undeveloped* state of electric force will correspond with the state of *no lateral action* of the magnetic state of the force; the electric current will correspond with the lateral effects commonly called magnetism; but the state of static induction which is between the normal condition and the current will still require a corresponding lateral condition in the magnetic series, presenting its own peculiar phenomena; for it can hardly be supposed that the normal electric, and the inductive or polarized electric, condition, can both have the same lateral relation. If magnetism be a separate and a higher relation of the powers developed, then perhaps the argument which presses for this third condition of that force would not be so strong.

1735. I cannot conclude these general remarks upon the relation of the electric and magnetic forces without expressing my surprise at the results obtained with the copper plate (1721, 1725). The experiments with the flat helices represent one of the simplest cases of the induction of electrical currents (1720); the effect, as is well known, consisting in the production of a momentary current in a wire at the instant when a current in the contrary direction begins to pass through a neighbouring parallel wire, and the production of an equally brief current in the reverse direction when the determining current is stopped (26). Such being the case, it seems very extraordinary that this induced current which takes place in the helix A when there is only air between A and C (1720) should be equally strong when that air is replaced by an enormous mass of that excellently conducting metal copper (1721). It might have been supposed that this mass would have allowed of the formation and discharge of almost any quantity of currents in it, which the helix C was competent to induce, and so in some degree have diminished if not altogether prevented the effect in A: instead of which, though we can hardly doubt that an infinity of currents are formed at the moment in the copper plate, still not the smallest diminution or alteration of the effect in A appears (65). Almost the only way of reconciling this effect with generally received notions is, as it appears to me, to admit that magnetic action is communicated by the action of the intervening particles (1729, 1733).

1736. This condition of things, which is very remarkable, accords perfectly with the effects observed in solid helices where wires are coiled over wires to the amount of five or six or more layers in succession, no diminution of effect on the outer ones being occasioned by those within.

§ 22. *Note on Electrical Excitation*

1737. That the different modes in which electrical excitement takes place will some day or other be reduced under one common law can hardly be doubted, though for the present we are bound to admit distinctions. It will be a great point gained when these distinctions are, not removed, but understood.

1738. The strict relation of the electrical and chemical powers renders the chemical mode of excitement the most instructive of all, and the case of two isolated combining particles is probably the simplest that we possess. Here however the action is local, and we still want such a test of electricity as shall apply to it, to cases of current electricity, and also to those of static induction. Whenever by virtue of the previously combined condition of some of the acting particles (923) we are enabled, as in the voltaic pile, to expand or convert the local action into a current, then chemical action can be traced through its variations to the production of *all* the phenomena of tension and the static state, these being in every respect the same as if the electric forces producing them had been developed by friction.

1739. It was Berzelius, I believe, who first spoke of the aptness of certain particles to assume opposite states when in presence of each other (959). Hypothetically we may suppose these states to increase in intensity by increased approximation, or by heat, &c., until at a certain point combination occurs, accompanied by such an arrangement of the forces of the two particles between themselves as is equivalent to a discharge, producing at the same time a particle which is throughout a conductor (1700).

1740. This aptness to assume an excited electrical state (which is probably polar in those forming non-conducting matter) appears to be a primary fact, and to partake of the nature of induction (1162), for the particles do not seem capable of retaining their particular state independently of each other (1177) or of matter in the opposite state. What appears to be definite about the particles of matter is their assumption of a *particular* state, as the positive or negative, in relation to each other, and not of either one or other indifferently; and also the acquirement of force up to a certain amount.

1741. It is easily conceivable that the same force which causes local action between two free particles shall produce current force if one of the particles is previously in combination, forming part of an electrolyte (923, 1738). Thus a particle of zinc, and one of oxygen, when in presence of each other, exert their inductive forces (1740), and these at last rise up to the point of combination. If the oxygen be previously in union with hydrogen, it is held so combined by an analogous exertion and arrangement of the forces; and as the forces of the oxygen and hydrogen are for the time of combination mutually engaged and related, so when the superior relation of the forces between the oxygen and zinc come into play, the induction of the former or oxygen towards the metal cannot be brought on and increased without a corresponding deficiency in its induction towards the hydrogen with which it is in combination (for the amount of force in a particle is considered as definite), and the latter therefore has its force turned towards the oxygen of the next particle of water; thus the effect may be considered as extended to sensible distances, and thrown into the condition of static induction, which being discharged and then removed by the action of other particles produces currents.

1742. In the common voltaic battery, the current is occasioned by the tendency of the zinc to take the oxygen of the water from the hydrogen, the effective action being at the place where the oxygen leaves the previously existing electrolyte. But Schœnbein has arranged a battery in which the effective action is at the other extremity of this essential part of the arrangement, namely, where oxygen goes to the electrolyte.[1] The first may be considered as a case where the current is put into motion by the abstraction of oxygen from hydrogen, the latter by that of hydrogen from oxygen. The direction of the electric current is in both cases the same, when referred to the direction in which the elementary particles of the electrolyte are moving (923, 962), and both are equally in accordance with the hypothetical view of the inductive action of the particles just described (1740).

1743. In such a view of voltaic excitement the action of the particles may be divided into two parts, that which occurs whilst the force in a particle of oxygen is rising towards a particle of zinc acting on it, and falling towards the particle of hydrogen with which it is associated (this being the progressive period of the inductive action), and that which occurs when the change of association takes place, and the particle of oxygen leaves the hydrogen and combines with the zinc. The former appears to be that which produces the current, or if there be no current, produces the state of tension at the termination of the battery; whilst the latter, by terminating for the time the influence of the particles which have been active, allows of others coming into play, and so the effect of current is continued.

1744. It seems highly probable that excitement by friction may very frequently be of the same character. Wollaston endeavoured to refer such excitement to chemical action,[2] but if by chemical action ultimate union of the acting particles is intended, then there are plenty of cases which are opposed to such a view. Davy mentions some such, and for my own part I feel no difficulty in admitting other means of electrical excitement than chemical action, especially if by chemical action is meant a final combination of the particles.

1745. Davy refers experimentally to the opposite states which two particles having opposite chemical relations can assume when they are brought into the close vicinity of each other, but *not* allowed to combine.[3] This, I think, is

the first part of the action already described (1743); but in my opinion it cannot give rise to a continuous current unless combination take place, so as to allow other particles to act successively in the same manner, and not even then unless one set of the particles be present as an element of an electrolyte (923, 963); i.e., mere quiescent contact alone without chemical action does not in such cases produce a *current*.

1746. Still it seems very possible that such a relation may produce a high charge, and thus give rise to excitement by friction. When two bodies are rubbed together to produce electricity in the usual way, one at least must be an insulator. During the act of rubbing, the particles of opposite kinds must be brought more or less closely together, the few which are most favourably circumstanced being in such close contact as to be short only of that which is consequent upon chemical combination. At such moments they may acquire by their mutual induction (1740) and partial discharge to each other, very exalted opposite states, and when, the moment after, they are by the progress of the rub removed from each other's vicinity, they will retain this state if both bodies be insulators, and exhibit them upon their complete separation.

1747. All the circumstances attending friction seem to me to favour such a view. The irregularities of form and pressure will cause that the particles of the two rubbing surfaces will be at very variable distances, only a few at once being in that very close relation which is probably necessary for the development of the forces; further, those which are nearest at one time will be further removed at another, and others will become the nearest, and so by continuing the friction many will in succession be excited. Finally, the lateral direction of the separation in rubbing seems to me the best fitted to bring many pairs of particles, first of all into that close vicinity necessary for their assuming the opposite states by relation to each other, and then to remove them from each other's influence whilst they retain that state.

1748. It would be easy, on the same view, to explain hypothetically, how, if one of the rubbing bodies be a conductor, as the amalgam of an electrical machine, the state of the other when it comes from under the friction is (as a mass) exalted; but it would be folly to go far into such speculation before that already advanced has been confirmed or corrected by fit experimental evidence. I do not wish it to be

[1] *Philosophical Magazine*, 1838, XII, 225, 315. See also De la Rive's results with peroxide of manganese. *Annales de Chimie*, 1836, LXI, p. 40., *Dec.* 1838.
[2] *Philosophical Transactions*, 1801, p. 427.
[3] *Ibid.*, 1807, p. 34.

supposed that I think all excitement by friction is of this kind; on the contrary, certain experiments lead me to believe that in many cases, and perhaps in all, effects of a thermo-electric nature conduce to the ultimate effect; and there are very probably other causes of electric disturbance influential at the same time, which we have not as yet distinguished.

Royal Institution, June, 1838

FIFTEENTH SERIES

§ 23. Notice of the Character and Direction of the Electric Force of the Gymnotus

RECEIVED NOVEMBER 15, READ DECEMBER 6, 1838

1749. WONDERFUL as are the laws and phenomena of electricity when made evident to us in inorganic or dead matter, their interest can bear scarcely any comparison with that which attaches to the same force when connected with the nervous system and with life; and though the obscurity which for the present surrounds the subject may for the time also veil its importance, every advance in our knowledge of this mighty power in relation to inert things, helps to dissipate that obscurity, and to set forth more prominently the surpassing interest of this very high branch of physical philosophy. We are indeed but upon the threshold of what we may, without presumption, believe man is permitted to know of this matter; and the many eminent philosophers who have assisted in making this subject known have, as is very evident in their writings, felt up to the latest moment that such is the case.

1750. The existence of animals able to give the same concussion to the living system as the electrical machine, the voltaic battery, and the thunder-storm, being with their habits made known to us by Richer, S'Gravesende, Firmin, Walsh, Humboldt, &c. &c., it became of growing importance to identify the living power which they possess, with that which man can call into action from inert matter, and by him named electricity (265, 351). With the *torpedo* this has been done to perfection, and the direction of the current of force determined by the united and successive labours of Walsh,[1] Cavendish,[2] Galvani,[3] Gardini,[4] Humboldt and Gay-Lussac,[5] Todd,[6] Sir Humphry

Davy,[7] Dr. Davy,[8] Becquerel,[9] and Matteucci.[10]

1751. The gymnotus has also been experimented with for the same purpose, and the investigations of Williamson,[11] Garden,[12] Humboldt,[13] Fahlberg,[14] and Guisan,[15] have gone very far in showing the identity of the electric force in this animal with the electricity excited by ordinary means; and the two latter philosophers have even obtained the spark.

1752. As an animal fitted for the further investigation of this refined branch of science, the gymnotus seems, in certain respects, better adapted than the torpedo, especially (as Humboldt has remarked) in its power of bearing confinement, and capability of being preserved alive and in health for a long period. A gymnotus has been kept for several months in activity, whereas Dr. Davy could not preserve torpedoes above twelve or fifteen days; and Matteucci was not able out of 116 such fish to keep one living above three days, though every circumstance favourable to their preservation was attended to.[16] To obtain gymnoti has therefore been a matter of consequence; and being stimulated, as much as I was honoured, by very kind communications from Baron Humboldt, I in the year 1835 applied to the Colonial Office, where I was promised every assistance in procuring some of these fishes, and continually expect to receive either news of them or the animals themselves.

1753. Since that time Sir Everard Home has also moved a friend to send some gymnoti over,

[1] *Philosophical Transactions*, 1773, p. 461.
[2] *Ibid.*, 1776, p. 196.
[3] Aldini's *Essai sur la Galvanism*, II, 61.
[4] *De Electrici ignis Natura*, § 71, Mantua, 1792.
[5] *Annales de Chimie*, XIV, 15.
[6] *Philosophical Transactions*, 1816, p. 120.
[7] *Ibid.*, 1829, p. 15.
[8] *Ibid.*, 1832, p. 259; and 1834, p. 531.
[9] *Traité de l'Électricité*, IV, 264.
[10] *Bibliothèque Universelle*, 1837, Vol. XII, 163.
[11] *Philosophical Transactions*, 1775, p. 94.
[12] *Ibid.*, 1775, p. 102.
[13] *Personal Narrative*, chap. xvii.
[14] *Swedish Transactions*, 1801, pp. 122, 156.
[15] *De Gymnoto Électrico*, Tubingen, 1819.
[16] *Bibliothèque Universelle*, 1837, XII, p. 174.

which are to be consigned to His Royal Highness our late President; and other gentlemen are also engaged in the same work. This spirit induces me to insert in the present communication that part of the letter from Baron Humboldt which I received as an answer to my inquiry of how they were best to be conveyed across the Atlantic. He says, "The gymnotus, which is common in the Llanos de Caracas (near Calabozo), in all the small rivers which flow into the Orinoco, in English, French or Dutch Guiana, is not of difficult transportation. We lost them so soon at Paris because they were too much fatigued (by experiments) immediately after their arrival. MM. Norderling and Fahlberg retained them alive at Paris above four months. I would advise that they be transported from Surinam (from Essequibo, Demerara, Cayenne) in summer, for the gymnotus in its native country lives in water of 25° centigrade (or 77° Fahr.). Some are five feet in height, but I would advise that such as are about twenty-seven or twenty-eight inches in length be chosen. Their power varies with their food, and their state of rest. Having but a small stomach they eat little and often, their food being cooked meat, *not salted,* small fish, or even bread. Trial should be made of their strength and the fit kind of nourishment before they are shipped, and those fish only selected already accustomed to their prison. I retained them in a box or trough about four feet long, and sixteen inches wide and deep. The water must be *fresh,* and be changed every three or four days: the fish must not be prevented from coming to the surface, for they like to swallow air. A net should be put over and round the trough, for the gymnotus often springs out of the water. There are all the directions that I can give you. It is, however, *important* that the animal should not be tormented or fatigued, for it becomes exhausted by frequent electric explosions. Several gymnoti may be retained in the same trough."

1754. A gymnotus has lately been brought to this country by Mr. Porter, and purchased by the proprietors of the Gallery in Adelaide Street: they immediately most liberally offered me the liberty of experimenting with the fish for scientific purposes; they placed it for the time exclusively at my disposal, that (in accordance with Humboldt's directions [1753]) its powers might not be impaired; only desiring me to have a regard for its life and health. I was not slow to take advantage of their wish to forward the interests of science, and with many thanks ac-

cepted their offer. With this gymnotus, having the kind assistance of Mr. Bradley of the Gallery, Mr. Gassiot, and occasionally other gentlemen, as Professors Daniell, Owen and Wheatstone, I have obtained every proof of the identity of its power with common electricity (265, 351, &c.). All of these had been obtained before with the torpedo (1750), and some, as the shock, circuit, and spark (1751), with the gymnotus; but still I think a brief account of the results will be acceptable to the Royal Society, and I give them as necessary preliminary experiments to the investigations which we may hope to institute when the expected supply of animals arrives (1752).

1755. The fish is forty inches long. It was caught about March 1838; it was brought to the Gallery on the 15th of August, but did not feed from the time of its capture up to the 19th of October. From the 24th of August Mr. Bradley nightly put some blood into the water, which was changed for fresh water next morning, and in this way the animal perhaps obtained some nourishment. On the 19th of October it killed and eat four small fish; since then the blood has been discontinued, and the animal has been improving ever since, consuming upon an average one fish daily.[1]

1756. I first experimented with it on the 3rd of September, when it was apparently languid, but gave strong shocks when the hands were favourably disposed on the body (1760, 1773, &c.). The experiments were made on four different days, allowing periods of rest from a month to a week between each. His health seemed to improve continually, and it was during this period, between the third and fourth days of experiment, that he began to eat.

1757. Beside the hands two kinds of collectors were used. The one sort consisted each of a copper rod fifteen inches long, having a copper disc one inch and a half in diameter brazed to one extremity, and a copper cylinder to serve as a handle, with large contact to the hand, fixed to the other, the rod from the disc upwards being well covered with a thick caoutchouc tube to insulate that part from the hand. By these the states of particular parts of the fish whilst in the water could be ascertained.

1758. The other kind of collectors were intended to meet the difficulty presented by the complete immersion of the fish in water; for even when obtaining the spark itself I did not think myself justified in asking for the removal of the animal into air. A plate of copper eight

[1] The fish eaten were gudgeons, carp, and perch.

inches long by two inches and a half wide, was bent into a saddle shape, that it might pass over the fish, and inclose a certain extent of the back and sides, and a thick copper wire was brazed to it, to convey the electric force to the experimental apparatus; a jacket of sheet caoutchouc was put over the saddle. the edges projecting at the bottom and the ends; the ends were made to converge so as to fit in some degree the body of the fish, and the bottom edges were made to spring against any horizontal surface on which the saddles were placed. The part of the wire liable to be in the water was covered with caoutchouc.

1759. These conductors being put over the fish, collected power sufficient to produce many electric effects; but when, as in obtaining the spark, every possible advantage was needful, then glass plates were placed at the bottom of the water, and the fish being over them, the conductors were put over it until the lower caoutchouc edges rested on the glass, so that the part of the animal within the caoutchouc was thus almost as well insulated as if the gymnotus had been in the air.

1760. *Shock.* The shock of this animal was very powerful when the hands were placed in a favourable position, i.e., one on the body near the head, and the other near the tail; the nearer the hands were together within certain limits the less powerful was the shock. The disc conductors (1757) conveyed the shock very well when the hands were wetted and applied in close contact with the cylindrical handles; but scarcely at all if the handles were held in the dry hands in an ordinary way.

1761. *Galvanometer.* Using the saddle conductors (1758) applied to the anterior and posterior parts of the gymnotus, a galvanometer was readily affected. It was not particularly delicate; for zinc and platina plates on the upper and lower surface of the tongue did not cause a permanent deflection of more than 25°; yet when the fish gave a powerful discharge the deflection was as much as 30°, and in one case even 40°. The deflection was constantly in a given direction, the electric current being always from the anterior parts of the animal through the galvanometer wire to the posterior parts. The former were therefore for the time externally positive, and the latter negative.

1762. *Making a magnet.* When a little helix containing twenty-two feet of silked wire wound on a quill was put into the circuit, and an annealed steel needle placed in the helix, the needle became a magnet, and the direction of its

polarity in every case indicated a current from the anterior to the posterior parts of the gymnotus through the conductors used.

1763. *Chemical decomposition.* Polar decomposition of a solution of iodide of potassium was easily obtained. Three or four folds of paper moistened in the soluticn (322) were placed between a platina plate and the end of a wire also of platina, these being respectively connected with the two saddle conductors (1758). Whenever the wire was in conjunction with the conductor at the fore part of the gymnotus, iodine appeared at its extremity; but when connected with the other conductor, none was evolved at the place on the paper where it before appeared. So that here again the direction of the current proved to be the same as that given by the former tests.

1764. By this test I compared the middle part of the fish with other portions before and behind it, and found that the conductor A, which being applied to the middle was negative to the conductor B applied to the anterior parts was, on the contrary, positive to it when B was applied to places near the tail. So that within certain limits the condition of the fish externally at the time of the shock appears to be such that any given part is negative to other parts anterior to it, and positive to such as are behind it.

1765. *Evolution of heat.* Using a Harris thermo-electrometer belonging to Mr. Gassiot, we thought we were able in one case, namely that when the deflection of the galvanometer was 40° (1761), to observe a feeble elevation of temperature. I was not observing the instrument myself, and one of those who at first believed they saw the effect now doubts the result.[1]

1766. *Spark.* The electric spark was obtained thus. A good magneto-electric coil, with a core of soft iron wire, had one extremity made fast to the end of one of the saddle collectors (1758), and the other fixed to a new steel file; another file was made fast to the end of the other collector. One person then rubbed the point of one of these files over the face of the other, whilst another person put the collectors over the fish, and endeavoured to excite it to action. By the friction of the files contact was made and broken very frequently; and the object was to catch the moment of the current through the wire and helix, and by breaking contact *during the current* to make the electricity sensible as a spark.

[1] In more recent experiments of the same kind we could not obtain the effect.

1767. The spark was obtained four times, and nearly all who were present saw it. That it was not due to the mere attrition of the two piles was shown by its not occurring when the files were rubbed together, independently of the animal. Since then I have substituted for the lower file a revolving steel plate, cut file fashion on its face, and for the upper file wires of iron, copper and silver, with all of which the spark was obtained.[1]

1768. Such were the general electric phenomena obtained from this gymnotus whilst living and active in his native element. On several occasions many of them were obtained together; thus a magnet was made, the galvanometer deflected, and perhaps a wire heated, by one single discharge of the electric force of the animal.

1769. I think a few further but brief details of experiments relating to the quantity and disposition of the electricity in and about this wonderful animal will not be out of place in this short account of its powers.

1770. When the shock is strong, it is like that of a large Leyden battery charged to a low degree, or that of a good voltaic battery of perhaps one hundred or more pair of plates, of which the circuit is completed for a moment only. I endeavoured to form some idea of the *quantity* of electricity by connecting a large Leyden battery (291) with two brass balls, above three inches in diameter, placed seven inches apart in a tub of water, so that they might represent the parts of the gymnotus to which the collectors had been applied; but to lower the intensity of the discharge, eight inches in length of six-fold thick wetted string were interposed elsewhere in the circuit, this being found necessary to prevent the easy occurrence of the spark at the ends of the collectors (1758), when they were applied in the water near to the balls, as they had been before to the fish. Being thus arranged, when the battery was strongly charged and discharged, and the hands put into the water near the balls, a shock was felt, much resembling that from the fish; and though the experiments have no pretension to accuracy, yet as the tension could be in some degree imitated by reference to the more or less ready production of a spark, and after that the shock be used to indicate whether the quantity was about the same, I think we may conclude that a single medium discharge of the

[1] At a later meeting, at which attempts were made to cause the attraction of gold leaves, the spark was obtained directly between fixed surfaces, the inductive coil (1766) being removed, and only short wires (by comparison) employed.

fish is at least equal to the electricity of a Leyden battery of fifteen jars, containing 3500 square inches of glass coated on both sides, charged to its highest degree (291). This conclusion, respecting the great quantity of electricity in a single gymnotus shock, is in perfect accordance with the degree of deflection which it can produce in a galvanometer needle (367, 860, 1761), and also with the amount of chemical decomposition produced (374, 860, 1763) in the electrolyzing experiments.

1771. Great as is the force in a single discharge, the gymnotus, as Humboldt describes, and as I have frequently experienced, gives a double and even a triple shock; and this capability of immediately repeating the effect with scarcely a sensible interval of time, is very important in the considerations which must arise hereafter respecting the origin and excitement of the power in the animal. Walsh, Humboldt, Gay-Lussac, and Matteucci have remarked the same thing of the torpedo, but in a far more striking degree.

1772. As, at the moment when the fish wills the shock, the anterior parts are positive and the posterior parts negative, it may be concluded that there is a current from the former to the latter through every part of the water which surrounds the animal, to a considerable distance from its body. The shock which is felt, therefore, when the hands are in the most favourable position, is the effect of a very small portion only of the electricity which the animal discharges at the moment, by far the largest portion passing through the surrounding water. This enormous external current must be accompanied by some effect within the fish *equivalent* to a current, the direction of which is from the tail towards the head, and equal to the sum of *all these external forces*. Whether the process of evolving or exciting the electricity within the fish includes the production of this internal current (which need not of necessity be as quick and momentary as the external one), we cannot at present say; but at the time of the shock the animal does not apparently feel the electric sensation which he causes in those around him.

1773. By the help of the accompanying diagram I will state a few experimental results which illustrate the current around the fish, and show the cause of the difference in character of the shock occasioned by the various ways in which the person is connected with the animal, or his position altered with respect to it. The large circle represents the tub in which the animal is confined; its diameter is forty-six inches, and the depth of water in it three inches and a half; it is supported on dry wooden legs. The figures represent the places where the hands or the disc conductors (1757) were applied, and where they are close to the figure of the animal, it implies that contact with the fish was made. I will designate different persons by A, B, C, &c., A being the person who excited the fish to action.

1774. When one hand was in the water the shock was felt in that hand only, whatever part of the fish it was applied to; it was not very strong, and was only in the part immersed in the water. When the hand and part of the arm were in, the shock was felt in all the parts immersed.

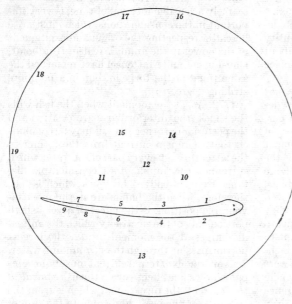

1775. When *both* hands were in the water at the *same* part of the fish, still the shock was comparatively weak, and only in the parts immersed. If the hands were on opposite sides, as at 1, 2, or at 3, 4, or 5, 6, or if one was above and the other below at the same part, the effect was the same. When the disc collectors were used in these positions no effect was felt by the person holding them (and this corresponds with the observation of Gay-Lussac on torpedoes),[1] whilst other persons, with both hands in at a distance from the fish, felt considerable shocks.

1776. When both hands or the disc collectors were applied at places separated by a part of the length of the animal, as at 1, 3, or 4, 6, or 3, 6, then strong shocks extending up the arms,

[1] *Annales de Chimie*, XIV, p. 18.

and even to the breast of the experimenter, occurred, though another person with a single hand in at any of these places, felt comparatively little. The shock could be obtained at parts very near the tail, as at 8, 9. I think it was strongest at about 1 and 8. As the hands were brought nearer together the effect diminished, until being in the same cross plane, it was, as before described, only sensible in the parts immersed (1775).

1777. B placed his hands at 10, 11, at least four inches from the fish, whilst A touched the animal with a glass rod to excite it to action; B quickly received a powerful shock. In another experiment of a similar kind, as respects the non-necessity of touching the fish, several persons received shocks independently of each other; thus A was at 4, 6; B at 10, 11; C at 16, 17; and D at 18, 19; all were shocked at once, A and B very strongly, C and D feebly. It is very useful, whilst experimenting with the galvanometer or other instrumental arrangements, for one person to keep his hands in the water at a moderate distance from the animal, that he may know and give information when a discharge has taken place.

1778. When B had both hands at 10, 11, or at 14, 15, whilst A had but one hand at 1, or 3, or 6. the former felt a strong shock, whilst the latter had but a weak one, though in contact with the fish. Or if A had both hands in at 1, 2, or 3, 4, or 5, 6, the effect was the same.

1779. If A had the hands at 3, 5, B at 14, 15, and C at 16, 17, A received the most powerful shock, B the next powerful, and C the feeblest.

1780. When A excited the gymnotus by his hands at 8, 9, whilst B was at 10, 11, the latter had a much stronger shock than the former, though the former touched and excited the animal.

1781. A excited the fish by one hand at 3, whilst B had both hands at 10, 11 (or along), and C had the hands at 12, 13 (or across); A had the pricking shock in the immersed hand only (1774); B had a strong shock up the arms; C felt but a slight effect in the immersed parts.

1782. The experiments I have just described are of such a nature as to require many repetitions before the general results drawn from them can be considered as established; nor do I pretend to say that they are anything more than indications of the direction of the force. It is not at all impossible that the fish may have the power of throwing each of its four electric organs separately into action, and so to a certain degree direct the shock, i.e., he may have the capability of causing the electric current to emanate from one side, and at the same time bring the other side of his body into such a condition, that it shall be as a non-conductor in that direction. But I think the appearances and results are such as to forbid the supposition, that he has any control over the direction of the currents after they have entered the fluid and substances around him.

1783. The statements also have reference to the fish when in a straight form; if it assume a bent shape, then the lines of force around it vary in their intensity in a manner that may be anticipated theoretically. Thus if the hands were applied at 1, 7, a feebler shock in the arms would be expected if the animal were curved with that side inwards, than if it were straight, because the distance between the parts would be diminished, and the intervening water therefore conduct more of the force. But with respect to the parts *immersed*, or to animals, as fish *in the water* between 1 and 7, they would be more powerfully, instead of less powerfully, shocked.

1784. It is evident from all the experiments, as well as from simple considerations, that all the water and all the conducting matter around the fish through which a discharge circuit can in any way be completed, is filled at the moment with circulating electric power; and this state might be easily represented generally in a diagram by drawing the lines of inductive action (1231, 1304, 1338) upon it: in the case of a gymnotus, surrounded equally in all directions by water, these would resemble generally, in disposition, the magnetic curves of a magnet, having the same straight or curved shape as the animal, i.e., provided he, in such cases, employed, as may be expected, his four electric organs at once.

1785. This gymnotus can stun and kill fish which are in very various positions to its own body; but on one day when I saw it eat, its action seemed to me to be peculiar. A live fish about five inches in length, caught not half a minute before, was dropped into the tub. The gymnotus instantly turned round in such a manner as to form a coil inclosing the fish, the latter representing a diameter across it; a shock passed, and there in an instant was the fish struck motionless, as if by lightning, in the midst of the waters, its side floating to the light. The gymnotus made a turn or two to look for its prey, which having found he bolted, and then went searching about for more. A second smaller fish was given him, which being hurt in the conveyance, showed but little signs of life, and this he swallowed at once, apparently without shocking it. The coiling of the gymnotus round its prey had, in this case, every appearance of being intentional on its part, to increase the force of the shock, and the action is evidently exceedingly well suited for that purpose (1783), being in full accordance with the well-known laws of the discharge of currents in masses of conducting matter; and though the fish may not always put this artifice in practice, it is very probable he is aware of its advantage, and may resort to it in cases of need.

1786. Living as this animal does in the midst of such a good conductor as water, the first thoughts are thoughts of surprise that it can sensibly electrify anything, but a little consideration soon makes one conscious of many points of great beauty, illustrating the wisdom of the whole arrangement. Thus the very conducting power which the water has; that which it gives to the moistened skin of the fish or animal to be struck; the extent of surface by which the fish and the water conducting the charge to it are in contact; all conduce to favour and increase the shock upon the doomed animal, and are in the most perfect contrast with the inefficient state of things which would exist if the gymnotus and the fish were surrounded by air; and at the same time that the power is one of low intensity, so that a dry skin wards it off, though a moist one conducts it (1760); so is it one of great quantity (1770), that though the surrounding water does conduct away much, enough to produce a full effect may take its course through the body of the fish that is to be caught for food, or the enemy that is to be conquered.

1787. Another remarkable result of the relation of the gymnotus and its prey to the medium around them is, that the larger the fish to be killed or stunned, the greater will be the shock to which it is subject, though the gymnotus may exert only an equal power; for the large fish has passing through its body those currents of electricity, which, in the case of a smaller one, would have been conveyed harmless by the water at its sides.

1788. The gymnotus appears to be sensible when he has shocked an animal, being made conscious of it, probably, by the *mechanical im-*

pulse he receives, caused by the spasms into which it is thrown. When I touched him with my hands, he gave me shock after shock; but when I touched him with glass rods, or the insulated conductors, he gave one or two shocks, felt by others having their hands in at a distance, but then ceased to exert the influence, as if made aware it had not the desired effect. Again, when he has been touched with the conductors several times, for experiments on the galvanometer or other apparatus, and appears to be languid or indifferent, and not willing to give shocks, yet being touched by the hands, they, by convulsive motion, have informed him that a sensitive thing was present, and he has quickly shown his power and his willingness to astonish the experimenter.

1789. It has been remarked by Geoffroy St. Hilaire that the electric organs of the torpedo, gymnotus, and similar fishes, cannot be considered as essentially connected with those which are of high and direct importance to the life of the animal, but to belong rather to the common teguments; and it has also been found that such torpedoes as have been deprived of the use of their peculiar organs, have continued the functions of life quite as well as those in which they were allowed to remain. These, with other considerations, lead me to look at these parts with a hope that they may upon close investigation prove to be a species of natural apparatus, by means of which we may apply the principles of *action and reaction* in the investigation of the nature of the *nervous influence*.

1790. The anatomical relation of the nervous system to the electric organ; the evident exhaustion of the nervous energy during the production of electricity in that organ; the apparently equivalent production of electricity in proportion to the quantity of nervous force consumed; the constant direction of the current produced, with its relation to what we may believe to be an equally constant direction of the nervous energy thrown into action at the same time; all induce me to believe, that it is not impossible but that, on passing electricity perforce through the organ, a reaction back upon the nervous system belonging to it might take place, and that a restoration, to a greater or smaller degree, of that which the animal expends in the act of exciting a current, might perhaps be effected. We have the analogy in relation to heat and magnetism. Seebeck taught us how to commute heat into electricity; and Peltier has more lately given us the strict converse of this, and shown us how to convert the electricity into heat, including both its relation of hot and cold. Oersted showed how we were to convert electric into magnetic forces, and I had the delight of adding the other member of the full relation, by reacting back again and converting magnetic into electric forces. So perhaps in these organs, where nature has provided the apparatus by means of which the animal can exert and convert nervous into electric force, we may be able, possessing in that point of view a power far beyond that of the fish itself, to reconvert the electric into the nervous force.

1791. This may seem to some a very wild notion, as assuming that the nervous power is in some degree analogous to such powers as heat, electricity, and magnetism. I am only assuming it, however, as a reason for making certain experiments, which, according as they give positive or negative results, will regulate further expectation. And with respect to the nature of nervous power, that exertion of it which is conveyed along the nerves to the various organs which they excite into action, is not the direct principle of *life*; and therefore I see no natural reason why we should not be allowed in certain cases to *determine* as well as observe its course. Many philosophers think the power is electricity. Priestley put forth this view in 1774 in a very striking and distinct form, both as regards ordinary animals and those which are electric, like the torpedo.[1] Dr. Wilson Philip considers that the agent in certain nerves is electricity modified by vital action.[2] Matteucci thinks that the nervous fluid or energy, in the nerves belonging to the electric organ at least, is electricity.[3] MM. Prevost and Dumas are of opinion that electricity moves in the nerves belonging to the muscles; and M. Prevost adduces a beautiful experiment, in which steel was magnetized, in proof of this view; which, if it should be confirmed by further observation and by other philosophers, is of the utmost consequence to the progress of this high branch of

[1] Priestley on *Air*, Vol. I, p. 277; edition of 1774.
[2] Dr. Wilson Philip is of opinion, that the nerves which excite the muscles and effect the chemical changes of the vital functions, operate by the electric power supplied by the brain and spinal marrow, in its effects, modified by the vital powers of the living animal; because he found, as he informs me, as early as 1815, that while the vital powers remain, all these functions can be as well performed by voltaic electricity after the removal of the nervous influence, as by that influence itself; and in the end of that year he presented a paper to the Royal Society, which was read at one of their meetings, giving an account of the experiments on which this position was founded.
[3] *Bibliothèque Universelle*, 1837, Vol. XII, 192.

knowledge.[1] Now though I am not as yet convinced by the facts that the nervous fluid is only electricity, still I think that the agent in the nervous system may be an inorganic force; and if there be reasons for supposing that magnetism is a higher relation of force than electricity (1664, 1731, 1734), so it may well be imagined that the nervous power may be of a still more exalted character, and yet within the reach of experiment.

1792. The kind of experiment I am bold enough to suggest is as follows. If a gymnotus or torpedo has been fatigued by frequent exertion of the electric organs, would the sending of currents of similar force to those he emits, or of other degrees of force, either continuously or intermittingly in the same direction as those he sends forth, restore him his powers and strength more rapidly than if he were left to his natural repose?

1793. Would sending currents through in the contrary direction exhaust the animal rapidly? There is, I think, reason to believe the torpedo (and perhaps the gymnotus) is not much disturbed or excited by electric currents sent only

1 *Ibid*, 1837, XII, 202; XIV, 200.

through the electric organ; so that these experiments do not appear very difficult to make.

1794. The disposition of the organs in the torpedo suggest still further experiments on the same principle. Thus when a current is sent in the natural direction, i.e., from below upwards through the organ on one side of the fish, will it excite the organ on the other side into action? or if sent through in the contrary direction, will it produce the same or any effect on that organ? Will it do so if the nerves proceeding to the organ or organs be tied? and will it do so after the animal has been so far exhausted by previous shocks as to be unable to throw the organ into action in any, or in a similar, degree of his own will?

1795. Such are some of the experiments which the conformation and relation of the electric organs of these fishes suggest, as being rational in their performance, and promising in anticipation. Others may not think of them as I do; but I can only say for myself that, were the means in my power, they are the very first I would make.

Royal Institution, November 9, 1838

SIXTEENTH SERIES

§ 24. *On the Source of Power in the Voltaic Pile* ¶ i. *Exciting Electrolytes, &c., Being Conductors of Thermo and Feeble Currents* ¶ ii. *Inactive Conducting Circles Containing a Fluid or Electrolyte* ¶ iii. *Active Circles Excited by Solution of Sulphuret of Potassium, &c.*

RECEIVED JANUARY 23, READ FEBRUARY 6, 1840

§ 24. *On the Source of Power in the Voltaic Pile*

1796. WHAT is the source of power in a voltaic pile? This question is at present of the utmost importance in the theory and to the development of electrical science. The opinions held respecting it are various; but by far the most important are the two which respectively find the source of power in contact, and in chemical force. The question between them touches the first principles of electrical action; for the opinions are in such contrast that two men respectively adopting them are thenceforward constrained to differ, in every point, respecting the probable and intimate nature of the agent or force on which all the phenomena of the voltaic pile depend.

1797. The theory of contact is the theory of Volta, the great discoverer of the voltaic pile itself, and it has been sustained since his day by a host of philosophers, amongst whom, in recent times, rank such men as Pfaff, Marianini, Fechner, Zamboni, Matteucci, Karsten, Bouchardat, and as to the excitement of the power, even Davy; all bright stars in the exalted regions of science. The theory of chemical action was first advanced by Fabroni,[1] Wollaston,[2] and Parrot,[3] and has been more or less devel-

1 A.D. 1792, 1799. Becquerel's *Traité de l'Électricité*, I, pp. 81–91; and *Nicholson's Quarto Journal*, III, 308; IV, 120; or *Journal de Physique*, VI, 348.
2 A.D. 1801. *Philosophical Transactions*, 1801, p. 427.
3 A.D. 1801. *Annales de Chimie*, 1829, XLII, 45; 1831, XLVI, 361.

oped since by Oersted, Becquerel, De la Rive, Ritchie, Pouillet, Schœnbein, and many others, amongst whom Becquerel ought to be distinguished as having contributed, from the first, a continually increasing mass of the strongest experimental evidence in proof that chemical action always evolves electricity;[1] and De la Rive should be named as most clear and constant in his views, and most zealous in his production of facts and arguments, from the year 1827 to the present time.[2]

1798. Examining this question by the results of definite electro-chemical action, I felt constrained to take part with those who believed the origin of voltaic power to consist in chemical action alone (875, 965), and ventured a paper on it in April 1834[3] (875, &c.), which obtained the especial notice of Marianini.[4] The rank of this philosopher, the observation of Fechner,[5] and the consciousness that over the greater part of Italy and Germany the contact theory still prevailed, have induced me to re-examine the question most carefully. I wished not merely to escape from error, but was anxious to convince myself of the truth of the contact theory; for it was evident that if contact electromotive force had any existence, it must be a power not merely unlike every other natural power as to the phenomena it could produce, but also in the far higher points of limitation, definite force, and finite production (2065).

1799. I venture to hope that the experimental results and arguments which have been thus gathered may be useful to science. I fear the detail will be tedious, but that is a necessary consequence of the state of the subject. The contact theory has long had possession of men's minds, is sustained by a great weight of authority, and for years had almost undisputed sway in some parts of Europe. If it be an error, it can only be rooted out by a great amount of forcible experimental evidence; a fact sufficiently clear to my mind by the circumstance, that De la Rive's papers have not already convinced the workers upon this subject. Hence the reason why I have thought it needful to add my further

testimony to his and that of others, entering into detail and multiplying facts in a proportion far beyond any which would have been required for the proof and promulgation of a new scientific truth (2017). In so doing I may occasionally be only enlarging, yet then I hope strengthening, what others, and expecially De la Rive have done.

1800. It will tend to clear the question, if the various views of contact are first stated. Volta's theory is, that the simple contact of conducting bodies causes electricity to be developed at the point of contact without any change in nature of the bodies themselves; and that though such conductors as water and aqueous fluids have this property, yet the degree in which they possess it is unworthy of consideration in comparison with the degree to which it rises amongst the metals.[6] The present views of the Italian and German contact philosophers are, I believe, generally the same, except that occasionally more importance is attached to the contact of the imperfect conductors with the metals. Thus Zamboni (in 1837) considers the metallic contact as the most powerful source of electricity, and not that of the metals with the fluids;[7] but Karsten, holding the contact theory, transfers the electromotive force to the contact of the fluids with the solid conductors.[8] Marianini holds the same view of the principle of contact, with this addition, that actual contact is not required to the exertion of the exciting force, but that the two approximated dissimilar conductors may affect each other's state, when separated by sensible intervals of the $\frac{1}{10000}$th of a line and more, air intervening.[9]

1801. De la Rive, on the contrary, contends for simple and strict chemical action, and, as far as I am aware, admits of no current in the voltaic pile that is not conjoined with and dependent upon a complete chemical effect. That admirable electrician Becquerel, though expressing himself with great caution, seems to admit the possibility of chemical attractions being able to produce electrical currents when they are not strong enough to overcome the force of cohesion, and so terminate in combination.[10] Schœnbein states that a current may be produced by a tendency to chemical action, i.e.,

[1] A.D. 1824, &c. *Annales de Chimie*, 1824, XXV, 405; 1827, XXXV, 113; 1831, XLVI, 265, 276, 337; XLVII, 113; XLIX, 131.
[2] *Ibid.*, 1828, XXXVII, 225; XXXIX, 297; 1836, LXII, 147: or *Mémoires de Genève*, 1829, IV, 285; 1832, VI, 149; 1835, VII.
[3] *Philosophical Transactions*, 1834, p. 425.
[4] *Memorie della Società Italiana in Modena*, 1837, XXI, p. 205.
[5] *Philosophical Magazine*, 1838, XIII, 205; or Poggendorf's *Annalen*, XLII, p. 481. Fechner refers also to Pfaff's reply to my paper. I never cease to regret that the German is a sealed language to me.

[6] *Annales de Chimie*, 1802, XL, p. 225.
[7] *Bibliothèque Universelle*, 1836, V, 387; 1837, VIII, 189.
[8] *L'Institut*, No. 150.
[9] *Mem. della Soc. Ital. in Modena*, 1837, XXI, 232–237.
[10] *Annales de Chimie*, 1835, LX, 171; and *Traité de l'Électricité*, I, pp. 253, 258.

that substances which have a tendency to unite chemically may produce a current, though that tendency is not followed up by the actual combination of the substances.[1] In these cases the assigned force becomes the same as the contact of Volta, inasmuch as the acting matters are not altered whilst producing the current. Davy's opinion was, that contact like that of Volta excited the current or was the cause of it, but that chemical changes supplied the current. For myself I am at present of the opinion which De la Rive holds, and do not think that, in the voltaic pile, mere contact does anything in the excitation of the current, except as it is preparatory to, and ends in, complete chemical action (1741, 1745).

1802. Thus the views of contact vary, and it may be said that they pass gradually from one to another, even to the extent of including chemical action: but the two extremes appear to me irreconcilable in principle under any shape; they are as follows. The contact theory assumes that when two different bodies being conductors of electricity are in contact, there is a force at the point of contact by which one of the bodies gives a part of its natural portion of electricity to the other body, which the latter takes in addition to its own natural portion; that, though the touching points have thus respectively given and taken electricity, they cannot retain the charge which their contact has caused, but discharge their electricities to the masses respectively behind them (2067): that the force which, at the point of contact, induces the particles to assume a new state, cannot enable them to keep that state (2069): that all this happens without any permanent alteration of the parts that are in contact, and has no reference to their chemical forces (2065, 2069).

1803. The chemical theory assumes, that at the place of action, the particles which are in contact act chemically upon each other and are able, under the circumstances, to throw more or less of the acting force into a dynamic form (947, 996, 1120): that in the most favourable circumstances, the whole is converted into dynamic force (1000): that then the amount of current force produced is an exact equivalent of the original chemical force employed; and that in no case (in the voltaic pile) can any electric current be produced, without the active exertion and consumption of an equal amount

of chemical force, ending in a given amount of chemical change.

1804. Marianini's paper[2] was to me a great motive for re-examining the subject; but the course I have taken was not so much for the purpose of answering particular objections, as for the procuring evidence, whether relating to controverted points or not, which should be satisfactory to my own mind, open to receive either one theory or the other. This paper, therefore, is not controversial, but contains further facts and proofs of the truth of De la Rive's views. The cases Marianini puts are of extreme interest, and all his objections must, one day be answered, when numerical results, both as to intensity and quantity of force, are obtained; but they are all debateable, and, to my mind, depend upon variations of quantity which do not affect seriously the general question. Thus, when that philosopher quotes the numerical results obtained by considering two metals with fluids at their opposite extremities which tend to form counter currents, the difference which he puts down to the effect of metallic contact, either made or interrupted, I think accountable for, on the facts partly known respecting opposed currents; and with me differences quite as great, and greater, have arisen, and are given in former papers (1046), when metallic contacts were in the circuit. So at page 213 of his memoir, I cannot admit that *e* should give an effect equal to the difference of *b* and *d*; for in *b* and *d* the opposition presented to the excited currents is merely that of a bad conductor, but in the case of *e* the opposition arises from the power of an opposed acting source of a current.

1805. As to the part of his memoir respecting the action of sulphuretted solutions,[3] I hope to be allowed to refer to the investigations made further on. I do not find, as the Italian philosopher, that iron with gold or platina, in solution of the sulphuret of potassa, is positive to them,[4] but, on the contrary, powerfully negative, and for reasons given in the sequel (2049).

1806. With respect to the discussion of the cause of the spark before contact,[5] Marianini admits the spark, but I give it up altogether. Jacobi's paper[6] convinces me I was in error as to *that proof* of the existence of a state of tension

[1] *Philosophical Magazine*, 1838, XII, 227, 311, 314; also *Bibliothèque Universelle*, 1838, XIV, 155, 395.

[2] *Memorie della Società Italiana in Modena*, 1827, XXI, p. 205.
[3] *Ibid.*, 1827, XXI, p. 217.
[4] *Ibid.*, p. 217.
[5] *Ibid.*, p. 225.
[6] *Philosophical Magazine*, 1838, XIII, 401.

PLATE XII

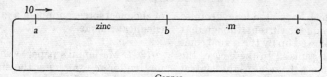

Fig. 1

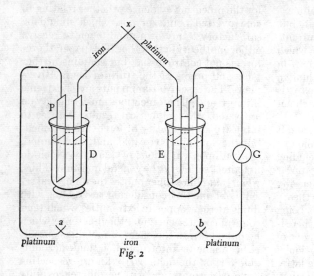

Fig. 2

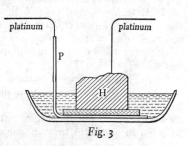

Fig. 3

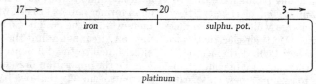

Fig. 4

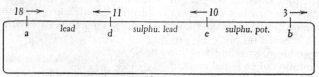

Fig. 5

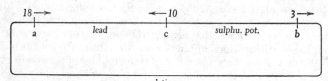

Fig. 6

in the metals before contact (915, 956). I need not therefore do more at present than withdraw my own observations.

1807. I now proceed to address myself to the general argument, rather than to particular controversy, or to the discussion of cases feeble in power and doubtful in nature; for I have been impressed from the first with the feeling that it is no weak influence or feeble phenomenon that we have to account for, but such as indicates a force of extreme power, requiring, therefore, that the cause assigned should bear some proportion, both in intensity and quantity, to the effects produced.

1808. The investigations have all been made by aid of currents and the galvanometer, for it seemed that such an instrument and such a course were best suited to an examination of the electricity of the voltaic pile. The electrometer is no doubt a most important instrument, but the philosophers who do use it are not of accord in respect to the safety and delicacy of its results. And even if the few indications as yet given by the electrometer be accepted as correct, they are far too general to settle the question of, whether contact or chemical action is the exciting force in the voltaic battery. To apply that instrument closely and render it of any force in supplying affirmative arguments to either theory, it would be necessary to construct a table of contacts, or the effects of contacts, of the different metals and fluids concerned in the construction of the voltaic pile, taken in pairs (1868), expressing in such table both the *direction* and the *amount* of the contact force.

1809. It is assumed by the supporters of the contact theory, that though the metals exert strong electromotive forces at their points of contact with each other, yet these are so balanced in a metallic circuit that no current is ever produced whatever their arrangement may be. So in Pl. XII, *Fig. 1*, if the contact force of copper and zinc is 10 $\longrightarrow$, and a third metal be introduced at *m*, the effect of its contacts, whatever that metal may be, with the zinc and copper at *b* and *c*, will be an amount of force in the opposite direction = 10. Thus, if it were potassium, its contact force at *b* might be 5 $\longrightarrow$, but then its contact force at *c* would be $\longleftarrow$ 15: or if it were gold, its contact force at *b* might be $\longleftarrow$ 19, but then its contact force at *c* would be 9 $\longrightarrow$. This is a very large assumption, and that the theory may agree with the facts is necessary: still it is, I believe, only an assumption, for I am not aware

of any data, independent of the theory in question, which prove its truth.

1810. On the other hand, it is assumed that fluid conductors, and such bodies as contain water, or, in a word, those which I have called electrolytes (664, 823, 921), either exert no contact force at their place of contact with the metals, or if they do exert such a power, then it is with this most important difference, that the forces are not subject to the same law of compensation or neutralization in the complete circuit, as holds with the metals (1809). But this, I think I am justified in saying, is an assumption also, for it is supported not by any independent measurement or facts (1808), but only by the theory which it is itself intended to support.

1811. Guided by this opinion, and with a view to ascertain what is, in an active circle, effected by contact and what by chemical action, I endeavoured to find some bodies in this latter class (1810) which should be without chemical action on the metals employed, so as to exclude that cause of a current, and yet such good conductors of electricity as to show any currents due to the contact of these metals with each other or with the fluid: concluding that any electrolyte which would conduct the thermo current of a single pair of bismuth and antimony plates would serve the required purpose, I sought for such, and fortunately soon found them.

¶ i. *Exciting Electrolytes, &c., Being Conductors of Thermo and Feeble Currents*

1812. *Sulphuret of potassium.* This substance and its solution were prepared as follows. Equal weights of caustic potash (*potassa fusa*) and sulphur were mixed with and heated gradually in a Florence flask, till the whole had fused and united, and the sulphur in excess began to sublime. It was then cooled and dissolved in water, so as to form a strong solution, which by standing became quite clear.

1813. A portion of this solution was included in a circuit containing a galvanometer and a pair of antimony and bismuth plates; the connection with the electrolyte was made by two platinum plates, each about two inches long and half an inch wide: nearly the whole of each was immersed, and they were about half an inch apart. When the circuit was completed, and all at the same temperature, there was no current; but the moment the junction of the antimony and bismuth was either heated or cooled, the corresponding thermo current was produced, causing the galvanometer-needle to be permanently deflected, occasionally as much as 80°. Even the small difference of temperature occasioned by touching the Seebeck element with the finger, produced a very sensible current through the electrolyte. When in place of the antimony-bismuth combination mere wires of *copper and platinum*, or *iron and platinum* were used, the application of the spirit-lamp to the junction of these metals produced a thermo current which instantly travelled round the circuit.

1814. Thus this electrolyte will, as to high conducting power, fully answer the condition required (1811). It is so excellent in this respect, that I was able to send the thermo current of a single Seebeck's element across five successive portions connected with each other by platinum plates.

1815. *Nitrous acid*. Yellow anhydrous nitrous acid, made by distilling dry nitrate of lead, being put into a glass tube and included in a circuit with the antimony-bismuth arrangement and the galvanometer, gave no indication of the passage of the thermo current, though the immersed electrodes consisted each of about four inches in length of moderately thick platinum wire, and were not above a quarter of an inch apart.

1816. A portion of this acid was mixed with nearly its volume of pure water; the resulting action caused depression of temperature, the evolution of some nitrous gas, the formation of some nitric acid, and a dark green fluid was produced. This was now such an excellent conductor of electricity, that almost the feeblest current could pass it. That produced by Seebeck's circle was sensible when only one-eighth of an inch in length of the platinum wires dipped in the acid. When a couple of inches of each electrode was in the fluid, the conduction was so good, that it made very little difference at the galvanometer whether the platinum wires touched each other in the fluid, or were a quarter of an inch apart.[1]

1817. *Nitric acid*. Some pure nitric acid was boiled to drive off all the nitrous acid, and then cooled. Being included in the circuit by platinum plates (1813), it was found to conduct so badly that the effect of the antimony-bismuth pair, when the difference of temperature was at the greatest, was scarcely perceptible at the galvanometer.

1818. On using a pale yellow acid, otherwise pure, it was found to possess rather more conducting power than the former. On employing a red nitric acid, it was found to conduct the thermo current very well. On adding some of the green nitrous acid (1816) to the colourless nitric acid, the mixture acquired high conducting powers. Hence it is evident that nitric acid is not a good conductor when pure, but that the presence of nitrous acid in it (conjointly probably with water), gives it this power in a very high degree amongst electrolytes.[2] A very red strong nitric acid, and a weak green acid (consisting of one vol. strong nitric acid and two vols. of water, which had been rendered green by the action of the negative platinum electrode of a voltaic battery), were both such excellent conductors that the thermo current could pass across five separate portions of them connected by platinum plates, with so little retardation that I believe twenty interruptions would not have stopped this feeble current.

1819. *Sulphuric acid*. Strong oil of vitriol, when between platinum electrodes (1813), conducted the antimony-bismuth thermo current sensibly, but feebly. A mixture of two volumes acid and one volume water conducted much better, but not nearly so well as the two former electrolytes (1814, 1816). A mixture of one volume of oil of vitriol and two volumes saturated solution of sulphate of copper conducted this feeble current very fairly.

Potassa. A strong solution of caustic potassa, between platinum plates, conducted the thermo current sensibly, but very feebly.

1820. I will take the liberty of describing here, as the most convenient place, other results relating to the conducting power of bodies, which will be required hereafter in these investigations. Galena, yellow sulphuret of iron, arsenical pyrites, native sulphuret of copper and iron, native gray artificial sulphuret of copper, sulphurets of bismuth, iron, and copper, globules of oxide of burnt iron, oxide of iron by heat or scale oxide, conducted the thermo current very well. Native peroxide of manganese and peroxide of lead conducted it moderately well.

1821. The following are bodies, in some respect analogous in nature and composition, which did not sensibly conduct this weak current when the contact surfaces were small:—

---

[1] De la Rive has pointed out the facility with which an electric current passes between platinum and nitrous acid. *Annales de Chimie*, 1828, XXXVII, 278.

[2] Schœnbein's experiments on a compound of nitric and nitrous acids will probably bear upon and illustrate this subject. *Bibliothèque Universelle*, 1817, X, 406.

artificial gray sulphuret of tin, blende, cinnabar, hæmatite, Elba iron-ore, native magnetic oxide of iron, native peroxide of tin or tinstone, wolfram, fused and cooled protoxide of copper, peroxide of mercury.

1822. Some of the foregoing substances are very remarkable in their conducting power. This is the case with the solution of sulphuret of potassium (1813) and the nitrous acid (1816), for the great amount of this power. The peroxide of manganese and lead are still more remarkable for possessing this power, because the *protoxides* of these metals do not conduct either the feeble thermo current or a far more powerful one from a voltaic battery. This circumstance made me especially anxious to verify the point with the peroxide of lead. I therefore prepared some from red-lead by the action of successive portions of nitric acid, then boiled the brown oxide, so obtained, in several portions of distilled water, for days together, until every trace of nitric acid and nitrate of lead had been removed; after which it was well and perfectly dried. Still, when a heap of it in powder, and consequently in very imperfect contact throughout its own mass, was pressed between two plates of platinum and so brought into the thermo-electric circuit (1813), the current was found to pass readily.

¶ ii. *Inactive Conducting Circles Containing a Fluid or Electrolyte*

1823. De la Rive has already quoted the case of potash, iron and platina,[1] to show that where there was no chemical action there was no current. My object is to increase the number of such cases; to use other fluids than potash, and such as have good conducting power for weak currents; to use also strong and weak solutions; and thus to accumulate the conjoint experimental and argumentative evidence by which the great question must finally be decided.

1824. I first used the sulphuret of potassium as an electrolyte of good conducting power, but chemically inactive (1811) when associated with iron and platinum in a circuit. The arrangement is given in Pl. XII, *Fig. 2*, where D, E represent two test-glasses containing the strong solution of sulphuret of potassium (1812); and also four metallic plates, about 0.5 of an inch wide and two inches long in the immersed part, of which the three marked P, P, P were platinum, and that marked I, of clean iron: these were connected by iron and platinum wires, as in *Fig. 2*, a galvanometer being introduced at G. In this arrangement there were three metallic contacts of platinum and iron, *a b* and *x*: the first two, being opposed to each other, may be considered as neutralizing each other's forces; but the third, being unopposed by any other metallic contact, can be compared with either the difference of *a* and *b* when one is warmer than the other, or with itself when in a heated or cooled state (1830), or with the force of chemical action when any body capable of such action is introduced there (1831).

1825. When this arrangement is completed and in order, there is absolutely no current circulating through it, and the galvanometer-needle rests at 0°; yet is the whole circuit open to a very feeble current, for a difference of temperature at any one of the junctions *a, b*, or *x*, causes a corresponding thermo current, which is instantly detected by the galvanometer, the needle standing permanently at 30° or 40°, or even 50°.

1826. But to obtain this proper and normal state, it is necessary that certain precautions be attended to. In the first place, if the circuit be complete in every part except for the immersion of the iron and platinum plates into the cup D, then, upon their introduction, a current will be produced directed from the platinum (which appears to be positive) through the solution to the iron; this will continue perhaps five or ten minutes, or if the iron has been carelessly cleaned, for several hours; it is due to an action of the sulphuretted solution on *oxide of iron*, and not to any effect on the metallic iron; and when it has ceased, the disturbing cause may be considered as exhausted. The experimental proofs of the truth of this explanation, I will quote hereafter (2049).

1827. Another precaution relates to the effect of accidental movements of the plates in the solution. If two platinum plates be put into a solution of this sulphuret of potassium, and the circuit be then completed, including a galvanometer, the arrangement, if perfect, will show no current; but if one of the plates be lifted up into the air for a few seconds and then replaced, it will be negative to the other, and produce a current lasting for a short time.[2] If the two plates be iron and platinum, or of any other metal or substance not acted on by the sulphuret, the same effect will be produced. In these cases, the current is due to the change

---

[1] *Philosophical Magazine*, 1837, XI, 275.

[2] Marianini observed effects of this kind produced by exposure to the air, of one of two plates dipped in nitric acid. *Annales de Chimie*, 1830, XLV, p. 42.

wrought by the air on the film of sulphuretted solution adhering to the removed plate;[1] but a far less cause than this will produce a current, for if one of the platinum plates be removed, washed well, dried, and even heated, it will, on its re-introduction, almost certainly exhibit the negative state for a second or two.

1828. These or other disturbing causes appear the greater in these experiments in consequence of the excellent conducting power of the solution used; but they do not occur if care be taken to avoid any disturbance of the plates or the solution, and then as before said, the whole acquires a normal and perfectly inactive state.

1829. Here then is an arrangement in which the contact of platinum and iron at x is at liberty to produce any effect which such a contact may have the power of producing; and yet what is the consequence? absolutely nothing. This is not because the electrolyte is so bad a conductor that a current of contact cannot pass, for currents far feebler than this is assumed to be, pass readily (1813); and the electrolyte employed is vastly superior in conducting power to those which are commonly used in voltaic batteries or circles, in which the current is still assumed to be dependent upon contact. The simple conclusion to which the experiment should lead is, in my opinion, that the contact of iron and platinum is absolutely without any electromotive force (1835, 1859, 1889).

1830. If the contact be made really active and effective, according to the beautiful discovery of Seebeck, by making its temperature different to that of the other parts of the circuit, then its power of generating a current is shown (1824). This enables us to compare the supposed power of the mere contact with that of a thermo contact; and we find that the latter comes out as infinitely greater than the former, for the former is nothing. The same comparison of mere contact and thermo contact may be made by contrasting the effect of the contact c at common temperatures, with either the contact at a or at b, either heated or cooled. Very moderate changes of temperature at these places produce instantly the corresponding current, but the mere contact at x does nothing.

1831. So also I believe that a true and philosophic and even rigid comparison may be

[1] Becquerel long since referred to the effect of such exposure of a plate, dipped in certain solutions, to the air. Generally the plate so exposed became positive on re-immersion. *Annales de Chimie*, 1824, XXV, 405.

made at x, between the assumed effect of mere contact and that of chemical action. For if the metals at x be separated, and a piece of paper moistened in dilute acid, or a solution of salt, or if only the tongue or a wet finger be applied there, then a current is caused, stronger by far than the thermo currents before produced (1830), passing from the iron through the introduced acid or other active fluid to the platinum. This is a case of current from chemical action without any metallic contact in the circuit on which the effect can for a moment be supposed to depend (879); it is even a case where metallic contact is changed for chemical action, with the result, that where contact is found to be quite ineffectual, chemical action is very energetic in producing a current.

1832. It is of course quite unnecessary to say that the same experimental comparisons may be made at either of the other contacts, a or b.

1833. Admitting for the moment that the arrangement proves that the contact of platinum and iron at x has no electromotive force (1835, 1859), then it follows also that the contact of either platinum or iron with any other metal has no such force. For if another metal, as zinc, be interposed between the iron and platinum at x (Pl. XII, *Fig. 2*), no current is produced; and yet the test application of a little heat at a or b, will show by the corresponding current, that the circuit being complete will conduct any current that may tend to pass. Now that the contacts of zinc with iron and with platinum are of equal electromotive force, is not for a moment admitted by those who support the theory of contact activity; we ought therefore to have a resulting action equal to the differences of the two forces, producing a certain current. No such current is produced, and I conceive, with the admission above, that such a result proves that the contacts *iron-zinc* and *platinum-zinc* are entirely without electromotive force.

1834. Gold, silver, potassium, and copper were introduced at x with the like negative effect; and so no doubt might every other metal, even according to the relation admitted amongst the metals by the supporters of the contact theory (1809). The same negative result followed upon the introduction of many other conducting bodies at the same place; as, for instance, those already mentioned as easily conducting the thermo current (1820); and the effect proves, I think, that the contact of any of these with either iron or platinum is utterly ineffective as a source of electromotive force.

1835. The only answer which, as it appears to me, the contact theory can set up in opposition to the foregoing facts and conclusions is, to say that the solution of sulphuret of potassium in the cup D (Pl. XII, *Fig. 2*), acts as a metal would do (1809), and so the effects of all the contacts in the circuit are exactly balanced. I will not stop at this moment to show that the departure with respect to electrolytes, or the fluid bodies in the voltaic pile, *from the law* which is supposed to hold good with the metals and solid conductors, though only an assumption, is still essential to the contact theory of the voltaic pile (1810, 1861);[1] nor to prove that the electrolyte is no otherwise like the metals than in having no contact electromotive force whatever. But believing that this will be very evident shortly, I will go on with the experimental results, and resume these points hereafter (1859, 1889).

1836. The experiment was now repeated with the substitution of a bar of *nickel* for that of iron, (Pl. XII, *Fig. 2*) (1824), all other things remaining the same.[2] The circuit was again found to be a good conductor of a feeble thermo current, but utterly inefficient as a voltaic circuit when all was at the same temperature, and due precautions taken (2051). The introduction of metals at the contact *x* was as ineffective as before (1834); the introduction of chemical action at *x* was as striking in its influence as in the former case (1831); all the results were, in fact, parallel to those already obtained; and if the reasoning then urged was good, it will now follow that the contact of platinum and nickel with each other, or of either with any of the different metals or solid conductors introduced at *x*, is entirely without electromotive force.[3]

[1] See Fechner's words. *Philosophical Magazine*, 1838, XIII, 377.

[2] There is another form of this experiment which I sometimes adopted, in which the cup E (Pl. XII, *Fig. 2*), with its contents, was dismissed, and the platinum plates in it connected together. The arrangement may then be considered as presenting three contacts of iron and platinum, two acting in one direction, and one in the other. The arrangement and the results are virtually the same as those already given. A still simpler but equally conclusive arrangement for many of the arguments, is to dismiss the iron between *a* and *b* altogether, and so have but one contact, that at *x*, to consider.

[3] One specimen of nickel was, on its immersion, positive to platinum for seven or eight minutes, and then became neutral. On taking it out it seemed to have a yellowish tint on it, as if invested by a coat of sulphuret; and I suspected this piece had acted like lead (1885) and bismuth (1895). It is difficult to get pure and also perfectly compact nickel; and if porous, then the matter retained in the pores produces currents.

1837. Many other pairs of metals were compared together in the same manner; the solution of sulphuret of potassium connecting them together at one place, and their mutual contact doing that office at another. The following are cases of this kind: iron and gold; iron and palladium; nickel and gold; nickel and palladium; platina and gold; platina and palladium. In all these cases the results were the same as those already given with the combinations of platinum and iron.

1838. It is necessary that due precaution be taken to have the arrangements in an unexceptionable state. It often happened that the first immersion of the plates gave deflections; it is, in fact, almost impossible to put two plates of the *same metal* into the solution without causing a deflection; but this generally goes off very quickly, and then the arrangement may be used for the investigation (1826). Sometimes there is a feeble but rather permanent deflection of the needle; thus when platinum and palladium were the metals, the first effect fell and left a current able to deflect the galvanometer-needle 3°, indicating the platinum to be positive to the palladium. This effect of 3°, however, is almost nothing compared to what a mere thermo current can cause, the latter producing a deflection of 60° or more; besides which, even supposing it an essential effect of the arrangement, it is in the wrong direction for the contact theory. I rather incline to refer it to that power which platinum and other substances have of effecting combination and decomposition without themselves entering into union; and I have occasionally found that when a platinum plate has been left for some hours in a strong solution of sulphuret of potassium (1812) a small quantity of sulphur has been deposited upon it. Whatever the cause of the final feeble current may be, the effect is too small to be of any service in support of the contact theory; while, on the other hand, it affords delicate, and, therefore, strong indications in favour of the chemical theory.

1839. A change was made in the form and arrangement of the cup D (Pl. XII, *Fig. 2*), so as to allow of experiments with other bodies than the metals. The solution of sulphuret of potassium was placed in a shallow vessel, the platinum plate was bent so that the immersed extremity corresponded to the bottom of the vessel; on this a piece of loosely folded cloth was laid in the solution, and on that again the mineral or other substance to be compared with the platinum; the fluid being of such depth that only part of that substance was in it, the rest being clean and dry; on this portion the platinum wire, which completed the circuit, rested. The arrangement of this part of the circuit is given in section at Pl. XII, *Fig. 3*, where H represents a piece of galena to be compared with the platinum P.

1840. In this way galena, compact yellow copper pyrites, yellow iron pyrites, and globules of oxide of burnt iron, were compared with platinum (the solution of sulphuret of potassium being the electrolyte used in the circuit), and with the same results as were before obtained with metals (1829, 1833).

1841. Experiments hereafter to be described gave arrangements in which, with the same electrolyte, sulphuret of lead was compared with gold, palladium, iron, nickel, and bismuth (1885, 1886); also sulphuret of bismuth with platinum, gold, palladium, iron, nickel, lead, and sulphuret of lead (1894), and always with the same result. Where no chemical action occurred there no current was formed; although the circuit remained an excellent conductor, and the contact existed by which, it is assumed in the contact theory, such a current should be produced.

1842. Instead of the strong solution, a dilute solution of the yellow sulphuret of potassium, consisting of one volume of strong solution (1812) and ten volumes of water, was used. Plates of platinum and iron were arranged in this fluid as before (1824): at first the iron was negative (2049), but in ten minutes it was neutral, and the needle at 0°.[1] Then a weak chemical current excited at x (1831) easily passed: and even a thermo current (1830) was able to show its effects at the needle. Thus a strong or a weak solution of this electrolyte showed the same phenomena. By diluting the solution still further, a fluid could be obtained in which the iron was, after the first effect, permanently but feebly positive. On allowing time, however, it was found that in all such cases black sulphuret formed here and there on the iron. Rusted iron was negative to platinum (2049) in this very weak solution, which by direct chemical action could render metallic iron positive.

1843. In all the preceding experiments the electrolyte used has been the sulphuret of po-

[1] Care was taken in these and the former similar cases to discharge the platinum surface of any reacting force it might acquire from the action of the previous current, by separating it from the other metals, and touching it in the liquid for an instant with another platinum plate.

tassium solution; but I now changed this for another, very different in its nature, namely the *green nitrous acid* (1816), which has already been shown to be an excellent conductor of electricity. Iron and platinum were the metals employed, both being in the form of wires. The vessel in which they were immersed was a tube like that formerly described (1815); in other respects the arrangement was the same in principle as those already used (1824, 1836). The first effect was the production of a current, the iron being positive in the acid to the platina; but this *quickly ceased*, and the galvanometer-needle came to 0°. In this state, however, the circuit could not in all things be compared with the one having the solution of sulphuret of potassium for its electrolyte (1824); for although it could conduct the thermo current of antimony and bismuth in a certain degree, yet that degree was very small compared to the power possessed by the former arrangement, or to that of a circle in which the nitrous acid was between two platinum plates (1816). This remarkable retardation is consequent upon the assumption by the iron of that peculiar state which Schœnbein has so well described and illustrated by his numerous experiments and investigations. But though it must be admitted that the iron in contact with the acid is in a peculiar state (1951, 2001, 2033), yet it is also evident that a circuit consisting of platinum, iron, peculiar iron, and nitrous acid, does not cause a current though it have sufficient conducting power to carry a thermo current.

1844. But if the contact of platinum and iron has an electromotive force, why does it not produce a current? The application of heat (1830), or of a little chemical action (1831) at the place of contact, does produce a current, and in the latter case a strong one. Or if any other of the contacts in the arrangement can produce a current, why is not that shown by some corresponding effect? The only answers are to say that the peculiar iron has the same electromotive properties and relations as platinum, or that the nitrous acid is included under the same law with the metals (1809, 1835); and so the sum of the effects of all the contacts in the circuit is nought, or an exact balance of forces. That the iron is like the platinum in having no electromotive force at its contacts without chemical action, I believe; but that it is unlike it in its electrical relations, is evident from the difference between the two in strong nitric acid, as well as in weak acid; from their difference in the power of transmitting electric currents to either nitric acid or sulphuret of potassium, which is very great; and also by other differences. That the nitrous acid is, as to the power of its contacts, to be separated from other electrolytes and classed with the metals in what is, with them, only an assumption, is a gratuitous mode of explaining the difficulty, which will come into consideration, with the case of sulphuret of potassium, hereafter (1835, 1859, 1889, 2060).

1845. To the electro-chemical philosopher, the case is only another of the many strong instances, showing that where chemical action is absent in the voltaic circuit, there no current can be formed; and that whether solution of sulphuret of potassium or nitrous acid be the electrolyte or connecting fluid used, still the results are the same, and contact is shown to be inefficacious as an active electromotive condition.

1846. I need not say that the introduction of different metals between the iron and platinum at their point of contact produced no difference in the results (1833, 1834) and caused no current; and I have said that heat and chemical action applied there produced their corresponding effects. But these parallels in action and non-action show the identity in nature of this circuit (notwithstanding the production of the surface of peculiar iron on that metal), and that with solution of sulphuret of potassium: so that all the conclusions drawn from it apply here; and if that case ultimately stand firm as a proof against the theory of contact force, this will stand also.

1847. I now used oxide of iron and platinum as the extremes of the solid part of the circuit, and the nitrous acid as the fluid; i.e., I heated the iron wire in the flame of a spirit-lamp, covering it with a coat of oxide in the manner recommended by Schœnbein in his investigations, and then used it instead of the clean iron (1843).

The oxide of iron was at first in the least degree positive, and then immediately neutral. This circuit, then, like the former, gave no current at common temperatures; but it differed much from it in conducting power, being a very excellent conductor of a thermo current, the oxide of iron not offering that obstruction to the passage of the current which the peculiar iron did (1843, 1844). Hence scale oxide of iron and platinum produce no current by contact, the third substance in the proof circuit being nitrous acid; and so the result agrees with that obtained in the former case, where that third substance was solution of sulphuret of potassium.

1848. In using nitrous acid it is necessary that certain precautions be taken, founded on the following effect. If a circuit be made with the green nitrous acid, platinum wires, and a galvanometer, in a few seconds all traces of a current due to first disturbances will disappear; but if one wire be raised into the air and instantly returned to its first position, a current is formed, and that wire is negative, across the electrolyte, to the other. If one wire be dipped only a small distance into the acid, as for instance one fourth of an inch, then the raising that wire not more than one eighth of an inch and instantly restoring it, will produce the same effect as before. The effect is due to the evaporation of the nitrous acid from the exposed wire (1937). I may perhaps return to it hereafter, but wish at present only to give notice of the precaution that is required in consequence, namely, to retain the immersed wires undisturbed during the experiment.

1849. Proceeding on the facts made known by Schœnbein respecting the relation of iron and nitric acid, I used that acid as the fluid in a voltaic circuit formed with iron and platinum. Pure nitric acid is so deficient in conducting power (1817) that it may be supposed capable of stopping any current due to the effect of contact between the platinum and iron; and it is further objectionable in these experiments, because, acting feebly on the iron, it produces a chemically excited current, which may be considered as mingling its effect with that of contact: whereas the object at present is, by excluding such chemical action, to lay bare the influence of contact alone. Still the results with it are consistent with the more perfect ones already described; for in a circuit of iron, platinum, and nitric acid, the joint effects of the chemical action on the iron and the contact of iron and platinum, being to produce a current of a certain constant force indicated by the galvanometer, a little chemical action, brought into play where the iron and platinum were in contact as before (1831), produced a current far stronger than that previously existing. If then, from the weaker current, the part of the effect due to chemical action be abstracted, how little room is there to suppose that any effect is due to the contact of the metals!

1850. But a *red nitric acid* with platinum plates conducts a thermo current well, and will do so even when considerably diluted (1818). When such red acid is used between iron and platinum, the conducting power is such, that one half of the permanent current can be overcome by a counter thermo current of bismuth and antimony. Thus a sort of comparison is established between a thermo current on the one hand, and a current due to the joint effects of chemical action on iron and contact of iron and platinum on the other. Now considering the admitted weakness of a thermo current, it may be judged what the strength of that part of the second current due to contact can, at the utmost, be; and how little it is able to account for the strong currents produced by ordinary voltaic combinations.

1851. If for a clean iron wire, one oxidized in the flame of a spirit-lamp be used, being associated with platinum in pure strong nitric acid, there is a feeble current, the oxide of iron being positive to the platinum, and the facts mainly as with iron. But the further advantage is obtained of comparing the contact of strong and weak acid with this oxidized wire. If one volume of the strong acid and four volumes of water be mixed, this solution may be used, and there is even less deflection than with the strong acid: the iron side is now not sensibly active, except the most delicate means be used to observe the current. Yet in both cases if a chemical action be introduced in place of the contact, the resulting current passes well, and even a thermo current can be made to show itself as more powerful than any due to contact.

1852. In these cases it is safest to put the whole of the oxidized iron under the surface and connect it in the circle by touching it with a platinum wire; for if the oxidized iron be continued through from the acid to the air, it is almost certain to suffer from the joint action of the acid and air at their surface of contact.

1853. I proceeded to use a fluid differing from any of the former: this was solution of *potassa*, which has already been employed by De la Rive (1823) with iron and platina, and which when strong has been found to be a substance conducting so well, that even a thermo current could pass it (1819), and therefore fully sufficient to show a contact current, if any such exists.

1854. Yet when a strong solution of this substance was arranged with silver and platinum (bodies differing sufficiently from each other when connected by nitric or muriatic acid), as in the former cases, a very feeble current was produced, and the galvanometer-needle stood nearly at zero. The contact of these metals therefore did not appear to produce a sensible current; and, as I fully believe, because no elec-

tromotive power exists in such contact. When that contact was exchanged for a very feeble chemical action, namely, that produced by interposing a little piece of paper moistened in dilute nitric acid (1831), a current was the result. So here, as in the many former cases, the arrangement with a little chemical action and no metallic contact produces a current, but that without the chemical action and with the metallic contact produces none.

1855. Iron or nickel associated with platinum in this strong solution of potassa was positive. The force of the produced current soon fell, and after an hour or so was very small. Then annulling the metallic contact at *x* (Pl. XII, *Fig. 2*), and substituting a feeble chemical action there, as of dilute nitric acid, the current established by the latter would pass and show itself. Thus the cases are parallel to those before mentioned (1849, &c.), and show how little contact alone could do, since the effect of the conjoint contact of iron and platinum and chemical action of potash and iron were very small as compared with the contrasted chemical action of the dilute nitric acid.

1856. Instead of a strong solution of potassa, a much weaker one consisting of one volume of strong solution and six volumes of water was used, but the results with the silver and platinum were the same: no current was produced by the metallic contact as long as that only was left for exciting cause, but on substituting a little chemical action in its place (1831), the current was immediately produced.

1857. Iron and nickel with platinum in the weak solution also produced similar results, except that the positive state of these metals was rather more permanent than with the strong solution. Still it was so small as to be out of all proportion to what was to be expected according to the contact theory.

1858. Thus these different contacts of metals and other well-conducting solid bodies prove utterly inefficient in producing a current, as well when solution of potassa is the third or fluid body in the circuit, as when that third body is either solution of sulphuret of potassium, or hydrated nitrous acid, or nitric acid, or mixed nitric and nitrous acids. Further, all the arguments respecting the inefficacy of the contacts of bodies interposed at the junction of the two principal solid substances, which were advanced in the case of the sulphuret of potassium solution (1833), apply here with potassa; as they do indeed in every case of a conducting circuit where the interposed fluid is without chemical action and no current is produced. If a case could be brought forward in which the interposed fluid is without action, is yet a sufficiently good conductor, and a current *is* produced; then, indeed, the theory of contact would find evidence in its favour, which, as far as I can perceive, could not be overcome. I have most anxiously sought for such a case, but cannot find one (1798).

1859. The argument is now in a fit state for the resumption of that important point before adverted to (1835, 1844), which, if truly advanced by an advocate for the contact theory, would utterly annihilate the force of the previous experimental results, though it would not enable that theory to give a reason for the activity of, and the existence of a current in, the pile; but which, if in error, would leave the contact theory utterly defenceless and without foundation.

1860. A supporter of the contact theory may say that the various conducting electrolytes used in the previous experiments are like the metals; i.e., that they have an electromotive force at their points of contact with the metals and other solid conductors employed to complete the circuit; but that this is of such consistent strength at each place of contact, that, in a complete circle, the sum of the forces is 0 (1809). The actions at the contacts are tense electromotive actions, but balanced, and so no current is produced. But what experiment is there to support this statement? where are the measured electromotive results proving it (1808)? I believe there are none.

1861. The contact theory, after assuming that mere contacts of dissimilar substances have electromotive powers, further assumes a difference between metals and liquid conductors (1810) without which it is impossible that the theory can explain the current in the voltaic pile: for whilst the contact effects in a metallic circuit are assumed to be always perfectly balanced, it is also assumed that the contact effects of the electrolytes or interposed fluid with the metals are not balanced, but are so far removed from anything like an equilibrium, as to produce most powerful currents, even the strongest that a voltaic pile can produce. If so, then why should the solution of sulphuret of potassium be an exception? it is quite unlike the metals: it does not appear to conduct without decomposition; it is an excellent electrolyte, and an excellent *exciting* electrolyte in proper cases (1880), producing most powerful currents when

it acts chemically; it is in all these points quite unlike the metals, and, in its action, like any of the acid or saline exciting electrolytes commonly used. How then can it be allowed that, without a single direct experiment, and solely for the purpose of avoiding the force of those which are placed in opposition, we should suppose it to leave its own station amongst the electrolytes, and class with the metals; and that too, in a point of character, which, even with them, is as yet a mere assumption (1809)?

1862. But it is not with the sulphuret of potassium alone that this freedom must be allowed; it must be extended to the nitrous acid (1843, 1847), to the nitric acid (1849, &c.), and even to the solution of potash (1854); all these being of the class of electrolytes, and yet exhibiting no current in circuits where they do not occasion chemical action. Further, this exception must be made for *weak solutions* of sulphuret of potassium (1842) and of potassa (1856), for they exhibit the same phenomena as the stronger solutions. And if the contact theorists claim it for these weak solutions, then how will they meet the case of weak nitric acid which is not similar in its action on iron to strong nitric acid (1977), but can produce a powerful current?

1863. The chemical philosopher is embarrassed by none of these difficulties; for he first, by a simple direct experiment, ascertains whether any of the two given substances in the circuit are active chemically on each other. If they are, he expects and finds the corresponding current; if they are not, he expects and he finds no current, though the circuit be a good conductor and he look carefully for it (1829).

1864. Again; taking the case of iron, platina, and solution of sulphuret of potassium, there is no current; but for iron substitute zinc, and there is a powerful current. I might for zinc substitute copper, silver, tin, cadmium, bismuth, lead, and other metals; but I take zinc, because its sulphuret dissolves and is carried off by the solution, and so leaves the case in a very simple state; the fact, however, is as strong with any of the other metals. Now if the contact theory be true, and if the iron, platina, and solution of sulphuret of potassium give contacts which are in perfect equilibrium as to their electromotive force, then why does changing the iron for zinc destroy the equilibrium? Changing one metal for another in a metallic circuit causes no alteration of this kind: nor does changing one substance for another among the great number of bodies which, as solid conductors, may be used to form conducting (but chemically inactive) circuits (1867, &c.). If the solution of sulphuret of potassium is to be classed with the metals as to its action in the experiments I have quoted (1825, &c.), then, how comes it to act quite unlike them, and with a power equal to the *best* of the other class, in the new cases of zinc, copper, silver, &c. (1882, 1885, &c.)?

1865. This difficulty, as I conceive, must be met, on the part of the contact theorists, by a new assumption, namely, that this fluid sometimes acts as the best of the metals, or first class of conductors, and sometimes as the best of the electrolytes or second class. But surely this would be far too loose a method of philosophizing in an experimental science (1889); and further, it is most unfortunate for such an assumption, that this second condition or relation of it never comes on by itself, so as to give us a pure case of a current from contact alone; it never comes on *without* that chemical action to which the chemist so simply refers all the current which is then produced.

1866. It is unnecessary for me to say that the same argument applies with equal force to the cases where nitrous acid, nitric acid, and solution of potash are used; and it is supported with equal strength by the results which they have given (1843, 1849, 1853).

1867. It may be thought that it was quite unnecessary, but in my desire to establish contact electromotive force, to do which I was at one time very anxious, I made many circuits of three substances, including a galvanometer, all being conductors, with the hope of finding an arrangement, which, without chemical action, should produce a current. The number and variety of these experiments may be understood from the following summary; in which metals, plumbago, sulphurets and oxides, all being conductors even of a thermo current, were thus combined in various ways:

1. Platinum
2. Iron
3. Zinc
4. Copper
5. Plumbago
6. Scale oxide of iron
7. Native peroxide of manganese
8. Native gray sulphuret of copper
9. Native iron pyrites
10. Native copper pyrites
11. Galena
12. Artificial sulphuret of copper
13. Artificial sulphuret of iron
14. Artificial sulphuret of bismuth

1 and 2 with 5, 6, 7, 8, 9, 10, 11. 12, 13, 14, in turn
1 and 3 with 5, 6, 7, 8, 9, 10, 11, 12, 13, 14
1 and 5 with 6, 7, 8, 9, 10, 11, 12, 13, 14
3 and 6 with 7, 8, 9, 10, 11, 12, 13, 14
4 and 5 with 6, 7, 8, 9, 10, 11, 12, 13, 14
4 and 6 with 7, 8, 9, 10, 11, 12, 13, 14
4 and 7 with 8, 9, 10, 11, 12, 13, 14
4 and 8 with 9, 10, 11, 12, 13, 14
4 and 9 with 10, 11, 12, 13, 14
4 and 10 with 11, 12, 13, 14
4 and 11 with 12, 13, 14
4 and 12 with 13, 14
4 and 13 with 14
1 and 4 with 12

1868. Marianini states from experiment that copper is positive to sulphuret of copper:[1] with the Voltaists, according to the same philosopher, sulphuret of copper is positive to iron (1878), and with them also iron is positive to copper. These three bodies therefore ought to give a most powerful circle: but on the contrary, whatever sulphuret of copper I have used, I have found not the slightest effect from such an arrangement.

1869. As peroxide of lead is a body causing a powerful current in solution of sulphuret of potassium, and indeed in every case of a circuit where it can give up part of its oxygen, I thought it reasonable to expect that its contact with metals would produce a current, if contact ever could. A part of that which had been prepared (1822), was therefore well dried, which is quite essential in these cases, and formed into the following combinations:

Platinum	Zinc	Peroxide of lead
Platinum	Lead	Peroxide of lead
Platinum	Cadmium	Peroxide of lead
Platinum	Iron	Peroxide of lead

Of these varied combinations, not one gave the least signs of a current, provided differences of temperature were excluded; though in every case the circle formed was, as to conducting power, perfect for the purpose, i.e., able to conduct even a very weak thermo current.

1870. In the contact theory it is not therefore the metals alone that must be assumed to have their contact forces so balanced as to produce, in any circle of them, an effect amounting to nothing (1809); but all solid bodies that are able to conduct, whether they be forms of carbon, or oxides, or sulphurets, must be included in the same category. So also must the electrolytes already referred to, namely, the solutions of sulphuret of potassium and potash,

[1] *Memorie della Società Italiana in Modena*, 1827, XXI, 224.

and nitrous and nitric acids, in every case where they do not act chemically. In fact *all conductors* that do not act chemically in the circuit must be assumed, by the contact theory, to be in this condition, until a case of voltaic current without chemical action is produced (1858).

1871. Then, even admitting that the results obtained by Volta and his followers with the electrometer prove that mere contact has an electromotive force and can produce an effect, surely all experience with contact alone goes to show that the electromotive forces in a circuit are always balanced. How else is it likely that the above-named most varied substances should be found to agree in this respect? unless indeed it be, as I believe, that all substances agree in this, of having no such power at all. If so, then where is the source of power which can account by the theory of contact for the current in the voltaic pile? If they are not balanced, then where is the sufficient case of contact alone producing a current? or where are the numerical data which indicate that such a case can be (1808, 1868)? The contact philosophers are bound to produce, not a case where the current is infinitesimally small, for such cannot account for the current of the voltaic pile, and will always come within the debatable ground which De la Rive has so well defended, but a case and data of such distinctness and importance as may be worthy of opposition to the numerous cases produced by the chemical philosopher (1892); for without them the contact theory as applied to the pile appears to me to have *no* support, and, as it asserts contact electromotive force even *with* the balanced condition, to be almost without foundation.

1872. To avoid these and similar conclusions, the contact theory must bend about in the most particular and irregular way. Thus the contact of solution of sulphuret of potassium with iron must be considered as balanced by the joint force of its contact with platinum, and the contact of iron and platinum with each other; but changing the iron for lead, then the contact of the sulphuret with the latter metal is no longer balanced by the other two contacts, it has all of a sudden changed its relation: after a few seconds, when a film of sulphuret has been formed by the chemical action, then the current ceases, though the circuit be a good conductor (1885); and now it must be assumed that the solution has acquired its first relation to the metals and to the sulphuret of lead, and gives an equilibrium condition of the contacts in the circle.

1873. So also with this sulphuretted solution and with potassa, dilution must, by the theory, be admitted as producing *no change* in the character of the contact force; but with nitric acid, it, on the contrary, must be allowed to change the character of the force greatly (1977). So again acids and alkalies (as potassa) in the cases where the currents are produced by them, as with zinc and platinum for instance, must be assumed as giving the preponderance of electromotive force on the same side, though these are bodies which might have been expected to give opposite currents, since they differ so much in their nature.

1874. Every case of a current is obliged to be met, on the part of the contact advocates, by assuming powers at the points of contact, in *the particular case*, of such proportionate strengths as will consist with the results obtained, and the theory is made to bend about (1956, 1992, 2006, 2014, 2063), having no general relation for the acids or alkalies, or other electrolytic solution used. The result therefore comes to this: The theory can predict nothing regarding the results; it is accompanied by no case of a voltaic current produced without chemical action, and in those associated with chemical action, it bends about to suit the real results, these contortions being exactly parallel to the variations which the pure chemical force, by experiment, indicates.

1875. In the midst of all this, how simply does the chemical theory meet, include, combine, and even predict, the numerous experimental results! When there is a current there is also chemical action; when the action ceases, the current stops (1882, 1885, 1894); the action is determined either at the anode or the cathode, according to circumstances (2039, 2041), and the direction of the current is invariably associated with the direction in which the active chemical forces oblige the anions and cations to move in the circle (962, 2052).

1876. Now when in conjunction with these circumstances it is considered that the many arrangements without chemical action (1825, &c.) produce no current; that those with chemical action almost always produce a current; that hundreds occur in which chemical action without contact produces a current (2017, &c.); and that as many with contact but without chemical action (1867) are known and are inactive; how can we resist the conclusion, that the powers of the voltaic battery originate in the exertion of chemical force?

¶ iii. *Active Circles Excited by Solution of Sulphuret of Potassium, &c.*

1877. In 1812 Davy gave an experiment to show, that of two different metals, copper and iron, that having the strongest attraction for oxygen was positive in oxidizing solutions, and that having the strongest attraction for sulphur was positive in sulphuretting solutions.[1] In 1827 De la Rive quoted several such inversions of the states of two metals, produced by using different solutions, and reasoned from them, that the mere contact of the metals could not be the cause of their respective states, but that the chemical action of the liquid produced these states.[2]

1878. In a former paper I quoted Sir Humphry Davy's experiment (943), and gave its result as a proof that the contact of the iron and copper could not originate the current produced; since when a dilute acid was used in place of the sulphuret, the current was reverse in direction, and yet the contact of the metals remained the same. M. Marianini[3] adds that copper will produce the same effect with tin, lead, and even zinc; and also that silver will produce the same results as copper. In the case of copper he accounts for the effect by referring it to the relation of the iron and the new body formed on the copper, the latter being, according to Volta, positive to the former.[4] By his own experiment the same substance was negative to the iron across the same solution.[5]

1879. I desire at present to resume the class of cases where a solution of sulphuret of potassium is the liquid in a voltaic circuit; for I think they give most powerful proof that the current in the voltaic battery cannot be produced by contact, but is due altogether to chemical action.

1880. The solution of sulphuret of potassium (1812) is a most excellent conductor of electricity (1814). When subjected between platinum electrodes to the decomposing power of a small voltaic battery, it readily gave pure sulphur at the anode, and a little gas, which was probably hydrogen, at the cathode. When arranged with platinum surfaces so as to form a Ritter's secondary pile, the passage of a feeble primary current, for a few seconds only, makes this secondary battery effective in causing a counter current; so that, in accordance with the electrolytic conduc-

tion (923, 1343), it probably does not conduct without decomposition, or if at all, its point of electrolytic intensity (966, 983) must be very low. Its exciting action (speaking on the chemical theory) is either the giving an anion (sulphur) to such metallic and other bodies as it can act upon, or, in some cases, as with the peroxides of lead and manganese, and the protoxide of iron (2046), the abstraction of an anion *from* the body in contact with it, the current produced being in the one or the other direction accordingly. Its chemical affinities are such that in many cases its anion goes to that metal, of a pair of metals, which is left untouched when the usual exciting electrolytes are employed; and so a beautiful inversion of the current in relation to the metals is obtained; thus, when copper and nickel are used with it, the anion goes to the copper; but when the same metals are used with the ordinary electrolytic fluids, the anion goes to the nickel. Its excellent conducting power renders the currents it can excite very evident and strong; and it should be remembered that the strength of the resulting currents, as indicated by the galvanometer, depends jointly upon the energy (not the mere quantity) of the exciting action called into play, and the conductive ability of the circuit through which the current has to run. The value of this exciting electrolyte is increased for the present investigation, by the circumstance of its giving, by its action on the metals, resulting compounds, some of which are insoluble, whilst others are soluble; and, of the insoluble results, some are excellent conductors, whilst others have no conducting power at all.

1881. The experiments to be described were made generally in the following manner. Wires of platinum, gold, palladium, iron, lead, tin, and the other malleable metals, about one-twentieth of an inch in diameter and six inches long, were prepared. Two of these being connected with the ends of the galvanometer-wires, were plunged at the same instant into the solution of sulphuret of potassium in a test-glass, and kept there without agitation (1919), the effects at the same time being observed. The wires were in every case carefully cleansed with fresh fine sand-paper and a clean cloth; and were sometimes even burnished by a glass rod, to give them a smooth surface. Precautions were taken to avoid any difference of temperature at the junctions of the different metals with the galvanometer-wires.

1882. *Tin and platinum.* When tin was associated with platinum, gold, or, I may say, any

[1] *Elements of Chemical Philosophy*, p. 148.
[2] *Annales de Chimie*, 1828, XXXVII, 231–237; XXXIX, 299.
[3] *Memorie della Società Italiana in Modena*, 1837, XXI, p. 224.
[4] *Ibid.*, p. 219. [5] *Ibid.*, p. 224.

other metal which is chemically inactive in the solution of the sulphuret, a strong electric current was produced, the tin being positive to the platinum through the solution, or, in other words, the current being from the tin through the solution to the platinum. In a very short time this current fell greatly in power, and in ten minutes the galvanometer-needle was nearly at 0°. On then endeavouring to transmit the antimony-bismuth thermo current (1825) through the circuit, it was found that it could not pass, the circle having lost its conducting power. This was the consequence of the formation on the tin of an insoluble, investing, non-conducting sulphuret of that metal; the non-conducting power of the body formed is not only evident from the present result, but also from a former experiment (1821).

1883. Marianini thinks it is possible that (in the case of copper, at least [1878], and, so I presume, for all similar cases, for surely one law or principle should govern them) the current is due to the contact force of the sulphuret formed. But that application is here entirely excluded; for how can a *non-conducting* body form a current, either by contact or in any other way? No such case has ever been shown, nor is it in the nature of things; so that it cannot be the contact of the sulphuret that here causes the current; and if not in the present, why in any case? for nothing happens here that does not happen in any other instance of a current produced by the same exciting electrolyte.

1884. On the other hand, how beautiful a proof the result gives in confirmation of the chemical theory! Tin can take sulphur from the electrolyte to form a sulphuret; and whilst it is doing so, and in proportion to the degree in which it is doing so, it produces a current; but when the sulphuret which is formed, by investing the metal, shuts off the fluid and prevents further chemical action, then the current ceases also. Nor is it *necessary* that it should be a non-conductor for this purpose, for conducting sulphurets will perform the same office (1885, 1894), and bring about the same result. What, then, can be more clear, than that whilst the sulphuret is *being formed* a current is produced, but that when formed its mere contact can do nothing towards such an effect?

1885. *Lead.* This metal presents a fine result in the solution of sulphuret of potassium. Lead and platinum being the metals used, the lead was at first highly positive, but in a few seconds the current fell, and in two minutes the galvanometer-needle was at 0°. Still the arrangement conducted a feeble thermo current extremely well, the conducting power not having disappeared, as in the case of tin; for the investing sulphuret of lead is a conductor (1820). Nevertheless, though a conductor, it could stop the further chemical action; and that ceasing, the current ceased also.

1886. Lead and gold produced the same effect. Lead and palladium the same. Lead and iron the same, except that the circumstances respecting the tendency of the latter metal under common circumstances to produce a current from the electrolyte to itself, have to be considered and guarded against (1826, 2049). Lead and nickel also the same. In all these cases, when the lead was taken out and washed, it was found beautifully invested with a thin polished pellicle of sulphuret of lead.

1887. With lead, then, we have a *conducting* sulphuret formed, but still there is no sign that its contact can produce a current, any more than in the case of the *non-conducting* sulphuret of tin (1882). There is no new or additional action produced by this *conducting* body; there was no deficiency of action with the former *non-conducting* product; both are alike in their results, being in fact, essentially alike in their relation to that on which the current really depends, namely, an active chemical force. A piece of lead put *alone* into the solution of sulphuret of potassium, has its surface converted into sulphuret of lead, the proof thus being obtained, even when the current cannot be formed, that there is a force (chemical) present and active under such circumstances; and such force can produce a current of chemical force when the circuit form is given to the arrangement. The force at the place of excitement shows itself, both by the formation of sulphuret of lead and the production of a current. In proportion as the formation of the one decreases the production of the other diminishes, though all the bodies produced are conductors, and contact still remains to perform any work or cause any effect to which it is competent.

1888. It may perhaps be said that the current is due to the contact between the solution of sulphuret and the lead (or tin, as the case may be), which occurs at the beginning of the experiment; and that when the action ceases, it is because a new body, the sulphuret of lead, is introduced into the circuit, the various contacts being then balanced in their force. This would be to fall back upon the assumption before resisted (1861, 1865, 1872), namely, that the solution may class with metals and such like bodies, giving balanced effects of contact in relation to *some* of these bodies, as in this case, to the sulphuret of lead produced, but not with *others*, as the lead itself; both the lead and its sulphuret being in the same category as the metals generally (1809, 1870).

1889. The utter improbability of this as a natural effect, and the absence of all experimental proof in support of it, have been already stated (1861, 1871), but one or two additional reasons against it now arise. The state of things may perhaps be made clearer by a diagram or two, in which assumed contact forces may be assigned, in the absence of all experimental expression, without injury to the reasoning. Let *Fig. 4*, Pl. XII, represent the electromotive forces of a circle of platinum, iron, and solution of sulphuret of potassium; or platinum, nickel, and solution of sulphuret; cases in which the forces are, according to the contact theory, balanced (1860). Then *Fig. 5* may represent the circle of platinum, lead, and solution of sulphuret, which does produce a current, and, as I have assumed, with a resulting force of 11 ⟶. This in a few minutes becomes quiescent, i.e., the current ceases, and *Fig. 6* may represent this new case according to the contact theory. Now is it at all likely that by the intervention of sulphuret of lead at the contact *c*, *Fig. 5*, and the production of two contacts *d* and *e*, *Fig. 6*, such an enormous change of the contact force suffering alteration should be made as from 10 to 21? the intervention of the same sulphuret either at *a* or *b* (1834, 1840) being able to do nothing of the kind, for the sum of the force of the two new contacts is in that case exactly equal to the force of the contact which they replace, as is proved by such interposition making no change in the effects of the circle (1867, 1840). If therefore the intervention of this body between *lead* and platinum at *a*, or between solution of *sulphuret of potassium* and platinum at *b* (*Fig. 5*) causes no change, these cases including its contact with both lead and the solution of sulphuret, is it at all probable that its intervention between these two bodies at *c* should make a difference equal to double the amount of force previously existing, or indeed any difference at all?

1890. Such an alteration as this, in the sum assigned as the amount of the forces belonging to the sulphuret of lead by virtue of its two places of contact, is equivalent I think to saying that it partakes of the anomalous character already supposed to belong to certain fluids, namely, of sometimes giving balanced forces in circles of good conductors, and at other times not (1865).

1891. Even the metals themselves must in fact be forced into this constrained condition; for the effect at a point of contact, if there be *any at all*, must be the result of the *joint* and *mutual actions* of the bodies in contact. If therefore in the circuit, *Fig. 5*, the contact forces are not balanced, it must be because of the deficient *joint* action of the lead and solution at *c*.[1] If the metal and fluid were to act in their proper character, and as iron or nickel would do in the place of the lead, then the force there would be ⟵ 21, whereas it is less, or according to the assumed numbers only ⟵ 10. Now as there is no reason why the lead should have any superiority assigned to it over the solution, since the latter can give a balanced condition amongst good conductors in its proper situation as well as the former; how can this be, unless lead possess that strange character of sometimes giving equipoised contacts, and at other times not (1865)?

1892. If that be true of lead, it must be true of all the metals which, with this sulphuretted electrolyte, give circles producing currents; and this would include bismuth, copper, antimony, silver, cadmium, zinc, tin, &c., &c. With other electrolytic fluids iron and nickel would be included, and even gold, platinum, palladium; in fact all the bodies that can be made to yield in any way active voltaic circuits. Then is it possible that this can be true, and yet not a single combination of this extensive class of bodies be producible that can give the current without chemical action (1867), considered not as a result, but as a known and pre-existing force?

1893. I will endeavour to avoid further statement of the arguments, but think myself bound to produce (1799) a small proportion of the enormous body of facts which appear to me to bear evidence all in one direction.

1894. *Bismuth.* This metal, when associated with platinum, gold, or palladium in solution of the sulphuret of potassium, gives active circles, the bismuth being positive. In the course of less than half an hour the current ceases; but the circuit is still an excellent conductor of thermo currents. Bismuth with iron or nickel produces the same final result with the reservation before made (1826). Bismuth and lead give an active circle; at first the bismuth is positive;

---

[1] My numbers are assumed, and if other numbers were taken, the reasoning might be removed to contact *b*, or even to contact *a*, but the end of the argument would in every case be the same.

in a minute or two the current ceases, but the circuit still conducts the thermo current well.

1895. Thus whilst sulphuret of bismuth is in the act of formation the current is produced; when the chemical action ceases the current ceases also; though contact continues and the sulphuret be a good conductor. In the case of bismuth and lead the chemical action occurs at both sides, but is most energetic at the bismuth, and the current is determined accordingly. Even in that instance the cessation of chemical action causes the cessation of the current.

1896. In these experiments with *lead* and *bismuth* I have given their associations with platinum, gold, palladium, iron, and nickel; because, believing in the first place that the results prove all current to depend on chemical action, then, the quiescent state of the resulting or final circles shows that the contacts of these metals in their respective pairs are *without force* (1829): and upon that again follows the passive condition of all those contacts which can be produced by interposing other conducting bodies between them (1833); an argument that need not again be urged.

1897. *Copper.* This substance being associated with platinum, gold, iron, or any metal chemically inactive in the solution of sulphuret, gives an active circle, in which the copper is positive through the electrolyte to the other metal. The action, though it falls, does not come to a close as in the former cases, and for these simple reasons; that the sulphuret formed is not compact but porous, and does not adhere to the copper, but separates from it in scales. Hence results a continued renewal of the chemical action between the metal and electrolyte, and a continuance of the current. If after a while the copper plate be taken out and washed, and dried, even the wiping will remove part of the sulphuret in scales, and the nail separates the rest with facility. Or if a copper plate be left in abundance of the solution of sulphuret, the chemical action *continues*, and the coat of sulphuret of copper becomes thicker and thicker.

1898. If, as Marianini has shown,[1] a copper plate which has been dipped in the solution of sulphuret, be removed before the coat formed is so thick as to break up from the metal beneath, and be washed and dried, and then replaced, in association with platinum or iron, in the solution, it will at first be neutral, or, as is often the case, negative (1827, 1838) to the other metal, a result quite in opposition to the

[1] *Memorie della Società Italiana in Modena*, 1837, XXI. 224.

idea, that the mere presence of the sulphuret on it could have caused the former powerful current and positive state of the copper (1878, 1897). A further proof that it is not the mere *presence*, but the *formation*, of the sulphuret which causes the current, is, that, if the plate be left long enough for the solution to penetrate the investing crust of sulphuret of copper and come into activity on the metal beneath, then the plate becomes active, and a current is produced.

1899. I made some sulphuret of copper, by igniting thick copper wire in a Florence flask or crucible in abundance of vapour of sulphur. The body produced is in an excellent form for these experiments, and a good conductor; but it is not without action on the sulphuretted solution, from which it can take more sulphur, and the consequence is that it is positive to platinum or iron in such a solution. If such sulphuret of copper be left long in the solution, and then be washed and dried, it will generally acquire the final state of sulphuration, either in parts or altogether, and also be inactive, as the sulphuret formed on the copper was before (1898); i.e., when its chemical action is exhausted, it ceases to produce a current.

1900. *Native gray sulphuret of copper* has the same relation to the electrolyte: it takes sulphur from it and is raised to a higher state of combination; and, as it is also a conductor (1820), it produces a current, being itself positive so long as the action continues.

1901. But when the copper is *fully sulphuretted*, then all these actions cease; though the sulphuret be a conductor, the contacts still remain, and the circle can carry with facility a feeble thermo current. This is not only shown by the quiescent cases just mentioned (1898), but also by the utter inactivity of platinum and *compact yellow copper pyrites*, when conjoined by this electrolyte, as shown in a former part of this paper (1840).

1902. *Antimony.* This metal, being put alone into a solution of sulphuret of potassium, is acted on, and a sulphuret of antimony formed which does not adhere strongly to the metal, but wipes off. Accordingly, if a circle be formed of antimony, platinum, and the solution, the antimony is positive in the electrolyte, and a powerful current is formed, which continues. Here then is another beautiful variation of the conditions under which the chemical theory can so easily account for the effects, whilst the theory of contacts cannot. The sulphuret produced in this case is a non-conductor whilst in the solid state (402); it cannot therefore be that any contact of this sulphuret can produce the current; in that respect it is like the sulphuret of tin (1882). But that circumstance does not stop the occurrence of the chemical current; for, as the sulphuret forms a porous instead of a continuous crust, the electrolyte has access to the metal and the action goes on.

1903. *Silver*. This metal, associated with platinum, iron, or other metals inactive in this electrolyte, is strongly positive, and gives a powerful continuous current. Accordingly, if a plate of silver, coated with sulphuret by the simple action of the solution, be examined, it will be found that the crust is brittle and broken, and separates almost spontaneously from the metal. In this respect, therefore, silver and copper are alike, and the action consequently continues in both cases; but they differ in the sulphuret of silver being a non-conductor (434) for these feeble currents, and, in that respect, this metal is analogous to antimony (1902).

1904. *Cadmium*. Cadmium with platinum, gold, iron, &c., gives a powerful current in the solution of sulphuret, and the cadmium is positive. On several occasions this current continued for two or three hours or more; and at such times, the cadmium being taken out, washed and wiped, the sulphuret was found to separate easily in scales on the cloth used.

1905. Sometimes the current would soon cease; and then the circle was found not to conduct the thermo current (1813). In these cases, also, on examining the cadmium, the coat of sulphuret was strongly adherent, and this was more especially the case when prior to the experiment the cadmium, after having been cleaned, was burnished by a glass rod (1881). Hence it appears that the sulphuret of this metal is a non-conductor, and that its contact could not have caused the current (1883) in the manner Marianini supposes. All the results it supplies are in perfect harmony with the chemical theory and adverse to contact theory.

1906. *Zinc*. This metal, with platinum, gold, iron, &c., and the solution of sulphuret, produces a very powerful current, and is positive through the solution to the other metal. The current was permanent. Here another beautiful change in the circumstances of the general experiment occurs. Sulphuret of zinc is a nonconductor of electricity (1821), like the sulphurets of tin, cadmium, and antimony; but then it is soluble in the solution of sulphuret of potassium; a property easily ascertainable by putting a drop of solution of zinc into a portion

of the electrolytic solution, and first stirring them a little, by which abundance of sulphuret of zinc will be formed; and then stirring the whole well together, when it will be redissolved. The consequence of this solubility is, that the zinc when taken out of the solution is perfectly free from investing sulphuret of zinc. Hence, therefore, a very sufficient reason, on the chemical theory, why the action should go on. But how can the theory of contact refer the current to any contact of the metallic sulphuret, when that sulphuret is, in the first place, a non-conductor, and, in the next, is dissolved and carried off into the solution at the moment of its formation?

1907. Thus all the phenomena with this admirable electrolyte (1880), whether they be those which are related to it as an active (1879) or as a passive (1825, &c.) body, confirm the chemical theory, and oppose that of contact. With tin and cadmium it gives an impermeable non-conducting body; with lead and bismuth it gives an impermeable conducting body; with antimony and silver it produces a permeable non-conducting body; with copper a permeable conducting body; and with zinc a soluble nonconducting body. The chemical action and its resulting current are perfectly consistent with all these variations. But try to explain them by the theory of contact, and, as far as I can perceive, that can only be done by twisting the theory about and making it still more tortuous than before (1861, 1865, 1872, 1874, 1889); special assumptions being necessary to account for the effects which, under it, become so many special cases.

1908. *Solution of protosulphuret of potassium, or bihydrosulphuret of potassa*. I used a solution of this kind as the electrolyte in a few cases. The results generally were in accordance with those already given, but I did not think it necessary to pursue them at length. The solution was made by passing sulphuretted hydrogen gas for twenty-four hours through a strong solution of pure caustic potassa.

1909. Iron and platinum with this solution formed a circle in which the iron was first negative, then gradually became neutral, and finally acquired a positive state. The solution first acted as the yellow sulphuret in reducing the investing oxide (2049), and then, apparently, directly on the iron, dissolving the sulphuret formed. Nickel was positive to platinum from the first, and continued so though producing only a weak current. When weak chemical action was substituted for metallic contact at x

(Pl. XII, *Fig. 2*) (1831), a powerful current passed. Copper was highly positive to iron and nickel; as also to platinum, gold, and the other metals which were unacted upon by the solution. Silver was positive to iron, nickel, and even lead; as well as to platinum, gold, &c. Lead is positive to platinum, then the current falls, but does not cease. Bismuth is also positive at first, but after a while the current almost entirely ceases, as with the yellow sulphuret of potassium (1894).

1910. Native gray sulphuret of copper and artificial sulphuret of copper (1899) were positive to platinum and the inactive metals: but yellow copper pyrites, yellow iron pyrites, and galena, were inactive with these metals in this solution; as before they had been with the solution of yellow or bisulphuret of potassium. This solution, as might be expected from its composition, has more of alkaline characters in it than the yellow sulphuret of potassium.

1911. Before concluding this account of results with the sulphuretted solutions, as exciting electrolytes, I will mention the varying and beautiful phenomena which occur when copper and silver, or two pieces of copper, or two pieces of silver, form a circle with the yellow solution. If the metals be copper and silver, the copper is at first positive and the silver remains untarnished; in a short time this action ceases, and the silver becomes positive; at the same instant it begins to combine with sulphur and becomes covered with sulphuret of silver; in the course of a few moments the copper again becomes positive; and thus the action will change from side to side several times, and the current with it, according as the circumstances become in turn more favourable at one side or the other.

1912. But how can it be thought that the current first produced is due in any way to the *contact* of the sulphuret of copper formed, since its presence there becomes at last the reason why that first current diminishes, and enables the silver, which is originally the weaker in exciting force, and has no sulphuret as yet formed on it, to assume for a time the predominance, and produce a current which can overcome that excited at the copper (1911)? What can account for these changes, but chemical action which, as it appears to me, accounts, as far as we have yet gone, with the utmost simplicity, for *all* the effects produced, however varied the mode of action and their circumstances may be?

Royal Institution, December 12, 1839

SEVENTEENTH SERIES

§ 21. *On the Source of Power in the Voltaic Pile (continued)* ¶ iv. *The Exciting Chemical Force Affected by Temperature* ¶ v. *The Exciting Chemical Force Affected by Dilution* ¶ vi. *Differences in the Order of the Metallic Elements of Voltaic Circles* ¶ vii. *Active Voltaic Circles and Batteries without Metallic Contact* ¶ viii. *Considerations of the Sufficiency of Chemical Action* ¶ ix. *Thermo-electric Evidence* ¶ x. *Improbable Nature of the Assumed Contact Force*

RECEIVED JANUARY 30, READ MARCH 19, 1840

¶ iv. *The Exciting Chemical Force Affected by Temperature*

1913. ON the view that chemical force is the origin of the electric current in the voltaic circuit, it is important that we have the power of causing by ordinary chemical means, a variation of that force within certain limits, without involving any alteration of the metallic or even the other contacts in the circuit. Such variations should produce corresponding voltaic effects, and it appeared not improbable that these differences alone might be made effective enough to produce currents without any metallic contact at all.

1914. De la Rive has shown that the increased action of a pair of metals, when put into hot fluid instead of cold, is in a great measure due to the exaltation of the chemical affinity on that metal which was acted upon.[1] My object was to add to the argument by using but one metal and one fluid, so that the fluid might be alike at both contacts, but to exalt the chemical force at one only of the contacts by the ac-

[1] *Annales de Chimie*, 1828, XXXVII, p. 242.

PLATE XIII

Fig. 1

Fig. 2

Fig. 3

Fig. 4

Fig. 5

Fig. 6

Fig. 7

Fig. 8

iron

platinum

Fig. 10

Fig. 11

Fig. 12

tion of heat. If such difference produced a current with circles which either did not generate a thermo current themselves, or could not conduct that of an antimony and bismuth element, it seemed probable that the effect would prove to be a result of pure chemical force, contact doing nothing.

1915. The apparatus used was a glass tube (Pl. XIII, *Fig. 1*) about five inches long and 0.4 of an inch internal diameter, open at both ends, bent, and supported on a retort-stand. In this the liquid was placed, and the portion in the upper part of one limb could then easily be heated and retained so, whilst that in the other limb was cold. In the experiments I will call the left-hand side A, and the right-hand side B, taking care to make no change of these designations. C and D are the wires of metal (1881) to be compared; they were formed into a circuit by means of the galvanometer, and, often also, a Seebeck's thermo-element of antimony and bismuth; both these, of course, caused no disturbing effect so long as the temperature of their various junctions was alike. The wires were carefully prepared (1881), and when two of the same metal were used, they consisted of the successive portions of the same piece of wire.

1916. The precautions which are necessary for the elimination of a correct result are rather numerous, but simple in their nature.

1917. *Effect of first immersion.* It is hardly possible to have the two wires of the same metal, even platinum, so exactly alike that they shall not produce a current in consequence of their difference; hence it is necessary to alternate the wires and repeat the experiment several times, until an undoubted result independent of such disturbing influences is obtained.

1918. *Effect of the investing fluid or substance.* The fluid produced by the action of the liquid upon the metal exerts, as is well known, a most important influence on the production of a current. Thus when two wires of cadmium were used with the apparatus (Pl. XIII, *Fig. 1*) (1915) containing dilute sulphuric acid, hot on one side and cold on the other, the hot cadmium was at first positive, producing a deflection of about 10°; but in a short time this effect disappeared, and a current in the reverse direction equal to 10° or more would appear, the hot cadmium being now negative. This I refer to the quicker exhaustion of the chemical forces of the film of acid on the heated metallic surface (1003, 1036, 1037), and the consequent

final superiority of the colder side at which the action was thus necessarily more powerful (1953, &c.; 1966, 2015, 2031, &c.). Marianini has described many cases of the effects of investing solutions, showing that if two pieces of the same metal (iron, tin, lead, zinc, &c.) be used, the one first immersed is negative to the other, and has given his views of the cause.[1] The precaution against this effect was not to put the metals into the acid until the proper temperature had been given to both parts of it, and then to observe the *first effect* produced, accounting that as the true indication, but repeating the experiment until the result was certain.

1919. *Effect of motion.* This investing fluid (1918) made it necessary to guard against the effect of successive rest and motion of the metal in the fluid. As an illustration, if two tin wires (1881) be put into dilute nitric acid, there will probably be a little motion at the galvanometer, and then the needle will settle at 0°. If either wire be then moved, the other remaining quiet, that in motion will become positive. Again, tin and cadmium in dilute sulphuric acid gave a strong current, the cadmium being positive, and the needle was deflected 80°. When left, the force of the current fell to 35°. If the cadmium were then moved it produced very little alteration; but if the tin were moved it produced a great change, not showing, as before, an increase of its force, but the reverse, for it became more negative, and the current force rose up again to 80°.[2] The precaution adopted to avoid the interference of these actions, was not only to observe the first effect of the introduced wires, but to keep them moving from the moment of the introduction.

1920. The above effect was another reason for heating the acids, &c. (1918), before the wires were immersed; for in the experiment just described, if the cadmium side were heated

---

[1] *Annales de Chimie*, 1830, XLV, p. 40.
[2] Tin has some remarkable actions in this respect. If two tins be immersed in succession into dilute nitric acid, the one last in is positive to the other at the moment: if, both being in, one be moved, that is for the time positive to the other. But if dilute sulphuric acid be employed, the last tin is always negative: if one be taken out, cleaned, and reimmersed, it is negative: if, both being in and neutral, one be moved, it becomes negative to the other. The effects with muriatic acid are the same in kind as those with sulphuric acid, but not so strong. This effect perhaps depends upon the compound of tin first produced in the sulphuric and muriatic acids tending to acquire some other and more advanced state, either in relation to the oxygen, chlorine or acid concerned, and so adding a force to that which at the first moment, when only metallic tin and acid are present, tends to determine a current.

to boiling. the moment the fluid was agitated on the tin side by the boiling on the cadmium side, there was more effect by far produced by the motion than the heat: for the heat at the cadmium alone did little or nothing, but the jumping of the acid over the tin made a difference in the current of 20° or 30°.

1921. *Effect of air.* Two platinum wires were put into cold strong solution of sulphuret of potassium (1812), (Pl. XIII, *Fig. 1*); and the galvanometer was soon at 0°. On heating and boiling the fluid on the side A (1915) the platinum in it became negative; cooling that side, by pouring a little water over it from a jug, and heating the side B, the platinum there in turn became negative; and, though the action was irregular, the same general result occurred however the temperatures of the parts were altered. This was not due to the chemical effect of the electrolyte on the heated platinum. Nor do I believe it was a true thermo current (1933); but if it were the latter, then the heated platinum was *negative* through the electrolyte to the cold platinum. I believe it was altogether the increased effect of the air upon the electrolyte at the heated side; and it is evident that the application of the heat, by causing currents in the fluid and also in the air, facilitates their mutual action at that place. It has been already shown that lifting up a platinum wire in this solution, so as to expose it for a moment to the air (1827), renders it negative when reimmersed, an effect which is in perfect accordance with the assumed action of the heated air and fluid in the present case. The interference of this effect is obviated by raising the temperature of the electrolyte quietly before the wires are immersed (1918), and observing only the first effect.

1922. *Effect of heat.* In certain cases where two different metals are used, there is a very remarkable effect produced on heating the negative metal. This will require too much detail to be described fully here; but I will briefly point it out and illustrate it by an example or two.

1923. When two platinum wires were compared in hot and cold dilute sulphuric acid (1935), they gave scarcely a sensible trace of any electric current. If any real effect of heat occurred, it was that the hot metal was the least degree positive. When silver and silver were compared, hot and cold, there was also no sensible effect. But when platinum and silver were compared in the same acid, different effects occurred. Both being cold, the silver in the A side (Pl. XIII, *Fig. 1*) (1915) was positive

about 4°, by the galvanometer; moving the platina on the other side B did not alter this effect, but on heating the acid and platinum there, the current became very powerful, deflecting the needle 30°, and the silver was positive. Whilst the heat continued, the effect continued; but on cooling the acid and platinum it went down to the first degree. No such effect took place at the silver; for on heating that side, instead of becoming negative, it became more positive, but only to the degree of deflecting the needle 16°. Then, *motion* of the platinum (1919) facilitated the passing of the current and the deflection increased, but *heating* the platinum side did far more.

1924. *Silver and copper* in dilute sulphuric acid produced very little effect; the copper was positive about 1° by the galvanometer; moving the copper or the silver did nothing; heating the copper side caused no change; but on heating the silver side it became negative 20°. On cooling the silver side this effect went down, and then, either moving the silver or copper, or heating the copper side, caused very little change: but heating the silver side made it negative as before.

1925. All this resolves itself into an effect of the following kind; that where two metals are in the relation of positive and negative to each other in such an electrolyte as dilute acids (and perhaps others), heating the negative metal at its contact with the electrolyte enables the current, which tends to form, to pass with such facility, as to give a result sometimes tenfold more powerful than would occur without it. It is not displacement of the investing fluid, for motion will in these cases do nothing: it is not chemical action, for the effect occurs at that electrode where the chemical action is not active: it is not a thermo-electric phenomenon of the ordinary kind, because it depends upon a voltaic relation; i.e., the metal showing the effect must be negative to the other metal in the electrolyte; so silver heated does nothing with silver cold, though it shows a great effect with copper either hot or cold (1924); and platinum hot is as nothing to platinum cold, but much to silver either hot or cold.

1926. Whatever may be the intimate action of heat in these cases, there is no doubt that it is dependent on the current which tends to pass round the circuit. It is essential to remember that the increased effect on the galvanometer is not due to any increase in the electromotive force, but solely to the removal of obstruction to the current by an increase probably of discharge. M. de la Rive has described an effect of heat, on the passage of the electric current, through dilute acid placed in the circuit, by platinum electrodes. Heat applied to the negative electrode increased the deflection of a galvanometer needle in the circuit, from 12° to 30° or 45°; whilst heat applied to the positive electrode caused no change.[1] I have not been able to obtain this nullity of effect at the positive electrode when a voltaic battery was used (1639); but I have no doubt the present phenomena will prove to be virtually the same as those which that philosopher has described.

1927. The effect interferes frequently in the ensuing experiments when *two* metals, hot and cold, are compared with each other; and the more so as the negative metal approximates in inactivity of character to platinum or rhodium. Thus in the comparison of cold copper, with hot silver, gold, or platinum, in dilute nitric acid, this effect tends to make the copper appear more positive than it otherwise would do.

1928. *Place of the wire terminations.* It is requisite that the *end* of the wire on the hot side should be *in* the heated fluid. Two copper wires were put into diluted solution of sulphuret of potassium (Pl. XIII, *Fig. 2*); that portion of the liquid extending from C to D was heated, but the part between D and E remained cold. Whilst both ends of the wires were in the cold fluid, as in the figure, there were irregular movements of the galvanometer, small in degree, leaving the B wire positive. Moving the wires about, but retaining them as in the figure, made no difference; but on raising the wire in A, so that its termination should be in the hot fluid between C and D, then it became positive and continued so. On lowering the end into the cold part, the former state recurred; on raising it into the hot part, the wire again became positive. The same is the case with two silver wires in dilute nitric acid; and though it appears very curious that the current should increase in strength as the extent of bad conductor increases, yet such is often the case under these circumstances. There can be no reason to doubt that the part of the wire which is in the hot fluid at the A side is at all times equally positive or nearly so; but at one time the whole of the current it produces is passing through the entire circuit by the wire in B, and at another, a part, or the whole, of it is circulating to the cold end of its own wire, only by the fluid in tube A.

[1] *Bibliothèque Universelle*, 1837, VII, 388.

1929. *Cleaning the wires.* That this should be carefully done has been already mentioned (1881); but it is especially necessary to attend to the very extremities of the wires, for if these circular spaces, which occur in the most effective part of the circle, be left covered with the body produced on them in a preceding trial, an experimental result will often be very much deranged, or even entirely falsified.

1930. Thus the best mode of experimenting (1915) is to heat the liquid in the limb A or B (Pl. XIII, *Fig. 2*), first; and, having the wires well cleaned and connected, to plunge both in at once, and, retaining the *end* of the heated wire in the hot part of the fluid, to keep both wires in motion, and observe, especially, the first effects: then to take out the wires, reclean them, change them side for side and repeat the experiment, doing this so often as to obtain from the several results a decided and satisfactory conclusion.

1931. It next becomes necessary to ascertain whether any true thermo current can be produced by electrolytes and metals, which can interfere with any electro-chemical effects dependent upon the action of heat. For this purpose different combinations of electrolytes and metals not acted on chemically by them, were tried, with the following results.

1932. Platinum and a very *strong solution of potassa* gave, as the result of many experiments, the hot platinum positive across the electrolyte to the cold platinum, producing a current that could deflect the galvanometer needle about 5°, when the temperatures at the two junctures were 60° and 240°. Gold and the same solution gave a similar result. Silver and a moderately strong solution, of specific gravity 1070, like that used in the ensuing experiments (1948) gave the hot silver positive, but now the deflection was scarcely sensible, and not more than 1°. Iron was tried in the same solution, and there was a constant current and deflection of 50° or more, but there was also chemical action (1948).

1933. I then used *solution of the sulphuret of potassium* (1812). As already said, hot platinum is negative in it to the cold metal (1921); but I do not think the action was thermo-electric. Palladium with a weaker solution gave no indication of a current.

1934. Employing dilute nitric acid, consisting of one volume strong acid and fifty volumes water, platinum gave no certain indication: the hot metal was sometimes in the least degree positive, and at others an equally small degree negative. Gold in the same acid gave a scarcely sensible result; the hot metal was negative. Palladium was as gold.

1935. With dilute sulphuric acid, consisting of one by weight of oil of vitriol and eighty of water, neither platinum nor gold produced any sensible current to my galvanometer by the mere action of heat.

1936. *Muriatic acid* and platinum being conjoined, and heated as before, the hot platinum was very slightly negative in strong acid: in dilute acid there was no sensible current.

1937. *Strong nitric acid* at first seemed to give decided results. Platinum and pure strong nitric acid being heated at one of the junctions, the hot platinum became constantly negative across the electrolyte to the cold metal, the deflection being about 2°. When a yellow acid was used, the deflection was greater; and when a very orange-coloured acid was employed, the galvanometer needle stood at 70°, the hot platinum being still negative. This effect, however, is not a pure thermo current, but a peculiar result due to the presence of nitrous acid (1848). It disappears almost entirely when a dilute acid is used (1934); and what effect does remain indicates that the hot metal is negative to the cold.

1938. Thus the *potash solution* seems to be the fluid giving the most probable indications of a thermo current. Yet there the deflection is only 5°, though the fluid, being very strong, is a good conductor (1819). When the fluid was diluted, and of specific gravity 1070, like that before used (1932), the effect was only 1°, and cannot therefore be confounded with the results I have to quote.

1939. The dilute *sulphuric* (1935) and *nitric* acids used (1934) gave only doubtful indications in some cases of a thermo current. On trial it was found that the thermo current of an antimony-bismuth pair could not pass these solutions, as arranged in these and other experiments (1949, 1950); that, therefore, if the little current obtained in the experiments be of a thermo-electric nature, this combination of platinum and acid is far more powerful than the antimony-bismuth pair of Seebeck; and yet that (with the interposed acid) it is scarcely sensible by this delicate galvanometer. Further, when there is a current, the hot metal is generally negative to the cold, and it is therefore impossible to confound these results with those to be described where the current has a contrary direction.

1940. In strong nitric acid, again, the hot metal is negative.

1941. If, after I show that heat applied to metals in acids or electrolytes which *can act on them* produces considerable currents, it be then said that though the metals which are inactive in the acids produce no thermo currents, those which, like copper, silver, &c., act chemically, may; then, I say, that such would be a mere supposition, and a supposition at variance with what we know of thermo-electricity; for amongst the solid conductors, metallic or non-metallic (1867), there are none, I believe, which are able to produce thermo currents with some of the metals, and not with others. Further, these metals, copper, silver, &c., do not always show effects which can be mistaken or pass for thermo-electric, for silver in hot dilute nitric acid is scarcely different from silver in the same acid cold (1950); and in other cases, again, the hot metals become negative instead of positive (1953).

Cases of One Metal and One Electrolyte; One Junction Being Heated

1942. The cases I have to adduce are far too numerous to be given in detail; I will therefore describe one or two, and sum up the rest as briefly as possible.

1943. *Iron in diluted sulphuret of potassium.* The hot iron is well positive to the cold metal. The negative and cold wire continues quite clean, but from the hot iron a dark sulphuret separates which becoming diffused through the solution discolours it. When the cold iron is taken out, washed and wiped, it leaves the cloth clean; but that which has been heated leaves a black sulphuret upon the cloth when similarly treated.

1944. *Copper and the sulphuretted solution.* The hot copper is well positive to the cold on the first immersion, but the effect quickly falls, from the general causes already referred to (1918).

1945. *Tin and solution of potassa.* The hot tin is strongly and constantly positive to the cold.

1946. *Iron and dilute sulphuric acid* (1935). The hot iron was constantly positive to the cold, 60° or more. *Iron and diluted nitric acid* gave even a still more striking result.

I must now enumerate merely, not that the cases to be mentioned are less decided than those already given, but to economize time.

1947. *Dilute solution of yellow sulphuret of potassium*, consisting of one volume of the strong solution (1812), and eighteen volumes of water. Iron, silver, and copper, with this solution, gave good results. The hot metal was positive to the cold.

1948. *Dilute solution of caustic potassa* (1932). Iron, copper, tin, zinc, and cadmium gave striking results in this electrolyte. The hot metal was always positive to the cold. Lead produced the same effect, but there was a momentary jerk at the galvanometer at the instant of immersion, as if the hot lead was negative at that moment. In the case of iron it was necessary to continue the application of heat, and then the formation of oxide at it could easily be observed; the alkali gradually became turbid, for the protoxide first formed was dissolved, and becoming peroxide by degrees, was deposited, and rendered the liquid dull and yellow.

1949. *Dilute sulphuric acid* (1935). Iron, tin, lead, and zinc, in this electrolyte, showed the power of heat to produce a current by exalting the chemical affinity, for the hot side was in each case positive.

1950. *Dilute nitric acid* is remarkable for presenting only one case of a metal hot and cold exhibiting a striking difference, and that metal is iron. With silver, copper, and zinc, the hot side is at the first moment positive to the cold, but only in the smallest degree.

1951. *Strong nitric acid.* Hot iron is positive to cold. Both in the hot and cold acid the iron is in its peculiar state (1844, 2001).

1952. *Dilute muriatic acid: 1 volume strong muriatic acid, and 29 volumes water.* This acid was as remarkable for the number of cases it supplied as the dilute nitric acid was for the contrary (1950). Iron, copper, tin, lead, zinc, and cadmium gave active circles with it, the hot metal being positive to the cold; all the results were very striking in the strength and permanency of the electric current produced.

1953. Several cases occur in which the hot metal becomes *negative* instead of positive, as above; and the principal cause of such an effect I have already adverted to (1918). Thus with the solution of the *sulphuret of potassium* and zinc, on the first immersion of the wires into the hot and cold solution there was a pause, i.e., the galvanometer needle did not move at once, as in the former cases; afterwards a current gradually came into existence, rising in strength until the needle was deflected 70° or 80°, the hot metal being *negative* through the electrolyte to the cold metal. *Cadmium* in the same solution gave also the first pause and then a current, the hot metal being negative; but the effect was very small. Lead, hot, was

negative, producing also only a feeble current. Tin gave the same result, but the current was scarcely sensible.

1954. *In dilute sulphuric acid.* Copper and zinc, after having produced a first positive effect at the hot metal, had that reversed, and a feeble current was produced, the hot metal being negative. Cadmium gave the same phenomena, but stronger (1918).

1955. *In dilute nitric acid.* Lead produced no effect at the first moment; but afterwards an electric current, gradually increasing in strength, appeared, which was able to deflect the needle 20° or more, the hot metal being negative. Cadmium gave the same results as lead. Tin gave an uncertain result: at first the hot metal appeared to be a very little negative, it then became positive, and then again the current diminished, and went down almost entirely.

1956. I cannot but view in these results of the action of heat, the strongest proofs of the dependence of the electric current in voltaic circuits on the chemical action of the substances constituting these circuits: the results perfectly accord with the known influence of heat on chemical action. On the other hand, I cannot see how the theory of contact can take cognizance of them, except by adding new assumptions to those already composing it (1874). How, for instance, can it explain the powerful effects of iron in sulphuret of potassium, or in potassa, or in dilute nitric acid; or of tin in potassa or sulphuric acid; or of iron, copper, tin, &c., in muriatic acid; or indeed of any of the effects quoted? That they cannot be due to thermo contact has been already shown by the results with inactive metals (1931, 1941); and to those may now be added those of the active metals, silver and copper in dilute nitric acid, for heat produces scarcely a sensible effect in these cases. It seems to me that no other cause than chemical force (a very sufficient one) remains, or is needed to account for them.

1957. If it be said that, on the theory of chemical excitement, the experiments prove either too much or not enough, that, in fact, heat ought to produce the same effect with *all* the metals that are acted on by the electrolytes used, then, I say that that does not follow. The force and other circumstances of chemical affinity vary almost infinitely with the bodies exhibiting its action, and the added effect of heat upon the chemical affinity would, necessarily, partake of these variations. Chemical action often goes on without any current being produced; and it is well known that, in almost every voltaic circuit, the chemical force has to be considered as divided into that which is local and that which is current (1120). Now heat frequently assists the local action much, and, sometimes, without appearing to be accompanied by any great increase in the *intensity* of chemical affinity; whilst at other times we are sure, from the chemical phenomena, that it does affect the intensity of the force. The electric current, however, is not determined by the amount of action which takes place, but by the intensity of the affinities concerned; and so cases may easily be produced, in which that metal exerting the least amount of action is nevertheless the positive metal in a voltaic circuit; as with copper in weak nitric acid associated with other copper in strong acid (1975), or iron or silver in the same weak acid against copper in the strong acid (1996). Many of those instances where the hot side ultimately becomes negative, as of zinc in dilute solution of sulphuret of potassium (1953), or cadmium and lead in dilute nitric acid (1955), are of this nature; and yet the conditions and result are in perfect agreement with the chemical theory of voltaic excitement (1918).

1958. The distinction between currents founded upon that difference of intensity which is due to the difference in force of the chemical action which is their exciting cause, is, I think, a necessary consequence of the chemical theory, and in 1834 I adopted that opinion[1] (891, 908, 916, 988). De la Rive in 1836 gave a still more precise enunciation of such a principle,[2] by saying, that the intensity of currents is exactly proportional to the degree of affinity which reigns between the particles, the combination or separation of which produces the currents.

1959. I look upon the question of the origin of the power in the voltaic battery as abundantly decided by the experimental results not connected with the action of heat (1824, &c.; 1878, &c.). I further view the results with heat as adding very strong confirmatory evidence to the chemical theory; and the numerous questions which arise as to the varied results produced, only tend to show how important the voltaic circuit is as a means of investigation into the nature and principles of chemical affinity (1967). This truth has already been most strikingly illustrated by the researches of De la Rive made by means of the galvanometer, and the investigations of my friend Professor Daniell into the real nature of acid and other compound electrolytes.[3]

Cases of Two Metals and One Electrolyte; One Junction Being Heated

1960. Since heat produced such striking results with single metals, I thought it probable that it might be able to affect the mutual relation of the metals in some cases, and even invert their order: on making circuits with two metals and electrolytes, I found the following cases.

1961. In the solution of *sulphuret of potassium*, hot tin is well positive to cold silver: cold tin is very slightly positive to hot silver, and the silver then rapidly tarnishes.

1962. In the solution of *potassa*, cold tin is fairly positive to hot lead, but hot tin is much more positive to cold lead. Also cold cadmium is positive to hot lead, but hot cadmium is far more positive to cold lead. In these cases, therefore, there are great differences produced by heat, but the metals still keep their order.

1963. In *dilute sulphuric acid*, hot iron is *well positive* to cold tin, but hot tin is *still more positive* to cold iron. Hot iron is a little positive to cold lead, and hot lead is very positive to cold iron. These are cases of the actual inversion of order; and tin and lead may have their states reversed exactly in the same manner.

1964. *In dilute nitric acid*, tin and iron, and iron and lead may have their states reversed, whichever is the hot metal being rendered positive to the other. If, when the iron is to be plunged into the heated side (1930) the acid is only moderately warm, it seems at first as if the tin would almost overpower the iron, so beautifully can the forces be either balanced or rendered predominant on either side at pleasure. Lead is positive to tin in both cases; but far more so when hot than when cold.

1965. These effects show beautifully that, in many cases, when two different metals are taken, either can be made positive to the other at pleasure, by acting on their chemical affinities; though the contacts of the metals with each other (supposed to be an electromotive cause) remain *entirely unchanged*. They shew the effect of heat in reversing or strengthening the natural differences of the metals, according as its action is made to oppose or combine with their natural chemical forces, and thus add further confirmation to the mass of evidence already adduced.

[1] *Philosophical Transactions*, 1834, p. 428.
[2] *Annales de Chimie*, 1836. LXI. p. 44. &c.
[3] *Philosophical Transactions*, 1839, p. 97.

1966. There are here, as in the cases of one metal, some instances where the heat renders the metal more negative than it would be if cold. They occur, principally, in the solution of sulphuret of potassium. Thus, with zinc and cadmium, or zinc and tin, the coldest metal is positive. With lead and tin, the hot tin is a little positive, cold tin very positive. With lead and zinc, hot zinc is a little positive, cold zinc much more so. With silver and lead, the hot silver is a little positive to the lead, the cold silver is more, and well positive. In these cases the current is preceded by a moment of quiescence (1953), during which the chemical action at the hot metal reduces the efficacy of the electrolyte against it more than at the cold metal, and the latter afterwards shows its advantage.

1967. Before concluding these observations on the effects of heat, and in reference to the probable utility of the voltaic circuit in investigations of the intimate nature of chemical affinity (1959), I will describe a result which, if confirmed, may lead to very important investigations. Tin and lead were conjoined and plunged into cold dilute sulphuric acid; the tin was positive a little. The same acid was heated, and the tin and lead, having been perfectly cleaned, were reintroduced, then the lead was a little positive to the tin. So that a difference of temperature not limited to one contact, for the two electrolytic contacts were always at the same temperature, caused a difference in the relation of these metals the one to the other. Tin and iron in dilute sulphuric acid appeared to give a similar result; i.e., in the cold acid the tin was always positive, but with hot acid the iron was sometimes positive. The effects were but small, and I had not time to enter further into the investigation.

1968. I trust it is understood that, in every case, the precautions as to very careful cleansing of the wires, the places of the ends, simultaneous immersion, observation of the first effects, &c., were attended to.

¶ v. *The Exciting Chemical Force Affected by Dilution*

1969. Another mode of affecting the chemical affinity of these elements of voltaic circuits, the metals and acids, and also applicable to the cases of such circuits, is to vary the proportion of water present. Such variation is known, by the simplest chemical experiments, to affect very importantly the resulting action, and,

upon the chemical theory, it was natural to expect that it would also produce some corresponding change in the voltaic pile. The effects observed by Avogadro and Oersted in 1823 are in accordance with such an expectation, for they found that when the same pair of metals was plunged in succession into a strong and a dilute acid, in certain cases an inversion of the current took place.[1] In 1828 De la Rive carried these and similar cases much further, especially in voltaic combinations of copper and iron with lead.[2] In 1827 Becquerel[3] experimented with one metal, copper, plunged at its two extremities into a solution of the same substance (salt) of *different strengths*; and in 1828 De la Rive[4] made many such experiments with one metal and a fluid in different states of dilution, which I think of very great importance.

1970. The argument derivable from effects of this kind appeared to me so strong that I worked out the facts to some extent, and think the general results well worthy of statement. Dilution is the circumstance which most generally exalts the existing action, but how such a circumstance should increase the electromotive force of *mere contact* did not seem evident to me, without *assuming*, as before (1874), exactly those influences at the points of contact in the various cases, which the prior results, ascertained by experiments, would require.

1971. The form of apparatus used was the bent tube already described (1915) (Pl. XIII, *Fig. 1*). The precautions before directed with the wires, tube, &c., were here likewise needful. But there were others also requisite, consequent upon the current produced by combination of water with acid, an effect which has been described long since by Becquerel,[5] but whose influence in the present researches requires explanation.

1972. Pl. XIII, *Figs. 3* and *4* represent the two arrangements of fluids used, the part below *m* in the tubes being strong acid, and that above diluted. If the fluid was nitric acid and the platinum wires as in the figures, drawing the end of the wire D upwards above *m*, or depressing it from above *m* downwards, caused great changes at the galvanometer; but if they were preserved quiet at any place, then the electro-current ceased, or very nearly so. Whenever the current existed it was from the weak to the strong acid through the liquid.

[1] *Annales de Chimie*, 1823, XXII, p. 361.
[2] *Ibid.*, 1828, XXXVII, p. 234.
[3] *Ibid.*, 1827, XXXV, p. 120.
[4] *Ibid.*, 1828, XXXVII, p. 240, 241.
[5] *Traité de l'Electricité*, II, p. 81.

1973. When the tube was arranged, as in *Fig. 3*, with water or dilute acid on one side only, and the wires were immersed not more than one third of an inch, the effects were greatly diminished; and more especially, if, by a little motion with a platinum wire, the acids had been mixed at *m*, so that the transition from weak to strong was gradual instead of sudden. In such cases, even when the wires were moved, horizontally, in the acid, the effect was so small as to be scarcely sensible, and not likely to be confounded with the chemical effects to be described hereafter. Still more surely to avoid such interference, an acid moderately diluted was used instead of water. The precaution was taken of emptying, washing, and re-arranging the tubes with fresh acid after each experiment, lest any of the metal dissolved in one experiment should interfere with the results of the next.

1974. I occasionally used the tube with dilute acid on one side only, (Pl. XIII *Fig. 3*,) and sometimes that with dilute acid on both sides, *Fig. 4.* I will call the first No. 1 and the second No. 2.

1975. In illustration of the general results I will describe a particular case. Employing tube No. 1 with strong and dilute nitric acid,[1] and two copper wires, the wire in the dilute acid was powerfully positive to the one in the strong acid at the first moment, and continued so. By using tube No. 2 the galvanometer-needle could be held stiffly in either direction, simply by simultaneously raising one wire and depressing the other, so that the first should be in weak and the second in strong acid; the former was always the positive piece of metal.

1976. On repeating the experiments with the substitution of platinum, gold, or even palladium for the copper, scarcely a sensible effect was produced (1973).

1977. *Strong and dilute nitric acid.*[1] The following single metals being compared with themselves in these acids, gave most powerful results of the kind just described with copper (1975); silver, iron, lead, tin, cadmium, zinc. The metal in the weaker acid was positive to that in the stronger. Silver is very changeable, and after some time the current is often suddenly reversed, the metal in the strong acid becoming positive: this again will change back, the metal in the weaker acid returning to its positive state. With tin, cadmium, and zinc,

[1] The dilute acid consisted of three volumes of strong nitric acid and two volumes of water.

violent action in the acid quickly supervenes and mixes all up together. Iron and lead show the alternations of state in the tube No. 2 as beautifully as copper (1975).

1978. *Strong and dilute sulphuric acid.* I prepared an acid of 49 by weight, strong oil of vitriol, and 9 of water, giving a sulphuric acid with two proportions of water, and arranged the tube No.1 (1974) with this and the strongest acid. But as this degree of dilution produced very little effect with the iron, as compared with what a much greater dilution effected, I adopted the plan of putting strong acid into the tube, and then adding a little water at the top at one of the sides, with the precaution of stirring and cooling it previous to the experiment (1973).

1979. With *iron*, the part of the metal in the weaker acid was powerfully positive to that in the stronger acid. With copper, the same result, as to direction of the current, was produced; but the amount of the effect was small. With silver, cadmium, and zinc, the difference was either very small or unsteady, or nothing; so that, in comparison with the former cases, the electromotive action of the strong and weak acid appeared balanced. With lead and tin, the part of the metal in the *strong* acid was *positive* to that in the weak acid; so that they present an effect the reverse of that produced by iron or copper.

1980. *Strong and dilute muriatic acid.* I used the strongest pure muriatic acid in tube No. 1, and added water on the top of one side for the dilute extremity (1973), stirring it a little as before. With silver, copper, lead, tin, cadmium, and zinc, the metal in the *strongest acid* was positive, and the current in most cases powerful. With iron, the end in the strongest acid was first positive: but shortly after the weak acid side became positive and continued so. With palladium, gold, and platinum, nearly insensible effects were the results.

1981. *Strong and dilute solution of caustic potassa.* With iron, copper, lead, tin, cadmium, and zinc, the metal in the strong solution was positive: in the case of iron slightly, in the case of copper more powerfully, deflecting the needle 30° or 38°, and in the cases of the other metals very strongly. Silver, palladium, gold, and platinum, gave the merest indications (1973).

Thus potash and muriatic acid are, in several respects, contrasted with nitric and sulphuric acids. As respects muriatic acid, however, and perhaps even the potash, it may be admitted that, even in their strongest states, they are not fairly comparable to the very strong nitric and sulphuric acids, but rather to those acids when somewhat diluted (1985).

1982. I know it may be said in reference to the numerous changes with strong and dilute acids, that the results are the consequence of corresponding alterations in the contact force; but this is to change about the theory with the phenomena and with chemical force (1874, 1956, 1985, 2006, 2014, 2063); or it may be alleged that it is the contact force of the solutions produced at the metallic surfaces which, differing, causes difference of effect; but this is to put the effect before the cause in the order of *time*. If the liberty of shifting the point of efficacy from metals to fluids, or from one place to another, be claimed, it is at all events quite time that some definite statement and data respecting the active points (1808) should be given. At present it is difficult to lay hold of the contact theory by any argument derived from experiment, because of these uncertainties or variations, and it is in that respect in singular contrast with the definite expression as to the place of action which the chemical theory supplies.

1983. All the variations which have been given are consistent with the extreme variety which chemical action under different circumstances possesses, but, as it still appears to me, are utterly incompatible with, what should be, the simplicity of mere contact action; further they admit of even greater variation, which renders the reasons for the one view and against the other, still more conclusive.

1984. Thus if a contact philosopher say that it is only the very strongest acids that can render the part of the metals in it negative, and therefore the effect does not happen with muriatic acid or potash (1980, 1981), though it does with nitric and sulphuric acids (1977, 1978); then, the following result is an answer to such an assumption. Iron in *dilute nitric acid*, consisting of one volume of strong acid and twenty of water, is positive to iron in strong acid, or in a mixture of one volume of strong acid with one of water, or with three, or even with five volumes of water. Silver also, in the weakest of these acids, is positive to silver in any of the other four states of it.

1985. Or if, modifying the statement upon these results, it should be said that diluting the acid at one contact *always* tends to give it a certain *proportionate* electromotive force, and therefore diluting one side more than the other will still allow this force to come into play;

then, how is it that with muriatic acid and potassa the effect of dilution is the reverse of that which has been quoted in the cases with nitric acid and iron or silver (1977, 1984)? Or if, to avoid *difficulty*, it be assumed that each electrolyte must be considered apart, the nitric acid by itself, and the muriatic acid by itself, for that one may differ from another in the *direction* of the change induced by dilution, then how can the following results with a single acid be accounted for?

1986. I prepared four nitric acids:

A was very strong pure nitric acid;
B was one volume of A and one volume of water;
C was one volume of A and three volumes of water;
D was one volume of A and twenty volumes of water.

Experimenting with these acids and a metal, I found that copper in C acid was positive to copper in A or D acid. Nor was it the *first* addition of water to the strong acid that brought about this curious relation, for copper in the B acid was positive to copper in the strong acid A, but negative to the copper in the weak acid D: the negative effect of the stronger nitric acid with this metal does not therefore depend upon a very high degree of concentration.

1987. Lead presents the same beautiful phenomena. In the C acid it is positive to lead either in A or D acid: in B acid it is positive to lead in the strongest, and negative to lead in the weakest acid.

1988. I prepared also three sulphuric acids:

E was strong oil of vitriol;
F one volume of E and two volumes of water;
G one volume of E and twenty volumes of water.

Lead in F was well *negative* to lead either in E or G. Copper in F was also negative to copper in E or G, but in a smaller degree. So here are two cases in which metals in an acid of a certain strength are *negative* to the same metals in the same acid, either stronger or weaker. I used platinum wires ultimately in all these cases with the same acids to check the interference of the combination of acid and water (1973); but the results were then almost nothing, and showed that the phenomena could not be so accounted for.

1989. To render this complexity for the contact theory still more complicated, we have further variations, in which, with the same acid strong and diluted, some metals are positive in the strong acid and others in the weak. Thus, tin in the strongest sulphuric acid E

(1988) was positive to tin in the moderate or the weak acids F and G; and tin in the moderate acid F was positive to the same metal in G. Iron, on the contrary, being in the strong acid E was negative to the weaker acids F and G; and iron in the medium acid F was negative to the same metal in G.

1990. For the purpose of understanding more distinctly what the contact theory has to do here, I will illustrate the case by a diagram. Let Pl. XIII, *Fig. 5* represent a circle of metal and sulphuric acid. If A be an arc of iron or copper, and B C strong oil of vitriol, there will be no determinate current: or if B C be weak acid, there will be no such current: but let it be strong acid at B, and diluted at C, and an electric current will run round A C B. If the metal A be silver, it is equally indifferent with the strong and also with the weak acid, as iron has been found to be as to the production of a current; but, besides that, it is indifferent with the strong acid at B and the weak acid at C. Now if the dilution of the electrolyte at one part, as C, had so far increased the contact electromotive force there, when iron or copper was present, as to produce the current found by experiment; surely it ought (consistently with any reasonable limitations of the assumptions in the contact theory) to have produced the same effect with silver: but there was none. Making the metal A lead or tin, the difficulty becomes far greater; for though with the strong or the weak acid alone any effect of a determinate current is nothing, yet one occurs upon dilution at C, but now dilution must be supposed to *weaken* instead of *strengthen* the contact force, for the current is in the reverse direction.

1991. Neither can these successive changes be referred to a gradual progression in the effect of dilution, dependent upon the *order of the metals*. For supposing dilution more favourable to the electromotive force of the contact of an acid and a metal, *in proportion* as the metals were in a certain order, as for instance that of their efficacy in the voltaic battery; though such an assumption might seem to account for the gradual diminution of effect from iron to copper, and from copper to silver, one would not expect the reverse effects, or those on the other side of zero, to appear by a return back to such metals as lead and tin (1979, 1989), but rather look for them in platinum or gold, which, however, produce no results of the kind (1976, 1988). To increase still further this complexity, it appears, from what has been before stated, that on changing the *acids* the or-

der must again be changed (1981); nay, more, that with the same acid, and merely by changing the proportion of dilution, such alteration of the order must take place (1986, 1988).

1992. Thus it appears, as before remarked (1982), that to apply the theory of contact electromotive force to the facts, that theory must twist and bend about with every variation of chemical action; and after all, with every variety of contact, active and inactive, in no case presents phenomena independent of the active exertion of chemical force.

1993. As the influence of dilution and concentration was so strong in affecting the relation of different parts of the same metal to an acid, making one part either positive or negative to another, I thought it probable that, by mere variation in the strength of the interposed electrolyte, the order of metals when in acids or other solutions of uniform strength, might be changed. I therefore proceeded to experiment on that point, by combining together two metals, tin and lead, through the galvanometer (1915); arranging the electrolytic solution in tube No. 1, strong on one side and weak on the other: immersing the wires simultaneously, tin into the strong, and lead into the weak solution, and after observing the effect, re-cleaning the wires, re-arranging the fluid, and re-immersing the wires, the tin into the weak, and the lead into the strong portion. De la Rive has already stated[1] that inversions take place when dilute and strong sulphuric acid is used; these I could not obtain when care was taken to avoid the effect of the investing fluid (1918): the general statement is correct, however, when applied to another acid, and I think the evidence very important to the consideration of the great question of contact or chemical action.

1994. *Two metals in strong and weak solution of potash*. Zinc was positive to tin, cadmium, or lead, whether in the weak or strong solution. Tin was positive to cadmium, either in weak or strong alkali. Cadmium was positive to lead both ways, but most when in the strong alkali. Thus, though there were *differences in degree* dependent on the strength of the solution, there was *no inversion* of the order of the metals.

1995. *Two metals in strong and weak sulphuric acid*. Cadmium was positive to iron and tin both ways: tin was also positive to iron, copper, and silver; and iron was positive to copper and silver, whichever side the respective metals were in. Thus none of the metals tried

[1] *Annales de Chimie*, 1828, XXXVII, p. 240.

could be made to pass the others, and so take a different order from that which they have in acid uniform in strength. Still there were great variations in degree; thus iron in strong acid was only a little positive to silver in weak acid, but iron in weak acid was very positive to silver in strong acid. Generally the metal, usually called positive, was most positive in the weak acid; but that was not the case with lead, tin, and zinc.

1996. *Two metals in strong and weak nitric acid.* Here the degree of change produced by difference in the strength of the acid was so great, as to cause not merely difference in degree, but inversions of the order of the metals, of the most striking nature. Thus iron and silver being in tube No. 2 (1974), whichever metal was in the weak acid was positive to the other in the strong acid. It was merely requisite to raise the one and lower the other metal to make either positive at pleasure (1975). Copper in weak acid was positive to silver, lead, or tin, in strong acid. Iron in weak acid was positive to silver, copper, lead, zinc, or tin, in strong acid. Lead in weak acid was positive to copper, silver, tin, cadmium, zinc, and iron in strong acid. Silver in weak acid was positive to iron, lead, copper, and, though slightly, even to tin, in strong acid. Tin in weak acid was positive to copper, lead, iron, zinc, and silver, and either neutral or a little positive to cadmium in strong acid. Cadmium in weak acid is very positive, as might be expected, to silver, copper, lead, iron, and tin, and, moderately so, to zinc in the strong acid. When cadmium is in the strong acid it is slightly positive to silver, copper, and iron, in weak acid. Zinc in weak acid is very positive to silver, copper, lead, iron, tin, and cadmium in strong acid: when in the strong acid it is a little positive to silver and copper in weak acid.

1997. Thus wonderful changes occur amongst the metals in circuits containing this acid, merely by the effect of dilution; so that of the five metals, silver, copper, iron, lead, and tin, any one of them can be made either positive or negative to any other, with the exception of silver positive to copper. The order of these five metals only may therefore be varied about one hundred different ways in the same acid, merely by the effect of dilution.

1998. So also zinc, tin, cadmium, and lead; and likewise zinc, tin, iron, and lead, being groups each of four metals; any one of these metals may be made either positive or negative to any other metal of the same group, by dilution of this acid.

1999. But the case of variation by dilution may, as regards the opposed theories, be made even still stronger than any yet stated; for the *same metals* in the *same acid* of the *same strength at the two sides* may be made to change their order, as the chemical action of the acid on each particular metal is affected, by dilution, in a smaller or greater degree.

2000. A voltaic association of iron and silver was dipped, both metals at once, into the same strong nitric acid; for the first instant, the iron was positive; the moment after, the silver became positive, and continued so. A similar association of iron and silver was put into weak nitric acid, and the iron was immediately positive, and continued so. With iron and copper the same results were obtained.

2001. These, therefore, are *finally* cases of such an inversion (1999); but as the iron in the strong nitric acid acquires a state the moment after its immersion, which is probably not assumed by it in the weak acid (1843, 1951, 2033), and as the action on the iron in its *ordinary* state may be said to be, to render it positive to the silver or copper, both in the strong or weak acid, we will not endeavour to force the fact, but look to other metals.

2002. *Silver and nickel* being associated in weak nitric acid, the nickel was positive; being associated in strong nitric acid, the nickel was still positive at the first moment, but the silver was finally positive. The nickel lost its superiority through the influence of an investing film (1918); and though the effect might easily pass unobserved, the case cannot be allowed to stand, as fulfilling the statement made (1999).

2003. *Copper and nickel* were put into strong nitric acid; the copper was positive from the first moment. Copper and nickel being in dilute nitric acid, the nickel was slightly but clearly positive to the copper. Again, *zinc and cadmium* in strong nitric acid; the cadmium was positive strongly to the zinc; the same metals being in dilute nitric acid, the zinc was very positive to the cadmium. These I consider beautiful and unexceptionable cases (1999).

2004. Thus the nitric acid furnishes a most wonderful variety of effects when used as the electrolytic conductor in voltaic circles; and its difference from sulphuric acid (1995) or from potassa (1994) in the phenomena consequent upon dilution, tend, in conjunction with many preceding facts and arguments, to show that the electromotive force in a circle is not the consequence of any power in bodies generally, belonging to them in classes rather than as individuals, and having that simplicity of character which contact force has been assumed to have; but one that has all the variations which chemical force is *known* to exhibit.

2005. The changes occurring where any one of four or five metals, differing from each other as far as silver and tin, can be made positive or negative to the others (1997, 1998), appears to me to shut out the probability that the contact of these metals with each other can produce the smallest portion of the effect in these voltaic arrangements; and then, if not there, neither can they be effective in any other arrangements; so that what has been deduced in that respect from former experiments (1829, 1833) is confirmed by the present.

2006. Or if the scene be shifted, and it be said that it is the *contact* of the acids or solutions which, by dilution at one side, produce these varied changes (1874, 1982, 1991, 2014, 2060), then how *utterly unlike* such contact must be to that of the numerous class of conducting solid bodies (1809, 1867)! And, where, to give the assumption any show of support, is the case of such contact (apart from chemical action) producing such currents?

2007. That it cannot be an alteration of contact force by mere dilution at one side (2006) is also shown by making such a change, but using metals that are chemically inactive in the electrolyte employed. Thus when nitric or sulphuric acids were diluted at one side, and then the strong and the weak parts connected by platinum or gold (1976), there was no sensible current, or only one so small as to be unimportant.

2008. A still stronger proof is afforded by the following result. I arranged the tube (Pl. XIII, *Fig. 3*) (1972), with strong solution of yellow sulphuret of potassium (1812) from A to *m*, and a solution consisting of one volume of the strong solution, with six of water from *m* to B. The extremities were then connected by platinum and iron in various ways; and when the first effect of immersion was guarded against, including the first brief negative state of the iron (2049), the effects were as follows. Platinum being in A and in B, that in A, or the strong solution, was very slightly positive, causing a permanent deflection of 2°. Iron being in A and in B, the same result was obtained. Iron being in A and platinum in B, the iron was positive about 2° to the platinum. Platinum being in A and iron in B, the platinum was now positive to the iron by about 2°. So that not

only the contact of the iron and platinum passes for nothing, but the contact of strong and weak solution of this electrolyte with either iron or platinum, is ineffectual in producing a current. The current which is constant is very feeble, and evidently related to the mutual position of the strong and weak solutions, and is probably due to their gradual mixture.

2009. The results obtained by dilution of an electrolyte capable of acting on the metals employed to form with it a voltaic circuit, may in some cases depend on making the acid a better electrolyte. It would appear, and would be expected from the chemical theory, that whatever circumstance tends to make the fluid a more powerful chemical agent and a better electrolyte (the latter being a relation purely chemical and not one of contact) favours the production of a determinate current. Whatever the cause of the effect of dilution may be, the results still tend to show how valuable the voltaic circle will become as an investigator of the nature of chemical affinity (1959).

¶ vi. *Differences in the Order of the Metallic Elements of Voltaic Circles*

2010. Another class of experimental arguments, bearing upon the great question of the origin of force in the voltaic battery, is supplied by a consideration of the different order in which the metals appear as electromotors when associated with different exciting electrolytes. The metals are usually arranged in a certain order; and it has been the habit to say that a metal in the list so arranged is negative to any one above it, and positive to any one beneath it, as if (and indeed upon the conviction that) they possessed a certain direct power one with another. But in 1812 Davy showed inversions of this order in the case of iron and copper[1] (943); and in 1828 De la Rive showed many inversions in different cases[2] (1877); gave a strong contrast in the order of certain metals in strong and dilute nitric acid;[3] and in objecting to Marianini's result most clearly says, that any order must be considered in relation only to that liquid employed in the experiments from which the order is derived.[4]

2011. I have pursued this subject in relation to several solutions, taking the precautions before referred to (1917, &c.), and find that no such single order as that just referred to can be maintained. Thus nickel is negative to an-

[1] *Elements of Chemical Philosophy*, p. 149.
[2] *Annales de Chimie*, 1828, XXXVII, p. 232.
[3] *Ibid.*, p. 235.   [4] *Ibid.*, p. 243.

timony and bismuth in strong nitric acid; it is positive to antimony and bismuth in dilute nitric acid; it is positive to antimony and negative to bismuth in strong muriatic acid; it is positive to antimony and bismuth in dilute sulphuric acid; it is negative to bismuth and antimony in potash; and it is very negative to bismuth and antimony, either in the colourless or the yellow solution of sulphuret of potassium.

2012. In further illustration of this subject I will take ten metals, and give their order in seven different solutions.

1992, 2006, 2063), and yet never showing a case of the production of a current by contact alone, i.e., unaccompanied by chemical action.

2015. On the other hand, how simply does the chemical theory of excitement of the current represent the facts! as far as we can yet follow them they go hand in hand. Without chemical action, no current; with the changes of chemical action, changes of current; whilst the influence of the strongest cases of *contact*, as of silver and tin (1997) with each other, pass for nothing in the result. In further confirmation, the exciting power does not rise, but falls,

Dilute nitric acid	Dilute sulphuric acid	Muriatic acid	Strong nitric acid	Solution of caustic potassa	Colourless bi-hydrosulphuret of potassium	Yellow hydrosulphuret of potassium
1. Silver	1. Silver	3. Antimony	5. Nickel	1. Silver	6. Iron	6. Iron
2. Copper	2. Copper	1. Silver	1. Silver	5. Nickel	5. Nickel	5. Nickel
3. Antimony	3. Antimony	5. Nickel	3. Antimony	2. Copper	4. Bismuth	4. Bismuth
4. Bismuth	4. Bismuth	4. Bismuth	2. Copper	6. Iron	8. Lead	3. Antimony
5. Nickel	5. Nickel	2. Copper	4. Bismuth	4. Bismuth	1. Silver	8. Lead
6. Iron	6. Iron	6. Iron	6. Iron	8. Lead	3. Antimony	1. Silver
7. Tin	8. Lead	8. Lead	7. Tin	3. Antimony	7. Tin	7. Tin
8. Lead	7. Tin	7. Tin	8. Lead	9. Cadmium	2. Copper	9. Cadmium
9. Cadmium	9. Cadmium	9. Cadmium	10. Zinc	7. Tin	10. Zinc	2. Copper
10. Zinc	10. Zinc	10. Zinc	9. Cadmium	10. Zinc	9. Cadmium	10. Zinc

2013. The dilute nitric acid consisted of one volume strong acid and seven volumes of water; the dilute sulphuric acid, of one volume strong acid and thirteen of water; the muriatic acid, of one volume strong solution and one volume water. The strong nitric acid was pure, and of specific gravity 1.48. Both strong and weak solution of potassa gave the same order. The yellow sulphuret of potassium consisted of one volume of strong solution (1812) and five volumes of water. The metals are numbered in the order which they presented in the dilute acids (the negative above), for the purpose of showing, by the comparison of these numbers in the other columns, the striking departures there, from this, the most generally assumed order. Iron is included, but only in its ordinary state: its place in nitric acid being given as that which it possesses on its first immersion, not that which it afterwards acquires.

2014. The displacements appear to be most extraordinary, as extraordinary as those consequent on dilution (2005); and thus show that there is no general ruling influence of fluid conductors, or even of acids, alkalies, &c., as distinct classes of such conductors, apart from their pure chemical relations. But how can the contact theory account for these results? To meet such facts it must be bent about in the most extraordinary manner, following all the contortions of the string of facts (1874, 1956,

by the contact of the bodies produced, as the chemical actions producing these decay or are exhausted; the consequent result being well seen in the effect of the investing fluids produced (1918, 1953, 1966).

2016. Thus, as De la Rive has said, any list of metals in their order should be constructed in reference to the exciting fluid selected. Further, a zero point should be expressed in the series; for as the electromotive power may be either at the anode or cathode (2040, 2052), or jointly at both, that substance (if there be one) which is absolutely without any exciting action should form the zero point. The following may be given, by way of illustration, as the order of a few metals, and other substances in relation to muriatic acid:

> *Peroxide of lead,*
> *Peroxide of manganese,*
> *Oxide of iron,*
> PLUMBAGO,
> Rhodium,
> Platinum,
> Gold,
> Antimony,
> Silver,
> Copper,
> Zinc:

in which plumbago is the neutral substance; those in italics are active at the cathode, and those in Roman characters at the anode. The upper are of course negative to the lower. To make such lists as complete as they will shortly require to be, numbers expressive of the relative exciting force, counting from the zero point, should be attached to each substance.

¶ vii. *Active Voltaic Circles and Batteries without Metallic Contact*

2017. There are cases in abundance of electric currents produced by pure chemical action, but not one undoubted instance of the production of a current by pure contact. As I conceive the great question must now be settled by the weight of evidence, rather than by simple philosophic conclusions (1799), I propose adding a few observations and facts to show the number of these cases, and their force. In the Eighth Series of these *Researches*[1] (April, 1834) I gave the first experiment, that I am aware of, in which chemical action was made to produce an electric current and chemical decomposition at a distance, in a simple circuit, without any contact of metals (880, &c.). It was further shown, that when a pair of zinc and platinum plates were excited at one end of the dilute nitrosulphuric acid (880), or solution of potash (884), or even in some cases a solution of common salt (885), decompositions

[1] *Philosophical Transactions*, 1834, p. 426.

might be produced at the other end, of solutions of iodide of potassium (900), protochloride of tin (901), sulphate of soda, muriatic acid, and nitrate of silver (906); or of the following bodies in a state of fusion; nitre, chlorides of silver and lead, and iodide of lead (902, 906); no metallic contact being allowed in any of the experiments.

2018. I will proceed to mention new cases; and first, those already referred to, where the action of a little dilute acid produced a current passing through the solution of the sulphuret of potassium (1831), or green nitrous acid (1844), or the solution of potassa (1854); for here no metallic contact was allowed, and chemical action was the evident and only cause of the currents produced.

2019. The following is a table of cases of similar excitement and voltaic action, produced by chemical action without metallic contact. Each horizontal line contains the four substances forming a circuit, and they are so arranged as to give the direction of the current, which was in all cases from left to right through the bodies as they now stand. All the combinations set down were able to effect decomposition, and they are but a few of those which occurred in the course of the investigation.

2020.

Iron	Dilute nitric acid	Platinum	Sulph. of potassium (1812)	Full current
Iron	Dilute nitric acid	Platinum	Red nitric acid	Full current
Iron	Dilute nitric acid	Platinum	Pale nitric acid, strong	Good
Iron	Dilute nitric acid	Platinum	Green nitrous acid	Very powerful
Iron	Dilute nitric acid	Platinum	Iodide of potassium	Full current
Iron	Dilute sulphuric acid	Platinum	Sulphuret of potassium	Full
Iron	Dilute sulphuric acid	Platinum	Red nitric acid	Good
Iron	Muriatic acid	Platinum	Green nitrous acid	Most powerful
Iron	Dilute muriatic acid	Platinum	Red nitric acid	Good
Iron	Dilute muriatic acid	Platinum	Sulphuret of potassium	Good
Iron	Solution of salt	Platinum	Green nitrous acid	Most powerful
Iron	Common water	Platinum	Green nitrous acid	Good
Zinc	Dilute nitric acid	Platinum	Iodide of potassium	Good
Zinc	Muriatic acid	Platinum	Iodide of potassium	Good
Cadmium	Dilute nitric acid	Platinum	Iodide of potassium	Good
Cadmium	Muriatic acid	Platinum	Iodide of potassium	Good
Lead	Dilute nitric acid	Platinum	Iodide of potassium	Good
Lead	Muriatic acid	Platinum	Iodide of potassium	Good
Copper	Dilute nitric acid	Platinum	Iodide of potassium	
Copper	Muriatic acid	Platinum	Iodide of potassium	
Lead	Strong sulphuric acid	Iron	Dilute sulphuric acid	Strong
Tin	Strong sulphuric acid	Iron	Dilute sulphuric acid	Strong
Copper	Sulphuret of potassium	Iron	Dilute nitric acid	Powerful
Copper	Sulphuret of potassium	Iron	Iodide of potassium	
Copper	Strong nitric acid	Iron	Dilute nitric acid	Very powerful
Copper	Strong nitric acid	Iron	Iodide of potassium	
Silver	Strong nitric acid	Iron	Dilute nitric acid	Strong
Silver	Strong nitric acid	Iron	Iodide of potassium	Good
Silver	Sulphuret of potassium	Iron	Dilute nitric acid	Strong
Tin	Strong sulphuric acid	Copper	Dilute sulphuric acid	

2021. It appears to me probable that any one of the very numerous combinations which can be made out of the following table, by taking one substance from each column and arranging them in the order in which the columns stand, would produce a current without metallic contact, and that some of these currents would be very powerful.

Rhodium		Dilute nitric acid
Gold		Dilute sulphuric acid
Platinum		Muriatic acid
Palladium	Iron	Solution of vegetable acids
Silver		Iodide of potassium
Nickel		Iodide of zinc
Copper		Solution of salt
Lead		Many metallic solutions
Tin		
Zinc		
Cadmium		

Strong nitrous acid, or strong solution or sulphuret of potassium

2022. To these cases must be added the many in which one metal in a uniform acid gave currents when one side was heated (1942, &c.). Also those in which one metal with an acid strong and diluted gave a current (1977, &c.).

2023. In the cases where by dilution of the acid one metal can be made either positive or negative to another (1996, &c.), one half of the results should be added to the above, except that they are too strong; for instead of proving that chemical action can produce a current without contact, they go to the extent of showing a total disregard of it, and production of the current against the force of contact, as easily as with it.

2024. That it is easy to construct batteries without metallic contact was shown by Sir Humphry Davy in 1801,[1] when he described various effective arrangements including only one metal. At a later period Zamboni constructed a pile in which but one metal and one fluid was used,[2] the only difference being extent of contact at the two surfaces. The following forms, which are dependent upon the mere effect of dilution, may be added to these.

2025. Let *a b, a b, a b* (Pl. XIII, *Fig. 6*), represent tubes or other vessels, the parts at *a* containing strong nitric or sulphuric acid, and the parts at *b* dilute acid of the same kind; then connect these by wires, rods, or plates of one metal only, being copper, iron, silver, tin, lead, or any of those metals which become positive and negative by difference of dilution in the

acid (1979, &c.). Such an arrangement will give an effective battery.

2026. If the acid used be the sulphuric, and the metal employed be iron, the current produced will be in one direction, thus, ⟵—— through the part figured; but if the metal be tin, the resulting current will be in the contrary direction, thus ——⟶.

2027. Strong and weak solutions of potassa being employed in the tubes, then the single metals zinc, lead, copper, tin, and cadmium (1981), will produce a similar battery.

2028. If the arrangements be as in Pl. XIII, *Fig. 7*, in which the vessels 1, 3, 5, &c. contain strong sulphuric acid, and the vessels 2, 4, 6, &c. dilute sulphuric acid; and if the metals *a, a, a,* are tin, and *b, b, b,* are iron (1979), a battery electric current will be produced in the direction of the arrow. If the metals be changed for each other, the acids remaining; or the acids be changed, the metals remaining; the direction of the current will be reversed.

¶ viii. *Considerations of the Sufficiency of Chemical Action*

2029. Thus there is no want of cases in which chemical action alone produces voltaic currents (2017); and if we proceed to look more closely to the correspondence which ought to exist between the chemical action and the current produced, we find that the further we trace it the more exact it becomes; in illustration of which the following cases will suffice.

2030. *Chemical action does evolve electricity.* This has been abundantly proved by Becquerel and De la Rive. Becquerel's beautiful voltaic arrangement of acid and alkali[3] is a most satisfactory proof that chemical action is abundantly sufficient to produce electric phenomena. A great number of the results described in the present papers prove the same statement.

2031. *Where chemical action has been but diminishes or ceases, the electric current diminishes or ceases also.* The cases of tin (1882, 1884), lead (1885), bismuth (1895), and cadmium (1905), in the solution of sulphuret of potassium, are excellent instances of the truth of this proposition.

2032. If a piece of grain tin be put into strong nitric acid, it will generally exert no action, in consequence of the film of oxide which is formed upon it by the heat employed in the process of breaking it up. Then two platinum wires, connected by a galvanometer, may be put into the

[1] *Philosophical Transactions,* 1801, p. 397. Also *Journals of the Royal Institution,* 1802, p. 51; and *Nicholson's Journal,* 8vo, 1802, Vol. I, p. 144.
[2] *Quarterly Journal of Science,* VIII, 177; or *Annales de Chimie,* XI, 190, (1819).

[3] *Annales de Chimie,* 1827, XXXV, p. 122. *Bibliothèque Universelle,* 1838; XIV, 129, 171.

acid, and one of them pressed against the piece of tin, yet without producing an electric current. If, whilst matters are in this position, the tin be scraped under the acid by a glass rod or other non-conducting substance capable of breaking the surface, the acid acts on the metal newly exposed, and produces a current; but the action ceases in a moment or two from the formation of oxide of tin and an exhausted investing solution (1918), and the current ceases with it. Each scratch upon the surface of the tin reproduces the series of phenomena.

2033. The case of iron in strong nitric acid, which acts and produces a current at the first moment (1843, 1951, 2001), but is by that action deprived of so much of its activity, both chemical and electrical, is also a case in point.

2034. If lead and tin be associated in muriatic acid, the lead is positive at the first moment to the tin. The tin then becomes positive, and continues so. This change I attribute to the circumstance that the chloride of lead formed partly invests that metal, and prevents the continuance of the action there; but the chloride of tin, being far more soluble than that of lead, passes more readily into the solution; so that action goes on there, and the metal exhibits a permanent positive state.

2035. The effect of the investing fluid already referred to in the cases of tin (1919) and cadmium (1918), some of the results with two metals in hot and cold acid (1966), and those cases where metal in a heated acid became negative to the same metal in cold acid (1953, &c.), are of the same kind. The latter can be beautifully illustrated by two pieces of lead in dilute nitric acid: if left a short time, the needle stands nearly at 0°, but on heating either side, the metal there becomes negative 20° or more, and continues so as long as the heat is continued. On cooling that side and heating the other, that piece of lead which before was positive now becomes negative in turn, and so on for any number of times.

2036. *When the chemical action changes the current changes also.* This is shown by the cases of two pieces of the same active metal in the same fluid. Thus if two pieces of silver be associated in strong muriatic acid, first the one will be positive and then the other; and the changes in the direction of the current will not be slow as if by a gradual action, but exceedingly sharp and sudden. So if silver and copper be associated in a dulute solution of sulphuret of potassium, the copper will be chemically active and positive, and the silver will remain clean;

until of a sudden the copper will cease to act, the silver will become instantly covered with sulphuret, showing by that the commencement of chemical action there, and the needle of the galvanometer will jump through 180°. Two pieces of silver or of copper in solution of sulphuret of potassium produce the same effect.

2037. If metals be used which are inactive in the fluids employed, and the latter undergo no change during the time, from other circumstances, as heat, &c. (1838, 1937), then no currents, and of course no such alterations in direction, are produced.

2038. *Where no chemical action occurs no current is produced.* This in regard to ordinary solid conductors, is well known to be the case, as with metals and other bodies (1867). It has also been shown to be true when fluid conductors (electrolytes) are used, in every case where they exert no chemical action, though such different substances as acid, alkalies and sulphurets have been employed (1843, 1853, 1825, 1829). These are very striking facts.

2039. *But a current will occur the moment chemical action commences.* This proposition may be well illustrated by the following experiment. Make an arrangement like that in *Fig. 14*: the two tubes being charged with the same pure, pale, strong nitric acid, the two platinum wires *p p* being connected by a galvanometer, and the wire *i*, of iron. The apparatus is only another form of the simple arrangement (Pl. XIII, *Fig. 9*,) where, in imitation of a former experiment (889), two plates of iron and platinum are placed parallel, but separated by a drop of strong nitric acid at each extremity. Whilst in this state no current is produced in either apparatus; but if a drop of water be added at *b, Fig. 9*, chemical action commences, and a powerful current is produced, though without metallic or any additional contact. To observe this with the apparatus, (Pl. XIII, *Fig. 8*), a drop of water was put in at *b*. At first there was no chemical action and no electric current, though the water was there, so that contact with the water did nothing: the water and acid were moved and mixed together by means of the end of the wire *i*; in a few moments proper chemical action came on, the iron evolving nitrous gas at the place of its action, and at the same time acquiring a positive condition at that part, and producing a powerful electric current.

2040. *When the chemical action which either has or could have produced a current in one direction is reversed or undone, the current is reversed (or undone) also.*

2041. This is a principle or result which most strikingly confirms the chemical theory of voltaic excitement, and is illustrated by many important facts. Volta in the year 1802,[1] showed that crystallized *oxide of manganese* was highly negative to zinc and similar metals, giving, according to his theory, electricity to the zinc at the point of contact. Becquerel worked carefully at this subject in 1835,[2] and came to the conclusion, but reservedly expressed, that the facts were favourable to the theory of contact. In the following year De la Rive examined the subject,[3] and shows, to my satisfaction at least, that the peroxide is at the time undergoing chemical change and losing oxygen, a change perfectly in accordance with the direction of the current it produces.

2042. The peroxide associated with platinum in the green nitrous acid originates a current, and is negative to the platinum, at the same time giving up oxygen and converting the nitrous acid into nitric acid, a change easily shown by a common chemical experiment. In nitric acid the oxide is negative to platinum, but its negative state is much increased if a little alcohol be added to the acid, that body assisting in the reduction of the oxide. When associated with platinum in solution of potash, the addition of a little alcohol singularly favours the increase of the current for the same reason. When the peroxide and platinum are associated with solution of sulphuret of potassium, the peroxide, as might have been expected, is strongly negative.

2043. In 1835 M. Muncke[4] observed the striking power of peroxide of lead to produce phenomena like those of the peroxide of manganese, and these M. de la Rive in 1836 immediately referred to corresponding chemical changes.[5] M. Schœnbein does not admit this inference, and bases his view of "currents of tendency" on the phenomena presented by this body and its non-action with nitric acid.[6] My own results confirm those of M. de la Rive, for by direct experiment I find that the peroxide is acted upon by such bodies as nitric acid. Potash and pure strong nitric acid boiled on peroxide of lead readily dissolved it, forming protonitrate of lead. A dilute nitric acid was made and divided into two portions; one was tested by a solution of sulphuretted hydrogen, and showed no signs of lead: the other was mingled with a little peroxide of lead (1822) at common temperatures, and after an hour filtered and tested in the same manner, and found to contain plenty of lead.

2044. The peroxide of lead is negative to platinum in solutions of common salt and potash, bodies which might be supposed to exert no chemical action on it. But direct experiments show that they do exert sufficient action to produce all the effects. A circumstance in further proof that the current in the voltaic circuit formed by these bodies is chemical in its origin, is the rapid depression in the force of the current produced, after the first moment of immersion.

2045. The most powerful arrangement with peroxide of lead, platinum, and one fluid, was obtained by using a solution of the yellow sulphuret of potassium as the connecting fluid. A convenient mode of making such experiments was to form the peroxide into a fine soft paste with a little distilled water, to cover the lower extremity of a platinum plate uniformly with this paste, using a glass rod for the purpose, and making the coat only thick enough to hide the platinum well, then to dry it well, and finally, to compare that plate with a clean platinum plate in the electrolyte employed. Unless the platinum plate were perfectly covered, local electrical currents (1120) took place which interfered with the result. In this way, the peroxide is easily shown to be negative to platinum either in the solution of the sulphuret of potassium or in nitric acid. Red-lead gave the same results in both these fluids.

2046. But using this sulphuretted solution, the same kind of proof in support of the chemical theory could be obtained from protoxides as before from the peroxides. Thus, some pure protoxide of lead, obtained from the nitrate by heat and fusion, was applied on the platinum plate (2045), and found to be strongly negative to metallic platinum in the solution of sulphuret of potassium. White lead applied in the same manner was also found to acquire the same state. Either of these bodies when compared with platinum in dilute nitric acid was, on the contrary, very positive.

2047. The same effect is well shown by the action of oxidized iron. If a plate of iron be oxidized by heat so as to give an oxide of such aggregation and condition as to be acted on scarcely or not at all by the solution of sulphuret, then there is little or no current, such

[1] *Annales de Chimie*, 1802, XL, 224.
[2] *Ibid.*, 1835, LX, 164, 171.
[3] *Ibid.*, 1836, LXI, 40; and *Bibliothèque Universelle*, 1836, I, 152, 158.
[4] *Bibliothèque Universelle*, 1836, I, 160.
[5] *Ibid.*, 1836, I, 162, 154.
[6] *Philosophical Magazine*, 1838, XII, 226, 311; and *Bibliothèque Universelle*, 1838, XIV, 155.

an oxide being as platinum in the solution (1840). But if it be oxidized by exposure to air, or by being wetted and dried; or by being moistened by a little dilute nitric or sulphuric acid and then washed, first in solution of ammonia or potassa, and afterwards in distilled water and dried; or if it be moistened in solution of potassa, heated in the air, and then washed well in distilled water and dried; such iron associated with platinum and put into a solution of the sulphuret will produce a powerful current until all the oxide is reduced, the iron during the whole time being negative.

2048. A piece of rusty iron in the same solution is powerfully negative. So also is a platinum plate with a coat of protoxide, or peroxide, or native carbonate of iron on it (2045).

2049. This result is one of those effects which has to be guarded against in the experiments formerly described (1826, 1886). If what appears to be a clean plate of iron is put into a dilute solution of the sulphuret of potassium, it is first negative to platinum, then neutral, and at last generally feebly positive; if it be put into a strong solution, it is first negative, and then becomes neutral, continuing so. It cannot be cleansed so perfectly with sandpaper, but that when immersed it will be negative, but the more recently and well the plate has been cleansed, the shorter time does this state continue. This effect is due to the instantaneous oxidation of the surface of the iron during its momentary exposure to the atmosphere, and the after reduction of this oxide by the solution. Nor can this be considered an unnatural result to those who consider the characters of iron. Pure iron in the form of a sponge takes fire spontaneously in the air; and a plate recently cleansed, if dipped into water, or breathed upon, or only exposed to the atmosphere, produces an instant smell of hydrogen. The thin film of oxide which can form during a momentary exposure is, therefore, quite enough to account for the electric current produced.

2050. As a further proof of the truth of these explanations, I placed a plate of iron under the surface of a solution of the sulphuret of potassium, and rubbed it there with a piece of wood which had been soaking for some time in the same sulphuret. The iron was then neutral or very slightly positive to platinum connected with it. Whilst in connection with the platinum it was again rubbed with the wood so as to acquire a fresh surface of contact; it did not become negative, but continued in the least degree positive, showing that the former nega-

tive current was only a temporary result of the coat of oxide which the iron had acquired in the air.

2051. Nickel appears to be subject to the same action as iron, though in a much slighter degree. All the circumstances were parallel, and the proof applied to iron (2050) was applied to it also, with the same result.

2052. So all these phenomena with protoxides and peroxides agree in referring the current produced to chemical action; not merely by showing that the current depends upon the action, but also that the *direction* of the current depends upon the direction which the chemical affinity determines the exciting or electromotive anion to take. And it is I think a most striking circumstance that these bodies, which when they can and do act chemically produce currents, have not the least power of the kind when *mere contact only* is allowed (1869), though they are excellent conductors of electricity, and can readily carry the currents formed by other and more effectual means.

2053. With such a mass of evidence for the efficacy and sufficiency of chemical action as that which has been given (1878, 2052); with so many current circuits without metallic contact (2017) and so many non-current circuits with (1867); what reason can there be for referring the effect in the joint cases where both chemical action and contact occur, to contact, or to anything but the chemical force alone? Such a reference appears to me most unphilosophical: it is dismissing a proved and active cause to receive in its place one which is merely hypothetical.

¶ ix. *Thermo-electric Evidence*

2054. The phenomena presented by that most beautiful discovery of Seebeck, thermoelectricity, has occasionally and, also, recently been adduced in proof of the electromotive influence of contact amongst the metals, and such like solid conductors[1] (1809, 1867). A very brief consideration is, I think, sufficient to show how little support these phenomena give to the theory in question.

2055. If the contact of metals exert any exciting influence in the voltaic circuit, then we can hardly doubt that thermo-electric currents are due to the same force; i.e., to disturbance, by local temperature, of the balanced forces of the different contacts in a metallic or similar

[1] See Fechner's words. *Philosophical Magazine,* 1838, XIII, p. 206.

circuit. Those who quote thermo effects as proofs of the effect of contact must, of course, admit this opinion.

2056. Admitting contact force, we may then assume that heat either increases or diminishes the electromotive force of contact. For if in Pl. XIII, *Fig. 10*, A be antimony and B bismuth, heat applied at *x* causes a current to pass in the direction of the arrow; if it be assumed that bismuth in contact with antimony tends to become positive and the antimony negative, then heat diminishes the effect; but if it be supposed that the tendency of bismuth is to become negative, and of antimony positive, then heat increases the effect. How we are to decide which of these two views is the one to be adopted, does not seem to me clear; for nothing in the thermo-electric phenomena alone can settle the point by the galvanometer.

2057. If for that purpose we go to the voltaic circuit, there the situation of antimony and bismuth varies according as one or another fluid conductor is used (2012). Antimony, being negative to bismuth with the acids, is positive to it with an alkali or sulphuret of potassium; still we find they come *nearly together* in the midst of the metallic series. In the thermo series, on the contrary, their position is at the *extremes*, being as different or as much opposed to each other as they can be. This difference was long ago pointed out by Professor Cumming:[1] how is it consistent with the contact theory of the voltaic pile?

2058. Again, if silver and antimony form a thermo circle (Pl. XIII, *Fig. 11*), and the junction *x* be heated, the current there is from the silver to the antimony. If silver and bismuth form a thermo series (*Fig. 12*), and the junction *x* be heated, the current is from the bismuth to the silver; and assuming that heat increases the force of contact (2056), these results will give the direction of contact force between these metals, *antimony*←—*silver*, and *bismuth*—→*silver*. But in the voltaic series the current is *from the silver* to both the antimony and bismuth at their points of contact, whenever dilute sulphuric or nitric acid, or strong nitric acid, or solution of potassa (2012) are used; so that metallic contact, like that in the thermo circle, can at all events have *very little* to do here. In the yellow sulphuret of potassium the current is from both antimony and bismuth *to the silver* at their contacts, a result equally inconsistent with the thermo effect as

[1] *Annals of Philosophy*, 1823, VI, 177.

the former. When the colourless hydrosulphuret of potassium is used to complete the voltaic circle, the current is from bismuth to silver, and from silver to antimony at their points of contact; whilst, with strong muriatic acid, precisely the reverse direction occurs, for it is from silver to bismuth, and from antimony to silver at the junctions.

2059. Again; by the heat series copper gives a current to gold; tin and lead give currents to copper, rhodium, or gold; zinc gives one to antimony, or iron, or even plumbago; and bismuth gives one to nickel, cobalt, mercury, silver, palladium, gold, platinum, rhodium, and plumbago; at the *point of contact* between the metals: currents which are just the reverse of those produced by the same metals, when formed into voltaic circuits and excited by the ordinary acid solutions (2012).

2060. These, and a great number of other discrepancies, appear by a comparison, according to theory, of thermo contact and voltaic contact action, which can only be accounted for by assuming a specific effect of the contact of water, acids, alkalies, sulphurets, and other exciting electrolytes, for each metal; this assumed contact force being not only unlike thermo-metallic contact, in not possessing a balanced state in the complete circuit at uniform temperatures, but, also, having no relation to it as to the *order* of the metals employed. So bismuth and antimony, which are far apart in thermo-electric order, must have this extra character of acid contact very greatly developed in an opposite direction as to its result, to render them only a feeble voltaic combination with each other: and with respect to silver, which stands between tin and zinc thermoelectrically, not only must the same departure be required, but how great must the effect of this, its incongruous contact, be, to overcome so completely as it does, and even powerfully reverse the differences which the metals (according to the contact theory) tend to produce!

2061. In further contrast with such an assumption, it must be remembered that, though the series of thermo-electric bodies is different from the usual voltaic order (2012), it is perfectly consistent with itself, i.e., that if iron and antimony be weak with each other, and bismuth be strong with iron, it will also be strong with antimony. Also that if the electric current pass from bismuth to rhodium at the hot junction, and also from rhodium to antimony at the hot junction, it will pass far more powerfully from bismuth to antimony at the heated junction. To be at all consistent with this simple and true relation, sulphuric acid should not be strongly energetic with iron or tin and weakly so with silver, as it is in the voltaic circuit, since these metals are not far apart in the thermo series: nor should it be nearly alike to platinum and gold voltaically, since they are far apart in the thermo series.

2062. Finally, in the thermo circuit there is that relation to heat which shows that for every portion of electric force evolved, there is a corresponding change in another force, or form of force, namely heat, able to account for it; this, the united experiments of Seebeck and Peltier have shown. But contact force is a force which has to produce something from nothing, a result of the contact theory which can be better stated a little further on (2069, 2071, 2073).

2063. What evidence then for mere contact excitement, derivable from the facts of thermo-electricity, remains, since the power must thus be referred to the acid or other electrolyte used (2060) and made, not only to vary uncertainly for each metal, but to vary also in direct conformity with the variation of chemical action (1874, 1956, 1992, 2006, 2014)?

2064. The contact theorist seems to consider that the advocate of the chemical theory is called upon to account for the phenomena of thermo-electricity. I cannot perceive that Seebeck's circle has any relation to the voltaic pile, and think that the researches of Becquerel[1] are quite sufficient to authorize that conclusion.

¶ x. *Improbable Nature of the Assumed Contact Force*

2065. I have thus given a certain body of experimental evidence and consequent conclusions, which seem to me fitted to assist in the elucidation of the disputed point, in addition to the statements and arguments of the great men who have already advanced their results and opinions in favour of the chemical theory of excitement in the voltaic pile, and against that of contact. I will conclude by adducing a further argument founded upon the, to me, unphilosophical nature of the force to which the phenomena are, by the contact theory, referred.

2066. It is assumed by the theory (1802) that where two dissimilar metals (or rather bodies) touch, the dissimilar particles act on each other, and induce opposite states. I do

[1] *Annales de Chimie*, 1829, XLI, 355; XLVI, 275.

not deny this, but on the contrary think that in many cases such an effect takes place between contiguous particles; as for instance, preparatory to action in common chemical phenomena, and also preparatory to that act of chemical combination which, in the voltaic circuit, causes the current (1738, 1743).

2067. But the contact theory assumes that these particles, which have thus by their mutual action acquired opposite electrical states, can discharge these states one to the other, and yet remain in the state they were first in, being *in every point* entirely unchanged by what has previously taken place. It assumes also that the particles, being by their mutual action rendered plus and minus, can, whilst under this inductive action, discharge to particles of like matter with themselves and so produce a current.

2068. This is in no respect consistent with known actions. If in relation to chemical phenomena we take two substances, as oxygen and hydrogen, we may conceive that two particles, one of each, being placed together and heat applied, they induce contrary states in their opposed surfaces, according, perhaps, to the view of Berzelius (1739), and that these states becoming more and more exalted end at last in a mutual discharge of the forces, the particles being ultimately found combined, and unable to repeat the effect. Whilst they are under induction and before the final action comes on, they cannot spontaneously lose that state; but by removing the *cause* of the increased inductive effect, namely the heat, the effect itself can be lowered to its first condition. If the acting particles are involved in the constitution of an electrolyte, then they can produce current force (921, 924) proportionate to the amount of chemical force consumed (868).

2069. But the contact theory, which is obliged, according to the facts, to admit that the acting particles are not changed (1802, 2067) (for otherwise it would be the chemical theory), is constrained to admit also, that the force which is able to make two particles assume a certain state in respect to each other, is unable to make them *retain* that state; and so it virtually denies the great principle in natural philosophy, that cause and effect are equal (2071). If a particle of platinum by contact with a particle of zinc willingly gives of its own electricity to the zinc, because this by its presence tends to make the platinum assume a negative state, why should the particle of platinum take electricity from any other particle of platinum behind it, since that would only tend to destroy the very state which the zinc has just forced it into? Such is not the case in common induction; (and Marianini admits that the effect of contact may take place through air and measurable distances);[1] for there a ball rendered negative by induction, will not take electricity from surrounding bodies, however thoroughly we may uninsulate it; and if we force electricity into it, it will, as it were, be spurned back again with a power equivalent to that of the inducing body.

2070. Or if it be supposed rather, that the zinc particle, by its inductive action, tends to make the platinum particle positive, and the latter, being in connection with the earth by other platinum particles, calls upon them for electricity, and so acquires a positive state; why should it discharge that state to the zinc, the very substance, which, making the platinum assume that condition, ought of course to be able to sustain it? Or again, if the zinc tends to make the platinum particle positive, why should not electricity go to the platinum *from the zinc*, which is as much in contact with it as its neighbouring platinum particles are? Or if the zinc particle in contact with the platinum tends to become positive, why does not electricity flow to it from the zinc particles behind, as well as from the platinum?[2] There is no sufficient probable or philosophic cause assigned for the assumed action; or reason given why one or other of the consequent effects above mentioned should not take place: and, as I have again and again said, I do not know of a single fact, or case of contact current, on which, in the absence of such probable cause, the theory can rest.

2071. The contact theory assumes, in fact, that a force which is able to overcome powerful resistance, as for instance that of the conductors good or bad, through which the current passes, and that again of the electrolyte action where bodies are decomposed by it, can arise out of nothing; that, without any change in the acting matter or the consumption of any generating force, a current can be produced which

[1] *Memorie della Società Italiana in Modena*, 1837, XXI, 232, 233, &c.
[2] I have spoken, for simplicity of expression, as if one metal were active and the other passive in bringing about these induced states, and not, as the theory implies, as if each were mutually subject to the other. But this makes no difference in the force of the argument; whilst an endeavour to state fully the joint changes on both sides would rather have obscured the objections which arise and which yet are equally strong in either view.

shall go on for ever against a constant resistance, or only be stopped, as in the voltaic trough, by the ruins which its exertion has heaped up in its own course. This would indeed be *a creation of power*, and is like no other force in nature. We have many processes by which the form of the power may be so changed that an apparent *conversion* of one into another takes place. So we can change chemical force into the electric current, or the current into chemical force. The beautiful experiments of Seebeck and Peltier show the convertibility of heat and electricity; and others by Oersted and myself show the convertibility of electricity and magnetism. But in no cases, not even those of the gymnotus and torpedo (1790), is there a pure creation of force; a production of power without a corresponding exhaustion of something to supply it.[3]

2072. It should ever be remembered that the chemical theory sets out with a power the existence of which is pre-proved, and then follows its variations, rarely assuming anything which is not supported by some corresponding simple chemical fact. The contact theory sets out with an assumption, to which it adds others as the cases require, until at last the contact force, instead of being the firm unchangeable thing at first supposed by Volta, is as variable as chemical force itself.

2073. Were it otherwise than it is, and were the contact theory true, then, as it appears to me, the equality of cause and effect must be denied (2069). Then would the perpetual mo-

[3] (*Note*, March 29, 1840). I regret that I was not before aware of most important evidence for this philosophical argument, consisting of the opinion of Dr. Roget, given in his *Treatise on Galvanism* in the *Library of Useful Knowledge*, the date of which is January 1829. Dr. Roget is, upon the facts of the science, a supporter of the chemical theory of excitation; but the striking passage I desire now to refer to, is the following, at § 113 of the article *Galvanism*. Speaking of the voltaic theory of contact, he says, "Were any further reasoning necessary to overthrow it, a forcible argument might be drawn from the following consideration. If there could exist a power having the property ascribed to it by the hypothesis, namely, that of giving continual impulse to a fluid in one constant direction, without being exhausted by its own action, it would differ essentially from all the other known powers in nature. All the powers and sources of motion, with the operation of which we are acquainted, when producing their peculiar effects, are expended in the same proportion as those effects are produced; and hence arises the impossibility of obtaining by their agency a perpetual effect; or, in other words, a perpetual motion. But the electromotive force ascribed by Volta to the metals when in contact is a force which, as long as a free course is allowed to the electricity it sets in motion, is never expended, and continues to be excited with undiminished power, in the production of a never-ceasing effect. Against the truth of such a supposition, the probabilities are all but infinite." *Roget.*

tion also be true; and it would not be at all difficult, upon the first given case of an electric current by contact alone, to produce an electro-magnetic arrangement, which, as to its principle, would go on producing mechanical effects for ever.

Royal Institution, December 26, 1839

NOTE

2074. In a former series (925, &c.) I have said that I do not think any part of the electricity of the voltaic pile is due to the combination of the oxide of zinc with the sulphuric acid used, and that I agreed so far with Sir Humphry Davy in thinking that acids and alkalies did not in combining evolve electricity in large quantity when they were not parts of electrolytes.

This I would correct; for I think that Becquerel's pile is a perfect proof that when acid and alkali combine an electric current is produced.[1]

I perceive that Dr. Mohr of Coblentz appears to have shown that it is only nitric acid which amongst acids can in combining with alkalies produce an electric current.[2]

[1] *Bibliothèque Universelle*, 1838, XIV, 129, 171. *Comptes Rendus*, I, p. 455. *Annales de Chimie*, 1827, XXXV, 122.
[2] *Philosophical Magazine*, 1838, XIII, p. 382; or Poggendorf's *Annalen*, XLII, p. 76.

For myself, I had made exception of the hydracids (929) on theoretical grounds. I had also admitted that oxyacids when in solution might in such cases produce small currents of electricity (928 and *Note*); and Jacobi says that in Becquerel's improved acid and alkaline pile, it is not above a thirtieth part of the whole power which appears as current. But I now wish to say that though in the voltaic battery, dependent for its power on the oxidization of zinc, I do not think that the *quantity* of electricity is at all increased or affected by the combination of the oxide with the acid (933, 945), still the latter circumstance cannot go altogether for nothing. The researches of Mr. Daniell on the nature of compound electrolytes[3] ties together the electrolyzation of a salt and the water in which it is dissolved, in such a manner as to make it almost certain that, in the corresponding cases of the *formation* of a salt at the place of excitement in the voltaic circuit, a similar connection between the water and the salt formed must exist: and I have little doubt that the joint action of water, acids, and bases, in Becquerel's battery, in Daniell's electrolyzations, and at the zinc in the ordinary active pile, are, in principle, closely connected together.

[3] *Philosophical Transactions*, 1839, p. 97.

EIGHTEENTH SERIES

§ 25. *On the Electricity Evolved by the Friction of Water and Steam against Other Bodies*

RECEIVED JANUARY 26, READ FEBRUARY 2, 1843

2075. Two years ago an experiment was described by Mr. Armstrong and others,[1] in which the issue of a stream of high pressure steam into the air produced abundance of electricity. The source of the electricity was not ascertained, but was supposed to be the evaporation or change of state of the water, and to have a direct relation to atmospheric electricity. I have at various times since May of last year been working upon the subject, and though I perceive Mr. Armstrong has, in recent communications, anticipated by publication some of the facts which I also have obtained, the Royal Society may still perhaps think a compressed account of my results and conclusions, which in-

[1] *Philosophical Magazine*, 1840, XVII, pp. 370, 452, &c.

clude many other important points, worthy its attention.

2076. The apparatus I have used was not competent to furnish me with much steam or a high pressure, but I found it sufficient for my purpose, which was the investigation of the effect and its cause, and not necessarily an increase of the electric development. Mr. Armstrong, as is shown by a recent paper, has well effected the latter.[2] The boiler I used, belonging to the London Institution, would hold about ten gallons of water, and allow the evaporation of five gallons. A pipe 4½ feet long was attached to it, at the end of which was a large stop-cock and a metal globe, of the capacity of thirty-two cubic inches, which I will call the

[2] *Ibid.*, 1843, XXII, p. 1.

steam-globe, and to this globe, by its mouth-piece, could be attached various forms of apparatus, serving as vents for the issuing steam.[1] Thus a cock could be connected with the steam-globe, and this cock be used as the experimental steam-passage; or a wooden tube could be screwed in; or a small metal or glass tube put through a good cork, and the cork screwed in; and in these cases the steam way of the globe and tube leading to the boiler was so large, that they might be considered as part of the boiler, and these terminal passages as the obstacles which, restraining the issue of steam, produced any important degree of friction.

2077. Another issue piece consisted of a metal tube terminated by a metal funnel, and of a cone advancing by a screw more or less into the funnel, so that the steam as it rushed forth beat against the cone (Pl. XIV, *Fig. 2*); and this cone could either be electrically connected with the funnel and boiler, or be insulated.

2078. Another terminal piece consisted of a tube, with a stop-cock and feeder attached to the top part of it, by which any fluid could be admitted into the passage, and carried on with the steam (Pl. XIV, *Fig. 3*).

2079. In another terminal piece, a small cylindrical chamber was constructed (Pl. XIV, *Fig. 4*) into which different fluids could be introduced, so that, when the cocks were opened, the steam passing on from the steam-globe (2076) should then enter this chamber and take up anything that was there, and so proceed with it into the final passage, or out against the cone (2077), according as the apparatus had been combined together. This little chamber I will always call C.

2080. The pressure at which I worked with the steam was from eight to thirteen inches of mercury, never higher than thirteen inches, or about two-fifths of an atmosphere.

2081. The boiler was insulated on three small blocks of lac, the chimney being connected by a piece of funnel-pipe removable at pleasure. Coke and charcoal were burnt, and the insulation was so good, that when the boiler was attached to a gold-leaf electrometer and charged purposely, the divergence of the leaves did not alter either by the presence of a large fire, or the abundant escape of the results of the combustion.

2082. When the issuing steam produces electricity, there are two ways of examining the effect: either the insulated boiler may be observed, or the steam may be examined, but these states are always contrary one to the other. I attached to the boiler both a gold-leaf and a discharging electrometer, the first showed any charge short of a spark, and the second by the number of sparks in a given time carried on the measurement of the electricity evolved. The state of the steam may be observed either by sending it through an insulated wide tube in which are some diaphragms of wire gauze, which serves as a discharger to the steam, or by sending a puff of it near an electrometer when it acts by induction; or by putting wires and plates of conducting matter in its course, and so discharging it. To examine the state of the boiler or substance against which the steam is excited, is far more convenient, as Mr. Armstrong has observed, than to go for the electricity to the steam itself; and in this paper I shall give the state of the former, unless it be otherwise expressed.

2083. Proceeding to the cause of the excitation, I may state first that I have satisfied myself it is not due to evaporation or condensation, nor is it affected by either the one or the other. When the steam was at its full pressure, if the valve were suddenly raised and taken out, no electricity was produced in the boiler, though the evaporation was for the time very great. Again, if the boiler were charged by excited resin before the valve was opened, the opening of the valve and consequent evaporation did not affect this charge. Again, having obtained the power of constructing steam passages which should give either the positive or the negative, or the neutral state (2102, 2110, 2117), I could attach these to the steam way, so as to make the boiler either positive, or negative, or neutral at pleasure with the same steam, and whilst the evaporation for the whole time continued the same. So that the excitation of electricity is clearly independent of the evaporation or of the change of state.

2084. The issue of *steam alone* is not sufficient to evolve electricity.[2] To illustrate this point I may say that the cone apparatus (2077) is an excellent exciter: so also is a boxwood tube (2102) (Pl. XIV, *Fig. 5*) soaked in water, and screwed into the steam-globe. If with either of these arrangements, the steam-globe (*Fig. 1*) be empty of water, so as to catch and retain

---

[1] This globe and the pieces of apparatus are represented upon a scale of one-fourth in the Plate belonging to this paper.

[2] Mr. Armstrong has also ascertained that water is essential to a high development. *Phil. Mag.*, 1843, Vol. XXII, p. 2.

PLATE XIV

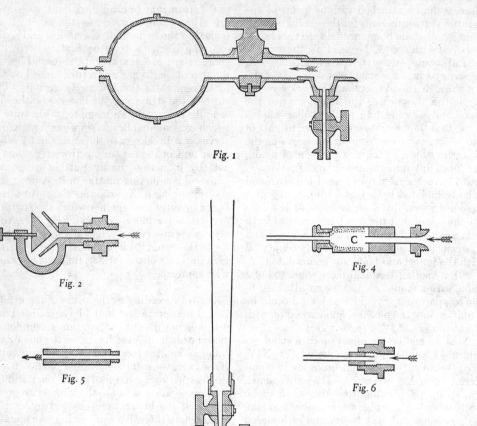

Fig. 1

Fig. 2

Fig. 4

Fig. 5

Fig. 6

Fig. 3

Description of the Apparatus represented in section,
and to a scale of one-fourth

Fig. 1 The steam-globe (2076), principal steam-cock, and drainage-cock to re-move the water condensed in the pipe. The current of steam, &c. travelled in the direction of the arrow-heads.

Fig. 2 The cone apparatus (2077) in one of its forms. The cone could be ad-vanced and withdrawn by means of the milled head and screw.

Fig. 3 The feeding apparatus (2078). The feeder was a glass tube or retort neck fitted by a cork into the cap of the feeding stop-cock. Other apparatuses, as those figured 2, 5, 6, could be attached by a connecting piece to this apparatus.

Fig. 4 The chamber C (2079) fitted by a cork on to a metal pipe previously screwed into the steam-globe; and having a metallic tube and adjusting piece screwed into its mouth. Other parts, as the cone *fig. 2,* or the wooden or glass tubes 5, 6, could be conjoined with this chamber.

Fig. 5 The boxwood tube (2102).

Fig. 6 A glass or thin metal tube (2076) attached by a cork to a mouthpiece fitting into the steam-globe.

that which is condensed from the steam, then after the first moment (2089), and when the apparatus is hot, the issuing steam excites no electricity; but when the steam-globe is filled up so far that the rest of the condensed water is swept forward with the steam, abundance of electricity appears. If then the globe be emptied of its water, the electricity ceases; but upon filling it up to the proper height, it immediately reappears in full force. So when the feeder apparatus (2078) was used, whilst there was no water in the passage-tube, there was no electricity; but on letting in water from the feeder, electricity was immediately evolved.

2085. The electricity is due entirely to the friction of the particles of water which the steam carries forward against the surrounding solid matter of the passage, or that which, as with the cone (2077), is purposely opposed to it, and is in its nature like any other ordinary case of excitement by friction. As will be shown hereafter (2130, 2132), a very small quantity of water properly rubbed against the obstructing or interposed body, will produce a very sensible proportion of electricity.

2086. Of the many circumstances affecting this evolution of electricity, there are one or two which I ought to refer to here. Increase of pressure (as is well illustrated by Mr. Armstrong's experiments) greatly increases the effect, simply by rubbing the two exciting substances more powerfully together. Increase of pressure will sometimes change the positive power of a passage to negative; not that it has power of itself to change the quality of the passage, but as will be seen presently (2108), by carrying off that which gave the positive power; no increase of pressure, as far as I can find, can change the negative power of a given passage to positive. In other phenomena hereafter to be described (2090, 2105), increase of pressure will no doubt have its influence; and an effect which has been decreased, or even annihilated (as by the addition of substances to the water in the steam-globe, or to the issuing current of water and steam), may, no doubt, by increase of pressure be again developed and exalted.

2087. The shape and form of the exciting passage has great influence, by favouring more or less the contact and subsequent separation of the particles of water and the solid substance against which they rub.

2088. When the mixed steam and water pass through a tube or stop-cock (2076), they may issue, producing either a hissing smooth sound, or a rattling rough sound;[1] and with the cone apparatus (2077) (Pl. XIV, *Fig. 2*), or certain lengths of tube, these conditions alternate suddenly. With the smooth sound little or no electricity is produced; with the rattling sound plenty. The rattling sound accompanies that irregular rough vibration, which casts the water more violently and effectually against the substance of the passage, and which again causes the better excitation. I converted the end of the passage into a steam-whistle, but this did no good.

2089. If there be no water in the steam-globe (2076), upon opening the steam-cock the *first effect* is very striking; a good excitement of electricity takes place, but it very soon ceases. This is due to water condensed in the cold passages, producing excitement by rubbing against them. Thus, if the passage be a stop-cock, whilst cold it excites electricity with what is supposed to be steam only; but as soon as it is hot, the electricity ceases to be evolved. If, then, whilst the steam is issuing, the cock be cooled by an insulated jet of water, it resumes its power. If, on the other hand, it be made hot by a spirit-lamp before the steam be let on, then there is *no* first effect. On this principle, I have made an exciting passage by surrounding one part of an exit tube with a little cistern, and putting spirits of wine or water into it.

2090. We find then that particles of water rubbed against other bodies by a current of steam evolve electricity. For this purpose, however, it is not merely water but *pure* water which must be used. On employing the feeding apparatus (2078), which supplied the rubbing water to the interior of the steam passage, I found, as before said, that with steam only I obtained no electricity (2084). On letting in distilled water, abundance of electricity was evolved; on putting a small crystal of sulphate of soda, or of common salt into the water, the evolution ceased entirely. Re-employing distilled water, the electricity appeared again; on using the common water supplied to London, it was unable to produce it.

2091. Again, using the steam-globe (2076), and a boxwood tube (2102) which excites well if the water distilling over from the boiler be allowed to pass with the steam, when I put a small crystal of sulphate of soda, of common salt, or of nitre, or the smallest drop of sulphuric acid, into the steam-globe with the water,

---

[1] Messrs. Armstrong and Schafhaeutl have both observed the coincidence of certain sounds or noises with the evolution of the electricity.

the apparatus was utterly ineffective, and no electricity could be produced. On withdrawing such water and replacing it by distilled water, the excitement was again excellent: on adding a very small portion of any of these substances, it ceased; but upon again introducing pure water it was renewed.

2092. Common water in the steam-globe was powerless to excite. A little potash added to distilled water took away all its power; so also did the addition of *any* of those saline or other substances which give conducting power to water.

2093. The effect is evidently due to the water becoming so good a conductor, that upon its friction against the metal or other body, the electricity evolved can be immediately discharged again, just as if we tried to excite lac or sulphur by flannel which was damp instead of dry. It shows very clearly that the exciting effect, when it occurs, is due to water and not to the passing steam.

2094. As ammonia increases the conducting power of water only in a small degree (554), I concluded that it would not take away the power of excitement in the present case; accordingly on introducing some to the pure water in the globe, electricity was still evolved though the steam of vapour and water was able to redden moist turmeric paper. But the addition of a very small portion of dilute sulphuric acid, by forming sulphate of ammonia, took away all power.

2095. When in any of these cases, the steam-globe contained water which could not excite electricity, it was beautiful to observe how, on opening the cock which was inserted into the steam-pipe before the steam-globe (Pl. XIV, *Fig.* 1), the use of which was to draw off the water condensed in the pipe before it entered the steam-globe, electricity was instantly evolved; yet a few inches farther on the steam was quite powerless, because of the small change in the quality of the water over which it passed, and which it took with it.

2096. When a wooden or metallic tube (2076) was used as the exciting passage, the application of solution of salts to the outside and end of the tube in no way affected the evolution. But when a wooden cone (2077) was used, and that cone moistened with the solutions, there was no excitement on first letting out the steam, and it was only as the solution was washed away that the power appeared; soon rising, however, to its full degree.

2097. Having ascertained these points respecting the necessity of water and its purity,

the next for examination was the influence of the substance against which the stream of steam and water rubbed. For this purpose I first used cones (2077) of various substances, either insulated or not, and the following, namely, brass, boxwood, beechwood, ivory, linen, kerseymere, white silk, sulphur, caoutchouc, oiled silk, japanned leather, melted caoutchouc and resin, all became negative, causing the stream of steam and water to become positive. The fabrics were applied stretched over wooden cones. The melted caoutchouc was spread over the surface of a boxwood or a linen cone, and the resin cone was a linen cone dipped in a strong solution of resin in alcohol, and then dried. A cone of wood dipped in oil of turpentine, another cone soaked in olive oil, and a brass cone covered with the alcoholic solution of resin and dried, were at first inactive, and then gradually became negative, at which time the oil of turpentine, olive-oil and resin were found cleared off from the parts struck by the stream of steam and water. A cone of kerseymere, which had been dipped in alcoholic solution of resin and dried two or three times in succession, was very irregular, becoming positive and negative by turns, in a manner difficult to comprehend at first, but easy to be understood hereafter (2113).

2098. The end of a rod of shellac was held a moment in the stream of steam and then brought near a gold-leaf electrometer: it was found excited negatively, exactly as if it had been rubbed with a piece of flannel. The corner of a plate of sulphur showed the same effect and state when examined in the same way.

2099. Another mode of examining the substance rubbed was to use it in the shape of wires, threads or fragments, holding them by an insulating handle in the jet, whilst they were connected with a gold-leaf electrometer. In this way the following substances were tried:

Platinum	Ivory
Copper	Shellac on silk
Iron	Sulphur on silk
Zinc	Sulphur in piece
Sulphuret of copper	Plumbago
Linen	Charcoal
Cotton	Asbestos
Silk	Cyanite
Worsted	Hæmatite
Wood	Rock-crystal
Horse-hair	Orpiment
Bear's hair	Sulphate of baryta
Flint glass	Sulphate of lime
Green glass	Carbonate of lime
Quill	Fluor-spar

All these substances were rendered negative, though not in the same degree. This apparent difference in degree did not depend *only* upon the specific tendency to become negative, but also upon the conducting power of the body itself, whereby it gave its charge to the electrometer; upon its tendency to become wet (which is very different, for instance in shellac or quill, to that of glass or linen), by which its conducting quality was affected; and upon its size or shape. Nevertheless I could distinguish that bear's hair, quill and ivory had very feeble powers of exciting electricity as compared to the other bodies.

2100. I may make here a remark or two upon the introduction of bodies into the jet. For the purpose of preventing condensation on the substance, I made a platinum wire white-hot by an insulated voltaic battery, and introduced it into the jet: it was quickly lowered in temperature by the stream of steam and water to 212°, but of course could never be below the boiling-point. No difference was visible between the effect at the first instant of introduction or any other time. It was always instantly electrified and negative.

2101. The threads I used were stretched across a fork of stiff wire, and the middle part of the thread was held in the jet of vapour. In this case, the string or thread, if held exactly in the middle of the jet and looked at end-ways to the thread, was seen to be still, but if removed the least degree to the right or left of the axis of the stream it (very naturally) vibrated, or rather rotated, describing a beautiful circle, of which the axis of the stream was the tangent: the interesting point was to observe, that when the thread rotated, travelling as it were with the current, there was little or no electricity evolved, but that when it was nearly or quite stationary there was abundance of electricity, thus illustrating the effect of friction.

2102. The difference in the quality of the substances above described (2099) gives a valuable power of arrangement at the jet. Thus if a metal, glass, or wood tube[1] (2076) be used for the steam issue, the boiler is rendered well negative and the steam highly positive; but if a quill tube or, better still, an ivory tube be used, the boiler receives scarcely any charge, and the stream of steam is also in a neutral state. This result not only assists in proving that the elec-

tricity is not due to evaporation, but is also very valuable in the experimental inquiry. It was in such a neutral jet of steam and water that the excitation of the bodies already described (2099) was obtained.

2103. Substances, therefore, may be held either in the neutral jet from an ivory tube, or in the positive jet from a wooden or metal tube; and in the latter case effects occurred which, if not understood, would lead to great confusion. Thus an insulated wire was held in the stream issuing from a glass or metal tube, about half an inch from the mouth of the tube, and was found to be unexcited: on moving it in one direction a little farther off, it was rendered positive; on moving it in the other direction, nearer to the tube, it was negative. This was simply because, when near the tube in the forcible part of the current, it was excited and rendered negative, rendering the steam and water more positive than before, but that when farther off, in a quieter part of the current, it served merely as a discharger to the electricity previously excited in the exit tube, and so showed the same state with it. Platinum, copper, string, silk, wood, plumbago, or any of the substances mentioned above (2099), excepting quill, ivory and bear's hair, could, in this way, be made to assume either one state or the other, according as they were used as exciters or dischargers, the difference being determined by their place in the stream. A piece of fine wire gauze held across the issuing jet shows the above effect very beautifully; the difference of an eighth of an inch either way from the neutral place will change the state of the wire gauze.

2104. If, instead of an excited jet of steam and water (2103), one issuing from an ivory tube (2102), and in the neutral state be used, then the wires, &c. can no longer be made to assume both states. They may be excited and rendered negative (2099), but at no distance can they become dischargers, or show the positive state.

2105. We have already seen that the presence of a very minute quantity of matter able to give conducting power to the water took away all power of excitation (2090, &c.) up to the highest degree of pressure, i.e., of mechanical friction that I used (2086); and the next point was to ascertain whether it would be so for all the bodies rubbed by the stream, or whether differences in degree would begin to manifest themselves. I therefore tried all these bodies again, at one time adding about two grains of sulphate of soda to the four ounces of

---

[1] A boxwood tube, 3 inches long and ⅕th of an inch inner diameter, well soaked in distilled water and screwed into the steam-globe, is an admirable exciter.

water which the steam-globe retained as a constant quantity when in regular action, and at another time adding not a fourth of this quantity of sulphuric acid (2091). In both cases all the substances (2099) remained entirely unexcited and neutral. Very probably, great increase of pressure might have developed some effect (2086).

2106. With dilute sulphuric acid in the steam-globe, varying from extreme weakness to considerable sourness, I used tubes and cones of zinc, but could obtain *no trace* of electricity. Chemical action, therefore, appears to have nothing to do with the excitement of electricity by a current of steam.

2107. Having thus given the result of the friction of the steam and water against so many bodies, I may here point out the remarkable circumstance of water being *positive* to them all. It very probably will find its place above all other substances, even cat's hair and oxalate of lime (2131). We shall find hereafter, that we have power, not merely to prevent the jet of steam and water from becoming positive, as by using an ivory tube (2102), but also of reducing its own power when passing through or against such substances as wood, metal, glass, &c. Whether, with a jet so reduced, we shall still find amongst the bodies above mentioned (2099) some that can render the stream positive and others that can make it negative, is a question yet to be answered.

2108. Advancing in the investigation, a new point was to ascertain what other bodies, than water, would do if their particles were carried forward by the current of steam. For this purpose the feeding apparatus (2078) was mounted and charged with oil of turpentine, to be let in at pleasure to the steam-exit passage. At first the feeder stop-cock was shut, and the issuing steam and water made the boiler negative. On letting down the oil of turpentine, this state was instantly changed, the boiler became powerfully positive, and the jet of steam, &c., as strongly negative. Shutting off the oil of turpentine, this state gradually fell, and in half a minute the boiler was negative, as at first. The introduction of more oil of turpentine instantly changed this to positive, and so on with perfect command of the phenomena.

2109. Removing the feeder apparatus and using only the steam-globe and a wooden exit tube (2076), the same beautiful result was obtained. With pure water in the globe the boiler was negative, and the issuing steam, &c., positive; but a drop or two of oil of turpentine, in-

troduced into the steam-globe with the water, instantly made the boiler positive and the issuing stream negative. On using the little interposed chamber C (2079), the effects were equally decided. A piece of clean new sail-cloth was formed into a ring, moistened with oil of turpentine and placed in the box; as long as a trace of the fluid remained in the box the boiler was positive and the issuing stream negative.

2110. Thus the positive or negative state can be given at pleasure, either to the substance rubbed or to the rubbing stream; and with respect to this body, oil of turpentine, its perfect and ready dissipation by the continuance of the passage of the steam soon causes the new effect to cease, yet with the power of renewing it in an instant.

2111. With olive oil the same general phenomena were observed, i.e., it made the stream of steam, &c., *negative*, and the substance rubbed by it *positive*. But from the comparative fixedness of oil, the state was much more permanent, and a very little oil introduced into the steam-globe (2076), or into the chamber C (2079), or into the exit tube, would make the boiler positive for a long time. It required, however, that this oil should be in such a place that the steam stream, after passing by it, should rub against other matter. Thus, on using a wooden tube (2076, 2102) as the exciter, if a little oil were applied to the inner termination, or that at which the steam entered it, the tube was made positive and the issuing steam negative; but if the oil were applied to the outer termination of the tube, the tube had its ordinary negative state, as with pure water, and the issuing steam was positive.

2112. Water is essential to this excitation by fixed oil, for when the steam-globe was emptied of water, and yet oil left in it and in the passages, there was no excitement. The first effect (2089) it is true was one of excitement, and it rendered the boiler positive, but that was an effect due to the water condensed in the passage, combined with the action of the oil. Afterwards when all was hot, there was no evolution of electricity.

2113. I tried many other substances with the chamber C and other forms of apparatus, using the wet wooden tube (2102) as the place and substance by which to excite the steam stream. Hog's-lard, spermaceti, bees'-wax, castor oil, resin applied dissolved in alcohol; these, with olive-oil, oil of turpentine, and oil of laurel, all rendered the boiler positive, and the issuing steam negative. Of substances which seemed to have the reverse power, it is doubtful if there are any above water. Sulphuret of carbon, naphthaline, sulphur, camphor, and melted caoutchouc, occasionally seemed in strong contrast to the former bodies, making the boiler very negative, but on trying pure water immediately after, it appeared to do so quite as powerfully. Some of the latter bodies with oil-gas liquid, naphtha and caoutchoucine, gave occasionally variable results, as if they were the consequence of irregular and complicated effects. Indeed, it is easy to comprehend, that according as a substance may adhere to the body rubbed, or be carried off by the passing stream, exchanging its mechanical action from rubbed to rubber, it should give rise to variable effects; this, I think, was the case with the cone and resin before referred to (2097).

2114. The action of salts, acids, &c., when present in the water to destroy its effect, I have already referred to (2090, &c.). In addition, I may note that sulphuric ether, pyroxylic spirit, and boracic acid did the same.

2115. Alcohol seemed at the first moment to render the boiler positive. Half alcohol and half water rendered the boiler negative, but much less so than pure water.

2116. It must be considered that a substance having the reverse power of water, but only in a small degree, may be able to indicate that property merely by diminishing the power of water. This diminution of power is very different in its cause to that dependent on increasing the conducting power of the water, as by saline matter (2090), and yet the apparent effect will be the same.

2117. When it is required to render the issuing steam permanently negative, the object is very easily obtained. A little oil or wax put into the steam-globe (2076), or a thick ring of string or canvas soaked in wax, or solution of resin in alcohol, and introduced into the box C (2079), supplies all that is required. By adjusting the application it is easy to neutralize the power of the water, so that the issuing stream shall neither become electric, nor cause that to be electrified against which it rubs.

2118. We have arrived, therefore, at three modes of rendering the jet of steam and water neutral, namely, the use of an ivory or quill tube (2102), the presence of substances in the water (2090, &c.), and the neutralization of its natural power by the contrary force of oil, resin, &c., &c.

2119. In experiments of the kind just described an ivory tube cannot be used safely with acid or alkalies in the steam-globe, for they, by their chemical action on the substance of the tube, in the evolution or solution of the oily matter for instance, change its state and make its particular power of excitement very variable. Other circumstances also powerfully affect it occasionally (2144).

2120. A very little oil in the rubbing passages produces a great effect, and this at first was a source of considerable annoyance, by the continual occurrence of unexpected results; a portion may lie concealed for a week together in the thread of an unsuspected screw, and yet be sufficient to mar the effect of every arrangement. Digesting and washing with a little solution of alkali, and avoiding all oiled washers, is the best way in delicate experiments of evading the evil. Occasionally I have found that a passage, which was in some degree persistently negative, from a little melted caoutchouc, or positive from oil, resin, &c., might be cleared out thoroughly by letting oil of turpentine be blown through it; it assumed for a while the positive state, but when the continuance of steam had removed that (2110), the passage appeared to be perfectly clear and good and in its normal condition.

2121. I now tried the effect of oil, &c., when a little saline matter or acid was added to the water in the steam-globe (2090, &c.), and found that when the water was in such a state as to have no power of itself, still oil of turpentine or, oil, or resin in the box C, showed their power, in conjunction with such water, of rendering the boiler positive, but their power appeared to be reduced: increase of the force of steam, as in all other cases, would, there is little doubt, have exalted it again. When alkali was in the steam-globe, oil and resin lost very much of their power, and oil of turpentine very little. This fact will be important hereafter (2126).

2122. We have seen that the action of such bodies as oil introduced into the jet of steam changed its power (2108), but it was only by experiment we could tell whether this change was to such an extent as to alter the electricity for few or many of the bodies against which the steam stream rubbed. With olive oil in the box C, *all* the insulated cones before enumerated (2097) were made positive. With acetic acid in the steam-globe all were made neutral (2091). With resin in the box C (2113), all the substances in the former list (2099) were made positive; there was not one exception.

2123. The remarkable power of oil, oil of turpentine, resin, &c., when in very small quantity, to change the exciting power of water, though as regards some of them (2112) they are inactive without it, will excuse a few theoretical observations upon their mode of action. In the first place it appears that steam alone cannot by friction excite the electricity, but that the minute globules of water which it carries with it being swept over, rubbed upon and torn from the rubbed body (2085) excite it and are excited, just as when the hand is passed over a rod of shellac. When olive oil or oil of turpentine is present, these globules are, I believe, virtually converted into globules of these bodies, and it is no longer water, but the new fluids which are rubbing the rubbed bodies.

2124. The reasons for this view are the following. If a splinter of wood dipped in olive oil or oil of turpentine touch the surface of water, a pellicle of the former instantly darts and spreads over the surface of the latter. Hence it is pretty certain that every globule of water passing through the box C, containing olive oil or oil of turpentine, will have a pellicle over it. Again, if a metal, wooden, or other balance-pan be *well cleaned* and *wetted* with water, and then put on the surface of clean water in a dish, and the other pan be loaded until almost, but not quite able to pull the first pan from the water, it will give a rough measure of the cohesive force of the water. If now the oily splinter of wood touch any part of the clean surface of the water in the dish, not only will it spread over the whole surface, but cause the pan to separate from the water, and if the pan be put down again, the water in the dish will no longer be able to retain it. Hence it is evident that the oil facilitates the separation of the water into parts by a mechanical force not otherwise sufficient, and invests these parts with a film of its own substance.

2125. All this must take place to a great extent in the steam passage: the particles of water there must be covered each with a film of oil. The tenuity of this film is no objection to the supposition, for the action of excitement is without doubt at that surface where the film is believed to exist, and such a globule, though almost entirely water, may well act as an oil globule, and by its friction render the wood, &c., positive, itself becoming negative.

2126. That water which is rendered ineffective by a little saline or acid matter should still be able to show the effect of the film of oil (2121) attached to it, is perfectly consistent with this view. So also is the still more striking fact that alkalized water (2092) having no power

of itself should deeply injure the power of olive-oil or resin, and hardly touch that of oil of turpentine (2121), for the olive-oil or resin would no longer form a film over it but dissolve in it; on the contrary the oil of turpentine would form its film.

2127. That resin should produce a strong effect and sulphur not is also satisfactory, for I find resin in boiling hot water melts, and has the same effect on the balance (2124) as oil, though more slowly; but sulphur has not this power, its point of fusion being too high.

2128. It is very probable that when wood, glass or even metal is rubbed by these oily currents, the oil may be considered as rubbing not merely against wood, &c., but water also, the water being now on the side of the thing rubbed. Under the circumstances water has much more attraction for the wood rubbed than oil has, for in the steam-current, canvas, wood, &c., which have been well soaked in oil for a long time are quickly dispossessed of it, and found saturated with water. In such case the effect would still be to increase the positive state of the substance rubbed, and the negative state of the issuing stream.

2129. Having carried the experiments thus far with steam, and having been led to consider the steam as ineffectual by itself, and merely the mechanical agent by which the rubbing particles were driven onwards, I proceeded to experiment with compressed air.[1] For this purpose I used a strong copper box of the capacity of forty-six cubic inches, having two stop-cocks, by one of which the air was always forced in, and the other retained for the exit aperture. The box was very carefully cleaned out by caustic potash. Extreme care was taken (and required) to remove and avoid oil, wax, or resin about the exit apertures. The air was forced into it by a condensing syringe, and in certain cases when I required dry air, four or five ounces of cylinder *potassa fusa* were put into the box, and the condensed air left in contact with the substance ten or fifteen minutes. The average quantity of air which issued and was used in each blast was 150 cubic inches. It was very difficult to deprive this air of the smell of oil which it acquired in being pumped through the condensing syringe.

2130. I will speak first of undried common air: when such compressed air was let suddenly

[1] Mr. Armstrong has also employed air in much larger quantities. *Philosophical Magazine*, 1841, Vol. XVIII, pp. 133, 328.

out against the brass or the wood cone (2077), it rendered the cone negative, exactly as the steam and water had done (2097). This I attributed to the particles of water suddenly condensed from the expanding and cooled air rubbing against the metal or wood: such particles were very visible in the mist that appeared, and also by their effect of moistening the surface of the wood and metal. The electricity here excited is quite consistent with that evolved by steam and water: but the idea of that being due to evaporation (2083) is in striking contrast with the actual condensation here.

2131. When however common air was let out against ice it rendered the ice *positive*, again and again, and that in alternation with the negative effect upon wood and metal. This is strongly in accordance with the high positive position which has already been assigned to water (2107).

2132. I proceeded to experiment with dry air (2129), and found that it was in all cases quite *incapable* of exciting electricity against wood or sulphur, or brass, in the form of cones (2077, 2097); yet if, in the midst of these experiments, I let out a portion of air immediately after its compression, allowing it no time to dry, then it rendered the rubbed wood or brass negative (2130). This is to me a satisfactory proof that in the former case the effect was due to the condensed water, and that neither *air alone* nor *steam alone* can excite these bodies, wood, brass, &c., so as to produce the effect now under investigation.

2133. In the next place the box C was attached to this air apparatus and experiments made with different substances introduced into it (2108), using common air as the carrying vehicle.

2134. With distilled water in C, the metal cone was every now and then rendered negative, but more frequently no effect was produced. The want of a continuous jet of air sadly interfered with the proper adjustment of the proportion of water to the issuing stream.

2135. With common water (2090), or a very dilute saline solution, or very dilute sulphuric acid (2091) or ammonia, I never could obtain any traces of electricity.

2136. With oil of turpentine only in box C, the metal cone was rendered positive; but when both distilled water and oil of turpentine were introduced, the cone was very *positive* indeed, far more so than before. When sent against ice, the ice was made positive.

2137. In the same manner olive-oil and water in C, or resin in alcohol and water in C, rendered the cone positive, exactly as if these substances had been carried forward in their course by steam.

2138. Although the investigation as respects the steam stream may here be considered as finished, I was induced in connection with the subject to try a few experiments with the air current and dry powders. *Sulphur* in powder (sublimed) rendered both metal and wood, and even the sulphur cone negative, only once did it render metal positive. *Powdered resin* generally rendered metal negative, and wood positive, but presented irregularities, and often gave *two states in the same experiment*, first diverging the electrometer leaves, and yet at the end leaving them uncharged. *Gum* gave unsteady and double results like the resin. *Starch* made wood negative. *Silica*, being either very finely powdered rock-crystal or that precipitated from fluo-silicic acid by water, gave very constant and powerful results, but both metal and wood were made strongly positive by it, and the silica when caught on a wet insulated board and examined was found to be negative.

2139. These experiments with powders give rise to two or three observations. In the first place the high degree of friction occurring between particles carried forward by steam or air was well illustrated by what happened with sulphur; it was found driven into the dry boxwood cone opposed to it with such force that it could not be washed or wiped away, but had to be removed by scraping. In the next place, the *double* excitements were very remarkable. In a single experiment, the gold-leaves would open out very wide at first, and then in an instant as suddenly fall, whilst the jet still continued, and remain at last either neutral or a very little positive or negative: this was particularly the case with gum and resin. The fixation upon the wood of some of the particles issuing at the beginning of the blast and the condensation of moisture by the expanding air, are circumstances which, with others present, tend to cause these variable results.

2140. Sulphur is nearly constant in its results, and silica very constant, yet their states are the reverse of those that might have been expected. Sulphur in the lump is rendered negative whether rubbed against wood or any of the metals which I have tried, and renders them *positive* (2141), yet in the above experiments it almost always made both negative.

Silica, in the form of a crystal, by friction with wood and metals renders them *negative*, but applied as above, it constantly made them strongly positive. There must be some natural cause for these changes, which at present can only be considered as imperfect results, for I have not had time to investigate the subject.

2141. In illustration of the effect produced by steam and water striking against other bodies, I rubbed these other substances (2099) together in pairs to ascertain their order, which was as follows:

1. Catskin or bearskin
2. Flannel
3. Ivory
4. Quill
5. Rock-crystal
6. Flint glass
7. Cotton
8. Linen, canvas
9. White silk
10. The hand
11. Wood
12. Lac
13. Metals—
14. Sulphur

Iron
Copper
Brass
Tin
Silver
Platinum

Any one of these became negative with the substances above, and positive with those beneath it. There are however many exceptions to this general statement: thus one part of a catskin is very negative to another part, and even to rock-crystal: different pieces of flannel also differ very much from each other.

2142. The mode of rubbing also makes in some cases a great difference, although it is not easy to say why, since the particles that actually rub ought to present the same constant difference; a feather struck lightly against dry canvas will become strongly negative, and yet the same feather drawn with a little pressure between the folds of the same canvas will be strongly positive, and these effects alternate, so that it is easy to take away the one state in a moment by the degree of friction which produces the other state. When a piece of flannel is halved and the two pieces drawn across each other, the two pieces will have different states irregularly, or the same piece will have both states in different parts, or sometimes both

pieces will be negative, in which case, doubtless, air must have been rendered positive, and then dissipated.

2143. Ivory is remarkable in its condition. It is very difficult of excitement by friction with the metals, much more so than linen, cotton, wood, &c., which are lower in the scale than it (2141), and withal are much better conductors, yet both circumstances would have led to the expectation that it would excite better than them when rubbed with metals. This property is probably very influential in giving character to it as a non-exciting steam passage (2102).

2144. Before concluding this paper, I will mention, that having used a thin ivory tube fixed in a cork (2076) for many experiments with oil, resin, &c., it at last took up such a state as to give not merely a non-exciting passage for the steam, but to exert upon it a nullifying effect, for the jet of steam and water passing through it produced no excitation against any of the bodies opposed, as on the former occasion, to it (2099). The tube was apparently quite clean, and was afterwards soaked in alcohol to remove any resin, but it retained this peculiar state.

2145. Finally, I may say that the cause of the evolution of electricity by the liberation of confined steam is not evaporation; and further, being, I believe, friction, it has no effect in producing, and is not connected with, the general electricity of the atmosphere: also, that as far as I have been able to proceed, pure gases, i.e., gases not mingled with solid or liquid particles do not excite electricity by friction against solid or liquid substances.[1]

[1] References to papers in the *Philosophical Magazine*, 1840–1843. Armstrong, *Phil. Mag.*, Vol. XVII, pp. 370, 452; Vol. XVIII, pp. 50, 133, 328; Vol. XIX, p. 25; Vol. XX, p. 5; Vol. XXII, p. 1. Pattinson, *Phil. Mag.*, Vol. XVII, pp. 375, 457. Schafhaeutl, *Phil. Mag.*, Vol. XVII, p. 449; Vol. XVIII, pp. 14, 95, 265. See also *Philosophical Magazine*, 1843, XXIII, p. 194, for Armstrong's account of the *Hydro-electric Machine*.

NINETEENTH SERIES[1]

§ 26. *On the Magnetization of Light and the Illumination of Magnetic Lines of Force*[2] ¶ i. *Action of Magnets on Light* ¶ ii. *Action of Electric Currents on Light* ¶ iii. *General Considerations*

RECEIVED NOVEMBER 6, READ NOVEMBER 20, 1845

¶ i. *Action of Magnets on Light*

2146. I HAVE long held an opinion, almost amounting to conviction, in common I believe with many other lovers of natural knowledge, that the various forms under which the forces of matter are made manifest have one common origin; or, in other words, are so directly related and mutually dependent, that they are convertible, as it were, one into another, and possess equivalents of power in their action.[3] In modern times the proofs of their convertibility have been accumulated to a very considerable extent, and a commencement made of the determination of their equivalent forces.

2147. This strong persuasion extended to the powers of light, and led, on a former occasion, to many exertions, having for their object the discovery of the direct relation of light and electricity, and their mutual action in bodies subject jointly to their power;[4] but the results were negative and were afterwards confirmed, in that respect, by Wartmann.[5]

2148. These ineffectual exertions, and many others which were never published, could not remove my strong persuasion derived from philosophical considerations; and, therefore, I recently resumed the inquiry by experiment in a most strict and searching manner, and have at last succeeded in *magnetizing and electrifying a ray of light, and in illuminating a magnetic line of force*. These results, without entering into the detail of many unproductive experiments, I will describe as briefly and clearly as I can.

2149. But before I proceed to them, I will define the meaning I connect with certain terms which I shall have occasion to use: thus, by *line of magnetic force*, or *magnetic line of force*, or *magnetic curve*, I mean that exercise of magnetic force which is exerted in the lines usually called magnetic curves, and which equally exist as passing from or to magnetic poles, or forming concentric circles round an electric current. By *line of electric force*, I mean the force exerted in the lines joining two bodies, acting on each other according to the principles of static electric induction (1161, &c.), which may also be either in curved or straight lines. By a *diamagnetic*, I mean a body through which lines of magnetic force are passing, and which does not by their action assume the usual magnetic state of iron or loadstone.

2150. A ray of light issuing from an Argand lamp, was polarized in a horizontal plane by reflexion from a surface of glass, and the polarized ray passed through a Nichol's eye-piece revolving on a horizontal axis, so as to be easily examined by the latter. Between the polarizing mirror and the eyepiece two powerful electromagnetic poles were arranged, being either the

---

[1] *Philosophical Transactions*, 1846, p. 1.

[2] The title of this paper has, I understand, led many to a misapprehension of its contents, and I therefore take the liberty of appending this explanatory note. Neither accepting nor rejecting the hypothesis of an ether, or the corpuscular, or any other view that may be entertained of the nature of light; and, as far as I can see, nothing being really known of a ray of light more than of a line of magnetic or electric force, or even of a line of gravitating force, except as it and they are manifest in and by substances; I believe that in the experiments I describe in the paper, light has been magnetically affected, i.e., that that which is magnetic in the forces of matter has been affected, and in turn has affected that which is truly magnetic in the force of light: by the term magnetic I include here either of the peculiar exertions of the power of a magnet, whether it be that which is manifest in the magnetic or the diamagnetic class of bodies. The phrase "illumination of the lines of magnetic force" has been understood to imply that I had rendered them luminous. This was not within my thought. I intended to express that the line of magnetic force was illuminated as the earth is illuminated by the sun, or the spider's web illuminated by the astronomer's lamp. Employing a ray of light, we can tell, *by the eye*, the direction of the magnetic lines through a body; and by the alteration of the ray and its optical effect on the eye, can see the course of the lines just as we can see the course of a thread of glass, or any other transparent substance, rendered visible by the light: and this is what I meant by *illumination*, as the paper fully explains.—December 15, 1845. M. F.

[3] *Experimental Researches*, 57, 366, 376, 877, 961, 2071.

[4] *Philosophical Transactions*, 1834. *Experimental Researches*, 951–955.

[5] *Archives de l'Électricité*, II, pp. 596–600.

poles of a horseshoe magnet, or the contrary poles of two cylinder magnets; they were separated from each other about 2 inches in the direction of the line of the ray, and so placed, that, if on the same side of the polarized ray, it might pass near them; or if on contrary sides, it might go between them, its direction being always parallel, or nearly so, to the magnetic lines of force (2149). After that, any transparent substance placed between the two poles, would have passing through it, both the polarized ray and the magnetic lines of force at the same time and in the same direction.

2151. Sixteen years ago I published certain experiments made upon optical glass,[1] and described the formation and general characters of one variety of heavy glass, which, from its materials, was called silicated borate of lead. It was this glass which first gave me the discovery of the relation between light and magnetism, and it has power to illustrate it in a degree beyond that of any other body; for the sake of perspicuity I will first describe the phenomena as presented by this substance.

2152. A piece of this glass, about 2 inches square and 0.5 of an inch thick, having flat and polished edges, was placed as a *diamagnetic* (2149) between the poles (not as yet magnetized by the electric current), so that the polarized ray should pass through its length; the glass acted as air, water, or any other indifferent substance would do; and if the eyepiece were previously turned into such a position that the polarized ray was extinguished, or rather the image produced by it rendered invisible, then the introduction of this glass made no alteration in that respect. In this state of circumstances the force of the electro-magnet was developed, by sending an electric current through its coils, and immediately the image of the lamp-flame became visible, and continued so as long as the arrangement continued magnetic. On stopping the electric current, and so causing the magnetic force to cease, the light instantly disappeared; these phenomena could be renewed at pleasure, at any instant of time, and upon any occasion, showing a perfect dependence of cause and effect.

[1] *Philosophical Transactions*, 1830, p. 1. I cannot resist the occasion which is thus offered to me of mentioning the name of Mr. Anderson, who came to me as an assistant in the glass experiments, and has remained ever since in the Laboratory of the Royal Institution. He has assisted me in all the researches into which I have entered since that time, and to his care, steadiness, exactitude, and faithfulness in the performance of all that has been committed to his charge, I am much indebted.—M. F.

2153. The voltaic current which I used upon this occasion, was that of five pair of Grove's construction, and the electro-magnets were of such power that the poles would singly sustain a weight of from twenty-eight to fifty-six, or more, pounds. A person looking for the phenomenon for the first time would not be able to see it with a weak magnet.

2154. The character of the force thus impressed upon the diamagnetic is that of *rotation;* for when the image of the lamp-flame has thus been rendered visible, revolution of the eye-piece to the right or left, more or less, will cause its extinction; and the further motion of the eye-piece to the one side or other of this position will produce the reappearance of the light, and that with complementary tints, according as this further motion is to the right- or left-hand.

2155. When the pole nearest to the observer was a marked pole, i.e., the same as the north end of a magnetic needle, and the farther pole was unmarked, the rotation of the ray was right-handed; for the eye-piece had to be turned to the right-hand, or clock fashion, to overtake the ray and restore the image to its first condition. When the poles were reversed, which was instantly done by changing the direction of the electric current, the rotation was changed also and became left-handed, the alteration being to an equal degree in extent as before. The direction was always the same for the same *line of magnetic force* (2149).

2156. When the diamagnetic was placed in the numerous other positions, which can easily be conceived, about the magnetic poles, results were obtained more or less marked in extent, and very definite in character, but of which the phenomena just described may be considered as the chief example: they will be referred to, as far as is necessary, hereafter.

2157. The same phenomena were produced in the silicated borate of lead (2151) by the action of a good ordinary steel horseshoe magnet, no electric current being now used. The results were feeble, but still sufficient to show the perfect identity of action between electro-magnets and common magnets in this their power over light.

2158. Two magnetic poles were employed end-ways, i.e., the cores of the electro-magnets were hollow iron cylinders, and the ray of polarized light passed along their axes and through the diamagnetic placed between them: the effect was the same.

2159. One magnetic pole only was used, that being one end of a powerful cylinder electro-magnet. When the heavy glass was beyond the magnet, being close to it but between the magnet and the polarizing reflector, the rotation was in one direction, dependent on the nature of the pole; when the diamagnetic was on the near side, being close to it but between it and the eye, the rotation for the same pole was in the contrary direction to what it was before; and when the magnetic pole was changed, both these directions were changed with it. When the heavy glass was placed in a corresponding position to the pole, but above or below it, so that the *magnetic curves* were no longer passing through the glass parallel to the ray of polarized light, but rather perpendicular to it, then no effect was produced. These particularities may be understood by reference to *Fig. 1*, where *a* and *b* represent the first positions of the diamagnetic, and *c* and *d* the latter positions, the course of the ray being marked by the dotted line. If also the glass were placed directly at the end of the magnet, then no effect was produced on a ray passing in the direction here described, though it is evident, from what has been already said (2155), that a ray passing *parallel* to the magnetic lines through the glass so placed, would have been affected by it.

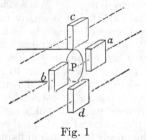

Fig. 1

2160. Magnetic lines, then, in passing through silicated borate of lead, and a great number of other substances (2173), cause these bodies to act upon a polarized ray of light when the lines are parallel to the ray, or in proportion as they are parallel to it: if they are perpendicular to the ray, they have no action upon it. They give the diamagnetic the power of rotating the ray; and the *law* of this action on light is, that if a magnetic line of force be *going from* a north pole, or *coming* from a south pole, along the path of a polarized ray coming to the observer, it will rotate that ray to the right-hand; or, that if such a line of force be coming from a north pole, or going from a south pole, it will rotate such a ray to the left-hand.

2161. If a cork or a cylinder of glass, representing the diamagnetic, be marked at its ends

with the letters N and S, to represent the poles of a magnet, the line joining these letters may be considered as a magnetic line of force; and further, if a line be traced round the cylinder with arrow-heads on it to represent direction, as in *Fig. 2*, such a simple model, held up before the eye, will express the whole of the law, and give every position and consequence of direction resulting from it. If a watch be considered as the diamagnetic, the north pole of a magnet being imagined against the face, and a south pole against the back, then the motion of the hand will indicate the direction of rotation which a ray of light undergoes by magnetization.

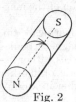

Fig. 2

2162. I will now proceed to the different circumstances which affect, limit, and define the extent and nature of this new power of action on light.

2163. In the first place, the rotation appears to be in proportion to the extent of the diamagnetic through which the ray and the magnetic lines pass. I preserved the strength of the magnet and the interval between its poles constant, and then interposed different pieces of the same heavy glass (2151) between the poles. The greater the extent of the diamagnetic in the line of the ray, whether in one, two, or three pieces, the greater was the rotation of the ray; and, as far as I could judge by these first experiments, the amount of rotation was exactly proportionate to the extent of diamagnetic through which the ray passed. No addition or diminution of the heavy glass on the *side* of the course of the ray made any difference in the effect of that part through which the ray passed.

2164. The power of rotating the ray of light *increased* with the intensity of the magnetic lines of force. This general effect is very easily ascertained by the use of electro-magnets; and within such range of power as I have employed, it appears to be directly proportionate to the intensity of the magnetic force.

2165. Other bodies, besides the heavy glass, possess the same power of becoming, under the influence of magnetic force, active on light (2173). When these bodies possess a rotative power of their own, as is the case with oil of turpentine, sugar, tartaric acid, tartrates, &c., the effect of the magnetic force is to add to, or subtract from, their specific force, according as the natural rotation and that induced by the magnetism is right- or left-handed (2231).

2166. I could not perceive that this power was affected by any degree of motion which I was able to communicate to the diamagnetic, whilst jointly subject to the action of the magnetism and the light.

2167. The interposition of copper, lead, tin, silver, and other ordinary non-magnetic bodies in the course of the magnetic curves, either between the pole and the diamagnetic, or in other positions, produced no effect either in kind or degree upon the phenomena.

2168. Iron frequently affected the results in a very considerable degree; but it always appeared to be, either by altering the direction of the magnetic lines, or disposing within itself of their force. Thus when the two contrary poles were on one side of the polarized ray (2150), and the heavy glass in its best position between them and in the ray (2152), the bringing of a large piece of iron near to the glass on the other side of the ray, caused the power of the diamagnetic to fall. This was because certain lines of magnetic force, which at first passed through the glass parallel to the ray, now crossed the glass and the ray; the iron giving two contrary poles opposite the poles of the magnet, and thus determining a new course for a certain portion of the magnetic power, and that across the polarized ray.

2169. Or if the iron, instead of being applied on the opposite side of the glass, were applied on the same side with the magnet, either near it or in contact with it, then, again, the power of the diamagnetic fell, simply because the power of the magnet was diverted from it into a new direction. These effects depend much of course on the intensity and power of the magnet, and on the size and softness of the iron.

2170. The electro-helices (2190) without the iron cores were very feeble in power, and indeed hardly sensible in their effect. With the iron cores they were powerful, though no more electricity was then passing through the coils than before (1071). This shows, in a very simple manner, that the phenomena exhibited by light under these circumstances is directly connected with the magnetic form of force supplied by the arrangement. Another effect which occurred illustrated the same point. When the contact at the voltaic battery is made, and the current sent round the electro-magnet, the image produced by the rotation of the polarized ray does not rise up to its full lustre immediately, but increases for a couple of seconds, gradually acquiring its greatest intensity; on breaking the contact, it sinks instantly and disappears apparently at once. The gradual rise in brightness is due to the *time* which the iron core of the magnet requires to evolve all that magnetic power which the electric current can develop in it; and as the magnetism rises in intensity, so does its effect on the light increase in power; hence the progressive condition of the rotation.

2171. I cannot as yet find that the heavy glass (2151), when in this state, i.e., with magnetic lines of force passing through it, exhibits any increased degree, or has any specific magneto-inductive action of the recognized kind. I have placed it in large quantities, and in different positions, between magnets and magnetic needles, having at the time very delicate means of appreciating any difference between it and air, but could find none.

2172. Using water, alcohol, mercury, and other fluids contained in very large delicate thermometer-shaped vessels, I could not discover that any difference in volume occurred when the magnetic curves passed through them.

2173. It is time that I should pass to a consideration of this power of magnetism over light as exercised, not only in the silicated borate of lead (2151), but in many other substances; and here we perceive, in the first place, that if all transparent bodies possess the power of exhibiting the action, they have it in very different degrees, and that up to this time there are some that have not shown it at all.

2174. Next, we may observe that bodies which are exceedingly different to each other in chemical, physical, and mechanical properties, develop this effect; for solids and liquids, acids, alkalies, oils, water, alcohol, ether, all possess the power.

2175. And lastly, we may observe, that in all of them, though the degree of action may differ, still it is always the same in kind, being a rotative power over the ray of light; and further, the direction of the rotation is, in every case, independent of the nature or state of the substance, and dependent upon the direction of the magnetic line of force, according to the law before laid down (2160).

2176. Amongst the substances in which this power of action is found, I have already distinguished the *silico-borate of lead* (2151) as eminently fitted for the purpose of exhibiting the phenomena. I regret that it should be the best, since it is not likely to be in the possession of many, and few will be induced to take the trouble of preparing it. If made, it should be well annealed, for otherwise the pieces will have considerable power of depolarizing light, and then the particular phenomena under consideration are much less strikingly observed. The *borate of lead*, however, is a substance much more fusible, softening at the heat of boiling oil, and therefore far more easily prepared in the form of glass plates and annealed; and it possesses as much magneto-rotative power over light as the silico-borate itself. *Flint-glass* exhibits the property, but in a less degree than the substances above. Crown-glass shows it, but in a still smaller degree.

2177. Whilst employing crystalline bodies as diamagnetics, I generally gave them that position in which they did not affect the polarized ray, and then induced the magnetic curves through them. As a class, they seemed to resist the assumption of the rotating state. *Rock-salt* and *fluor-spar* gave evidence of the power in a slight degree; and I think that a crystal of alum did the same, but its ray length in the transparent part was so small that I could not ascertain the fact decisively. Two specimens of transparent fluor, lent me by Mr. Tennant, gave the effect.

2178. Rock-crystal, 4 inches across, gave no indications of action on the ray; neither did smaller crystals, nor cubes about three-fourths of an inch in the side, which were so cut as to have two of their faces perpendicular to the axis of the crystal (1692, 1693), though they were examined in every direction.

2179. *Iceland spar* exhibited no signs of effect, either in the form of rhomboids, or of cubes like those just described (1695).

2180. *Sulphate of baryta, sulphate of lime*, and *carbonate of soda*, were also without action on the light.

2181. A piece of fine clear *ice* gave me no effect. I cannot however say there is none, for the effect of water in the same mass would be very small, and the irregularity of the flattened surface from the fusion of the ice and flow of water, made the observation very difficult.

2182. With some degree of curiosity and hope, I put gold-leaf into the magnetic lines, but could perceive no effect. Considering the extremely small dimensions of the length of the path of the polarized ray in it, any positive result was hardly to be expected.

2183. In experiments with liquids, a very good method of observing the effect is to enclose them in bottles from 1½ to 3 or 4 inches in diameter, placing these in succession between the magnetic poles (2150), and bringing the analysing eye-piece so near to the bottle that, by adjustment of the latter, its cylindrical form may cause a diffuse but useful image of the lamp-flame to be seen through it: the light of this image is easily distinguished from that which passes by irregular refraction through the striæ and deformations of the glass, and the phenomena being looked for in this light are easily seen.

2184. Water, alcohol, and ether, all show the effect; water most, alcohol less, and ether the least. All the fixed oils which I have tried, including almond, castor, olive, poppy, linseed, sperm, olein from hog's lard, and distilled resin oil, produce it. The essential oils of turpentine, bitter almonds, spike lavender, lavender, jessamine, cloves, and laurel, produce it. Also naphtha of various kinds, melted spermaceti, fused sulphur, chloride of sulphur, chloride of arsenic, and every other liquid substance which I had at hand and could submit in sufficient bulk to experiment.

2185. Of aqueous solutions I tried 150 or more, including the soluble acids, alkalies and salts, with sugar, gum, &c., the list of which would be too long to give here, since the great conclusion was that the exceeding diversity of substance caused no exception to the general result, for all the bodies showed the property. It is indeed more than probable, that in all these cases the water and not the other substance present was the ruling matter. The same general result was obtained with alcoholic solutions.

2186. Proceeding from liquids to air and gaseous bodies, I have here to state that, as yet, I have not been able to detect the exercise of this power in any one of the substances in this class. I have tried the experiment with bottles 4 inches in diameter, and the following gases: oxygen, nitrogen, hydrogen, nitrous oxide, olefiant gas, sulphurous acid, muriatic acid, carbonic acid, carbonic oxide, ammonia, sulphuretted hydrogen, and bromine vapour, at ordinary temperatures; but they all gave negative results. With air, the trial has been carried, by another form of apparatus, to a much higher degree, but still ineffectually (2212).

2187. Before dismissing the consideration of the substances which exhibited this power, and in reference to those in which it was superinduced upon bodies possessing, naturally, rotative force (2165, 2231), I may record, that the following are the substances submitted to experiment: castor oil, resin oil, oil of spike lavender, of laurel, Canada balsam, alcoholic solution of camphor, alcoholic solution of camphor and corrosive sublimate, aqueous solutions of sugar, tartaric acid, tartrate of soda, tartrate of potassa and antimony, tartaric and boracic acid, and sulphate of nickel, which rotated to the right-hand; copaiba balsam, which rotated the ray to the left-hand; and two specimens of camphene or oil of turpentine, in one of which the rotation was to the right-hand, and in the other to the left. In all these cases, as already said (2165), the superinduced magnetic rotation was according to the general law (2160), and without reference to the previous power of the body.

2188. Camphor being melted in a tube about an inch in diameter, exhibited high natural rotative force, but I could not discover that the magnetic curves induced additional force in it. It may be, however, that the shortness of the ray length and the quantity of coloured light left, even when the eye-piece was adjusted to the most favourable position for darkening the image produced by the naturally rotated ray, rendered the small magneto-power of the camphor insensible.

¶ ii. *Action of Electric Currents on Light*

2189. From a consideration of the nature and position of the lines of magnetic and electric force, and the relation of a magnet to a current of electricity, it appeared almost certain that an electric current would give the same result of action on light as a magnet; and, in the helix, would supply a form of apparatus in which great lengths of diamagnetics, and especially of such bodies as appeared to be but little affected between the poles of the magnet, might be submitted to examination and their effect exalted: this expectation was, by experiment, realized.

2190. Helices of copper wire were employed, three of which I will refer to. The first, or *long helix*, was 0.4 of an inch internal diameter; the wire was 0.03 of an inch in diameter, and having gone round the axis from one end of the helix to the other, then returned in the same manner, forming a coil 65 inches long, double in its whole extent, and containing 1240 feet of wire.

2191. The second, or *medium helix*, is 19 inches long, 1.87 inch internal diameter, and 3 inches external diameter. The wire is 0.2 of an inch in diameter, and 80 feet in length, being disposed in the coil as two concentric spirals. The electric current, in passing through it, is not divided, but traverses the whole length of the wire.

2192. The third, or *Woolwich helix*, was made under my instruction for the use of Lieut.-Colonel Sabine's establishment at Woolwich. It is 26.5 inches long, 2.5 inches internal diameter, and 4.75 inches external diameter. The wire is 0.17 of an inch in diameter, and 501 feet in length. It is disposed in the coil in four concentric spirals connected end to end, so that the whole of the electric current employed passes through all the wire.

2193. The long helix (2190) acted very feebly on a magnetic needle placed at a little distance from it; the medium helix (2191) acted more powerfully, and the Woolwich helix (2192) very strongly; the same battery of ten pairs of Grove's plate being employed in all cases.

2194. Solid bodies were easily subjected to the action of these electro-helices, being for that purpose merely cut into the form of bars or prisms with flat and polished ends, and then introduced as cores into the helices. For the purpose of submitting liquid bodies to the same action, tubes of glass were provided, furnished at the ends with caps; the cylindrical part of the cap was brass, and had a tubular aperture for the introduction of the liquids, but the end was a flat glass plate. When the tube was intended to contain aqueous fluids, the plates were attached to the caps, and the caps to the tube by Canada balsam; when the tube had to contain alcohol, ether or essential oils, a thick mixture of powdered gum with a little water was employed as the cement.

2195. The general effect produced by this form of apparatus may be stated as follows: the tube within the long helix (2190) was filled with distilled water and placed in the line of the polarized ray, so that by examination through the eye-piece (2150), the image of the lamp-flame produced by the ray could be seen through it. Then the eyepiece was turned until the image of the flame disappeared, and, afterwards, the current of ten pairs of plates sent through the helix; instantly the image of the flame reappeared, and continued as long as the electric current was passing through the helix; on stopping the current the image disappeared. The light did not rise up gradually, as in the case of electro-magnets (2170), but instantly. These results could be produced at pleasure. In this experiment we may, I think, justly say that a ray of light is electrified and the electric forces illuminated.

2196. The phenomena may be made more striking, by the adjustment of a lens of long focus between the tube and the polarizing mirror, or one of short focus between the tube and the eye; and where the helix, or the battery, or the substance experimented with, is feeble in power, such means offer assistance in working out the effects: but after a little experience, they are easily dispensed with, and are only useful as accessories in doubtful cases.

2197. In cases where the effect is feeble, it is more easily perceived if the Nichol eyepiece be adjusted, not to the perfect extinction of the ray, but a little short of or beyond that position; so that the image of the flame may be but just visible. Then, on the exertion of the power of the electric current, the light is either increased in intensity, or else diminished, or extinguished, or even re-illuminated on the other side of the dark condition; and this change is more easily perceived than if the eye began to observe from a state of utter darkness. Such a mode of observing also assists in demonstrating the rotatory character of the action on light; for, if the light be made visible beforehand by the motion of the eyepiece in one direction, and the power of the current be to *increase* that light, an instant only suffices, after stopping the current, to move the eye-piece in the other direction until the light is apparent as at first, and then the power of the current will be to *diminish* it; the tints of the lights being affected also at the same time.

2198. When the current was sent round the helix in one direction, the rotation induced upon the ray of light was one way; and when the current was changed to the contrary direction, the rotation was the other way. In order to express the direction, I will assume, as is usually done, that the current passes from the zinc through the acid to the platinum in the same cell (663, 667, 1627): if such a current pass under the ray towards the right, upwards on its right side, and over the ray towards the left, it will give left-handed rotation to it; or, if the current pass over the ray to the right, down on the right side, and under it towards the left, it will induce it to rotate to the right-hand.

2199. The LAW, therefore, by which an electric current acts on a ray of light is easily expressed. When an electric current passes round a ray of polarized light in a plane perpendicular to the ray, it causes the ray to revolve on its axis, as long as it is under the influence of the current, in the *same direction* as that in which the current is passing.

2200. The simplicity of this law, and its identity with that given before, as expressing the action of magnetism on light (2160), is very

beautiful. A model is not wanted to assist the memory; but if that already described (2161) be looked at, the line round it will express at the same time the direction both of the current and the rotation. It will indeed do much more; for if the cylinder be considered as a piece of iron, and not a piece of glass or other diamagnetic, placed between the two poles N and S, then the line round it will represent the direction of the currents, which, according to Ampère's theory, are moving round its particles; or if it be considered as a core of iron (in place of a core of water), having an electric current running round it in the direction of the line, it will also represent such a magnet as would be formed if it were placed between the poles whose marks are affixed to its ends.

2201. I will now notice certain points respecting the degree of this action under different circumstances. By using a tube of water (2194) as long as the helix, but placing it so that more or less of the tube projected at either end of the helix, I was able, in some degree, to ascertain the effect of length of the diamagnetic, the force of the helix and current remaining the same. The greater the column of water subjected to the action of the helix, the greater was the rotation of the polarized ray; and the amount of rotation seemed to be directly proportionate to the length of fluid round which the electric current passed.

2202. A short tube of water, or a piece of heavy glass, being placed in the axis of the Woolwich helix (2192), seemed to produce equal effect on the ray of light, whether it were in the middle of the helix or at either end; provided it was always within the helix and in the line of the axis. From this it would appear that every part of the helix has the same effect; and, that by using long helices, substances may be submitted to this kind of examination which could not be placed in sufficient length between the poles of magnets (2150).

2203. A tube of water as long as the Woolwich helix (2192), but only 0.4 of an inch in diameter, was placed in the helix parallel to the axis, but sometimes in the axis and sometimes near the side. No apparent difference was produced in these different situations; and I am inclined to believe (without being quite sure) that the action on the ray is the same, wherever the tube is placed, within the helix, in relation to the axis. The same result was obtained when a larger tube of water was looked through, whether the ray passed through the axis of the helix and tube, or near the side.

2204. If bodies be introduced into the helix possessing, naturally, rotating force, then the rotating power given by the electric current is superinduced upon them, exactly as in the cases already described of magnetic action (2165, 2187).

2205. A helix, 20 inches long and 0.3 of an inch in diameter, was made of uncovered copper wire, 0.05 of an inch in diameter, in close spirals. This was placed in a large tube of water, so that the fluid, both in the inside and at the outside of the helix, could be examined by the polarized ray. When the current was sent *through* the helix, the water within it received rotating power; but no trace of such an action on the light was seen on the outside of the helix, even in the line most close to the uncovered wire.

2206. The water was enclosed in brass and copper tubes, but this alteration caused not the slightest change in the effect.

2207. The water in the brass tube was put into an *iron* tube, much longer than either the Woolwich helix or the brass tube, and quite one-eighth of an inch thick in the side; yet when placed in the Woolwich helix (2192), the water rotated the ray of light apparently as well as before.

2208. An iron bar, 1 inch square and longer than the helix, was put into the helix, and the small water tube (2203) upon it. The water exerted as much action on the light as before.

2209. Three iron tubes, each 27 inches long and one-eighth of an inch in thickness in the side, were selected of such diameters as to pass easily one into the other, and the whole into the Woolwich helix (2192). The smaller one was supplied with glass ends and filled with water; and being placed in the axis of the Woolwich helix, had a certain amount of rotating power over the polarized ray. The second tube was then placed over this, so that there was now a thickness of iron equal to two-eighths of an inch between the water and the helix; the water had *more* power of rotation than before. On placing the third tube of iron over the two former, the power of the water *fell*, but was still very considerable. These results are complicated, being dependent on the new condition which the character of iron gives to its action on the forces. Up to a certain amount, by increasing the development of magnetic forces, the helix and core, *as a whole*, produce increased action on the water; but on the addition of more iron and the disposal of the forces through it, their action is removed in part from the water and the rotation is lessened.

2210. Pieces of heavy glass (2151), placed in iron tubes in the helices, produced similar effects.

2211. The bodies which were submitted to the action of an electric current in a helix, in the manner already described, were as follows: heavy glass (2151, 2176), water, solution of sulphate of soda, solution of tartaric acid, alcohol, ether, and oil of turpentine; all of which were affected, and acted on light exactly in the manner described in relation to magnetic action (2173).

2212. I submitted *air* to the influence of these helices carefully and anxiously, but could not discover any trace of action on the polarized ray of light. I put the long helix (2190) into the other two (2191, 2192), and combined them all into one consistent series, so as to accumulate power, but could not observe any effect of them on light passing through air.

2213. In the use of helices, it is necessary to be aware of one effect, which might otherwise cause confusion and trouble. At first, the wire of the long helix (2190) was wound directly upon the thin glass tube which served to contain the fluid. When the electric current passed through the helix it raised the temperature of the metal, and that gradually raised the temperature of the glass and the film of water in contact with it, and so the cylinder of water, warmer at its surface than its axis, acted as a lens, gathering and sending rays of light to the eye, and continuing to act for a time after the current was stopped. By separating the tube of water from the helix, and by other precautions, this source of confusion is easily avoided.

2214. Another point of which the experimenter should be aware is the difficulty, and almost impossibility, of obtaining a piece of glass which, especially after it is cut, does not depolarize light. When it does depolarize, difference of position makes an immense difference in the appearance. By always referring to the parts that do not depolarize, as the black cross, for instance, and by bringing the eye as near as may be to the glass, this difficulty is more or less overcome.

2215. For the sake of supplying a general indication of the amount of this induced rotating force in two or three bodies, and without any pretence of offering correct numbers, I will give, generally, the result of a few attempts to measure the force, and compare it with the natural power of a specimen of oil of turpentine. A very powerful electro-magnet was employed, with a *constant* distance between its poles of 2½ inches. In this space was placed different substances; the amount of rotation of the eyepiece observed several times and the average taken, as expressing the rotation for the ray length of substance used. But as the substances were of different dimensions, the ray lengths were, by calculation, corrected to one standard length, upon the assumption that the power was proportionate to this length (2163). The oil of turpentine was of course observed in its natural state, i.e., without magnetic action. Making water 1, the numbers were as follows:

Oil of turpentine	.	.	11.8	
Heavy glass (2151)	.	.	6.0	
Flint-glass	.	.	2.8	
Rock-salt	.	.	2.2	
Water	.	.	1.0	
Alcohol	.	.	.	less than water
Ether	.	.	.	less than alcohol

2216. In relation to the action of magnetic and electric forces on light, I consider, that to know the conditions under which there is no apparent action, is to add to our knowledge of their mutual relations; and will, therefore, very briefly state how I have lately combined these forces, obtaining no apparent result (955).

2217. Heavy glass, flint-glass, rock crystal, Iceland spar, oil of turpentine, and air, had a polarized ray passed through them; and, at the same time, lines of electro-static tension (2149) were, by means of coatings, the Leyden jar, and the electric machine, directed across the bodies, parallel to the polarized ray, and perpendicular to it, both in and across the plane of polarization; but without any visible effect. The tension of a rapidly recurring, induced secondary current, was also directed upon the same bodies and upon water (as an electrolyte), but with the same negative result.

2218. A polarized ray, powerful magnetic lines of force, and the electric lines of force (2149) just described, were combined in various directions in their action on heavy glass (2151, 2176), but with no other result than that due to the mutual action of the magnetic lines of light, already described in this paper.

2219. A polarized ray and electric currents were combined in every possible way in electrolytes (951–954). The substances used were distilled water, solution of sugar, dilute sulphuric acid, solution of sulphate of soda, using platinum electrodes; and solution of sulphate of copper, using copper electrodes: the current was sent along the ray, and perpendicular to it

in two directions at right angles with each other; the ray was made to rotate, by altering the position of the polarizing mirror, that the plane of polarization might be varied; the current was used as a continuous current, as a rapidly intermitting current, and as a rapidly alternating double current of induction; but in no case was any trace of action perceived.

2220. Lastly, a ray of polarized light, electric currents, and magnetic lines of force, were directed in every possible way through dilute sulphuric acid and solution of sulphate of soda, but still with negative results, except in those positions where the phenomena already described were produced. In one arrangement, the current passed in the direction of radii from a central to a circumferential electrode, the contrary magnetic poles being placed above and below; and the arrangements were so good that when the electric current was passing, the fluid rapidly rotated; but a polarized ray sent horizontally across this arrangement was not at all affected. Also, when the ray was sent vertically through it, and the eye-piece moved to correspond to the rotation impressed upon the ray in this position by the magnetic curves alone, the superinduction of the passage of the electric current made not the least difference in the effect upon the ray.

¶ iii. *General Considerations*

2221. Thus is established, I think for the first time,[1] a true, direct relation and dependence between light and the magnetic and electric forces; and thus a great addition made to the facts and considerations which tend to prove that all natural forces are tied together, and have one common origin (2146). It is, no doubt, difficult in the present state of our knowledge to express our expectation in exact terms; and, though I have said that another of the powers

---

[1] I say, for the first time, because I do not think that the experiments of Morrichini on the production of magnetism by the rays at the violet end of the spectrum prove any such relation. When in Rome with Sir H. Davy in the month of May 1814, I spent several hours at the house of Morrichini, working with his apparatus and under his directions, but could not succeed in magnetising a needle. I have no confidence in the effect as a *direct* result of the action of the sun's rays; but think that when it has occurred it has been secondary, incidental, and perhaps even accidental; a result that might well happen with a needle that was preserved during the whole experiment in a north and south position. *January* 2, 1846. I should not have written "for the first time" as above, if I had remembered Mr. Christie's experiments and papers on the "Influence of the Solar Rays on Magnets," communicated in the *Philosophical Transactions* for 1826, p. 219, and 1828, p. 379.—M. F.

of nature is, in these experiments, directly related to the rest, I ought, perhaps, rather to say that another form of the great power is distinctly and directly related to the other forms; or, that the great power manifested by particular phenomena in particular forms, is here further identified and recognized, by the direct relation of its form of light to its forms of electricity and magnetism.

2222. The relation existing between *polarized* light and magnetism and electricity, is even more interesting than if it had been shown to exist with common light only. It cannot but extend to common light; and, as it belongs to light made, in a certain respect, more precise in its character and properties by polarization, it collates and connects it with these powers, in that duality of character which they possess, and yields an opening, which before was wanting to us, for the appliance of these powers to the investigation of the nature of this and other radiant agencies.

2223. Referring to the conventional distinction before made (2149), it may be again stated that it is the magnetic lines of force *only* which are effectual on the rays of light, and they *only* (in appearance) when parallel to the ray of light, or as they tend to parallelism with it. As, in reference to matter not magnetic after the manner of iron, the phenomena of electric induction and electrolyzation show a vast superiority in the energy with which electric forces can act as compared to magnetic forces, so here, in another direction and in the peculiar and correspondent effects which belong to magnetic forces, they are shown, in turn, to possess great superiority, and to have their full equivalent of action on the same kind of matter.

2224. The magnetic forces do not act on the ray of light directly and without the intervention of matter, but through the mediation of the substance in which they and the ray have a simultaneous existence; the substances and the forces giving to and receiving from each other the power of acting on the light. This is shown by the non-action of a vacuum, of air or gases; and it is also further shown by the special degree in which different matters possess the property. That magnetic force acts upon the ray of light always with the same character of manner and in the same direction, independent of the different varieties of substance, or their states of solid or liquid, or their specific rotative force (2232), shows that the magnetic force and the light have a direct relation: but that substances are necessary, and that these act in different degrees, shows that the magnetism and the light act on each other through the intervention of the matter.

2225. Recognizing or perceiving *matter* only by its powers, and knowing nothing of any imaginary nucleus, abstract from the idea of these powers, the phenomena described in this paper much strengthen my inclination to trust in the views I have on a former occasion advanced in reference to its nature.[1]

2226. It cannot be doubted that the magnetic forces act upon and affect the internal constitution of the diamagnetic, just as freely in the dark as when a ray of light is passing through it; though the phenomena produced by light seem, as yet, to present the only means of observing this constitution and the change. Further, any such change as this must belong to opaque bodies, such as wood, stone, and metal; for as diamagnetics, there is no distinction between them and those which are transparent. The degree of transparency can at the utmost, in this respect, only make a distinction between the individuals of a class.

2227. If the magnetic forces had made these bodies magnets, we could, by light, have examined a transparent magnet; and that would have been a great help to our investigation of the forces of matter. But it does not make them magnets (2171), and therefore the molecular condition of these bodies, when in the state described, must be specifically distinct from that of magnetized iron, or other such matter, and must be *a new magnetic condition;* and as the condition is a state of tension (manifested by its instantaneous return to the normal state when the magnetic induction is removed), so the *force* which the matter in this state possesses and its mode of action, must be to us a *new magnetic force* or *mode of action* of matter.

2228. For it is impossible, I think, to observe and see the action of magnetic forces, rising in intensity, upon a piece of heavy glass or a tube of water, without also perceiving that the latter acquire properties which are not only *new* to the substance, but are also in subjection to very definite and precise laws (2160, 2199), and are equivalent in proportion to the magnetic forces producing them.

2229. Perhaps this state is a state of *electric tension tending to a current;* as in magnets, according to Ampère's theory, the state is a state of *current*. When a core of iron is put into a helix, everything leads us to believe that currents of electricity are produced within it, which

[1] See p. 850–855.

rotate or move in a plane perpendicular to the axis of the helix. If a diamagnetic be placed in the same position, it acquires power to make light rotate in the same plane. The state it has received is a state of tension, but it has not passed on into currents, though the acting force and every other circumstance and condition are the same as those which do produce currents in iron, nickel, cobalt, and such other matters as are fitted to receive them. Hence the idea that there exists in diamagnetics, under such circumstances, a tendency to currents, is consistent with all the phenomena as yet described, and is further strengthened by the fact, that, leaving the loadstone or the electric current, which by inductive action is rendering a piece of iron, nickel, or cobalt magnetic, perfectly unchanged, a mere change of temperature will take from these bodies their extra power, and make them pass into the common class of diamagnetics.

2230. The present is, I believe, the first time that the molecular condition of a body, required to produce the circular polarization of light, has been artificially given; and it is therefore very interesting to consider this known state and condition of the body, comparing it with the relatively unknown state of those which possess the power naturally: especially as some of the latter rotate to the right-hand and others to the left; and, as in the cases of quartz and oil of turpentine, the same body chemically speaking, being in the latter instance a liquid with particles free to move, presents different specimens, some rotating one way and some the other.

2231. At first one would be inclined to conclude that the natural state and the state conferred by magnetic and electric forces must be the same, since the effect is the same; but on further consideration it seems very difficult to come to such a conclusion. Oil of turpentine will rotate a ray of light, the power depending upon its particles and not upon the arrangement of the mass. Whichever way a ray of polarized light passes through this fluid, it is rotated in the same manner; and rays passing in every possible direction through it *simultaneously* are all rotated with equal force and according to one common law of direction; i.e., either all right-handed or else all to the left. Not so with the rotation superinduced on the *same* oil of turpentine by the magnetic or electric forces: it exists only in one direction, i.e., in a plane perpendicular to the magnetic line;

and being limited to this plane, it can be changed in direction by a reversal of the direction of the inducing force. The direction of the rotation produced by the natural state is connected invariably with the direction of the ray of light; but the power to produce it appears to be possessed in every direction and at all times by the particles of the fluid: the direction of the rotation produced by the induced condition is connected invariably with the direction of the magnetic line or the electric current, and the condition is possessed by the particles of matter, but strictly limited by the line or the current, changing and disappearing with it.

2232. Let *m*, in *Fig. 3*, represent a glass cell filled with oil of turpentine, possessing naturally the power of producing right-hand rotation, and *a b* a polarized ray of light. If the ray proceed from *a* to *b*, and the eye be placed at *b*, the rotation will be right-handed, or according to the direction expressed by the arrow-heads on the circle *c;* if the ray proceed from *b* to *a*, and the eye be placed at *a*, the rotation will still be right-handed *to the observer*, i.e., according to the direction indicated on the circle *d*. Let now an electric current pass round the oil of turpentine in the direction indicated on the circle *c*, or magnetic poles be placed so as to produce the same effect (2155); the particles will acquire a further rotative force (which no motion amongst themselves will disturb), and a ray coming from *a* to *b* will be seen by an eye placed at *b* to rotate to the right-hand more than before, or in the direction on the circle *c;* but pass a ray from *b* to *a*, and observe with the eye at *a*, and the phenomenon is no longer the same as before; for instead of the new rotation being according to the direction indicated on the circle *d*, it will be in the contrary direction, or to the observer's left-hand (2199). In fact the induced rotation will be added to the natural rotation as respects a ray passing from *a* to *b*, but it will be subtracted from the natural rotation as regards the ray passing from *b* to *a*. Hence the particles of this fluid which rotate by virtue of their natural force, and those which rotate by virtue of the induced force, cannot be in the same condition.

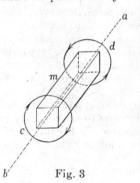

Fig. 3

2233. As respects the power of the oil of turpentine to rotate a ray in whatever direction it is passing through the liquid, it may well be that though all the particles possess the power of rotating the light, only those whose planes of rotation are more or less perpendicular to the ray affect it; and that it is the resultant or sum of forces in any one direction which is active in producing rotation. But even then a striking difference remains, because the resultant in the same plane is not absolute in direction, but relative to the course of the ray, being in the one case as the circle c, and in the other as the circle d, *Fig. 3;* whereas the resultant of the magnetic or electric induction is absolute, and not changing with the course of the ray, being always either as expressed by c or else as indicated by d.

2234. All these differences, however, will doubtless disappear or come into harmony as these investigations are extended; and their very existence opens so many paths, by which we may pursue our inquiries, more and more deeply, into the powers and constitution of matter.

2235. Bodies having rotating power of themselves, do not seem by that to have a greater or a less tendency to assume a further degree of the same force under the influence of magnetic or electric power.

2236. Were it not for these and other differences, we might see an analogy between those bodies, which possess at all times the rotating power, as a specimen of quartz which rotates only in one plane, and also those to which the power is given by the induction of other forces, as a prism of heavy glass in a helix, on the one hand; and, on the other, a natural magnet and a helix through which the current is passing. The natural condition of the magnet and quartz, and the constrained condition of the helix and heavy glass, form the link of the analogy in one direction; whilst the supposition of currents existing in the magnet and helix, and only a tendency or tension to currents existing in the quartz and heavy glass, supplies the link in the transverse direction.

2237. As to those bodies which seem as yet to give no indication of the power over light, and therefore none of the assumption of the new magnetic conditions, these may be divided into two classes, the one including air, gases and vapours, and the other rock crystal, Iceland spar, and certain other crystalline bodies. As regards the latter class, I shall give, in the next series of these researches, proofs drawn from phenomena of an entirely different kind, that they do acquire the new magnetic condition; and these being so disposed of for the moment, I am inclined to believe that even air and gases have the power to assume the peculiar state, and even to affect light, but in a degree so small that as yet it has not been made sensible. Still the gaseous state is such a remarkable condition of matter, that we ought not too hastily to assume that the substances which, in the solid and liquid state, possess properties even general in character, always carry these into their gaseous condition.

2238. Rock-salt, fluor-spar, and, I think, alum, affect the ray of light; the other crystals experimented with did not; these are equiaxed and singly refracting, the others are unequiaxed and doubly refracting. Perhaps these instances, with that of the rotation of quartz, may even now indicate a relation between magnetism, electricity, and the crystallizing forces of matter.

2239. All bodies are affected by helices as by magnets, and according to laws which show that the causes of the action are identical as well as the effects. This result supplies another fine proof in favour of the identity of helices and magnets, according to the views of Ampère.

2240. The theory of static induction which I formerly ventured to set forth (1161, &c.), and which depends upon the action of the contiguous particles of the dielectric intervening between the inductric and the inducteous bodies, led me to expect that the same kind of dependence upon the intervening particles would be found to exist in magnetic action; and I published certain experiments and considerations on this point seven years ago (1709–1736). I could not then discover any peculiar condition of the intervening substance or diamagnetic; but now that I have been able to make out such a state, which is not only a state of tension (2227), but dependent entirely upon the magnetic lines which pass through the substance, I am more than ever encouraged to believe that the view then advanced is correct.

2241. Although the magnetic and electric forces *appear* to exert no power on the ordinary or on the depolarized ray of light, we can hardly doubt but that they have some special influence, which probably will soon be made apparent by experiment. Neither can it be supposed otherwise than that the same kind of action should take place on the other forms of radiant agents as heat and chemical force.

2242. This mode of magnetic and electric action, and the phenomena presented by it, will, I hope, greatly assist hereafter in the investigation of the nature of transparent bodies, of light, of magnets, and their action one on another or on magnetic substances. I am at this time engaged in investigating the new magnetic condition, and shall shortly send a further account of it to the Royal Society. What the possible effect of the force may be in the earth as a whole or in magnets, or in relation to the sun, and what may be the best means of causing light to evolve electricity and magnetism, are thoughts continually pressing upon the mind; but it will be better to occupy both time and thought, aided by experiment, in the investigation and development of real truth, than to use them in the invention of suppositions which may or may not be founded on, or consistent with, fact.

Royal Institution, Oct. 29, 1845

TWENTIETH SERIES[1]

§ *27. On New Magnetic Actions, and on the Magnetic Condition of All Matter*[2] ¶ i. *Apparatus Required* ¶ ii. *Action of Magnets on Heavy Glass* ¶ iii. *Action of Magnets on Other Substances Acting Magnetically on Light* ¶ iv. *Action of Magnets on Metals Generally*

RECEIVED DECEMBER 6, READ DECEMBER 18, 1845

2243. THE contents of the last Series of these *Researches* were, I think, sufficient to justify

1 *Philosophical Transactions*, 1846, p. 21.
2 My friend Mr. Wheatstone has this day called my attention to a paper by M. Becquerel, "On the magnetic actions excited in all bodies by the influence of very energetic magnets," read to the Academy of Sciences on the 27th of September 1827, and published in the *Annales de Chimie*, XXXVI, p. 337. It relates to the action of the magnet on a magnetic needle, on soft iron, on the deutoxide and tritoxide of iron, on the tritoxide alone, and on a needle of wood. The author observed, and quotes Coulomb as having also observed, that a needle of wood under certain conditions, pointed *across* the magnetic curves; and he also states the striking fact that he had found a needle of wood place itself parallel to the wires of a galvanometer. These effects, however, he refers to a degree of magnetism less than that of the tritoxide of iron, but the same in character, for the bodies take the same position The polarity of steel and iron is stated to be in the direction of the length of the substance, but that of tritoxide of iron, wood and gum-lac, most frequently in the direction of the width, and always when one magnetic pole is employed. "This difference of effect, which establishes a line of demarcation between these two species of phenomena, is due to this, that the magnetism being very feeble in the tritoxide of iron, wood, &c., we may neglect the reaction of the body on itself, and therefore the direct action of the bar ought to overrule it."
As the paper does not refer the phenomena of wood and gum-lac to an elementary *repulsive* action, nor show that they are common to an immense class of bodies, nor distinguish this class, which I have called diamagnetic, from the magnetic class; and, as it makes all magnetic action of one kind, whereas I show that there are two kinds of such action, as distinct from each other as positive and negative electric action are in their way, so I do not think I need alter a word or the date of that which I have written; but am most glad here to acknowledge M. Becquerel's important facts and labours in reference to this subject.—M. F. Dec. 5, 1845.

the statement, that a new magnetic condition (i.e., one new to our knowledge) had been impressed on matter by subjecting it to the action of magnetic and electric forces (2227); which new condition was made manifest by the powers of action which the matter had acquired over light. The phenomena now to be described are altogether different in their nature; and they prove, not only a magnetic condition of the substances referred to unknown to us before, but also of many others, including a vast number of opaque and metallic bodies, and perhaps all except the magnetic metals and their compounds: and they also, through that condition, present us with the means of undertaking the correlation of magnetic phenomena, and perhaps the construction of a theory of general magnetic action founded on simple fundamental principles.

2244. The whole matter is so new, and the phenomena so varied and general, that I must, with every desire to be brief, describe much which at last will be found to concentrate under simple principles of action. Still, in the present state of our knowledge, such is the only method by which I can make these principles and their results sufficiently manifest.

¶ i. *Apparatus Required*

2245. The effects to be described require magnetic apparatus of great power, and under perfect command. Both these points are obtained by the use of electro-magnets, which can be raised to a degree of force far beyond that of natural or steel magnets; and further, can be suddenly altogether deprived of power, or made energetic to the highest degree, without the slightest alteration of the arrangement, or of any other circumstance belonging to an experiment.

2246. One of the electro-magnets which I use is that already described under the term Woolwich helix (2192). The soft iron core belonging to it is 28 inches in length and 2.5 inches in diameter. When thrown into action by ten pair of Grove's plates, either end will sustain one or two half-hundred weights hanging to it. The magnet can be placed either in the vertical or the horizontal position. The iron core is a cylinder with flat ends, but I have had a cone of iron made, 2 inches in diameter at the base and 1 inch in height, and this placed at the end of the core, forms a conical termination to it, when required.

2247. Another magnet which I have had made has the horseshoe form. The bar of iron is 46 inches in length and 3.75 inches in diameter, and is so bent that the extremities forming the poles are 6 inches from each other; 522 feet of copper wire 0.17 of an inch in diameter, and covered with tape, are wound round the two straight parts of the bar, forming two coils on these parts, each 16 inches in length, and composed of three layers of wire: the poles are, of course, 6 inches apart, the ends are planed true, and against these move two short bars of soft iron, 7 inches long and 2½ by 1 inch thick, which can be adjusted by screws, and held at any distance less than 6 inches from each other. The ends of these bars form the opposite poles of contrary name; the magnetic field between them can be made of greater or smaller extent and the intensity of the lines of magnetic force be proportionately varied.

2248. For the suspension of substances between and near the poles of these magnets, I occasionally used a glass jar, with a plate and sliding wire at the top. Six or eight lengths of cocoon silk being equally stretched, were made into one thread and attached, at the upper end, to the sliding rod, and at the lower end to a stirrup of paper, in which anything to be experimented on could be sustained.

2249. Another very useful mode of suspension was to attach one end of a fine thread, 6 feet long, to an adjustable arm near the ceiling of the room, and terminating at the lower end by a little ring of copper wire; any substance to be suspended could be held in a simple cradle

of fine copper wire having 8 or 10 inches of the wire prolonged upward; this being bent into a hook at the superior extremity, gave the means of attachment to the ring. The height of the suspended substance could be varied at pleasure, by bending any part of the wire at the instant into the hook form. A glass cylinder placed between the magnetic poles was quite sufficient to keep the suspended substance free from any motion, due to the agitation of the air.

2250. It is necessary, before entering upon an experimental investigation with such an apparatus, to be aware of the effect of any magnetism which the bodies used may possess; the power of the apparatus to make manifest such magnetism is so great, that it is difficult on that account to find writing-paper fit for the stirrup above mentioned. Before therefore any experiments are instituted, it must be ascertained that the suspending apparatus employed does not point, i.e., does not take up a position parallel to the lines joining the magnetic poles, by virtue of the magnetic force. When copper suspensions are employed, a peculiar effect is produced (2309), but when understood, as it will be hereafter, it does not interfere with the results of experiment. The wire should be fine, not magnetic as iron, and the form of the suspending cradle should not be elongated horizontally, but be round or square as to its general dimensions, in that direction.

2251. The substances to be experimented with should be carefully examined, and rejected if not found free from magnetism. Their state is easily ascertained; for, if magnetic, they will either be attracted to the one or the other pole of the great magnet, or else point between them. No examination by smaller magnets, or by a magnetic needle, is sufficient for this purpose.

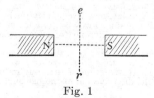

Fig. 1

2252. I shall have such frequent occasion to refer to two chief directions of position across the magnetic field, that to avoid periphrasis, I will here ask leave to use a term or two, conditionally. One of these directions is that from pole to pole, or along the line of magnetic force; I will call it the *axial direction:* the other is the direction perpendicular to this, and across the line of magnetic force; and for the time, and as respects the space between the poles, I will call it the *equatorial direction*. Other terms that I may use, I hope will explain themselves.

¶ ii. *Action of Magnets on Heavy Glass*

2253. The bar of silicated borate of lead, or heavy glass already described as the substance in which magnetic forces were first made effectually to bear on a ray of light (2152), and which is 2 inches long, and about 0.5 of an inch wide and thick, was suspended centrally between the magnetic poles (2247), and left until the effect of torsion was over. The magnet was then thrown into action by making contact at the voltaic battery: immediately the bar moved, turning round its point of suspension, into a position across the magnetic curve or line of force, and after a few vibrations took up its place of rest there. On being displaced by hand from this position, it returned to it, and this occurred many times in succession.

2254. Either end of the bar indifferently went to either side of the axial line. The determining circumstance was simply inclination of the bar one way or the other to the axial line, at the beginning of the experiment. If a particular or marked end of the bar were on one side of the magnetic, or axial line, when the magnet was rendered active that end went farther outwards, until the bar had taken up the equatorial position.

2255. Neither did any change in the magnetism of the poles, by change in the direction of the electric current, cause any difference in this respect. The bar went by the shortest course to the equatorial position.

2256. The power which urged the bar into this position was so thoroughly under command that if the bar were swinging it could easily be hastened in its course into this position, or arrested as it was passing from it, by seasonable contacts at the voltaic battery.

2257. There are two positions of equilibrium for the bar; one stable, the other unstable. When in the direction of the axis or magnetic line of force, the completion of the electric communication causes no change of place; but if it be the least oblique to this position, then the obliquity increases until the bar arrives at the equatorial position; or if the bar be originally in the equatorial position, then the magnetism causes no further changes, but retains it there (2298, 2299, 2384).

2258. Here then we have a magnetic bar which points east and west, in relation to north and south poles, i.e., points perpendicularly to the lines of magnetic force.

2259. If the bar be adjusted so that its point of suspension, being in the axial line, is not equidistant from the poles, but near to one of them, then the magnetism again makes the bar take up a position perpendicular to the magnetic lines of force; either end of the bar being on the one side of the axial line, or the other, at pleasure. But at the same time there is another effect, for at the moment of completing the electric contact, the centre of gravity of the bar recedes from the pole and remains repelled from it as long as the magnet is retained excited. On allowing the magnetism to pass away, the bar returns to the place due to it by its gravity.

2260. Precisely the same effect takes place at the other pole of the magnet. Either of them is able to repel the bar, whatever its position may be, and at the same time the bar is made to assume a position, at right angles, to the line of magnetic force.

2261. If the bar be equidistant from the two poles, and in the axial line, then no repulsive effect is or can be observed.

2262. But preserving the point of suspension in the equatorial line, i.e., equidistant from the two poles, and removing it a little on one side or the other of the axial line (2252), then another effect is brought forth. The bar points as before across the magnetic line of force, but at the same time it recedes from the axial line, increasing its distance from it, and this new position is retained as long as the magnetism continues, and is quitted with its cessation.

2263. Instead of two magnetic poles, a single pole may be used, and that either in a vertical or a horizontal position. The effects are in perfect accordance with those described above; for the bar, when near the pole, is repelled from it in the direction of the line of magnetic force, and at the same time it moves into a position perpendicular to the direction of the magnetic lines passing through it. When the magnet is vertical (2246) and the bar by its side, this action makes the bar a tangent to the curve of its surface.

2264. To produce these effects, of pointing across the magnetic curves, the form of the heavy glass must be long; a cube, or a fragment approaching roundness in form, will not point, but a long piece will. Two or three rounded pieces or cubes, placed side by side in a paper tray, so as to form an oblong accumulation, will also point.

2265. Portions, however, of any form, are *repelled:* so if two pieces be hung up at once in the axial line, one near each pole, they are repelled by their respective poles, and approach, seeming to attract each other. Or if two pieces be hung up in the equatorial line, one on each side of the axis, then they both recede from the axis, seeming to repel each other.

2266. From the little that has been said, it is evident that the bar presents in its motion a complicated result of the force exerted by the magnetic power over the heavy glass, and that, when cubes or spheres are employed, a much simpler indication of the effect may be obtained. Accordingly, when a cube was thus used with the two poles, the effect was repulsion or recession from either pole, and also recession from the magnetic axis on either side.

2267. So, the indicating particle would move, either along the magnetic curves, or across them; and it would do this either in one direction or the other; the only constant point being, that its tendency was to move from stronger to weaker places of magnetic force.

2268. This appeared much more simply in the case of a single magnetic pole, for then the tendency of the indicating cube or sphere was to move outwards, in the direction of the magnetic lines of force. The appearance was remarkably like a case of weak electric repulsion.

2269. The cause of the pointing of the bar, or any oblong arrangement of the heavy glass, is now evident. It is merely a result of the tendency of the particles to move outwards, or into the positions of weakest magnetic action. The joint exertion of the action of all the particles brings the mass into the position, which, by experiment, is found to belong to it.

2270. When one or two magnetic poles are active at once, the courses described by particles of heavy glass free to move, form a set of lines or curves, which I may have occasion hereafter to refer to; and as I have called air, glass, water, &c., diamagnetic (2149), so I will distinguish these lines by the term *diamagnetic curves*, both in relation to, and contradistinction from, the lines called magnetic curves.

2271. When the bar of heavy glass is immersed in water, alcohol, or ether, contained in a vessel between the poles, all the preceding effects occur; the bar points and the cube recedes exactly in the same manner as in air.

2272. The effects equally occur in vessels of wood, stone, earth, copper, lead, silver, or any of those substances which belong to the diamagnetic class (2149).

2273. I have obtained the same equatorial direction and motions of the heavy glass bar as those just described, but in a very feeble degree, by the use of a good common steel horseshoe magnet (2157). I have not obtained them by the use of the helices (2191, 2192) without the iron cores.

2274. Here therefore we have magnetic repulsion without polarity, i.e., without reference to a particular pole of the magnet, for either pole will repel the substance, and both poles will repel it at once (2262). The heavy glass, though subject to magnetic action, cannot be considered as magnetic, in the usual acceptation of that term, or as iron, nickel, cobalt, and their compounds. It presents to us, under these circumstances, a magnetic property new to our knowledge; and though the phenomena are very different in their nature and character to those presented by the action of the heavy glass on light (2152), still they appear to be dependent on, or connected with, the same condition of the glass as made it then effective, and therefore, with those phenomena, prove the reality of this new condition.

¶ iii. *Action of Magnets on Other Substances Acting Magnetically on Light*

2275. We may now pass from heavy glass to the examination of the other substances, which when under the power of magnetic or electric forces, are able to affect and rotate a polarized ray (2173), and may also easily extend the investigation to bodies which, from their irregularity of form, imperfect transparency, or actual opacity, could not be examined by a polarized ray, for here we have no difficulty in the application of the test to all such substances.

2276. The property of being thus repelled and affected by magnetic poles was soon found not to be peculiar to heavy glass. Borate of lead, flint-glass, and crown-glass set in the same manner equatorially, and were repelled when near to the poles, though not to the same degree as the heavy glass.

2277. Amongst substances which could not be subjected to the examination by light, phosphorus in the form of a cylinder presented the phenomena very well; I think as powerfully as heavy glass, if not more so. A cylinder of sulphur, and a long piece of thick India rubber, neither being magnetic after the ordinary fashion, were well directed and repelled.

2278. Crystalline bodies were equally obedient, whether taken from the single or double refracting class (2237). Prisms of quartz, calcareous spar, nitre and sulphate of soda, all pointed well, and were repelled.

2279. I then proceeded to subject a great number of bodies, taken from every class, to the magnetic forces, and will, to illustrate the variety in the nature of the substances, give a com-

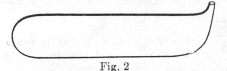

Fig. 2

paratively short list of crystalline, amorphous, liquid and organic bodies below. When the bodies were fluids, I enclosed them in thin glass tubes. Flint-glass points equatorially, but if the tube be of very thin glass, this effect is found to be small when the tube is experimented with alone; afterwards, when it is filled with liquid and examined, the effect is such that there is no fear of mistaking that due to the glass for that of the fluid. The tubes must not be closed with cork, sealing-wax, or any ordinary substance taken at random, for these are generally magnetic (2285). I have usually so shaped them in the making, and drawn them off at the neck, as to leave the aperture on one side, so that when filled with liquid they require no closing.

2280.

Rock crystal	Water
Sulphate of lime	Alcohol
Sulphate of baryta	Ether
Sulphate of soda	Nitric acid
Sulphate of potassa	Sulphuric acid
Sulphate of magnesia	Muriatic acid
Alum	Solutions of various al-
Muriate of ammonia	kaline and earthy salts
Chloride of lead	Glass
Chloride of sodium	Litharge
Nitrate of potassa	White arsenic
Nitrate of lead	Iodine
Carbonate of soda	Phosphorus
Iceland spar	Sulphur
Acetate of lead	Resin
Tartrate of potash and	Spermaceti
antimony	Caffeine
Tartrate of potash and	Cinchonia
soda	Margaric acid
Tartaric acid	Wax from shellac
Citric acid	Sealing-wax
Olive oil	Mutton, dried
Oil of turpentine	Beef, fresh
Jet	Beef, dried
Caoutchouc	Blood, fresh
Sugar	Blood, dried
Starch	Leather
Gum-arabic	Apple
Wood	Bread
Ivory	

2281. It is curious to see such a list as this of bodies presenting on a sudden this remarkable property, and it is strange to find a piece of wood, or beef, or apple, obedient to or repelled by a magnet. If a man could be suspended, with sufficient delicacy, after the manner of Dufay, and placed in the magnetic field, he would point equatorially; for all the substances of which he is formed, including the blood, possess this property.

2282. The setting equatorially depends upon the form of the body, and the diversity of form presented by the different substances in the list was very great; still the general result, that elongation in one direction was sufficient to make them take up an equatorial position, was established. It was not difficult to perceive that comparatively large masses would point as readily as small ones, because in larger masses more lines of magnetic force would bear in their action on the body, and this was proved to be the case. Neither was it long before it evidently appeared that the form of a plate or a ring was quite as good as that of a cylinder or a prism; and in practice it was found that plates and flat rings of wood, spermaceti, sulphur, &c., if suspended in the right direction, took up the equatorial position very well. If a plate or ring of heavy glass could be floated in water, so as to be free to move in every direction, and were in that condition subject to magnetic forces diminishing in intensity, it would immediately set itself equatorially, and if its centre coincided with the axis of magnetic power, would remain there; but if its centre were out of this line, it would then, perhaps, gradually pass off from this axis in the plane of the equator, and go out from between the poles.

2283. I do not find that division of the substance has any distinct influence on the effects. A piece of Iceland spar was observed, as to the degree of force with which it set equatorially; it was then broken into six or eight fragments, put into a glass tube and tried again; as well as I could ascertain, the effect was the same. By a second operation, the calcareous spar was reduced into coarse particles; afterwards to a coarse powder, and ultimately to a fine powder: being examined as to the equatorial set each time, I could perceive no difference in the effect, until the very last, when I thought there might be a slight diminution of the tendency; but if so, it was almost insensible. I made the same experiment on silica with the same result, of no diminution of power. In reference to this point I may observe that starch and other bodies in fine powder exhibited the effect very well.

2284. It would require very nice experiments and great care to ascertain the specific degree of this power of magnetic action possessed by different bodies, and I have made very little progress in that part of the subject. Heavy glass stands above flint-glass, and the latter above plate-glass. Water is beneath all these, and I think alcohol is below water, and ether below alcohol. The borate of lead is I think as high as heavy glass, if not above it, and phosphorus is probably at the head of all the substances just named. I verified the equatorial set of phosphorus between the poles of a common magnet (2273).

2285. I was much impressed by the fact that blood was not magnetic (2280), nor any of the specimens tried of red muscular fibre of beef or mutton. This was the more striking, because as will be seen hereafter, iron is *always* and in almost *all states* magnetic. But in respect to this point it may be observed, that the ordinary magnetic property of matter and this *new property* are in their effects opposed to each other; and that when this property is strong it may overcome a very slight degree of ordinary magnetic force, just as also a certain amount of the magnetic property may oppose and effectually hide the presence of this force (2422). It is this circumstance which makes it so necessary to be careful in examining the magnetic condition of the bodies in the first instance (2250). The following list of a few substances which were found slightly magnetic, will illustrate this point: paper, sealing-wax, china ink, Berlin porcelain, silkworm-gut, asbestos, fluor-spar, red lead, vermilion, peroxide of lead, sulphate of zinc, tourmaline, plumbago, shellac, charcoal. In some of these cases the magnetism was generally diffused through the body, in other cases it was limited to a particular part.

2286. Having arrived at this point, I may observe, that we can now have no difficulty in admitting that the phenomena abundantly establish the existence of a magnetic property in matter, new to our knowledge. Not the least interesting of the consequences that flow from it is the manner in which it disposes of the assertion which has sometimes been made, that all bodies are magnetic. Those who hold this view, mean that all bodies are magnetic as iron is, and say that they point between the poles. The new facts give not a mere negative to this statement, but something beyond, namely, an affirmative as to the existence of forces in all

ordinary bodies, directly the opposite of those existing in magnetic bodies, for whereas those practically produce attraction, these produce repulsion; those set a body in the axial direction, but these make it take up an equatorial position: and the facts, with regard to bodies generally, are exactly the reverse of those which the view quoted indicates.

¶ iv. *Action of Magnets on Metals Generally*

2287. The metals, as a class, stand amongst bodies having a high and distinct interest in relation both to magnetic and electric forces, and might at first well be expected to present some peculiar phenomena, in relation to the striking property found to be possessed in common by so large a number of substances, so varied in their general characters. As yet no distinction associated with conduction or non-conduction, transparent or opaque, solid or liquid, crystalline or amorphous, whole or broken, has presented itself; whether the metals, distinct as they are as a class, would fall into the great generalization, or whether at last a separation would occur, was to me a point of the highest interest.

2288. That the metals, iron, nickel and cobalt, would stand in a distinct class, appeared almost undoubted; and it will be, I think, for the advantage of the inquiry, that I should consider them in a section apart by themselves. Further, if any other metals appeared to be magnetic, as these are, it would be right and expedient to include them in the same class.

2289. My first point, therefore, was to examine the metals for any indication of ordinary magnetism. Such an examination cannot be carried on by magnets anything short in power of those to be used in the further investigation; and in proof of this point I found many specimens of the metals, which appeared to be perfectly free from magnetism when in the presence of a magnetic needle, or a strong horseshoe magnet (2157), that yet gave abundant indications when suspended near to one or both poles of the magnets described (2246).

2290. My test of magnetism was this. If a bar of the metal to be examined, about 2 inches long, was suspended (2249) in the magnetic field, and being at first oblique to the axial line was upon the supervention of the magnetic forces drawn into the axial position instead of being driven into the equatorial line, or remaining in some oblique direction, then I considered it magnetic. Or, if being near one magnetic pole, it was attracted by the pole, instead of being repelled, then I concluded it was magnetic. It is evident that the test is not strict, because, as before pointed out (2285), a body may have a slight degree of magnetic force, and yet the power of the new property be so great as to neutralize or surpass it. In the first case, it might seem neither to have the one property nor the other; in the second case, it might appear free from magnetism, and possessing the special property in a *small* degree.

2291. I obtained the following metals, so that when examined as above, they did not appear to be magnetic; and in fact, if magnetic, were so to an amount so small as not to destroy the results of the other force, or to stop the progress of the inquiry.

Antimony	Lead
Bismuth	Mercury
Cadmium	Silver
Copper	Tin
Gold	Zinc

2292. The following metals were, and are as yet to me, magnetic, and therefore companions of iron, nickel and cobalt:

Platinum
Palladium
Titanium

2293. Whether all these metals are magnetic, in consequence of the presence of a little iron, nickel, or cobalt in them, or whether any of them are really so of themselves, I do not undertake to decide at present; nor do I mean to say that the metals of the former list are free. I have been much struck by the apparent freedom from iron of almost all the specimens of zinc, copper, antimony and bismuth, which I have examined; and it appears to me very likely that some metals, as arsenic, &c., may have much power in quelling and suppressing the magnetic properties of any portion of iron in them, whilst other metals, as silver or platinum, may have little or no power in this respect.

2294. Resuming the consideration of the influence exerted by the magnetic force over those metals which are not magnetic after the manner of iron (2291), I may state that there are two sets of effects produced which require to be carefully distinguished. One of these depends upon induced magneto-electric currents, and shall be resumed hereafter (2309). The other includes effects of the same nature as those produced with heavy glass and many other bodies (2276).

2295. All the non-magnetic metals are subject to the magnetic power, and produce the same general effects as the large class of bodies already described. The force which they then manifest, they possess in different degrees. Antimony and bismuth show it well, and bismuth appears to be especially fitted for the purpose. It excels heavy glass, or borate of lead, and perhaps phosphorus; and a small bar or cylinder of it about 2 inches long, and from 0.25 to 0.5 of an inch in width, is as well fitted to show the various peculiar phenomena as anything I have yet submitted to examination.

2296. To speak accurately, the bismuth bar which I employed was 2 inches long, 0.33 of an inch wide, and 0.2 of an inch thick. When this bar was suspended in the magnetic field, between the two poles, and subject to the magnetic force, it pointed freely in the equatorial direction, as the heavy glass did (2253), and if disturbed from that position, returned *freely* to it. This latter point, though perfectly in accordance with the former phenomena, is in such striking contrast with the phenomena presented by copper and some other of the metals (2309), as to require particular notice here.

2297. The comparative sensibility of bismuth causes several movements to take place under various circumstances, which being complicated in their nature, require careful analysis and explanation. The chief of these, with their causes, I will proceed to point out.

2298. If the cylinder electro-magnet (2246) be placed vertically so as to present one pole upwards, that pole will exist in the upper end of an iron cylinder, having a flat horizontal face $2\frac{1}{2}$ inches in diameter. A small indicating sphere (2266) of bismuth, hung over the centre of this face and close to it, does not move by the magnetism. If the ball be carried outwards, half-way, for instance, between the centre and the edge, the magnetism makes it move inwards, or towards the axis (prolonged) of the iron cylinder. If carried still farther outwards, it still moves inwards under the influence of the magnetism, and such continues to be the case until it is placed just over the edge of the terminal face of the core, where it has no motion at all (here, by another arrangement of the experiment, it is known to tend in what is at present an upward direction from the core).

If carried a little farther outwards, the magnetism then makes the bismuth ball tend to go outwards or be repelled, and such continues to be the direction of the force in any further position, or down the side of the end of the core.

2299. In fact, the circular edge formed by the intersection of the end of the core with its sides, is virtually the apex of the magnetic pole, to a body placed like the bismuth ball close to it, and it is because the lines of magnetic force issuing from it diverge as it were, and weaken rapidly in all directions from it, that the ball also tends to pass in all directions either inwards or upwards, or outwards from it, and thus produces the motions described. These same effects do not in fact all occur when the ball, being taken to a greater distance from the iron, is placed in magnetic curves, having generally a simpler direction. In order to remove the effect of the edge, an iron cone was placed on the top of the core, converting the flat end into a cone, and then the indicating ball was urged to move upwards, only when over the apex of the cone, and upwards and outwards, as it was more or less on one side of it, being always repelled from the pole in that direction, which transferred it most rapidly from strong to weaker points of magnetic force.

2300. To return to the vertical flat pole: when a horizontal bar of bismuth was suspended concentrically and close to the pole, it could take up a position in any direction relative to the axis of the pole, having at the same time a tendency to move upwards or be repelled from it. If its point of suspension was a little eccentric, the bar gradually turned, until it was parallel to a line joining its point of suspension with the prolonged axis of the pole, and the centre of gravity moved inwards. When its point of suspension was just outside the edge of the flat circular terminating face, and the bar formed a certain angle with a radial line joining the axis of the core and the point of suspension, then the movements of the bar were uncertain and wavering. If the angle with the radial line were less than that above, the bar would move into parallelism with the radius and go inwards: if the angle were greater, the bar would move until perpendicular to the radial line and go outwards. If the centre of the bar were still farther out than in the last case, or down by the side of the core, the bar would always place itself perpendicular to the radius and go outwards. All these complications of motion are easily resolved into their simple elementary origin, if reference be had to the character of the circular angle bounding the end of the core; to the direction of the magnetic lines of force issuing from it and the other parts of the pole; to the position of the different parts of the bar in these lines; and the ruling principle that each particle tends

to go by the nearest course from *strong* to *weaker* points of magnetic force.

2301. The bismuth points well, and is well repelled (2296) when immersed in water, alcohol, ether, oil, mercury, &c., and also when enclosed within vessels of earth, glass, copper, lead, &c. (2272), or when screens of 0.75 or 1 inch in thickness of bismuth, copper, or lead intervene. Even when a bismuth cube (2266) was placed in an iron vessel $2\frac{1}{2}$ inches in diameter and 0.17 of an inch in thickness, it was well and freely repelled by the magnetic pole.

2302. Whether the bismuth be in one piece or in very fine powder, appears to make no difference in the character or in the degree of its magnetic property (2283).

2303. I made many experiments with masses and bars of bismuth suspended, or otherwise circumstanced, to ascertain whether two pieces had any mutual action on each other, either of attraction or repulsion, whilst jointly under the influence of the magnetic forces, but I could not find any indication of such mutual action: they appeared to be perfectly indifferent one to another, each tending only to go from stronger to weaker points of magnetic power.

2304. Bismuth, in very fine powder, was sprinkled upon paper, laid over the horizontal circular termination of the vertical pole (2246). If the paper were tapped, the magnet not being excited, nothing particular occurred; but if the magnetic power were on, then the powder retreated in both directions, inwards and outwards, from a circular line just over the edge of the core, leaving the circle clear, and at the same time showing the tendency of the particles of bismuth in all directions from that line (2299).

2305. When the pole was terminated by a cone (2246) and the magnet not in action, paper with bismuth powder sprinkled over it being drawn over the point of the cone, gave no particular result; but when the magnetism was on, such an operation cleared the powder from every point which came over the cone, so that a mark was traced or written out in clear lines running through the powder, and showing every place where the pole had passed.

2306. The bar of bismuth and a bar of antimony was found to set equatorially between the poles of the ordinary horseshoe magnet.

2307. The following list may serve to give an idea of the apparent order of some metals, as regards their power of producing these new effects, but I cannot be sure that they are perfectly free from the magnetic metals. In addition to that, there are certain other effects produced by the action of magnetism on metals (2309) which greatly interfere with the results due to the present property.

Bismuth	Cadmium
Antimony	Mercury
Zinc	Silver
Tin	Copper

2308. I have a vague impression that the repulsion of bismuth by a magnet has been observed and published several years ago. If so, it will appear that what must then have been considered as a peculiar and isolated effect, was the consequence of a general property, which is now shown to belong to all matter.[1]

2309. I now turn to the consideration of some peculiar phenomena which are presented by copper and several of the metals when they are subjected to the action of magnetic forces, and which so tend to mask effects of the kind already described that if not known to the inquirer they would lead to much confusion and doubt. These I will first describe as to their appearances, and then proceed to consider their origin.

2310. If instead of a bar of bismuth (2296) a bar of copper of the same size be suspended between the poles (2247), and magnetic power be developed whilst the bar is in a position oblique to the axial and equatorial lines, the experimenter will perceive the bar to be affected, but this will not be manifest by any tendency of the bar to go to the equatorial line; on the contrary, it will advance towards the axial position as if it were magnetic. It will not, however, continue its course until in that position, but, unlike any effect produced by magnetism, will stop short, and making no vibration beyond or about a given point, will remain there, coming at once to a dead rest: and this it will do even though the bar by the effect of torsion or momentum was previously moving with a force that would have caused it to make several gyrations. This effect is in striking contrast with that which occurs when antimony, bismuth, heavy glass, or other such bodies are employed, and it is equally removed from an ordinary magnetic effect.

2311. The position which the bar has taken up it retains with a considerable degree of tenacity, provided the magnetic force be continued. If pushed out of it, it does not return into it, but takes up its new position in the same manner, and holds it with the same stiffness; a push, however, which would make the bar spin round several times if no magnetism were present, will now not move it through more than 20° or 30°. This is not the case with bismuth or heavy glass; they vibrate freely in the magnetic field, and always return to the equatorial position.

2312. The position taken up by the bar may be any position. The bar is moved a little at the instant of superinducing the magnetism, but allowing and providing for that, it may be finally fixed in any position required. Even when swinging with considerable power by torsion or momentum, it may be caught and retained in any place the experimenter wishes.

2313. There are two positions in which the bar may be placed at the beginning of the experiment, from which the magnetism does not move it; the equatorial and the axial positions. When the bar is nearly midway between these, it is usually most strongly affected by the first action of the magnet, but the position of most effect varies with the form and dimensions of the magnetic poles and of the bar.

2314. If the centre of suspension of the bar be in the axial line, but near to one of the poles, these movements occur well, and are clear and distinct in their direction: if it be in the equatorial line, but on one side of the axial line, they are modified, but in a manner which will easily be understood hereafter.

2315. Having thus stated the effect of the supervention of the magnetic force, let us now remark what occurs at the moment of its cessation; for during its continuance there is no change. If, then, after the magnetism has been sustained for two or three seconds, the electric current be stopped, there is instantly a strong action on the bar, which has the appearance of a revulsion (for the bar returns upon the course which it took for a moment when the electric contact was made), but with such force, that whereas the advance might be perhaps 15° or 20°, the revulsion will cause the bar occasionally to move through two or three revolutions.

---

[1] M. de la Rive has this day referred me to the *Bibliothèque Universelle* for 1829, Vol. XL, p. 82, where it will be found that the experiment spoken of above is due to M. la Baillif of Paris. M. la Baillif showed sixteen years ago that both bismuth and antimony repelled the magnetic needle. It is astonishing that such an experiment has remained so long without further results. I rejoice that I am able to insert this reference before the present series of these *Researches* goes to press. Those who read my papers will see here, as on many other occasions, the results of a memory which becomes continually weaker; I only hope that they will be excused, and that omissions and errors of that nature will be considered as involuntary.—M. F. Dec. 30, 1845.

2316. Heavy glass or bismuth present no such phenomena as this.

2317. If, whilst the bar is revolving from revulsion the electric current at the magnet be renewed, the bar instantly stops with the former appearances and results (2310), and then upon removing the magnetic force is affected again, and, of course, now in a contrary direction to the former revulsion.

2318. When the bar is caught by the magnetic force in the axial or equatorial position, there is no revulsion. When inclined to these positions, there is; and the places most powerful in this respect appear to be those most favourable to the first brief advance (2313). If the bar be in a position at which strong revulsion would occur, and whilst the magnetism is continued, be moved by hand into the equatorial or axial position, then on taking off the magnetic force there is no revulsion.

2319. If the continuance of the electric current and consequently of the magnetism be for a moment only, the revulsion is very little, and the shorter the continuance of the magnetic force the less is the revulsion. If the magnetic force be continued for two or three seconds and then interrupted and *instantly* renewed, the bar is loosened and caught again by the power before it sensibly changes its place; and now it may be observed that it does not advance on the *renewal* of the force as it would have done had it been acted on by a first contact in that place (2310); i.e., if the bar be in a certain place inclined to the axial position, the first supervention of the magnetic power causes it to advance towards the axial position; but the bar being in the same place and the magnetic power suspended and *instantly* renewed, the second supervention of force does not move the bar as the first did.

2320. When the copper bar is immersed in water, alcohol, or even mercury, the same effects take place as in the air, but the movements are, of course, not to the same extent.

2321. When plates of copper or bismuth, an inch in thickness, intervene between the poles and the copper bar, the same results occur.

2322. If one magnetic pole only be employed the effects occur near it as well as before, provided that pole have a face large in proportion to the bar, as the end of the iron core (2246): but if the pole be pointed by the use of the conical termination, or if the bar be opposite the edge of the end of the core, then they become greatly enfeebled or disappear altogether; and only the general fact of repulsion remains (2295).

2323. The peculiar effects which have just been described are perhaps more strikingly shown if the bar of copper be suspended perpendicularly, and then hung opposite and near to the large face of a single magnetic pole, or the pole being placed vertically, as described (2246, 2263), anywhere near to its side. The bar, it will be remembered, is 2 inches in length by 0.33 of an inch in width, and 0.2 of an inch in thickness, and as it now will revolve on an axis parallel to its length, the two smaller dimensions are those which are free to move into new positions. In this case the establishment of the magnetic force causes the bar to turn a little in accordance with the effects before described, and the removal of the magnetic force causes a revulsion, which sends the bar spinning round on its axis several times. But at any moment the bar can again be caught and held in a position as before. The tendency on making contact at the battery is to place the longest moving dimension, i.e., the width of the bar, parallel to the line joining the centre of action of the magnet and the bar.

2324. The bar, as before (2311), is extremely sluggish and as if immersed in a dense fluid, as respects rotation on its own axis; but this sluggishness does not affect the bar as a whole, for any pendulum vibration it has, continues unaffected. It is very curious to see the bar, jointly vibrating from its point of suspension (2249) and rotating on its axis, when first affected by the magnetic force, for instantly the latter motion ceases, but the former goes on with undiminished power.

2325. The same effect of sluggishness occurs with a cube or a globe of copper as with the bar, but the phenomena of the first turn and the revulsion cease (2310, 2315).

2326. The bars of bismuth and heavy glass present no appearance of this kind. The peculiar phenomena produced by copper are as distinct from the actions of these substances as they are from ordinary magnetic actions.

2327. Endeavouring to explain the cause of these effects, it appears to me that they depend upon the excellent conducting power of copper for electric currents, the *gradual* acquisition and loss of magnetic power by the iron core of the electro-magnet, and the production of those induced currents of magneto-electricity which I described in the first series of these *Experimental Researches* (55, 109).

2328. The obstruction to motion on its own axis, when the bar is subjected to the magnetic forces, belongs equally to the form of a sphere or a cube. It belongs to these bodies, however, only when their axes of rotation are perpendicular or oblique to the lines of magnetic force, and not when they are parallel to it; for the horizontal bar, or the vertical bar, or the cube or sphere, rotate with perfect facility when they are suspended *above* the vertical pole (2246), the rotation and vibration being then equally free, and the same as the corresponding movements of bismuth or heavy glass. The obstruction is at a maximum when the axis of rotation is perpendicular to the lines of magnetic force, and when the bar or cube, &c., is near to the magnet.

2329. Without going much into the particular circumstances, I may say that the effect is fully explained by the electric currents induced in the copper mass. By reference to the second series of these *Researches* (160),[1] it will be seen that when a globe, subject to the action of lines of magnetic force, is revolving on an axis perpendicular to these lines, an electric current runs round it in a plane parallel to the axis of rotation and to the magnetic lines, producing consequently a magnetic axis in the globe, at right angles to the magnetic curves of the inducing magnet. The magnetic poles of this axis therefore are in that direction which, in conjunction with the chief magnetic pole, tends to draw the globe back against the direction in which it is revolving. Thus, if a piece of copper be revolving before a north magnetic pole, so that the parts nearest the pole move towards the right-hand, then the right-hand side of that copper will have a south magnetic state, and the left-hand side a north magnetic state; and these states will tend to counteract the motion of the copper towards the right-hand: or if it revolve in the contrary direction, then the right-hand side will have a south magnetic state, and the left-hand side a north magnetic state. Whichever way, therefore, the copper tends to revolve on its own axis, the instant it moves, a power is evolved in such a direction as tends to stop its motion and bring it to rest. Being at rest in reference to this direction of motion, then there is no residual or other effect which tends to disturb it, and it remains still.

2330. If the whole mass be moving parallel to itself, and be small in comparison with the face of the magnetic pole opposite to which it is placed, then, though it pass through the magnetic lines of force, and consequently have a tendency to the formation of magneto-electric currents within it, yet as all parts move

[1] *Philosophical Transactions*, 1832, p. 168.

with equal velocity and in the same direction through similar magnetic lines of force, the tendency to the formation of a current is the same in every part, and there is no actual production of current, and consequently nothing occurs which can in any way interfere with its freedom of motion. Hence the reason that though the rotation of the bar or cube (2324, 2328) upon its own axis is stopped, its vibration as a pendulum is not affected.

2331. That neither the one nor the other motion is affected when the bar or cube is over the vertical pole (2328) is simply because in both cases (with the given dimensions of the pole and the moving metal) the lines of particles through which the induced currents tend to move are parallel throughout the whole mass; and therefore, as there is no part by which the return of the current can be carried on, no current can be formed.

2332. Before proceeding to the explanation of the other phenomena, it will be necessary to point out the fact generally understood and acknowledged, I believe, that *time* is required for the development of magnetism in an iron core by a current of electricity; and also for its fall back again when the current is stopped. One effect of the gradual rise in power was referred to in the last series of these *Researches* (2170). This time is probably longer with iron not well annealed than with very good and perfectly annealed iron. The last portions of magnetism which a given current can develop in a certain core of iron, are also apparently acquired more slowly than the first portions; and these portions (or the condition of iron to which they are due) also appear to be lost more slowly than the other portions of the power. If electric contact be made for an instant only, the magnetism developed by the current disappears as instantly on the breaking of the current, as it appeared on its formation; but if contact be continued for three or four seconds, breaking the contact is by no means accompanied by a disappearance of the magnetism with equal rapidity.

2333. In order to trace the peculiar effect of the copper, and its cause, let us consider the condition of the horizontal bar (2310, 2313) when in the equatorial position, between the two magnetic poles, or before a single pole; the point of suspension being in a line with the axis of the pole and its exciting wire helix. On sending an electric current through the helix, both it and the magnet it produces will conduce to the formation of currents in the copper bar in the contrary direction. This is shown from my former *Researches* (26), and may be proved, by placing a small or large wire helix-shaped (if it be desired) in the form of the bar, and carrying away the currents produced in it, by wires to a galvanometer at a distance. Such currents, being produced in the copper, only continue whilst the magnetism of the core is rising, and then cease (18, 39), but *whilst* they continue, they give a virtual magnetic polarity to that face of the copper bar which is opposite to a certain pole, the polarity being the same in kind as the pole it faces. Thus on the side of the bar facing the north pole of the magnet, a north polarity will be developed; and on that side facing the south pole, a south polarity will be generated.

2334. It is easy to see that if the copper during this time were opposite only one pole, or being between two poles, were nearer to one than the other, this effect would cause its repulsion. Still, it cannot account for the whole amount of the repulsion observed alike with copper as with bismuth (2295), because the currents are of but momentary duration, and the repulsion due to them would cease with them. They do, however, cause a brief repulsive effort, to which is chiefly due the first part of the peculiar effect.

2335. For if the copper bar, instead of being parallel to the face of the magnetic pole, and therefore at right angles to the resultant of magnetic force, be inclined, forming, for instance, an angle of 45° with the face, then the induced currents will move generally in a plane corresponding more or less to that angle, nearly as they do in the examining helix (2333), if it be inclined in the same manner. This throws the polar axis of the bar of copper on one side, so that the north polarity is not directly opposed to the north pole of the inducing magnet, and hence the action both of this and the other magnetic pole upon the two polarities of the copper will be to send it farther round, or to place it edgeways to the poles, or with its breadth parallel to the magnetic resultant passing through it (2323): the bar therefore receives an impulse, and the angle of it nearest to the magnet appears to be pulled up towards the magnet. This action of course stops the instant the magnetism of the helix core ceases to rise, and then the motion due to this cause ceases, and the copper is simply subject to the action before described (2295). At the same time that this twist or small portion of a turn round the point of suspension occurs, the cen-

tre of gravity of the whole mass is repelled, and thus I believe all the actions up to this condition of things are accounted for.

2336. Then comes the *revulsion* which occurs upon the cessation of the electric current, and the falling of the magnetism in the core. According to the law of magneto-electric induction, the disappearance of the magnetic force will induce brief currents in the copper bar (28), but in the contrary direction to those induced in the first instance; and therefore the virtual magnetic pole belonging to the copper for the moment, which is nearest the north end of the electro-magnet, will be a south pole; and that which is farthest from the same pole of the magnet will be a north pole. Hence will arise an exertion of force on the bar tending to turn it round its centre of suspension in the contrary direction to that which occurred before, and hence the apparent revulsion; for the angle nearest the magnetic pole will recede from it, the broad face (2323) or length (2315) of the bar will come round and face towards the magnet, and an action the reverse in every respect of the first action will take place, except that whereas the motion was then only a few degrees, now it may extend to two or three revolutions.

2337. The cause of this difference is very obvious. In the first instance, the bar of copper was moving under influences powerfully tending to retard and stop it (2329); in the second case these influences are gone, and the bar revolves freely with a force proportionate to the power exerted by the magnet upon the currents induced by its own action.

2338. Even when the copper is of such form as not to give the oblique resultant of magnetic action from the currents induced in it, when, for instance, it is a cube or a sphere, still the effect of the action described above is evident (2325). When a plate of copper about three-fourths of an inch in thickness, and weighing two pounds, was sustained upon some loose blocks of wood and placed about 0.1 of an inch from the face of the magnetic pole, it was repelled and held off a certain distance upon the making and continuing of electric contact at the battery; and when the battery current was stopped, it returned towards the pole; but the return was much more powerful than that due to gravity alone (as was ascertained by an experiment), the plate being at that moment actually *attracted*, as well as tending by gravitation towards the magnet, so that it gave a strong tap against it.

2339. Such is, 1 believe, the explanation of the peculiar phenomena presented by copper in the magnetic field; and the reason why they appear with this metal and not with bismuth or heavy glass, is almost certainly to be found in its high electro-conducting power, which permits the formation of currents in it by inductive forces, that cannot produce the same in a corresponding degree in bismuth, and of course not at all in heavy glass.

2340. Any ordinary magnetism due to metals by virtue of their inherent power, or the presence of small portions of the magnetic metals in them, must oppose the development of the results I have been describing; and hence metals not of absolute purity cannot be compared with each other in this respect. I have, nevertheless, observed the same phenomena in other metals; and as far as regards the sluggishness of rotatory motion, traced it even into bismuth. The following are the metals which have presented the phenomena in a greater or smaller degree:

Copper	Mercury
Silver	Platinum
Gold	Palladium
Zinc	Lead
Cadmium	Antimony
Tin	Bismuth

2341. The accordance of these phenomena with the beautiful discovery of Arago,[1] with the results of the experiments of Herschel and Babbage,[2] and with my own former inquiries (81),[3] is very evident. Whether the effect obtained by Ampère, with his copper cylinder and helix,[4] was of this nature, I cannot judge, inasmuch as the circumstances of the experiment and the energy of the apparatus are not sufficiently stated; but it probably may have been.

2342. As, because of other duties, three or four weeks may elapse before I shall be able to complete the verification of certain experiments and conclusions, I submit at once these results to the attention of the Royal Society, and will shortly embody the account of the action of magnets on magnetic metals, their action on gases and vapours, and the general considerations in another series of these *Researches*.

Royal Institution, Nov. 27, 1845

[1] *Annales de Chimie*, XXVII, 363; XXVIII, 325; XXXII, 213. I am very glad to refer here to the *Comptes Rendus* of June 9, 1845, where it appears that it was M. Arago who first obtained his peculiar results by the use of electro- as well as common magnets.
[2] *Philosophical Transactions*, 1825, p. 467.
[3] *Ibid.*, 1832, p. 146.
[4] *Bibliothèque Universelle*, XXI, p. 48.

TWENTY-FIRST SERIES[5]

§ 27. *On New Magnetic Actions, and on the Magnetic Condition of All Matter (continued)* ¶ v. *Action of Magnets on the Magnetic Metals and Their Compounds* ¶ vi. *Action of Magnets on Air and Gases* ¶ vii. *General Considerations*

RECEIVED DECEMBER 24, 1845, READ JANUARY 8, 1846

¶ v. *Action of Magnets on the Magnetic Metals and Their Compounds*

2343. THE magnetic characters of iron, nickel and cobalt, are well known; and also the fact that at certain temperatures they lose their usual property and become, to ordinary test and observation, non-magnetic; then entering into the list of diamagnetic bodies and acting in like manner with them. Closer investigation, however, has shown me that they are still very different to other bodies, and that though inactive when hot, on common magnets or to common tests, they are not so absolutely, but retain a certain amount of magnetic power

[5] *Philosophical Transactions*, 1846, p. 41.

whatever their temperature; and also that this power is the same in character with that which they ordinarily possess.

2344. A piece of iron wire, about 1 inch long and 0.05 of an inch in diameter, being thoroughly cleaned, was suspended at the middle by a fine platinum wire connected with the suspending thread (2249) so as to swing between the poles of the electro-magnet. The heat of a spirit-lamp was applied to it, and it soon acquired a temperature which rendered it quite insensible to the presence of a good ordinary magnet, however closely it was approached to the heated iron. The temperature of the iron was then raised considerably higher by adjustment of the flame, and the electro-magnet thrown into action. Immediately the hot iron became magnetic and pointed between the poles. The power was feeble, and in this respect the state of the iron was in striking contrast with that which it had when cold; but in character the force was precisely the same.

2345. The iron was then allowed to fall in temperature slowly so that its assumption of the higher magnetic condition might be observed. The intensity of the force did not appear to increase until the temperature arrived near a certain point, and then as the heat continued to diminish, the iron rapidly, but not instantaneously, acquired its high magnetic power; at which time it could not be kept from the magnet, but flew to it, bending the suspending wire and trembling as it were with magnetic energy as it adhered by one end to the core.

2346. A small bar of nickel was submitted to an experimental examination in the same manner. This metal, as I have shown,[1] loses its magnetism as respects ordinary tests at a heat below that of boiling oil, and hence it is very well fitted to show whether the magnetic metals can have their power entirely removed by heat or not; and also whether the disappearance of the whole or greater portion of their power is sudden or gradual. The smallness of the mass to be experimented on assisted much in the determination of the latter point. Upon being heated the nickel soon became indifferent to ordinary magnets; but however high the temperature, still it pointed to and was attracted by the electro-magnet. The power was very feeble, but certain. It was scarcely enough to sustain the weight of the nickel by the magnetic action alone; but was abundantly evident when the metal was supported as described (2344).

2347. On carefully lowering the temperature of the nickel, it was again found that the transition from one degree of magnetic force to the other was progressive and not instantaneous. With iron it is difficult to preserve all the parts, either in heating or cooling, so nearly at the same temperature as to be sure that it is not the union of hotter and colder portions which gives the appearance of an intermediate degree of magnetism; but with nickel that is not so difficult, for the progression is more gradual, so that when in cooling the power began to increase, the cooling might be continued some time before the full degree of power came on; at any time in that period the temperature might be slightly raised, and though the power would then diminish a little, it could yet be retained at a degree stronger than the weakest. In fact it was easy to *keep* the nickel at many of the intermediate degrees of power, and thus to remove all doubt of the progressive assumption of the full degree of force.

2348. I have expressed an opinion, founded on the different temperatures at which the magnetic metals appeared to lose their peculiar power,[2] that all the metals would probably have the same character of magnetism if their temperature could be lowered sufficiently. The facts just described appear to me entirely against such an opinion. The metals which are magnetic retain a portion of their power after the great change has been effected, or in what might be called their diamagnetic state; but the other metals, such as bismuth, tin, &c., present no trace of this power, and therefore are not in the condition of the heated iron, nickel, or cobalt; for in fact whilst these point axially and are attracted, the others point equatorially and are repelled. I therefore hope to be allowed to withdraw the view I then put forth.

2349. I next proceeded to examine the peroxides of iron, and in accordance with the observations of M. Becquerel[3] and others found them all, both natural and artificial, possessed of magnetic power at common temperatures. I heated them in tubes but found them still magnetic, suffering *no* diminution of the force by such temperature as I could apply to them.

2350. Different specimens of the oxide of nickel were found to present the same phenomena. They were magnetic both when hot and cold; and that heat should cause no change in this respect is the more striking, because the hot oxide had a temperature given to it far higher than that necessary to produce the great magnetic change in the metal itself (2346).

2351. The oxide of cobalt also was magnetic, and equally magnetic whether hot or cold. Glass coloured blue by cobalt is magnetic in consequence of the presence of the oxide of that metal, and is so whether hot or cold. In all these cases the degree of power retained was very small compared to that of the pure metal.

2352. Proceeding to the *salts* of iron, I found them magnetic. Clean crystals of the proto-

[1] *Philosophical Magazine*, 1836, Vol. VIII, p. 179, or *Experimental Researches*, Vol. II, p. 219.

[2] *Philosophical Magazine*, 1836, Vol. VIII, p. 177; *ibid.*, 1839, Vol. XIV, p. 161; or *Experimental Researches*, Vol. II, pp. 217, 225.
[3] *Annales de Chimie*, 1827, Vol. XXXVI, p. 337, *Comptes Rendus*, 1845, Vol. XX, p. 1708.

sulphate of iron were attracted and pointed axially very well; so also did the dry salt. As I proceeded I found that every salt and compound containing iron in the basic part was magnetic. To enumerate the different substances subjected to trial would be tedious; the following are selected as illustrations of the variety in kind:

Protochloride	Protophosphate
Perchloride	Perphosphate
Iodide	Nitrate
Protosulphate	Carbonate
Persulphate	Prussian Blue

2353. Amongst native compounds

Bog iron ore	Yellow sulphuret of iron
Hæmatite	Arsenical pyrites
Chromate of iron	Copper pyrites, and many others were magnetic

2354. Green bottle-glass is comparatively very magnetic from the iron it contains, and cannot be used as tubes to hold other substances. Crown glass is magnetic from the same cause. Flint glass is not magnetic, but points equatorially.

2355. Crystals of the yellow ferro-prussiate of potassa[1] were not magnetic, but were repelled and set equatorially; and such was the case also with red ferro-prussiate.

2356. According to my hopes, even the solutions of the ferruginous salts, whether in water or alcohol, were magnetic. A tube filled with a clear solution of proto- or persulphate of iron, or proto- or perchloride, or tincture of muriate of iron, was attracted by the poles, and pointed very well between them in the axial direction.

2357. These solutions supply a very important means of advancing magnetical investigation, for they present us with the power of making a magnet, which is at the same time liquid, transparent, and within certain limits, adjustable to any degree of strength. Hence the power of examining a magnet optically. Hence also, the capability of placing magnetic portions of matter one within another, and so observing dynamic and other phenomena within magnetic media. In fact, not only may these substances be placed as magnets in the magnetic field, but the field generally may be filled with them, and then other bodies and other magnets examined as to their joint or separate actions in it (2361, &c.).

2358. In reference to the salts of *nickel* and *cobalt*, pure crystals of the sulphate of nickel were found to be well magnetic, and also pure

[1] Ferro-prussiate of potassa: now known as potassium ferricyanide.—ED.

crystals of sulphate of cobalt. Solutions of the sulphate of nickel, the chloride of nickel, and the chloride of cobalt, were also magnetic. That I might be perfectly safe in these conclusions I applied to Mr. Askin of Birmingham, whose power of separating nickel and cobalt from each other and other metals is well known, as also the scale upon which he carries on these operations; and he favoured me with a solution of chloride of nickel and another of chloride of cobalt perfectly pure, both of which proved to be well magnetic between the poles of my magnet.

2359. Heat applied to any of these magnetic solutions did not diminish or affect their power.

2360. These results with the salts of the magnetic metals conjoin with those before quoted, as tending to show that the non-magnetic metals could not by any change of temperature be rendered magnetic (2398), but as a class are distinct from iron, nickel, and cobalt; for none of the compounds of the non-magnetic metals show, as yet, any indication of ordinary magnetic force, whereas in respect of these three substances all their compounds possess it.

2361. In illustration of the power which the iron and other similar solutions give in the investigation of magnetic phenomena (2357), as well as in reference to the general conclusions to be drawn from all the facts described in this paper, I will proceed to describe certain anticipated results which were obtained by the employment of these solutions in the magnetic field.

2362. A clear solution of the proto-sulphate of iron was prepared, in which one ounce of the liquid contained seventy-four grains of the hydrated crystals; a second solution was prepared containing one volume of the former and three volumes of water: a third solution was made of one volume of the stronger solution and fifteen volumes of water. These solutions I will distinguish as Nos. 1, 2, and 3; the proportions of crystals of sulphate of iron in them were respectively as 16, 4, and 1 per cent nearly. These numbers may, therefore, be taken as representing (generally only [2423]) the strength of the magnetic part of the liquids.

2363. Tubes like that before described (2279) were prepared and filled respectively with these solutions and then hermetically sealed, as little air as possible being left in them. Glasses of the solutions were also prepared, large enough to allow the tubes to move freely in them, and yet of such size and shape as would permit of their being placed between the magnetic poles. In this manner the action of the magnetic forces upon the matter in the tubes could be examined and observed, both when the tubes were in diamagnetic media, as air, water, alcohol, &c., and also in magnetic media, either stronger or weaker in magnetic force, than the substances in the tubes.

2364. When these tubes were suspended in air between the poles, they all pointed axially or magnetically, as was to be expected; and with forces apparently proportionate to the strengths of the solutions. When they were immersed in alcohol or water, they also pointed in the same direction; the strongest solution very well, and also the second, but the weakest solution was feeble in its action, though very distinct in its character (2422).

2365. When the tubes, immersed in the different ferruginous solutions, were acted upon, the results were very interesting. The tube No. 1 (the strongest magnetically), when in solution No. 1, had no tendency, under the influence of the magnetic power, to any particular position, but remained wherever it was placed. Being placed in solution No. 2, it pointed well axially, and in solution No. 3 it took the same direction, but with still more power.

2366. The tube No. 2, when in the solution No. 1, pointed equatorially, i.e., as heavy glass, bismuth, or a diamagnetic body generally, in air. In solution No. 2 it was indifferent, not pointing either way; and in solution No. 3 it pointed axially, or as a magnetic body. The tube No. 3, containing the weakest solution, pointed equatorially in solutions No. 1 and 2, and not at all in solution No. 3.

2367. Several other ferruginous solutions varying in strength were prepared, and, as a general and constant result, it was found that any tube pointed axially if the solution in it was stronger than the surrounding solution, and equatorially if the tube solution was the weaker of the two.

2368. The tubes were now suspended vertically, so that being in the different solutions they could be brought near to one of the magnetic poles, and employed in place of the indicating cube or sphere of bismuth, or heavy glass (2266). The constant result was that when the tube contained a stronger solution than that which surrounded it, it was attracted to the pole, but when its solution was the weaker of the two, it was repelled. The latter phenomena were as to appearance in every respect the same as those presented in the repulsion of heavy glass, bismuth, or any other diamagnetic body in air.

2369. Having described these phenomena, I will defer their further consideration until I arrive at the last division of this paper, and proceed to certain results more especially belonging to the present part of these *Researches*.

2370. As the magnetic metals, iron, nickel and cobalt, present in their compounds substances also distinguished by the possession of magnetic properties (2360), so it appeared very probable that other metals, of whose magnetic character doubts were entertained, because of the possible presence of iron in the specimens experimented with, might in this way have their magnetic character tested; for it seemed likely, from analogy, that every metal well magnetic *per se*, would be magnetic in its compounds; and, judging from the character of the great class of diamagnetic bodies (2275), that no magnetic compounds would be obtained of a metal not magnetic of itself. Accordingly I proceeded to apply this kind of test to the combinations of many of the metals, and obtained the following results:

2371. *Titanium.* Wollaston has described the magnetic effects of crystals of titanium, expressing at the same time a belief that they are due to iron.[1] I took a specimen of the oxide of titanium, which I believe to be perfectly free from iron, and inclosing it in a tube (2279), subjected it to the action of the electro-magnet (2246, 2247). It proved to be freely magnetic. Another specimen obtained from Mr. Johnson, and believed by him to be perfectly free from iron, was also magnetic. Hence I conclude that titanium is truly a magnetic metal.

2372. *Manganese.* Berthier, as far as I am aware, first announced that this metal was magnetic at very low temperatures.[2] On submitting specimens of the various oxides, which were considered as pure, to the magnetic force, they were all found to be magnetic, especially the protoxide. So were the following compounds of manganese in the pure, dry, or crystallized state: chloride, sulphate, ammonio-sulphate, phosphate, carbonate, borate; and also the chloride, nitrate, sulphate, and ammonio-sulphate when in solution. A specimen of the ammonio-sulphate was rendered alkaline by the addition of a little carbonate of ammonia boiled and then carefully crystallized thrice: after that the crystals and solution of the purified salt were perfectly and well magnetic. I have no doubt, therefore, that manganese is a mag-

[1] *Philosophical Transactions*, 1823, p. 400.
[2] *Traité des Essais par la Voie Sèche*, Vol. I, p. 532. *Philosophical Magazine*, 1845, Vol. XXVII, p. 2.

netic metal, as Berthier said. If any opinion may be drawn concerning the magnetic force of the metal from the degree of magnetism of the compounds, I should expect that manganese possesses considerable power of this kind when at a sufficiently low temperature.[1]

2373. *Cerium.* I am not aware that cerium has as yet been classed with the magnetic metals. Having made experiments with the hydrated protoxide, the carbonate, and the chloride of this metal, and also with the double sulphate of the oxide and potassa prepared with great care, I found them all magnetic; and those that are soluble are magnetic in the state of solution. Hence, as the compounds are undoubtedly magnetic, there is every reason to believe that cerium also is a magnetic metal (2370).

2374. *Chromium.* The magnetic phenomena of chromium compounds are very interesting. Portions of the chromate and the bichromate of potassa were purified by three careful crystallizations each; part of the bichromate was heated in a platinum crucible, until the second equivalent of chromic acid was converted into the crystallized oxide, and this being washed cut and dried was found to be well magnetic. So were all the other specimens of oxide of chromium which were examined.

A specimen of Warrington's chromic acid was found to be very feebly magnetic.

2375. Chromate of lead, when subjected to the magnet, pointed equatorially and was repelled. Such was the case also with crystals of the chromate of potassa. Crystals of the bichromate, however, did not act thus; for if in any way affected they were in the least degree magnetic, showing the influence of the increased proportion of chromic acid. Solutions of either salt pointed well equatorially and were repelled; thus showing the diamagnetic influence of the water present (2422).

2376. As just stated, a solution of the bichromate contained in a tube, pointed equatorially and was repelled; but if the same solution had a little alcohol added to it, and also some pure muriatic or sulphuric acid, and were then heated for a few minutes to reduce the chromic acid to the state of oxide or chloride, then, on being returned to the tube and subjected to the magnet, it was found strongly magnetic.

2377. I think it has before been said that chromium is a magnetic metal; as these results have been obtained with its pure compounds,

[1] *Philosophical Magazine,* 1845, Vol. XXVII, p. 2.

there is no longer any doubt in my mind that such is the case.

2378. *Lead.* The compounds of lead point equatorially and are repelled. The substances tried were the chloride, iodide, sulphuret, nitrate, sulphate, phosphate, carbonate, protoxide fused, and the acetate. A portion of very carefully crystallized nitrate being dissolved was precipitated by pure zinc, and the lead obtained washed with dilute nitric acid, to remove subsalts. Such lead was free from magnetism, and therefore the metal ranks in the diamagnetic class, both directly and by its compounds. Lead usually appears to be magnetic, and it is not very easy to obtain the metal in the pure diamagnetic state.

2379. *Platinum.* I have, as yet, found no wrought specimens of this metal free from magnetism, not even those prepared by Dr. Wollaston himself, and left with the Royal Society. Specimens of the purest platinum obtained from Mr. Johnson were also found to be slightly magnetic.

2380. Clean platinum foil and cuttings were dissolved in pure nitro-muriatic acid, and the solution evaporated to dryness. Both the solution and the dry chloride pointed equatorially and were repelled by the magnet. A part of the chloride, being dissolved and rendered acid, was precipitated by an acid solution of muriate of ammonia, and the ammonio-chloride of platinum washed and dried: it also, at the magnet, pointed equatorially and was repelled. A portion of this ammonio-chloride, decomposed in a flint-glass tube by heat, gave spongy platinum, which being pressed together into a cake, pointed *axially* and was attracted at the side of the magnetic pole, being magnetic.

2381. At present I believe that platinum is as a metal magnetic, though very slightly so; and that in the compounds, the change of state and the presence of other substances having the diamagnetic character, are sufficient to cover this property and make the whole compound diamagnetic (2422).

2382. *Palladium.* All the palladium in the possession of the Royal Society, prepared by Dr. Wollaston, amounting to ten ingots and rolled plates, is magnetic. Specimens of the metal from Mr. Johnson, considered as pure, were also slightly magnetic. The chloride, the ammonio-bichloride, and the cyanuret of palladium, pointed equatorially and were repelled by the magnet. The same cyanuret, reduced by heat either in open platinum vessels or in close glass tubes, gave palladium possessing a feeble degree of magnetic property. Some of Wollaston's palladium was dissolved in pure nitro-muriatic acid, and the solution slowly acted upon by pure zinc, free from iron, and not magnetic. Five successive portions of the precipitated metal were collected, and *all* were *magnetic*. Ammonio-bichloride of palladium was prepared from the same solution by pure acid muriate of ammonia, and digested in nitro-muriatic acid. The salt itself was repelled, being diamagnetic; but when reduced by heat in glass tubes, or in Berlin capsules, the palladium obtained was magnetic. From the result of all the experiments, I believe the metal to be feebly but truly magnetic.

2383. *Arsenic.* This metal required very particular examination, and even when carefully sublimed twice or thrice in succession, presented appearances which sometimes made me class it with the magnetic, and at other times with the diamagnetic bodies. On the whole, I incline to believe that it belongs to the latter series of substances, being only in a very small degree removed from the zero or medium point. Pure white arsenic points freely in an equatorial direction, and is repelled by a magnetic pole.

2384. In reference to the pointing of short bars between magnetic poles exposing large flat faces, I ought to observe, that such bars will sometimes point axially and seem to be magnetic when they do not belong to that class, and are repelled by a single pole. The cause of this effect has been already given (2298, 2299), and is obviated by the use of poles having wedge-shaped or conical terminations.

2385. *Osmium.* Osmic acid from Mr. Johnson, in fine transparent crystals, was clearly diamagnetic, being repelled. Specimens of the metal and of the protoxide were both slightly magnetic. The protoxide had been obtained by the action of alcohol on a solution of osmic acid which had twice been distilled with water, and the metal was believed to be perfectly free from other substances. Probably, therefore, osmium belongs to the magnetic class.

2386. *Iridium.* Mr. Johnson supplied me with several preparations of iridium. The oxide, chloride, and ammonio-chloride were magnetic; and so was a sample of the metal. One specimen of the metal, which seemed to be very pure, was scarcely at all magnetic; and on the whole, I incline to believe that iridium does not stand in the magnetic class.

2387. *Rhodium.* A well-fused specimen of this metal, prepared by Dr. Wollaston, was mag-

netic; but crystals of the chloride and the sodio-chloride of rhodium prepared by the same philosopher, and others also from Mr. Johnson, were not magnetic, but pointed well equatorially. I conclude, therefore, that the metal is probably not magnetic, or if magnetic, is but little removed from the zero point.

2388. *Uranium.* Peroxide of this metal was obtained not magnetic; protoxide very slightly magnetic: I have set the metal for the present in the diamagnetic class.

2389. *Tungsten.* The oxide of this metal, and also the acid, were submitted to examination, and found to point well equatorially. The acid was distinctly repelled by a single magnetic pole; the oxide appeared nearly neutral. Hence I have, for the present, considered tungsten as a diamagnetic metal.

2390. *Silver* is not magnetic (2291), nor its compounds.

2391. *Antimony* is not magnetic (2291), nor its compounds.

2392. *Bismuth* is not magnetic (2291), nor its compounds.

Having tried many of the compounds of each of these three metals, I thought it well to record the accordance existing between them and their metallic bases (2370).

2393. *Sodium.* A fine large globule, equal to half a cubic inch in size, was well repelled, and is therefore diamagnetic.

2394. *Magnesium.* None of the compounds or salts of this base is magnetic.

2395.

Calcium	Sodium
Strontium	Potassium
Barium	Ammonia

None of the compounds or salts of these substances is magnetic.

2396. From the characters, therefore, of the compounds, as well as from direct evidence in respect of some of the metals, it would appear that, besides iron, nickel, and cobalt, the following are also magnetic; namely, titanium, manganese, cerium, chromium, palladium, platinum. It is, however, very probable that there may be metals possessing distinct magnetic power, yet in so slight a degree, as, like platinum and palladium, not to exhibit in their compounds any sensible trace of it. Such may be the case with tungsten, uranium, rhodium, &c.

2397. I have heated several of the diamagnetic metals, even up to their fusing-points, but have not been able to observe any change, either in the character or degree of their magnetic relations.

2398. Perhaps the cooling of some of the metals, whose compounds, like those of iron, nickel and cobalt, are magnetic, might develop in them a much higher degree of force, than any which they have as yet been known to possess. Manganese, chromium, cerium, titanium, are metals of much interest in this point of view. Osmium, iridium, rhodium and uranium ought to be subjected with them to the same trial.

2399. The following is an attempt to arrange some of the metals in order, as respects their relation to magnetic force. The 0° or medium point is supposed to be the condition of a metal or substance indifferent to the magnetic force as respects attraction or repulsion in air or space. The farther substances are placed from this point, the more distinctive are they as regards their attraction or repulsion by the magnet. Nevertheless this order may, very probably, be found inaccurate by more careful observation.

Magnetic	Diamagnetic
	Bismuth
	Antimony
	Zinc
	Tin
	Cadmium
	Sodium
Iron	Mercury
Nickel	Lead
Cobalt	Silver
Manganese	Copper
Chromium	Gold
Cerium	Arsenic
Titanium	Uranium
Palladium	Rhodium
Platinum	Iridium
Osmium	Tungsten

0°

¶ vi. *Action of Magnets on Air and Gases*

2400. It was impossible to advance in an experimental investigation of the kind now described, without having the mind impressed with various theoretical views of the mode of action of the bodies producing the phenomena. In the passing consideration of these views, the apparently middle condition which *air* held between magnetic and diamagnetic substances was of the utmost interest, and led to many experiments upon its probable influence, which I will now proceed briefly to describe.

2401. A thin flint-glass tube, in which common air was hermetically enclosed, was placed between the magnetic poles (2249) surrounded by air, and the effect of the magnetic force observed upon it. There was a very feeble tendency of the tube to an equatorial position, due to the substance of the tube in which the air was enclosed.

2402. The air was then withdrawn from around the tube more or less, and at last up to the highest amount which a good air-pump would effect; but whatever the degree of rarefaction, the tube of air still seemed to be affected exactly in the same manner as if surrounded by air of its own density.

2403. I then surrounded the air-tube with hydrogen and carbonic acid in succession; but in both these, and in each of them at different degrees of rarefaction, the tube of air remained as indifferent as before.

2404. Hence there appears to be no sensible distinction between dense or rare air; or, as far as these experiments go, between one gas or vapour and another.

2405. As it did not seem at all unlikely that the equatorial and axial set of bodies, or their repulsions and attractions, might depend upon converse actions of the media by which they were surrounded (2361), so I proceeded to examine what would occur with diamagnetic substances, when the air or gas which surrounded them was changed in its density or nature, or what would happen to air itself when surrounded by these substances.

2406. The air tube (2401) was suspended horizontally in water (being retained below the surface by a cube of bismuth attached to it, just beneath the point of suspension, which therefore could have no power of giving it direction); it was then subjected to the magnetic forces, and immediately pointed well in an axial direction, or as a magnet would have done. Being brought near to one pole, it moved, on the supervention of the magnetic force, appearing as if *attracted* after the manner of a magnetic body; and this continued as long as the magnetic force was sustained in action.

2407. The air-tube was in like manner subjected to the action of the magnetic force, when surrounded by alcohol, and also by oil of turpentine, with precisely the same results as in water. In all these cases the action of air in the fluids was precisely the same as the action of a magnetic body in air. The air-tube was subjected to the action of the magnet even when under the surface of mercury, and here also it pointed axially.

2408. In order to extend the experimental relations of air and gases, I proceeded to place substances of the diamagnetic class in them. Thus the bar of heavy glass (2253) was suspended in a jar of air, and then the air about it more or less rarefied, but as before, in the case of the air-tube (2402), alterations of this kind produced no effect. Whether the bar were in air at the ordinary pressure, or as rare as the pump could render it, it still pointed equatorially, and apparently always with the same degree of force.

2409. The bar of bismuth (2296) was suspended in the jar and the same alteration in the density of the air made as before; but this caused no difference in the action of the bismuth, either in kind or degree. Carbonic acid and hydrogen gases were then introduced in succession into the jar, and these also were employed in different degrees of rarefaction, but the results were the same; no change took place in the action on the bismuth.

2410. A bismuth cube was suspended in air and gases at ordinary pressure, and also rarefied as much as could be, and under these circumstances it was brought near the magnetic pole and its repulsion observed; its action was in all these cases precisely the same as in the atmosphere.

2411. The perpendicular copper bar (2323) was suspended near the magnetic pole *in vacuo*, but its set, sluggish movements and revulsion were just the same as before in air (2324).

2412. The following preparations in tubes (2401), namely, a vacuum, air, hydrogen, carbonic acid gas, sulphurous acid gas, and vapour of ether, were surrounded by water, and then subjected to the magnetic force; they all pointed axially, and, as far as I could perceive, with equal force. Being placed in alcohol, the same effect occurred.

2413. The same preparations being surrounded by air, or by carbonic acid gas, all set equatorially.

2414. The axial position of the tubes in the liquid (2412) depends, doubtless, upon the relation of the contents of the tube to the surrounding medium; for as far as the matter of the tube is concerned, it alone would have tended to give the equatorial position. In the following succeeding experiments (2413), where the tubes of gases were in surrounding gases, the equatorial position is due to this effect of the glass of the tube; and that it should produce its constant feeble effect, undisturbed by all the variations of the gases and vapours, is a proof how like and how indifferent these are one to the other.

2415. I suspended a tube of liquid sulphurous acid in gaseous sulphurous acid; when un-

der the magnetic influence, the liquid pointed well equatorially. I surrounded liquid nitrous acid by gaseous nitrous acid; the liquid pointed well equatorially. I placed liquid ether in the vapour of ether; the former pointed equatorially. Upon suspending the tube of vapour of ether in liquid ether, the vapour pointed axially.

2416. In every kind of trial, therefore, and in every form of experiment, the gases and vapours still occupy a medium position between the magnetic and the diamagnetic classes. Further, whatever the chemical or other properties of the substances, however different in their specific gravity, or however varied in their own degree of rarefaction, they all become alike in their magnetic relation, and apparently equivalent to a perfect vacuum. Bodies which are very marked as diamagnetic substances, immediately lose all traces of this character when they become vaporous (2415). It would be exceedingly interesting to know whether a body from the magnetic class, as chloride of iron, would undergo the same change.

¶ vii. *General Considerations*

2417. Such are the facts which, in addition to those presented by the phenomena of light, establish a magnetic action or condition of matter new to our knowledge. Under this action, an elongated portion of such matter usually (2253, 2384) places itself at right angles to the lines of magnetic force; this result may be resolved into the simpler one of repulsion of the matter by either magnetic pole. The set of the elongated portion, or the repulsion of the whole mass, continues as long as the magnetic force is sustained, and ceases with its cessation.

2418. By the exertion of this new condition of force, the body moved may pass either *along* the magnetic lines or *across* them; and it may move along or across them in either or any direction. So that two portions of matter, simultaneously subject to this power, may be made to approach each other as if they were mutually attracted, or recede as if mutually repelled. All the phenomena resolve themselves into this; that a portion of such matter, when under magnetic action, tends to move from stronger to weaker places or points of force. When the substance is surrounded by lines of magnetic force of equal power on all sides, it does not tend to move, and is then in marked contradistinction with a linear current of electricity under the same circumstances.

2419. This condition and effect are new, not *only* in respect to the exertion of power by a magnet over bodies previously supposed to be indifferent to its influence, but are *new* as a magnetic action, presenting us with a second mode in which the magnetic power can exert its influence. These two modes are in the same general antithetical relation to each other as positive and negative in electricity, or as northness and southness in polarity, or as the lines of electric and magnetic force in magneto-electricity; and the diamagnetic phenomena are the more important, because they extend largely, and in a new direction, that character of duality which the magnetic force already, in a certain degree, was known to possess.

2420. All matter appears to be subject to the magnetic force as universally as it is to the gravitating, the electric and the chemical or cohesive forces; for that which is not affected by it in the manner of ordinary magnetic action, is affected in the manner I have now described; the matter possessing for the time the solid or fluid state. Hence substances appear to arrange themselves into two great divisions; the magnetic, and that which I have called the diamagnetic classes; and between these classes the contrast is so great and direct, though varying in degree, that where a substance from the one class will be attracted, a body from the other will be repelled; and where a bar of the one will assume a certain position, a bar of the other will acquire a position at right angles to it.

2421. As yet I have not found a single solid or fluid body, not being a mixture, that is perfectly neutral in relation to the two lists; i.e., that is neither attracted nor repelled in air. It would probably be important to the consideration of magnetic action, to know if there were any natural simple substance possessing this condition in the solid or fluid state. Of compound or mixed bodies there may be many; and as it may be important to the advancement of experimental investigation, I will describe the principles on which such a substance was prepared when required for use as a circumambient medium.

2422. It is manifest that the properties of magnetic and diamagnetic bodies are in opposition as respects their dynamic effects; and, therefore, that by a due mixture of bodies from each class, a substance having any intermediate degree of the property of either may be obtained. Protosulphate of iron belongs to the magnetic, and water to the diamagnetic class; and using these substances, I found it easy to make a solution which was neither attracted nor repelled, nor pointed when in air. Such a solution pointed axially when surrounded by water. If made somewhat weaker in respect of the iron, it would point axially in water but equatorially in air; and it could be made to pass more and more into the magnetic or the diamagnetic class by the addition of more sulphate of iron or more water.

2423. Thus a *fluid* medium was obtained, which, practically, as far as I could perceive, had every magnetic character and effect of a gas, and even of a vacuum; and as we possess both magnetic and diamagnetic glass (2354), it is evidently possible to prepare a *solid* substance possessing the same neutral magnetic character.

2424. The endeavour to form a general list of substances in the present imperfect state of our knowledge would be very premature: the one below is given therefore only for the purpose of conveying an idea of the singular association under which bodies come in relation to magnetic force, and for the purpose of general reference hereafter:

Iron
Nickel
Cobalt
Manganese
Palladium
Crown-glass
Platinum
Osmium
0° Air and vacuum
Arsenic
Ether
Alcohol
Gold
Water
Mercury
Flint glass
Tin
Heavy glass
Antimony
Phosphorus
Bismuth

2425. It is very interesting to observe that metals are the substances which stand at the extremities of the list, being of all bodies those which are most powerfully opposed to each other in their magnetic condition. It is also a very remarkable circumstance, that these differences and departures from the medium condition are in the metals at the two extremes, iron and bismuth, associated with a small conducting power for electricity. At the same time the *contrast* between these metals, as to their fibrous and granular state, their malleable and brittle character, will press upon the mind whilst contemplating the possible condition of their molecules when subjected to magnetic force.

2426. In reference to the metals, as well as the diamagnetics not of that class (2286), it is satisfactory to have such an answer to the opinion that all bodies are magnetic as iron, as does not consist in a mere negation of that which is affirmed, but in proofs that they are in a different and opposed state, and are able to counteract a very considerable degree of magnetic force (2448).

2427. As already stated, the magnetic force is so strikingly distinct in its action upon bodies of the magnetic and the diamagnetic class, that when it causes the attraction of the one it produces the repulsion of the other; and this we cannot help referring, in some way, to an action upon the molecules or the mass of the substances acted upon, by which they are thrown into different conditions and affected accordingly. In that point of view it is very striking to compare the results with those which are presented to us by a polarized ray, especially as then a remarkable difference comes into view; for if transparent bodies be taken from the two classes, as for instance, heavy glass or water from the diamagnetic, and a piece of green glass or a solution of green vitriol from the magnetic class, then a given line of magnetic force will cause the repulsion of one and the attraction of the other; but this same line of force, which thus affects the particles so differently, affects the polarized ray when passing through them precisely in the *same* manner in both cases; for the two bodies cause its rotation in the *same* direction (2160, 2199, 2224).

2428. This consideration becomes even more important when we connect it with the diamagnetic and the optical properties of bodies which rotate a polarized ray. Thus the iron solution and a piece of quartz, having the power to rotate a ray, point by the influence of the *same* line of magnetic force, the one axially and the other equatorially; but the rotation which is impressed on a ray of light by these two bodies, as far as they are under the influence of the same magnetic force, is the *same* for both. Further, this rotation is quite independent of, and quite unlike that of the quartz in a most important point; for the quartz by itself can only rotate the ray in one direction, but under the influence of the magnetic force it can rotate it both to the right and left, according to the course of the ray (2231, 2232). Or, if two pieces

of quartz (or two tubes of oil of turpentine) be taken which can rotate the ray *different* ways, the further rotative force manifested by them when under the dominion of the magnetism is always the *same* way; and the direction of that way may be made either to the right or left in either crystal of quartz. All this time the *contrast* between the quartz as a diamagnetic, and the solution of iron as a magnetic body remains undisturbed. Certain considerations regarding the character of a ray, arising from these contrasts, press strongly on my mind, which, when I have had time to submit them to further experiment, I hope to present to the Society.

2429. Theoretically, an explanation of the movements of the diamagnetic bodies, and all the dynamic phenomena consequent upon the actions of magnets on them, might be offered in the supposition that magnetic induction caused in them a contrary state to that which it produced in magnetic matter; i.e., that if a particle of each kind of matter were placed in the magnetic field both would become magnetic, and each would have its axis parallel to the resultant of magnetic force passing through it; but the particle of magnetic matter would have its north and south poles opposite, or facing towards the contrary poles of the inducing magnet, whereas with the diamagnetic particles the reverse would be the case; and hence would result approximation in the one substance, recession in the other.

2430. Upon Ampère's theory, this view would be equivalent to the supposition, that as currents are induced in iron and magnetics parallel to those existing in the inducing magnet or battery wire; so in bismuth, heavy glass and diamagnetic bodies, the currents induced are in the contrary direction. This would make the currents in diamagnetics the same in direction as those which are induced in diamagnetic conductors at the *commencement* of the inducing current; and those in magnetic bodies the same as those produced at the *cessation* of the same inducing current. No difficulty would occur as respects non-conducting magnetic and diamagnetic substances, because the hypothetical currents are supposed to exist not in the mass, but round the particles of the matter.

2431. As far as experiment yet bears upon such a notion, we may observe, that the known inductive effects upon masses of magnetic and diamagnetic metals *are the same*. If a straight rod of iron be carried across magnetic lines of force, or if it, or a helix of iron rods or wire, be held near a magnet, as the power in it rises, electric currents are induced, which move through the bars or helix in certain determinate directions (38, 114, &c.). If a bar or a helix of bismuth be employed under the same circumstances the currents are again induced, and precisely in the same direction as in the iron, so that here no difference occurs in the direction of the induced current, and not very much in its force, nothing like so much indeed as between the current induced in either of these metals and a metal taken from near the neutral point (2399). Still there is this difference remaining between the conditions of the experiment and the hypothetical case; that in the former the induction is manifested by currents in the masses, whilst in the latter, i.e., in the special magnetic and diamagnetic effects, the currents, if they exist, are probably about the particles of the matter.

2432. The magnetic relation of aeriform bodies is exceedingly remarkable. That oxygen or nitrogen gas should stand in a position intermediate between the magnetic and diamagnetic classes; that it should occupy the place which *no* solid or liquid element can take; that it should show no change in its relations by rarefaction to any possible degree, or even when the space it occupies passes into a vacuum; that it should be the same magnetically with any other gas or vapour; that it should not take its place at one end but in the very middle of the great series of bodies; and that all gases or vapours should be alike, from the rarest state of hydrogen to the densest state of carbonic acid, sulphurous acid, or ether vapour, are points so striking, as to presuade one at once that air must have a great and perhaps an active part to play in the physical and terrestrial arrangement of magnetic forces.

2433. At one time I looked to air and gases as the bodies which, allowing attenuation of their substance without addition, would permit of the observation of corresponding variations in their magnetic properties; but now all such power by rarefaction appears to be taken away; and though it is easy to prepare a liquid medium which shall act with other bodies as air does (2422), still it is not truly in the same relation to them; neither does it allow of dilution, for to add water or any such substance is to add to the diamagnetic power of the liquid; and if it were possible to convert it into vapour and so dilute it by heat, it would pass into the class of gases and be magnetically undistinguishable from the rest.

2434. It is also very remarkable to observe the apparent disappearance of magnetic condition and effect when bodies assume the vaporous or gaseous state, comparing it at the same time with the similar relation to light; for as yet no gas or vapour has been made to show any magnetic influence over the polarized ray, even by the use of powers far more than enough to manifest such action freely in liquid and solid bodies.

2435. Whether the negative results obtained by the use of gases and vapours depend upon the smaller quantity of matter in a given volume, or whether they are direct consequences of the altered physical condition of the substance, is a point of very great importance to the theory of magnetism. I have imagined, in elucidation of the subject, an experiment with one of M. Cagniard de la Tour's ether tubes, but expect to find great difficulty in carrying it into execution, chiefly on account of the strength, and therefore the mass of the tube necessary to resist the expansion of the imprisoned heated ether.

2436. The remarkable condition of air and its relation to bodies taken from the magnetic and the diamagnetic classes, causes it to point equatorially in the former and axially in the latter. Or, if the experiment presents its results under the form of attraction and repulsion, the air moves as if repelled in a magnetic medium and attracted in a medium from the diamagnetic class. Hence it seems as if the air were magnetic when compared with diamagnetic bodies, and of the latter class when compared with magnetic bodies.

2437. This result I have considered as explained by the assumption that bismuth and its congeners are absolutely repelled by the magnetic poles, and would, if there were nothing else concerned in the phenomenon than the magnet and the bismuth, be equally repelled. So also with the iron and its similars, the attraction has been assumed as a direct result of the mutual action of them and the magnets; further, these actions have been admitted as sufficient to account for the pointing of the air both axially and equatorially, as also for its apparent attraction and repulsion; the effect in these cases being considered as due to the travelling of the air to those positions which the magnetic or diamagnetic bodies tended to leave.

2438. The effects with air are, however, in these results precisely the same as those which were obtained with the solutions of iron of various strengths (2365), where *all* the bodies belonged to the magnetic class, and where the effect was evidently due to the greater or smaller degree of magnetic power possessed by the solutions. A weak solution in a stronger pointed equatorially and was repelled like a diamagnetic, not because it did not tend by attraction to an axial position, but because it tended to that position with less force than the matter around it; so the question will enter the mind, whether the diamagnetics, when in air, are repelled and tend to the equatorial position for any other reason, than that the air is more magnetic than they are, and tends to occupy the axial space. It is easy to perceive that if all bodies were magnetic in different degrees, forming one great series from end to end, with air in the middle of the series, the effects would take place as they do actually occur. Any body from the middle part of the series would point equatorially in the bodies above it and axially in those beneath it; for the matter which, like bismuth, goes from a strong to a weak point of action, may do so only because that substance, which is already at the place of weak action, tends to come to the place where the action is strong; just as in electrical induction the bodies best fitted to carry on the force are drawn into the shortest line of action. And so air in water, or even under mercury, is, or appears to be, drawn towards the magnetic pole.

2439. But if this were the true view, and air had such power amongst other bodies as to stand in the midst of them, then one would be led to expect that rarefaction of the air would affect its place, rendering it, perhaps, more diamagnetic, or at all events altering its situation in the list. If such were the case, bodies that set equatorially in it in one state of density, would, as it varied, change their position, and at last set axially: but this they do not do; and whether the rarefied air be compared with the magnetic or the diamagnetic class, or even with dense air, it keeps its place.

2440. Such a view also would make mere space magnetic, and precisely to the same degree as air and gases. Now though it may very well be, that space, air and gases, have the same general relation to magnetic force, it seems to me a great additional assumption to suppose that they are all absolutely magnetic, and in the midst of a series of bodies, rather than to suppose that they are in a normal or zero state. For the present, therefore, I incline to the former view, and consequently to the opinion that diamagnetics have a specific action antithetically distinct from ordinary magnetic action,

and have thus presented us with a magnetic property new to our knowledge.

2441. The amount of this power in diamagnetic substances seems to be very small, when estimated by its dynamic effect, but the motion which it can generate is perhaps not the most striking measure of its force; and it is probable that when its nature is more intimately known to us, other effects produced by it and other indicators and measurers of its powers, than those so imperfectly made known in this paper, will come to our knowledge; and perhaps even new classes of phenomena will serve to make it manifest and indicate its operation. It is very striking to observe the feeble condition of a helix when alone, and the astonishing force which, in giving and receiving, it manifests by association with a piece of soft iron. So also here we may hope for some analogous development of this element of power, so new as yet to our experience. It cannot for a moment be supposed that, being given to natural bodies, it is either superfluous or insufficient, or unnecessary. It doubtless has its appointed office, and that one which relates to the whole mass of the globe; and it is probably because of its relation to the whole earth that its amount is necessarily so small (so to speak) in the portions of matter which we handle and subject to experiment. And small as it is, how vastly greater is this force, even in dynamic results, than the mighty power of gravitation, for instance, which binds the whole universe together, when manifested by masses of matter of equal magnitude!

2442. With a full conviction that the uses of this power in nature will be developed hereafter, and that they will prove, as all other natural results of force do, not merely important but essential, I will venture a few hasty observations.

2443. Matter cannot thus be affected by the magnetic forces without being itself concerned in the phenomenon, and exerting in turn a due amount of influence upon the magnetic force. It requires mere observation to be satisfied that when a magnet is acting upon a piece of soft iron, the iron itself, by the condition which its particles assume, carries on the force to distant points, giving it direction and concentration in a manner most striking. So also here the condition which the particles of intervening diamagnetics acquire, may be the very condition which carries on and causes the transfer of force through them. In former papers (1161, &c.)[1] I

[1] *Philosophical Transactions*, 1838, Part I.

proposed a theory of electrical induction founded on the action of contiguous particles with which I am now even more content than at the time of its proposition: and I then ventured to suggest that probably the lateral action of electrical currents which is equivalent to electrodynamic or *magnetic* action, was also conveyed onwards in a similar manner (1663, 1710, 1729, 1735). At that time I could discover no peculiar condition of the intervening or diamagnetic matter; but now that we are able to distinguish such an action, so *like* in its nature in bodies so *unlike* in theirs, and by that so like in character to the manner in which the magnetic force pervades all kinds of bodies, being at the same time as universal in its presence as it is in its action; now that diamagnetics are shown not to be indifferent bodies, I feel still more confidence in repeating the same suggestion, and asking whether it may not be by the action of the contiguous or next succeeding particles that the magnetic force is carried onwards, and whether the peculiar condition acquired by diamagnetics when subject to magnetic action, is not that condition by which such propagation of the force is affected?

2444. Whichever view we take of solid and liquid substances, whether as forming two lists, or one great magnetic class (2424, 2437), it will not, as far as I can perceive, affect the question. They are all subject to the influence of the magnetic lines of force passing through them, and the virtual difference in property and character between any two substances taken from different places in the list (2424) will be the same; for it is the differential relation of the two which governs their mutual effects.

2445. It is that group which includes air, gases, vapours, and even a vacuum which presents any difficulty to the mind; but here there is such a wonderful change in the physical constitution of the bodies, and such high powers in some respects are retained by them, whilst others seem to vanish, that we might almost expect some peculiar condition to be assumed in regard to a power so universal as the magnetic force. Electric induction being an action through distance is varied enough amongst solid and liquid bodies; but, when it comes to be exerted in air or gases, where it most manifestly exists, it is alike in amount in all (1292); neither does it vary in degree in air however rare or dense it may be (1284). Now magnetic action may be considered as a mere function of electric force, and if it should be found to correspond with the latter in this particular rela-

tion to air, gases, &c., it would not excite in my mind any surprise.

2446. In reference to the manner in which it is possible for electric force, either static or dynamic, to be transferred from particle to particle when they are at a distance from each other, or across a vacuum, I have nothing to add to what I have said before (1614, &c.). The supposition that such can take place, can present nothing startling to the mind of those who have endeavoured to comprehend the radiation and the conduction of heat under one principle of action.

2447. When we consider the magnetic condition of the earth as a whole, without reference to its possible relation to the sun, and reflect upon the enormous amount of diamagnetic matters which, to our knowledge, forms its crust; and when we remember that magnetic curves of a certain amount of force and universal in their presence, are passing through these matters and keeping them constantly in that state of tension, and therefore of action, which I hope successfully to have developed, we cannot doubt but that some great purpose of utility to the system, and us its inhabitants, is thereby fulfilled, which now we shall have the pleasure of searching out.

2448. Of the substances which compose the crust of the earth, by far the greater portion belongs to the diamagnetic class; and though ferruginous and other magnetic matters, being more energetic in their action, are consequently more striking in their phenomena, we should be hasty in assuming that therefore they overrule entirely the effect of the former bodies. As regards the ocean, lakes, rivers, and the atmosphere, they will exert their peculiar effect almost uninfluenced by any magnetic matter in them; and as respects the rocks and mountains, their diamagnetic influence is perhaps greater than might be anticipated. I mentioned that by adjusting water and a salt of iron together, I obtained a solution inactive in air (2422); that is, by a due association of the forces of a body from each class, water and a salt of iron, the magnetic force of the latter was entirely counteracted by the diamagnetic force of the former, and the mixture was neither attracted nor repelled. To produce this effect, it required that more than 48.6 grains of crystallized protosulphate of iron should be added to 10 cubic inches of water (for these proportions gave a solution which still set equatorially), a quantity so large, that I was greatly astonished on observing the power of the water to overcome it. It is not therefore at all unlikely that many of the masses which form the crust of this our globe may have an excess of diamagnetic power and act accordingly.

2449. Though the general disposition of the magnetic curves which permeate and surround our globe resemble those of a very short magnet, and therefore give lines of force rapidly diverging in their general form, yet the magnitude of the system prevents us from observing any diminution of their power within small limits; so that probably any attempt on the surface of the earth to observe the tendency of matter to pass from stronger to weaker places of action would fail. Theoretically, however, and at first sight, I think a pound of bismuth or of water, estimated at the equator, where the magnetic needle does not dip, ought to weigh less when taken into latitudes where the dip is considerable; whilst a pound of iron, nickel or cobalt, ought, under the same change of circumstances, to weigh more. If such should really prove to be the case, then a ball of iron and another of bismuth, attached to the ends of a delicate balance beam, should cause that beam to take different inclinations on different parts of the surface of the earth; and it does not seem quite impossible that an instrument to measure one of the conditions of terrestrial magnetic force might be constructed on such a principle.

2450. If one might speculate upon the effect of the whole system of curves upon very large masses, and these masses were in plates or rings, then they would, according to analogy with the magnetic field, place themselves equatorially. If Saturn were a magnet as the earth is, and his ring composed of diamagnetic substances, the tendency of the magnetic forces would be to place it in the position which it actually has.

2451. It is a curious sight to see a piece of wood, or of beef, or an apple, or a bottle of water repelled by a magnet, or taking the leaf of a tree and hanging it up between the poles, to observe it take an equatorial position. Whether any similar effects occur in nature among the myriads of forms which, upon all parts of the earth's surface, are surrounded by air, and are subject to the action of lines of magnetic force, is a question which can only be answered by future observation.

2452. Of the interior of the earth we know nothing, but there are many reasons for believing that it is of a high temperature. On this supposition I have recently remarked, that at a certain distance from the surface downwards, magnetic substances must be entirely destitute, either of the power of retaining magnetism, or becoming magnetic by induction from currents in the crust or otherwise.[1] This is evidently an error; that the iron, &c., can retain no magnetic condition of itself, is very probably true, but that the magnetic metals and all their compounds retain a certain power of becoming magnetic by induction, whatever their temperature, has now been proved (2344, &c.). The deep magnetic contents of the earth, therefore, though they probably do not constitute of themselves a central magnet, are just in the condition to act as a very weak iron core to the currents around them, or other inducing actions, and very likely are highly important in this respect. What the effect of the diamagnetic part may be under the influence of such inductive forces, we are not prepared to state; but as far as I have been able to observe, such bodies have not their power diminished by heat (2397).

2453. If the sun has anything to do with the magnetism of the globe, then it is probable that part of its effect is due to the action of the light that comes to us from it; and in that expectation the air seems most strikingly placed round our sphere, investing it with a transparent diamagnetic, which therefore, is permeable to its rays, and at the same time moving with great velocity across them. Such conditions seem to suggest the possibility of magnetism being there generated; but I shall do better to refrain from giving expression to these vague thoughts (though they will press in upon the mind), and first submitting them to rigid investigation by experiment, if they prove worthy, then present them hereafter to the Royal Society.

Royal Institution, Dec. 22, 1845

Feb. 2, 1846. I add the following notes and references to these *Researches:*

Brugmans first observed the repulsion of bismuth by a magnet in 1778. *Antonii Brugmans Magnetismus seu de affinitatibus magneticis observationes magneticæ.* Lugd. Batav. 1778, § 41.

M. le Baillif on the "Repulsion of a Magnet by Bismuth and Antimony," *Bulletin Universel,* 1827, Vol. VII, p. 371; Vol. VIII, pp. 87, 91, 94.

Saigey on the "Magnetism of certain natural combinations of Iron, and on the mutual repulsions of Bodies in general," *Ibid.,* 1828, Vol. IX, pp. 89, 167, 239.

Seebeck on the "Magnetic Polarity of different Metals, Alloys and Oxides," *Ibid.,* 1828, Vol. IX, p. 175.

[1] *Philosophical Magazine,* 1845, Vol. XXVII, p. 3.

TWENTY-SECOND SERIES[1]

§ 28. *On the Crystalline Polarity of Bismuth (and Other Bodies), and on its Relation to the Magnetic Form of Force* ¶ i. *Crystalline Polarity of Bismuth* ¶ ii. *Crystalline Polarity of Antimony* ¶ iii. *Crystalline Polarity of Arsenic*

RECEIVED OCTOBER 4, READ DECEMBER 7, 1848

2454. MANY results obtained by subjecting bismuth to the action of the magnet have at various times embarrassed me, and I have either been contented with an imperfect explanation, or have left them for a future examination: that examination I have now taken up, and it has led to the discovery of the following results. I cannot, however, better enter upon the subject than by a brief description of the anomalies which occurred, and which may be obtained at pleasure.

2455. If a small open glass tube have a bulb formed in its middle part and some clean good bismuth be placed in the bulb and melted by a spirit-lamp, it is easy afterward, by turning the metal into the tubular part of the arrangement, to cast it into long cylinders: these are very clean, and when broken are seen to be crystallized, usually giving cleavage planes, which run across the metal. I prepare them from 0.05 to 0.1 of an inch in diameter, and, if the glass be thin, usually break both it and the bismuth together, and then keep the little cylinders in their vitreous cases.

2456. Taking some of these cylinders at random and suspending them horizontally between the poles of the electro-magnet (2247), they presented the following phenomena. The first pointed axially; the second, equatorially; the third, equatorial in one position, and obliquely equatorial if turned round on its axis 50° or 60°; the fourth, equatorially and axially under the same treatment; and all of them, if suspended perpendicularly, pointed well, vibrating about a final fixed position which seemed to have no reference to the form of the cylinders. In all these cases the bismuth was strongly diamagnetic (2295, &c.), being repelled by a single magnetic pole, or passing off on either side from the axial line between two poles. A similar piece of finely-grained or granular bismuth was, under the same circumstances and at the same time, affected in a perfectly regular manner, taking up the equatorial position (2253), as a body simply diamagnetic ought to do. The cause of these variations was finally traced to the regularly crystalline condition of the metallic cylinders.

¶ i. *Crystalline Polarity of Bismuth*

2457. Some bismuth was crystallized in the usual manner by melting it in a clean iron ladle, allowing it partly to congeal, and then pouring away the internal fluid portion. Pieces so obtained were then broken up by copper hammers and tools, and groups of the crystals separated, each group or piece consisting only of those crystals which were symmetrically arranged, and therefore likely to act in one direction. If any part of the fragments had been in contact with the iron ladle, it was cleared away by rubbing on sandstone and sandpaper. Pieces weighing from 18 grains to 100 grains were thus easily obtained.

2458. The electro-magnet employed in the first instance was that already described (2247), having moveable terminations which supplied either conical, round, or flat-faced poles. That the suspension of the bismuth might be readily effected and unobjectionable as to magnetic influence, the following arrangement was generally adopted. A single fibre of cocoon silk, from 12 to 24 inches in length, was attached to a fit support above, and made fast below to the end of a piece of fine, straight, well-cleaned copper wire, about 2 inches in length; the lower end of this wire was twisted up into a little head, and then furnished with a pellet of cement, made by melting together a portion of pure white wax with about one-fourth its weight of Canada balsam. The cement was soft enough to adhere by pressure to any dry substance, and sufficiently hard to sustain weights up to 300 grains, or even more. When prepared, the

[1] *Philosophical Transactions*, 1849, p. 1. The Bakerian Lecture.

633

suspender was subjected by itself to the action of the magnet, to ascertain that it was free from any tendency to point, or be affected; without which precaution no confidence could be reposed in the results of the experiments.

2459. A piece of selected bismuth (2457), weighing 25 grains was hung up between the poles of the magnet, and moved with great freedom. The constituent cubes were associated in the usual manner, being attached to each other chiefly in the line joining two opposite solid angles; and this line was in the greatest length of the piece. The instant that the magnetic force was on, the bismuth vibrated strongly about a given line, in which, at last, it settled; and if moved out of that position, it returned, when at liberty, into it; pointing with considerable force, and having its greatest length *axial*.

2460. Another piece was then selected, having a flatter form, which when subjected to the magnetic power, pointed with the same facility and force, but its greatest length was equatorial: still the line according to which the cubes tended to associate diametrally, was, as before, in the *axial* direction. Other pieces were then taken of different forms, or shaped into various forms by rubbing them down on stone, but they all pointed well; and took up a final position, which had no reference to the shape, but was manifestly dependent on the crystalline condition of the substance.

2461. In all these cases the bismuth was diamagnetic, and strongly repelled by either magnetic pole, or from the axial line. It was affected only whilst the magnetic force was present. It set in a given constant position perfectly determinate; and, if moved, always returned to it, unless the extent of motion was above 90°, and then the piece moved farther round and took up a new position diametrically opposed to the former, which it then retained with equal force, and in the same manner. This phenomenon is general in all the results I have to refer to, and I will express it by the word diametral: diametral set or position.

2462. The effect occurs with a single magnetic pole, and it is then striking to observe a long piece of a substance, so diamagnetic as bismuth, repelled, and yet at the same moment set round with force, axially or end on, as a piece of magnetic substance would do.

2463. Whether the magnetic poles employed (2458) are pointed, round, or flatfaced, still the effect on the bismuth is the same: nevertheless, the form of the poles has an important

influence of a subordinate kind; and some forms are much more fitted for these investigations than others. When pointed poles are employed, the lines of magnetic force (2149) rapidly diverge, and the force itself diminishes in intensity to the middle distance from each pole. But when flat-faced poles are used, though the lines of power are curved and vary in intensity at and towards the edges of the flat faces, yet there is a space at the middle of the magnetic field where they may be considered as parallel to the magnetic axes, and of equal force throughout. If the flat faces of the poles be square or circular, and their distance apart about one-third of their diameter, this space of uniform power is of considerable extent. In my experience the central or axial portion of the magnetic field is sensibly weaker than the circumjacent parts; but, then, there is a small screw-hole in the middle of each pole face, for the attachment of other forms of termination.

2464. Now the law of action of bismuth, as a *diamagnetic* body, is that it tends to go from stronger to weaker places of magnetic force (2267, 2418); but as a *magnecrystallic* body it is subject to no effect of the kind; and is as powerfully affected by lines of equal force as by any other. So a piece of amorphous bismuth, suspended in a magnetic field of uniform power, seems to have lost its diamagnetic force altogether, and tends to acquire no motion but what is due to torsion of the suspending fibre, or currents of air: but a piece of regularly crystallized bismuth is, in the same situation, very powerfully affected by virtue of its magnecrystallic condition.

2465. Hence the great value of a magnetic field of uniform force; and, if, hereafter, in the extension of these investigations to bodies having only a small degree of crystalline power, a perfectly uniform field should be required, it could easily be given by making the form of the pole face somewhat convex, and rounded at the edges more or less. The required shape could be ascertained by calculation, or perhaps better in practice, by the use of a little test cylinder of bismuth in the granular or amorphous state, or of phosphorus.

2466. In addition to these observations, it may be remarked that small crystals, or masses of crystals, and such as approach in their general shape to that of a cube or a sphere, are better than large or elongated pieces; inasmuch, as if there be irregularities in the force of a magnetic field, such pieces are less likely to be affected by them.

2467. When the crystal of bismuth is in a magnetic field of equal strength, it is equally affected whether it be in the middle of the field or close up to one or the other magnetic pole; i.e. the number of vibrations in equal times appears to be equal. Much care, however, is required in estimating it by such means, because, from the occurrence of two positions of unstable equilibrium in the equatorial direction, the vibrations in large arcs are much slower than those in small arcs; and it is difficult in different cases to adjust them to the same extent of vibration.

2468. Whether the bismuth be in a field of intense magnetic force or one of feeble powers; whether the magnetic poles are close up to the piece, or are opened out until they are five or six inches or even a foot asunder; whether the bismuth be in the line of maximum force, or raised above, or lowered beneath it; whether the electric current be strong or weak, and the magnetic force, therefore, more or less in that respect; if the bismuth be affected at all it is always affected in the same manner.

2469. The results are, altogether, very different from those produced by diamagnetic action (2418). They are equally distinct from those discovered and described by Plücker, in his beautiful researches into the relation of the optic axis to magnetic action; for there the force is equatorial, whereas here it is axial. So they appear to present to us a new force, or a new form of force, in the molecules of matter, which, for convenience sake, I will conventionally designate by a new word, as the *magnecrystallic* force.

2470. The direction of this force is, in relation to the magnetic field, *axial* and *not equatorial:* this is proved by several considerations. Thus, when a piece of regularly crystallized bismuth was suspended in the magnetic field, it pointed; keeping it in this position, the point of suspension was removed 90° in the equatorial plane (2252), so that when again freely suspended, the line through the crystal, which was before horizontal in the equatorial plane, was now vertical; the piece again pointed, and generally with more force than before. The line passing through the crystal, coincident with the magnetic axis, may now be taken as a line of force; and if the process of a quarter revolution in the equatorial plane be repeated, however often, the crystal still continues to point with the assumed line of force in the magnetic axis, and with a maximum degree of power. But now, if the point of suspension be removed

90° in the plane of the axis, i.e., to the end of the assumed line of force, so, that when the crystal is again freely suspended this line is vertical; then, the crystal presents its peculiar effect at a *minimum*, being almost or entirely devoid of pointing power, and exhibits in relation to the magnet, only the ordinary diamagnetic force (2418).

2471. Now if the power had been equatorial and polar, its maximum effect would not have been produced by a change of the point of suspension through 90° in the equatorial plane, but by the same change in the axial plane, and any similar change after that in the axial plane, would not have disturbed the maximum force; whereas a single change of 90° in the equatorial plane, would have brought the line of force vertical (as in Plücker's case of Iceland spar), and reduced the results to a minimum or zero.

2472. The directing force, therefore, and the set of the crystal are in the *axial* direction. This force is, doubtless, resident in the particles of the crystal. It is such, that the crystal can set with equal readiness and permanence in two diametral positions; and that between these there are two positions of equatorial equilibrium, which are, of course, unstable in their nature. Either end of the mass or of its molecules is, to all intents and purposes, both in these phenomena, and in the ordinary results of crystallization, like the other end; and in many cases, therefore, the words *axial* and *axiality* would seem more expressive than the words *polar* and *polarity.* In presenting the ideas to my own mind, I have found the meaning belonging to the former words the more useful.

2473. On placing the *metal* in other positions, and therefore in a constrained condition, no alteration of the state or power of the bismuth, either in force or direction, is produced by the power of the magnet, however strong its enforcement or long its continuance.

2474. It is difficult readily to describe the position of this force in relation to the crystal, though most easy to ascertain it experimentally. The form of the bismuth crystals is said to be that of a cube, and of its primitive particle a regular octohedron. To me the crystals do not seem to be cubes, but either rhomboids or rhombic prisms, approaching very nearly to cubes. My measurements were very imperfect and the crystals not regular; but as an average of several observations, the planes were inclined to each other at angles of $91\frac{1}{2}°$ and $88\frac{1}{2}°$; and the boundary lines of a plane at $87\frac{1}{2}°$ and $92\frac{1}{2}°$. Whatever be the true form, it is manifest, upon inspection, that the aggregating force tends to produce crystals having more or less of the rhomboidal shape and rhombic planes; and that these crystals run together in symmetric groups, generally in the direction of their longest diameters. Now the line of *magnecrystallic* force almost always coincides with this direction where the latter is apparent.

2475. The *cleavage* of bismuth crystals removes the solid angles and replaces them by planes; so that there are four directions producing the octohedron. These cleavages are not (in my experience) made with equal facility, nor do they produce planes equally bright and perfect. Two, and more frequently one, of these planes are more perfect than the others; and this, the most perfect plane, is that which is produced at the most acute solid angle (2474); and is generally easily recognized. When a bismuth crystal presents many planes of cleavage and is suspended in the magnetic field, one of these planes faces towards one of the magnetic poles, and its corresponding plane, if it be there, towards the other; so that the line of magnecrystallic force is perpendicular to this plane: and this plane corresponds to the one which I have already described as being, generally, the most perfect, and replacing the acute angle of the crystal.

2476. A single crystal of bismuth was selected and cut out from the mass by copper tools, and the places where it had adhered were rubbed down on sand-paper, so as to give the fragment a cube-like form with six planes; four of these planes were natural. One of the solid angles, expected to be that terminating or in the direction of the line of magnecrystallic force, was removed, so as to expose a small cleavage plane, which was bright and perfect, as also was expected. When suspended in the magnetic field with this plane vertical, the crystal instantly pointed with considerable force, and with the plane towards either one or the other magnetic pole; so that the magnecrystallic axis appeared now to be horizontal and acting with its greatest power. When this axial line was made vertical, and the plane therefore horizontal, the position being carefully adjusted, the crystal did not point at all. Being now suspended in succession at all the angles and faces of the cube, it always pointed with more or less force; but always so that a line drawn perpendicularly through the indicating cleavage plane (representing therefore the line of force) was in the same vertical plane as that including the magnetic axis: and, finally, when the bright

cleavage plane was horizontal and the line of directive force therefore vertical, inclining it a little in a given direction would make any given part of the crystal point to the magnetic poles.

2477. A *group* of bismuth crystals, the apex of which was terminated by a single small cleavage facet, was found to give the same results.

2478. Occasionally groups of crystals (2457) occurred which did not seem capable of being placed in some one position in which they lost all directive power, but seemed to retain a minimum degree of force. It is very unlikely, however, that all the groups should be perfectly symmetric in the arrangement of their parts. It is more surprising that they should be so distinct in their action as they are. In reference to bismuth, and many other bodies, it is probable that magnetic force will give a more important indication in relation to the essential and real crystalline structure of the mass than its form can do.

2479. I have already stated that the *magnecrystallic* force does not manifest itself by attraction or repulsion, or, at least, does not cause approach or recession, but gives *position* only. The *law* of action appears to be that *the line or axis* of MAGNECRYSTALLIC *force* (being the resultant of the action of all the molecules), *tends to place itself parallel, or as a tangent, to the magnetic curve or line of magnetic force, passing through the place where the crystal is situated.*

2480. I now broke up masses of bismuth which had been melted and solidified in the ordinary way, and selecting those fragments which appeared to be most regularly crystallized, submitted them to experiment. It was almost impossible to take a small piece which did not obey the magnet and point more or less readily. By selecting the thin plates with perfect cleavage planes, I readily obtained specimens which corresponded in all respects with the crystals; but thicker plates or angular pieces often proved complicated in the results, though apparently simple and regular as to form. Occasionally, the cleavage plane, which I have hitherto taken for that perpendicular to the line of force (2475), has proved not to be the plane supposed; but, after observing experimentally the direction of the magnecrystallic power, I have always either found, or else obtained by cleavage, a plane corresponding to it, possessing the appearance and character before described (2475). Bismuth plates from the one-twentieth to the one-tenth of an inch in thickness, and bounded by parallel and similar planes, when broken up, often proved, upon ocular examination, to be compounded and irregular.

2481. When a well-selected plate of bismuth (mine are about 0.3 of an inch in length and breadth, and 0.05, more or less, in thickness) is hung up by the edge in the magnetic field, it vibrates and points, presenting its faces to the magnetic poles, and setting diametrically (2461). By whatever part of the edge it is suspended, the same results follow. But if it be suspended horizontally, the cleavage planes of the fragment and of the magnetic axis being parallel to the plane of motion of the plate, then it is perfectly indifferent; for then the line of magnecrystallic force is perpendicular to the line of magnetic force in every position that it can take.

2482. But if the plate be inclined at only a very small angle from this position, it points, and that with more force as the planes become more nearly vertical (2475); and the phenomena before described with a crystal (2476), can here be obtained with a fragment from a mass, and any part of the edge of the plate made to point axially, by elevating or depressing it above or below the horizontal plane.

2483. If a number of these crystalline plates be selected at the magnet, they may afterwards be built up together, with a little good cement (2458), into a mass which has perfectly regular magnecrystallic action; and in that respect resembles the crystals before spoken of (2459, 2468, 2476). In this manner, also, the *diamagnetic* effect of the bismuth may be neutralized; for it is easy to build up a prism whose breadth and thickness are equal, and this being hung with the length vertical, points well and without any interference of diamagnetic action.

2484. By placing three equal plates at right angles to each other, a system is obtained, which has lost all power of pointing under the influence of the magnet, the force being, in every direction, neutralized. This represents the case of finely crystallized or amorphous bismuth. The same result (having the same nature) may be obtained by taking a selected uniform mass of crystals (2457), melting it in a glass tube and resolidifying it: unless the crystallization is large and distinct, which rarely happens, the piece obtained is apparently without magnecrystallic force. A like result is also obtained by breaking up the crystal and putting the small fragments or powder into a tube, and submitting the whole to the force of the magnet.

2485. These experiments on bismuth are not difficult of repetition; for, except those which require the sudden production or cessation of the magnetic force, the whole may be repeated with an ordinary horseshoe magnet. A magnet, with which I have wrought considerably, consists of seven bars placed side by side, and being fixed in a box with the poles upwards, presents two magnet cheeks, an inch and a quarter apart, between which is the magnetic field, having the lines of force in a horizontal direction. The poles of the magnet should be covered, each with paper, to prevent communication of particles of iron or rust. The best place for the piece of bismuth is, of course, between the poles; not level, however, with their tops, but from 0.4 to 1.0 inch lower down (2463), that the effect of flat-faced poles may be obtained. If it be desired to strengthen the lines of magnetic force, this may be done by introducing a piece of iron between the poles of the magnet, and so, by virtually causing them to approach, lessen the width of the magnetic field between them.

2486. The magnet I used would sustain 30 lbs. at the keeper; but employing small pieces of bismuth, I have easily obtained the effects with magnets weighing themselves not more than 7 ounces, and able to sustain only 22 ounces; so that the experiments are within the reach of every one.

2487. Whilst the crystal of bismuth is in the magnetic field, it is affected very distinctly, and even strongly, by the near approximation of soft iron or magnets, and after the following

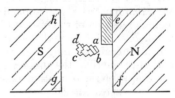

Fig. 1

manner. Let *Fig. 1* represent in plan the position of the two chief magnetic poles, and of a piece of crystallized bismuth between them, which, by its magnecrystallic condition, points axially. Then, if a piece of soft iron be applied against the cheek of the pole, as at *e*, and also near to the bismuth, as at *a*, it will affect the latter and cause its approach to the iron. If the iron be applied in a similar manner at *f*, *g*, or *h*, it will have a like result in causing motion of the bismuth, and the parts marked *b*, *c*, and *d*, will in turn approach it, seeming to be attracted. If the soft iron do not touch the magnetic pole, but be held between it and the bismuth so as to represent generally the same positions, the same effects, but in a weaker degree, are produced.

2488. Though these motions seem to indicate an effect of attraction, I do not believe them to be due to any such cause, but simply to the influence of the law of action (2479) before expressed. The previously uniform condition of the magnetic field is destroyed by the presence of the iron; lines of magnetic force, of greater intensity than the others, proceed from the angle *a* of the iron in the position represented, or from the corresponding angles in the other positions (the shape of the pole now approximating more or less to the conical or pointed form), and therefore the crystal of bismuth moves round on the axis of suspension, that it may place the line of magnecrystallic force parallel or as a tangent to the resultant of the magnetic forces which pass through its mass.

2489. When in place of the group of crystals a crystalline plate of bismuth (2481) is employed, the appearances produced under similar circumstances, are those of *repulsion;* for if *Fig. 2* be allowed to represent this state of

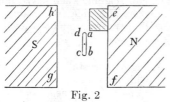

Fig. 2

things, the piece of iron applied at *e* causes the plate to recede from it at *a*, or if applied at *f, g*, or *h*, it causes recession of the bismuth from it at the points *b, c,* and *d*. Now though these effects look like repulsion, they are, as I conclude, nothing more than the consequences of the endeavour which the bismuth makes under the law before expressed (2479), to place the magnecrystallic line of force parallel to, or as a tangent to the resultant of magnetic force passing through the bismuth.

2490. A piece of iron wire about 1½ inches long, and 0.1 or 0.2 of an inch thick, being held in the equatorial plane to the edge of the plate (*Fig. 3*), did not alter its position; but if the end *e* were inclined to either pole, the plate began to move, and moved most when the iron touched the pole as in the figure. When it approached or touched the N pole, the inclination of the crystal plate of bismuth was as indicated by the dotted figure. When it touched the S, the inclination was the contrary way. If the end *e* were kept in contact with the N pole,

and the other end of the soft iron rod placed in the position *m*, the bismuth was not affected; but if then this subsidiary pole were moved the one way or the other towards the edge of the plate, the latter turned as the pole moved,

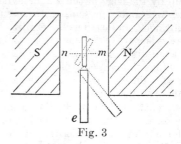

Fig. 3

always tending to keep its face towards it, and evidently by the tendency of the magnecrystallic axis to place itself parallel to the resultant of magnetic force passing through the bismuth. The same results were obtained with the crystal (2487) under similar circumstances, and corresponding results were obtained when the soft iron rod was applied between the S cheek of the magnet and the bismuth. The like effects were also obtained with plates of arsenic and antimony.

2491. When a magnet is used instead of soft iron, corresponding effects are produced; only it must be remembered, that if the chief magnet be very powerful, it may often neutralize, and even change, the magnetism of the small approximated magnet; and this can happen with the latter (as to external influence), whilst in the magnetic field, even though when withdrawn it may appear to remain unaltered.

2492. Thus, when the plate of bismuth was suspended between the cheeks of the horseshoe magnet (2485), *Fig. 2*, and the north pole of a small magnet (the blade of a pocket-knife) was placed at *a* or *b*, it caused recession of the part of the bismuth near it, and precisely for the same reasons as those that existed when the soft iron was there. When the extra pole was placed at *c* or *d*, the action was more feeble than in the former case, and consisted in an approximation of that part of the bismuth to the pole. As this position of the subordinate pole would terminate and neutralize certain of the lines of magnetic force proceeding from the south pole of the horseshoe magnet, so the resultant of the lines of force passing through the bismuth would be changed in direction, being rendered oblique to their former course, and precisely in the manner represented by the motion of the bismuth, in its tendency to place its line of force parallel with them in their new position.

2493. An approximated south pole caused motions in the contrary direction.

2494. When the subordinate pole was applied to the edge of the plate, the little magnet being in the equatorial position (*Fig. 3*), then instead of being neutral, as the iron was, it caused the plate to move in a tangential direction, either to the right or the left, according as it was either a south or a north pole, just indeed as the iron did when, by inclining it, the approximated end became a pole (2490). This effect was shown in a still more striking degree by using the crystal of bismuth (2487), because, from its form and position the magnetic curves most affected by the extra pole were more included in the bismuth than when the plate was used.

2495. Innumerable variations of these motions may be caused, and appearances of attraction or repulsion, or tangential action be obtained at pleasure by the use of crystals having the magnecrystallic axis corresponding with their length, or plates where it accords with their thickness; and either permanent or temporary subsidiary magnetic poles. By making the moveable pole travel slowly round the bismuth from the neutral point m to the other neutral point n, *Fig. 3*, a summary of the whole can be obtained, and it is found that they all resolve themselves into the general law before expressed (2479); the magnecrystallic axis and the resultant of magnetic force passing through the bismuth, tending to become parallel.

2496. Hence a small crystal or plate of bismuth (or arsenic [2532]) may become a very useful and important indicator of the direction of the lines of force in a magnetic field, for at the same time that it takes up a position showing their course, it does not by its own action tend sensibly to disturb them.

2497. Many of these motions are similar to, and have relation with, those described by Plücker, Reich, and others, as obtained by the action of iron and magnets on bismuth, in its simple diamagnetic condition. These results are by them and others considered as indicating that the bismuth, as I had originally supposed (2429, &c.), has really, in its diamagnetic state, a magnetic condition the reverse of that of iron. I am not acquainted with all of them, or with the reasoning thereon (being in the German language); but such as I am aware of, and have re-obtained, seem to me to be simple results of the law I formerly laid down (2267, 2418), namely, that diamagnetic bodies tend to proceed from stronger to weaker places of magnetic force; and give no additional or other

proof of the assumed reverse polarity of bismuth than the former cases of action which I had given, coming under that law.

2498. Supposing that the intervening or surrounding matter might, in some manner, affect the magnecrystallic action of bismuth and other bodies, I fixed the magnetic poles at a given distance (about two inches) asunder, suspended a crystal of bismuth in the middle of the magnetic field, and observed its vibrations and set. Then, without any other change, I introduced screens of bismuth, being blocks about two inches square and 0.75 of an inch in thickness, between the poles and the crystal, but I could not perceive that any change in the phenomena was produced by their presence.

2499. The bismuth crystal (2459) was suspended in water between the magnetic poles of the horseshoe magnet. It set well in accordance with the general law (2479), and it took five revolutions of the torsion index at the upper end of the suspending silk filament to displace it, and cause it to turn into the diametral position. This is, as well as I could observe the results, the same amount of torsion force required to effect its displacement when the crystal was placed in the same position, but surrounded with air only.

2500. The same bismuth was then suspended in a saturated solution of protosulphate of iron (adapted as a magnetic medium); it set as before with apparently no change of any kind, and when the torsion force was put on, it still required five turns of the index, as before, to cause the displacement of the crystal, and its passage into the diametral position.

2501. Whether therefore crystals of bismuth be immersed in air, or water, or solution of sulphate of iron, or placed between thick masses of bismuth, if they be subject to the same magnetic force, the magnecrystallic force exerted by them is the same both in nature, direction and amount.

2502. It seemed possible and probable that magnetic force might affect the crystallization of bismuth, if not of other bodies. For, as the force affects the mass of a crystal by that power which its particles possess, and which they give to the crystal as a whole by their polar (or axial [2472]) and symmetric condition; and, as the final position of the crystalline mass in the magnetic field may be considered as that of the least constraint, so it was likely enough that, if the bismuth in a fluid state were placed under the influence of the magnetism, the individual particles would tend to assume one and the same axial condition, and the crystalline arrangement and direction of the mass upon its solidification, be in some degree determined and under government.

2503. Some bismuth, therefore, was fused in a glass tube and held in a fixed position in the strong magnetic field until it had become solid; then, being removed from the glass, it was suspended so that it might assume the same position under the influence of the magnet; but no signs of *magnecrystallic* force were evident. It was not expected that the whole would become regularly crystallized, but that a *difference* between one direction and another might appear. Nothing of the kind however occurred, whatever the direction in which the piece was suspended; and when it was broken open, the crystallization within was found to be small, confused, and in all directions. Perhaps if longer time were allowed, and a permanent magnet used, a better result might be obtained. I had built many hopes upon the process, in reference to the crystalline condition of gold, silver, platina, and the metals generally, and also in respect of other bodies.

2504. I cannot find that crystals of bismuth acquire any power, either temporary or permanent, which they can *bring away* from the magnetic field. I held crystals in different positions in the field of intense action of a powerful electro-magnet, having conical terminations very near to each other; and, after some time, removed them and applied them instantly to a very delicate astatic magnetic needle; but I could not perceive that they had the least extra effect upon it, because of such treatment.

2505. As a crystal of bismuth is subject to, and obeys the influence of, the lines of magnetic force (2479), so it follows that it ought to obey even the earth's action, and point, though with a very feeble degree of power. I have suspended a good crystal by a long filament of cocoon silk, and sheltered it as well as I could from currents of air by concentric glass tubes, and I think have observed indications of a set or pointing. The crystal was so hung that the magnecrystallic axis made the same angle with the horizontal plane (about 70°) as the magnetic dip, and the indication was, that the axis and the dip tended to coincide: but the experiments require careful repetition.

2506. A more important point, as to the nature of the polar or axial forces of bismuth, is to know whether two crystals, or uniformly crystallized masses of bismuth, can mutually affect each other; and if so, what the nature of these affections are? what is the relation of the equatorial and terminal parts? and what, the direction of the forces? I have made many experiments, in relation to this subject, both in and out of the magnetic field, but obtained only negative results. I employed however small masses of bismuth, and it is my purpose to repeat and extend them at a more convenient season with larger masses, built up, if necessary, in the manner already described (2483).

2507. I need hardly say that a crystal of bismuth ought to point in a helix or ring of wire carrying an electric current, and so that its magnecrystallic axis should be parallel to the axis of the ring or helix. This I find experimentally to be the case.

¶ ii. *Crystalline Polarity of Antimony*

2508. *Antimony* is a *magnecrystallic* body. Some crystalline masses, procured in the manner before described (2457), were broken up with copper tools, and some excellent groups of crystals were obtained, weighing from ten to twenty grains each, in which all the constituent crystals appeared to be uniformly placed. The individual crystals were very good on the whole, and much more frequently complete and full at the faces than those of bismuth. They were very bright, having a steel-gray or silvery appearance, and to the eye appeared more surely as cubes than bismuth, though here and there distinctly rhomboidal faces presented themselves. Planes of cleavage can be made to replace the solid angles; and, as with bismuth, there is one plane generally brighter and more nearly perfect than the others.

2509. In the first place, it was ascertained that all these crystals were diamagnetic and strongly so.

2510. In the next it was ascertained, as with bismuth, that all of them exhibited the magnecrystallic phenomena with considerable power, showing the existence of a line of force (2470), which, when placed vertically, left the crystal free to move in any direction (2476); but when placed horizontally, caused the crystal to point, and in so doing took up its own position parallel to the resultant of magnetic force passing through the crystal (2479). This line proceeded, as in bismuth, from one of the solid angles to the opposite one, and was perpendicular to the bright cleavage plane just spoken of (2508).

2511. So, generally, the action of the magnet upon these crystals was the same as upon the crystals of bismuth; but there are some points of variation which require to be more distinctly stated and distinguished.

2512. In the first place, when the magne-crystallic axis was horizontal, and a certain crystal used, upon the evolution of the magnetic force, the crystal went up to its position slowly, and pointed, as with a dead set. If the crystal were moved from this position on either side, it returned to it at once: there was no vibration. Other crystals did the same imperfectly; and others again made one or perhaps two vibrations, but all appeared as if they were moving in a thick fluid, and were, in that respect, utterly unlike bismuth, in the freedom and mobility with which it vibrated (2459).

2513. In the next place, when the crystals were so suspended as to have the magnecrystallic axis vertical, there was no pointing nor any other signs of magnecrystallic force; but other appearances presented themselves. For, if the crystalline mass was revolving when the magnetic force was excited, it suddenly stopped, and was caught in a position which might, as was found by experience, be any position; but if the greatest length was out of the axial or equatorial position, the arrest was followed by a *revulsive* motion on the discontinuance of the electric current (2315). This revulsive motion was never great, but was most when the length of the mass formed about an angle of 45° with the axis of the magnetic field.

2514. On further examination it appeared that this arresting and revulsive effect was precisely the same in kind as that observed on a former occasion with copper and other metals (2309), and due to the same cause, namely, the production of circular electric currents in the metal under the inductive force of the magnet. Now, the reason appeared why, in the former case, the crystals of antimony did not oscillate (2512); and why, also, they went up to their position of rest with a dead set; for the currents produced by the motion are just those which tend to stop the motion (2329);[1] and though the magnecrystallic force was sufficient to make the crystal move and point, yet the very motion so produced generated the current

[1] Anyone who wishes to form a sufficient idea of the arresting powers of these induced currents, should take a lump of solid copper, approaching to the cubical or globular form, weighing from a quarter to half a pound; should suspend it by a long thread, give it a rapid rotation, and then introduce it, spinning, into the magnetic field of the electro-magnet; he will find its motion to be instantly stopped; and if he further tries to spin it, whilst in the field, will find it impossible to do so.

which reacted upon the tendency to motion, and so caused the mass to advance towards its position of rest as if it moved in a thick fluid.

2515. Having this additional knowledge respecting the arrest and revulsion of the antimony (effects dependent upon its superior conducting power, in this compact crystalline state, as compared with bismuth), one has no difficulty in identifying the magnecrystallic force of this metal with that of the former, and establishing the correspondence of the results in all essential characters and particulars. In most of the pieces of crystals of antimony the force seemed less than in bismuth, but, in fact, this may not really be so, for the inductive current action just described tends to hide the magnecrystallic phenomena.

2516. Different pieces of antimony also seem to differ from each other in their setting force, and also in their tendency to exhibit revulsive effects; but these differences are either only apparent, or may easily be explained. The arresting and revulsive action depends much upon the continuity of the mass, so that one large piece shows it much better than several small pieces, and these again better than a powdered substance. Even the revulsive action of copper may be entirely destroyed by reducing the single lump to filings. It is easy to perceive, therefore, that of two groups of antimony crystals, each symmetrically disposed within itself, the one may have larger crystals well connected together, as regards the induction of currents through the whole mass, and the other smaller crystals less favourably united. These would present very different appearances, as regards the arrest of motion and succeeding revulsive action; and further, on that very account, would differ in their readiness to present the magnecrystallic phenomena, though they might possess precisely equal degrees of that force.

2517. On proceeding to experiment with plates of antimony, further illustrations of the effects resulting from the causes just described were obtained, with abundant accompanying evidence of the existence of the magnecrystallic condition in the metal. The plates were selected from broken masses, as with bismuth (2480). Some were soon found which acted simply, instantly, and well; their large surfaces were bright cleavage planes. When suspended by any part of the edge, these planes faced towards the magnetic poles; and the plate oscillated on each side of its final position, gradually acquiring its state of rest.

2518. When these plates were suspended with their planes horizontal, they had no power of pointing in the magnetic field. When they were inclined, the points which were most depressed below and raised above the horizontal plane, were those which took up their places nearest the magnetic poles (2482).

2519. When several plates were arranged together into a consistent bundle (2483), the *diamagnetic* effect was removed, and the magnecrystallic oscillation and pointing became very ready a characteristic.

2520. Thus it is evident that, in all these cases, there was a line of magnecrystallic force perpendicular to the planes of the plates, and perfectly consistent in its position and action with the force before found in the solid crystals of antimony.

2521. But another plate of antimony was now selected, which had every appearance of being able to present all the phenomena of the former plates; and yet, when hung up by its edge, it showed no signs of magnecrystallic results; for it first advanced a little (2310), then was arrested and kept in its place, and if standing between the axial and equatorial positions, was revulsed when the battery current was interrupted, exhibiting effects equal to those of copper (2315). Many other plates were tried with precisely the same result.

2522. When this plate (2521) was placed in the field of intense power between two *conical* magnetic poles, it exhibited the same phenomena; but notwithstanding the arresting action, it moved slowly until it stood in the equatorial position; a result which was probably due to the exertion of both *magnecrystallic* and *diamagnetic* force. When the plate was suspended with its planes horizontal, the arresting and revulsive actions were gone; for the induced currents which before caused them could not now exist in the necessary vertical plane; further, it had no setting power, which showed that there was no axis of magnecrystallic force in the length or breadth of the plates.

2523. Other plates were then found able to produce mixed effects, and those in different degrees. Thus, some, like the first, vibrated freely, pointed well, and presented no indication of the arrest and revulsive phenomena. Others vibrated sluggishly, set well, and showed a tendency to be arrested. Others pointed well, going up to their place with a dead set, but moving as if in a fluid; or, if the magnetic force were taken off before the piece had settled, it was revulsed feebly: and others were caught at

once, did not set (within the time of my observation), and were strongly revulsed.

2524. Finally, a careful investigation, carried on by means both of the horseshoe (2485) and the great electro-magnet (2247), made the cause of these differences in the effects apparent.

2525. It may be observed, in the first place, that sometimes a plate of antimony being selected (2517), having planes very bright and perfect in their appearance, and, therefore, giving reason to think that it may point well in the magnetic field, when submitted to the horseshoe magnet does not do so; but points obliquely, feebly, and perhaps in two undiametral positions. This is, I have no doubt, because the crystallization is complicated and confused. Such a plate, if it be sufficiently broad and long (i.e., not less than a quarter or one-third of an inch), when submitted to the electro-magnet, will show the arresting (2310) and revulsive (2315) action well.

2526. In the next place, we have to remember that, for the development of the induced currents which cause the arresting and revulsive action, the plate must have certain sufficient dimensions in a vertical plane (2329). The currents occur in the mass and not round the separate particles (2329), and the resultant of the magnetic lines of force passing through the substance, is the axis round which these currents are produced. Hence the reason why the effect does not occur with plates suspended in the horizontal position, which yet produce it well in the vertical position; a result which a disc half an inch in diameter of thin foil or plate, being copper, silver, gold, tin, or almost any malleable metal, will show; though the best conductors are the fittest for the purpose. Now this condition is of no consequence in respect to *magnecrystallic* action, and a narrow plate has as much force as a broad one, having the same mass. The first plate that I happened to select (2517) was well crystallized, thick and narrow; hence it was favourable for magnecrystallic action, unfavourable to the arresting and revulsive action, and showed no signs, comparatively, of the latter.

2527. When a broad and well-crystallized plate is obtained, then both sets of effects appear: thus, if the plate is revolving when the magnetic force is brought into action, it quickens its velocity for an instant, then is stopped; and if the magnetic force is at once taken off, it is revulsed, exactly as a piece of copper would be (2315). But if the magnetic force be continued, it will then be perceived that the stop is only apparent; for the plate moves, though with a greatly reduced velocity, and continues to move until it has taken up its magnecrystallic position. It moves as if in a thick fluid. Hence the magnecrystallic force is there and produces its full effect; and the reason why the appearances have changed is, that the very motion which the force tends to give, and does give to the mass, causes those magneto-electric currents (2329) which by their mutual action with the magnet tends to stop the motion; and therefore its slowness and the final dead set (2512, 2523).

2528. A magnet which is weaker (as the horse-shoe instrument described [2485]) produces the currents by induction in a much weaker degree, and yet manifests the magnecrystallic power well; hence it is more favourable, under certain circumstances, for such investigations; as it helps to distinguish the one effect from the other.

2529. It will readily be seen that plates, whether of the same metal or of different metals, cannot, even roughly, be compared with each other as to magnecrystallic force by their vibrations; for under the influence of these induced currents, plates of the same magnecrystallic force oscillate in very different manners. I took a plate, and by cement (2458) attached selected paper to its faces, and then observed how it acted in the magnetic field; it set slowly and it showed the arresting and revulsive effects (2521). I then pressed it in a mortar, so as to break it up into many parts, which still kept their place; and now it set more freely and quickly, and showed very little of the revulsive action.

2530. Though the indication by vibration is thus uncertain, the torsion force still remains to us, I believe, a very accurate indication of the strength of the set (2500), and, therefore, of the degree of the magnecrystallic force; and though the suspending silk fibre may give way a little, a glass thread, according to Ritchie's suggestion, would answer perfectly.

2531. Antimony must be a good conductor of electricity in the direction of the plates of the crystals, or it would not give, so freely, these indications of revulsive action. The groups of

crystals of antimony (2508) showed the effect in such a degree as to make me think that the constituent cubes possessed the power nearly equally in all directions. A piece of finely crystallized or granular antimony does not, however, show it in the same proportion; from which it would seem as if an effect equivalent in some degree to that of division occurs, either at the meeting of two incongruous crystals, or between the contiguous plates of the crystals, and affects the conducting power in these directions.

¶ iii. *Crystalline Polarity of Arsenic*

2532. A mass of the metal arsenic exhibiting crystalline structure (2480), was broken up, and several plates selected from the fragments, having good cleavage plane surfaces, about 0.3 of an inch in length, 0.1 inch in width, and 0.03 in thickness. These, when suspended opposite one conical pole, proved to be perfectly diamagnetic; and when before it or between two poles strongly *magnecrystallic*. I have a pair of flat-faced poles with screw-holes in the centre of the faces, and these so much weaken the intensity of the lines of magnetic force about the middle of the field, when the faces are within half an inch of each other, that a cylinder of granular bismuth 0.3 in length sets *axially*, or from pole to pole (2384). But with the plates of arsenic between the same poles there was no tendency of this kind; so much was the magnecrystallic force predominant over the diamagnetic force of the substance.

2533. When the plates of arsenic were suspended with their planes horizontal, then they did not point at all between the flat-faced poles. Any inclination of the planes to the horizontal line produced pointing, with more or less force as the planes approached more or less to the vertical position, exactly in the manner already described in relation to bismuth and antimony (2482, 2518).

2534. Thus, arsenic with bismuth and antimony are found to possess the magnecrystallic force or condition.

Royal Institution September 23, *1848*

TWENTY-SECOND SERIES, *Continued*[1]

§ 28. *On the Crystalline Polarity of Bismuth and Other Bodies, and on its Relation to the Magnetic and Electric Form of Force (continued)* ¶ iv. *Crystalline Condition of Various Bodies* ¶ v. *Nature of the Magnecrystallic Force, and General Observations*

RECEIVED OCTOBER 31, READ DECEMBER 7, 1848

¶ iv. *Crystalline Condition of Various Bodies*

2535. *ZINC.* Plates of zinc broken out of crystallized masses gave irregular indications, and, being magnetic from the impurity in them, the effects might be due entirely to that circumstance. Pure zinc was thrown down electrochemically on platina from solutions of the chloride and the sulphate. The former occurred in ramifying dendritic associations of small crystal; the latter in a compact close form. Both were free from magnetic action and freely diamagnetic, but neither showed any trace of the magnecrystallic action.

2536. *Titanium.*[2] Some good crystals of titanium obtained from the bottom of an iron furnace, were cleansed by the alternate action of acids and fluxes until as clear from iron as I could procure them. They were bright, well-formed and magnetic (2371), and contained iron, I think, diffused through their whole mass, for nitromuriatic acid, by long boiling, continually removed titanium and iron from them. These crystals had a certain magnetic property which I am inclined to refer to their crystalline condition. When between the poles of the electro-magnet, they set; and when the electric current was discontinued, they still set between the poles of the enfeebled magnet as they did before. If left to itself, a crystal always took the *same* position, showing that it was constantly rendered magnetic in the same direction. But if a crystal was placed and kept in another position between the magnetic poles whilst the electric current was on, and afterwards the current suspended, and then the crystal set free, it pointed between the poles of the enfeebled magnet in this new direction; showing that the magnetism was in a different direction in the body of the crystal to that which it had before. If now the magnet were reinvigorated by the electric current, the crystal instantly spun round and took a magnetic state in the first or original direction. The crystals could in fact become magnetized in any direction, but there was one direction in which they could be magnetized with a facility and force greater than in any other. From the appearances I am inclined to refer this to the crystalline condition, but it may be due to an irregular diffusion of iron in the masses of titanium. The crystals were too small for me to make out the point clearly.

2537. *Copper.* I selected some good crystals of native copper, and, having carefully separated them from the mass, examined them in respect of their magnecrystallic force. At the horseshoe magnet (2486) they gave no signs of such power, whatever the direction in which they were suspended, but stood in any position; and any degree of torsion, however small, applied at the upper extremity of the suspending filament, was obeyed at once, and to the full extent, by the crystal beneath. When subjected to the electro-magnet, the phenomena of arrest and revulsion were produced (2513, 2310), as was to be expected. If after the arrest the magnetic force were continued, there was no slow advance of the crystal up to a distinct pointing position (2512); it stood perfectly still in any position. So there is no evidence of magnecrystallic action in this case.

2538. *Tin.* I selected from block and grain tin some pieces which appeared, by their external forms and the surface produced under the action of acids, to have a regular crystalline structure internally; and, cutting off portions, carefully submitted them to the power of the magnets, but there was no appearance of any magnecrystallic phenomena. Indications of the arresting and revulsive actions were presented, and also of diamagnetic force, but nothing else. I also examined some crystals of tin

---

[1] *Philosophical Transactions,* 1849, p. 19.
[2] For these and many other crystals I am indebted to the kindness of Sir Henry T. De la Beche and Mr. Tennant.

obtained by electro-chemical deposition. They were pure and diamagnetic: they were arrested and revulsed, but they showed no signs of magnecrystallic action.

2539. *Lead.* Lead was crystallized by fusion, partial solidification, and pouring off (2457), and some very fair crystals, having the general form of octohedra, were obtained. Observed at the magnets, these were arrested and revulsed feebly, but presented no magnecrystallic phenomena. Some fine crystalline plates of lead obtained electro-chemically from the decomposition of the acetate by zinc, were submitted to the magnet: they were pure, diamagnetic, and were arrested and revulsed, but presented no appearance of magnecrystallic action.

2540. *Gold.* Three fine large crystals of gold were examined. They were diamagnetic, and easily arrested (2310, 2340); the revulsion did not take place, because of their octohedral or orbicular form. They presented no magnecrystallic indications.

2541. *Tellurium.* Two fractured pieces of this substance, presenting large and parallel planes of cleavage, were examined: both pointed, and the greatest length was across the axial line between flat-faced poles (2463). I think the effects were in part, if not altogether, due to the magnecrystallic state of the substance; but I do not think the evidence was quite conclusive.

2542. *Iridium and Osmium alloy.* The native grains of iridium and osmium are often flat, presenting two planes looking like crystal planes, which are parallel to each other even when the grains are thick. Some of the largest and most crystalline were selected, and, after ignition with flux and digestion in nitromuriatic acid, were examined at the magnet. Some were more magnetic than others, being attracted; others were very little magnetic: the latter were selected and examined more carefully. These all pointed with great readiness and force, comparatively speaking; for they were not above one-fifteenth of an inch long, and yet they set freely when the magnetic poles were 3 or 4 inches apart. The faces of the crystalline particles were *always* towards the poles, and their length consequently not *in* but *across* the axial line; and this was true whether the distance between the poles was small or great, or whether flat-faced or conical poles were used. I believe they were magnecrystallic.

2543. *Fusible metal.* Crystals of fusible metal (2457) pointed, but the crystals, which were apparently quadrangular plates or prisms, were not good, and the evidence not clear and distinct.

2544. *Wires.* I thought it possible that thin wires, which by the action of acids exhibited fibrous arrangements, might have their particles in a state approaching to the crystalline condition, and therefore submitted bundles of platinum, copper, and tin wire to the action of the magnet; but no indications of magnecrystallic action appeared.

2545. I submitted several metallic compounds to the power of the magnet, applied so as to develop any indication of the magnecrystallic phenomena. Galena, native cinnabar, oxide of tin, sulphuret of tin, native red oxide of copper, Brookite or oxide of titanium, iron pyrites, and also diamond, fluor spar, rock-salt and boracite, being all well crystallized and diamagnetic, presented no evidence of the magnecrystallic force. Native and well-crystallized sulphuret of copper, sulphuret of zinc, cobalt glance and leucites were magnetic. Arsenical iron, specular iron and magnetic oxide of iron were still more so. I could not in any of them distinguish any magnetic results due to crystallization.

2546. On examining magnetic salts, several of them presented very striking magnecrystallic phenomena. Thus, with *sulphate of iron*, the first crystal which I employed was suspended with the magnecrystallic axis vertical, and it presented no particular appearances; only the longest horizontal direction went into the magnetic axis pointing feebly. But on turning the piece 90° (2470), instantly it pointed with much force, and the greatest length went equatorially. The crystal was compounded of superposed flat crystals or plates, and the magnecrystallic axis went directly across these; it was easy therefore, after one or two experiments, to tell beforehand how the crystal should be suspended, and how it would point. Whether the crystals were long, or oblique, or irregular, still the magnecrystallic force predominated and determined the position of the crystal, and this happened whether pointed or flat poles were used, and whether they were near together or far asunder. The magnecrystallic axis is perpendicular, or nearly so, to two of the sides of the rhomboidal prism. I have some small prismatic crystals of which the length is nearly three times the width of the prism; but when both the length and the magnecrystallic axis are horizontal, no power of the magnet, or shape, or position of the poles, will cause the length to take the axial direction, for that is constantly retained by the magnecrystallic axis, so greatly does it predominate in power over the mere magnetic force of the crystal. Yet this latter is so great as at times to pull the suspending fibre asunder when the crystal is above the poles (2615).

2547. *Sulphate of nickel.* When a crystal of sulphate of nickel was suspended in the magnetic field, its length set axially. This might be due, either to mere magnetic force, or partly to magnecrystallic force. Therefore I cut a cube out of the crystal, two faces of which were perpendicular to the length of the original prism. This cube pointed well in the magnetic field, and the line coincident with the axis of the prism was that which pointed axially, and represented the magnecrystallic axis. Even when the cube was reduced in this direction and converted into a square plate whose thickness coincided with the magnecrystallic axis, it pointed as well as before, though the shortest dimensions of the piece were now axial.

2548. The *persulphate of ammonia and iron*, and the *sulphate of manganese*, did not give any indication of magnecrystallic phenomena; the *sulphate of ammonia and manganese* I think did, but the crystals were not good. The sulphate of potassa and nickel is magnecrystallic. All three salts were magnetic.

2549. Thus it seems that other bodies besides bismuth, antimony and arsenic, present magnecrystallic effects. Amongst these are the alloy of iridium and osmium, probably tellurium and titanium, and certainly the sulphates of iron and nickel. Before leaving this part of the subject, I may remark that this property has probably led me into error at times on a former occasion (2290). A mistake with arsenic (2383) might very easily arise from this cause.

¶ v. *On the Nature of the Magnecrystallic Force, and General Observations*[1]

2550. The magnecrystallic force appears to be very clearly distinguished from either the magnetic or diamagnetic forces, in that it causes neither approach nor recession; consisting not in attraction or repulsion, but in its giving a certain determinate position to the mass under its influence, so that a given line in relation to the mass is brought by it into a given relation with the direction of the external magnetic power.

2551. I thought it right very carefully to examine and prove the conclusion, that there was no connection of the force with either attractive or repulsive influences. For this purpose I constructed a torsion-balance, with a bifilar suspension of cocoon silk, consisting of two bundles of seven filaments each, 4 inches long and one-twelfth of an inch apart; and suspended a crystal of bismuth (2457) from one end of the lever, so that it might be fixed and retained in any position. This balance was protected by a glass case, outside of which the conical terminal of one pole of the great electro-magnet (2247) was adjusted, so as to be horizontal, at right angles to the lever of the torsion-balance, and in such a position that the bismuth crystal was in the prolongation of the axis of the pole, and about half an inch from its extremity when all was at rest. The other pole, 4 inches off, was left large so that the lines of magnetic force should diverge, as it were, and rapidly diminish in strength from the end of the conical pole. The object was to observe the degree of repulsion exerted by the magnet on the bismuth, as a diamagnetic body, either by the distance to which it was repelled, or by the torsion required to bring it back to its first position; and to do this with the bismuth, having its magnecrystallic axis at one time axial or parallel to the lines of magnetic force, at another equatorial, observing whether any difference was produced.

2552. The crystal was therefore placed with its magnecrystallic axis first parallel to the lines of magnetic force, and then turned four times in succession 90° in a horizontal plane, so as to observe it under all positions of the magnecrystallic axis; but in no case could any difference in the amount of the repulsion be observed. In other experiments the axis was placed oblique, but still with the same result. If there be therefore any difference it must be exceedingly small.[2]

2553. A corresponding experiment was made, hanging the crystal as a pendulum by a bifilar suspension of cocoon silk 30 feet in length, with the same result.

2554. Another very striking series of proofs that the effect is not due to attraction or repulsion, was obtained in the following manner. A skein of fifteen filaments of cocoon silk, about 14 inches long, was made fast above, and then a weight of an ounce or more hung to the lower end; the middle of this skein was about the middle of the magnetic field of the electro-magnet, and the square weight below rested against the side of a block of wood, so as to give a steady, silken vertical axis, without swing or revolution. A small strip of card, about half

[1] See onwards, 2836. &c.

[2] See now 2839, &c.

an inch long, and the tenth of an inch broad, was fastened across the middle of this axis by cement; and then a small prismatic crystal of sulphate of iron about 0.3 of an inch long, and 0.1 in thickness, was attached to the card, so that the length, and also the magnecrystallic axis, were in the horizontal plane; all the length was on one side of the silken axis, so that as the crystal swung round, the length was radius to the circle described, and the magnecrystallic axis parallel to the tangent.

2555. This crystal took a position of rest due to the torsion force of the suspending skein of silk; and the position could be made any one that was desired, by turning the weight below. The torsion force was such that, when the crystal was made to vibrate on its silken axis, forty complete (or to and fro) vibrations were performed in a minute.

2556. When the crystal was made to stand between the flat-faced poles (2463) obliquely, as in *Fig. 4*, the moment the magnet was ex-

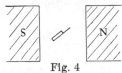

Fig. 4

cited it moved, tending to stand with its length equatorial or its magnecrystallic axis parallel to the lines of magnetic force. When the N pole was removed, and the experiment repeated, the same effect took place, but not as strongly as before; and when, finally, the pole S was brought as near to the crystal as it could be, without touching it, the same result occurred, and with more strength than in the last case.

2557. In the two latter experiments, therefore, the crystal of sulphate of iron, though a magnetic body and strongly attracted by such a magnet as that used, actually *receded* from the pole of the magnet under the influence of the magnecrystallic condition.

2558. If the pole S be removed and that marked N be retained for action on the crystal, then the latter approaches the pole, urged by both the magnetic and magnecrystallic forces; but if the crystal be revolved 90° to the left, or 180° to the right, round the silken axis, so as to come into the contrary or opposite position, then this pole repels or rather causes the removal to a distance of the crystal, just as the former did. The experiment requires care, and I find that conical poles are not good; but with attention I could obtain the results with the utmost readiness.

2559. The sulphate of iron was then replaced by a crystalline plate (2480) of bismuth, placed as before on one side of the silk suspender, and with its magnecrystallic axis horizontal. Making the position the same as that which the crystal had in relation to the N pole in the former experiment (2556), so that to place its axis parallel to the lines of magnetic force it must approach this magnetic pole, and then throwing the magnet into an active state, the bismuth moved accordingly, and did approach the pole, against its diamagnetic tendency, but under the influence of the magnecrystallic force. The effect was small but distinct.

2560. Anticipating, for a short time, the result of the reasoning to be given farther on (2607), I will describe a corresponding effect obtained with the red ferro-prussiate of potassa. A crystal of this salt had its acute linear angles ground away, so as to convert it into a plate with faces parallel to the plane of the optic axis, and was then made to replace the plate of bismuth. Being in the position before represented (2556), and the magnet rendered active, it moved, placing the plane of the optic axes equatorially, as Plücker describes. When the pole N was removed and S brought up to the crystal, the same motion occurred, the crystal *retreating from* the pole; and when S pole was removed and N brought towards the crystal, it moved as before, the whole body now *approaching* towards the pole. On inclining the crystal the other way, i.e., making its place on the other side of the equatorial line, the S pole caused it to *approach* and the N pole to *recede*. So that the same pole seemed able either to attract or repel the same side of the crystal; and either pole could be made to show this apparent attractive and repulsive force.

2561. Hence a proof that neither attraction nor repulsion causes the set, or governs the final position of the body, or of any of the bodies whose movements are due to the same cause (2607).

2562. This force then is distinct in its character and effects from the magnetic and diamagnetic forms of force. On the other hand, it has a most manifest relation to the crystalline structure of the bismuth and other bodies; and therefore to the molecules, and to the power by which these molecules are able to build up the crystalline masses. It appears to me impossible to conceive of the results in any other way than by a mutual reaction of the magnetic force, and the force of the particles of the crystal on each other: and this leads the mind to another conclusion, namely, that as far as they can act on each other they partake of a like nature; and brings, I think, fresh help for the solution of that great problem in the philosophy of molecular forces, which assumes that they all have one common origin (2146).

2563. Whether we consider a crystal or a particle of bismuth, its polarity has a very extraordinary character, as compared with the polarity of a particle in the ordinary magnetic state, or when compared with any other of the dual conditions of physical force; for the opposite poles have *like* characters; as is shown first of all by the diametral pointing of the masses (2461), and also by the physical characters and relations of crystals generally. As the molecules lie in the mass of a crystal, therefore, they can in no way represent, or be represented by, the condition of a parcel of iron filings between the poles of a magnet, or the particles of iron in the keeper when in its place; for these have poles of *different* names and quality adhering together, and so giving a sort of structure; whereas, in the crystal, the molecules have poles of like nature towards each other, for, so to say, all the poles are alike.

2564. As made manifest by the phenomena, the magnecrystallic force is a force acting at a distance; for the crystal is moved by the magnet at a distance (2556, 2574), and the crystal also can move the magnet at a distance. To produce the latter result, I converted a steel bodkin, about 3 inches long, into a magnet; and then suspended it perpendicularly by a single cocoon filament 4 inches long, from a small horizontal rod, which again was suspended by its centre and another length of cocoon filament, from a fixed point of support. In this manner the bodkin was free to move on its own axis, and could also describe a circle about $1\frac{1}{2}$ inches in diameter; and the latter motion was not hindered by any tendency of the needle to point under the earth's influence, because it could take any position in the circle and yet remain parallel to itself.

2565. A support perfectly free from magnetic action was constructed of glass rod and copper wire, which passing through the bottom of the stand, and being in the prolongation of the upper axis of motion, was concentric with the circle which the little magnet could describe; its height was such that it could sustain a crystal or any other substance level with the pole at the lower end of the needle, and in the centre of the small circle in which the latter could revolve around it. By moving the lower end of the support, the upper end also could be made to approach to or recede from the magnet. The whole was covered with a glass shade, and when left to become of uniform temperature, and at rest, the needle magnet was found to take up a *constant* position under the torsion force of the suspending filaments. Further, any rotation of the glass and copper wire support did not produce a final change in the position of the magnet; for though the motion of the air would carry the magnet away, it returned, ultimately, to the same spot. When removed from this spot, the torsion force of the silk suspension made the system oscillate; the time of a half oscillation, or a passage in one direction, was about three minutes, and of a whole oscillation therefore six minutes.

2566. When a crystal of bismuth was fixed on the support with the magnecrystallic axis in a horizontal direction, it could be placed near the lower pole of the magnet in any position, and being then left for two or three hours, or until by repeated examination the magnetic pole was found to be stationary, the place of the latter could be examined and the degree and direction in which it was affected by the bismuth ascertained. Extreme precaution was required in these observations, and all steel or iron things, as spectacles, knives, keys, &c., had to be removed from the observer before he entered the place of experiment; and glass candlesticks were used. The effect produced was but small, but the result was, that if the direction of the magnecrystallic axis made an angle of 10°, 20°, or 30° with the line from the magnetic pole to the middle of the bismuth crystal, then the pole followed it, tending to bring the two lines into parallelism; and this it did whichever end of the magnecrystallic axis was towards the pole, or whichever side it was inclined to. By moving the bismuth at successive times, the deviation of the magnetic pole could be carried up to 60°.

2567. The crystal of bismuth therefore is able to react upon and affect the magnet at a distance.

2568. But though it thus take up the character of a force acting at a distance, still it is due to that power of the particles which makes them cohere in regular order, and gives the mass its crystalline aggregation; which we call at other times the attraction of aggregation, and so often speak of as acting at *insensible* distances.

2569. For the further explication of the nature of this force, I proceeded to examine the effect of heat on crystals of bismuth when in the magnetic field. The crystals were suspended either by platina or fine copper wire, and heated, sometimes by a small spirit-lamp flame applied directly, sometimes in an oil-bath placed between the magnetic poles; and though the upward currents of air and fluid were strong in these cases, they were far too weak to overcome the set caused by magnecrystallic action, and helped rather to show when that action was weakened or ceased.

2570. When the temperature was gradually raised in the air the bismuth crystal continued to point, until of a sudden it became indifferent in that respect, and turned in any direction under the influence of the rising currents of air. Instantly removing the lamp flame the bismuth revolved slowly and regularly, as if there were no tendency to take up one position more than another, or no remains of magnecrystallic action; but in a few seconds, as the temperature fell, it resumed its power of pointing; and, apparently, in an instant and with full force, and the pointing was precisely in the same direction as at first. On examining the crystal carefully, its external shape and its cleavage showed that, as a crystal, it was unchanged; but the appearance of a minute globule of bismuth, which had exuded upon the surface in one place, showed that the temperature had been close upon the point of fusion.

2571. The same result occurred in the oil-bath, except that as removing the lamp from the oil-bath did not immediately stop the addition of heat to the bismuth, so more of the latter was melted; and about one-fourth of the metal appeared as a drop hanging at the lower part. Still the whole mass lost its power at the high temperature, and the power was regained in the same direction, but in a less degree on cooling. The diminished force was accounted for on breaking up the crystal; for the parts which had been liquefied were now crystallized irregularly, and therefore, though active at the beginning of the experiment, were neutral at the end.

2572. As heat has this effect, the expectation entertained (2502) of crystallizing bismuth regularly *in the magnetic field* is of course unfounded; for the metal must acquire the solid state, and be lowered through several degrees probably, before it can exhibit the magnecrystallic phenomena. If heat has the same effect on all bodies prior to their liquefaction, then, of course, such a process can be applied to none of them.

2573. A crystallized piece of antimony was subjected to the same experiment, and it also lost its magnecrystallic power below a dull red heat, and just as it was softening so as to take the impression of the copper loop in which it was hung. On being cooled it did not resume its former state, but then became ordinarily magnetic and pointed. This I conclude arose from iron affected by the flame and heat of the spirit-lamp; for, as the heat was high enough to burn off part of the antimony and make it rise in fumes of oxide of antimony, so this might set a certain portion of iron free which the carbon and hydrogen of the flame would leave in a very magnetic state (2608).

2574. In further elucidation of the mutual action of the bismuth and the magnet, the bismuth was suspended, as already described (2551), on the bifilar balance, but so turned, that its magnecrystallic axis, being horizontal, was not parallel or perpendicular to the arm of the lever, but a little inclined, as in the Figure (5),

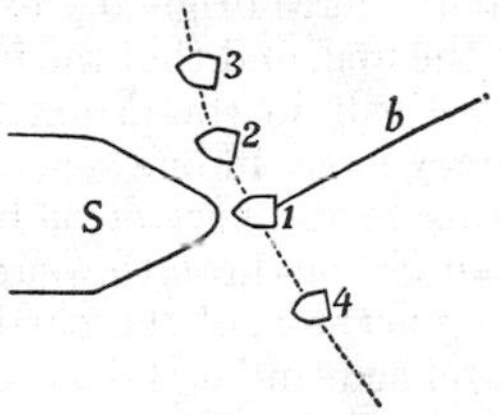

Fig. 5

where 1 represents the crystal of bismuth attached to the balance arm *b*, the axis of which is so placed that the crystal can swing through the various positions 1, 2, 3, 4; S is the pole of the magnet separated only by the glass of the shade. It is manifest, that in position 1 the magnecrystallic axes and the lines of magnetic force are parallel to each other; whereas in the positions 2, 3, 4, they are oblique. When the apparatus was so arranged that the crystal of bismuth rested at 1, the superinduction of the full magnetic force sent it towards 4; a result of diamagnetic action. When however the bismuth had its place of rest at 2, the development of the magnetic force did not make it pass towards 3, in accordance with the former result, but towards 1, which it usually attained and often passed, going a little towards 4. In this case the magnecrystallic and the diamagnetic forces were opposed to each other, and the former gained the advantage up to position 1.

2575. But though the crystal of bismuth in these cases moves across the lines of force in the magnetic field, it cannot be expected to do so in a field where the lines are parallel and of equal force, as between flat-faced poles; the crystal being restrained so as to move only parallel to itself; for under such circumstances the forces are equal in both directions and on both sides of the mass, and the only tendency the crystal has, in relation to its magnecrystallic condition, is to turn round a vertical axis until it is in its natural position in the magnetic field.

2576. A most important question next arises in relation to the magnecrystallic force, namely whether it is an original force inherent in the crystal of bismuth, &c., or whether it is induced under the magnetic and electric influences. When a piece of soft iron is held in the vicinity of a magnet it acquires new powers and properties; some persons assume this to depend upon the development by induction of a new force in the iron and its particles, like in nature to that in the inducing magnet: by others it is considered that the force originally existed in the particles of the iron, and that the inductive action consisted only in the arrangement of all the elementary forces in one general direction. Applying this to the crystal of bismuth, we cannot make use of the latter supposition in the same manner; for all the particles are arranged beforehand, and it is that very arrangement of them and their forces which gives the bismuth its power. If the particles of a substance be in the heterogeneous condition possessed by those of the iron in its unmagnetic state, then the magnetic force may develop the magnetic, and also the diamagnetic condition, which probably is a condition of induction; but it does not appear at once, that it can develop a state of the kind now under consideration.

2577. That the particles hold their own to a great extent in all the results is manifest, by the consideration that they have an inherent power or force, the crystalline force, which is so unchangeable that no treatment to which they can be subjected can alter it; that it is this very force which, placing the particles in a regular position in the mass, enables them to act jointly on the magnet or the electric current, and affect or be affected by them; and that if the particles are not so arranged, but are in all directions in the mass, then the sum of their forces externally is nothing, and no inductive exertion of the magnet or current can develop the slightest trace of the phenomena.

2578. And that particles even before crystallization can act in some degree at a distance, by virtue of their crystallizing force, is, I think, shown by the following fact. A jar containing about a quart of solution of sulphate of soda, of such strength as to crystallize when cold by the touch of a crystal of the salt or an extraneous body, was left, accidentally, for a week or more unattended and undisturbed. The solution remained fluid; but on the jar being touched, crystallization took place throughout the whole mass at once, producing clear, distinct, transparent plates, which were an inch or more in length, up to half an inch in breadth; and very thin, perhaps about the one-fiftieth or one-sixtieth of an inch. These were all horizontal, and of course parallel to each other; and I think, if I remember rightly, had their length in the same direction; and they were alike in character, and, apparently, in quantity in every part of the jar. They almost held the fluid in its place when the jar was tilted; and when the liquid was poured off presented a beautiful and uniform assemblage of crystals. The result persuaded me, at the time, that though the influence of a particle in solution and about to crystallize, must be immediately and essentially upon its neighbours, yet that it could exert an influence beyond these, without which influence, the whole mass of solution could hardly have been brought into such a uniform crystallizing state. Whether the horizontality of the plates can have any relation to the almost vertical lines of magnetic force, which from the earth's magnetism was pervading the solution during the whole time of its rest, is more than I will venture to say.

2579. The following are considerations which bear upon this great question (2576) of an original or an induced state.

2580. In the first place, the bismuth carries off no power or particular state from the magnetic field, able to make it affect a magnet (2504); so that if the condition acquired by the crystal be an induced condition, it is probably a transient one, and continues only whilst under induction. The fact, therefore, though negative in its evidence, agrees, as far as it tells, with that supposition.

2581. In the next place, if the effect were wholly due, as far as the crystal is concerned, to an original power inherent in the mass, we might expect to find the earth's magnetism, or any weak magnet, affecting the crystal. It is true that a weak magnetic force ought to *induce* any given condition in a crystal of bismuth just as well as a stronger, only proportionally. But if the given condition were inherent in the crystal, and did not change in its amount by the degree of magnetic force to which it was subjected, then a weak magnetic force ought to act more decidedly on the bismuth than it would do if the condition were induced in the bismuth, and only in proportion to its own force. Whatever the value of the argument, I was induced to repeat the experiment of the earth's influence (2505) very carefully, and by sheltering the suspended crystals in small flasks or jars contained within the larger covering jar, and making the experiment in an underground place of uniform and constant temperature, I was able to exclude every effect of currents of air, so that the crystals obeyed the slightest degree of torsion given to the suspending fibre by the index above. Under these circumstances I could obtain no indications of pointing by the earth's action, either with crystals of bismuth or of sulphate of iron. Perhaps at the equator, where the lines of force are horizontal, they might be rendered sensible.

2582. In the third place, assuming that there is an original force in the crystals and their molecules, it might be expected that they would show some direct influence upon each other, independent of the magnetic force, and if so the best possible argument would be thus obtained that the force which is rendered manifest in the magnetic field was inherent in them. But on placing a large crystal with its magnecrystallic axis horizontal under a smaller and suspended one, or side by side with it, I could procure no signs of mutual action; even when the approximated parts of the crystals were ground or dissolved away, so as to let the two masses come as near as possible to each other, having large surfaces at the smallest possible distance. Extreme care is required in such experiments (2581), or else many results are produced which seem to show a mutual affection of the bodies.

2583. Neither could I find any trace of mutual action between crystals of bismuth, or of sulphate of iron, when they were both in the *magnetic field*, the one being freely suspended and the other brought in various positions near to it.

2584. From the absence therefore or extreme weakness of any power in the crystals to affect each other, and also from the action of heat which can take away the power of the crystal before it has lost its mere crystalline condition (2570), I am induced to believe that the force manifested in the crystal when in the magnetic

field, which appears by external actions, and causes the motion of the mass, is chiefly and almost entirely *induced*, in a manner, subject indeed to the crystalline force, and finally additive to it; but at the same time exalting the force and the effects to a degree which they could not have approached without the induction.

2585. In that case the word *magnetocrystallic* ought probably to be applied to this force, as it is generated or developed under the influence of the magnet. The word *magnecrystallic* I used purposely to indicate that which I believed belonged to the crystal itself, and I shall still speak of the magnecrystallic axis, &c., in that sense.

2586. This force appears to me to be very strange and striking in its character. It is not polar, for there is no attraction or repulsion. Then what is the nature of the mechanical force which turns the crystal round (2460), or makes it affect a magnet (2564)? It is not like a turning helix of wire acted on by the lines of magnetic force; for there, there is a current of electricity required, and the ring has polarity all the time and is powerfully attracted or repelled.[1]

2587. If we suppose for a moment that the axial position is that in which the crystal is unaffected, and that it is in the oblique position that the magnecrystallic axial direction is affected and rendered polar, giving two tensions pulling the crystal round, then there ought to be attractions at these times, and an obliquely presented crystal ought to be attracted by a single pole, or the nearest of two poles; but no action of this kind appears.

2588. Or we might suppose that the crystal is a little more apt for magnetic induction, or a little less apt for diamagnetic induction, in the direction of the magnecrystallic axis than in other directions. But, if so, it should surely show polar attractions in the case of the magnetic bodies, as sulphate of iron (2557, 2583); and in the case of diamagnetic bodies, as bismuth, a difference in the degree of repulsion when presented with the magnecrystallic axis parallel and perpendicular to the lines of magnetic force (2552); which it does not do.

2589. I do not remember heretofore such a case of force as the present one, where a body is brought into position only, without attraction or repulsion.

[1] Perhaps these points may find their explication hereafter in the action of contiguous particles (1663, 1710, 1729, 1735, 2443).

2590. If the power be induced, it must be like, generally, to its inducing predominants; and these are, at present, the magnetic and electric forces. If induced, subject to the crystalline force (2577), it must show an intimate relation between it and them. How hopeful we may be, therefore, that the results will help to throw open the doors which may lead us to a full knowledge of these powers (2146), and the combined manner in which they dwell in the particles of matter, and exert their influence in producing the wonderful phenomena which they present!

2591. I cannot resist throwing forth another view of these phenomena which may possibly be the true one. The lines of magnetic force may perhaps be assumed as in some degree resembling the rays of light, heat, &c.; and may find difficulty in passing through bodies, and so be affected by them, as light is affected. They may, for instance, when a crystalline body is interposed, pass more freely, or with less disturbance, through it in the direction of the magnecrystallic axis than in other directions. In that case, the position which the crystal takes in the magnetic field with its magnecrystallic axis parallel to the lines of magnetic force, may be the position of no, or of least resistance; and therefore the position of rest and stable equilibrium. All the diametral effects would agree with this view. Then, just as the optic axis is to a ray of polarized light, namely, the direction in which it is not affected, so would the magnecrystallic axis be to the lines of magnetic force. If such were the case, then, also, as the phenomena are developed in crystalline bodies, we might hope for the discovery of a series of effects dependent upon retardation and influence in direction, parallel to the beautiful phenomena presented by light with similar bodies. In making this supposition, I do not forget the points of inertia and momentum; but such an idea as I can form of inertia does not exclude the above view as altogether irrational. I remember too, that, when a magnetic pole and a wire carrying an electric current are fastened together, so that one cannot turn without the other, if the one be made axis the other will revolve round and carry the first with it; and also, that if a magnet be floated in mercury and a current sent down it, the magnet will revolve by the powers which are *within* its mass. With my imperfect mathematical knowledge, there seems as much difficulty in these motions as in the one I am supposing, and therefore I venture to put forth the

idea.[1] The hope of a polarized bundle of magnetic forces is enough of itself to make one work earnestly with such an object, though only in imagination, before us; and I may well say that no man, if he take industry, impartiality and caution with him in his investigations of science, ever works experimentally in vain.

2592. I have already referred, in the former paper (2469), to Plücker's beautiful discovery and results in reference to the repulsion of the optic axis[2] of certain crystals by the magnet, and have distinguished them from my own obtained with bismuth, antimony and arsenic, which are not cases of either repulsion or attraction; believing then, with Plücker, that the force there manifested is an optic axis force, exerted in the equatorial direction; and therefore existing in a direction at right angles to that which produces the magnecrystallic phenomena.

2593. But the relations of *both* to crystalline structure, and therefore to the force which confers that condition, are most evident. Other considerations as to position, set, and turning, also show that the two forces, so to say, have a very different relation to each other to that which exists between them and the magnetic or diamagnetic force. As, therefore, this strong likeness on the one hand, and distinct separation on the other are clearly indicated, I will endeavour to compare the two sets of effects, with the view of ascertaining whether the force exerted in producing them is not identical.

2594. I had the advantage of verifying Plücker's results under his own personal tuition in respect of tourmaline, staurolite, red ferro-prussiate of potassa, and Iceland spar. Since then, and in reference to the present inquiry, I have carefully examined calcareous spar, as being that one of the bodies which was at the same time free from magnetic action, and so simple in its crystalline relations as to possess but one optic axis.

2595. When a small rhomboid, about 0.3 of an inch in its greatest dimension, is suspended, with its optic axis horizontal, between the pointed poles (2458) of the electro-magnet, approximated as closely as they can be to allow free motion, the rhomboid sets in the equatorial direction, and the optic axis coincides with the magnetic axis; but, when the poles were separated to the distance of half, or three-quarters of an

---

[1] See *note* (2639).
[2] "On the Repulsion of the Optic Axes of Crystals by the Poles of a Magnet," Poggendorff's *Annalen*, Vol. LXXII, October 1847, or Taylor's *Scientific Memoirs*, Vol. V, p. 353.

inch, the rhomboid turned through 90°, and set with the optic axis in the equatorial direction, and the greatest length axial. In the first instance the diamagnetic force overcame the optic axis force; in the second the optic axis force was the stronger of the two.

2596. To remove the diamagnetic effect I used flat poles (2463), and then the little rhomboid always set in, or vibrated about, that position in which its optic axis was equatorial.

2597. I also took three cubes of calcareous spar (1695), in which the optic axes were perpendicular to two of the faces, of the respective dimensions of 0.3, 0.5, and 0.8 of an inch in the side, and placed these in succession in the magnetic field, between either flat or pointed poles. In all cases, the optic axis, if horizontal, passed into the equatorial position; or, if vertical, left the cubes indifferent as to direction. It was easy by the method of two positions (2470) to find the line of force, which, being vertical, left the mass unaffected by the magnet; or being horizontal, went into the equatorial position; and then examining the cube by polarized light, it was found that this line coincided with the optic axis.

2598. Even the horseshoe magnet (2485) is sufficiently strong to produce these effects.

2599. I tried two similar cubes of rock-crystal (1692), but could perceive no traces of any phenomena having either magneoptic, or magnecrystallic, or any other relation to the crystalline structure of the masses.

2600. But though it is thus very certain that there is a line in a crystal of calcareous spar coinciding with the optic axis, which line seems to represent the resultant of the forces which make the crystal take up a given position in the magnetic field; and, though it is equally certain that this line takes up its position in the equatorial direction; yet, considered as a line of force, i.e., as representing the direction of the force which places the crystal in that position, it seems to me to have something anomalous in its character. For, that a directing and determining *line* of force should have, as its full effect, the result of going into a *plane* (the equatorial), in which it can take up any one of an infinite number of positions indifferently, leaves an imperfect idea on my mind; and a thought, that there is some other effect or residual phenomena to be recognized and accounted for.

2601. On further consideration, it appears that a simple combination of the magnecrystalline condition, as it exists in bismuth, will supply us with a perfect representation of the state of calcareous spar; for, by placing two equal pieces of bismuth with their magnecrystallic axes perpendicular to each other (2484), we have a system of forces which seems to possess, as a resultant, a line setting in the equatorial direction. When that line is vertical, the system is, as regards position, indifferent; but when horizontal, the system so stands, that the line is in the equatorial plane. Still, the real force is not in the equatorial direction, but axial; and the system is moved by what may be considered a *plane of axial force* (resulting from the union of the two axes at right angles to each other), rather than by a *line of equatorial force*.

2602. Doubtless, the rhomboid or cube (2597) of calcareous spar is not a compound crystal, like the system of bismuth crystals just referred to (2601); but its molecules may possess a compound disposition of their forces, and may have two or more axes of power, which at the same time that they cause the crystalline structure, may exert such force in relation to the magnet, as to give results in the same manner, and of the same kind, as those of the double crystal of bismuth (2601). Indeed, that there should be but one axis of crystalline force, either in the particle of Iceland spar, or in those of bismuth, does not seem to me to be any way consistent with the cleavage of the substances in three or more directions.

2603. The optic axis in a piece of calcareous spar, is simply the line in which, if a polarized, or ordinary ray of light moves, it is the least affected. It may be a line which, as a resultant of the molecular forces, is that of the least intensity; and, certainly, as regards ordinary and mechanical means of observing cohesion, a piece of calcareous spar is sensibly, and much harder on the faces and parts which are parallel to the optic axis, than on those perpendicular to it. An ordinary file or a piece of sandstone shows this. So that the plane equatorial to the optic axis, as it represents directions in which the force causing crystallization is greater in degree than in the direction of the optic axis, may also be that in which the resultant of its magnecrystallic force is exerted.

2604. I am bound to state, as in some degree in contrast with such considerations, that, with bismuth, antimony and arsenic, the cleavage is very facile perpendicular to the magnecrystallic axis (2475, 2510, 2532). But we must remember that the cleavage (and therefore the cohesive) force is not the only thing to be considered, for in calcareous spar it does not coincide with either the axial or the equatorial direction of the substance in the magnetic field: we must endeavour to look beyond this to the polar (or axial) condition of the particles of the masses, for the full understanding and true relation of all these points.

2605. I am bound, also, to admit that, if we consider calcareous spar as giving the simple system of force, we may, by the juxtaposition of two crystals with their optic axes at right angles to each other, produce a compound mass, which will truly represent the bismuth in the direction of the force; i.e., it will, in the magnetic field, point with apparently one line of force only, and that in the axial direction, whilst it may be really moved by a system of forces lying in the equatorial plane. I will not at present pretend to say that this is not the state of things; but I think, however, that the metals, bismuth, antimony and arsenic, present us with the simplest as they do the strongest cases of magnecrystallic force; and whether that be so or not, I am still of opinion that the phenomena discovered by Plücker and those of which I have given an account in these two papers, have one common origin and cause.

2606. I went through all the experiments and reasonings with Plücker's crystals (as the carbonate of lime, tourmaline and red ferro-prussiate of potassa), in reference to the question of original or induced power (2576), as before, and came to the same conclusion as in the former case (2584).

2607. I could not find that crystals of red ferro-prussiate of potassa or tourmaline were affected by the earth's magnetism (2581), or that they had the power of affecting each other (2582). Neither could I find that Plücker's effect with calcareous spar, or red ferro-prussiate of potassa, was either an attractive or repulsive effect, but one connected with position only (2550, 2560). All which circumstances tend to convince me that the force active in his experiments, and that in my results with bismuth, &c., is the same.[1]

2608. A small rhomboid of Iceland spar was raised to the highest temperature in the magnetic field which a spirit-lamp could give (2570);

[1] The optic axis is the direction of least optic force; and by Plücker's experiments, coincides with what I consider in my results as the direction of minimum magnecrystallic force. It is more than probable that, wherever the two sets of effects (whether really or only nominally different) can be recognized in the same body, the directions of maximum effect, and also those of minimum effect, will be found to coincide. November 23, 1848.

it was at least equal to the full red heat of copper, but it pointed as well then as before. A short thick tourmaline was heated to the same degree, and it also pointed equally well. As it cooled, however, it became highly magnetic, and seemed to be entirely useless for experiments at low temperatures; but on digesting it for a few seconds in nitromuriatic acid, a little iron was dissolved from the surface, after which it pointed as well, and in accordance with Plücker's law, as before. A little peroxide upon the surface had been reduced by the flame and heat to protoxide, and caused the magnetic appearances.

2609. There is a general and, as it appears to me, important relation between Plücker's magneto-optical results and those I formerly obtained with heavy glass and other bodies (2152, &c.). When any of these bodies is subject to strong induction under the influence of the magnetic or electric forces, it acquires a peculiar state, in which it can influence a polarized ray of light. The effect is a rotation of the ray, if it be passed through the substance parallel to the lines of magnetic force, or in other words, in the axial direction; but if it be passed in the equatorial direction, no effect is produced. The equatorial plane, therefore, is that plane in which the condition of the molecular forces is the least disturbed as respects their influence on light. So also in Plücker's results, the optic axis, or the optic axes, if there be two, go into that plane under the same magnetic influence, they also being the lines in which there is the least, or no action on polarized light.

2610. If a piece of heavy glass, or a portion of water, could be brought beforehand into this constrained condition, and then placed in the magnetic field, I think there can be no doubt that it would move, if allowed to do so, and place itself naturally, so that the plane of no action on light should be equatorial, just as Plücker shows that a crystal of calcareous spar or tourmaline does in his experiments. And, as in his case, the magnetic or diamagnetic character of the bodies, makes no difference in the general result; so in my experiments, the optical effect is produced in the same direction, and subject to the same laws, with both classes of substances (2185, 2187).

2611. But though thus generally alike in this great and leading point, there is still a vast difference in the disposition of the forces in the heavy glass and the crystal; and there is a still greater difference in this, that the heavy glass takes up its state only for a time by constraint and under induction, whilst the crystal possesses it freely, naturally and permanently. In both cases, however, whether natural or induced, it is a state of the particles; and com · paring the effect on light of the glass under constraint with that of the crystal at liberty, it indicates a power in the magnet of inducing something like that condition in the particles of matter which is necessary for crystallization; and that even in the particles of fluids (2184).

2612. If there be any weight in these considerations, and if the forces manifested in the crystals of bismuth and Iceland spar be the same (2607), then there is further reason for believing that, in the case of bismuth and the other metals named, there is, when they are subjected to the power of the magnet, both an induced condition of force (2584), and also a pre-existing force (2577). The latter may be distinguished as the crystalline force, and is shown, first, by such bodies exhibiting optic axes and lines of force when not under induction; by the symmetric condition of the whole mass, produced under circumstances of ordinary occurrence; and by the fixity of the line of magnecrystallic force in the bodies shown experimentally to possess it.

2613. Though I have spoken of the magnecrystallic axis as a given line or direction, yet I would not wish to be understood as supposing that the force decreases, or state changes, in an equal ratio all round from it. It is more probable that the variation is different in degree in different directions, dependent on the powers which give difference of form to the crystals. The knowledge of the disposition of the force can be ascertained minutely hereafter, by the use of good crystals, an unchangeable ordinary magnet (2485, 2528), or a regulated electromagnet, flat-faced poles (2463), and torsion (2500, 2530).

2614. I cannot conclude this series of *Researches* without remarking how rapidly the knowledge of molecular forces grows upon us, and how strikingly every investigation tends to develop more and more their importance, and their extreme attraction as an object of study. A few years ago magnetism was to us an occult power, affecting only a few bodies; now it is found to influence all bodies, and to possess the most intimate relations with electricity, heat, chemical action, light, crystallization, and, through it, with the forces concerned in cohesion; and we may, in the present state of things, well feel urged to continue in our labours, encouraged by the hope of bringing it into a bond of union with gravity itself.

Royal Institution, October 20, 1848

¶ vi. NOTE. *On the Position of a Crystal of Sulphate of Iron in the Magnetic Field*

RECEIVED DECEMBER 7, 1848, READ DECEMBER 7, 1848

2615. Though effects of the following nature are general, yet I think it convenient to state that I obtained them chiefly by the use of magnetic poles (2247), the form of which is given in the plan and side-view annexed (*Fig.* 6). The

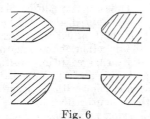

Fig. 6

crystals submitted to their action were suspended by cocoon silk, so as to be level with the upper surface of the poles.

2616. A prismatic crystal of protosulphate of iron was selected, which was nearly 0.9 of an inch in length, 0.1 in breadth, and 0.05 in thickness; by examination the magnecrystallic axis was found to coincide with the thickness, and therefore to be perpendicular, or nearly so (2546), to the plate. Being suspended as above described, and the magnet (2247) excited by ten pair of Grove's plates, the crystal stood transverse, or with its *magnecrystallic axis* parallel to the axis of magnetic force, when the distance between the poles was 2.25 inches or more; but when the distance was about 2 inches or less, then it stood with its length axial, or nearly so, and its magnecrystallic axis therefore transverse to the lines of magnetic force. In the intermediate distances between 2 and 2.25 inches, the prism assumed an oblique position (2634), more or less inclined to the axial line, and so passing gradually from the one position to the other. This intermediate distance I will for the present call *n* (neutral) distance.

2617. If the poles be 2 inches apart and the crystal be gradually lowered, it passes through the same intermediate oblique positions into the transverse position; or if the crystal be raised, the same transitions occur; at any less distance the changes are the same, but later. They occur more rapidly when the crystal is raised than when it is lowered; but this is only because of the unsymmetric disposition and intensity of the lines of magnetic force around the magnetic axis, due to the horseshoe form of the magnet and shape of the poles. If two cylinder magnets with equal conical terminations were employed, there is no doubt that for equal amounts of elevation or depression, corresponding changes would take place in the position of the crystal.

2618. These changes however are not due to mere diminution of the magnetic force by distance, but to differences in the *forms* or *direction* of the resultants of force. This is shown by the fact that, if the crystal be left in its first position, and so pointing with the length axially, no diminution of the force of the magnet alters the position; thus, whether one or ten pair of plates be used to excite the magnet, the *n* distance (2616) remains unchanged; and even descending to the use of an ordinary horseshoe magnet, I have found the same result.

2619. Variation in the length of the prismatic crystal has an important influence over the result. As the crystal is shorter, the distance *n* diminishes, all the other phenomena remaining the same. A crystal 0.7 of an inch long, but thicker than the last, had for its maximum *n* distance 1.7 inch. A still shorter crystal had for its maximum *n* distance 1.1 inch. In all these cases variation of the force of the magnet caused no sensible change.

2620. Variation in that dimension of the crystal coincident with the magnecrystallic axis affected the *n* distance: thus, increase in the length of the magnecrystallic axis diminished the distance, and diminution of it in that direction increased the distance. This was shown in two ways; first, by placing a second prismatic crystal by the side of the former in a symmetric position (2636), which reduced the *n* distance to between 1.75 and 2 inches; and next, by employing two crystals in succession of the same length but different thicknesses. The thicker one had the smaller *n* distance.

2621. Variation in the depth of the crystal, i.e. its vertical dimension, did not produce any sensible effect on the *n* distance: nor by theory should it do so, until the extension upwards or downwards brings the upper or lower parts into the condition of raised or depressed portions (2617).

2622. Variation in the form of the poles affects the *n* distance. As they are more acute, the distance increases; and as they are more obtuse up to flat-faced poles (2463), the distance diminishes.

2623. With the shorter crystals, or with obtuse poles, it is often necessary to diminish the power of the magnet, or else the crystal is liable to be drawn to the one or other pole. This, however, may be avoided by employing a vertical axis which is confined below as well as above (2554); and then the difference in *strength* of the magnet is shown to be indifferent to the results, or very nearly so.

2624. These effects may probably be due to the essential difference which exists between the ordinary magnetic and the magnecrystallic action, in that the first is *polar*, and the second only *axial* (2472) in character. If a piece of magnetic matter, iron for instance, be in the magnetic field, it immediately becomes polar (i.e., has terminations of different qualities). If many iron particles be there, they all become polar; and if they be free to move, arrange themselves in the direction of the axial line, being joined to each other by contrary poles; and by that the polarity of the extreme particles is increased. Now this does not appear to be at all the case with particles under the influence of the magnecrystallic force; the force seems to be altogether *axial*, and hence probably the difference above, and in many other results.

2625. Thus, if four or more little cubes of iron be suspended in a magnetic field of equal force (2465), they will become polar; if also four similar cubes of crystallized bismuth be similarly circumstanced, they will be affected and point. If the iron cubes be arranged together in the direction of the equatorial line, they will form an aggregate in a position of unstable equilibrium, and will immediately, as a whole, turn and point with the length axially; whereas the bismuth cubes by such approximation will suffer no sensible change.

2626. The *extreme* (and the other) associated cubes of the elongated iron arrangement now have a polar force above that which they had before; and the whole group serves, as it were, as a conductor for the lines of magnetic power; for many of them concentrate upon the iron, and the intensity of power is much stronger between the ends of the iron arrangement and the magnetic poles than it is in other parts of the magnetic field. Such is not the case with the bismuth cubes; for however they be arranged, the intensity of force in the magnetic field is, as far as experiments have yet gone, unaffected by them; and the intensity of the molecules of the crystals appears to remain the same. Hence the iron stands lengthways between the poles; the bismuth crystals, on the contrary, whether arranged side by side, as respects the magnecrystallic axis, so as to stand to length equatorially; or end to end, so as to stand axially, are perfectly indifferent in that respect, vibrating and setting equally both ways.

2627. A given piece of iron when introduced into a field of equal magnetic force, and brought towards the pole, adheres to it and disturbs the intensity of the field, producing a pointed form of pole in one part with diverging lines of force: a crystal of bismuth vibrates with sensibly equal force in every part of the field (2467), and does not disturb the distribution of the power.

2628. Considering all these actions and conditions, it appears to me that the occurrence of the *n* distance with a body which is at the same time magnetic and magnecrystallic, may be traced to that which causes them and their differences, namely, the *polarity* belonging to the magnetic condition, and the *axiality* belonging to the magnecrystallic condition. Thus, suppose an uniform magnetic field three inches from pole to pole, and a bar of magnetic matter an inch long, suspended in the middle of it; by virtue of the polarity it acquires, it will point axially, and carry on, or conduct, with its mass, the magnetic force, so much better than it was conducted in the same space before, that the lines of force between the ends of this bar and the magnetic poles will be concentrated and made more intense than anywhere else in the magnetic field. If the poles be made to approach towards the bar, this effect will increase, and the bar will conduct more and more of the magnetic force, and point with proportionate intensity. It is not merely that the magnetic field becomes more intense by the approximation of the poles, but the proportion of force carried on by the bar becomes greater as compared to that conveyed onwards by an equal space in the magnetic field at its side.

2629. But if a similar bar of magnecrystallic substance be placed in the magnetic field, its power does not rise in the same manner, or in the same great proportion, by approximation of the poles. There can be no doubt that such approximation increases the intensity of the lines of force, and therefore increases the intensity of the magneto-crystallic state; but this state does not appear to be due to polarity, and the bar does not convey more power through it than is conveyed onwards elsewhere through an equal space in the magnetic field. Hence its directive force does not increase in the same rapid degree as the directive force of the magnetic bar just referred to.

2630. If then we take a bar which, like a prism of sulphate of iron, is magnetic, and also magnecrystallic, having the magnecrystallic axis perpendicular to its length, such a bar, properly suspended, ought to have an *n* distance of the poles, within which the forces ought to be nearly in equilibrium; whilst at a greater distance of the poles, the magnecrystallic force ought to predominate; and at a lesser distance, the magnetic force ought to have the advantage; simply, because the magnetic force, in consequence of the true polarity of the molecules, grows up more rapidly and diminishes more rapidly than the magneto-crystallic force.

2631. This view, also, is consistent with the fact that variation of the force of the magnet does not affect the *n* distance (2618, 2619); for, whether the force be doubled or quadrupled, both the magnetic and magneto-crystallic forces are at the same time doubled or quadrupled; and their proportion therefore remains the same.

2632. The raising or lowering of the crystal above or below the line of maximum magnetic force is manifestly equivalent in principle to the separation of the magnetic poles; and therefore should produce corresponding effects: and that is the case (2617). Besides that, when the crystal is raised above the level of the poles, such resultants of magnetic force as pass through it, are no longer parallel to its length, but more or less curved, so that they probably cannot act with the same amount of power in throwing the whole crystal into a consistent polarized magnetic condition, as if they were parallel to it: whereas, as respects the induction of the magneto-crystallic condition, each of the particles appears to be affected independently of the others; and, therefore, any loss of an effect dependent upon joint action would not be felt here.

2633. M. Plücker told me, when in England in August last, that the repulsive force on the optic axis diminishes and increases less rapidly than the magnetic force, by change of distance; but is not altered in its proportion to the magnetic force by employing a stronger or weaker magnet. This is manifestly the same effect as that I have been describing; and makes me still more thoroughly persuaded that his results and mine are due to one and the same cause (2605, 2607).

2634. I have said that, within the *n* distance, the crystal of sulphate of iron pointed more or less obliquely (2616); I will now state more particularly what the circumstances are. If the distance *n* be so adjusted, that the prismatic crystal, which is at the time between the magnetic poles, shall make an angle of 30° (or any quantity) with the axial line; then it will be found that there is another stable position, namely, the diametral position (2461), in which it can stand; but that the obliquity is always on the same side of the axial line; and that the crystal will not stand with the like obliquity of 30° on the opposite side of the magnetic axis.

2635. If the crystal be turned 180° round a vertical axis, or end for end, then the inclination, and the direction in which it occurs, remain unchanged; in fact, it is simply giving the crystal the diametral position. But if the crystal be revolved 180° round a horizontal axis; either that coinciding with its length, which represents its maximum magnetic direction; or that corresponding with its breadth, and therefore with the magnecrystallic axis; then the inclination is the same in amount as before, but it is on the *other* side of the axial line.

2636. This is the case with all the prismatic crystals of sulphate of iron which I have tried. The effect is very determinate; and, as would be expected, when two crystals correspond in the direction of the inclination, they also correspond in the position of their form and direction of the various planes.

2637. All these variations of position indicate an oblique resultant of setting force, derived from the joint action of the magnetic and magnecrystallic forces; and would be explained by the supposition that the magnecrystallic axis or line of maximum magnecrystallic force was not perpendicular to the chief planes of the crystal (or those terminating it), but a little inclined in the direction of the length.

2638. Whether this be the case, or whether the maximum line of magnetic force may not, even, be a little inclined to the length of the prism; still, the *n* distance supplies an excellent experimental opportunity of examining this inclination, however small its quantity may be; because of the facility with which the influence of either the one or the other may be made predominant in any required degree.

Royal Institution, December 5, 1848

2639. *Note.* (2591) Another supposition may be thrown out for consideration. I have already said that the assumption of a mere axial condition (2587, 2591) would account for the set without attraction or repulsion. Now if we suppose it possible that the molecules should become polar in relation to the north and south poles of the magnet, but with *no mutual relation amongst themselves*, then the bismuth or other crystal might set as if induced with mere axial power: but it seems to me very improbable that polarities of a given particle in a crystal should be subject to the influence of the polarities of the distant magnet poles, and not also to the *like polarities* of the contiguous particles.—*January 24, 1849*

TWENTY-THIRD SERIES[1]

§ 29. *On the Polar or Other Condition of Diamagnetic Bodies*

Received January 1, Read March 7 and 14, 1850

2640. Four years ago I suggested that all the phenomena presented by diamagnetic bodies, when subjected to the forces in the magnetic field, might be accounted for by assuming that they then possessed a polarity the same in kind as, but the reverse in direction of, that acquired by iron, nickel and ordinary magnetic bodies under the same circumstances (2429, 2430). This view was received so favourably by Plücker, Reich and others, and above all by W. Weber,[2] that I had great hopes it would be confirmed;

[1] *Philosophical Transactions*, 1850, p. 171.

[2] Poggendorff's *Annalen*, January 7, 1848; or Taylor's *Scientific Memoirs*, V, p. 477.

and though certain experiments of my own (2497) did not increase that hope, still my desire and expectation were in that direction.

2641. Whether bismuth, copper, phosphorus, &c., when in the magnetic field, are polar or not, is however an exceedingly important question; and very essential and great differences, in the mode of action of these bodies under the one view or the other, must be conceived to exist. I found that in every endeavour to proceed by induction of experiment from that which is known in this department of science to the unknown, so much uncertainty, hesitation and discomfort arose from the unsettled state of my mind on this point that I determined, if possible, to arrive at some experimental proof either one way or the other. This was the more needful, because of the conclusion in the affirmative to which Weber had come in his very philosophical paper; and so important do I think it for the progress of science, that, in those imperfectly developed regions of knowledge, which form its boundaries, our conclusions and deductions should not go far beyond, or at all events not aside from the results of experiment (except as suppositions), that I do not hesitate to lay my present labours, though they arrive at a negative result, before the Royal Society.

2642. It appeared to me that many of the results which had been supposed to indicate a polar condition were only consequences of the law that diamagnetic bodies tend to go from stronger to weaker places of action (2418;) others again appeared to have their origin in induced currents (26, 2338); and further consideration seemed to indicate that the differences between these modes of action and that of a real polarity, whether magnetic or diamagnetic, might serve as a foundation on which to base a mode of investigation, and also to construct an apparatus that might give useful conclusions and results in respect of this inquiry. For, if the polarity exists it must be in the particles and for the time permanent, and therefore distinguishable from the momentary polarity of the mass due to induced temporary currents; and it must also be distinguishable from ordinary magnetic polarity by its contrary direction.

2643. A straight wooden lever, 2 feet in length, was fixed by an axis at one end, and by means of a crank and wheel made to vibrate in a horizontal plane, so that its free extremity passed to and fro through about 2 inches. Cylinders or cores of metal or other substances, 5½ inches long and three-quarters of an inch diameter, were fixed in succession to the end of a brass rod 2 feet long, which itself was attached

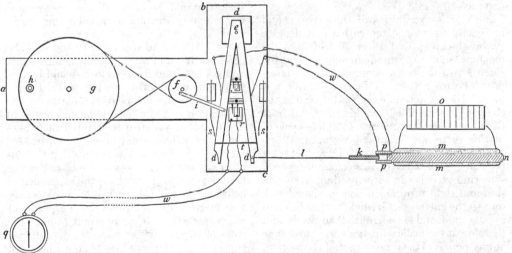

Fig. 1

a, b, c, frame board; *d, d, d* wooden lever, of which *e* is the axis, *f* the crank-wheel, and *g* the great wheel with its handle *h; i* the bar connecting the crank-wheel and lever; *k* a cylinder or core of metal to be submitted to experiment; *l* the rod connecting it with the lever; *m* the helix of the electro-magnet; *n* the iron core, and *o* the exciting battery; *p* the experimental helix; *q* the galvanometer, 20 feet from the electro-magnet; *r* the commutator; *w, w* connecting wires; *s, s* springs of brass or copper; *t* a copper rod connecting the two arms of the lever, to give strength. The plan is to a scale of one-sixteenth: the part at the electro-magnet and experimental helix is in section; the further description is contained in paragraphs 2643, 2644, 2645 and 2648.

at the other end to the moving extremity of the lever, so that the cylinders could be moved to and fro in the direction of their length through the space of 2 inches. A large cylinder electro-magnet was also prepared (2191), the iron core of which was 21 inches long, and 1.7 inch in diameter; but one end of this core was made smaller for the length of 1 inch, being in that part only 1 inch in diameter.

2644. On to this reduced part was fixed a hollow helix consisting of 516 feet of fine covered copper wire: it was 3 inches long, 2 inches external diameter, and 1 inch internal diameter: when in its place, 1 inch of the central space was occupied by the reduced end of the electro-magnet core which carried it; and the magnet and helix were both placed concentric with the metal cylinder above mentioned, and at such a distance that the latter, in its motion, would move within the helix in the direction of its axis, approaching to and receding from the electro-magnet in rapid or slow succession. The least and greatest distances of the moving cylinder from the magnet during the journey were one-eighth of an inch and 2.2 inches. The object of course was to observe any influence upon the experimental helix of fine wire which the metal cylinders might exert, either whilst moving to or from the magnet, or at different distances from it.[1]

2645. The extremities of the experimental helix wire were connected with a very delicate galvanometer, placed 18 or 20 feet from the machine, so as to be unaffected directly by the electro-magnet; but a commutator was interposed between them. This commutator was moved by the wooden lever (2643), and as the electric currents which would arrive at it from the experimental helix, in a complete cycle of motion or to and fro action of the metal cylinder (2643), would consist of two contrary portions, so the office of this commutator was, sometimes to take up these portions in succession and send them on in one consistent current to the galvanometer, and at other times to oppose them and to neutralize their result; and therefore it was made adjustable, so as to change at any period of the time or part of the motion.

2646. With such an arrangement as this, it is known that, however powerful the magnet, and however delicate the other parts of the apparatus, no effect will be produced at the gal-

vanometer as long as the magnet does not change in force, or in its action upon neighbouring bodies, or in its distance from, or relation to, the experimental helix; but the introduction of a piece of iron into the helix, or anything else that can influence or be influenced by the magnet, can, or ought to, show a corresponding influence upon the helix and galvanometer. My apparatus I should imagine, indeed, to be almost the same in principle and practice as that of M. Weber (2640), except that it gives me contrary results.

2647. But to obtain correct conclusions, it is most essential that extreme precaution should be taken in relation to many points which at first may seem unimportant. All parts of the apparatus should have perfect steadiness, and be fixed almost with the care due to an astronomical instrument; for any motion of any portion of it is, from the construction, sure to synchronize with the motion of the commutator; and portions of effect, inconceivably small, are then gathered up and made manifest as a whole at the galvanometer; and thus, without care, errors might be taken for real and correct results. Therefore, in my arrangements, the machine (2643, &c.), the magnet and helix, and the galvanometer stood upon separate tables, and these again upon a stone floor laid upon the earth; and the table carrying the machine was carefully strutted to neighbouring stonework.

2648. Again, the apparatus should itself be perfectly firm and without shake in its motion, and yet easy and free. No iron should be employed in any of the moving parts. I have springs to receive and convert a portion of the momentum of the whole at the end of the to and fro journey; but it is essential that these should be of hammered brass or copper.

2649. It is absolutely necessary that the cylinder or core in its motion should not in the least degree disturb or shake the experimental helix and the magnet. Such a shake may easily take place and yet (without much experience) not be perceived. It is important to have the cores of such bodies as bismuth, phosphorus, copper, &c., as large as may be, but I have not found it safe to have less than one-eighth of an inch of space between them and the interior of the experimental helix. In order to float, as it were, the core in the air, it is convenient to suspend it in the bight or turn of a fine copper wire passing once round it, the ends of which rise up, and are made fast to two fixed points at equal heights but wide apart, so that the

---

[1] It is very probable that if the metals were made into cylinders shorter, but of larger diameter than those described above, and used with a corresponding wider helix, better results than those I have obtained would be acquired.

wire has a V form. This suspension keeps the core parallel to itself in every part of its motion.

2650. The magnet, when excited, is urged by an electric current from five pairs of Grove's plates, and is then very powerful. When the battery is not connected with it, it still remains a magnet of feeble power, and when thus employed may be referred to as in the *residual state*. If employed in the residual state, its power may for the time be considered constant, and the experimental helix may at any moment be connected with the galvanometer without any current appearing there. But if the magnet be employed in the excited state, certain important precautions are necessary; for upon connecting the magnet with the battery and then connecting the experimental helix with the galvanometer, a current will appear at the latter, which will, in certain cases, continue for a minute or more, and which has the appearance of being derived at once from that of the battery. It is not so produced, however, but is due to the *time* occupied by the iron core in attaining its maximum magnetic condition (2170, 2332), during the whole of which it continues to act upon the experimental helix, producing a current in it. This time varies with several circumstances, and in the same electro-magnet varies especially with the period during which the magnet has been out of use. When first employed, after two or three days' rest, it will amount to eighty or ninety seconds, or more. On breaking battery contact and immediately renewing it, the effect will be repeated, but occupy only twenty or thirty seconds. On a third intermission and renewal of the current, it will appear for a still shorter period; and when the magnet has been used at short intervals for some time, it seems capable of receiving its maximum power almost at once. In every experiment it is necessary to wait until the effect is shown by the galvanometer to be over; otherwise the last remains of such an effect might be mistaken for a result of polarity, or some peculiar action of the bismuth or other body under investigation.

2651. The galvanometer employed was made by Ruhmkorff and was very sensible. The needles were strengthened in their action and rendered so nearly equal that a single vibration to the right or to the left occupied from sixteen to twenty seconds. When experimenting with such bodies as bismuth or phosphorus, the place of the needle was observed through a lens. The perfect communication in all parts of the circuit was continually ascertained by a feeble thermo-electric pair, warmed by the fingers. This was done also for every position of the commutator, where the film of oxide formed on any part by two or three days' rest was quite sufficient to intercept a feeble current.

2652. In order to bring the phenomena afforded by magnetic and diamagnetic bodies into direct relation, I have not so much noted the currents produced in the experimental helix, as the effects obtained at the galvanometer. It is to be understood, that the standard of deviation, as to direction, has always been that produced by an iron wire moving in the same direction at the experimental helix, and with the same condition of the commutator and connecting wires, as the piece of bismuth or other body whose effects were to be observed and compared.

2653. A thin glass tube, of the given size (2643), $5\frac{1}{2}$ by $\frac{3}{4}$ inches, was filled with a saturated solution of protosulphate of iron, and employed as the experimental core: the velocity given to the machine at this and all average times of experiment was such as to cause five or six approaches and withdrawals of the core in one second; yet the solution produced no sensible indication at the galvanometer. A piece of magnetic glass tube (2354), and a core of foolscap paper, magnetic between the poles of the electro-magnet, were equally inefficient. A tube filled with small crystals of protosulphate of iron caused the needle to move about 2°, and cores formed out of single large crystals, or symmetric groups of crystals of sulphate of iron, produced the same effect. Red oxide of iron (colcothar) produced the least possible effect. Iron scales and metallic iron (the latter as a thin wire) produced large effects.

2654. Whenever the needle moved, it was consistent in its direction with the effect of a magnetic body; but in many cases with known magnetic bodies, the motion was little or none. This proves that such an arrangement is by no means so good a test of magnetic polarity as the use of a simple or an astatic needle. This deficiency of power in that respect does not interfere with its ability to search into the nature of the phenomena that appear in the experiments of Weber, Reich and others.

2655. Other metals than iron were now employed and with perfect success. If they were magnetic, as nickel and cobalt, the deflection was in the same direction as for iron. When the metals were diamagnetic, the deflection was in the contrary direction; and for some of the metals, as copper, silver and gold, it amounted to 60° or 70°, which was permanently sustained as long as the machine continued to work. But the deflection was not the greatest for the most diamagnetic substances, as bismuth or antimony, or phosphorus; on the contrary, I have not been able to assure myself, up to this time, that these three bodies can produce any effect. Thus far the effect has been proportionate to the *conducting power* of the substance for electricity. Gold. silver and copper have produced large deflections, lead and tin less. Platina very little. Bismuth and antimony none.

2656. Hence there was every reason to believe that the effects were produced by the currents induced in the mass of the moving metals, and not by any polarity of their particles. I proceeded therefore to test this idea by different conditions of the cores and the apparatus.

2657. In the first place, if produced by induced currents, the great proportion of these would exist in the part of the core near to the dominant magnet, and but little in the more distant parts; whereas in a substance like iron, the polarity which the whole assumes makes length a more important element. I therefore shortened the core of copper from 5½ inches (2643) to 2 inches, and found the effect not sensibly diminished; even when 1 inch long it was little less than before. On the contrary, when a fine iron wire, 5½ inches in length, was used as core, its effects were strong; when the length was reduced to 2 inches, they were greatly diminished; and again, with a length of 1 inch, still further greatly reduced. It is not difficult to construct a core of copper, with a fine iron wire in its axis, so that when above a certain length it should produce the effects of iron, and beneath that length the effects of copper.

2658. In the next place, if the effect were produced by induced currents in the mass (2642), division of the mass would stop these currents and so alter the effect; whereas if produced by a true diamagnetic polarity, division of the mass would not affect the polarity seriously, or in its essential nature (2430). Some copper filings were therefore digested for a few days in dilute sulphuric acid to remove any adhering iron, then well-washed and dried, and afterwards warmed and stirred in the air, until it was seen by the orange colour that a very thin film of oxide had formed upon them: they were finally introduced into a glass tube (2653) and employed as a core. It produced no effect whatever, but was now as inactive as bismuth.

2659. The copper may however be divided so as either to interfere with the assumed currents or not, at pleasure. Fine copper wire was cut up into lengths of 5½ inches, and as many of these associated together as would form a compact cylinder three-quarters of an inch in diameter (2643); it produced no effect at the galvanometer. Another copper core was prepared by associating together many *discs* of thin copper plate, three-quarters of an inch in diameter, and this affected the galvanometer, holding its needle 25° or 30° from zero.

2660. I made a solid helix cylinder, three-quarters of an inch in diameter and 2 inches long, of covered copper wire, one-sixteenth of an inch thick, and employed this as the experimental core. When the two ends of its wire were unconnected, there was no effect upon the experimental helix, and consequently none at the galvanometer; but when the ends were soldered together, the needle was well affected. In the first condition, the currents, which tended to be formed in the mass of moving metal, could not exist because the metal circuit was interrupted; in the second they could, because the circuit was not interrupted; and such division as remained did not interfere to prevent the currents.

2661. The same results were obtained with other metals. A core cylinder of gold, made of half-sovereigns, was very powerful in its effect on the galvanometer. A cylinder of silver, made of sixpenny pieces, was very effectual; but a cylinder made of precipitated silver, pressed into a glass tube as closely as possible, gave no indications of action whatever. The same results were obtained with disc cylinders of tin and lead, the effects being proportionate to the condition of tin and lead as bad conductors (2655).

2662. When iron was divided, the effects were exactly the reverse in kind. It was necessary to use a much coarser galvanometer and apparatus for the purpose; but that being done, the employment of a solid iron core, and of another of the same size or weight formed of lengths of fine iron wire (2659), showed that the division had occasioned no inferiority in the latter. The excellent experimental researches of Dove[1] on the electricity of induction, will show that this ought to be the case.

2663. Hence the result of division in the diamagnetic metals is altogether of a nature to confirm the conclusion, that the effects pro-

[1] Taylor's *Scientific Memoirs*, V, p. 129. I do not see a date to the paper.

duced by them are due to induced currents moving through their masses, and not to any polarity correspondent in its general nature (though opposed in its direction) to that of iron.

2664. In the third place (2656), another and very important distinction in the actions of a diamagnetic metal may be experimentally established according as they may be due either to a true polarity, or merely to the presence of temporary induced currents; and as for the consideration of this point diamagnetic and magnetic polarity are the same, the point may best be considered, at present, in relation to iron.

2665. If a core of any kind be advanced towards the dominant magnet and withdrawn from it by a motion of uniform velocity, then a complete journey, or *to* and *from* action, might be divided into four parts; the *to*, the *stop* after it; the *from*, and the *stop* succeeding that. If a core of iron make this journey, its end towards the dominant magnet becomes a pole, rising in force until at the nearest distance, and falling in force until at the greatest distance. Both this effect and its *progression* inwards and outwards, cause currents to be induced in the surrounding helix, and these currents are in one direction as the core advances, and in the contrary direction as it recedes. In reality, however, the iron does not travel with a constant velocity; for, because of the communication of motion from a revolving crank at the machine (2643), it, in the *to* part of the journey, gradually rises from a state of rest to a maximum velocity, which is half-way, and then as gradually sinks to rest again near the magnet: and the *from* part of the journey undergoes the same variations. Now as the maximum effect upon the surrounding experimental helix depends upon the velocity conjointly with the intensity of the magnetic force in the end of the core, it is evident that it will not occur with the maximum velocity, which is in the middle of the *to* or *from* motion; nor at the *stop* nearest to the dominant magnet, where the core end has greatest magnetic force, but somewhere between the two. Nevertheless, during the *whole* of the advance, the core will cause a current in the experimental helix in one direction, and during the whole of the recession it will cause a current in the other direction.

2666. If diamagnetic bodies, under the influence of the dominant magnet, assume also a polar state, the difference between them and iron being only that the poles of like names or

forces are changed in place (2429, 2430), then the same kind of action as that described for iron would occur with them; the only difference being, that the two currents produced would be in the reverse direction to those produced by iron.

2667. If a commutator, therefore, were to be arranged to gather up these currents, either in the one case or the other, and send them on to the galvanometer in one consistent current, it should change at the moments of the two *stops* (2665), and then would perform such duty perfectly. If, on the other hand, the commutator should change at the times of maximum velocity or maximum intensity, or at two other times equidistant either from the one *stop* or from the other, then the parts of the opposite currents intercepted between the changes would exactly neutralize each other, and no final current would be sent on to the galvanometer.

2668. Now the action of the iron is, by experiment, of this nature. If an iron wire be simply introduced or taken out of the experimental helix with different conditions of the commutator, the results are exactly those which have been stated. If the machine be worked with an iron wire core, the commutator changing at the stops (2665), then the current gathered up and sent on to the galvanometer is a maximum; if the commutator change at the moments of maximum velocity, or at any other pair of moments equidistant from the one stop or the other, then the current at the commutator is a minimum, or 0.

2669. There are two or three precautions which are necessary to the production of a pure result of this kind. In the first place, the iron ought to be soft and not previously in a magnetic state. In the next, an effect of the following kind has to be guarded against. If the iron core be away from the dominant magnet at the beginning of an experiment, then, on working the machine, the galvanometer will be seen to move in one direction for a few moments, and afterwards, notwithstanding the continued action of the machine, will return and gradually take up its place at 0°. If the iron core be at its shortest distance from the dominant magnet at the beginning of the experiment, then the galvanometer needle will move in the contrary direction to that which it took before, but will again settle at 0°. These effects are due to the circumstance, that, when the iron is away from the dominant magnet, it is not in so strong a magnetic state, and when at the nearest to it is in a stronger state, than the *mean* or *average state*, which it acquires during the continuance of an experiment; and that in rising or falling to this average state, it produces two currents in contrary directions, which are made manifest in the experiments described. These existing only for the first moments, do, in their effects at the galvanometer, then appear, producing a vibration which gradually passes away.

2670. One other precaution I ought to specify. Unless the commutator changes accurately at the given points of the journey, a little effect is gathered up at each change, and may give a permanent deflection of the needle in one direction or the other. The tongues of my commutator, being at right angles to the direction of motion and somewhat flexible, dragged a little in the *to* and *from* parts of the journey: in doing this they approximated, though only in a small degree, to that which is the best condition of the commutator for gathering up (and not opposing) the currents; and a deflection to the right or left appeared (2677). Upon discovering the cause and stiffening the tongues so as to prevent their flexure, the effect disappeared, and the iron was perfectly inactive.

2671. Such therefore are the results with an iron core, and such would be the effects with a copper or bismuth core if they acted by a diamagnetic polarity. Let us now consider what the consequences would be if a copper or bismuth core were to act by currents, induced for the time, in its moving mass, and of the nature of those suspected (2642). If the copper cylinder moved with uniform velocity (2665), then currents would exist in it, parallel to its circumference, during the whole time of its motion; and these would be at their maximum force just before and just after the *to* or inner stop, for then the copper would be in the most intense parts of the magnetic field. The rising current of the copper core for the *in* portion of the journey would produce a current in one direction in the experimental helix, the stopping of the copper and consequent falling of its current would produce in the experimental helix a current contrary to the former; the first instant of motion *outwards* in the core would produce a maximum current in it contrary to its former current, and producing in the experimental helix its inductive result, being a current the same as the last there produced; and then, as the core retreated, its current would fall, and in so doing and by its final stop, would produce a fourth current in the experimental helix, in the same direction as the first.

2672. The four currents produced in the experimental helix alternate by twos, i.e., those produced by the falling of the first current in the core and the rising of the second and contrary current, are in one direction. They occur at the instant before and after the stop at the magnet, i.e., from the moment of maximum current (in the core) before, to the moment of maximum current after, the stop; and if that stop is momentary, they exist only for that moment, and should during that brief time be gathered up by the commutator. Those produced in the experimental helix during the falling of the second current in the core and the rising of a third current (identical with the first) in the return of the core to the magnet, are also the same in direction, and continue from the beginning of the retreat to the end of the advance (or from maximum to maximum) of the core currents, i.e., for almost the whole of the core journey; and these, by its change at the maximum moments, the commutator should take up and send on to the galvanometer.

2673. The motion however of the core is not uniform in velocity, and so, sudden in its change of direction, but, as before said (2665), is at a maximum as respects velocity in the middle of its approach to and retreat from the dominant magnet; and hence a very important advantage. For its stop may be said to commence immediately after the occurrence of the maximum velocity; and if the lines of magnetic force were equal in position and power there to what they are nearer to the magnet, the contrary currents in the experimental helix would commence at those points of the journey; but, as the core is entering into a more intense part of the field, the current in it still rises though the velocity diminishes, and the consequence is, that the maximum current in it neither occurs at the place of greatest velocity, nor of greatest force, but at a point between the two. This is true both as regards the approach and the recession of the core, the two maxima of the currents occurring at points equidistant from the place of rest near the dominant magnet.

2674. It is therefore at these two points that the commutator should change, if adjusted to produce the greatest effect at the galvanometer by the currents excited in the experimental helix, through the influence of, or in connexion with, currents of induction produced in the core; and experiment fully justifies this conclusion. If the length of the journey from the stop out to the stop in, which is 2 inches (2643, 2644), be divided into 100 parts, and the dominant magnet be supposed to be on the right-hand, then such an expression as the following, 50|50, may represent the place where the commutator changes, which in this illustration would be midway in the to and from motion, or at the places of greatest velocity.

2675. Upon trial of various adjustments of the commutator I have found that from 77|23 to 88|12, gave the best results with a copper core. On the whole, and after many experiments, I conclude that with the given strength of electro-magnet, distance of the experimental core when at the nearest from the magnet, length of the whole journey, and average velocity of the machine, 86|14 may represent the points where the induced currents in the core are at a maximum and where the commutator ought to change.

2676. From what has been said before (2667), it will be seen that both in theory and experiment these are the points in which the effect of any polarity, magnetic or diamagnetic, would be absolutely nothing. Hence the power of submitting by this machine metals and other bodies to experiment, and of eliminating the effects of magnetic polarity, of diamagnetic polarity, and of inductive action, the one from the others: for either by the commutator or by the direction of the polarity, they can be separated; and further, they can also be combined in various ways for the purpose of elucidating their joint and separate action.

2677. For let the arrows in the diagram represent the to and from journey, and the intersections of the lines, *a, b* or *c, d,* &c., the periods in the journey when the commutator changes

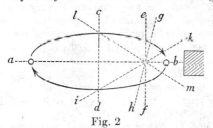

Fig. 2

(in which case *c, d* will correspond to 50|50, and *e, f* to 86|14), then *a, b* will represent the condition of the commutator for the maximum effect of iron or any other polar body. If the line *a b* be gradually revolved until parallel to *c, d,* it will in every position indicate points of commutator change, which will give the iron effect at the galvanometer by a deflection of the needle always in the same direction; it is only when the ends *a* and *b* have passed the

points *c* and *d,* either above or below, that the direction of the deflection will change for iron. But the line *a, b* indicates those points for the commutator with which no effect will be produced on the galvanometer by the induction of *currents* in the mass of the core. If the line be inclined in one direction, as *i, k,* then these currents will produce a deflection at the galvanometer on one side; if it be inclined in the other direction, as *l, m,* then the deflection will be on the other side. Therefore the effects of these induced currents may be either combined with, or opposed to, the effects of a polarity, whether it be magnetic or diamagnetic.

2678. All the metals before mentioned (2655), namely, gold, silver, copper, tin, lead, platina, antimony and bismuth, were submitted to the power of the electro-magnet under the best adjustment (2675) of the commutator. The effects were stronger than before, being now at a maximum, but in the same order; as regarded antimony and bismuth, they were very small, amounting to not more than half a degree, and may very probably have been due to a remainder of irregular action in some part of the apparatus. All the experiments with the divided cores (2658, &c.) were repeated with the same results as before. Phosphorus, sulphur and gutta percha did not, either in this or in the former state of the commutator, give any indication of effect at the galvanometer.

2679. As an illustration of the manner in which this position of the commutator caused a separation of the effects of copper and iron, I had prepared a copper cylinder core 2 inches in length having an iron wire in its axis, and this being employed in the apparatus gave the pure effect of the copper with its induced currents. Yet this core, as a whole, was highly magnetic to an ordinary test-needle; and when the two changes of the commutator were not equidistant from the one stop or the other (2670, 2677), the iron effect came out powerfully, overruling the former and producing very strong contrary deflections at the needle. The platinum core which I have used is an imperfect cylinder, 2 inches long and 0.62 of an inch thick: it points magnetically between the poles of a horseshoe electro-magnet (2381), making a vibration in less than a second, but with the above condition of the commutator (2675) gives 4° of deflection due to the induced currents, the magnetic effect being annulled or thrown out.

2680. Some of the combined effects produced by oblique position of the commutator points were worked out in confirmation of the former conclusions (2677). When the commutator was so adjusted as to combine any polar power which the bismuth, as a diamagnetic body, might possess, with any conducting power which would permit the formation of currents by induction in its mass (2676), still the effects were so minute and uncertain as to oblige me to say that, experimentally, it is without either polar or inductive action.

2681. There is another distinction which may usefully be established between the effects of a true sustainable polarity, either magnetic or diamagnetic, and those of the transient induced currents dependent upon *time*. If we consider the resistance in the circuit, which includes the experimental helix and the galvanometer coil, as nothing, then a magnetic pole of constant strength passed a certain distance into the helix would produce the same amount of current electricity in it, whether the pole were moved into its place by a quick or a slow motion. Or if the iron core be used (2668) the same result is produced, provided, in any alternating action, the core is left long enough at the extremities of its journey to acquire, either in its quick or slow alternation, the same state. This I found to be the fact when no commutator nor dominant magnet was used; a single insertion of a weak magnetic pole gave the same deflection, whether introduced quickly or slowly; and when the residual dominant magnet, an iron wire core, and the commutator in its position *a, b* (2677) were used, four journeys to and from produced the *same* effect at the galvanometer when the velocities were as 1:5 or even as 1:10.

2682. When a copper, silver, or gold core is employed in place of the iron, the effect is very different. There is no reason to doubt, that, as regards the core itself, the same amount of electricity is thrown into the form of induced circulating currents within it, by a journey to or from, whether that journey is performed quickly or slowly: the above experiment (2681) in fact confirms such a conclusion. But the effect which is produced upon the experimental helix is not proportionate to the whole amount of these currents, but to the maximum intensities to which they rise. When the core moves slowly, this intensity is small; when it moves rapidly, it is great, and necessarily so, for the same current of electricity has to travel in the two differing periods of time occupied by the journeys. Hence the quickly moving core should produce a far higher effect on the experimental helix than the slowly moving core; and this also I found to be the fact.

2683. The short copper core was adjusted to the apparatus, and the machine worked with its average velocity until forty journeys to and from had been completed; the galvanometer needle passed 39° west. Then the machine was worked with a greater rapidity, also for forty journeys, and the needle passed through 80° or more west; finally, being worked at a slow rate for the same number of journeys, the needle sent through only 21° west. The extreme velocities in this experiment were probably as 1:6; the time in the longest case was considerably less than that of one vibration of the needle (2651), so that I believe all the force in the slowest case was collected. The needle is very little influenced by the swing or momentum of its parts, because of the deadening effect of the copper plate beneath it, and, except to return to zero, moves very little after the motion of the apparatus ceases. A silver core produced the same results.

2684. These effects of induced currents have a relation to the phenomena of revulsion which I formerly described (2310, 2315, 2338), being the same in their exciting cause and principles of action, and so the two sets of phenomena confirm and illustrate each other. That the revulsive phenomena are produced by induced currents, has been shown before (2327, 2329, 2336, 2339); the only difference is, that with them the induced currents were produced by exalting the force of a magnet placed at a fixed distance from the affected metal; whilst in the present phenomena, the force of the magnet does not change, but its distance from the piece of metal does.

2685. So also the same circumstances which affect the phenomena here affect the revulsive phenomena. A plate of metal will, as a whole, be well-revulsed; but if it be divided across the course of the induced currents it is not then affected (2529). A ring helix of copper wire, if the extremities be unconnected, will not exhibit the phenomena, but if they be connected then it presents them (2660).

2686. On the whole, the revulsive phenomena are a far better test and indication of these currents than the present effects; especially if advantage be taken of the division of the mass into plates, so as to be analogous, or rather superior, in their action to the disc cylinder cores (2659, 2661). Platinum, palladium and lead in leaf or foil, if cut or folded into squares half an inch in the side, and then packed regularly together, will show the phenomena of revulsion very well; and that according to the direction of the leaves, and not of the external form. Gold, silver, tin and copper have the revulsive effects thus greatly exalted. Antimony, as I have already shown, exhibits the effect well (2514, 2519). Both it and bismuth can be made to give evidence of the induced currents produced in them when they are used in thin plates, either single or associated, although, to avoid the influence of the diamagnetic force, a little attention is required to the moments of making and breaking contact between the voltaic battery and the electro-magnet.

2687. Copper, when thus divided into plates, had its revulsive phenomena raised to a degree that I had not before observed. A piece of copper foil was annealed and tarnished by heat, and then folded up into a small square block, half an inch in the side and a quarter of an inch thick, containing seventy-two folds of the metal. This block was suspended by a silk film as before (2248), and whilst at an angle of 30° or thereabouts with the equatorial line (2252), the electro-magnet was excited; it immediately advanced or turned until the angle was about 45° or 50°, and then stood still. Upon the interruption of the electric current at the magnet the revulsion came on very strongly, and the block turned back again, passed the equatorial line, and proceeded on until it formed an angle of 50° or 60° on the other side; but instead of continuing to revolve in that direction as before (2315), it then returned on its course, again passed the equatorial line, and almost reached the axial position before it stood still. In fact, as a mass, it vibrated to and fro about the equatorial line.

2688. This however is a simple result of the principles of action formerly developed (2329, 2330). The revulsion is due to the production of induced currents in the suspended mass during the falling of the magnetism of the electro-magnet; and the effect of the action is to bring the axis of these induced currents parallel to the axis of force in the magnetic field. Consequently, if the time of the fall of magnetic force, and therefore of the currents dependent thereon, be greater than the time occupied by the revulsion of the copper block as far as the equatorial line, any further motion of it by momentum will be counteracted by a contrary force; and if this force be strong enough the block will return. The conducting power of the copper and its division into laminæ, tend to set up these currents very readily and with extra power; and the very power which they possess tends to make the time of a vibration so short,

that two or even three vibrations can occur before the force of the electro-magnet has ceased to fall any further. The effect of *time*, both in the rising and falling of power, has been referred to on many former occasions (2170, 2650), and is very beautifully seen here.

2689. Returning to the subject of the assumed polarity of bismuth, I may and ought to refer to an experiment made by Reich, and described by Weber,[1] which, if I understand the instruction aright, is as follows: a strong horseshoe magnet is laid upon a table in such a position that the line joining its two poles is perpendicular to the magnetic meridian and to be considered as prolonged on one side; in that line, and near the magnet, is to be placed a small powerful magnetic needle, suspended by cocoon silk, and on the other side of it, the pole of a bar magnet, in such a position and so near, as exactly to counteract the effect of the horseshoe magnet, and leave the needle to point exactly as if both magnets were away. Then a mass of bismuth being placed between the poles of the horseshoe magnet is said to react upon the small magnet needle, causing its deflection in a particular direction, and this is supposed to indicate the polarity of the bismuth under the circumstances, as it has no such action when the magnets are away. A piece of iron in place of the bismuth produces the contrary deflection of the needle.

2690. I have repeated this experiment most anxiously and carefully, but have never obtained the slightest trace of action with the bismuth. I have obtained action with the iron; but in those cases the action was far less than if the iron were applied outside between the horseshoe magnet and the needle, or to the needle alone, the magnets being entirely away. On using a garnet, or a weak magnetic substance of any kind, I cannot find that the arrangement is at all comparable for readiness of indication or delicacy, with the use of a common or an astatic needle, and therefore I do not understand how it could become a test of the polarity of bismuth when these fail to show it. Still I may have made some mistake; but neither by close reference to the description, nor to the principles of polar action, can I discover where.

2691. There is an experiment which Plücker described to me, and which at first seems to indicate strongly the polarity of bismuth. If a bar of bismuth (or phosphorus) be suspended

[1] Taylor's *Scientific Memoirs*, V, p. 480.

horizontally between the poles of the electro-magnet, it will go to the equatorial position with a certain force, passing, as I have said, from stronger to weaker places of action (2267). If a bar of iron of the same size be fixed in the equatorial position a little below the plain in which the diamagnetic bar is moving, the latter will proceed to the equatorial position with much greater force than before, and this is considered as due to the circumstance, that, on the side where the iron has N polarity, the dia-magnetic body has S polarity, and that on the other side the S polarity of the iron and the N polarity of the bismuth also coincide.

2692. It is however very evident that the lines of magnetic force have been altered suf-ficiently in their intensity of direction, by the presence of the iron, to account fully for the increased effect. For, consider the bar as just leaving the axial position and going to the equatorial position; at the moment of starting its extremities are in places of stronger mag-netic force than before, for it cannot be doubted for a moment that the iron bar determines more force from pole to pole of the electro-magnet than if it were away. On the other hand, when it has attained the equatorial pos-ition, the extremities are under a much weaker magnetic force than they were subject to in the *same places* before; for the iron bar deter-mines downwards upon itself much of that force, which, when it is not there, exists in the plane occupied by the bismuth. Hence, in pass-ing through 90°, the diamagnetic is urged by a much greater difference of intensity of force when the iron is present than when it is away; and hence, probably, the whole additional re-sult. The effect is like many others which I have referred to in magnecrystallic action (2487-2497), and does not, I think, add any-thing to the experimental proof of diamagnetic polarity.

2693. Finally, I am obliged to say that I can find no experimental evidence to support the hypothetical view of diamagnetic polarity (2640), either in my own experiments, or in the repetition of those of Weber, Reich, or others. I do not say that such a polarity does not exist; and I should think it possible that Weber, by far more delicate apparatus than mine, had obtained a trace of it, were it not that then also he would have certainly met with the far more powerful effects produced by copper, gold, silver, and the better conducting diamagnetics. If bismuth should be found to give any effect, it must be checked and distinguished by refer-ence to the position of the commutator, divi-sion of the mass by pulverization, influence of time, &c. It appears to me also, that, as the magnetic polarity conferred by iron or nickel in very small quantity, and in unfavourable states, is far more readily indicated by its ef-fect on an astatic needle, or by pointing be-tween the poles of a strong horseshoe magnet, than by any such arrangement as mine or Web-er's or Reich's, so diamagnetic polarity would be much more easily distinguished in the same way, and that no indication of that polarity has as yet reached to the force and value of those already given by Brugmann and myself.

2694. So, at present, the actions represented or typified by iron, by copper and by bismuth, remain distinct; and their relations are only in part made known to us. It cannot be doubted that a larger and simpler law of action than any we are yet acquainted with, will hereafter be discovered, which shall include all these ac-tions at once; and the beauty of Weber's sug-gestion in this respect was the chief induce-ment to me to endeavour to establish it.

2695. Though from the considerations above expressed (2693) I had little hopes of any use-ful results, yet I thought it right to submit cer-tain magnecrystallic cores to the action of the apparatus. One core was a large group of sym-metrically disposed crystals of bismuth (2457); another a very large crystal of red ferrop+rus-siate of potassa; a third a crystal of calcareous spar; and a fourth and fifth large crystals of protosulphate of iron. These were formed into cylinders of which the first and fourth had the magnecrystallic axes (2479) parallel to the axis of the cylinder, and the second, third and fifth, had the equatorial direction of force (2546, 2594, 2595) parallel to the axis of the cylinder. None of them gave any effect at the galva-nometer, except the fourth and fifth, and these were alike in their results, and were dependent for them on their ordinary magnetic property.

2696. Some of the expressions I have used may seem to imply that, when employing the copper and other cores, I imagine that currents are first induced in them by the dominant mag-net, and that these induce the currents which are observed in the experimental helix. Wheth-er the cores act directly on the experimental helix or indirectly through their influence on the dominant magnet, is a very interesting question, and I have found it difficult to select expressions, though I wished to do so, which should not in some degree prejudge that ques-tion. It seems to me probable, that the cores act indirectly on the helix, and that their immediate action is altogether directed towards the dominant magnet, which, whether they consist of magnetic or diamagnetic metals, raises them into power either permanently or transiently, and has their power for that time directed towards it. Before the core moves to approach the magnet, the magnet and experimental helix are in close relation; and the latter is situated in the intense field of magnetic force which belongs to the pole of the former. If the core be iron, as it approaches the magnet it causes a strong convergence and concentration of the lines of magnetic force upon itself; and these, as they so converge, passing through the helix and across its convolutions, are competent to produce the currents in it which are obtained (2653, 2668). As the iron retreats these lines of force diverge, and again crossing the line of the wire in the helix in a contrary direction to their former course, produce a contrary current. It does not seem necessary, in viewing the action of the iron core, to suppose any direct action of it on the helix, or any other action than this which it exerts upon the lines of force of the magnet. In such a case its action upon the helix would be indirect.

2697. Then, by all parity of reasoning, when a copper core enters the helix its action upon it should be indirect also. For the currents which are produced in it are caused by the direct influence of the magnet, and must react equivalently upon it. This they do, and because of their direction and known action, they will cause the lines of force of the magnet to diverge. As the core diminishes in its velocity of motion, or comes to rest, the currents in it will cease, and then the lines of force will converge; and this divergence and convergence, or passage in two directions across the wire of the experimental helix, is sufficient to produce the two currents which are obtained in the advance of the core towards the dominant magnet (2671, 2673). A corresponding effect in the contrary direction is produced by the retreat of the core.

2698. On the idea that the actions of the core were not of this kind, but more directly upon the helix, I interposed substances between the core and the helix during the times of the experiment. A thick copper cylinder 2.2 inches long, 0.7 of an inch external diameter, and 0.1 of an inch internal diameter, and consequently 0.3 of an inch thick in the sides, was placed in the experimental helix, and an iron wire core (2668) used in the apparatus. Still, whatever the form of the experiment, the kind and amount of effect produced were the same as if the copper were away, and either glass or air in its place. When the dominant magnet was removed and the wire core made a magnet, the same results were produced.

2699. Another copper lining, being a cylinder 2.5 inches long, 1 inch in external diameter, and one-eighth of an inch in thickness, was placed in the experimental helix, and cores of silver and copper five-eighths of an inch in thickness, employed as before, with the best condition of the commutator (2675): the effects, with and without the copper, or with and without the glass, were absolutely the same (2698).

2700. There can be no doubt that the copper linings, when in place, were full of currents at the time of action, and that when away no such currents would exist in the air or glass replacing them. There is also full reason to admit, that the divergence and convergence of the magnetic lines of force supposed above (2697) would satisfactorily account for such currents in them, supposing the indirect action of the cores were assumed. If that supposition be rejected, then it seems to me that the whole of the bodies present, the magnet, the helix, the core, the copper lining, or the air or glass which replaces it, must all be in a state of tension, each part acting on every other part, being in what I have occasionally elsewhere imagined as the electro-tonic state (1729).

2701. The advance of the copper makes the lines of magnetic force diverge, or, so to say, drives them before it (2697). No doubt there is reaction upon the advancing copper, and the production of currents in it in such a direction as makes them competent, if continued, to continue the divergence. But it does not seem logical to say that the currents which the lines of force cause in the copper, are the cause of the divergence of the lines of force. It seems to me, rather, that the lines of force are, so to say, diverged, or bent outward by the advancing copper (or by a connected wire moving across lines of force in any other form of the experiments). and that the reaction of the lines of force upon the forces in the particles of the copper cause them to be resolved into a current, by which the resistance is discharged and removed, and the line of force returns to its place. I attach no other meaning to the words *line of force* than that which I have given on a former occasion (2149).

Royal Institution, Dec. 14, 1849

TWENTY-FOURTH SERIES[1]

§ 30. *On the Possible Relation of Gravity to Electricity*

RECEIVED AUGUST 1, READ NOVEMBER 28, 1850

2702. THE long and constant persuasion that all the forces of nature are mutually dependent, having one common origin, or rather being different manifestations of one fundamental power (2146), has made me often think upon the possibility of establishing, by experiment, a connexion between gravity and electricity, and so introducing the former into the group, the chain of which, including also magnetism, chemical force and heat, binds so many and such varied exhibitions of force together by common relations. Though the researches I have made with this object in view have produced only negative results, yet I think a short statement of the matter, as it has presented itself to my mind, and of the result of the experiments, which offering at first much to encourage, were only reduced to their true value by most careful searchings after sources of error, may be useful, both as a general statement of the problem, and as awakening the minds of others to its consideration.

2703. In searching for some principle on which an experimental inquiry after the identification or relation of the two forces could be founded, it seemed that if such a relation existed, there must be something in gravity which would correspond to the dual or antithetical nature of the forms of force in electricity and magnetism. To my mind it appeared possible that the ceding to the force or the approach of gravitating bodies on the one hand, and the effectual reversion of the force or separation of the bodies on the other, might present the points of correspondence; quiescence (as to motion) being the neutral condition. The final unchangeability of gravity did not seem affected by such an assumption; for the acting bodies when at rest would ever have the same relation to each other, and it would only be at the times of motion to and fro that any results related to electricity could be expected. Such results, if possible, could only be exceedingly small; but, *if possible*, i.e., if true, no terms could exaggerate the value of the relation they would establish.

2704. The thought on which the experiments were founded was that as two bodies moved towards each other by the force of gravity, currents of electricity might be developed either in them or in the surrounding matter in one direction; and that as they were by extra force moved from each other against the power of gravitation, the opposite currents might be produced. Also, that these currents would have relation to the line of approach and recession, and not to space generally, so that two bodies approaching would have currents in the opposite direction as to space generally, but the same as to the direction of their motion along the line joining them. It will be unnecessary to go further into the suppositions which arose concerning these points, or regarding the effect of forced motions either coinciding with, or across the direction of the earth's gravitation, and many other matters, than to say that as the effect looked for was exceedingly small so no hope was entertained of any result except by means of the gravitation of the earth. The earth was therefore made to be the one body, and the indicating mass of matter to be experimented with the other.

2705. First of all, a body, which was to be allowed to fall, was surrounded by a helix, and then its effect in falling sought for. Now a body may either fall with a helix or through a helix. Covered copper wire, to the amount of 350 feet in length, was made into a hollow cylindrical helix, about 4 inches long, its internal diameter being 1 inch and its external diameter 2 inches. It was attached to a line running upon an easy pulley, so that it could be raised 36 feet, and then allowed to fall with an accelerated velocity on to a very soft cushion, its axis remaining vertical the whole time. Long covered wires were made fast to its two extremities, and these being twisted round each other, were attached to a very delicate galvanometer, placed about 50 feet aside from the line of fall, and on a level midway with its

[1] *Philosophical Transactions*, 1851, p. 1. The Bakerian lecture.

course. The accuracy of the connexion and the direction of the set of the needle, were then both ascertained by the introduction of a feeble thermo-electric combination into the current. Such a helix, either in rising or falling, can produce no deviation at the galvanometer by any current due to the magnetism of the earth; for as it remains parallel to itself during the fall, so the lines of equal magnetic force, which being parallel to the dip, are intersected by the wire convolutions of the descending helix, are cut with an equal velocity on both sides of the helix, and consequently no effect of magneto-electric induction is produced. Neither in rising nor in falling did this helix present any trace of action at the galvanometer; whether the connection with the galvanometer was continued the whole time, or whether it was cut off just before the diminution or cessation of motion either way, or whether the rising and the falling were made to occur isochronously with the times of vibration of the galvanometer needle. So, though no effect of gravity appeared in the helix itself, still no source of error appeared to arise in this mode of using it.

2706. A solid cylinder of copper, three-fourths of an inch in diameter and 7 inches in length, was now introduced into the helix and carefully fastened in it, being bound round with a cloth so as not to move, and this compound arrangement was allowed to fall as before (2705). It gave very minute but remarkably regular indications of a current at the galvanometer; and the probability of these being related to gravity appeared the greater, when it was found that on raising the helix or core, similar indications of contrary currents appeared. It was some time before I was able to refer these currents to their true cause, but at last I traced them to the action of a part of the connecting wires proceeding from the helix to the galvanometer. The two wires had been regularly twisted together, but the effect of many falls had opened a part near the middle distance into a sort of loop, so that the wires, instead of being tightly twisted together like the strands of a rope, were separate for 3 feet, as if the strands were open. In falling, this loop opened out more or less, but always in the same manner; and the consequence was that the part of it representing the transverse opening, which was farthest from the galvanometer, travelled over a larger space than the corresponding part nearest the galvanometer. Now had they travelled through equal spaces, the effect of the magnetic lines of force of the earth upon them would have been

equal, and no effect at the galvanometer would have been produced; as it was, currents in opposite directions, but of unequal amounts of force, tended to be produced, and a current equal to the difference actually appeared. Such a case is described in my earliest researches on terrestrial magno-electro induction (171). It is evident that the current should appear in the reverse direction, as the helix and wires are raised in the air, and thus arose the reverse effect described above. Therefore no positive or favourable evidence was supplied in favour of the original assumption by this use of a copper core in the helix.

2707. The copper was selected as a heavy body and an excellent conductor of electricity. On its dismissal, a bismuth cylinder of equal size was employed to replace it as a substance eminently diamagnetic, and a bad conductor amongst metals. Uncertain evidence arose; but by close attention, first to one point and then to another, all the indications disappeared, and then the rising or falling of the bismuth produced no effect on the galvanometer.

2708. An *iron* cylinder was also employed as a magnetic metal, but when made perfectly secure, so as to prevent any motion relative to the helix, it was equally indifferent with the copper and bismuth (2706, 2707).

2709. Cylinders of glass and shellac were employed as non-conducting substances, but without effect.

2710. In other experiments the helix was *fixed*, and the different substances in the form of cylinders, three-fourths of an inch in diameter and 24 inches long, were dropped through it, or else raised through it with an accelerated velocity; but in neither case was any effect produced. Rods of copper, bismuth, glass, shellac and sulphur were employed. Occasionally these rods were made to rotate rapidly before and during their fall; and many other conditions were devised and carried into effect, but always with negative results, when sources of error were avoided or accounted for.

2711. On further consideration of the original assumption, namely a relation between the forces, and of the effects that might be looked for consequent upon a condition of tension in and around the particles of the body, which, as we know, are at the same moment the residence of both gravitating and electric forces, and are subject to the gravitation of the earth, it seemed probable that the stopping of the up and down motion (2703, 2704) in the line of gravity would produce contrary effects to the coming on of the motion, and that, whether the stopping was sudden or gradual; also that a motion downward quicker than that which gravity could communicate, would give more effect than the gravity result by itself, and that a corresponding increase in the velocity upwards would be proportionally effectual. In such case a machine which could give a rapid alternating up and down motion, might be very useful in producing many minute units of inductive action in a small space and moderate time; for then, by proper commutators, the accelerated and retarded parts of each half-vibration could be separated and recombined into one consistent

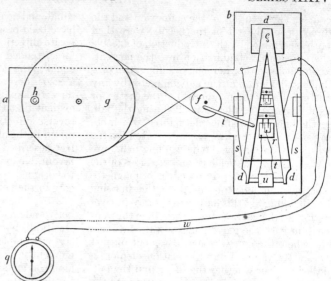

current, and this current could be sent through the galvanometer during the time its needle was swinging in one direction, and afterwards reversed for the time of a swing in the other direction; and so on alternately until the effect had become sensible, if any were produced by the assumed cause.

2712. The machine which I had made for this purpose is that described in the last series of these *Researches* (2643), the electro-magnet, the experimental core and the rod which carried them being removed: *a, b, c* frame-board; *d,d,d* wooden lever, of which *e* is the axis; *f* the crank-wheel, and *g* the great wheel with its handle *h; i* the bar connecting the crank-wheel and lever; *q* the galvanometer; *r* the commutator; *w*, connecting wires; *s, s* springs of brass or copper; *t* a copper rod connecting the two arms of the lever to give strength; *u* the hollow helix fixed, or moveable at pleasure. The plan is to a scale of one-fifteenth. Being on a moveable frame, it could be placed in any position. The cylinder of metal or other substance to be submitted to its action, was $5\frac{1}{2}$ inches long and three-fourths of an inch in diameter, and was firmly held between the ends *d, d* of the lever arms. The extent of the alternating motion was 3 inches. A hollow cylindrical helix *u*, $2\frac{1}{2}$ inches in length, and of such internal diameter that the cylinders could complete their rapid journeys to and fro within it without any danger of striking against its sides, was constructed, containing 516 feet of covered copper wire; this cylinder could be either fixed immoveably or attached firmly to the cylinder under ex-

periment so as to move with it. The wires from this helix passed to the commutators and from them to the galvanometer. Part of the momentum of this machine was taken up by springs *s, s* (2648), and converted into the contrary motion; but so much remained undisposed of thus, that great care was required in fixing and strutting to render the action of the whole very steady, or else derangement quickly occurred at the cylinder and helix, and electro-currents were frequently produced.

2713. The employment of cylinders of iron, copper and other substances in this machine was competent to produce electro-currents in various ways. Thus, iron might produce magneto-electric currents consequent upon its polar condition under the influence of the earth; these it would be easy to detect and separate by the use of adjusted magnets, which should neutralize or reverse the lines of magnetic force passing through the iron. Currents like those induced in copper cylinders and good conductors (2663, 2684), might be produced by the earth's action; but as the lines of gravitating force and of terrestrial magnetic force are inclined to each other, these might be separated by position; and it appeared that there was no source of error that might not by care be eliminated. I will not occupy time by describing how this long lesson of care was learned, but pass at once to the chief results.

2714. The copper cylinder (2712) was placed in the machine, and the helix fixed immoveably around it, the whole being in such a position that the cylinder should be vertical, and move up and down parallel to the line of gravitating force within the helix. However rapidly the machine was worked, or whatever the position of the commutator, there was no result at the galvanometer. Cylinders of bismuth, glass, sulphur, gutta percha, &c., were also employed, but with the same negative conclusion.

2715. Then the helix was taken from its fixed support and fastened on to the copper cylinder so as to move with it, and now very regular and comparatively large effects were produced. After a while, however, these were traced to causes other than gravity, and of the following kind. The helix was fixed at one end of a lever, at a point 22 inches from its axis, and being 2 inches in diameter its wires on one side were only 21 inches, and on the other side 23 inches from this axis. Hence, in vibrating these parts travelled with velocities and through spaces which are as 21:23. When therefore their paths were *across* the lines of magnetic force of the earth, electro-currents tended to form in these different parts proportionate in amount or strength to these numbers; and the differences of these currents being continually gathered up by the commutators, were made sensible at the galvanometer. This was rendered manifest by placing the machine so that though the plane of vibration was still vertical the place of the helix was just under the centre of motion, and the central line of the helix therefore, instead of being vertical, was horizontal. Now the convolutions of the helix cut the lines of magnetic force in the most favourable manner; and the consequence was that the commutators were not required, for a single motion of the helix in one direction was sufficient to show at the galvanometer the magneto-electric currents induced. If, on the contrary, the plane of motion was made horizontal, then no current was produced by any amount of motion; for though the helix was as horizontal as, and not sensibly more so than before, yet the parts of the convolutions which intersected the magnetic lines of force (being the upper and the lower parts) now moved with exactly equal velocity, and no differential result was produced.

2716. The former small result (2715) was therefore probably dependent upon an effect of this kind; and this was confirmed by placing the machine in such a position that the axis of the moving copper cylinder and helix should in its medium position be parallel to the line of the dip, and then no effect was produced. Other bodies in the same position were equally unable to produce any effect.

2717. Here end my trials for the present. The results are negative. They do not shake my strong feeling of the existence of a relation between gravity and electricity, though they give no proof that such a relation exists.

Royal Institution, July 19, 1850

TWENTY-FIFTH SERIES[1]

§ 31. *On the Magnetic and Diamagnetic Condition of Bodies* ¶ i. *Non-expansion of Gaseous Bodies by Magnetic Force* ¶ ii. *Differential Magnetic Action* ¶ iii. *Magnetic Characters of Oxygen, Nitrogen and Space*

RECEIVED AUGUST 15, READ NOVEMBER 28, 1850

¶ i. *Non-expansion of Gaseous Bodies by Magnetic Force*

2718. THERE can be no doubt that the magnetic force, the diamagnetic force, and the magneoptic or magnecrystallic force, will, when thoroughly understood, be found to unite or exist under one form of power, and be essentially the same. Hence the great interest which exists in the development of any one of these modes of action; for differing so greatly as they do in very peculiar points, it is hardly possible that any one of them should be advanced in its illustration or comprehension, without a corresponding advance in the knowledge of the others. Stimulated by such a feeling, I have been engaged with Plücker, Weber, Reich and others, in endeavouring to make out, with some degree of precision, the mode of action of diamagnetic as well as magnecrystallic bodies; and the recent investigation (2640, &c.) and endeavour to confirm the idea of polarity in

[1] *Philosophical Transactions,* 1851, p. 7.

bismuth and diamagnetic bodies, the reverse of that in a magnet or in iron bodies, was one of the results of that conviction and desire.

2719. Having failed however to establish the existence of such an antipolarity, and having shown, as I think, that the phenomena which were supposed to be due to it are in fact dependent upon other conditions and causes, I was induced, in the search after something precise as to the nature of diamagnetic bodies, to examine another idea which had arisen in consequence of the development of magnetic and diamagnetic phenomena amongst gaseous substances: this thought, with some of the results which have grown out of it during its experimental examination, I purpose making the subject of the present paper.

2720. Bancalari first showed that flame was diamagnetic.[1] The effect, as I proved, was due chiefly to the heated state of gaseous portions of the flame;[2] but besides that, it appeared that at common temperatures diamagnetic phenomena could be exhibited by gases; and also that in their production the gases differed very much one from another;[3] so that, taking common air, for instance, as a standard, nitrogen, and many other gases, were strongly diamagnetic in relation to it, whilst oxygen took on the appearance of a magnetic body; for *they* were repelled from, while it was attracted to, the place of maximum force in the magnetic field.

2721. Recalling the general law given respecting the action of magnetic and diamagnetic bodies (2267, 2418), namely, that the former tended to go from weaker to stronger places, and the latter from stronger to weaker places of magnetic power, and applying it to such bodies as the gases, which are at the same time both highly elastic and easily changed in bulk by the superaddition of very small degrees of force, it would seem to follow, that if the particles of a diamagnetic gas tended to go from strong to weak places of action, in consequence of the direct and immediate effect of the magnetic power on them, then such a gas should tend to become enlarged or expanded in the magnetic field. For, the amount of power by which the particles would tend to recede from the axis of the magnetic field, would be added to the expansive force by which they before resisted the pressure of the atmosphere; that pressure would therefore be in part sustained by the new force, and expansion would of ne-

cessity be the result. On the other hand, if a gas were magnetic (as for instance oxygen), then the force cast upon the particles, by such a direct and immediate action of the magnetic power upon them, would urge them *towards* the axis of the magnetic field, and so coinciding with, and being superadded to the pressure of the atmosphere, would tend to cause contraction and diminution of bulk.

2722. If such supposititious cases were to prove true, we should then be able to arrive at the knowledge of the real zero-point (2416, 2432, 2440),[4] not amongst gases only, but amongst all bodies, and should be able to tell whether such a gas as oxygen were a magnetic or a diamagnetic body, and also able to range individual gases and other substances in their proper places. And though I had originally endeavoured to ascertain whether there was any change in the bulk of air in the magnetic field, and found none, still Plücker's statement that he had obtained such an effect,[5] and the great enlargement of knowledge respecting the gases which since then we have acquired relating to their diamagnetic relations, and especially of the great difference which exists between them, encouraged me to proceed.

2723. I first endeavoured to determine whether there was any affection of the layer of air (or other gas) immediately in contact with the magnetic pole, which, either by the consequent expansion or contraction of that layer, could render it able to affect the course of a ray of light and thus make manifest the changes occurring within. A metal screen, with a pin-hole in it, was set up before the flame of a bright lamp in a dark room, and thus an artificial star or small definite luminous object was formed. Forty-six feet from it was placed the great horseshoe magnet (2247), ready to be excited by twenty pairs of Grove's plates; the poles were in a line, so that the ray from the lamp passed for 4 inches close to the surface of the first pole, then through 6 inches of air, and then, for 4 inches, close to the surface of the second pole. A very fine refracting telescope, belonging to Sir James South, having an aperture of 3 inches and 46 inches focal length, received the ray. The telescope was furnished with a perfect micrometer, so that the smallest change in the place of the luminous image could be observed on the threads. The axis of the telescope was just above the level of the magnetic poles.

---

[1] *Philosophical Magazine*, 1847, Vol. XXXI, pp. 401, 421.
[2] *Ibid.*, pp. 404, 406.
[3] *Ibid.*, p. 409.
[4] *Ibid.*, p. 420.
[5] *Annales de Chimie*, 1850, Vol. XXIX, p. 134.

Not the smallest change in either the character or place of the luminous image could be observed, either on the making or the breaking of the contact between the voltaic battery and the magnetic wire.

2724. As the chief part of the light which came to the telescope consisted of rays which passed at some distance above the magnetic poles, these were cut off by a screen, which rising only one-eighth of an inch above the level of the poles, allowed no ray to pass that was not within that distance. The intensity of the light was of course diminished, and the image was distorted by inflection; still its place was well marked by the micrometer. Not the slightest change in that or any other character occurred in the supervention or the withdrawal of the magnetic force.

2725. The terminals of the magnetic poles were then varied, so that the ray sometimes passed parallel and close to a long right-angled edge, or parallel to and between two right-angled edges, a little above or below them, or over the line joining two hemispherical poles, placed close together (and also in many other ways), but in no case did the magnetic action produce any effect upon the course of the ray.

2726. In another form of the experiment the telescope was dismissed, and a simple card, with a pin-hole $\frac{1}{60}$th or $\frac{1}{100}$th of an inch in diameter, employed in its place. The image of the star of light could be seen through the pin-hole in the dark room, and yet every ray tending to its formation passed within $\frac{1}{60}$th of an inch of the surface of the magnetic pole; still no effect due to the magnetic force could be observed.

2727. By another arrangement of the polar terminations, analogous to one I had formerly employed when experimenting on the diamagnetic relations of the gases,[1] I was able to surround them with other gaseous substances than air, and subject the ray for 2 inches of its course to these gases whilst under the influence of the magnet. Though the glass of the enclosing vessel disturbed the image of the object, i.e. the point of light, yet it was easy to perceive that no additional effect occurred when the magnetism was superinduced.

2728. Oxygen, nitrogen, hydrogen and coal-gas were thus employed; but whether any one of these, or whether air itself was submitted to examination, when in contact with the active pole of a very powerful magnet, it did not appear to be either expanded or condensed to

[1] *Philosophical Magazine*, 1847, Vol. XXXI, pp. 414, 415.

such a degree as to cause any sensible change in its refractive force.

2729. In order to compare the expected result with the real result due to change of volume, I took a bar of iron 7 inches long, and placed it so that the ray from the luminous object in passing to the eye should proceed by the side of the bar at not more than $\frac{1}{60}$th of an inch from it, and then raised the temperature of the bar gradually, until by expanding the air in contact with it, the course of the ray of light was sensibly affected; to do this it required to be exalted many degrees. When the air of the place was at 60° and the iron raised to 100° Fahr., the effect was not distinct. Hence it seemed, that observation of the expected change of volume of the air would be rendered far more sensible by some arrangement, measuring that change directly, than by such means as those referred to above, dependent on refractive force; for it is certain that the change of volume, in a very small quantity of air, raised from 60° to 100°, would be very evident by the former method. On the other hand, it was just possible that if the air or gas was affected by the magnet, it might only be in that film immediately contiguous to the pole; and also that great differences in the degree of change might exist along the *edge* of a solid angle, and along the *sides* of the planes forming that angle. Hence the assumed necessity for examining those parts by a ray of light; and every precaution was taken, by inclining the course of the ray a little more or less to the sides or edges of the poles, and by making the sides or edges very slightly convex, to include every variation of the experiment, that might help to make any magnetic or diamagnetic effect, whether special or local, or general, manifest; but without effect.

2730. I proceeded, as these attempts had failed, to endeavour to determine and compare the *volume* of air subjected to the magnetic force, before and after its subjection; and there seemed to be the greater hope of obtaining some results in this way, provided any such change was a consequence of the action of magnetic power, because air and gases, at a considerable distance from the surface of the magnet, are known to be strongly affected diamagnetically, and because Plücker had already said he had obtained such change of volume (2722).

2731. The first instrument constructed for this purpose was of the following kind. Two blocks of soft iron, each 1 inch thick and 3 inches square, having filed and flattened surfaces, were prepared; and also a sheet of copper, 1/60th of an inch in thickness and 3 inches square, having its middle part cut away to within 0.3 of an inch of the edge all round. This plate or frame was then placed between the iron blocks, and the whole held together very tightly by copper screws, so as to make an air-chamber 1/60th of an inch wide and 2.4 inches square, having the faces of the blocks, which were to become the magnetic poles, for its sides. Three apertures and corresponding passages gave access to the interior of this chamber; small stop-cocks were attached to each. By two of these, any gas, after it had been properly dried, could be sent into the chamber, or swept out of it, by any other entering gas; and to the third was attached a gauge (2732) for the purpose of indicating and measuring any change of volume which might occur. The edges of the central copper plate and the heads of the countersunk screws, were touched with white hard varnish, and the chamber thus rendered perfectly tight, under every condition to which it had to be subjected (*Fig. 1*).

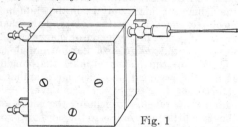

Fig. 1

2732. The gauges were formed of small capillary tubes from 1.5 to 3 inches in length, the diameter in the middle of their length being less than one-half of that at either termination. These were fixed at one end into a small socket, which screwed on to the third, or gauge-cock

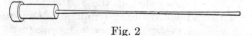

Fig. 2

mentioned above (2731). A minute portion of spirit, coloured by cochineal, being put into the external end of this gauge, from a slip of wood or glass, immediately advanced to the middle or narrowest part, forming, as it always should do, a single portion of fluid. By shutting the cock, this little cylinder could be easily retained in its place undisturbed during the filling of the air-chamber with gas, and the adjustment of its pressure to equality with that of the atmosphere. On shutting the other cocks

and opening the gauge-cock, the gauge was then ready to show any change of volume which the supervention of the magnetic force might cause; but to give it the highest degree of sensibility, it was necessary previously to make the liquid cylinder travel right and left of its place of rest, that the tube might be moistened on each side of the indicating fluid; an effect easily obtained by inclining the chamber to and fro, the gravity of the fluid making it pass one way or the other. But this and many other necessary precautions as to position, temperature, &c., can only be learned from experience.

2733. When this box was in its place, it stood between the poles of the great electro-magnet, with the plane of the gas-chamber in the equatorial position; then square blocks of soft iron, resting on the magnet poles, were made to abut and bear against the sides of the box, so that in fact the inner faces of the air-chamber were the virtual magnetic poles, and being 3 inches square were only 1/60th of an inch apart. Hence, whatever air or gas was within the chamber, would be subjected to a very powerful magnetic action, and could have very small changes in its bulk measured; but it is perhaps necessary to observe that it would be contained in a field having everywhere lines of equal magnetic power (2463, 2465).

2734. *Air* was introduced into the box, and when all was properly arranged, the place of the indicating fluid was observed by a microscope. Then the magnet was rendered powerfully active, and there appeared a very slight motion of the fluid, as if the air were a little expanded; on taking off the magnetic force the fluid returned to its first place. The same effect recurred again and again. The amount of this change was very small, and there was reason to refer it to the pressure exercised by the magnet, when in action, upon the sides of the iron box; for afterwards, when the box was placed in a vice and squeezed, the same motion in the fluid occurred; and further, when the square blocks of soft iron (2733) were kept apart by an under block of wood, so as not absolutely to touch and press the box, the effect was reduced to almost nothing.

2735. Oxygen, nitrogen, carbonic acid and nitrous oxide gases, were then introduced successively into the iron box, and with exactly the same result as with air. No difference appeared between oxygen and the other gases, greatly as they differ in magnetic and diamagnetic force and relations. Hydrogen and coal-gas were also subjected to experiment; but when these gases were in the box there was a gradual recession of the indicating fluid, due, as I found, to the absorption of the gases, probably either by the varnish or cement or cork used at the gauge, or at the joints of the box. The delicacy of the gauge was thus made manifest; but when the effect was taken into account, it was found that these gases were equally unaffected in bulk as the other gases by the magnetic influence.

2736. The diameter of the gauge, at the place where the fluid was placed, was rather less than $\frac{1}{100}$th of an inch. An amount of motion equal to $\frac{1}{100}$th of an inch was easily discerned. Comparing these numbers with the capacity of the gas-chamber, it would appear that if the gas in the latter had expanded or contracted to the extent of $\frac{1}{100,000}$th part, the result would have been visible; or any *difference* approaching to this amount, between oxygen and nitrogen or the other gases, would have become sensible, *but no such effects or differences appeared.*

2737. As the establishment of either the *occurrence* or the *absence* of change of volume in gases, when under the magnetic influence, appeared to me to be of great and almost equal importance, I was led to consider whether, in the experiment just described, the circumstance of the gases having been subjected to the magnetic power in a field of equal force (2733) might not have interfered with the production of the effect sought for; for such a field is that where the diamagnetic phenomena, of solid and liquid bodies, occur in the most unfavourable manner, and where indeed they almost entirely disappear. I therefore constructed another apparatus so that this condition was removed, and in which, if the particles of the diamagnetic gas, by any unknown disposition of the powers in action, tended only to pass from strong to weaker places of force, and being thus incapable of enlargement in the axial direction, would only show that effect equatorially, the opportunity for their doing so should be present.

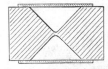

Fig. 3

2738. A cylinder of soft iron had the central parts removed in a lathe, until it had assumed the form of an hour-glass, or that represented in *Fig. 3*, which is to a scale of one-third. When placed between the poles of the magnet instead of the former box, it was expected that the continuation of the iron throughout would prevent any diminution of its length, from the pressure of the poles (2734), and that the diamagnetic phenomena would be abundantly produced in the parts from whence the iron had been removed. The latter was found to be the fact, for flame, smoke, bismuth and other diamagnetic matter, when placed there, passed equatorially very freely.

2739. A copper tube, 2.5 inches long, made of metal 0.1 of an inch thick, was fitted to the iron, so that when in its place it should occupy the position represented (*Fig. 3*), and could easily be made perfectly gas-tight by a little soft cement. In this way it formed an annular air-chamber round the iron, which, when measured, was found to have a capacity of rather more than 2 cubic inches, and included the most intense part of the magnetic field. Three stopcocks were fitted into this copper jacket, by two of which gas was passed into and out of the chamber, and the third was appropriated to the pressure-gauge as before. Whilst naked, this apparatus could not be used, because of its ever-varying temperature, and the consequent disturbance and ejectment of the fluid in the gauge; but when clothed in three thicknesses of flannel its temperature was perfectly steady; and by the further use of wooden keys to turn the cocks the apparatus became unexceptionable.

2740. Before proceeding to employ this apparatus with different gases, and in order to obtain some idea of what might be expected by comparing one gas with another, I made a preliminary experiment, dependent on the relative specific gravities of air and hydrogen, of the following nature. It is easy to diffuse a trace of ammonia through the air of a jar, by putting a little paper wetted with a strong solution into it;[1] and it is equally easy to send a jet of hydrogen, containing the smallest portion of muriatic acid gas, by a horizontal tube into the ammoniated air. When this is done, the course of the light hydrogen in the heavy air is rendered very distinctly visible; and it is seen, on leaving the horizontal tube, to turn at once upwards and to ascend rapidly, becoming wiredrawn in its course, in consequence of its small specific gravity compared to air.

2741. Two hemispherical iron pole terminations, associated with the great magnet, were then placed in contact with each other, so that they might be surrounded either by air or oxygen,[2] and the jet of hydrogen, delivering at the

[1] *Philosophical Magazine*, 1847, Vol. XXXI, p. 415.
[2] *Philosophical Magazine*, 1847, Vol. XXXI, pp. 413, 414.

rate of 6 cubic inches per minute, was placed exactly beneath the axial line, in the centre of the magnetic field. When there was no magnetic force employed the hydrogen rose vertically, breaking against the points where the hemispherical poles touched; but when the magnetic power was on, the stream of hydrogen divided into two parts, moving right and left, and ascended in two streams at a distance from the point of contact. Now this division took place at a certain distance *below* the axial line; and at that point, notwithstanding the ascensive power of hydrogen in air or oxygen, it was constrained to go horizontally by the apparently repulsive power of the magnetic force, and did not in its further course approach nearer to the axial line, but formed a curve concentric with it, or nearly so, so that the compound streams of gas assumed exactly the shape of a tuning-fork.

2742. When air occupied the magnetic field, the division of the stream of hydrogen was 0.3 or 0.32 of an inch below the axial line. When oxygen was about the poles, then the division of the hydrogen took place as far off as 0.55 of an inch below the axial line. Hence at these distances the power which tended to make the hydrogen pass from the axial line, equatorially in the direction of the radius, was equal to the difference of the specific gravity of hydrogen compared with that of air and oxygen respectively. At lesser distances the power would be much greater; and indeed, if in any experiment the hydrogen was delivered nearer to the axial line, it was blown downwards and away with much force. Calculating with these data, and still assuming that the diamagnetic gases receded from the axial line, in consequence of the direct action of the magnet and that only, causing them to pass from stronger to weaker places of action, I found, as I thought, reason to believe that the more diamagnetic gases, occupying the space within the copper box (2739), might probably be expanded at least $\frac{1}{60,000}$th part of their volume by the magnetic force. Now the gauges that I employed were sensible when the fluid in them moved the $\frac{1}{100}$th of an inch (2736), yet that space is only the $\frac{1}{2,500,000}$th part of the capacity of the chamber, and therefore such an expansion as that above would have made it move through 0.4 of an inch; a quantity abundantly sufficient to render the result sensible if the fundamental assumption were correct.

2743. *Air* was first submitted to the power of the great horseshoe magnet, urged by twenty pairs of Grove's plates in this apparatus (2739). The fluid moved very slightly outwards, as if a little expansion occurred on putting on the magnetic force, and returned when the force was taken off. This small effect was found afterwards to be due to compression, occasioned by the tendency of the magnetic poles to approximate (2734).

2744. *Oxygen* presented exactly the same appearances as common air and to the same amount, so that no effect, due to magnetic or diamagnetic action, was here evident, but only that of the compression observed in the case of air (2743).

2745. *Nitrogen* gave exactly the same results as oxygen and air. Now nitrogen is probably more diamagnetic than hydrogen, and should therefore have given a striking contrast with oxygen, if any positive results were to be obtained.

2746. *Carbonic acid* and nitrous oxide gases yielded the same negative results, and, as I believe, when the apparatus was in an unexceptionable condition.

2747. There is at the Pharmaceutical Society an excellent electro-magnet, of the horseshoe form, similar in arrangement to our own (2247), but far more powerful, and this through Mr. Redwood I was favoured with the use of, for the repetition of the foregoing experiments at the house of the Society. The iron, which is very soft and good in quality, is a square bar, 5 inches in thickness, and the medium line is 50 inches in length. It has 1500 feet of copper wire, 0.175 of an inch in thickness, coiled round it and arranged (when I used it) in one continuous length. The moveable terminal pieces for the poles are massive in proportion to the magnet. Eighty pairs of Grove's plates were used to excite this magnet, and as it was found, by preliminary trials, that these were most powerful when arranged as four twenties, with their similar ends connected, they were so used, constituting a battery of twenty pairs of plates, in which each platinum plate was 4 x 9 inches in the immersed part, and therefore presented 72 square inches of surface towards the active zinc.

2748. On repeating the former experiments (2743) the effect of pressure was again evident, and it was manifest that the magnet itself, though 5 inches in thickness, was a little bent by the mutual attraction of its poles. The effect was very small, because of the unity of the iron core passing through the centre of the experimental gas-chamber (2738). It was the only effect indicated by the gauge and was the same for all the gases; and when allowance was made for it, nothing remained to indicate any change in volume of the gas itself.

2749. *Air, oxygen, nitrogen, carbonic acid* and *nitrous oxide* were submitted, in varying order, to the effect of this very powerful magnet, but not the slightest trace of change of bulk in any of them appeared.

2750. I think that the experiments are in every respect sufficient to decide that these gases, whether they are considered as magnetic or diamagnetic bodies, or whether they include bodies of both classes (for oxygen is in striking contrast to the rest), are not affected in volume by the magnetic force, whether in fields of equal power (2737), or in places where the power is rapidly diminishing. I think this decision very important in relation to the true nature of the magnetic force, either as existing in, or acting upon the particles of bodies; and as in the magnetic field the force exhibits itself, not as a central but as an axial power, so the further distinction of the phenomena, into such as are related to the axial direction (2733), and such as are related to or include the equatorial direction (2737), is not unimportant, for they show that the particles do not tend to separate either parallel to the lines of magnetic power, or in a direction perpendicular to these lines. Without the experiments, the mind might have considered it very possible that one of these modes of expansion might have occurred and not the other.

2751. No doubt it is true that even yet changes in volume in these directions may occur, provided the change in one direction is expansion and in the other contraction, and that these are in amount equal to each other. It was partly in reference to such possible changes (which may be considered as molecular), that the experiments with the ray of light were made (2723, 2729), and also that in these and other experiments instituted for the purpose, a polarized ray was employed as the examiner; but the results were always negative, when by repetition and care sources of error were removed.

2752. The great differences in the degree of diamagnetic susceptibility and condition which the gases employed in the foregoing experiments possess or can assume, are such as to make one ready to suppose, that if they show no tendency in any case to change in volume under the action of the magnet, so neither would any other gas or vapour do so, but that all the individuals belonging to this great class

of bodies would be alike in that respect. In connexion with this conclusion I may state that I have on former occasions, and more lately, endeavoured to ascertain, by the use of very delicate apparatus and powerful electro-magnets, whether any change was produced in the volume of such fluids as water, alcohol and solution of sulphate of iron, but could observe no effect of the kind, and I do not believe in its existence. Still more recently, and in reference to the class of solid bodies, I have submitted iron as a magnetic metal, and bismuth as a diamagnetic body, to the same examination; the metals were employed both in the state of solid cylinders and of filings or fragments. The cylinders were put into glass tubes and the particles into glass bottles; gauges, like those described (2732), were applied to them, and that part of the containing vessel which was not filled with metal, was occupied, in one set of experiments, by air, and in another by alcohol, yet in no case could the least change in the volume of the iron or bismuth be observed, however powerful the magnetic force to which they were submitted.

2753. One other result of a repulsive force seemed possible even in cases when, according to a former supposition (2751), the tendency to expand equatorially might be compensated by an equal amount of tendency to contract in the axial direction, namely, that of the production of currents outwards or equatorially, i.e. in lines perpendicular to the magnetic axis, where pointed poles or the hour-glass core, already described, were used, and of other currents setting in towards that line along the inclined surfaces of the polar terminations; in some degree like those occurring so powerfully, and traced so readily when flame or hot air is observed in air, or when a stream of one gas is observed in another gas.[1]

2754. When however the gas occupying the whole of the magnetic field was uniform in nature and alike in temperature, not the slightest trace of such currents as these could be observed. It is not easy to devise unexceptionable tests of such motions, because visible bodies introduced into such a magnetic field to test the movements of the air there are themselves diamagnetic; and if they form a little isolated cloud, are moved together and away as a diamagnetic body would be; but when the whole field was occupied pretty equally by very light

[1] *Philosophical Magazine*, 1847, Vol. XXXI. pp. 402, 404, 409.

particles of dust or lycopodium, and the magnet in powerful action, no signs of currents in the air were visible. Further, when a faint stream of diffuse cold smoke from a taper spark[1] was allowed to fall or rise a little on one side of the axial line, it was determined outwards and equatorially; but though it went outwards with the most force when equidistant from the two conical poles, or their representative parts in the double iron core (2738), still when it was made to pass near to one side, it continued to go outwards and equatorially, even when, from its close vicinity to the iron surface, it had as it were to move over it; showing that the tendency of the smoke was outwards in *every part* of the magnetic field occupied by air or gas, and that therefore its motion was due to the action of the magnet on it as a diamagnetic, and not to currents of the air, which, if existing, would be inwards in one place or direction, and outwards in another.

2755. When magnetic or diamagnetic fluids were subject to the magnetic force upon a plate of mica over the poles, according to the ingenious arrangement of Plücker, they quickly assumed the different forms correspondent to their nature, but after that there was no further motion or current in them. The cases are no doubt different to those where the whole of the magnetic field is occupied by the same medium; still, as far as it goes, it helps to confirm the conclusion that no currents are formed. On putting the same liquids between the poles in glass cells, no magnetic currents could be observed in them, though fine particles were introduced into the fluids, for the purpose of making such changes of place visible, if they occurred.

2756. So there is no evidence, either by the action on a ray of light (2727, 2729), or by any expansion or contraction (2750), or by the production of any currents (2754), that the magnet exerts any direct power of attraction or repulsion on the particles of the different gases tried, or that they move in the magnetic field, as they are known to do, by any such immediate attraction or repulsion.

¶ ii. *Differential Magnetic Action*

2757. Then what is the cause of the diamagnetic change of place? The effect is evidently a differential result, depending upon the *differences* of the two portions or masses of matter occupying the magnetic field, as the air and the

streams of other gas in it,[2] or mercury and the tube of air in it (2407), or water and the piece of bismuth in it (2301); and though exhibited only in the action of masses, the latter must no doubt owe their differences to the qualities of the particles composing them. Yet it is to be observed that no attempt to separate the perfectly mixed particles of very different substances has ever succeeded, though made with most powerful magnets. Oxygen and nitrogen differ exceedingly, yet no appearance of the least degree of separation occurred in very powerful magnetic fields.[3] In other experiments I have enclosed a dilute solution of sulphate of iron in a tube, and placed the lower end of the tube between the poles of a powerful horseshoe magnet for days together, in a place of perfectly uniform temperature, and yet without the least appearance of any concentration of the solution in that end which might indicate a tendency in the particles to separate.

2758. The diamagnetic phenomena of the gases, when considered as the differential result of the action of volumes of these bodies, may be produced and examined in a very useful manner by the employment of soap-bubbles, as follows: a glass tube was fitted with a cap, stopcock and bladder, so that any given gas contained in the bladder might be sent through it, and also with a foot or stand so that it might be placed in any required position. The end of the tube was drawn down, bent at right angles, and cut off straight across at the extremity, being of the size and shape represented in *Fig. 4.*

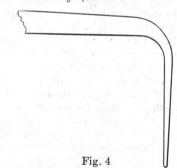

Fig. 4

2759. It is easy to blow soap-bubbles at the end of such a tube, of any size up to an inch in diameter, and retain them for the time required by the action of the stopcock. The soapy water

[1] *Philosophical Magazine*, 1847, Vol. XXXI, p. **403.**

[2] *Philosophical Magazine*, 1847, Vol. XXXI, p. 409.
[3] *Ibid.*, p. 416.

should be prepared, when wanted (and not be-forehand), by putting a cutting or two of soap into a little cold distilled water, for then bub-bles of the thinnest and most equable texture can be blown, which are more mobile than if thicker suds be used, and if a little care be tak-en, quite permanent enough for every useful experiment. The end of the pipe should be per-fectly clean and free from heterogeneous mat-ter (which is often destructive of the bubble), and should be wetted both inside and outside with the soap-water, and *left awhile in it before use.*

2760. If a bubble be blown with the end of the tube downwards, and be half an inch in di-ameter, it will usually have a little extra water at the bottom, and will hang from the slender extremity of the tube by an attachment so small as to allow it great freedom of motion. Hence it will swing to and fro like a pendulum; and according as there is more or less water at the bottom, it will vibrate more or less rapidly, will, as a whole, gravitate more or less power-fully, and therefore will retain its perpendicu-larly dependent position with more or less sta-bility,—circumstances which are very useful in the employment of the bubble as a magnetic or diamagnetic indicator.

2761. The regulation of the relative quantity of water which is in or upon the bubble is easily obtained within certain limits. If, after the pipe is dipped in the soap-water, the end be touched with a piece of wood or glass rod, which has also been kept in the soap-water, more or less of the liquid may be removed; and by ob-serving the height at which the fluid stands by capillary action within the tube, which may be varied between ⅒th and ½ an inch, it is easy, after a few experimental trials, to observe how much is required to make a bubble charged with a certain amount of water, and how little to give a bubble without any dependent water be-low; and then it is just as easy, by arranging the amount of water beforehand, to blow a bubble of any required character. Even when no drop of water is left at the bottom, still a range of thickness or thinness in the film itself can be obtained.

2762. As the bubbles contain less and less of water, so are they rendered more sensitive in their action. They vibrate slower, and are more easily moved by forces applied laterally to them. The diamagnetic effect of the soap-water constituting them is less, and therefore that of the gas contained within them compar-atively greater. If the bubble is very thin, the

dependent position becomes a position of un-stable equilibrium, for any inclination of the tube, or any lateral force, however small, then causes the bubble to pass to one side, and to run up and adhere to the side of the tube, *Fig. 5.* The dependent position supplies, in inclosed

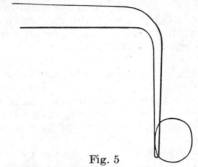

Fig. 5

spaces or atmospheres, an exceedingly delicate indicator; and even when the bubble is on the side of the tube it still forms a very valuable instrument, for it freely moves round the tube as axis; and as it possesses a certain degree of steadiness, it can be held in the magnetic field in any position, and by its motion to or from the axial line, shows very well the magnetic or diamagnetic condition of the gas contained in it in relation to the surrounding air.

2763. If the mouth of the tube be turned up-wards, bubbles of the thinnest texture can be blown; but they are then also very unstable in position, and run to the side of the tube; they can be used as indicators, as above (2762). If the mouth of the tube be made broader, the bubbles, being thin, can be retained standing on the extremity; but as their attachment is larger, so they require more force to move them sideways, and they lose in delicacy of indica-tion. It is convenient, in working with such bubbles, to make them nearly equal in size and thickness for the same set of comparative ex-periments. I usually employ them about half an inch in diameter.

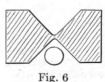

Fig. 6

2764. On blowing such a bubble with *air*, in the de-pendent position, placing it in the angle of the double pole on a level with the ax-ial line (*Fig. 6*), and then putting on the magnetic power by the use of twenty pair of plates, the bubble was deflected outwards from the axial line (or equatorially) with a certain amount of force, and returned to its first position on the interruption of the electric current. The deflection was not great, and being due to the water of the bubble, gave an indication of the amount of that effect, to be used as a correction in experiments with other gases.

2765. *Nitrogen in air.* A bubble of nitrogen went outwards or equatorially in common air with a force much surpassing the outward tendency of a bubble of air (2764), in a very striking and illustrative manner. It was often driven up from the end to the side of the tube; and when on the side, if presented inwards, it was driven to the outside of the tube, and however the tube was turned round, kept that position as long as the magnetic force was maintained. This effect is the more striking when it is considered that four-fifths of the air itself is nitrogen gas.

2766. *Oxygen in air.* The effect was very impressive, the bubble being pulled inwards or towards the axial line sharply and suddenly, exactly as if the oxygen were highly magnetic. The result was expected, being in accordance with the phenomena presented by oxygen and nitrogen in a former investigation of the diamagnetic phenomena of the gases.[1]

2767. *Nitrous oxide and olefiant gases in air.* The bubbles went outwards or diamagnetically with a force much greater than that due to the effect of the water of the bubble, proving the relation of these gases to air, and according with the results formerly obtained with streams of these substances.[2]

2768. There is no difficulty in applying this method of observation to experiments with gases in atmospheres of other gases than air, provided they be such as do not destroy the bubble; but I do not consume time by detailing the results of such experiments, which accorded perfectly with those before obtained.[3] The description given is quite sufficient to illustrate the point stated, namely, that the motion of the gases, one in another, when in the magnetic field, is a differential result, and supply sufficient cases for reference hereafter.

2769. The same conclusion, that the effect is a differential result of the masses of matter present in the magnetic field, is also manifest from the consideration of the cases of gaseous, liquid, and solid diamagnetic bodies, advanced in a former part of these *Researches* (2405–14); and a conclusion of the same kind, as regards magnetic bodies, may also be drawn from experiments then described (2361–68).

¶ iii. *Magnetic Characters of Oxygen, Nitrogen, and Space*

2770. The differential action of two portions of gas, or of any two bodies, may, by a more elaborate method, be examined in a manner far more interesting and important than that just described. The mode of action referred to may even be made the basis of instruments, by which, probably, most important indications and measurements of both magnetic and diamagnetic actions may be obtained, leading to results which are not even as yet contemplated by the imagination.

2771. If two portions of matter, gaseous or liquid, are tied together and placed in a symmetric magnetic field, on opposite sides of the magnetic axis, they will be simultaneously affected. If both are diamagnetic, or less magnetic than the medium occupying the magnetic field, both will tend to go outwards or equatorially; equally if they are alike, but unequally if they differ. The consequence will be that, if they are placed, in the first instance, equidistant from the magnetic axis, the supervention of the magnetic force will not alter their position, provided they be alike; but if they differ, then their position will be changed; for the most diamagnetic will move outwards equatorially, pulling the least diamagnetic inwards until the two are in such new positions that the forces acting on them are equipoised, and they will assume a position of stable equilibrium. Now the distance through which they will move may be used indirectly, or better still, the force required to restore them to their equidistant position may be employed directly to estimate the tendency each had to go from the magnetic axis; that is, to give their relative diamagnetic intensities.

2772. That I might submit gases to such a method of examination, I selected a piece of very thin and regular flint-glass tube, about $5/16$ths of an inch external diameter, and not more than $1/60$th of an inch in thickness, and drawing at the blow-pipe lamp two equable portions of this tube into the shape and size represented, *Fig. 7*, in which the barrel part is $1\frac{1}{2}$ inches long, I filled one with oxygen gas and the other with nitrogen gas, and then sealed them up hermetically. The end of the prolonged part of each was touched whilst warm with sealing-wax and a thread fastened to it, which thread was tied into a loop, also represented of full size. By these the tubes were to be suspended perpendicularly from a torsion balance, so that the middle of each should, when in place, be on a level with the magnetic axis.

[1] *Philosophical Magazine*, 1847, Vol. XXXI, pp. 410, 415.
[2] *Ibid.*, p. 411.　　　　[3] *Ibid.*, pp. 414, 415.

Fig. 7

2773. The torsion balance consisted of a bundle of sixty equally-stretched cocoon silk fibres, made fast above to a vertical axis carrying a horizontal index and graduated plate, and below to a horizontal lever. A cross-bar, about 1½ inches long, was attached to one end of this lever, also in the horizontal plane; and on the extremities of this cross bar, and 8½ inches from the centre of motion, were hung the two tubes of oxygen and nitrogen (2772), counterbalanced by a weight on the other arm of the horizontal level. The whole was thus so placed and adjusted in relation to the electro-magnet, furnished at the time with the double cone core or keeper (2764), that the middle part of each tube was level with the middle of the core, and equidistant on each side from it. Under these circumstances, if any motion was given to the balance, so as to make its arm vibrate, the vibrations were made with great slowness, in consequence of the weight of the whole moving arrangement, and the small amount of torsion force in the cocoon silk.

2774. The moment the magnetic force was thrown into action all things changed. The oxygen tube was immediately carried inwards towards the axis, and the nitrogen tube driven outwards on the contrary side. The balance swung beyond its new place of rest and then returned with considerable power, vibrating many times in the period, which before was filled by a single oscillation; and when it had come to its place of rest, or of stable equilibrium, the oxygen tube was about one-eighth of an inch from the iron of the core, and the nitrogen tube four-eighths distant. Ten revolutions of the torsion axis altered only in a slight degree these relative distances.

2775. The actions which determine the mutual self-adjustment of the oxygen and nitrogen, as regards their place in relation to the magnetic axis, are very simple and evident. In the first place, the *glass* of the tubes is more diamagnetic than the surrounding medium or air (2424), and therefore each tends to move outwards; but being equal in nature and condition to each other, they tend to move with equal force when at equal distances, and at those distances compensate each other. If one be driven inwards, it is subjected to a greater exertion of force by coming into a more intense part of the magnetic field; and the other, being

at the same time carried outwards, is for a corresponding reason in a place of less intense action; and therefore, as soon as the constraint is removed, the system returns to its position of stable equilibrium, in which the two bodies are equidistant from the magnetic axis.

2776. The *contents* also of the tubes are subject to the magnetic forces, and as the result shows (2774), in very different degrees. Either the oxygen tends inwards much more forcibly than the nitrogen, or the nitrogen tends outwards more powerfully than the oxygen; and the difference must exist to a very great degree, for it is such as to carry the glass of the oxygen tube up to a position so near the axis that it could not by itself, or with mere air inside, retain it for a moment without the aid of considerable restraint. The power with which the tubes only would retain their equidistant position, combined with the extent to which they are displaced from this position, shows the great amount of force which this conjoint action of the oxygen and the nitrogen leaves free to be exerted in the one direction, namely, from the oxygen inwards or axially, for though the action be complicated the result is simple. By former experiments, the nitrogen is known to pass equatorially and the oxygen axially in air,[1] and the nitrogen tube will pass equatorially according to a certain differential force, depending on the flint-glass and the nitrogen on the one hand, and the bulk of air displaced by them on the other. The oxygen tube in like manner will tend to pass axially by a differential force, the amount of which will depend upon the tendency of the oxygen to go axially, of its tube to go equatorially, and of their joint relation to the air they displace. But both the tubes and their contents are by their joint relation to the air and their mechanical connexion so related to each other, that when a force (as of torsion) is employed to restore them to their equidistant position from the magnetic axis, all consideration of the matter of the tubes and of the air as a surrounding medium may be dismissed. The gases within them may be considered as in immediate relation with each other and the magnetic axis, and disembarrassed from all other actions: and the force which may be found needful to place them

[1] *Philosophical Magazine*, 1847, Vol. XXXI, p. 409.

equidistant, is the measure of their magnetic or diamagnetic differences.

2777. Having thus explained the general principles of action, I will not at present go into their application in the construction of a measuring instrument or the results obtained with it, further than is required for the general elucidation of magnetic and diamagnetic bodies, and the determination of the true zero-point (2721, 2722).

2778. The principles just described enabled me to return to a method of investigation which on a former occasion greatly excited my hopes (2433), but which seemed then suddenly cut off by want of power. Various bodies, whether considered as magnetic or diamagnetic substances, admit of two modes of treatment, which promise to be exceedingly instructive as regards their properties and their destined purposes in natural operation. A gas may be *heated* or *cooled*, and the effect of temperature, which is known to be very influential,[1] may now be ascertained without any change in the bulk of the gas; or it may be *rarefied* and *condensed* through a very extensive range, and the effect of this kind of change upon it ascertained independent of temperature or the presence of any other substance. Solids and liquids do not admit of these methods of examination, and do not therefore assist in the determination of the zero-point and of the true distinction of magnetic and diamagnetic bodies in the same manner that the gases do.

2779. It appeared to me that if a gaseous body were magnetic, then its magnetic properties ought to be diminished in proportion as it was rarefied, i.e., that equal volumes of such a gas at different pressures ought to be more magnetic, as they are denser; on the other hand, that if a gas were diamagnetic, rarefaction ought to diminish its diamagnetic character, until, when reduced to the condition of a vacuum, it should disappear. In other words, if two opposed portions of the same magnetic gas, one rarer than the other, were subjected at once to the magnetic force, the *denser* ought to approach the axial line, or be drawn into the place of most intense action; whereas if two similarly opposed portions of a diamagnetic gas were subjected to the magnetic action, the more expanded or *rarer* gas ought to go inwards to the place of strongest action.

2780. Several bulbs of oxygen (*Fig. 8*), similar in arrangement to those already described

(2772), and very nearly alike in size, were prepared and hermetically sealed, after that the quantity of gas within them had been reduced to a certain degree by the air-pump. The first contained the gas at the pressure of one atmosphere; the second had the gas at half an atmosphere, or 15 inches of mercury; the third contained gas at the pressure of 10 inches of mercury; and the fourth, after being filled with oxygen, was reduced to as good a vacuum as an excellent air-pump could effect. When the first of these was compared with the other three, the effect was most striking; opposed to the half atmosphere, it went towards the axis, driving the expanded portion away; when in relation to the one-third atmosphere, it went inwards or axially with still more power; and when opposed to the oxygen vacuum, it took its place as close to the iron

Fig. 8

core as in the former case, when contrasted with nitrogen (2774); and it was manifest that the diamagnetic power of the glass tube which inclosed it (2775), was the only thing which prevented the oxygen from pressing against the iron core occupying the centre of the magnetic field.

2781. On experimenting with the other tubes exactly the same result was obtained. Thus the tube with one-third of an atmosphere, in association with the vacuum tube, went inwards, driving the other outwards, i.e., it was more magnetic than the vacuum; but in association with the one-half atmosphere tube it went outwards, whilst the denser gas passed inwards. Any one of the tubes, if associated with another having a rarer atmosphere, passed inwards or magnetically, whilst if associated with others having denser atmospheres it passed outwards, being driven off by the superior magnetic force of the denser gas. As far as I could ascertain in these preliminary forms of experiment, the tendency inwards or axially appeared to be in proportion to the density of the gas; but the exact measurement of these forces will be given hereafter.

2782. Thus oxygen appears to be a very magnetic substance, for it passes axially, or from weaker to stronger places of force, with considerable power; a conclusion in accordance with the result of former observations.[2] Moreover

[1] *Philosophical Magazine*, 1847, Vol. XXXI, pp. 406, 417.

[2] *Philosophical Magazine*, 1847, Vol. XXXI, pp. 410, 415.

it passes more powerfully when dense than when rare, its tendency inwards being apparently in proportion to its density. Hence, as the oxygen is removed, the magnetic force disappears with it, until when a vacuum is obtained, little or no trace of attraction or inward force remains. No doubt it may be said that dense oxygen is less diamagnetic than rare oxygen, or a vacuum. This however would imply, that the acting force of a substance, as the oxygen, could increase in proportion as the quantity of the substance diminished, which is not, I think, a philosophical assumption; and besides that, other reasons will soon appear to show that the magnetic condition which disappears as the oxygen is removed, belongs to and is dependent upon that substance, and that oxygen is therefore a truly magnetic body.

2783. *Nitrogen,* being the other and larger part of the atmosphere, was then subjected to experiment, and three tubes, one containing the gas at a pressure of 30 inches of mercury, another with the gas at the pressure of 15 inches, and the third reduced as nearly as it could be to a vacuum, were prepared (2780). When these were compared one with another in the magnetic field, they were found to be so nearly alike as not to be distinguishable from each other, i.e., they remained equidistant from the magnetic axis. I do not mean to imply that nitrogen at these different pressures is absolutely the same bulk for bulk (an instrument now under construction will enable me hereafter to compare and measure with infinitely greater accuracy, and to ascertain these points); but as compared with oxygen, the great and extraordinary differences produced by rarefaction there, have no corresponding differences here. If there are any, they are insensible at present, and may, for the chief purpose of this paper and the determination of the zero-point between magnetics and diamagnetics, be taken as nothing.

2784. Nitrogen therefore appears to be neither magnetic nor diamagnetic; if it were either, it could not but fall in its specific condition as it was rarefied; as it is, it is equivalent to a vacuum. If a given space be considered as a vacuum, into which oxygen or nitrogen is to be gradually introduced, as oxygen is added the space becomes more and more magnetic, i.e. more competent to admit of the kind of action distinguished by that word; but the corresponding gradual addition of nitrogen to an empty space produces no effect of that kind, or the contrary, and the nitrogen is therefore neither magnetic nor diamagnetic, but like space itself.

2785. As yet I have found no gas, which, being on the diamagnetic side of zero, can at all compare with oxygen in the range of effect produced by rarefaction. For the present, I may mention olefiant gas and cyanogen as substances which appear to proceed inwards, or towards the axial line, as they are more rarefied. They are therefore not merely at zero, but are in opposition to oxygen and are diamagnetic bodies. But if we want a body that is strongly and undeniably diamagnetic, and which, being added to or introduced into space, will make it diamagnetic, as oxygen renders it magnetic, then flint glass or phosphorus presents us with such a substance. When these bodies are made into forms similar to the volumes of nitrogen, or the vacua in size and shape, and are compared with them on the torsion balance, they pass outwards with much force; and it is probably the great diamagnetic force of the glass of the tubes that prevents the effect of rarefaction from being more evident in olefiant and other gases.

2786. When a tube has been filled with a particular gas, then exhausted as much as possible, and sealed up hermetically, it may be considered as inclosing what is commonly called a vacuum. I have prepared many such vacua, and may be permitted to distinguish them by the name of the gas, traces of which still remain. In comparing these vacua in the magnetic field (2773), they appeared to me to be in all respects alike; the oxygen vacuum was not more magnetic than the hydrogen, nitrogen, or olefiant vacuum. Their differences, if any, were far smaller than the differences which could be produced by the variations of size and other conditions of the glass bulbs, and can only be made manifest by the means hereafter to be used (2783); and I am fully persuaded that they will ultimately be nearly alike, ranging close *up to and about a perfect* vacuum.

2787. Before determining the place of zero amongst magnetic and diamagnetic bodies, we have to consider the true character and relation of *space* free from any material substance. Though one cannot procure a space perfectly free from matter, one can make a close approximation to it in a carefully prepared Torricellian vacuum. Perhaps it is hardly necessary for me to state, that I find both iron and bismuth in such vacua perfectly obedient to the magnet. From such experiments, and also from general observations and knowledge, it seems manifest that the lines of magnetic force (2149) can traverse pure space, just as gravitating force does, and as static electrical forces do (1616); and therefore space has a magnetic relation of its own, and one that we shall probably find hereafter to be of the utmost importance in natural phenomena. But this character of space is not of the same kind as that which, in relation to matter, we endeavour to express by the terms magnetic and diamagnetic. To confuse them together would be to confound space with matter, and to trouble all the conceptions by which we endeavour to understand and work out a progressively clearer view of the mode of action and the laws of natural forces. It would be as if, in gravitation or electric forces (1613), one were to confound the particles acting on each other with the space across which they are acting, and would, I think, shut the door to advancement. Mere space cannot act as matter acts, even though the utmost latitude be allowed to the hypothesis of an ether; and admitting that hypothesis, it would be a large additional assumption to suppose that the lines of magnetic force are vibrations carried on by it (2591); whilst as yet, we have no proof or indication that time is required for their propagation, or in what respect they may in general character assimilate to, or differ from, the respective lines of gravitating, luminiferous, or electric forces.

2788. Neither can space be supposed to have those circular currents round points diffused through it, which Ampère's theory assumes to exist around the particles of ordinary magnetic matter, and which I had for a moment supposed might exist in the contrary direction round the particles of diamagnetic matter (2429, 2640, &c.). The imagination, restrained by philosophical considerations, fails to find anything in pure space about which the currents could circulate, or to which they could by any association be attached; and the difficulty, if already not immeasurable, would be still greater to those, if there be any, who, assuming that magnetic and diamagnetic bodies are alike in nature, must assume that there are like currents in both; for it does not seem possible to add (for instance) phosphorus having such a magnetic constitution, to space supposed to be of a similar constitution, and yet to have as a result a diminution of the magnetic powers of the space so occupied.

2789. As space therefore comports itself independently of matter, and after another manner, the different varieties of matter must, in relation to their respective qualities, be considered amongst themselves. Those which produce no effect when added to space, appear to me to be neutral or to stand at zero. Those which bring with them an effect of one kind will be on the one side of zero, and those which produce an effect of the contrary kind will be on the other side of zero; by this division they constitute the two subdivisions of magnetic and diamagnetic bodies. The law which I formerly ventured to give (2267, 2418), still expresses accurately their relations; for in an absolute vacuum or free space, a magnetic body tends from weaker to stronger places of magnetic action, and a diamagnetic body under similar conditions from stronger to weaker places of action.

2790. Now that the *true zero* is obtained, and the great variety of material substances satisfactorily divided into two general classes, it appears to me that we want another name for the magnetic class, that we may avoid confusion. The word *magnetic* ought to be general, and include *all* the phenomena and effects produced by the power. But then a word for the subdivision, opposed to the diamagnetic class, is necessary. As the language of this branch of science may soon require general and careful changes, I, assisted by a kind friend, have thought that a word not selected with particular care might be provisionally useful; and as the magnetism of iron, nickel and cobalt, when in the magnetic field, is like that of the earth as a whole, so that when rendered active they place themselves parallel to its axes or lines of magnetic force, I have supposed that they and their similars (including oxygen now) might be called paramagnetic bodies, giving the following division:

Magnetic | Paramagnetic
Diamagnetic

If the attempt to facilitate expression be not accepted, I hope it will be excused.

2791. From the presence of oxygen in the air, the latter is, as a whole, a magnetic medium of no small power. Hence all the comparative experiments on the diamagnetic condition of other gases, made by passing streams of them through it and through each other,[1] require a correction, which occasionally may place some of these bodies on the paramagnetic side of zero. Even solid and fluid substances may be

[1] *Philosophical Magazine*, 1847, Vol. XXXI, pp. 407, 420, &c.

thus affected; and the preliminary list, which I formerly gave (2424), will need alteration in this respect. I hope soon however to have the means of ascertaining, not only the place of bodies, but also their relative degrees of force, at the same and at different temperatures, with a degree of accuracy that will serve great purposes in the further development of this branch of science.

2792. Amongst the gases hitherto examined there is nothing that compares with oxygen. The following are comparatively indifferent by the side of it: chlorine and bromine vapour, cyanogen, nitrogen, hydrogen, carbonic acid, carbonic oxide, olefiant gas, nitrous oxide, nitric oxide, nitrous acid vapour, muriatic acid, sulphurous acid, hydriodic acid, ammonia, sulphuretted hydrogen, coal-gas, ether vapour and sulphuret of carbon vapour; for though some, as olefiant and cyanogen gases, appear to be a little diamagnetic, and others, as nitrous oxide and nitric oxide, are magnetic, yet their effects disappear in comparison with the results produced by oxygen.

2793. I hope to give the correct expression of the paramagnetic force of oxygen (2783) hereafter; in the meantime I am tempted to give one or two rough illustrations of its degree in this place, in addition to the former one (2774). The capacity of the oxygen bulb, containing one atmosphere, is not quite 0.34 of a cubic inch, and the weight therefore of the oxygen within 0.117 of a grain. I endeavoured to compare this quantity in the first place with soft iron, and therefore attached a portion of that metal, having one-tenth of this weight or 0.012 of a grain, to a fine platinum wire fixed into one end of a vessel, corresponding in size to that containing the oxygen, so as to bring the iron into the middle, and then the bulb was exhausted and hermetically sealed. Being now opposed to the oxygen tube in the magnetic field, it was found, as expected, far to surpass the oxygen in magnetic power. As it was inconvenient further to reduce the iron or to enlarge the oxygen, another magnetic substance was employed for the comparison.

2794. One hundred grains of clean, good, crystallized protosulphate of iron were dissolved in distilled water, and diluted until a glass bulb, of nearly the same size as the oxygen bulb when filled with the solution, was equal to the oxygen bulb in force, and stood equidistant from the axial line, as far as I could judge by the present modes of observation. When the solution had this strength, it occupied the bulk

of $17\frac{1}{2}$ cubic inches. As the bulk of the oxygen is only 0.34 of a cubic inch (2793), that volume of this solution would contain very nearly two grains of crystallized sulphate of iron, equivalent to 0.4 of a grain of metallic iron; so that, bulk for bulk, oxygen is equally magnetic with a solution of sulphate of iron in water containing seventeen times the weight of the oxygen in crystallized protosulphate of iron, or 3.4 times its weight of metallic iron in that state of combination.

2795. Again, the oxygen tubes, containing respectively one atmosphere and a vacuum (2780), were adjusted about an inch apart, and placed on each side of the magnetic axis, and the force of the magnet developed. The oxygen of course approached the magnetic axis, and the vacuum passed equatorially. A slender glass filament, about 6 inches in length, had been drawn out at the lamp and fixed to a foot; and the end of this filament was then employed to press back the oxygen tube into its original place, and render it equidistant from the magnetic axis with the vacuum tube. In this position the two tubes would, as respects the glass, neutralize each other (2775); and considering the vacuum as zero, the oxygen alone may be considered as active, and the force required to hold it out may be looked upon as the force with which the oxygen, at that distance of half an inch, tended to go to the magnetic axis. The deflection of the glass filament or spring, at the place where the oxygen tube was held by it, was rather more than one inch from its position when relieved from the pressure of the tube. Being taken away, it was set up in the horizontal position (after being turned 90° on its axis, so that the flexure might be in the same direction, relative to the filament, as before); and the position of the end being marked, weights were put on it at the place of former contact with the oxygen tube, until they produced the same amount of deflection as before. It required rather more than the tenth of a grain to produce this effect; and this, considering that the whole oxygen only weighed 0.117 of a grain, and that no part of it was nearer than half an inch, whilst the average distance of the mass was above an inch from the magnetic axis, gives a high expression for the magnetic power.

2796. It is hardly necessary for me to say here that this oxygen cannot exist in the atmosphere, exerting such a remarkable and high amount of magnetic force, without having a most important influence on the disposition of the magnetism of the earth as a planet, especially if it be remembered that its magnetic condition is greatly altered by variations in its density (2781) and by variations in its temperature.[1] I think I see here the real cause of many of the variations of that force, which have been, and are now, so carefully watched on different parts of the surface of the globe. The daily variation and the annual variation both seem likely to come under it; also very many of the irregular continual variations which the photographic process of record renders so beautifully manifest. If such expectations be confirmed, and the influence of the atmosphere be found able to produce results like these, then we shall probably find a new relation between the aurora borealis and the magnetism of the earth, namely, a relation established, more or less, through the air itself in connection with the space above it; and even magnetic relations and variations which are not as yet suspected, may be suggested and rendered manifest and measurable, in the further development of what I will venture to call *atmospheric magnetism* (2847, &c.). I may be over-sanguine in these expectations, but as yet I am sustained in them by the apparent reality, simplicity and sufficiency of the cause assumed, as it at present appears to my mind. As soon as I have sufficiently submitted these views to a close consideration and the test of accordance with observation, and where applicable with experiments also, I will do myself the honour to bring them before the Royal Society.

Royal Institution, August 2, 1850

[1] *Philosophical Magazine*, 1847, Vol. XXXI, p. 417.

TWENTY-SIXTH SERIES[2]

§ 32. *Magnetic Conducting Power* ¶ i. *Magnetic Conduction* ¶ ii. *Conduction Polarity* ¶ iii. *Magnecrystallic Conduction* § 33. *Atmospheric Magnetism* ¶ i. *General Principles*

RECEIVED OCTOBER 9,[3] READ NOVEMBER 28, 1850

¶ i. *Magnetic Conduction*

2797. THE remarkable results given in a former series of these *Researches* (2757, &c.) respecting the powerful tendency of certain gaseous substances to proceed either to or from the central line of magnetic force, according to their relation to other substances present at the same time, and yet the absence of all condensation or expansion of these bodies (2756) which might be supposed to be consequent on such an amount of attractive or repulsive force as would be thought needful to produce this tendency and determination to particular places, have, upon consideration, led me to the idea, that if bodies possess different degrees of *conducting power* for magnetism, that difference may account for all the phenomena; and, further, that if such an idea be considered, it may assist in developing the nature of magnetic force. I shall therefore venture to think and speak freely on this matter for a while, for the purpose of drawing others into a consideration of the subject; though I run the risk, in doing

so, of falling into error through imperfect experiments and reasoning. As yet, however, I only state the case hypothetically, and use the phrase *conducting power* as a general expression of the capability which bodies may possess of affecting the transmission of magnetic force; implying nothing as to how the process of conduction is carried on. Thus limited in sense, the phrase may be very useful, enabling us to take, for a time, a connected, consistent and general view of a large class of phenomena; may serve as a standard of meaning amongst them, and yet need not necessarily involve any error, inasmuch as whatever may be the principles and condition of conduction, the phenomena dependent on it must consist among themselves.

2798. If a medium having a certain conducting power occupy the magnetic field, and then a portion of another medium or substance be placed in the field having a greater conducting power, the latter will tend to draw up towards the place of greatest force, displacing the former. Such at least is the case with bodies that are freely magnetic, as iron, nickel, cobalt and their combinations (2357, 2363, 2367, &c.), and

[2] *Philosophical Transactions*, 1851, p. 29.
[3] Revised by the author and returned by him November 12, 1850.

such a result is in analogy with the phenomena produced by electric induction. If a portion of still higher conducting power be brought into play, it will approach the axial line and displace that which had just gone there; so that a body having a certain amount of conducting power will appear as if attracted in a medium of weaker power, and as if repelled in a medium of stronger power by this differential kind of action (2367, 2414).

2799. At the same time that this idea of conduction will thus account for the place which a given substance would take up, as of oxygen in the axial line if in nitrogen, or of nitrogen at a distance if in oxygen, it also harmonizes with the fact, that there are no currents induced in a single gas occupying the magnetic field (2754), for any one particle can then conduct as well as any other, and therefore will keep its place; and it also agrees, I think, with the unchangeability of volume (2750).

2800. In reference to the latter point, we have to consider that the force which urges such a body as oxygen towards the middle of the field is not a central force like gravitation, or the mutual attraction of a set of particles for each other; but an axial force, which, being very different in character in the direction of the axis and of the radii, may, and must produce its effect in a very different manner to a purely central force. That these differences exist, is manifest by the action of transparent bodies, when in the magnetic field, upon a ray of light; and also by the ordinary action of magnetic bodies: and hence, perhaps, the reason, that when oxygen is drawn into the middle of the field, in consequence of its conducting power, still its particles are not compressed together (2721) by a force that otherwise would seem equal to that effect (2766).

2801. So when two separate portions of oxygen or nitrogen are in the magnetic field, the one passes inwards and the other outwards, without any contraction or expansion of their relative volumes; and the result is differential, the two bodies being in *relation to and dependence on* each other, by being simultaneously related to the lines of magnetic force which pass conjointly through them both, or through them and the medium in which they are conjointly immersed.

2802. I have already said, in reference to the transference onwards of magnetic force (2787), that pure space or a vacuum permits that transference, independent of any function that can be considered as of the same nature as the conducting power of matter; and in a manner more analogous to that in which the lines of gravitating force, or of static electric force, pass across mere space. Then as respects those bodies which, like oxygen, facilitate the transmission of this power more or less, they class together as magnetic or paramagnetic substances (2790); and those bodies, which, like olefiant gas or phosphorus, give more or less obstruction, may be arranged together as the diamagnetic class. Perhaps it is not correct to express both these qualities by the term *conduction;* but in the present state of the subject, and under the reservation already made (2797), the phrase may I think be employed conveniently without introducing confusion.

2803. If such be a correct general view of the nature and differences of paramagnetic and diamagnetic substances, then the internal processes by which they perform their functions can hardly be the same, though they might be similar. Thus they *may* have circular electric currents in opposite directions, but their distinction can scarcely be supposed to depend upon the difference of force of currents in the *same* direction. If the view be correct also, though the results obtained when two bodies are simultaneously present in the magnetic field may be considered as differential (2768, 2770) even though one of them be the general medium, yet the consequence of the presence of conducting power in matter renders a *single* body, when in space, subject to the magnetic force; and the result is, that when a paramagnetic substance is in a magnetic field of unequal force, it tends to proceed from weaker to stronger places of action, or is *attracted;* and when a diamagnetic body is similarly circumstanced, it tends to go from stronger to weaker places of action, or is *repelled* (2756).

2804. Matter, when its powers are under consideration, may, as to its quantity, be considered either by weight or by volume. In the present case, where the effects produced have an immediate reference to mere space (2787, 2802), it seems proper that the volume should be considered as the representation, and that in comparing one substance with another, equal volumes should be employed to give correct results. No other method could be used with the differential system of observation (2772, 2780).

2805. Some experimental evidence, other than that of change of situation, of the existence of this conducting power, by differences in which, I am endeavouring to account for the peculiar characteristics of paramagnetic and diamagnetic bodies, may well be expected. This evidence exists; but as certain considerations connected with polarity preclude me from calling too freely upon iron, cobalt, or nickel (2832) for illustrations, and as in other bodies which are paramagnetic, as well as in those that are diamagnetic, the effects are very weak, they will be better comprehended after some further general consideration of the subject (2843).

2806. I will now endeavour to consider what the influence is which paramagnetic and diamagnetic bodies, viewed as conductors (2797), exert upon the lines of force in a magnetic field. Any portion of space traversed by lines of magnetic power, may be taken as such a field, and there is probably no space without them. The condition of the field may vary in intensity of power, from place to place, either along the lines or across them; but it will be better to assume for the present consideration a field of equal force throughout, and I have formerly described how this may, for a certain limited space, be produced (2465). In such a field the power does not vary either along or across the lines, but the distinction of direction is as great and important as ever, and has been already marked and expressed by the term axial and equatorial, according as it is either parallel or transverse to the magnetic axis.

2807. When a paramagnetic conductor, as for instance, a sphere of oxygen, is introduced into such a magnetic field, considered previously as free from matter, it will cause a concentration of the lines of force on and through it, so that the space occupied by it transmits more magnetic power than before (*Fig. 1*). If, on the other hand, a sphere of diamagnetic matter be placed in a similar field, it will cause a divergence or opening out of the lines in the equatorial direction (*Fig. 2*); and less magnetic power will be transmitted through the space it occupies than if it were away.

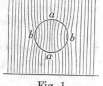

Fig. 1

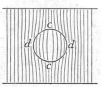

Fig. 2

2808. In this manner these two bodies will be found to affect *first* the *direction* of the lines of force, not only within the space occupied by themselves, but also in the neighbouring space, into which the lines passing through them are prolonged; and this change in the course of the lines will be in the contrary direction for the two cases.

2809. *Secondly*, they will affect the *amount* of force in any particular part of the space within or near them; for as every section across the line of such a magnetic field must be definite in amount of force, and be in that respect the same as every other section, so it is impossible to cause a concentration within the sphere of oxygen (*Fig. 1*) without causing also a simultaneous concentration in the parts axially situated as *a a* outside of it, and a corresponding diminution in the parts equatorially placed, *b b*. On the other hand, the diamagnetic body (*Fig. 2*) will cause diminution of the magnetic force in the parts of space axially placed in respect of it, *c c*, and concentration in the near equatorial parts, *d d*. If the magnetic field be considered as limited in its extent by the wails of iron forming the faces of opposed poles (2465), then even the distribution of the magnetism within the iron itself will be affected by the presence of the paramagnetic or diamagnetic bodies; and this will happen to a very large extent indeed, when, from among the paramagnetic class, such substances as iron, nickel or cobalt are selected.

2810. The influence of this disturbance of the forces upon the place and position of either a paramagnetic or a diamagnetic body placed within the magnetic field, is readily deduced upon consideration and easily made manifest by experiment. A small sphere of iron placed within a field of equal magnetic power, bounded by the iron poles, has a position of unstable equilibrium, equidistant from the iron surfaces, and at such time a great concentration of force takes place through it, and at the iron faces opposite to it, and through the intervening axial spaces. If the sphere be on either side of the middle distance, it flies to the nearest iron surface, and then can determine the greatest amount of magnetic force to or upon the axial lines which pass through it.

2811. If the iron be a spheroid, then its greatest diameter points axially, whether it be in the position of unstable equilibrium, nearer to or in contact with the iron walls of the field. As the circumstances are now more favourable for the concentration of force in the axial line passing through the body than before, so this result can be produced by much weaker paramagnetics than iron, and I have no doubt could easily be produced by a vessel of oxygen or nitric oxide gas (2782, 2792). It now becomes indeed a form, though not the best, of that experiment by which the magnetic condition of bodies is considered as most sensitively tested.

2812. The relative deficiency of power in diamagnetic bodies renders any attempt to obtain the converse phenomena to those of iron somewhat difficult; in order therefore to exalt the conditions, I used a saturated solution of protosulphate of iron in the magnetic field; by this means I strengthened the lines of power passing across it, without disturbing its equality in the parts employed, or introducing any error into the principle of the experiment, and then used bismuth as the diamagnetic body. A cylinder of this substance, suspended vertically, tended well towards the middle distance, finding its place of stable equilibrium in the spot where the paramagnetic body had unstable equilibrium. When the cylinder was suspended horizontally, then the direction it took was equatorial; and this effect also was very clear and distinct.

2813. These relative and reverse positions of paramagnetic and diamagnetic bodies, in a field of equal magnetic force, accord well with their known relations to each other, and with the kind of action already laid down in principle (2807) as that which they exert on the magnetic power to which they are subjected. One may retain them in the mind by conceiving that if a liquid sphere of a paramagnetic conductor were in the place of action, and then the magnetic force developed, it would change in form and be prolonged axially, becoming an oblong spheroid; whereas if such a sphere of diamagnetic matter were placed there, it would be extended in the equatorial direction and become an oblate spheroid.

2814. The *mutual action* of two portions of paramagnetic matter, when they are both in such a field of equal magnetic force, may be anticipated from the principles (2807, 2830), or from the corresponding facts, which are generally known. Two spheres of iron, if retained in the same equatorial plane, repel each other strongly; but as they are allowed to depart out of that plane, they first lose their mutual repulsive force and then attract each other, and that they do most powerfully when in an axial direction.

2815. With diamagnetic bodies the mutual action is more difficult to determine, because of the comparative lowness of their condition. I therefore resorted to the expedient, before described, of using a saturated solution of protosulphate of iron as the medium occupying the field of equal magnetic force, and employ-

ing two cylinders of phosphorus, about an inch long and half an inch in diameter, as the diamagnetic bodies. One of these was suspended at the end of a lever, which was itself suspended by cocoon-silk, so as to have extremely free motion, and the adjustments were such that when the phosphorus cylinder was in the middle of the magnetic field it was free to move equatorially or across the lines of magnetic force; it however had *no tendency* to do so under the influence of the magnetic force. The other cylinder was attached to a copper wire handle and could be placed in a fixed position on either side of the former cylinder; it was therefore adjusted close by the side of it, and the two retained together, until all disturbance from motion of the fluid or of the air had ceased; then the retaining body was removed, the two phosphorus cylinders still keeping their places; finally, the magnetic power was brought into action, and immediately the moveable cylinder separated slowly from the fixed one and passed to a distance. If brought back again whilst the magnet was active, when left at liberty it receded; but if restored to close vicinity, when the magnetic force was away, it retained that situation. The effect took place either in the one direction or the other, according as the fixed cylinder was on this or that side of the moving one; but the motion was in both cases across the lines of magnetic force, and was indeed mechanically and purposely limited to that direction by the mode of suspension. When two bismuth balls were placed, in respect of each other, in the direction of the magnetic axis, so that one might move, but only in the direction of that axis, its place was not sensibly affected by the other; the tendency of the free one to go to the middle of the field (2812) overpowered any other tendency that might really exist.

2816. Thus two diamagnetic bodies, when in the magnetic field, do truly affect each other; but the result is not opposed in its direction to that of paramagnetic bodies, being in both cases a separation of the substances from each other.

2817. The comparison of the action of paramagnetic and diamagnetic bodies on each other, was completed by using water as the medium in a field of equal magnetic force, and suspending a piece of phosphorus from the torsion balance. When the magnetic power was on, this phosphorus was repelled equatorially, as before, by another piece of phosphorus, but it was attracted by a tube filled with a saturated solution of protosulphate of iron; so paramagnetic and diamagnetic bodies attract each other equatorially in a mean medium, but each repels bodies of its own kind (2831).

¶ ii. *Conduction Polarity*

2818. Having thus considered briefly the effects which the disturbance of the lines of force, by the presence of paramagnetic and diamagnetic bodies, is competent to produce (2807, &c.), I will ask attention to that which may be considered as their polarity: not wishing by the term to indicate any internal condition of the substances or their particles, but the condition of the mass as a whole, in respect to the state into which it is brought by its own disturbance of the lines of magnetic force; and that, both in regard to its condition with respect to other bodies similarly affected; and also in regard to differences existing in different parts of its own mass. Such a condition concerns what may be called *conduction polarity*. Bodies in free space, when under magnetic action, will possess it in its simplest condition; but bodies immersed in other media will also possess it under more complicated forms, and its amount may then be varied, being reversed or increased, or diminished to a very large extent.

2819. Taking the simplest case of paramagnetic polarity, or that presented in Fig. 1 (2807), it consists in a convergence of the lines of magnetic force on to two opposed parts of the body, which are to each other in the direction of the magnetic axis. The difference in character of the two poles at these parts is very great, being that which is due to the known difference of quality in the two opposite directions of the line of magnetic force. Whether polar attraction or repulsion exists amongst paramagnetic bodies, when they present mere cases of conduction (as oxygen, for instance), is not yet certain (2827), but it probably does; and if so, will doubtless be consistent with the attraction and repulsion of *magnets* having correspondent poles.

2820. When we consider the conduction polarity of a diamagnetic body, matters appear altogether different. It has not a polarity like that of a paramagnetic substance, or one the mere reverse (in name or direction of the lines of force) of such a substance, as I, Weber and others have at times assumed (2640), but a state of its own altogether special. Its polarity consists of a divergence of the lines of power on to, or a convergence from the parts, which being opposite, are in the direction of the mag-

netic axis; so that these poles, having the *same* general and opposite relations to each other, which correspond to the differences in the poles of paramagnetic bodies, have still, under the circumstances, that striking contrast and difference from the polarity of the latter bodies which is given by convergence and divergence of the lines of force.

2821. Let *Fig. 3* represent a limited magnetic field with a paramagnetic body P, and a diamagnetic body D, in it, and let N and S represent the two walls of iron associated with the magnet (2465) which form its boundary, we shall then be able to obtain a clear idea of the direction of the lines of magnetic force in the field. Now the two bodies, P and D, cannot be represented by supposing merely that they have the same polarities in opposite directions. The 1 polarity of P is importantly unlike the 3 polarity of D; but if D be considered as having the reverse polarities of P, then the one polarity of P should be like the 4 polarity of D, whereas it is more unlike to that than to the 3 polarity of D, or even to its own 2 polarity.

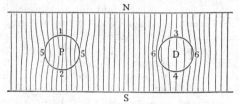
Fig. 3

2822. There are therefore two essential differences in the nature of the polarities dependent on conduction: the difference in the direction of the lines of force abutting on the polar surfaces, when the comparison is with a magnet reversed, and the difference of convergence and divergence of these lines, when compared with a magnet not reversed; and hence a diamagnetic body is not in that condition of polarity which may be represented by turning a paramagnetic body end for end, while it retains its magnetic state.

2823. Diamagnetic bodies in media more diamagnetic than themselves would have the polar condition of paramagnetic bodies (2819); and in like manner paramagnetic conductors in media more paramagnetic than themselves would have the polarity of diamagnetic bodies.

2824. Besides these differences the bodies must have an equatorial condition, which, in the two classes of conductors, would be able to produce corresponding effects. The whole of the equatorial part of P (*Fig. 3*) is alike in po- lar relation to the body P, or to the lines of force in the surrounding space; and there is a like correspondence in the equatorial parts of D, either to itself or to space; but these parts in P or in D differ in intensity of power one from the other, and both from the general in- tensity of the space. Such equatorial conditions must, I think, exist as a consequence of the definite character of any given section of the magnetic field (2809).

2825. Though the experimental results of these polarities are not absent, still they are not very evident or capable of being embodied in many striking forms; and that because of the extreme weakness of the forces brought in- to play, as compared with those larger forces exhibited in the mutual action of magnets. Hence it is, that the many attempts to show a polarity in bismuth have either failed, or other phenomena have been mistaken for those prop- erly referable to such a cause. The highest, and therefore the most delicate, test of polarity we possess, is in the subjection of the polar body to the line of direction of magnetic forces of a very high degree, when developed around it; and hence it is, that the pointing of a sub- stance between the poles of a powerful magnet is continually referred to for such a purpose. It would be, and is utterly in vain to look for any mutual action between the poles of two weak paramagnetic or diamagnetic conductors in many cases, when the action of these same poles is abundantly manifest in their relation to the almost infinitely stronger poles of a pow- erful horseshoe or electro-magnet.

2826. I took a tube *a* (*Fig. 4*), filled with a saturated solution of sulphate of cobalt, and suspended it between the poles of the great electro-magnet; it set readily and well. Another tube, *b*, was then filled with a saturated solution of sulphate of iron, and being associ- ated with the S pole of the magnet, was brought near the cobalt tube in the manner shown, but not the slightest effect on the position of *a* was observable. The tube *b* was changed into the position *c*, to double any effect that might be present, but no trace of mutual action between the poles of *a* and *b* was visible (2819).

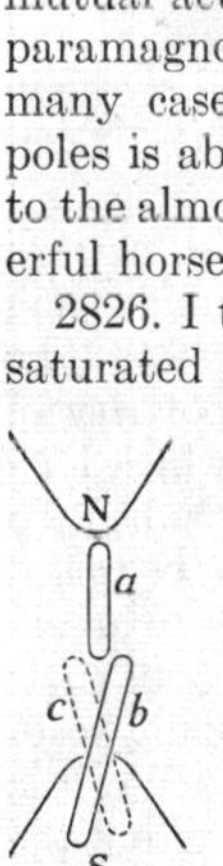

Fig. 4

2827. To increase the effect, the magnetic solution tube was suspended in water, as a good diamagnetic medium, between flat-faced poles (*Fig. 5*). It pointed well. Two bottles of

saturated solution of sulphate of iron were placed at *d* and *e*, but they did not alter the po- sition of *a*; being removed into the positions *f* and *g*, neither was any sensible alteration of

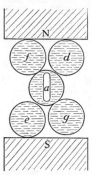

Fig. 5

the position of *a* produced. I made the same kind of exper- iment with an air-tube in water, in which case it points axially (2406), with the same negative result. I do not mean to assert that there was absolutely no effect pro- duced in these cases (2819); but if any, it must have been inappreciably small, and shows how unfit such means are to compare with those which are supplied by the pointing of a body when under the influence of powerful magnets. If polarity cannot be found by these methods in paramagnetic bodies so strongly influential as saturated solution of iron, nickel or cobalt, it can hardly be expected to manifest itself by analogous actions in the much weaker cases of diamagnetic substances.

2828. When a spherical paramagnetic con- ductor is placed midway in a field of equal mag- netic force, it occupies a place of unstable equi- librium, from which, if it be displaced ever so little, it will continue to move until it has gained the iron boundary walls of the field (2465, 2810); this is a consequence of its par- ticular polar condition. If the sphere were free to change its form, it would elongate in the di- rection of the magnetic axis; or if it were a sol- id of an elongated form, it would point axially, both consequences of its polar condition (2811).

2829. So also in the case of diamagnetic bod- ies, their peculiar condition of polarity is shown by corresponding facts, namely, by a spherical portion having its place of stable equilibrium in the middle of the magnetic field (2812), by a fluid portion tending to expand equatorially and become an oblate spheroid (2813), and by the equatorial pointing of an elongated por- tion (2812). If pointed magnetic poles are used, then the effects are very much stronger, but are exactly the same in kind, and de- pendent upon the same causes and polar con- ditions.

2830. There are another set of effects pro- duced, which are either the results of the axial polarity just referred to, or else may be consid- ered as consequences of the condition of the equatorial parts of the conductors (2824). Two balls of iron, in a field of equal force, if retained in a plane at right angles to the line of force, i.e., with their equatorial parts in juxtaposition, separate from each other with considerable power (2814), and the probability is that two infinitely weaker bodies of the paramagnetic class would separate in like manner. Two portions of phosphorus, being a diamagnetic substance, have been found also to separate under the same circumstances (2815).

2831. The motions here are of the same kind, whereas they might have been expected to be the reverse (2816) of each other; still they are perfectly consistent. The diamagnetics ought to separate, for the field is stronger in lines of magnetic force between them than on the outsides, as may easily be seen by considering the two spheres D D in *Fig. 6*; and therefore this motion is consistent, and is in accordance generally with the opening or set equatorially, either of separate portions or of a continuous mass of such substances (2829), in their tendency to go from stronger to weaker places of action. On the other hand, the two balls of iron, P P, have weaker lines of force between them than on the outside; and as their tendency is to pass from weaker to stronger places of action, they also separate to fulfil the requisite condition of equilibrium of forces. Finally, a paramagnetic and a diamagnetic body attract each other (2817); and they ought to do so, for the diamagnetic body finds a place of weaker action towards the paramagnetic body, and the paramagnetic substance finds a place of stronger action in the vicinity of the diamagnetic body, D P, *Fig. 6*.

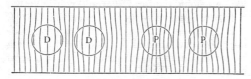

Fig. 6

2832. I have frequently spoken of iron in illustration of the action of paramagnetic conductors, and considered the polarity which it acquires as the same with that of these conductors; but I must now make clear a distinction, which exists in my mind, with regard to the polarity of a magnet, and the polarity, as I have called it, due to mere conduction. This distinction has an important influence in the case of iron. A permanent magnet has a polarity in itself, which is possessed also by its par-

ticles; and this polarity is essentially dependent upon the power which the magnet inherently possesses. It, as well as the power which produces it, is of such a nature, that we cannot conceive a mere space void of matter to possess either the one or the other, whatever form that space may be supposed to have, or however strong the lines of magnetic force passing across it. The polarity of a conductor is not necessarily of this kind; is not due to a determinate arrangement of the cause or source of the magnetic action, which in its turn overrules and determines the special direction of the lines of force (2807); but is simply a consequence of the condensation or expansion of these lines of force, as the substance under consideration is more or less fitted to convey their influence onwards. It is evidently a very different thing to originate such lines of power and *determine their direction* on the one hand, and only to assist or retard their progression without any reference to their direction on the other. Speaking figuratively, the difference may be compared to that of a voltaic battery and the conducting wires, or substances, which connect its extremities. The stream of force passes through both, but it is the battery which originates it, and also determines its direction; the wire is only a better or worse conductor, however by variation of form or quality it may diffuse, condense, or vary the stream of power.

2833. If this distinction be admitted, we have to consider whether iron, when under the influence of lines of magnetic power, becomes a magnet and has its proper polarity, or is a mere paramagnetic conductor with conducting powers of the highest possible degree. In the first place, it would have the real polarity of the magnet, in the second only that which I assign to oxygen and other conducting bodies. To my mind the iron is a magnet. It can be raised as a *source* of lines of magnetic power to an extreme degree of energy in the electro-magnet; and though, when very soft, it usually loses nearly all this power upon the cessation of the electric current, yet such is not the case if the mass of metal forms a continuous circuit or ring, for then it can retain the force for hours and weeks together, and is evidently for the time an original source of power independent of any voltaic current. Hence I think that the iron under the influence of lines of magnetic power becomes a magnet; and though it then has the same kind of polarity, as to direction, as a mere paramagnetic conductor, subject to the same lines of force, still with a great difference; for as the internal particles of iron become in a degree each a system producing magnetism, so their polarity is correlated and combined together into a polar whole, which, being infinitely more intense, may also be very different in the disposition of its force in different parts, to that equivalent to polarity, which a mere conductor possesses.

2834. It appears to me also as very probable that when iron, nickel and cobalt, are heated up to the respective temperatures at which they lose their wonderful degree of power (2347) and retain only so small a portion of it as to require the most sensible test to make it manifest (2343), they then have passed into the condition of paramagnetic conductors, have lost all ability to acquire that state of internal polarity they could assume as magnets, and now have no other polarity than that which belongs to them as masses of paramagnetic matter (2819). It is also probable that in many states of combination these metals may take up the mere conducting state; for instance, that whilst in the protoxide, iron may constitute a magnet, in the peroxide it is only a conductor; and in this respect it is not a little curious to find oxygen, which as a gas is a paramagnetic body (2782), reducing iron down to, and indeed far below its own condition, weight for weight. In their various salts also and solutions, these metals may, in conjunction with the combined matter, be acting only as conductors.

2835. Perhaps I ought not to have called the condition of concentration or expansion of the lines of magnetic force in the bodies acting as conductors a *polarity,* inasmuch as true magnetic polarity depends essentially and entirely on the *direction* of the line of force, and not on any mere compression or divergence of these lines. I have done so only that I might point with the more facility to facts and views that have heretofore been associated with some supposed polarity in the bodies which, whether paramagnetic or diamagnetic, I have been considering as mere conductors, and I hope that no mistake of my meaning will arise in consequence. I have already asked for such liberty in the use of phrases (*lines of force, conducting power*, &c.) (2149, 2797) as may, for the time, set me free from the bondage of preconceived notions; these are, for that very reason, exceedingly useful, provided they are for the time sufficiently restricted in their meaning, and do not admit of any hurtful looseness or inaccuracy in the representation of facts.

¶ iii. *Magnecrystallic Conduction*[1]

2836. The beautiful researches of Plücker in relation to magneoptic phenomena cannot have been forgotten, and I hope that my own experiments on magnecrystallic results (2454, &c.) are remembered in conjunction with his; the phenomena described by us are, as I believe, due to a common cause, and are the same in kind; and as far as they are presented by pure transparent bodies, are I think brought by Plücker into a proper relation to the positive and negative optic axis of such bodies.[2] In these cases a crystalline body sets powerfully, or takes up a particular position when placed in a field of magnetic force (2464, 2479, 2550), without reference to its paramagnetic or diamagnetic character (2562), and also without assuming any state which it can on its removal bring away with it (2504).

2837. If the idea of conduction be applied to these magnecrystallic bodies, it would seem to satisfy all that requires explanation in their special results. A magnecrystallic substance would then be one which in the crystallized state could conduct onwards, or permit the exertion of the magnetic force with more facility in one direction than another; and that direction would be the magnecrystallic axis. Hence, when in the magnetic field, the magnecrystallic axis would be urged into a position coincident with the magnetic axis, by a force correspondent to that difference, just as if two different bodies were taken, when the one with the greater conducting power displaces that which is weaker.

2838. The effect of position would thus be accounted for (2586); and also the greater aptness for magnetic conduction in one direction than in another (2588, 2591): and, what appeared to me as an anomaly in the supposition, that a line of force could have reference indifferently to any part of a plane (2600) disappears. That heat should take away this conducting power (2570) seemed perfectly consistent with what we know of the effect of heat on the magnetic condition of iron, oxygen, &c., and also upon the conducting power for electricity in such cases as platinum, sulphuret of silver, &c. Finally, the assumption did not appear inconsistent with the state which the body seems to assume for the time during which it is under the magnetic force (2609, &c.).

<hr>

[1] I must refer here to the important paper by MM. Tyndall and H. Knoblauch on this subject in the *Philosophical Magazine*, 1850, Vol. XXXVII, p. 1. M. F. January 6, 1851.
[2] *Philosophical Magazine*, 1849. Vol. XXXIV, p. 450.

2839. But if such a view were correct, it would appear to follow that a diamagnetic body like bismuth ought to be less diamagnetic when its magnecrystallic axis is parallel (as nearly as may be) to the magnetic axis, than when it is perpendicular to it. In the two positions it should be equivalent to two substances having different conducting powers for magnetism, and therefore, if submitted to the differential balance, ought to present differential phenomena, corresponding in kind to those of oxygen and nitrogen (2774), or phosphorus and bismuth, or any other two differing bodies. Though I have given certain results on a former occasion which seemed to bear on this point (2551, 2552, 2553), they are not satisfactory in the present state of our knowledge, because the difference, if any, would be small (2552), and quickly hidden by the employment of a single pointed pole. Other experiments, formerly described (2554–2561), would not show a small difference in diamagnetic force (though quite fitted for their intended purpose), because they were made with flat-faced poles, and a field nearly equal in magnetic power.

2840. The differential torsion balance (2773) enabled me to return to this matter with better hopes of success. A consistent group of bismuth crystals was selected (2457) and hung up on one side of the double cone core (2738), whilst a cylinder of flint-glass was opposed to it on the other. The flint-glass was to be a standard of reference, and therefore neither its place on the balance nor condition was altered during the experiment. The bismuth group was placed with its magnecrystallic axis horizontal, and so that it could be turned in a horizontal plane, that the axis might be at one time parallel to the magnetic axis (or lines of force), and at other times perpendicular to it, but without any alteration of the distance of its centre of gravity from the opposed glass cylinder. Hence, having either one position or the other, it could still be compared with the cylinder.

2841. The magnecrystallic axis was first made parallel to the core or magnetic axis, the magnetic power developed, and when the diamagnetic bodies had taken their position of rest or stable equilibrium, the place of the balance lever was observed and recorded by means of a ray of light reflected from a mirror attached to it. Then the bismuth was turned through 90°, or until its magnecrystallic axis was perpendicular to the axis of the double cone core; and now, when the magnet was excited, the place of the bismuth was found to be farther out from the core than before. On being turned through 90° more, so as to be in a position diametral to the first (2461), its place was again a little nearer to the magnet; and when in the fourth position, which is diametral to the second, then it was farther out. Thus the crystallized bismuth proved to be diamagnetic in different degrees, according with certain directions of its magnecrystallic axis, being more diamagnetic when this axis was perpendicular or transverse to the lines of magnetic force, than when it was parallel to them; and thus the expectation founded upon theoretical considerations (2839) was confirmed.

2842. I tried to obtain similar results with a cube of calcareous spar (2597); for it is evident that if its optic axis, being in a horizontal plane, is first placed parallel to the magnetic axis and then perpendicular to it, the body ought to be more diamagnetic in the first position than in the second, inasmuch as the latter is the position which it takes up under the influence of its magnecrystallic or magneoptic condition. I could not however obtain any distinct results, partly because its power is in all respects very inferior to the bismuth, partly because of the present imperfection of my torsion balance, and partly because of the size and shape of the calcareous spar. A sphere or a cylinder, having the optic axis perpendicular to the axis of the cylinder, would be more correct as forms of the substances to be tried.

2843. In concluding this part of the subject relating to the magnetic conducting power, I will now refer to some of the cases which I think experimentally establish its *existence* in the two subdivisions of magnetic bodies (2805). The place and position of iron in a field of equal force (2810, 2811) is no doubt a result of the extraordinary power which this body has of transmitting the magnetic force across the space which it occupies, whether the particles of the iron be considered as polar or not (2832), and therefore I accept the converse phenomena as to place and position of a diamagnetic body (2812, 2813) as proof that it has less power of transmitting the magnetic force than the space it occupies, and from that conclude that it conducts diamagnetically (2802).

2844. The separation of paramagnetic bodies in the equatorial direction is a proof of the manner in which, by their better conduction, they disturb the position of the lines of force in the medium around them (2831). The separation of two diamagnetic bodies, under the same circumstances, is an equal proof of the manner in which, by difference of conducting power, they also disturb the disposition of the force (2831). The equatorial attraction of a para-magnetic and a diamagnetic body for each other, when they are in a medium, which in conducting power is between the two (2831) is a proof not only of conduction in both but also of their reverse condition in respect to each other and the medium.

2845. The place of a crystal of bismuth, either nearer to or farther from the magnetic axis (2841), according as its magnecrystallic axis is parallel or perpendicular to the axial line, is also a case of the difference of conducting power, and therefore of the possession of that power by the diamagnetic body. Many other cases might be quoted in illustration of the existence of that power which I assumed as conducting power (2797), and which probably nobody may be inclined to deny. I will suppose that the above are enough to explain my meaning.

2846. It is hardly necessary for me to say that magnetic conduction does not mean electro-conduction, or anything like it. The very best electro-conductors, as silver, gold and copper, are below mere space in their ability to favour the transmission of magnetic force, so deficient are they in what I have called magnetic conduction. There is a striking analogy between this conduction of magnetic force and what I formerly called specific inductive capacity (1252, &c.) in relation to static electricity, which I hope will lead to further development of the manner in which lines of power are affected in bodies, and in part transmitted by them.

§ 33. *Atmospheric Magnetism*[1]

¶ 1. *General Principles*

2847. It is to me an impossible thing to perceive, that two ninths of the atmosphere by

[1] A most important paper by Professor Christie, "On the Theory of the Diurnal Variation of the Magnetic Needle," appears in the *Philosophical Transactions* for 1827, p. 308. Led by the discoveries of Seebeck in thermo-magnetism and the experiments of Cumming, he was induced to search how far the idea of thermo-currents or thermo-magnetic polarity would apply to the natural phenomena, and concludes (p. 327), that, admitting that the *earth and the atmosphere* are substances in which such action can under any circumstances take place, these experiments would indicate that *any portion of the earth bounded by parallel planes with the atmosphere surrounding it, would become similarly polarized if one part were more heated than another.* Thus considering alone *the equatorial regions of the earth,* we should have *two magnetic poles on the northern side, and on the southern side two poles similarly posited; the poles of different names being opposed to each other on the contrary sides of the equator.*

weight, is a highly magnetic body, subject to great changes in its magnetic character, by variations in its physical conditions of temperature and condensation or rarefaction (2780), and at the same time subject to these physical changes in a high degree, by annual and diurnal variations, in its relation to the sun, without being persuaded that it must have much to do with the disposition of the magnetic forces upon the surface of the earth (2796), and may perhaps account for a large part of the annual, diurnal and irregular variations, for short periods, which are found to occur in relation to that power. I cannot pretend to discuss this great question with much understanding, seeing that I have very little of that special knowledge which has been accumulated by the exertions of the great and distinguished labourers, Humboldt, Hansteen, Arago, Gauss, Sabine,

I ought to refer the readers of my paper to a theory of the *cause* of the daily variations by M. A. de la Rive, founded upon the idea of thermo-electric currents in the atmosphere and earth; it will be found in a memoir entitled "On the Diurnal Variation of the Magnetic Needle," *Annales de Chimie,* 1849, XXV, p. 310.

A friend has recently called my attention to an observation by M. E. Becquerel, which has reference to the present subject, and is in the following words. "If we reflect that the earth is encompassed by a mass of air, equivalent in weight to a layer of mercury of 30 inches, we may inquire whether such a mass of magnetic gas, continually agitated and submitted to the regular and irregular variations of pressure and temperature does not intervene in some of the phenomena dependent on terrestrial magnetism. If we calculate in fact what is the magnetic force of this fluid mass, we find that it is equivalent to an immense plate of iron, of a thickness a little more than $^1/_{10}$th of a millimetre of diameter (?), and which covers the whole surface of the globe." This passage is at pp. 311, 342, of Vol. XXVIII, *Annales de Chimie,* 1850, being contained in an excellent memoir, in which the author has well worked out those differential actions of different media, which I developed generally *five* years ago: *Experimental Researches,* 2357, 2361, 2406, 2414, 2423, &c. By such means he has rediscovered the magnetic character of oxygen and taken measurements of its force, being evidently unacquainted with the account that I gave of this substance in relation to nitrogen and other gases *three* years ago, in a letter published in the *Philosophical Magazine* for 1847, Vol. XXXI, p. 401, and also in Poggendorff's *Annalen* and elsewhere; hence the observations above. I cannot wonder at this, for I myself was not aware of M. E. Becquerel's paper until very lately. In my letter of 1847, I speak of oxygen as being magnetic in common air, p. 410; in carbonic acid, p. 414; in coal gas, p. 415; in hydrogen, p. 415, its power then being equal to its gravity. I say that air owes its place to the oxygen and nitrogen in it, p. 416, and tried to separate these constituents by attracting the oxygen and repelling the nitrogen. At the end of the paper I hesitate in deciding where the true zero between magnetic and diamagnetic bodies is to be placed, and refer to the atmosphere as being liable to affections under the magnetic influence of the earth. It was these old results which led me on to the present researches. —M. F. Nov. 28, 1850.

and many others, who have wrought so zealously at terrestrial magnetism over the surface of the whole earth. But as it has fallen to my lot to introduce certain fundamental physical facts, and as I have naturally thought much upon the general principles which tend to establish their relation to the magnetic actions of the atmosphere, I may be allowed to state these principles as well as I can, that others may be placed in possession of the subject. If the principles are right, they will soon find their special application to magnetic phenomena as they occur at various parts of the globe.

2848. The earth presents us with a spheroidal body, which, consisting of both paramagnetic and diamagnetic substances, disposed with much irregularity as regards its large divisions of earth and ocean, are also equally irregularly disposed and intermingled in its smaller portions. Nevertheless it is, on the whole, a magnet, and, as far as we at this moment are concerned, an original source of that power. And though we cannot conceive at present that all the particles of the earth contribute, as sources, to its magnetism, inasmuch as many of them are diamagnetic, and many non-conductors of electric currents, yet it is difficult to say that any large portion is not concerned in the production of the force; hereafter it may be necessary, perhaps, to consider certain parts as mere conductors, i.e., as parts merely permeated by the lines of force, originating elsewhere, but for the present the whole may be assumed, according to the theory of Gauss, as a mighty compound magnet.

2849. The magnetic force of this great system is disposed with a certain degree of regularity. We have the opportunity of recognising it only as it is exhibited in one shell or surface, which, being very irregular in form, is always the same to us, for we rarely, if ever, pass out of it; or if we do, as in a balloon, only to an insensible extent. This is the surface of the earth and water of our planet. The magnetic lines of force which pass in or across *this surface* are made known to us, as respects their direction and intensity, by their action on small standard magnets; but their average course or their temporary variations *below or above*, i.e., in the air above, or the earth beneath, are only dimly indicated by variations of the force at the surface of the earth, and these variations are so limited in their information, that they do not tell us whether the cause is above or below.

2850. The lines of force issue from the earth in the northern and southern parts with different but corresponding degrees of inclination, and incline to and coalesce with each other over the equatorial parts. Their general disposition is represented by the system, which emanates from a globe having within one or two short magnets adjusted in relation to the axis. There seems reason to believe, from the analogy of such globes to the earth, that the lines of magnetic force which proceed from the earth return to it; but in their circuitous course they may extend through space to a distance of many diameters of the earth, to tens of thousands of miles. Messrs. Gay-Lussac and Biot, in their ascent in a balloon, perceived some indication of a diminution in the intensity of the magnetic force at a height of about four miles from the surface; but we shall shortly perceive that they might be at the time in the midst of influences sufficient to account for all the effect, so that none of it might be occasioned by removal from the earth as a magnet. The increase of the intensity of the magnetic force, as we proceed from the equator towards the poles, accords with the idea of the enormous extension of this power.

2851. These lines proceed through space with a certain degree of facility, of which a general idea may be gained from ordinary knowledge, or from experiments and observations formerly made (2787). Whether there are any circumstances which can affect their passage through mere space, and so cause variations in their condition; whether variations in what has been called the temperature of space could, if they occurred, alter its power of transmitting the magnetic influence, are questions which cannot be answered at present, although the latter does not seem to be entirely beyond the reach of experiment.

2852. This space forms the great abyss into which such lines of force as we are able to take cognizance of by our observing instruments, which issue from the earth, proceed, at least at all parts of the globe where there is a sensible dip. But, as it were, between the earth and this space, there is interposed the atmosphere; which, however considerable we may estimate it in height, is so small when compared to the size of the earth, or to the extent of space beyond it into which the lines of force pass, that the idea of its being a changeable, active something interposed *between* two systems far more extensive and steady in their nature and condition, will not lead to any serious error. It is at the bottom of this atmosphere that we live and make all our inquiries, whether by observation or experiment.

2853. The atmosphere consists, as far as we are concerned at present, of four volumes of nitrogen and one volume of oxygen, or by weight, of three and a half parts of the former and one part of the latter. These substances are nearly uniformly mixed throughout, so that, as regards their manner of investing the earth, they act magnetically as a single medium; nor does there seem to be any tendency in the terrestrial magnetic forces to cause their separation,[1] though they differ very strikingly in their constitution as regards this power.

2854. *The nitrogen* of the air does not appear to be either paramagnetic or diamagnetic; if removed from zero, in either of these respects, it is only to a very small extent (2783, 2784). Whether dense or rare, it has apparently the same relation to and equality with space, as far as the present means of observation have proceeded. As respects the other element of change, namely, temperature, I concluded, from former imperfect experiments,[2] that nitrogen became more diamagnetic when heated than before; but as it was then mixed with the oxygen of the air, and the results were mingled together, I have, for the purposes of the present research, repeated the experiments far more carefully.

2855. A small helix of platinum wire, fixed at the end of thicker copper wires, could be placed in any position beneath the poles of the great electro-magnet, and being ignited by a voltaic battery, served to raise the temperature of the gas around it. The magnetic poles were raised; were terminated by hemispheres of soft iron 0.76 of an inch in diameter and 0.2 of an inch apart; and were covered by a glass shade, resting upon a thick flat bed of vulcanized caoutchouc. A tube passed through the bed, rising up to the top of the shade, by which any required gas could be introduced. A very thin plate of mica, about 3 inches square, was covered with an attenuated coat of wax on the upper side, and fixed horizontally over the magnetic poles within the shade. The small platinum helix was so placed as to be beneath the space, between the poles, and a little on one side of the axial line, so that a current of hot air rising upwards from it, could pass to the mica plate, and by melting the wax show where it came against the mica.

2856. All acted exceedingly well, *air* being in the glass shade. When there was no magnetic power on, the hot air from the ignited helix rose perpendicularly, and melted a neat round portion of the wax, showing the place of the current under natural circumstances; but when the magnet was thrown into action, then the wax on the mica remained unchanged, the hot air being thrown so far away from the axial line, and so cooled by its forcible mixture with the neighbouring air, as to be unable to melt a spot of wax anywhere. The moment the magnetic power was suspended, the column of hot air rose vertically and regained its original position.

2857. *Carbonic acid gas* was then sent into the shade, until twice as much as the contents of the shade had passed through the pipe (2855); but as it was heavy and the common air could make its way out only at the bottom of the shade, there was no doubt air mixed with the carbonic acid, which at last remained about the poles. The platinum coil being now heated, the column of hot gas rose vertically, as before. On putting on the magnetic force it was deflected from the axial line, passing equatorially, and melted the wax about half an inch off from the former place. Believing that even this effect might be due to the air mingled with the gas, other two volumes of carbonic acid gas were directed into and through the vessel. After this the magnetic force caused much less deflection of the rising column. Two volumes more of carbonic acid were sent through, and now the hot current of gas rose so nearly vertical that there was scarcely any sensible difference of its place when the magnetic power was in full action, or when it was entirely absent. Hence I conclude that carbonic acid gas is very little affected in its diamagnetic relations by a difference of temperature equal to that between natural temperatures and a full red heat.

2858. *Nitrogen.* This gas was prepared by passing common air slowly over burning phosphorus, and after being washed for twelve or fourteen hours, was sent into the shade so as to displace the carbonic acid. As it was lighter than the latter, it performed that service very well, and the portion remaining in the vessel probably contained no other oxygen or air than that it carried in with it. This nitrogen being then heated by the platinum coil, was almost as indifferent to the magnet as the carbonic acid. The heated column rose (nearly) to the same spot against the mica, whether the magnetic power was active or not. It went outwards or equatorially a very small degree when the mag-

[1] *Philosophical Magazine*, 1847, Vol. XXXI, p. 416.
[2] *Ibid.*, p. 418.

net was active, but this I attributed to a little oxygen still left with the nitrogen; and indeed nitric oxide gas shows oxygen in nitrogen so prepared. The platinum coil was raised to as high a temperature as it could well support without fusion, and yet there was only this small effect sensible; hence I conclude that hot nitrogen is not more diamagnetic than cold nitrogen, and that indeed its magnetic relation is noways affected by such change of temperature.

2859. I raised the French shade (2855) an inch for a moment, and then instantly placed it down again; and now, on making the magnet active and the coil hot, there was so much effect of dispersion of the gas within that the melted spot of wax appeared nearly an inch outside of the standard place, yet only a very small portion of air or of oxygen could have entered the vessel under these circumstances.

2860. The nitrogen of the air is therefore, as regards the magnetic force, a very indifferent body; it does not appear to be either paramagnetic or diamagnetic; neither does it present any difference in its relation, whether it be dense or rare, or at high or low temperatures. I formerly found that the diamagnetic metals, when heated, did not seem to change in their relation to the magnet (2397), and this now appears to be the case with such neutral or diamagnetic bodies as nitrogen and carbonic acid gases.

2861. *The oxygen* of the air differs in a most extraordinary degree from the nitrogen. It is highly paramagnetic, being, bulk for bulk, equivalent to a solution of protosulphate of iron, containing, of the crystallized salt, seventeen times the weight of the oxygen (2794). It becomes less paramagnetic, volume for volume (2780), as it is rarefied, and apparently in the simple proportion of its rarefaction, the temperature remaining the same. When its temperature is *raised*, the expansion consequent thereon being permitted,[1] it loses very greatly of its paramagnetic force; and there is sufficient reason, from a former result with air,[2] to conclude, that when its temperature is lowered its paramagnetic condition is exalted. How much its paramagnetic intensity might be increased by lowering it to the temperature of freezing mercury, as at the north or south poles of the earth, we cannot at present tell. Though a gas, it is apparently like the solid metals, iron, nickel or cobalt, when they are within the range of temperature which affects their magnetic forces;

[1] *Philosophical Magazine*, 1847, Vol. XXXI, p. 417.
[2] *Ibid.*, p. 406.

and it may, perhaps, like them, rise by cooling to a very high state.

2862. These relations it preserves when mingled with nitrogen in the air, as long as its physical and chemical conditions remain unchanged; but it is not irrelevant to remark, that every operation by which this active part of the atmosphere changes in its nature and passes into combinations, takes away its paramagnetic powers, whether the result be solid, liquid or gaseous.

2863. Hence the atmosphere is, in common phrase, a highly magnetic medium. The air that stands upon every square foot of surface on the earth, is equivalent, in magnetic force, to 8160 lbs. of crystallized protosulphate of iron (2794, 2861). This medium is, by every change in its density, whether of the kind indicated by the barometer, or caused by the presence or absence of the sun, changed in its magnetic relations. Further, every variation of temperature produces apparently its own change of force, in addition to that caused by the mere expansion or contraction in volume, and none of these alterations can happen without affecting the magnetic force emanating from the earth, and causing variations, both in its intensity and direction, at the earth's surface. Whether these changes are in the right direction and sufficient in quantity to supply a cause for the variations of the terrestrial magnetic power is the point now to be considered, for the illustration of which I will endeavour to construct a type case, and then apply it, as well as I can, to the natural facts.

2864. Let us assume the existence of two globes of air distinct from the surrounding atmosphere, by a difference of temperature or by a difference of density: the assumption is not too extravagant for an illustration, since Prout showed that there were masses of air, larger or smaller, floating about in the atmosphere, and singularly distinct from the surrounding parts, by temperature and other circumstances. Not to complicate the expression, we will leave out of view, at present, the attenuation upwards, and will consider one of these globes as *colder* or denser than the contiguous parts, and that it is in a portion of space which without it would present a field of equal magnetic force, i.e., having parallel lines of equal intensity of force passing across it.

2865. The air of such a globe will *facilitate* the transmission of the magnetic force through the space which it occupies (2807), making it superior, in that respect, to the surrounding atmosphere or space, and therefore more lines of magnetic force will pass through it than elsewhere (2809). The disposition of these lines, in respect to the line of the dip of the place, will be something like what is represented in *Fig.* 7 (2874), and consequently the globe will be polarized as a conductor (2821, 2822) of the paramagnetic class. Hence the intensity of the magnetic force and its direction will vary, not only within but without the globe, and these will vary in opposite directions, in different places, under the influence of laws which are perfectly regular and well known.

2866. First, as regards the *intensity*, which before was uniform (2864). If the intensity is to be considered as expressing the amount of force which passes through any given place, then, in consequence of the definite amount of power which belongs to any section, as *a a*, of a given amount of lines of magnetic force (2809), a concentration of these lines towards the middle, P, will cause an increase of intensity at that part, and a diminution at some other parts, as *b b*, from whence the influence of the power has been partly removed. Hence, supposing the normal condition to exist at *a*, if a test of intensity were carried from *a* to P, it would gradually enter parts *b* and *c*, in which the intensity was less than the normal condition, and these might be either without or within the globe P, or both (according to its temperature relative to the surrounding air, its size and other circumstances); it would then arrive at parts having the normal intensity; and lastly, at parts, P, having an intensity greater than the surrounding space; as it went outwards, on the opposite side of P, corresponding variations would occur in the reverse order.

2867. On transporting the test upwards, in the direction of the dip from *e*, where the intensity may be considered as normal, it would gradually occupy positions at *f g*, &c., in which the intensity would increase until it arrived at P, after which it would pass through places of less and less intensity, until at *p* it would again find the force in the normal state. If the test, in being carried upwards, be not taken along *the line of the dip*, then it will of course pass through variations like those described on the line *a* P, growing more and more in extent until the direction coincides with the line *a* P, which is at right angles to the dip and where they are at a maximum. Hence, to pass upwards through such a globe of cold air in our latitude, where the dip is 70° nearly, and at the equator, where

it is 0°, would be a very different matter, and the necessary natural results of such a difference ought to appear hereafter.

2868. But a magnetic needle or bar is not a test of such intensity, i.e., it will not tell these differences, or it may tell them in a contrary direction. To understand this point, we have to consider that a needle vibrates by gathering upon itself, because of its magnetic condition and polarity, a certain amount of the lines of force, which would otherwise traverse the space about it; and assuming that it underwent no change by change of temperature, it would be affected in proportion to any variations in the intensity of these lines, provided everything else remained the same. But being under natural circumstances surrounded by the atmosphere, which is a medium liable to variation in its magnetic condition, both by heat and rarefaction, and by these variations affects the intensity or quantity of the force, it will vary in its indications by variations in these conditions. Thus, for instance, if it were in a large sphere of oxygen, I expect that it would, by its number of vibrations or otherwise, indicate a certain intensity; if the oxygen were expanded, that it would indicate a higher intensity, although the same amount of lines of force and magnetic energy were passing through the oxygen as before. If the oxygen were made dense, then becoming a better conductor, I presume it would convey onwards *more* of the force and the magnet *less*, for the power would be partly transferred from the unchanging magnet to the improving conductor around it.

2869. These experiments can hardly be made with oxygen except by means of extremely delicate apparatus, but like effects are easily shown experimentally in selected analogous cases. Thus let a thin small tube of flint-glass, about 1 inch long and ½ an inch in diameter, be filled with a saturated solution of protosulphate of iron, and suspended horizontally by cocoon-silk (2270) between the poles of the electro-magnet, in a vessel which may either contain air or water, or other media (2406). In air it will point axially, and will be analogous to a needle under the earth's influence, and it will point with a certain amount of force. Fill the vessel with water, and now it will point with more force than before, though the water is a worse magnetic conductor than the air which was previously there; and it is precisely because the water *is* a worse conductor that the liquid magnet or test indicates more power. Increase the conducting power of the surrounding medium by adding sulphate of iron to it, and the indication of strength by the tube goes on diminishing, first returning to the degree of power it had in air, and then descending to lower gradations, for it returns with less and less force to its axial position when disturbed from it. So the magnetic needle employed for measuring intensity or magnetic force (for the same meaning is at present understood by the two terms) indicates, in a certain manner, the power thrown upon itself and, I conclude, accurately, provided the condition of the surrounding medium remains magnetically unchanged; but if it be placed in different media or in an altering medium, I expect that it will not measure accurately the intensity in them, i.e. it will not measure directly the amount of force passing relatively through them. The difference in air under different conditions would be very small, still it is that difference which concerns us in *atmospheric magnetism;* and it is very important to know whether, when the magnet indicates an increased intensity of force, it is altogether due to a real increase of the amount of the power at its source as it comes to us from the earth, or in part to a change in the magnetic constitution of the space around the magnet hitherto unknown to us.

2870. If what is now often indifferently called magnetic force or intensity have its results distinguished as of two kinds, namely, those of *quantity* and those of *tension*, then we shall more readily comprehend this matter. At present a needle shows both these as magnetic force, making no distinction between them, yet they produce effects on it often in opposite directions; for as they increase or diminish they both affect the needle alike; but as it is assumed that the tension can change whilst the quantity remains the same, and the quantity can be altered, yet the tension remain unaffected, the result by the needle will then be uncertain. If the tension in a given region be increased by diminishing the conducting power, the needle will show *increased force;* if it be increased by an increase of magnetic power in the earth from some internal action, the needle will still show *increased force*, and will not distinguish the one effect from the other. If the quantity in a region be increased by increasing the conducting power, the needle will show no such increase; on the contrary, it will indicate *diminution* of force, because the tension is diminished; or if the quantity be diminished by diminishing the conducting power, it will show *increased* force. The force might even lose in quantity and gain

in tension in such proportions that the needle should show no change; or it might gain in quantity and lose in tension, and the needle still be entirely indifferent to the whole result.

2871. If my view be correct, then the magnet is not, as at present applied, a perfect measure of the earth's magnetic force; for that may not change when the magnet by the influence of the different conditions of day and night, or of summer and winter, may show a difference. How *far* these uncertainties in its indication may affect the value of the observations made on the horizontal and vertical components of the earth's magnetic force as indications of that which they are expected to tell us, I do not know; but involving, as the effects do, two very different conditions, namely, variation of the conducting power and variation of the amount of force at its source, the one of which is chiefly in the atmosphere and the other in the earth, it seems to me to be of great consequence to the development of the theory of terrestrial magnetism, to have some method if possible, of distinguishing these two points or effects from each other.

2872. Referring again to the model globe, *Fig. 7* (2874), it appears to me, that if a magnet be used as the intensity test, it will indicate a less intensity at P rather than a greater one, for the very reason that the conducting power of the whole globe has been increased; and also, though the apparent diminution of intensity will probably be greater there than elsewhere, that the effect will occur in other parts, especially those on the right and left, and even at *b* and *b*, where the power transmitted, instead of being more, as at P, is really less than the portion transmitted in the normal or equable state of the magnetic field. With a diamagnetic globe of air, i.e., one warmer or more rarefied than the surrounding space (2877), though it would convey less power as being a worse conductor, still it should cause the magnet to set with greater force, and so give an indication of increased intensity, and that also both within and equatorially without the globe.

2873. If it be true that the changes of the medium (2869) can thus affect the magnet and that such changes can rise up to a sensible degree in the gases, then a magnet might make a different number of vibrations in a given time in oxygen and nitrogen gases of the same density, for they are very different in their magnetic relations. It should make the greatest number in nitrogen; perhaps a delicate torsion balance would be a still more sensible test of such a result; but it is probable that the space around the needle should be large, and it would be requisite to ascertain that the two media opposed equal mechanical resistance to the vibrating needle.

2874. The variation of the *direction* caused by the typical globe (2864) might be oblique to the horizontal and vertical planes, and consequently give results of declination and inclination, either separately or together. The direction would not vary in a central line parallel to the general dip of the surrounding space (*Fig.* 7). Along another central line perpendicular to

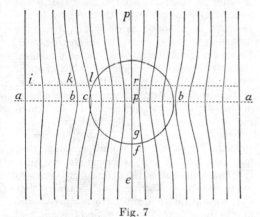

Fig. 7

this (i.e., any line in the equatorial plane), *a* P, there would also be no variation of the direction, but in any other position there would be variations. Thus in the line *i r*, as the free needle passed from *i* to *k*, its lower end would be carried inwards towards the central line of dip P; this effect, after attaining a maximum, perhaps at *l*, would gradually diminish again, and by the time the needle had reached *r* the dip would be normal. Corresponding effects would occur on the opposite side of the axial line *p e;* and if a needle be considered as in any place the dip of which is thus affected, and then be conceived as travelling in a circle round the axial line *p e*, it would always be in the surface of a cone, the apex of which is below.

2875. On the other hand, if the variations of the dip below the equatorial plane *a* P be considered, they will be equal in amount, but in the reverse direction, so that the magnetic needle, when deflected from its normal position, would have its upper end inclined inwards towards the axial line *p e;* or if moved round the axial line would always be in a conical surface, the apex of which is above.

2876. So the dip would vary in such a globe of air in every azimuth; and it would also vary in opposite directions in the upper and lower parts of the globe, and of the affected surrounding space.

2877. If we assume the existence of another typical globe of air (2864), having a higher temperature than the surrounding atmosphere, then its condition will be that of a diamagnetic conductor, and will be represented by *Fig. 9*

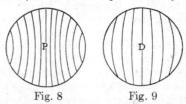

Fig. 8　　　　　　Fig. 9

(2807); and it will have power to affect both the intensity and the direction of the lines of force, in conformity with the action of the former globe, but in the contrary order. As regards the action of these globes, consequent upon the direction of the lines of force in and about them upon a needle coming within their influence, it may, in part, be represented by a magnet placed either in the direction of the needle for the cold globe, or in the reverse direction for the warm one; but as the lines of force of the combined system of the earth and such a magnet are very different in their arrangement to the lines of the earth affected by masses of warm or cold air having only conduction polarity (2820), it would be too much to say that they correspond, or that the effects on the intensity or direction would be the same for similar distance from the centre of the globe of air and the representative magnet.

2878. In endeavouring to proceed, from these hypothetical and comparatively simple cases, which are given only to lead the mind on from the results of experiment to the supposed condition of matters as regards our atmosphere and the earth, we have to consider that though there will be an effect, and though the intensity and direction of the magnetic force, upon the surface of the earth, must vary with changes of temperature and density of the atmosphere, still it will be in a manner very different from that represented by the typical globe of air, for the latter is a case which will never occur, though the variations of the natural case are almost infinite. Still the comparison holds in principle, and we may expect that as the sun leaves us on the west, some effect, correspondent to that of the approach of a body of cold air from the east, will be produced, which will increase and then diminish, and be followed by another series of effects as the sun rises again and brings warm air with him.

2879. The atmosphere diminishes in density upwards, and that diminution will affect the transmission of the magnetic force, but as far as it is constant, the effect produced by it will be constant too. The portion of the atmosphere which lies under the heating influence of the sun, as compared to its depth, will more resemble a slice of air wrapped round the earth than a globe. Still the inflection of the lines of force, both above and below this stratum, will occur, extending into space above and into the earth beneath (2848), according to the known influence of magnetic power and its perfectly definite character (2809). We are placed at the bottom of this layer of air, but as the atmosphere is denser there than higher up, and is also in many cases more affected there by changes of temperature, we are probably in a position where the inflections and variations due to the assumed causes exist in a considerable degree.

2880. There are innumerable circumstances that will break up, more or less, any general or average arrangement of the air temperature. For instance, the diversity of sea and land causes variations of temperature differently in different times of the year, and the extent to which this goes may be learned from the beautiful isothermal charts of Dove, now fortunately to be had in this country.[1] These variations may be expected to give, not merely differences in the regularity, direction and degree of magnetic variation; but because of vicinity, differences so large as to be manifold greater than the mean difference for a given short period, and they may also cause irregularities in the times of their occurrence.

2881. On considering the probable results of the magnetic action of the atmosphere, it appears to me that if the terrestrial magnetic force could be freed from all periodical and small perturbations, and its disposition ascertained for any given time, it might still include certain effects constituting a part of atmospheric magnetism. For instance, there is more air, by weight, over a given portion of the surface of the earth at latitudes from 24° to 34°, than there is either at higher latitudes or at the equator; and that should cause a difference from the disposition of the lines of force which

[1] *Report of the British Association*, 1848, *Reports*, p. 85.

would exist if there were equality in that respect, or if the atmosphere were away. Again, the temperature of the air is greater at the equatorial parts than in latitudes north or south of it; and as elevation of temperature diminishes the conducting power for magnetism, so the proportion of force passing through these parts ought to be less, and that passing through the colder parts greater, than if the temperature of the air were at the same mean degree over the whole surface of the globe, or than if the air were away. Again, there is a greater difference in range of temperature of the air at the equator as we rise upwards than in other parts, and hence the lower part is not so good a conductor proportionately to the upper part, or to space, as elsewhere, where the difference is not so great; the magnetic power, therefore, should be in some degree weakened there, the lines of force being diverted, more or less, from the warm air and thrown into other parts, as the cooler atmosphere and space above, or the earth beneath, according to the principles before explained (2808, 2821, 2877).

2882. The result of *annual variation* that may be expected from the magnetic constitution and condition of the atmosphere seems to me to be of the following kind. Assuming that the axis of rotation of the earth was perpendicular to the plane of its orbit round the sun, and dismissing for the present other causes of magnetic variation than those due to the atmosphere, the two hemispheres of the earth, and the portions of air covering them, would be affected and warmed alike by the sun, or at least would come into a constant relative state, dependent upon the arrangement of land and water; and the lines of magnetic force having taken up their position under the influence of the great dominant causes, whatever they may be, would not be altered by any annual change due to the atmosphere, since the daily mean of the atmospheric effect in a given place would at all parts of the year be alike. Under such circumstances the intensity and direction of the magnetic forces might be considered constant, presuming no sensible change to take place by the difference in distance from the sun which would occur in different parts of the orbit; and, as regards the two magnetic hemispheres, each would be the equivalent of and equal to the other, and they may for the time be considered in their mean or normal state.

2883. But as the axis of the earth's rotation is inclined 23° 28' to the plane of the ecliptic, the two hemispheres will become alternately warmer and colder than each other, and then a variation in the magnetic condition may arise. The air of the cooled hemisphere will conduct magnetic influence more freely than if in the mean state, and the lines of force passing through it will increase in amount, whilst in the other hemisphere the warmed air will conduct with less readiness than before, and the intensity will diminish. In addition to this effect of temperature, there ought to be another due to the increase of the ponderable portion of the air in the cooled hemisphere, consequent upon its contraction and the coincident expansion of the air in the warmer half, both of which circumstances tend to increase the variation in power of the two hemispheres from the normal state. Then as the earth rolls on in its annual journey, that which at one time was the cooler becomes the warmer hemisphere, and consequently in its turn sinks as far below the average magnetic intensity as it before had stood above it, whilst the other hemisphere changes its magnetic condition from less to more intense.

2884. As the sum of the magnetic forces which crop out from the earth wherever there is dip on one side of the magnetic equator must correspond to the sum of like force on the other side (2809), so they would not become more intense in one hemisphere, or more feeble in the other, without a corresponding contraction on the one hand, and enlargement on the other. The line of no dip round the globe may therefore be expected to move alternately north and south every year, or some effect equivalent to that take place. The condition of the two hemispheres under this view may be conceived by supposing an annual undulation of the force to and fro between them, during which, though neither the character nor the general disposition of the power be altered, there is in our winter a concentration and increase of intensity in the northern parts coincident with a diffused and diminished intensity in the south, and in summer the reverse.

2885. In respect to *direction*, alterations may also be anticipated. In the first place, and assuming that the magnetic poles and the poles of the earth coincide, the dip would increase in the cooling hemisphere towards the middle and polar parts; but it ought to diminish towards the magnetic equator, to accord with the concentration of the hemisphere of stronger power and enlargement of the weaker one; whilst on the other hand the dip ought to diminish at the polar and middle parts of the warming hemisphere and increase towards the magnetic equator. The magnetic equator would shift a little north and south of its mean place during each year, simultaneously with the whole system of magnetic lines. But as the magnetic poles do not coincide with those of the earth, or with what may be called the poles of the changing temperatures, so a cause of difference in direction will here arise.

2886. Again, it may be that as oxygen is cooled, its paramagnetic power may increase in a more rapid proportion than that of the change of temperature, so that the chief alteration of the disposition of the earth's force may be in the extreme northern and southern parts; and in combination with the holding power of the earth (2907) may even cause a change the reverse of that expected above in lower latitudes. If in our winter the lines of force were to close together in the polar parts and to open out in lower latitudes, the balance of magnetic force would just as well be sustained as if *all* the lines in our hemisphere were to be compressed and strengthened, and be compensated for by a corresponding change in the south. In the former case, each hemisphere would balance its own forces, in the latter they would be balanced against each other. There can, I think, be no doubt that as far as the mass of the earth and the space above our atmosphere are unchangeable in relation to annual and diurnal variation, so far they would tend to restrain any variation which might depend only on the varying temperature and state of the air; holding as it were the two sides of the variations, the increase and diminution of intensity, or the right and left hand in change of direction, nearer together than they otherwise would be.

2887. Further, if it be supposed that the whole of a hemisphere *is affected at once* in the same direction by change of temperature, it will *not be affected alike, but differently in different latitudes*, because of the difference in amount of that change.

2888. The difference of land and water (2880) will still further break up any expected uniformity of the general result, and cause that certain parts of the cooling hemisphere shall increase in power more in proportion than other parts; and when these parts lie on opposite sides of the magnetic meridian of any given place, they would probably have power to cause an alteration in the declination of the needle at that place.

2889. As the annual changes of temperature are less at the equator than in parts more north or south, so there, probably, little or no annual variation would occur: none indeed as regards the varying temperature or expansion of the air, but only that portion which is consequent upon the alternate changes of the parts on its opposite sides (2884).

2890. Another effect, which may be considered as an annual variation, but which is connected with the diurnal change, may be expected. As the daily changes in temperature of the atmosphere, influential upon a given place in north or south medium latitudes, are greater in extent in summer than in winter, so the corresponding magnetic variations may be expected to vary also, being larger in the northern hemisphere, when the sun is on the north side of the equator, and less when he is present in the southern hemisphere, and producing like correspondent change there.

2891. From a most important investigation by Colonel Sabine,[1] founded on the results of observations at Toronto and Hobarton, the facts appear to be that the magnetic intensity is greater in both hemispheres in those months which are winter in the northern hemisphere, and summer in the southern. Similar results are greatly wanted for other localities, and would show whether the different disposition of land and sea has anything to do with the question, or whether the results at Toronto and Hobarton are true exponents of hemispherical effects. Assuming Toronto and Hobarton as being such exponents, the dip in both hemispheres is greater (i.e., greater north dip at Toronto and south dip at Hobarton) in those months which are winter in the northern, and summer in the southern hemisphere. Whether there is any *annual* variation of the dip or total force in the equatorial parts of the globe is very important to determine. It would be well worth while to take up a station for the express purpose; the instruments are very simple, and the observations would require only a single observer. They are described in the paper referred to. Unfortunately such observations are not even made in Great Britain.

2892. The manner in which the diurnal variation may be produced or affected by the action of the sun on our atmosphere as the earth revolves in its beams has been already generally referred to. The whole portion of atmosphere exposed to the sun receives power to refract the lines of magnetic force which traverse it, and the whole of that which covers the darker hemisphere assumes an equally altered, but contrary state relative to the mean condition of the air. It is as if the earth were inclosed within two enormous magnetic lenses competent to affect the direction of the lines of force passing through them.

2893. I have already said that the action of the atmosphere thus affected might in some degree be compared at night-time to that of an enormous, diffuse, and very feeble ordinary magnet, having the position that it would naturally take according to the line of dip, passing over us from east to west, and including us for the time within its influence: in the day-time the action would be like that of the similar journey, not of a corresponding magnet reversed in direction, but of a corresponding globe of diamagnetic matter (2821). Assuming the maximum heat and cold to occur at midday and midnight, we might expect that the maximum effects would also occur near those periods as regards the variations of intensity (2824, 2866); for, other things being the same, the central parts of the heated and cooled masses are those where the difference of intensity should be greatest.

2894. It might be expected that this variation in the *intensity* would be greatest at those parts of the globe over which the sun passes vertically, or nearly so; but that may depend upon two circumstances at least; first, whether the difference in the day and night temperature is greater there than at other places, because the extent of the variation may be dependent in part upon that difference; and next, whether the amount of effect to be expected is the same for the same difference in number of degrees of temperature at every part of the scale (2886). If the conducting power of oxygen (2800) should be found by future experimental measurements (2960) to increase in a greater proportion for a fall of a given number of degrees at lower temperature than at high ones (including the effect of contraction for that fall [2861]), then it may be that parts more distant from the sun will be more affected than those under it; or if the contrary be the case, less affected than otherwise would be expected.

2895. With regard to the daily variations, as respects the *direction* of the lines of terrestrial magnetic force, or the inclination and declination of the magnetic needle, the principles of the changes that may be expected to occur

[1] "On the means adopted for determining the Absolute Values, Secular Change, and Annual Variation of the Magnetic Force," *Philosophical Transactions*, 1850, p. 201.

have been already referred to (2879); and it remains for me to compare these expectations with a few simple cases of observation, in such a general manner as will tend to show whether the *direction* of action is, both in theory and fact, the same; and whether there is any probability that the effect has been assigned to its true cause; for this purpose I will confine myself entirely at present to a part of the daily variation, namely, the effect of the sun and air as the luminary arrives at and passes over the meridian.

2896. Profiting by the last volume which has issued from the powerful mind and careful hands of Colonel Sabine,[1] I will take the case of Hobarton. The observatory there is in latitude 42° 52′.5 south, and longitude 147° 27′.5 east of Greenwich. The absolute declination is 9° 60′.8 east, and the dip is 70° 39′ south. In order to have the place of the sun and the time of maximum and minimum temperatures at hand, I have transferred the mean temperature for January (summer) for seven years, 1841–48, and the mean temperature for June (winter) for the same period, corresponding to every hour in the day and night, from pp. lxxxiv and cviii to *Fig. 10*, P. 709, where the middle series of numbers represents the hours, the line next below them a base line of temperature at 30° Fahr., and the two curves still lower down the mean hourly temperature for summer and winter. The short lines show generally the direction of the needle east or west of its mean position, the upper end being of course the north extremity. The positions about noon are distinguished by full lines, being those required for more immediate illustration.

2897. The north end of the magnetic needle at Hobarton is most east at 2 o'clock, and most west about 21 o'clock. Being at the extreme west at the latter hour, it passes through the full range of variation, or to the extreme east in five hours, or by 2 o'clock, and then requires the remaining nineteen hours to return to the utmost west. The maximum east and west declination is at 2 and 21 o'clock for summer, and at 3 and 22 o'clock for winter. The vertical positions show at what hours the declination was 0, and correspond with Sabine's zero. From 21 to 2 o'clock the needle passes from one extremity of its variation to the other, the north or upper end travelling in the reverse direction to the sun, so that it and the sun cross the meridian together in opposite directions, nearly about

[1] *Magnetical and Meteorological Observations*, Hobarton, Vol. I, 1850.

or a little before noon. About 2 o'clock the needle is arrested, and after that time returns west, following the sun. It will be proper to state, that the north end of the needle, the motion of which has just been described, is the end towards the equator, and also, the upper end of a dipping-needle at Hobarton. This distinction will receive more significance presently.

2898. Hence the cause which affects the needle appears to be far more powerful, and more concentrated in time when the sun is present than when he is away. In this there is accordance between the time of the effect and the time when the sun could exert most influence on those magnetic conditions of the atmosphere, which are for the present supposed to govern that effect.

2899. It will be seen by examination of *Fig. 10* that the time of maximum temperature is not when the sun is on the meridian, but two hours after it, both in summer and winter. But in reference to temperature and its effect on the magnetic condition of the air, and through that on the needle, it is not the local temperature which is supposed to influence the needle, but that which affects enormous masses of air, above as well as below, and of which the temperature at the spot, however important it may become when we can properly interpret it gives us as yet little or no knowledge. Still there are some points on which temperature has a more direct bearing. Thus the amount of variation of temperature is in summer double what it is in winter, and the amount of variation in the declination increases in the same proportion (2890). The minimum temperature in winter is later than in summer, and the extreme western declination of the needle is also later at the same period.

2900. The varying *direction* of the magnetic lines of the earth is made known to us by observations in two planes, one the horizontal plane, to which the position east and west is referred, constituting declination, and the other a vertical plane passing through the line of mean declination, and supplying observations of inclination. The direction of the line of force referred to this plane might change so as either to increase or diminish the inclination, and it does increase at some places for the same hour of local time for which it diminishes at others; thus it increases at Greenwich whilst it diminishes at St. Helena, which is nearly in the same meridian. At Hobarton it changes rapidly at the east and west extremes of the variation, i.e., about 2 and 21 o'clock. From noon it diminishes until about 3 o'clock; it then continues nearly the same in summer, when the variation is greatest until 18 or 19 o'clock, from that time it increases until about 22 o'clock, and is nearly a maximum from thence till noon. Hence it will be understood, that the inclination is generally greatest during the rapid journey of the north end of the needle from west to east between 21 and 2 o'clock, and least in the other or prolonged half of the journey; and though this is partly broken up in the night effect, to be considered hereafter, still as a general result it always appears.

2901. All this may be roughly represented by *Fig. 11* (2909), in which E. W. represents the path of the sun between the tropics as he comes up with the hours 21^h, 22^h, &c., in his daily journey, and *e* the path described by the north or upper end of the needle, freely suspended at Hobarton, and therefore showing both declination and inclination, i.e., the whole direction. Looking down upon such a needle, its upper end will take the course indicated by the arrow, and its position at any given hour is shown sufficiently by the leading lines.

2902. This relation of the motion of the needle to that of the sun has long been known; it has great significance in relation to my hypothesis of the physical cause of these variations. As regards the part of the action which I am considering, it is as if the pole of a magnet came on with the sun, of like nature to the upper end of the Hobarton needle, at first driving that end west. Towards 19 o'clock the tendency westward diminishes, but the tendency south increases. At 21 o'clock, the increase in the sun's power, acting not directly from the sun but from a region in the atmosphere beneath it, is not sufficient to compensate for his more unfavourable position; the earth's force brings the needle back as regards declination, and then it passes eastwards, but the southerly motion or inclination still increases; about 24 o'clock, or noon, the sun is as to east or west declination indifferent, but powerful in southern action, making the inclination then, or soon after, a maximum. Then as the sun goes west of the needle, its power in driving the pole behind it eastward will increase for a time, whilst the power producing inclination will diminish, until at 2 or 3 o'clock the earth's force will regain preponderance as the sun's power diminishes by distance, and the needle will return towards its least dip and mean inclination.

2903. All this may be represented experimentally by carrying a magnetic pole north of

the dipping-needle, so as to represent the place of the sun-heated air to Hobarton, provided that pole be of the same kind as the north or upper pole of the needle. I have already stated (2863, 2877), that when a portion of air is heated in a field of magnetic power, it loses in magnetic conduction power, and if in association with air less heated deflects the lines, assuming the state which I have distinguished as that of diamagnetic conduction polarity; then presenting the very polarity, or rather the very inflection of the lines of force, which would affect the needle, as it is affected. As the sun rises and passes north of such a place as Hobarton, the atmosphere under his coming influence becomes more and more heated and expanded; and referring to the model globes of air (2864, 2877), it is as if such a warm mass passed with the sun through all the regions of the equator, extending also far north and south of it; and, having Hobarton within its influence, produced the effects there observed.

2904. In such a view one sees a reason for the short time occupied in the return of the needle from west to east as the sun passes immediately over its meridian, and for the long time during which it is passing from east to west as the influence of the sun is slowly withdrawn, and then again slowly renewed during the remaining part of his journey, exception being made for the present of the paramagnetic effects due to cold.

2905. I will now consider the Toronto case of diurnal variation as it is presented to us in the volume of magnetical observations, issuing from the same authority and hands as the former volume,[1] and also in further observations down to 1848, sent to me by the kindness of Colonel Sabine. The position of the observatory is in lat. 43° 39′ 35″ N. and long. 79° 21′ 30″ W. The absolute declination is 1° 21′ 3″ W., and the mean or absolute dip is 75° 15′ N., so that as regards Hobarton it is on the other side of the equator, and nearly on the other side of the world. The results for the months of June and December are placed in a diagram corresponding to that for Hobarton (2896), employing the Toronto time for the hours, *Fig. 12*.

2906. The north end of the needle is that universally referred to in speaking of the declination; its course at Toronto, during the immediate sun effect, is as follows: Having gradually moved east from 16^h, it is at extreme east at 20 o'clock, and then returns from the east to

[1] *Magnetical and Meteorological Observations,* Toronto, 1840, 1841, 1842, Sabine.

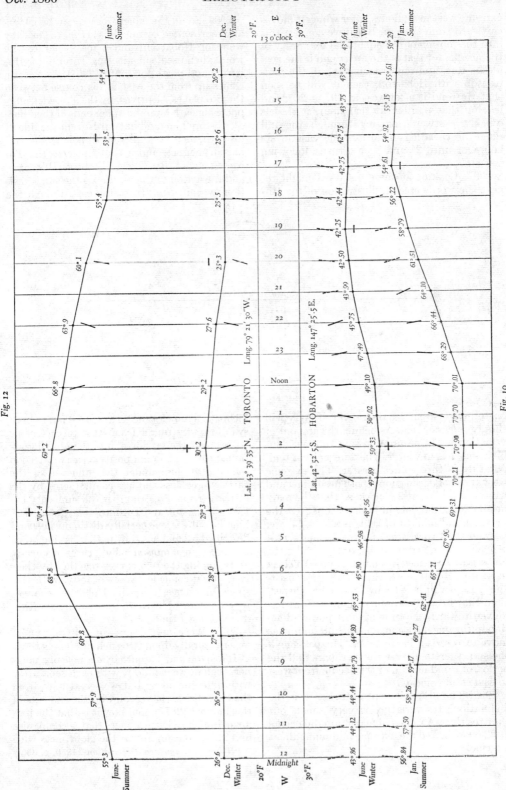

Fig. 12

June Summer

Dec. Winter

20°F.

E
13 o'clock

30°F.

June Winter

Jan. Summer

TORONTO Long. 79° 21′ 30″ W.

Lat. 43° 39′ 35″ N.

HOBARTON Long. 147° 25′·5 E.

Lat. 42° 52′·5 S.

Fig. 10

20°F

W

30°F.

June Summer

Dec. Winter

June Winter

Jan. Summer

extreme west in six hours, after which it moves eastward from the sun. But if we convert this into the motion of the equatorial extremity of the needle, for that is the *upper* end if the needle be free, and concerns us most in the comparison with Hobarton, then it will be seen that this end is most west at 19^h or 20^h; and leaving that position at that hour, it travels quickly eastward, passing through the full range of variation or to extreme east in six hours, or until 2^h, and then returns, following the sun.

2907. Looking at these results, I might repeat the words used in illustration of the Ho-

2909. So all the effects may again be generally represented by an ellipse (*Fig. 13*) as they were for Hobarton; and I may refer to the words then used, substituting Toronto for Hobarton and north for south (2901). As the sun comes up from the east in his course between the two places, he drives, by the altered atmosphere beneath him, the upper ends of their needles before him, and outwards from the line of his path, as if he were a north pole to the Hobarton magnet, and a south pole to the Toronto magnet. By 22 o'clock, the earth's force, and the action of the air due to the sun's position, permit a return to the east, though the

Fig. 13

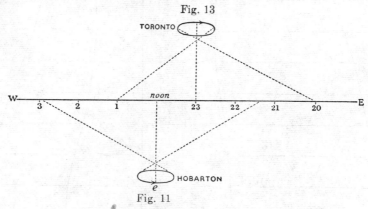

Fig. 11

barton effects, but for the sake of brevity will simply refer to them. As before, the amount of variation in the declination is in summer double what it is in winter. The difference of temperature is three times greater. The extreme west and east declination is both in summer and winter at 20 and at 2 o'clock, so that the magnet holds to the time in both seasons; but the maxima and minima of cold, as shown before, vary in the two seasons, for the former is at 4 o'clock in summer and 2 in winter, whilst the latter is at 16 o'clock in summer, and 20 o'clock in winter. But this is a variation with consistency; for it will be seen by a moment's inspection, that in winter the maximum of heat has moved towards the time of most powerful action in the one direction, and the minimum has moved towards it in the other. The passage of the sun, therefore, over the meridian, and the period of rapid motion of the needle from west to east, still coincide.

2908. The other element of direction is the inclination. Its variation is very small, but changes thus. A principal maximum dip occurs at 22 o'clock, and the extreme minimum dip at 4 o'clock.

inclination for a time increases (2902); both swing rapidly round from west to east as he passes over the meridian, and then having attained their maximum position eastward, soon follow after him under the influence of the earth's force, less and less counteracted by the retreating sun. So striking is the similarity between Hobarton and Toronto, that Colonel Sabine has already especially distinguished and described it,[1] and has shown, that, laying down the direction of motion in both cases by curves, and bringing the two curves together by their faces, they coincide almost exactly, with this single difference, that the Hobarton changes precede those at Toronto by an hour, or rather more, of local time.

2910. We cannot represent this day effect experimentally upon two such needles as those at Hobarton and Toronto by *one* pole of a magnet, though we can do it with each separately with different poles: but we see at once from the hypothesis, the reason why the sun acts in this manner (2877), and how it is that the region of influential atmosphere that accompanies him in his journey round the globe, acts with

[1] *Hobarton Magnetical Observations*, 1850, p. 35.

one effect in the northern latitude and another in southern positions (2903). The reasons also for the short time of the day journey and the lengthened period of the night return (2904), are manifest. The occurrence of disturbances or secondary waves of power in the night-time, and the condition both of the chief variation and the subordinate oscillations in summer and winter, will be considered hereafter.

2911. *Greenwich.* The following results are taken from the volume of *Greenwich Observations* for 1847. The latitude is 51° 31′ N., and being removed nearly 80° in longitude from Toronto, the station is well contrasted with it and also with Hobarton. The mean declination is 22° 51′ 18″ W., and the mean inclination is 69° N. As it is the upper end of the dipping-needle which we have to consider for the purpose of a ready comparison with the sun's observed day action (2906), I will describe those parts of its course and place for Greenwich time which concern us now. Moving westward before 19^h and 20^h, it then returns towards the east, and in six hours, or by 1^h or 2^h, has completed the great sun swing, after which it returns west, following the luminary. The vertical force is given as greatest between 3 and 4 o'clock, and least between 11 and 13 o'clock. The south end of the needle therefore is more upright at the former time and less at the latter; and as the latter occurs during the prolonged return part of the journey from east to west, including the night hours, so we perceive that the upper end of the needle performs its daily journey in an irregular closed curve, which the ellipse for Toronto, *Fig. 13* (2909), may generally represent; it passes from east to west slowly during the night hours, approaching the equator at the same time, and then it returns from west to east with far greater rapidity, performing this part of its journey at a greater distance from the equator and nearer to the pole.

2912. *Washington, U.S.* Latitude 38° 54′ N.; longitude 77° 2′ W.; the mean declination 1° 25′ W.; the mean dip 71° 20′ N. The south or upper end of the needle is in the morning at extreme west, about 20 to 22 o'clock, and at extreme east about 2 o'clock; it then returns slowly west, with the night action as in former cases, regaining extreme west at 20 to 22 o'clock. This is exactly the same movement for declination, in relation to the place of the sun, as for the former localities. I have not the variation of the dip, but theory would lead one to conclude that it is greatest between 22 and 2 o'clock, and least in the evening and night-

time. The total amount of declination variation is greatest in summer, as before, being 9′.87 in July and only 4′ in December. The greatest difference in the earth's temperature is also in July, being then nearly 20° Fahr., whereas in December and January it is only 10 Fahr. The shortest period between the extreme temperature, including therefore the quickest change of temperature, is from 16 or 18 to 2 o'clock, and consequently includes noon. All these conditions combine to produce the greatest magnetic action, and it is in the direction pointed out by the hypothesis.

2913. *Lake Athabasca.* Latitude 58° 41′ N.; longitude 111° 18′ W. of Greenwich; mean declination 28° E. The observations are only for five months, but as the position is in a high latitude and may be important for future considerations, I give the results here. The extreme western position of the upper end of the needle is about 17 or 18 o'clock, and its extreme eastern position about 1 or 2 o'clock; so that as far as declination is concerned, the action of the sun and atmosphere is as in former cases. The amount of declination variation is very great, being in October 21′.32; in November 10′.8; in December 9′.78; in January 16′.29, and in February 14′.87.

2914. *Fort Simpson.* Latitude 61° 52′ N.; longitude 121° 30′ W. of Greenwich; mean declination 38° E. These observations are only for two months, i.e., April and May 1844. The extreme western place of the upper or south end of the needle was at 19 o'clock, and its extreme eastern position at 2 o'clock. The result therefore is in perfect accordance with the preceding observations and conclusions. The amount of variation, as given in the horizontal plane, is very large, being 36′.26 in April and 32′ in May.

2915. *St. Petersburgh.* Latitude 59° 57′ N.; longitude 30° 15′ E. of Greenwich; mean declination 6° 10′ W.; the dip 70° 30′ N. The observations are the mean of six years, and show that the upper end of the needle is extreme west in regard to noon, about 19^h and 20^h for the months of March to August, and that for the other months there is a western position about the same hours. The extreme east position is, for *all* the months, about half-past 1 o'clock, so that the sun's effect in passing over at the noon period is as in former cases. The greatest amount of variation is 11′.52 in June; in winter it dwindles away to as little as 1′.77. From theory the dip may be expected to increase during the day hours and diminish at night.

2916. Thus these cases, which, including the chief feature of diurnal variation and sun action, were selected as a first and trial-test of the hypothesis, join their evidence together, as far as they go, in favour of that view which I am offering for their cause; nor have I yet found any instance of even an apparent contradiction in regard to the sun action. They assist the mind greatly in forming a precise notion of the manner in which the influence of the sun and air is supposed to act, not only in similar cases, but in respect of other consequences, i.e. in all that properly comes under the term of atmospheric magnetism; I will therefore now restate more particularly the principles which, according to the hypothesis, govern them, in hopes that I may be fortunate enough to assist in developing by degrees the *true physical cause* of the magnetic variations in question.

2917. Space, void of matter, admits of the transmission of the magnetic force through it (2787, 2851). Paramagnetic and diamagnetic bodies either increase or diminish the degree in which the transmission takes place (2789). This, their influence, I have expressed, for the time, by the phrase of *magnetic conducting power*, and I think have given sufficient first experimental evidence of the existence of the power and its effects in disturbing the lines of magnetic force (2843). The atmosphere is, by the oxygen it contains (2861, 2863), a paramagnetic medium, and has its conducting force greatly diminished by elevation of temperature (2856) and by rarefaction (2782, 2783), as has also been fully proved by experiment. The sun is an agent which both heats and rarefies the atmosphere, and in its diurnal course, the place of greatest heat and rarefaction must, speaking generally, be beneath it. The irregularities in the condition of the earth's surface and other causes do produce local departures from an exact relation of place, but they probably disappear partly, if not altogether, in the upper regions of the air.

2918. Assuming that *the air under the sun* is most changed magnetically, and confining the attention to a spot where the sun is vertical, for the purpose of considering the condition of the atmosphere there and at other parts in relation to it, the supposition of a globe of air over the spot will of course find no fit application (2877). We are first to suppose the sun far away and the atmosphere in a mean state as to temperature, and then consider the sun as present in the meridian of a given place; and it is *the degree of alteration* in temperature and expansion of the air beneath and around the place of the sun, and the manner in which the change comes on and passes away, which concern us. In relation to the surface of the earth, that alteration will be greatest somewhere beneath the sun, and will diminish in every direction around, becoming nearly nothing as to direct action at that part or circle of the earth where the sun's rays are tangent. In relation to elevation, it is a question yet whether the effect is greatest in amount at the surface, diminishing upwards. As regards the atmosphere, it must of course end with it, though as respects space itself (2851), a reservation-thought may arise. With regard to any alteration occasioned by the sun's influence in the opposite hemisphere, though there is none produced directly, yet indirectly there is that due to the falling of the temperature of the air, from the condition to which the sun, whilst above the horizon, had brought it. This change must be more tardy, irregular and disturbed, by local and other circumstances, than the opposite alterations produced by the direct influence of the luminary; and is that which occasions, by the hypothesis, the second maximum or minimum or other recurring night actions, made manifest by the needle in the hours when the sun is away.

2919. The lines of force which issue from a magnet are, as it were, located and fixed by their roots in a way well understood experimentally by those who have worked upon this subject. In the same manner the lines which issue from the earth more or less suddenly, according to the amount of inclination, are held beneath by a force of location; and because of the unchanging action of the earth in respect to atmospheric effect, are restrained more or less from alteration beneath during the changing action of the atmosphere. This fixation in the earth is a chief cause of certain peculiarities in the atmospheric phenomena as we observe them; and is productive of that rotation of the line of force about the mean position which we have already considered during the sun swing, and shall meet with again under the action of cold air. This condition of fixation at the lower parts of the lines of force occurs at every station where there is any dip at all, and gives for each the point of convergence round which the motion of the upper end of the needle takes place (2909, 2932).

2920. So the atmosphere, under the influence of the sun, lies upon the earth altered most at the part beneath the luminary. It has received power to affect the lines of magnetic force differently to the manner in which it affected them in the sun's absence. It has become a great magnetic lens, able to refract the lines,

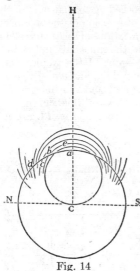

Fig. 14

and the manner in which it does so appears to be of the following nature. All the lines passing through this heated and expanded air, surrounded by other air not so much heated, will, because of its being a worse magnetic conductor than the latter (2861, 2862), tend to open out (2807); and the mass of heated air, as a whole, will assume the condition of diamagnetic polarity. If, therefore, for the sake of simplicity, the magnetic and astronomical poles of our earth be supposed as coincident, and *Fig. 14* represent a section taken through them and the place of the sun, then N and S will be the magnetic poles, and the different curves cutting the outline of the circle will sufficiently represent the course of the magnetic lines as they occur at or about the surface of the earth, H being the sun, and *a* the place immediately beneath it, which is also coincident with the magnetic equator. By this diagram we shall have an illustration of the hypothetical effect on the inclination of the needle.

2921. Considering the point *a* first, and assuming as yet that the maximum of change in the air is always at the surface of the earth, we shall find that there the lines of force will open out, preserving in some degree their parallel or concentric relation. Consequently a magnetic needle, free to move in every direction, and therefore taking up its position *in* the line of force, ought not, if placed at this spot, to be al-

tered in its position. It ought to show perhaps a diminution of magnetic force transmitted through that spot; but, for the reason before given (2868), I conclude it would indicate a greater intensity, the increased power thrown upon it through the diminution of the conducting power of the air in that place causing it to act as a more powerful needle.

2922. Proceeding to a point *b*, there the lines of force have dip. The same physical effect will be produced upon them here as before, i.e., the portions in the atmosphere will open out; but neither here nor in the former case will they continue to have the same curvature as before, for towards and in the earth, where they have their origin, they are restrained more or less from altering by the unchanging action of the earth (2919); whilst at their more advanced parts, as at *c*, they enter into portions of the atmosphere which are nearer to the most intense lines of solar action, H C, probably also into the region of most intense action, and also into space, circumstances which cause more displacement of the lines, tending to separate by the tension of the parts altered in the air, than can happen *in* the earth (2848). So the magnetic line of force at *b* will not move parallel to itself, but being inclined a certain degree to the horizon, when in the normal condition, will be more inclined, i.e., will have more dip given to it by the presence of the sun. This is the fact made manifest by the needle when indicating the position of the line as to inclination (2908) at Hobarton, Toronto or elsewhere, by the motion of its upper end; for it is manifest that whatever happens on one side of the place of the sun and magnetic equator, when, as in our supposition (2920), they coincide, will happen on the other.

2923. The case may be more simply stated, for the facility of recollection, by saying that the effect of the sun is to raise the magnetic curves, over the equatorial and neighbouring parts, from their normal position, in doing which the north and south dip are simultaneously affected and increased.

2924. At the place *d* like effects on the inclination must be produced, and theoretically it should be affected in the same direction even at N. and S. At the point *a* the inclination is supposed to be not at all altered; but going either north or south, the changes appear and increase. It is not probable that the maximum alteration will be at N. or S., but the latitude where it will occur must depend upon the many conjoined circumstances that belong to the case of a globe round which a magnetic lens, such as I have endeavoured to describe, is continually revolving.

2925. Instead of assuming that the sun is at H, let us suppose that we are looking at the diagram in a vertical position and towards the east; the sun coming up from the east and passing over our heads, and bringing with it that condition of our atmosphere which is the cause of the change. As it does so, all the magnetic curves would rise; the inclination would increase at *b, d,* and every place where there was any previously, in opposite directions on the two sides of *a;* this would go on until the sun was in the zenith, and then as it passed away and sank behind us, the lines would draw in again and the dip diminish to what it was at first. The maximum of dip would be when the sun was near the zenith, and the minimum when he was quite away.

2926. But if the resultant of force be above in the atmosphere (2937), which is by far the most probable, as it is the whole atmosphere which acts by heat diamagnetically, then the results would be modified; for if over *a,* the lines of force might be *depressed,* and any inclination there would be diminished; at *b* it might not for the moment be affected; whilst in higher latitudes it would be increased, according as the line of force from the resultant in the atmosphere, wherever that might be, fell outside of the angle formed by the inclination with the horizon of a given place or within it. St. Helena, the Cape of Good Hope, and Hobarton, furnish instances of the three cases.

2927. At the same time the total force would undergo a change in its amount; that transmitted through a given space would be least when the sun was in the zenith, and most when he was away (2863). The total variation in the force should be greatest at *a,* and diminish from thence towards north and south. The daily variations of the inclination are so imperfectly known to us at present that we cannot say how far the natural changes will accord with these expected variations, but as far as the observations go they agree with the theory.

2928. If the sun, instead of being over the equator, is at a tropic and so vertical, for instance, over *b,* then the effects will be modified; and the resultant still being assumed as above, the lines of force which before were not affected, may be expected to descend and lessen the inclination, whilst other lines in higher latitudes, which before were increased in inclination, may now be but little affected, and other

lines in still higher latitudes have, as before their inclination, increased. On the other side of the equator, the tendency of the lines would be to increase in inclination.

2929. Proceeding to that part of the expected change of position of the free needle which produces variations of *declination,* let *e r* in *Fig. 15* represent the sun's path in the equator, and *t c, t' c'* the same at the tropics; let *m r* be a magnetic meridian, and *a a', i i', o o'* places of equal north and south inclination on opposite sides of the equator. The curves of magnetic force seen in front in *Fig. 14,* are now in the

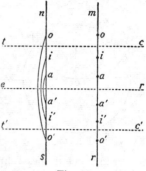

Fig. 15

plane of the magnetic meridian, but may be considered as rising on opposite sides of the equator and coalescing over it. If the air on all sides were in its mean condition and the sun entirely away, these curves would be in the vertical plane *m r;* or if the sun near midday was so placed that the resultant of the heated and changed atmosphere was in the meridian *m r,* though effects of inclination would occur (2922), still the curves would remain in the same vertical plane. But if the resultant were either to the east or the west of *m r,* variations of declination would be produced. For suppose the sun to be advancing from the east or *r;* because it gives the air a diamagnetic condition, the lines of force would tend to expand (2877), and therefore move westward, as represented in the meridian *n s;* and the deflection caused thereby would be greatest upon the surface of the earth, because it is there that the curves as they enter the earth are held and restrained in respect to their normal position (2919). As the warmed atmosphere came on, the western deflection would increase to a certain extent, and then diminish to nothing when the resultant was in the meridian; but as the latter passed on, the deflection would grow up on the eastern side of *n s,* and, after attaining a maximum, would diminish and cease as the warm air retreated.

2930. If the sun's path was in the northern tropic, *t c*, and the resultant in the atmosphere therefore to the north of the stations *a* or *i*, though that would make a difference in the amount of the declination variation, it would not alter its *direction*, for still the curves *a a'* and *i i'* would bear to the west as the sun came up, and would be on the meridian when the resultant was there also. There would be more effect produced at *i* than at *i'*, but the contrary character of the dip, in respect to the sun's place, would not alter the direction of the declination variation.

2931. A cold region of air acting, as at the coming on of night, upon the lines of magnetic force of the earth, would, by virtue of its paramagnetic character (2865), produce corresponding effects both of inclination and declination, but in the contrary direction.

2932. Thus the lines of force which issue from the earth at all places upon its surface where there is any dip, will, by the hypothesis, under the daily influence of the sun, describe by their ascending parts a closed curve or irregular cone, the apex of which is below. As a fact this result is perfectly well known, but its accordance with the hypothesis is important for the latter. The mean position of the free needle will be in the axis of this curve or cone, and its return, either in declination or inclination, to the mean is an important indication of the amount and position of the variable forces which influence it at such times.

2933. My hypothesis does not at all assume that the heated or cooled air has become magnetic so as to act directly on the needle after the manner of a piece of iron, either magnetically polar or rendered so under induction. There is no assumed polarity of the oxygen of the air other than the conduction polarity (2822, 2835) consequent upon a slight alteration of the direction of the lines of force. The change in the magnetic conducting power causes this deflection of the lines; just as a worse conductor of heat introduced into a medium of better conducting power disturbs the previous equable transfer of heat, and gives a new direction to that which is conducted; or as in static electricity, a body of more or less specific inductive capacity introduced into a uniform medium disturbs the equable lines of force which were previously passing across it.

2934. The sole action of the atmosphere is to bend the lines of force. The needle being held by these lines and, when free, being parallel to them, changes in position with the changes of the lines. It is not necessary even that the lines, which are immediately affected in direction by the altered air, should be those about the needle, but may be very distant. The whole of the magnetic lines about the earth are held by their mutual tension in one connected sensitive system, which has no sluggishness anywhere, but feels in every part a change in any one particular place. There may be, and is continually, a new distribution of force, but no suppression. So when any change in direction happens, near or distant, the needle in a given place will feel and indicate it, and that the more sensibly according to the vicinity of the place and the kind of change induced; but the disposition of the *whole* system has been affected at the same moment, and therefore all the other needles will be affected in obedience to the change in the lines of force which govern them individually.

2935. The needle is a balance on which all the magnetic power around a given locality fastens itself, even to the antipodes, and it shows for each place every variation in their amount or disposition, whether that occurs near or far off. Its mean position is the normal position; and as regards atmospheric changes, the fixation of the lines of force in the earth (2919) is that which tends to give the lines a standard position (exclusive of secular changes), and so bring them and the needle back from their disturbed to their normal state. Hence, whilst considering the causes which disturb either the declination or the inclination, arises the importance of keeping in mind the mean position or place of the needle (2932), and not merely the direction in which it is moving.

2936. So the well-known action of the sun on the needle is, by my hypothesis, very indirect; the sun at a given place affects the atmosphere; the atmosphere affects the direction of the lines of force there; the lines of force there affect those at any distance, and these affect the needles which they respectively govern.

2937. I have, for the sake of convenience in considering a special action of the atmosphere, spoken of the resultant in the atmosphere dependent on the sun's presence; and will do so a little while longer without implying any direct action of this resultant, or that portion of air which yields it, upon the needle (2933), for the sake of considering at what probable height it is situated in the air. That it cannot be on the surface of the earth, is shown by the depression of the lines and diminution of the dip at St. Helena and Singapore during the middle of the day; and that it is not even under the sun, is shown by the manner in which the greatest action precedes, in some degree, the sun, as at Hobarton and Toronto, and other places by different amounts of time; neither the time when the sun is on the meridian, nor the time when the observed temperature is highest (for that is after the sun), is the time of greatest action, but one before either of these periods. The changes in the temperature of the air produced by the sun, will not take place below and above at the same time. The upper regions of the atmosphere over a given spot are affected by the sun at his rising and afterwards, before the air below is heated; and therefore the effect from above would be expected to precede that below. The temperature observed on the earth does not show us, for the same time, the course of the changes above, and may be a very imperfect indication of them. The maximum temperature below is often two, three, or four hours after the sun, whereas, whatever heat the sun gives by his rays directly to the atmosphere, must be acquired far more rapidly than that. It is very probable, and almost certain, that at 4 or 5 o'clock A.M. in the summer months, the upper regions may be rising in temperature, whilst on the surface of the earth, through radiation and other causes, it is falling. The well-known effect of cold just before sunrise in some parts of India, and even in our country, is in favour of such a supposition. We must remember that it is not the absolute temperature of the air at any spot that renders it influential in producing magnetic variations, but the *differences* of temperature between it and surrounding regions. Though the upper regions be colder than the lower, their changes may be as great or greater; they happen at a range of temperature which is probably more influential than a higher range (2967); and, what is of importance, they occur more quickly and directly upon the presence of the sun. The quantity of heat which the atmosphere can take directly from the sun's rays, is indicated by the different proportions we receive from him when he is either vertical or oblique to us, and so sending his beams through less or more air; and when he has departed, the upper parts of the air are far more favourably circumstanced for rapid cooling by radiation than the portions below. So that the final changes may be as great or greater than below, and we may learn little of them, or their order, or time, by observations of temperature at the earth's surface. In addition therefore to observations of magnetic effect, as depression of the lines of

force at St. Helena, &c., there are apparently reasons deducible from physical causes, why the chief seat of action should be above in the atmosphere.

2938. In the midday effect the upper end of the needle passes the mean position (2935) on its return to the east generally before the sun passes the meridian going westward. At Toronto it is about an hour in advance; at St. Helena and Washington an hour and a half; at Greenwich and Petersburgh two hours; at Hobarton and the Cape of Good Hope the passage is about noon. Such results appear to indicate that the place of maximum action is in advance of the sun; and it probably is so in some degree, but not so much as at first may be supposed, as will appear, I think, from the following considerations.

2939. The precession of the time of maximum action may depend in part upon some such condition as the following. As the sun advances towards and passes over a meridian, the air is first raised in temperature and then allowed to fall, and these actions produce the differences in different places on which the magnetic variations depend. But they depend also upon the *suddenness* with which or the vicinity at which these differences occur. Thus two masses of air, having equal differences of temperature, will affect the lines of force more if they be near together, and to the needle, than if they be far apart. And again, if a body of air were of a certain low temperature at one part, and, proceeding horizontally, were to increase rapidly to a certain high temperature and then diminish slowly to the first low temperature, such a body passing across a set of lines of magnetic force would affect them in opposite directions at the fore and after part; but it would affect them most on the rapidly altering side.

2940. Now the air as heated by the sun must be in this condition. According to analogy with solid and liquid bodies, being exposed to heat and then withdrawn, the changes of temperature that it would undergo would be more rapid in the elevation than in the falling, and so the changes in the preceding would be more rapid than in the following parts. To this would be added the effect of the atmosphere warmed by the earth; for as that is slower in attaining heat, as is shown by the time of maximum temperature, so its effects being gradually communicated to the air above, as the sun passed away, would tend to retard its fall and enlarge the difference already spoken of. Applying these considerations to the natural case, the strongest effect and the greatest variation should be towards the west, and the following or lesser action towards the east of the sun; and the mean condition of the needle for the whole change would be in advance of that body.

2941. Mr. Broun has made observations of the daily variation at different heights, namely, at Makerstoun and the top of the Cheviot Hills, where the height differs by nearly half a mile, and finds, I believe, no difference in the intensity, but that the progress is *first* at the higher station. It would be very interesting to have an observatory up above, but to give the results required it should have air and not solid matter beneath it.

2942. There is another circumstance which importantly influences the *times* of the passages of the declination variation. If two places north and south of the equator have equal dip and contrary declinations, i.e., if both their upper ends point east or west, then the effects ought to correspond and form a pair. But if both have east or west declination, according to the usual mode of marking this effect by the north end of the magnet, then the variations already described should come on as the sun passes midway between them, but there should be a difference in *time*. As the luminary appears and approaches, the needles *a* and *b* (*Fig. 16*)

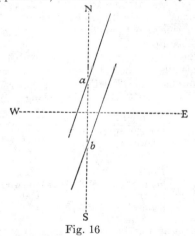

Fig. 16

will most probably be affected together; but, as he draws nigh, if the places have eastern declination, the one that is south will be soonest affected, and for the time most strongly, but will in a period more or less extended, be followed by the corresponding action at the other place. For as each needle will have returned from the first half of its series of changes to 0° by the time the sun is on its magnetic merid-

ian, and as it will arrive at this meridian, as regards the south needle, before it does so for the north needle, so the south magnet should precede the other in its changes. If the declination of both were westerly, then the north needle would precede the south.

2943. The hypothesis advanced, besides agreeing with the facts regarding the direction of the needle's motions, as is the case generally, and if my hopes are well-founded, will be the case also in more careful comparisons; should also agree in the *amount* of force required for the observed declinations at given hours. I have endeavoured to obtain experimental evidence of the difference of action of oxygen and nitrogen on needles subjected to the earth's power, but have not yet succeeded. This however is not surprising, since a saturated solution of protosulphate of iron has failed under the same circumstances. More delicate apparatus may perhaps yield a positive result.

2944. That small masses of oxygen should not give an indication of that which is shown by the atmosphere as a whole is not surprising, if we consider that the mass of air is exceeding great, and includes a vast extent of the curves on which it, by the hypothesis, acts; and yet that the effect to be accounted for is exceeding small. The extreme declination at Greenwich is 12′, equal to about 4′ 24″ of east and west alteration on the free needle, so that that is the whole of what has to be accounted for. One could scarcely expect such an effect to be shown by small masses of oxygen and nitrogen acting on only a few inches in length of the magnetic curves passing through them, unless one could use an apparatus of extreme and almost infinite sensibility; but from what I have seen of oxygen when compared at different degrees of dilution (2780), or at different temperatures (2861), I am led to believe that the effects on it produced by the sun in the atmosphere will ultimately be found competent to produce these variations.

2945. Where the air is changed in temperature or volume, there it acts and there it alters the directions of the lines of force; and these by their tension carry on the effect to more distant lines (2934), whose needles are accordingly affected. The transferred effect will be greater or less according as the distances are less or greater, and hence a change near at hand may overpower that at a distance, and a cloud close to a station may for the moment do more than the rising sun. These are the irregular variations; and the extent of their influence is well shown by the photographic records of Greenwich and Toronto. The volume of *Greenwich Observations* for 1847 contains a photographic record of the declination changes, February 18–19, 1849. Between 6 and 7 o'clock there is a variation of 16′ occurring in 18 minutes of time, or at the rate nearly of 1′ for each minute of time. The course of the mean variation for the same date and time is 1′.95 in two hours, or at the rate of 1 second for each minute of time, so that the irregular variation (which may be considered as a local variation in respect to the sun's power for the time) is sixty times that due to the effect of the great resultant; moreover it was in the reverse direction, for the temporary variation was from east to west, whilst the mean variation was from west to east.

2946. Another mode of showing how much the action of nearer portions of the atmosphere may overpower and hide the effect of the whole mass, is to draw the line of mean variation for the twenty-four hours through such a photographic record as that just referred to, and then it will be seen in every part of the course how small the mean effect on the needle is, compared to the irregular or comparatively local effect for the same moment of time. The magnet with which these observations were made, is a bar of steel 2 feet long, 1½ inch broad and a quarter of an inch thick, and therefore not obedient to sudden impulses; it is probable that a short, quick magnet would show numerous cases in which the irregular variation would be several hundred of times greater than the mean. Still all these irregularities and overpowering influences of near masses are eliminated by taking the mean of several years' observation, and thus a true result is obtained, to which the hypothesis advanced may be applied and so tested.

2947. Returning for a short time to the annual variation (2882), I may observe, that it has been a good deal considered in discussing the daily variation. The arrangement of the magnetic effects by Colonel Sabine at Hobarton, Toronto, St. Helena and elsewhere, into monthly portions, proves exceedingly instructive and important, especially for places between and near the tropics. It supplies that kind of analysis of the annual variation which is given by the hours for the daily variation. Every month, by a comparison of its curve with those of other months, tells its own story, at the same time that it links its predecessor and successor together.

2948. I shall have occasion to trace these monthly means hereafter; but in the meantime refer to the effect of the sun's annual approach and recession indicated by these means, as according with the hypothesis in respect to near and distant actions (2945). Hobarton and Toronto are in opposite hemispheres, so that the sun whilst approaching one recedes from the other, and the amount of variations therefore changes in opposite directions. Below is the average for each month, derived in the case of Hobarton from a mean of seven years, and in that of Toronto from a mean of two years.

	Hobarton Lat. 42° 52′.5 S.	Toronto Lat. 43° 39′.35 N.
January	11.66	6.51
February	11.80	6.40
March	9.50	8.50
April	7.26	9.52
May	4.56	10.34
June	3.70 Winter	11.99
July	4.61	12.70 Summer
August	5.89	12.68
September	8.24	9.72
October	11.01	7.59
November	12.05 Summer	5.75
December	11.81	4.47 Winter

The two stations are in latitudes differing only 47′ from each other; and the extreme difference of the atmospheric effect between summer and winter differs as little, being at Hobarton, which has the highest latitude, 8′.35, and at Toronto 8′.23.

2949. According to Dove, the northern hemisphere is warmer in July than the southern hemisphere by 17°.4 Fahr., and colder in winter by only 10°.7; the numbers being as follows:

July
Northern hemisphere 71°.0
Southern hemisphere 53°.6
| 62°.3 the whole globe

January
Northern hemisphere 48°.8
Southern hemisphere 59°.5
| 54°.15 the whole globe

The mean for the whole year is 59°.9 for the northern hemisphere, and 56°.5 for the southern. Therefore, as Dove further shows, the whole earth is in July, when the sun is shining over the terraqueous parts, 8° higher in temperature than in January, when it is over the watery regions: and from the influence of the same cause, the mean of the southern hemisphere is 3°.4 below the mean of the northern half of the globe. The difference between Jannary and July is for the northern hemisphere 22°.2, and for the southern only 5°.9. These differences are so peculiar in their arrangement and so large in amount, that they must have an effect upon the distribution of the magnetic forces of the earth, but the data are not yet sufficient to enable one to trace the results. Sabine indicates a probability from his analysis of observations that the sum of the earth's magnetic force is increased in intensity when the sun is in the southern signs, i.e. in our winter (2891). I should have expected from theory that such results would have been the case, at least in those parts where the dip was not very great; because a colder atmosphere ought to conduct the lines of magnetic force better, and therefore the systems round the earth ought at such a time to condense, as it were, in the cooler parts. It would be doubtful, however, whether the needle would show this difference, because the lines of power would not be restrained above, as in the case formerly supposed (2922), but could gather in from space freely. From what has been said, however, it will be evident that such a conclusion can only be drawn with any degree of confidence from observations made pretty equally over both hemispheres.

2950. If we should ever attain a good knowledge of the annual variation for several stations in different parts of both hemispheres, it would help to give data by which the depth at which the magnetic power is virtually situated might be estimated; for, as this power is expected to undergo undulations over very large portions of the earth's surface by the annual changes of temperature (2884), so they would differ in character and extent according as the origin of the lines should prove to be more or less deeply situated.

2951. With regard to the many variations of magnetic force, not periodic or not so in relation to the sun, which yet produce the irregular and overruling changes already referred to (2945), dependent, as I suppose, on local variations of the atmosphere, I may be allowed to notice briefly such points as have occurred to my mind.

2952. The *varying pressure* of the atmosphere, over a given part of the earth's surface, ought to cause a variation in the magnetic condition of that part of the earth. It is represented to us by a difference of 3 inches of mercury, or one-tenth of the weight of the atmosphere. Now the oxygen in a given space is paramagnetic in proportion to its quantity (2780), and there-

fore it does not seem possible that that quantity over a given space of the earth's surface, whether it be recognized by volume as above, or by weight as in a given volume at the earth's surface, should be varied to the extent of one-tenth of the whole sum without producing a corresponding alteration in the distribution of the magnetic force; the lines being drawn together and the force made more intense by an increase of the quantity or of the barometric pressure, and the reverse effects produced at the occurrence of diminished pressure.

2953. At any spot which is towards the confines of that space where the air is increasing or diminishing in pressure, there will probably occur variations in the directions of the lines of force, and these will be more marked at such places as happen to be between two others, in one of which atmosphere is accumulating, whilst from the other it is retreating. Whether these changes (which I think must occur) produce by vicinity effects large enough to become sensible in our magnetic instruments is a question to be resolved hereafter. To suggest the cause is useful, because to know of the existence, nature, and action of a cause, is important to the arrangement of the best means of observing and evolving its effects.

2954. *Winds and large currents of air above* may often be accompanied by magnetic changes if they endure for a time only. A constant stream like the trade-wind, may have a constant effect; but if, when the arrangement of the lines of magnetic force through the atmosphere is in a given state consequent upon the condition of the atmosphere at that time, a wind arises which mixes regions of cold and warm air together, or makes the air more dense in one region than another, or proceeding from one to another, balances regions which before were in different conditions, then every such change will be accompanied by a corresponding change in the disposition of the magnetic force, to which we may perhaps hereafter be able to refer by means of our instruments. Even tides in the air ought to produce an effect, though it may be far too small to be rendered sensible.

2955. The precipitation of *rain or snow* is a theoretical reason for the change of magnetic relations in the space where it takes place; because it alters the temperature where such precipitation occurs, and relieves it from a quantity of diluting diamagnetic or neutral matter. A *chilling hail-storm might* affect the needle in a summer's day. *Clouds* may have a sensible influence in several ways; acting at one time by their difference from neighbouring regions of clear air, and at other times by absorbing the sun's rays, and causing the evolution of sensible heat at different altitudes in the atmosphere at different places, or preventing its evolution more or less at the surface of the earth. Those masses of warmer or colder air of which meteorologists speak, which being transparent are not sensible to the eye, will produce their proportionate effect. And hypothetically speaking, it is not absolutely impossible that the hot and partially deoxygenated air of a large town like London, may affect instruments in its vicinity; and if so, it will affect them differently at different times, according to the direction of the wind.

2956. If one imagines on the surface of the earth a spot which shall represent the resultant there of the atmospheric actions above, and can conceive its course as it wanders to and fro, under the influence of the various causes of action which have been in part referred to, whilst it still travels onwards with the sun, one may have an idea of the manner in which it may affect the various observatories scattered over the earth. I believe that its course, as regards the east and west direction of its wanderings, is partly told in the photographic registerings of Greenwich and Toronto, being there mingled in effect with other causes of variation. This spot may be concentrated or diffuse; it may pass away and reappear elsewhere; there may even be two or more at once sufficiently strong to cause vibrations of the needle between them.

2957. The aurora borealis or australis can hardly be independent of the magnetic constitution of the atmosphere, occurring as it does within its regions, and perhaps in the space above. The place of the aurora is generally in those latitudes the air of which has a distinct magnetic relation, by difference of temperature and quantity, to that at the equator, and the magnetic character both of the aurora and of the medium in which it occurs ties them together; therefore, to be aware of and to understand in some degree the latter, will probably direct us to a better comprehension of the former. The aurora is already connected with magnetic disturbances and storms; it may in time connect them with changes in the atmosphere in a manner not at present anticipated, and as the suggestion is founded upon principle it seems deserving of consideration.

2958. Can the magnetic storms of Humboldt be due to atmospheric changes? This is a question on which I would offer the following observations. Supposing a magnetic rest in the atmosphere, and that all local or irregular variations remained unchanged for the time, then if a change happened in one place it would be felt instantly everywhere else over the whole earth, and in proportion to the distance from the place of change. It would be felt instantly, because the impulse would not be conveyed chiefly or importantly through the matter of the earth or air, but through the space above, for the lines there are affected by changes in that part of them which passes through the atmosphere, and, as I conceive would affect the other lines in space round our globe, which would in turn affect those parts of their lines, which, passing downwards to the earth, govern the needles below. In space, I conceive that the magnetic lines of force, not being dependent on or associated with matter (2787, 2917), would have their changes transmitted with the velocity of light, or even with that higher velocity or instantaneity which we suppose to belong to the lines of gravitating force, and if so, then a magnetic disturbance at one place would be felt instantaneously over the whole globe.

2959. But the difficulty is to conceive an atmospheric change sufficiently extensive and sudden to make itself perceived everywhere at the same time amongst the comparatively local variations that are continually occurring. Still, if there were a lull in these disturbances by the opposition of contrary actions or otherwise for the same moment of time at two or more places, those places might show a simultaneous effect of disturbance, and that even when the cause might be very little or not at all sensible in the place where it occurred. A simultaneous change over an area of 600 or 800 miles in diameter, might produce less alteration in the middle of that area than at the extremities of radii of 1000 miles.

2960. It becomes a fair question of principle to inquire how far masses of the air may be *moved* by the power of the magnetic force which pervades them. When two bulbs of oxygen in different states of density are subjected to a powerful magnet with an intense field of force, the mechanical displacement of one by the other is most striking. Whether in nature the enormous volumes of air concerned, and the difference in intensity of the earth's magnetic force at the different latitudes where these may be supposed to be located, combined with the difference of temperature, are sufficient to compensate for the small portions of oxygen in the air and the smaller variations in density, is a matter that cannot at present be determined. The differential result of motion, as has been shown, is very great where the direct result, as of compression, is not merely very small but nothing (2750, 2774), and the atmosphere is a region where the differential action of enormous masses is concerned.

2961. Now in the matter of difference of intensity, Gay-Lussac and Biot conclude from their observations,[1] that the magnetic force is the same at a height of four miles as at the surface of the earth. M. Kupffer, however, draws from Gay-Lussac's results the conclusion, that there was a little diminution, and Professor Forbes, from his experiments made in different parts of Europe,[2] concludes that there is a decrease of the force upwards. Such decrease may be a real consequence due to the difference of distance from the source of the terrestrial magnetic force; or, as is more likely, it may be due to the different proportions of oxygen there and at the surface of the earth. According to Gay-Lussac's account of the air brought from above, it was as 0.5 to 1.0, compared with the density below. Hence the paramagnetic power added to space in the place above, from whence the air was taken, would not be more than one-half of that added by the presence of the denser atmosphere below This I think ought to make a change in the distribution of the magnetic force; it would almost certainly do so at the equator, where the lines of force are parallel to the general direction of the atmosphere (2881); and I think it would do so, as to the horizontal component, in the latitude where Gay-Lussac and Biot made their aerial voyages. It is also just possible that the observers may have been in such relation to the heated or cooled air about them as to have had the difference observed produced, or rather affected, by some of the circumstances just described (2951).

2962. Whether the result obtained by Gay-Lussac and Biot indicate a change of power due to distance or not, this we know, that there *are* great changes from the magnetic equator toward the north and south; and that, as Humboldt and Bessel say, it is doubled in proceeding from the equator to the western limits of Baffin's Bay. And when so little as one-third of a cubic inch of oxygen can exert a force equal to the tenth of a grain, subject to the action of our powerful magnet, we may well conceive that the enormous sum of oxygen present, in only a few miles of heated or cooled atmosphere, can compensate for the great difference of magnetic force, and so by a change of place, cause currents or winds having their origin in magnetic power. In such a case we should have a relation of magnets to storms; and the magnetic force of the earth would have to do with the mechanical adjustments and variations of the atmosphere, sometimes causing currents which without it might not exist, and at other times opposing those which might else arise, according as the great differential relations by which it would act (2757) should combine with or oppose the other natural causes of motion in the air. Such movements would react upon the magnetic forces, so that these would readjust themselves, and so there would be magnetic storms, both material and potential, in the atmosphere, as there are supposed to be of the latter kind in the earth.

2963. In bringing this communication to a close, I have to express my obligations to two kind and able friends, Colonel Sabine and Professor Christie, for the interest they have taken in the subject, and on the part of the former for the extreme facilities afforded me in the use of observations and the data derived from them; but in doing so I must be careful not to convey any idea that they are at all responsible for the peculiar views I have ventured to put forth. I may well acknowledge that much which I have written has been upon very insufficient consideration; but hoping that there might be some foundation of truth in the account of the physical cause of the variations which I have ventured to suggest, I have not hesitated to put it forth, trusting that it might be for the advantage of science. The magnetic properties and relations of oxygen are perfectly clear and distinct, and are established by experiment (2774, 2780); and it is no assumption to carry these properties into the atmosphere, because the atmosphere, as a mere mixture of oxygen and nitrogen, is shown to possess them also (2862).[3] It varies in its magnetic powers, by causes which act upon it under natural circumstances, and make it able to produce some such effects as those I have endeavoured generally to describe.

2964. If it be a cause, in part only, of the observed magnetic variations, it is most important to identify and distinguish such a source of action, even though imperfectly; for the attention is then truly and intelligently directed in

---

[1] *Annales de Chimie*, Ann. XIII, Vol. LII, p. 86.
[2] *Edin. Phil. Trans.*, 1836, Vol. XIV, p. 25.

[3] *Philosophical Magazine*, 1847, Vol. XXXI, pp. 406, 409.

respect to the action and the phenomena it can produce. The assigned cause has the advantage of occurring periodically and for the same periods, as a large class of the effects supposed to be produced by it; and if the agreement should appear at first only general, still that agreement will greatly strengthen its claim to our attention. It has the advantage of offering explanations and even suggestions of many other magnetic events besides those which are periodical, and it presents itself at a time when we have no clear knowledge of any other physical cause for the variations, but are constrained vaguely to refer them to imaginary currents of electricity in the air or space above, or in the earth beneath.

2965. The causes, both of the original power and of its secular variations, are unknown to us. But if, accepting the earth as a magnet, we should be able to distinguish largely between internal and external action, and so separate a great class of phenomena from the rest, we should be enabled to define more exactly that which we require to know in both directions, should be competent to state distinctly the problems which need solution, and be far better able to appreciate any new hints from nature respecting the *source* of the power and the effects that it presents to us.

2966. The magnetic constitution of oxygen seems to me wonderful. It is in the air what iron is in the earth. The almost entire disappearance of this property also, when it enters into combination, is most impressive, as in the oxynitrogens and oxycarbons, and even with iron, which it reduces into a condition far below either the metal or the oxygen, weight for weight. Again, its striking contrast with the nitrogen, which dilutes it, impresses the mind, and by the difference recalls that which also exists between them in relation to static electricity (1464) and the lightning flash. Chlorine bromine, cyanogen and its congeners, chemically speaking, have no magnetic relation to oxygen. In nature it stands in this respect, as in all its chemical actions, alone.

2967. There is much to do with oxygen relative to atmospheric magnetism. Its proportion of paramagnetic force at different temperatures and different degrees of rarefaction, will require to be accurately ascertained, and this I hope to effect by a torsion balance, in course of construction (2783). Indeed, I hope that this great subject may be largely touched and tried by experiment as well as by observation, and therefore gladly make it part of these experimental researches.

2968. One can scarcely think upon the subject of atmospheric magnetism without having another great question suggested to the mind (2442): What is the final purpose in nature of this magnetic condition of the atmosphere, and its liability to annual and diurnal variations, and its entire loss by entering into combination either in combustion or respiration? No doubt there is one or more, for nothing is superfluous there. We find no remainders or surplusage of action in physical forces. The smallest provision is as essential as the greatest. None is deficient, none can be spared.

Royal Institution, September 14, 1850

APPENDIX

Received November 12, 1850

The following tables of data obtained at Toronto, St. Petersburgh, Washington, Lake Athabasca and Fort Simpson, supplied to me by the kindness of Colonel Sabine, have not yet been published. The data for Hobarton and Greenwich are in the volumes of observations for those stations.

TORONTO. Longitude 79° 5′ W. Latitude 43° 40′ N. Approximate declination 1° 25′ W. Mean inclination 75° 15′ N.

Diurnal variation of the Declination in the several months, from July 1842 to June 1848 inclusive.

Increasing numbers denote a movement of the south or upper end of the magnet towards the West.

Toronto mean time	0h Noon	1h	2h	3h	4h	5h	6h	7h	8h	9h	10h	11h	12h Midn.	13h	14h	15h	16h	17h	18h	19h	20h	21h	22h	23h	Daily means
Jan.	0.87	0.00	0.00	0.53	1.44	2.28	2.89	3.47	4.03	4.53	4.39	4.06	3.66	3.42	3.63	3.87	4.46	3.84	3.88	4.44	5.48	5.80	4.79	3.03	3.30
Feb.	0.78	0.00	0.06	0.94	1.58	1.91	2.73	3.13	4.02	4.44	4.69	4.45	4.31	3.81	3.54	4.07	3.97	4.86	4.95	5.20	5.97	5.70	4.64	2.53	3.43
Mar.	1.44	0.01	0.00	0.59	1.74	2.90	3.82	4.77	5.53	6.60	6.47	6.86	6.04	6.42	6.55	6.34	6.69	6.59	7.10	8.30	9.38	9.40	7.15	4.22	5.21
Apr.	1.25	0.00	0.16	1.02	2.76	4.12	5.14	6.31	7.05	7.14	7.60	7.66	7.39	7.32	7.65	7.82	8.08	8.33	9.46	10.09	10.20	9.10	6.87	3.74	6.09
May	1.16	0.00	0.29	1.56	3.24	5.11	6.08	6.27	6.18	6.75	7.36	7.49	7.40	7.26	6.72	7.10	7.80	9.70	11.02	12.16	12.03	10.28	6.90	3.52	6.39
June	1.37	0.00	0.02	0.94	2.53	4.35	5.45	6.11	6.10	6.66	6.66	6.87	6.77	6.50	6.37	6.36	7.29	9.03	11.34	12.34	12.09	10.54	7.67	4.04	6.12
July	1.53	0.09	0.00	0.84	2.18	3.98	5.20	5.77	6.31	6.34	7.31	7.38	7.67	7.06	6.42	6.37	6.86	8.53	10.54	12.01	12.22	10.69	7.65	4.27	6.13
Aug.	1.11	0.00	0.73	2.61	4.52	6.12	7.60	7.52	8.35	8.97	8.51	8.40	8.14	7.69	7.65	7.83	8.24	9.50	9.79	13.89	13.79	11.51	7.31	3.73	7.31
Sept.	0.03	0.00	0.76	2.92	4.62	6.04	6.78	6.83	7.32	8.51	7.83	7.08	7.50	7.66	7.53	7.77	8.45	8.38	9.79	11.16	10.24	8.60	5.34	2.25	6.37
Oct.	0.48	0.00	0.31	1.38	2.38	3.06	3.84	4.33	4.22	5.76	5.68	5.48	5.00	5.21	4.89	5.16	5.82	5.74	5.50	6.39	7.32	7.02	5.17	2.63	3.89
Nov.	0.75	0.00	0.34	1.37	2.21	2.91	3.96	4.89	5.16	5.70	5.54	5.26	4.51	3.79	3.80	4.51	4.44	4.99	4.95	5.70	6.31	6.08	4.57	2.35	3.92
Dec.	1.20	0.18	0.00	0.61	1.67	2.56	3.30	3.89	4.39	4.62	4.95	4.48	4.09	3.49	3.04	3.56	3.92	4.02	3.81	4.18	4.50	5.22	4.67	2.83	3.30

Mean Diurnal variation of the Inclination in the several months; from July 1842 to June 1848.

Increasing numbers denote increasing inclination.

Toronto mean time	0h Noon	1h	2h	3h	4h	5h	6h	7h	8h	9h	10h	11h	12h Midn.	13h	14h	15h	16h	17h	18h	19h	20h	21h	22h	23h	Daily means
Jan.	1.02	0.77	0.53	0.22	0.00	0.09	0.16	0.21	0.25	0.33	0.34	0.38	0.47	0.54	0.58	0.45	0.33	0.28	0.22	0.21	0.36	0.54	1.04	1.06	0.43
Feb.	0.86	0.61	0.36	0.12	0.01	0.00	0.09	0.12	0.19	0.26	0.27	0.31	0.37	0.45	0.49	0.44	0.41	0.30	0.27	0.44	0.69	0.70	0.79	0.86	0.39
Mar.	1.02	0.77	0.47	0.14	0.00	0.00	0.12	0.22	0.24	0.35	0.40	0.44	0.45	0.53	0.50	0.61	0.60	0.46	0.47	0.62	0.81	0.95	1.00	1.05	0.50
Apr.	0.99	0.52	0.54	0.17	0.05	0.00	0.14	0.35	0.49	0.53	0.49	0.61	0.56	0.59	0.64	0.89	0.92	0.66	0.74	0.80	0.90	1.03	1.16	1.16	0.61
May	0.83	0.60	0.22	0.06	0.00	0.11	0.27	0.33	0.47	0.62	0.64	0.66	0.76	0.86	0.87	0.89	0.92	1.05	1.00	1.01	1.11	1.29	1.30	1.12	0.70
June	0.89	0.60	0.26	0.05	0.00	0.00	0.16	0.34	0.53	0.68	0.73	0.83	0.84	0.90	0.91	0.98	1.03	0.91	1.08	1.12	1.28	1.17	1.37	1.19	0.75
July	0.67	0.55	0.17	0.07	0.00	0.06	0.17	0.24	0.39	0.40	0.51	0.56	0.62	0.56	0.66	0.78	0.83	0.87	0.81	0.80	0.88	1.03	1.14	0.93	0.57
Aug.	0.85	0.51	0.21	0.00	0.02	0.04	0.25	0.40	0.42	0.44	0.48	0.55	0.53	0.64	0.65	0.73	0.74	0.84	0.89	1.00	1.28	1.25	1.26	1.13	0.62
Sept.	1.35	0.82	0.35	0.10	0.00	0.10	0.29	0.49	0.53	0.55	0.57	0.63	0.68	0.70	0.70	0.75	0.75	0.65	0.55	0.55	0.85	1.28	1.64	1.71	0.75
Oct.	0.93	0.67	0.39	0.14	0.00	0.18	0.21	0.30	0.37	0.39	0.40	0.49	0.62	0.45	0.40	0.33	0.22	0.22	0.32	0.08	0.42	1.04	1.15	1.11	0.48
Nov.	0.94	0.75	0.45	0.22	0.11	0.01	0.12	0.18	0.20	0.20	0.23	0.33	0.33	0.31	0.21	0.22	0.12	0.07	0.00	0.00	0.17	0.14	0.89	1.00	0.32
Dec.	0.91	0.88	0.51	0.27	0.05	0.01	0.02	0.16	0.21	0.27	0.33	0.30	0.38	0.34	0.28	0.22	0.14	0.08	0.09	0.00	0.17	0.34	0.66	0.81	0.31
Hourly means	0.94	0.69	0.37	0.13	0.02	0.05	0.17	0.28	0.36	0.42	0.45	0.51	0.55	0.57	0.57	0.58	0.53	0.54	0.55	0.63	0.81	0.93	1.13	1.10	0.54

Toronto. Mean Diurnal variation of the Total Force in the several months, from July 1842 to June 1848.

Increasing numbers denote increasing Force. Mean Total Force at Toronto 13.9.

The figures express the changes in parts of the whole Force.

(All values below are in the form .00x, i.e. prefixed by ".00".)

Toronto mean time	0h	1h	2h	3h	4h	5h	6h	7h	8h	9h	10h	11h	12h	13h	14h	15h	16h	17h	18h	19h	20h	21h	22h	23h	Daily means
Jan.	005	011	017	023	022	024	023	023	023	020	019	015	010	009	004	003	004	005	008	009	010	003	000	000	012
Feb.	006	012	019	022	024	026	026	027	025	023	019	017	009	005	003	004	003	006	009	010	016	004	000	001	013
Mar.	004	011	019	026	029	031	031	031	028	025	020	014	005	002	002	002	003	003	010	013	013	007	002	000	014
Apr.	012	020	031	039	045	045	044	039	034	027	020	012	008	007	003	003	009	011	013	012	012	009	006	006	019
May	004	013	015	031	038	042	038	035	029	025	017	011	004	002	002	003	008	010	015	013	009	003	000	000	015
June	003	008	017	025	029	031	030	028	022	018	014	011	006	002	002	001	006	011	014	017	010	005	003	000	013
July	015	019	030	038	044	047	043	039	031	026	021	015	007	004	000	002	005	011	016	026	015	014	010	002	020
Aug.	027	034	044	042	057	057	051	046	041	032	023	010	006	001	003	000	006	018	026	022	024	019	019	021	026
Sept.	029	043	053	060	060	056	052	050	044	038	034	029	019	007	000	001	004	009	018	022	028	015	010	021	030
Oct.	013	021	027	032	032	033	033	034	031	026	023	018	007	003	005	002	000	005	011	014	014	011	008	006	017
Nov.	007	014	022	026	028	025	025	028	024	018	015	011	007	004	001	003	000	003	007	009	008	002	001	003	011
Dec.	004	010	019	020	023	021	021	021	019	018	017	012	010	008	006	007	003	003	007	006	006	006	001	000	011
Means	011	018	026	032	036	037	035	033	029	025	020	015	008	005	003	002	004	008	013	014	014	008	005	006	017

Mean Temperature of the Air in the several months, from July 1842 to June 1848, in degrees of Fahrenheit's scale.

Toronto mean time	0h	1h	2h	3h	4h	5h	6h	7h	8h	9h	10h	11h	12h	13h	14h	15h	16h	17h	18h	19h	20h	21h	22h	23h	Daily means
Jan.	27.8	28.3	28.6	28.5	28.0	27.1	26.3	25.8	25.5	25.3	26.3	24.6	25.6	23.5	23.4	21.6	23.2	23.0	23.7	23.6	23.9	24.8	26.0	27.1	25.48
Feb.	27.4	28.2	28.5	28.5	28.0	26.9	25.6	24.6	23.8	23.2	22.7	22.2	22.0	21.7	21.3	20.9	20.5	20.2	20.0	19.9	20.9	22.9	24.9	26.3	23.80
Mar.	33.8	34.4	35.0	34.9	34.3	33.6	31.9	30.5	29.5	28.6	28.0	27.3	27.3	26.8	26.3	26.2	25.8	25.5	25.0	25.9	27.8	29.9	31.6	32.8	29.71
Apr.	47.6	48.5	49.0	49.0	48.6	47.9	46.1	43.5	41.8	40.7	39.8	39.3	39.1	38.9	37.9	37.3	37.0	36.6	36.8	39.2	41.5	43.6	45.2	46.6	42.55
May	59.0	59.9	60.2	60.3	60.3	59.9	58.1	55.2	52.6	50.7	49.7	48.8	48.0	46.9	46.3	45.6	45.1	45.2	47.6	50.6	53.0	55.2	56.8	58.0	53.04
June	66.7	67.5	67.9	68.3	68.5	68.1	66.6	63.9	60.6	57.0	57.0	56.1	55.7	54.8	54.1	53.3	52.7	52.9	55.6	58.5	60.8	62.7	64.4	65.6	60.86
July	72.9	73.7	74.5	74.8	74.7	74.3	72.7	69.2	65.1	61.8	61.8	60.7	59.8	58.9	58.3	57.6	56.9	56.9	59.8	63.4	66.0	68.2	70.1	71.5	66.02
Aug.	73.0	73.9	74.5	74.8	74.6	74.1	72.5	68.4	65.3	63.6	62.4	61.6	60.7	60.0	59.4	58.7	58.3	58.1	59.6	63.2	66.0	68.7	70.6	72.1	66.43
Sept.	63.9	64.5	64.9	64.9	64.7	63.7	61.1	58.3	57.1	56.0	54.9	54.2	53.8	53.3	52.7	52.2	51.6	51.1	51.7	54.2	57.0	59.5	61.5	62.9	57.90
Oct.	49.7	50.3	50.5	50.3	49.6	47.8	45.8	44.7	43.9	43.1	42.3	41.6	41.0	40.4	40.1	39.9	39.5	39.4	39.6	40.4	42.8	45.6	47.5	48.9	44.35
Nov.	39.5	40.0	40.1	39.9	39.0	37.7	36.9	36.3	35.9	35.7	35.3	34.9	34.3	34.0	33.7	33.4	33.2	33.3	33.6	33.6	34.6	36.2	37.7	38.8	36.15
Dec.	29.9	30.4	30.7	30.5	29.8	28.9	28.2	27.9	27.5	27.3	27.0	26.9	26.6	26.0	25.7	25.5	25.5	25.5	25.1	25.0	25.4	26.6	27.9	29.1	27.44
Means	49.27	49.97	50.37	50.39	50.01	49.17	47.65	45.69	44.05	42.96	42.27	41.52	41.16	40.41	39.93	39.35	39.11	38.97	39.84	41.46	43.33	45.32	47.02	48.31	44.48

St. Petersburgh. Longitude 38° 18′ East. Latitude 59° 57′ North. Mean declination 6° 10′ West.

Mean Diurnal variation of the Declination in the several months, from 1841 to 1845 inclusive.

Increasing numbers denote a movement of the south or upper end of the magnet towards the West.

(All readings taken at 21½ minutes past the hour.)

Mean time	Noon 0	1	2	3	4	5	6	7	8	9	10	11	Midn. 12	13	14	15	16	17	18	19	20	21	22	23	Means
Jan.	0.27	0.00	0.36	1.24	1.59	1.99	2.39	3.28	4.03	4.65	4.56	4.65	4.43	3.72	3.77	3.10	2.57	2.22	2.35	2.17	2.08	1.86	1.42	1.02	2.49
Feb.	0.84	0.00	0.09	0.57	1.55	2.84	3.54	3.63	4.03	5.18	5.67	5.49	5.27	4.52	4.34	4.65	4.34	3.90	4.03	3.77	3.50	3.23	2.61	1.46	3.29
Mar.	0.89	0.00	0.04	1.15	2.88	4.16	5.36	6.29	6.73	6.78	7.40	7.84	6.69	6.51	5.76	6.11	6.38	6.16	6.65	6.56	6.73	6.38	4.96	2.79	5.05
Apr.	1.59	0.00	0.36	2.17	4.03	5.54	7.04	7.93	8.33	8.02	9.30	9.17	8.68	8.46	8.73	8.59	9.17	9.30	9.48	10.01	10.68	9.75	7.58	4.61	7.01
May	1.02	0.00	0.62	2.13	3.68	5.49	6.96	7.44	7.18	6.82	7.44	8.24	7.49	8.28	8.82	9.66	9.70	10.23	11.30	11.39	11.12	9.92	7.35	4.12	7.01
June	1.77	0.00	0.00	1.37	2.92	4.52	5.76	6.25	6.25	6.56	7.13	7.13	6.82	7.44	7.13	8.24	8.73	8.55	9.83	9.75	9.04	6.96	5.67	3.90	6.70
July	1.46	0.04	0.00	1.11	2.39	3.94	4.96	5.27	5.98	5.93	6.78	7.27	7.66	7.71	8.42	8.55	9.30	9.52	10.19	10.19	9.44	8.46	5.67	3.15	6.02
Aug.	0.27	0.00	0.40	2.44	4.16	5.94	6.94	7.27	7.97	8.06	8.33	7.49	8.02	8.11	8.06	8.55	9.30	9.88	10.19	10.19	9.44	8.42	5.67	3.15	6.47
Sept.	0.57	0.00	0.84	2.57	4.30	6.33	6.78	7.49	8.06	8.33	6.91	7.49	7.04	7.31	7.40	6.78	7.04	6.91	7.27	7.31	7.13	6.25	4.12	1.95	5.72
Oct.	0.31	0.00	0.48	1.77	3.59	4.08	4.87	5.76	6.02	6.56	6.56	6.20	5.71	5.18	4.78	4.39	4.16	3.99	4.21	4.83	5.09	4.65	3.32	1.59	4.10
Nov.	0.09	0.00	0.36	1.55	1.90	2.71	3.15	3.68	3.81	4.39	4.47	4.34	3.68	3.06	2.75	2.35	2.22	1.82	1.82	1.90	1.77	1.77	0.93	0.57	2.26
Dec.	0.53	0.00	0.36	1.24	1.82	2.39	2.79	2.97	4.03	4.56	4.56	4.52	3.68	3.10	2.88	2.53	2.04	1.82	1.77	1.77	1.82	1.68	1.28	0.93	2.29
Means	0.80	0.00	0.33	1.61	2.90	4.16	5.02	5.52	5.99	6.24	6.66	6.65	6.41	6.22	6.20	6.25	6.42	6.43	6.67	6.75	6.66	6.04	4.47	2.47	4.87

Mean Temperature of the Air in the several months, from 1841 to 1845 inclusive. Fahrenheit's scale.

(All readings taken at 21½ minutes past the hour. Values in °.)

Mean time	Noon 0	1	2	3	4	5	6	7	8	9	10	11	Midn. 12	13	14	15	16	17	18	19	20	21	22	23	Means
Jan.	20.28	20.71	20.67	20.41	19.82	19.89	19.73	19.71	19.74	19.76	19.67	19.49	19.38	19.33	19.29	19.19	19.04	18.90	18.79	18.74	18.79	18.81	18.74	19.24	19.98
Feb.	18.34	18.58	18.70	18.65	18.27	18.27	17.35	16.88	16.52	16.32	16.09	15.95	15.67	15.55	15.48	15.39	15.19	14.97	14.88	14.76	14.65	15.19	15.66	16.61	17.35
Mar.	25.61	26.30	26.97	27.01	27.01	26.13	24.74	23.88	23.20	22.44	21.94	21.31	20.70	20.07	19.62	19.26	18.84	18.54	18.34	18.74	19.87	21.38	22.95	24.53	24.53
Apr.	37.85	38.07	38.58	38.81	39.53	38.63	36.54	34.62	32.35	32.38	31.42	30.72	30.07	29.55	29.08	28.61	28.36	28.42	29.21	30.63	32.16	33.75	35.39	36.79	36.79
May	53.46	53.80	54.31	54.72	55.10	54.29	52.23	49.84	47.91	46.19	45.38	45.38	44.19	43.16	42.37	41.83	41.47	41.56	42.73	44.19	46.06	47.88	49.57	51.17	52.65
June	63.03	63.48	63.83	64.36	64.97	64.07	61.90	59.97	58.19	56.56	55.04	54.07	53.26	52.58	52.00	51.50	52.27	53.33	54.95	56.57	58.21	59.72	60.59	62.06	62.15
July	66.44	66.93	67.21	67.46	67.93	67.26	65.28	63.61	62.01	60.57	59.56	58.86	58.05	57.33	56.86	56.48	56.68	57.53	58.86	60.59	62.06	63.43	64.76	65.90	65.90
Aug.	67.10	68.00	68.56	68.69	69.23	68.56	65.73	63.70	62.26	60.08	60.08	59.22	58.14	57.60	57.20	56.57	56.14	56.73	57.65	59.45	61.29	63.12	64.71	66.06	66.06
Sept.	54.50	55.66	55.91	55.78	55.83	54.56	52.62	51.16	50.56	49.43	48.89	48.31	47.75	47.25	46.85	46.44	46.26	46.06	47.21	48.76	50.56	52.20	53.37	53.37	53.37
Oct.	41.92	44.80	42.76	41.98	41.78	40.92	40.30	39.89	38.56	39.31	38.86	38.52	38.32	38.14	38.00	37.85	37.73	37.67	37.71	37.53	38.28	39.11	40.12	41.04	41.04
Nov.	29.73	30.22	30.88	29.75	29.26	29.26	28.83	28.67	28.49	28.52	28.41	28.49	28.52	28.45	28.47	28.04	28.13	28.04	27.95	28.00	28.07	28.42	28.83	29.37	29.37
Dec.	26.04	26.45	26.40	26.27	26.13	25.91	25.70	26.02	25.52	25.48	25.48	25.32	25.21	25.12	24.96	24.85	24.85	24.92	25.03	25.03	25.14	25.25	25.39	25.79	25.79

Washington, U.S.—Longitude 77° 2' West. Latitude 38° 54' North. Mean declination 1° 25' West. Mean dip 71° 20' North.

Mean Diurnal variation of the Declination in minutes, and temperature in Fahrenheit's scale, of the months of the years 1840, 1841, 1842, which are specified.

Increasing numbers denote a movement of the south or upper end towards the East.

Mean time	Noon h m 0 12	h m 2 12	h m 4 12	h m 6 12	h m 8 12	h m 10 12	h m 12 12	h m 14 12	h m 16 12	h m 18 12	h m 20 12	h m 22 12	Mean
Jan. 1841–42	4.10	5.20	3.96	2.52	0.87	0.68	1.01	1.62	1.66	1.71	0.91	0.29	2.04
Feb. 1841–42	3.55	5.28	4.22	2.89	1.59	0.94	0.84	1.26	0.81	0.82	0.60	0.35	1.76
Mar. 1841–42	6.34	7.51	6.26	4.25	2.88	2.31	2.50	3.00	1.71	1.13	0.00	1.76	3.30
Apr. 1841–42	6.56	8.33	6.42	4.41	3.22	1.97	2.24	1.35	0.73	0.46	0.00	2.18	3.15
May 1841–42	7.72	8.57	6.36	4.45	3.82	3.47	3.25	3.05	2.63	0.33	0.00	4.25	3.99
June 1841–42	8.55	9.47	8.00	5.33	4.91	4.24	4.05	4.32	3.44	0.63	0.00	4.53	4.79
July 1840–41	8.42	9.87	8.07	5.75	4.57	3.52	3.60	3.40	2.99	0.98	0.00	3.82	4.56
Aug. 1840–41	10.94	10.81	7.95	6.00	4.03	3.55	4.48	4.64	4.04	1.35	0.00	5.99	5.30
Sept. 1840–41	8.76	8.44	5.43	4.45	2.62	3.31	2.83	2.86	2.44	0.87	0.00	4.22	3.85
Oct. 1840–41	5.65	5.83	4.35	2.47	1.41	0.58	1.41	1.80	1.51	1.35	0.00	1.75	2.34
Nov. 1840–41	4.69	4.79	3.33	1.60	0.51	0.74	1.14	1.41	0.82	0.71	0.00	1.83	1.79
Dec. 1840–41	3.93	4.90	3.39	1.92	0.10	0.36	0.62	1.53	0.93	2.00	1.02	0.87	1.79

Temperature

Mean time	Noon h m 0 12	h m 2 12	h m 4 12	h m 6 12	h m 8 12	h m 10 12	h m 12 12	h m 14 12	h m 16 12	h m 18 12	h m 20 12	h m 22 12
Jan. 1841–42	38.28	40.83	40.18	36.68	35.47	34.24	32.37	32.10	31.71	30.53	31.63	36.96
Feb. 1841–42	40.03	42.51	42.28	38.22	35.38	33.86	32.58	31.22	30.51	30.18	31.44	36.72
Mar. 1841–42	51.39	53.61	53.28	49.96	46.20	44.37	42.48	41.26	40.06	39.87	42.28	48.06
Apr. 1841–42	57.68	59.81	60.20	57.21	52.18	49.12	47.91	46.91	46.12	46.49	49.93	54.02
May 1841–42	66.37	68.48	68.69	65.93	59.83	56.70	55.19	53.34	52.42	55.50	59.72	63.23
June 1841–42	79.32	81.85	82.75	76.89	72.29	68.70	66.83	66.04	65.07	68.26	73.63	77.37
July 1841	81.13	81.53	84.60	81.33	74.93	71.56	68.78	68.09	66.78	70.64	75.–9	78.38
Aug. 1840–41	78.70	80.73	80.09	75.93	71.48	68.00	66.82	65.12	64.17	65.69	65.73	76.09
Sept. 1841	74.66	76.50	76.30	72.30	68.59	64.90	62.70	61.90	61.00	61.29	65.73	71.02
Oct. 1841	55.30	57.00	56.20	52.94	48.40	46.60	44.90	43.70	42.30	41.70	45.00	51.61
Nov. 1841	48.00	49.20	48.50	47.30	44.20	43.20	41.80	40.70	39.40	38.80	39.50	44.10
Dec. 1841	39.20	41.30	40.60	37.95	36.26	34.70	33.50	33.16	32.20	31.60	31.69	36.00

Lake Athabasca. Longitude 111° 18' West. Latitude 58° 41' North. Mean declination 28° East.

Diurnal variation of the Declination in the months of October, November and December 1843, and Jan. and Feb. 1844.

Increasing readings denote a movement of the south or upper end of the magnet towards the West.

Mean time }	15 minutes past midnight h m 12 15	h m 12 55 13	h m 13 55 14	h m 14 55 15	h m 15 55 16	h m 16 55 17	h m 17 55 18	h m 18 55 19	h m 19 55 20	h m 20 55 21	h m 21 55 22	5 minutes to noon h m 23 55	h m 0 55 1	h m 1 55 2	h m 2 55 3	h m 3 55 4	h m 4 55 5	h m 5 55 6	h m 6 55 7	h m 7 55 8	h m 8 55 9	h m 9 55 10	h m 10 55	5 minutes to midnight h m 11 55	Mean time
Oct. 1843	1.13	7.49	6.23	18.95	21.32	8.55	13.35	9.90	10.72	7.03	2.29	2.70	0.00	0.29	0.02	0.98	0.49	2.88	1.88	3.75	3.47	3.30	8.42	0.49	13 days obs. in Oct. 1843.
Nov. 1843	3.73	5.17	6.74	9.07	10.35	10.80	9.40	8.80	7.63	8.54	1.10	0.00	1.06	1.57	1.93	2.73	2.94	3.34	4.52	4.97	5.43	7.08	3.04	3.63	25 days obs. in Nov. 1843.
Dec. 1843	3.04	6.16	5.57	5.65	9.23	7.61	9.78	6.73	6.58	5.53	1.94	0.55	0.03	0.00	0.83	2.37	2.63	3.81	4.18	3.57	4.35	7.19	4.05	6.05	25 days obs. in Dec. 1843.
Jan. 1844	5.69	8.48	6.97	12.57	16.29	10.05	9.97	10.02	9.96	7.55	4.99	2.10	0.39	0.00	2.75	1.67	2.47	3.63	4.72	5.15	5.44	3.97	6.71	2.18	25 days obs. in Jan. 1844.
Feb. 1844	4.27	4.93	8.46	10.55	14.80	14.87	14.06	12.10	12.76	8.64	2.82	2.93	1.55	0.00	1.48	3.24	3.76	4.52	4.96	5.48	5.58	4.99	6.98	5.40	25 days obs. in Feb. 1844.

Fort Simpson. Longitude 121° 30' West. Latitude 61° 52' North.

Diurnal variation of the Declination in the months of April and May 1844.

Increasing numbers denote a movement of the south or upper end of the magnet towards the West.

Mean time }	15 minutes past midnight h m 12 15	h m 13 15 14	h m 14 15 15	h m 15 15 16	h m 16 15 17	h m 17 15 18	h m 18 15 19	h m 19 15 20	h m 20 15 21	h m 21 15 22	h m 22 15 23	h m 23 15	15 minutes past noon h m 0 15	h m 1 15 2	h m 2 15 3	h m 3 15 4	h m 4 15 5	h m 5 15 6	h m 6 15 7	h m 7 15 8	h m 8 15 9	h m 9 15 10	h m 10 15 11	h m 11 15	Mean time
Apr. 1844	5.82	6.03	17.45	25.16	22.90	36.80	36.26	37.60	33.14	25.27	18.77	8.27	5.72	2.16	0.00	1.37	1.23	0.43	0.30	4.04	4.62	1.26	2.86	5.55	20 days obs. in Apr. 1844.
May 1844	1.56	7.77	11.71	15.63	17.19	23.73	28.22	32.69	23.80	20.29	15.51	9.49	4.74	3.75	0.70	0.75	0.00	0.80	0.19	1.90	6.72	3.51	2.29	1.67	18 days obs. in May 1844.

§ 33. *On Atmospheric Magnetism* (*continued*)

RECEIVED NOVEMBER 19, READ NOVEMBER 28, 1850

¶ ii. *Experimental Inquiry into the Laws of Atmospheric Magnetic Action, and their Application to Particular Cases*

2969. BELIEVING that experiment may do much for the development of the general principles of atmospheric magnetism, and produce rapidly a body of facts on which philosophers may proceed hereafter to raise a superstructure, I endeavoured to find some means of representing practically the action of the atmosphere, when heated by the sun, upon the terrestrial magnetic curves. The object was to obtain some central arrangement of force which should deflect these curves or lines as they are deflected in a diamagnetic conductor or globe of hot air (2877), and then apply the results obtained by such an arrangement as a partial test to the various cases supplied by the magnetic observatories scattered over the earth. At first I endeavoured, for the sake of convenience, to attain this desired end by means of a horseshoe magnet, employing the lines which passed from pole to pole to disturb and re-arrange the earth's force; but the comparative weakness of the terrestrial force near the magnet, and the great prominence of the poles of the latter, gave rise to many inconveniences, which soon caused me to reject that method and have recourse to a ring-helix and voltaic apparatus. Considering the new use to which this helix is to be applied, the interest of the results, and the instruction that may be drawn from them, I shall be excused for being somewhat elementary in the description of its character and action.

2970. The helix consisted of about 12 feet of covered copper wire formed into a ring having about twenty-five convolutions, and being $1\frac{1}{2}$ inch in external diameter. The continuations of the wire were twisted together so as to neutralize any magnetic effect which they could produce, and were long enough to reach to a voltaic arrangement, and yet allow free motion of the helix. The requisite amount of magnetic power in the helix may be judged of by the following considerations: suppose a declination

[1] *Philosophical Transactions*, 1851, p. 85.

needle freely suspended; and then the *helix* placed at a distance in the prolongation of the needle with its axis in a line with the latter, and with that side towards the needle which will at small distances cause repulsion. The needle will point, in the magnetic meridian, with a certain amount of force; but as the helix is brought near it will point with less force, and within a certain distance will no longer point in the magnetic meridian, but either on one or the other side of it. There is a given distance within which the needle, when in the magnetic meridian, is in a position of unstable equilibrium, but beyond which it has a position of stable equilibrium, the distance varying with the strength of the exciting electric current. The power of the helix should be such that when end on to the needle the latter has a position of stable equilibrium in the meridian. One pair of plates is quite sufficient to make the helix as magnetic as is needful for distances varying from 4 to 24 inches. When a needle is properly arranged with either a magnet or a helix to the north or south of it as above described, if the magnet or helix be moved west the near end of the needle will move east, and contrariwise.

2971. As is well known, such a helix has a system of magnetic lines, which, passing through its axis, then opens out and turning round on the outside re-enters again at the axis, the circles of magnetic force being everywhere perpendicular to the electric current traversing the convolutions of the helix; and now I had, at a moment's notice, a source of lines of magnetic power exactly of the kind required to produce, in association with those of the earth, a disposition of the forces coinciding either with those of paramagnetic or diamagnetic polarization (2865, 2877).

2972. For let *Fig. 17* represent a section parallel to the axis of the ring-helix, then the two circles may represent the disposition of the magnetic force in that section, and the arrowheads may serve to indicate that magnetic direction which belongs to lines of force issuing out of the north end of a magnet. If such a system be suddenly produced in the midst of the earth's lines, it acts upon them according to the position of the helix in relation to the direction of the earth's power. Choosing the two positions in which the axis of the helix is parallel to the natural direction of the power, as shown by a free needle, at the place of observation, then two contrary effects are produced, which, as regards the lines exterior to the helix system, correspond to the polarity of paramagnetic and diamagnetic conductors. If, for instance, the helix is so placed that the polarity of its magnetic lines, exterior to and in the plane of the ring, accords with that of the earth's force, as in *Fig. 18*, then the earth's lines are de-

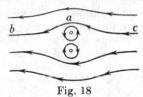

Fig. 17

Fig. 18

flected as represented, and a magnetic needle placed at *a*, which had taken up its position by the earth's influence, will not tend to alter its position as the helix approaches it, though it will be acted on with more power. In other parts of the line, *b a c*, it will alter its position, standing as a tangent to the curvature, and therefore will be deflected sometimes one way and sometimes another, as it is carried along the line (or through the neighbouring lines), in place of remaining parallel to itself, as it would do if the electro-magnetic helix were away.

2973. On the other hand, if the helix were turned round into the second position (2972), then the effect upon the direction of the neighbouring lines of force would be as in *Fig. 19*.

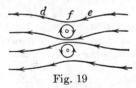

Fig. 19

Needles placed at *d* and *e* would again be deflected from the natural position given to them by the earth, but they would be deflected in a contrary direction to that which would be taken if they were in corresponding situations under the former arrangement. This figure and state of things represents the paramagnetic dis-

position of the forces, as the former did the diamagnetic condition.

2974. It is not pretended that the whole of these arrangements of forces is like those of the cases of paramagnetic and diamagnetic conductors. Independent systems are here introduced into the midst of the earth's magnetic power, and the central part of each arrangement must therefore be excepted; there are also attractions inwards and repulsions outwards, when the needle is at *a* and *f*, which do not take place in the cases of mere magnetic conduction. But external to these helix systems, the arrangement imposed upon the lines of force from the earth is in accordance with that produced by diamagnetic and paramagnetic conductors, and at distances from 2 inches to 2 or 3 feet; the lines of force thus altered, and those contorted by the sun and atmosphere in the great field of nature, are comparable in their direction, and may be considered as representing each other.

2975. In order to obtain a simple result of the action of such a centre of force on the magnetic lines of the earth, I adjusted a rod in the direction of the dipping-needle, and also a plane at the foot of it parallel to the magnetic equator at London. Then suspending a small magnet, half an inch long, from cocoon-silk, so that when hanging it should be parallel to the magnetic equator, it was adjusted so as to be near to the plane at the foot of the rod representing dip. The ring-helix (2970) was then associated with the voltaic pair, so that contact could be completed at any moment, and being always retained parallel to itself and to the plane of the magnetic equator, could be brought into the vicinity of the needle on all sides, above or below, and its action upon it observed. As the object was to represent the sun's action, the current was so sent through the helix that its upper face would repel the north end of a magnetic needle; for then a magnet, outside of and in the plane of the ring, would not tend to have its position changed, and the disposition of the forces of the earth under the influence of the helix was as in *Fig. 18*, or like that of a diamagnetic conductor.

2976. In making observations of this kind, and especially if the ring-helix is purposely retained at a considerable distance from the needle, it is better not to connect the helix permanently with the battery and then carry it towards and by the needle, but rather to choose the place where the helix action is to be observed, and when the helix is there to make contact with the battery; the motion and direction of the needle is then easily observed; or if it still, through reason of distance, be feeble, making and breaking contact a few times isochronously with the vibrations of the needle soon raises the effect to any degree required.

2977. There are certain positions in respect to the needle as a centre which must be clearly comprehended. The magnetic axis is a line through the centre of the free regular needle parallel to the direction of the earth's lines of force, whatever that may be, at the place where the experiments may be made. The magnetic equator plane is a plane passing through the centre of the needle perpendicular to the magnetic axis. The plane of the magnetic meridian is that plane which coincides with the magnetic axis, and also with the direction in which the declination needle points. This position always occurs with the magnets that are employed for observation, being a consequence of the method in which they are supported; it would not be taken by a needle placed at right angles on its mechanical axis, the latter being in the magnetic axis.

2978. When the ring-helix, situated as before explained (2975), was anywhere in the plane of the *magnetic meridian*, it exerted no action on the declination needle tending to change its position. When the helix was anywhere in the plane of the magnetic equator, it exerted no action on the needle to make it change its direction. These are the only places in which the helix does not affect the position of the needle.

2979. These two planes of no variation divide the space around the magnet into four quadrants, and the helix being in any one of these, affects the needle, altering its declination. The deflection of the line of force for two neighbouring quadrants is in the contrary direction, so that as the helix passes from the neutral line into one or the other quadrant, the declination of the needle changes.

2980. If the helix be above or below the magnetic equator and be carried round the magnetic axis travelling along a line of latitude, then the needle makes *one* large oscillation to the right, and another to the left during the circuit. Supposing that the experiment commences with the helix above the equator, and in the plane of the magnetic meridian north of the needle, if it then proceeds by west to south and on by east to its original position the north end of the needle will first go westward; will then stop and return eastward, passing the mean position, and will finally return westward and

settle in its first or original direction. All the time the helix is to magnetic east of the needle it will cause the same deflection, and also as long as it is in the west; the deflection will be more or less, but not change in direction as regards the neutral place. The position of the helix north or south of the needle is of no consequence as to the direction of the declination, provided it remain on the same side of the magnetic meridian, though it is to the amount. If the helix be below the magnetic equator the direction of the declination is reversed, but then again it does not change whilst the helix remains east or west of the needle and its plane of mean declination.

2981. If we carry the helix round the needle in a plane perpendicular to the planes of the magnetic equator and meridian, so as to traverse in succession the four quadrants, then the needle makes *two* to and fro vibrations (instead of one) during the circuit. Thus, beginning with the helix in the neutral position over the needle and going round by west and below, and then upwards on the east side to its first position, the north end of the needle will first pass westward, then eastward, then westward, after that eastward, and finally westward to its original or neutral position.

2982. As the helix is carried from the neutral planes (2978) into any of the quadrants, the power of affecting the declination of the needle is first developed, and then increases every way, from the edges of the quadrant until it attains its maximum force at the middle. Hence the maximum deflection east or west is when the helix is in the middle of each quadrant. Therefore, when the helix is carried from the middle of one quadrant to the middle of the next, only *one motion* in the needle appears; as for instance, an increasing westerly declination, though the direction of the declination in relation to the mean position has been reversed in that time, and there was a moment when the needle had no extra declination, but was *in* that mean position. So also as the helix moves over one quadrant from one neutral plane to another, though the declination of the needle produced by it has not changed in direction, but has been, for instance, all the time west, still the needle will have exhibited two motions going first west during the increase of the power, and then east whilst it is diminishing; and hence it is that though there are *four* departures of the needle from and return to the neutral or mean position, whilst the helix circumscribes it in an east and west vertical plane

(2981), there are only *two* complete journeys of the needle.

2983. The amount of the deflection diminishes as the distance of the helix from the needle increases; and the contrary.

2984. Two other needles were slung (2975) very oblique to the magnetic axis, one with its north end upwards and the other with its north end downwards, and these were submitted to the action of the helix as the former had been (2978). They were affected exactly in the same manner, showing no difference; i.e., a given end always moved the same way for the same change in position of the helix. If the helix was very near, then one pole was a little more influenced than the other in certain positions; but its removal farther off took away that difference (which is easily accounted for [2970]) and produced pure results. The place of the helix above or below the prolongation of the line of the needle made *no difference*, provided it was in the same place as regarded the magnetic equator of the earth's lines of force passing through the needle.

2985. For the purpose of establishing the nature of the action which such a helix, always in the given or diamagnetic position (2975), would exert upon the *inclination*, a small dipping-needle was submitted to its action and the following results obtained. The needle could move in the plane passing through the magnetic meridian of London.

2986. There was no deflection of the needle when the helix was in the plane of the magnetic equator, or in a plane perpendicular to that containing the mechanical axis of the needle. In every other position it affected it; so that these two planes divided the sphere of action into four segments, as before.

2987. As the helix passes from one quadrant to another, the direction in which the needle is deflected changes as before (2982). If the helix is in the upper north segment or the lower south segment, the upper or south end of the needle is deflected towards the south; if the helix be in the upper south or lower north segments, the upper or south end of the needle is deflected towards the north. If the helix be carried round the needle in the direction of the plane of motion, which in this case is that of the magnetic meridian, the end of the needle starting from a mean or unaffected position will move first one way, as for instance, north and then south; north again and south again, and finally north to regain its place of rest: so that there are two extreme deflections of the end in each

direction, as before, in the case of the declination magnet (2982).

2988. In other words, when the helix was anywhere below the magnetic equator, the *lower* or north end of the needle tended to point outwards from it or outside of it, being as it were *repelled* by the axis of the helix but *drawn* by the outer curved lines of force, *Fig. 20* (2992). Or if the helix were above the equator, then the *upper* or south end of the needle went outwards from the helix, moving exactly in the same direction in relation to the helix as the lower pole did before.

2989. The support of the needle was turned round 90°, which therefore removed the plane in which the needle could move 90° from the magnetic meridian. This carried the plane of no action on the needle 90° round, so that it now coincided with the magnetic meridian; and the plane, which, standing east and west was before neutral, was no longer a plane of indifference, but in fact passed at the middle of the segments through the places of strongest action.

2990. Here, with *inclination*, as before with *declination*, it is not the direction in which the needle stands that determines what action the helix may have upon it; for it may be loaded or otherwise restrained, as all horizontal needles are; but it is the *direction* of the lines of force at the needle which, with the helix, governs all. The helix may be above or below the prolongation of the needle indifferently; for if it still continues on the same side of the line of force, under the influence of which the needle acts, then the end of the needle moves in the same direction, though it may travel towards the helix in one instance and from it in another.

2991. I suspended a needle so that it was free to move in every direction, and now I obtained the simple natural effect of the helix, or a diamagnetic globe (2877) on a given line of force, and it is well to have it in mind. For, though we are obliged for the sake of practical observation to divide the position into two parts, declination and inclination, yet the results in each case are much better compared and remembered when the simple law of change in the whole line of force is ready in the mind for reference. The equatorial plane and the magnetic axis are now the only parts in which the helix can be without affecting the position of the needle; the first gives places (for the helix) with a stable position for the needle, and the second such as have either stable or unstable positions, according to the helix distance.

2992. If the helix be out of the plane and axis, then the end of the needle nearest to it leans from it as if repelled. If the helix be carried round in a circle of latitude, the end of the needle moves round before it just like the upper end of the needles at Hobarton and Toronto, in respect to the sun, during the midday hours. Instead of moving the helix round the needle, we may carry the needle into different positions as regards the helix, and then *Fig. 20* will represent the result. A result exceedingly simple, and in perfect accordance with the diamagnetic disposition of the forces produced by the helix (2972), as the two dotted lines indicate.

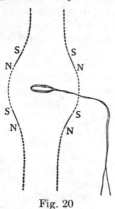

Fig. 20

2993. As an expression of the facts for use in applying them to the explanation and illustration of natural phenomena, it may be said in respect to *declination*, that the helix being above the needle in a plane having dip, and therefore above its magnetic equator, if on the east of a needle having north dip, it will send the south or upper end west, or if on the east of a needle having south dip (being of course then itself inverted [2972]), it will cause the north or upper end to pass westward; seeming to repel the end of the free needle or part of the line of force nearest to it. In reference to the *inclination*, it may be said that the helix being above the needle tends to send the upper end of the needle or line of force from it. If the helix is north of the magnetic axis, it will tend to send the upper end of the needle south; if it is south, the upper end will go north. As in the case of the declination, it is as if the end of the free needle or line of force nearest to it was repelled. In fact every case is included in this result, that if the helix be diamagnetically adjusted (2975) for a free needle, whether it is above or below the needle, or on this side or that, the nearest end of the needle will be as if repelled, provided the helix is not in a neutral position.

2994. I repeated all these experiments with the helix reversed, so as to give the effect of a paramagnetic globe of air (2865, 2973). I need only say, that the effects were precisely the same in nature and order, only in the *reverse* direction. They will be required in the explication of the night and early morning actions,

due to the cooling of the atmosphere (3003, 3010).

2995. In these experiments, that the laws of deflection might appear in their simplicity, the needle was suspended in the air, and the representation of the sun's action carried round it in all directions. But in nature the air is only above the needle, and the earth as a magnet is beneath it. In the natural case also, there is the fixation of the lines in the earth (2919), which tends, by holding them below the surface, to give them an amount of deflection *at* the surface, far beyond what they would have if they were as free to move in the earth beneath as in the space above;[1] and though this deflection would coincide with that produced by the helix alone, still it was important to verify its effect. I therefore took a bar magnet 30 inches long, and weak in condition, and suspended the needle above it in various parts, as so to have the effect of north or south dip to any degree, or no dip at all near the middle parts. The effect of absence of air from beneath was also in a certain degree represented; and to make this point more striking, I occasionally put masses of iron on and under the middle part of the magnet. The results with the helix were now influenced greatly in the *amount* of the deflection, but not in the direction. When the helix affected the direction of the needle, it was according to the above laws.

2996. In the consideration of natural phenomena, the magnetic axis, and also the planes of the magnetic equator and meridian, being circles or planes of no deflection, are very important. Changing as they do with every change, either of place or declination or dip, they require some ready means of illustration, and can hardly be comprehended in their effects without a model. I have prepared a globe on which, after marking the places of the observatories, I have drawn the magnetic meridians of these places as they were last estimated. I have then in another colour drawn for each place its magnetic equator, making that a great circle parallel to the equatorial plane of the dipping-needle at the place. I have also marked on the globe the mean path of the sun for each month, and by the use of adjustable pins to indicate the hours before and after noon of any given

---

[1] Referring to the typical globe of cold air (2874), it is manifest that if the space below the horizontal lines *a*, *c*, &c., were occupied by matter holding the lines in it, then the deflections now represented on the lower parts would appear above the holding surfaces, and to a much greater degree, though extending downwards to a much smaller space.

place, I have the means of ascertaining with sufficient accuracy when the sun is in any particular quadrant, or what part of the quadrant; when it passes a neutral line, and what its position in relation to the place of observation is, in a manner which no diagrams or figures could supply. I have found the globe very useful; and I accustom myself to place it always in a certain position, namely, with the axis of rotation horizontal, the north pole to my right hand, and the astronomical meridian of the place of observation towards the zenith. The observer can then regard it as from the place of the rising sun.

2997. Though we thus have the experimental conditions of a needle under an action like that resulting in nature from the presence of the sun (2920), I do not pretend that they can be applied without modification to natural phenomena, but only that they give very important aid in the study of the latter and the rationale of their action. The atmosphere, instead of being illimitable, wraps the earth round as a garment; the influence, as it extends from the region of action, must, in respect to that portion which is conveyed through its mass (2920), curve with its curvature, and give a result in any particular place, which only refined calculations founded upon careful observations can determine accurately. In regard to the development of the air action, it would, I think, be very interesting to ascertain, even roughly, the daily variations of a magnet at the bottom of a deep mine, half-way up, and at the mouth of the shaft. The results might tell us much about the holding power of the earth and the depths to which the deflections of the magnetic lines of force penetrate, and might even give us a rough expression of the changes of the internal power (or the absence of such changes) when freed from those dependent upon the atmosphere.

2998. Another reason why the experimental results must not be applied too closely is as follows. If the lines of force of the earth were perfectly regular, then the change produced amongst them by the sun and air would be regular also. But as the natural system is not regular either between the tropics, as at Sister's Walk and Longford in St. Helena, or in the higher latitudes, as at Hudson's Bay, so apparent inconsistences may and must result. The probability is that the greatest irregularities in the arrangement of the earth's magnetism are in and near the surface of the earth, and that above they tend to adjust with each other into a more regular order. Still the irregularities must extend their influence very far upwards, so that the contortions of the magnetic meridians or lines of force are not likely to be effaced, or much diminished, at the region coinciding with the place of the atmosphere's effect.

2999. But though the lines are irregular in the large space affected by the sun, the result will be expansion of the whole as a system and diamagnetic polarity. The lines of force below will be affected by those above; and so, though a perfect similarity between different places is not to be expected, still the kind of change at the earth's surface is not likely to be so uncertain as it might at first appear. Therefore I believe the globe (2996) will be found very useful in giving information regarding the probable effects of the magnetic meridian and equator, due to the place of the sun in the two chief quadrants for any given month of the year, or hour of the day.

3000. The passage of the magnetic meridian is important, and appears far more so after the experiment described (2978) than it did on a former occasion (2942). Being very often inclined to the astronomical meridian, it must have great influence in deciding when the daily declination changes in its direction. The place of greatest action, and its travelling north or south along a line of magnetic force according as the declination was west or east in relation to the helix as a sun, was confirmed by an experiment; and the further observation (a consequence of the former), that when the sun was equidistant from a place more north or south than itself, its action was far stronger on that side at which its path and the declination direction made an acute angle than on the other side where it was obtuse, was also confirmed. Thus if the helix, moving from east to west, were passing a place north of it having western declination, then the action was stronger on the western side of the place than on the east for equal distances of the helix from the magnet.

3001. The passage of the magnetic equator by the sun is also important, since the direction of the diurnal variation of the experimental needle is then altered; and this is of the more consequence, because by the great degree of natural declination in many places, even far north and south, this passage is thrown forward towards the astronomical meridian, either on the east side or the west, and comes into effect during the more influential hours of the sun or the cold. In all those places too where the dip is little, as at St. Helena, and in or near the sun's path, it may be important in influencing the amount of action. From the change of place of the sun between the tropics, and the variety of dip and declination at different places, the passing of the neutral planes by the sun and acting region must take place under an extreme variety of conditions; the unravelling of which I think will be much assisted by knowledge such as that which the preceding experiments and principles give. The sun may be astronomically either north or south of the needle, and yet the declination of the needle not change in direction (2980); or if there were much mean declination, as at Greenwich, then it might be astronomically east or west of it, and yet the declination produced not change its direction. The sun region may be south of a place and yet send its upper end farther south (2990); for all will depend upon its position in relation to the magnetic meridian and the magnetic axis, which are in most cases very far removed from those that are astronomical: added to all these causes of variety, there is the fixation of the lines of force in the earth (2919), which tends to give a further diversity to them.

3002. In the former paper I considered only the effect of air raised in temperature above the mean condition (2895), illustrating it by the sun's effect in the middle of the day; *now* I purpose considering that which will be produced by the cold of night, which reduces the air of a given region below the mean air temperature of that place. When a portion of air is so cooled, its conduction power is increased; in conjunction with the warmer air of surrounding regions it deflects the lines of magnetic force passing through both, as indicated by the type globe (2864, 2874), and acquires what I have called *conduction polarity* (paramagnetic), meaning thereby simply that the lines of force draw together in the middle of the cooled air.

3003. Theoretically, the effect of a cold region of air coming up from the east would be to make the magnetic lines of force, as they leave the earth, advance or bend towards it, because those in and about the cold air are inflected into it; and as those immediately west of the cold region move into or towards it, so those farther west, being in part relieved from their tension, will also move east, and thus an effect, the reverse of that of the sun (2877, 2972), or the same as that of the helix in the paramagnetic position (2973, 2994), will be produced. The upper ends of needles at places having dip show this deflection of the upper part of the lines of force, because they move by, with, and in them.

3004. So as cold approaches, the lines will lean towards it until it is in the position of maximum action in the eastern quadrant; then they will return (in declination) before the cold, until both it and the line (or needle) are in the magnetic meridian; after which, as the cold travels on westward, the needle will follow it west until the cold has attained its place of maximum action in the west quadrant (2982); and then, as the cold retreats, the needle will return east to its mean place; assuming that there is no other action for the time than that of the cold region. The upper end of the free needle, therefore, at any given place will tend *towards* the cold region, just as before it tended *from* a warm region; and as the declination is affected, so also the inclination will be. If the cold be on the magnetic meridian of a place within the tropics, as St. Helena or Singapore, it will increase the dip there, whilst at the same moment it is diminishing the dip at places south or north of it having considerable dip, a result which follows directly from the inflection of the lines of force into or towards the cold region.

3005. The chief regions of heat and cold on the same parallel of latitude, do not follow each other at equal intervals of time. It is difficult to make a judgement regarding their interval in the atmosphere above; but the maximum of cold on the earth for the twenty-four hours, is assumed by many as being seventeen hours after the preceding noon, and only seven hours from the coming noon. This brings into consideration the joint effect of hot and cold regions in deflecting the lines of force, especially during the forenoon and middle of the day. If a cold region be only three and a half hours west of a place at the same time that the warm region is three and a half hours east of it, it is very manifest that the joint effect of the two, for both act then to cause the same deflection, will be far greater than that of the heat or cold alone, or than any corresponding effect at other periods, for neither twelve hours after, nor at any other time will there be an equivalent condition of circumstances; and so it is also for other combinations of hot and cold regions, the effect of which will vary both by position and by their extent. A free needle is held in tension by the lines, which are themselves governed by the hot and cold regions of atmosphere; it probably never occupies its mean place, but is always in the resultant of these ever-present and ever-varying causes of change.

3006. As the earth revolves under the sun, each place would have, speaking generally, a maximum and a minimum of temperature for its atmosphere in the twenty-four hours. But looking at the globe as a whole, there would be one maximum and two minima, i.e., there would be a maximum region somewhere beneath the sun in his path, and a minimum in each of the polar regions; which, as regards the twenty-four hours, would not be at the pole, but in some place of high latitude, and perhaps, as before, seven or eight hours before noon. These cold regions will be very seriously affected in their extent and place and power by the position of the sun between the tropics; for as he advances to one tropic the cold region there will diminish in extent and force, whilst the other will grow up in importance; and whilst they thus vary in their power of influencing the general direction of the lines of force, they will vary in their own position also, and have at different times very various relations of place to the sun in different months, and so produce very various effects. It is these differences which are made manifest to us, as I believe, in the night and morning actions at the numerous observatories scattered over the globe.

3007. I will proceed to apply these views, and the additional knowledge gained by experiment, to the localities formerly considered, and to some new ones between the tropics, for the purpose of explaining, if I can, the principles of night action; of retardation, more or less, of the effects in relation to local time; of the difference in direction of the declination variation in different months, for the same place at the same hours, as pointed out by Colonel Sabine; of the diminution of dip in one place, and increase of it at another for the same local time. In doing so, it will be necessary to refer continually to that place which may be considered, in respect to the station, as the centre of hot or cold action for the time. I will endeavour to use the word *region* for that purpose, meaning thereby not the whole extent of heated or warmed air, nor the centre, but the chief place of the altered portion. It is very manifest that in some days in March or September, *all* the air that is east of the meridian at 21ʰ or 22ʰ may be considered warm in comparison to that which is then west of the same meridian, and that a resultant of action, which shall be the same for all places, cannot exist.

3008. We are to remember that the *eastening* and the *westening* of the upper end of the needle, of which I always speak, is produced in

two ways. The needle travels as positively by the withdrawal of a direct cause of action as it does under the immediate direct action of that cause, but in the contrary direction (2982). A westening may be the result either of the coming up of the sun on the east of the place of observation, or of its withdrawal in the west, after he has passed over the meridian and produced the great east swing.

3009. *St. Petersburgh* has a mean declination of 6° 10′ W., and a dip of 70° 30′ N.; therefore, though the magnetic and astronomical meridians are not very oblique to each other, still the sun or warm region reaches the former from 20′ to 40′ before the latter, and hence the time of the great sun-swing, which is from 20 to 1 o'clock, is made earlier than it otherwise would be. The magnetic equator of the needle (2977) forms an angle of about 40° with the earth's equator, and being thus tilted, it disposes the two quadrants chiefly concerned in the daily variation (2979), so that in the St. Petersburgh summer the warmest region is not only far nearer to the needle, but passes through the strongest places of action of the quadrants, whereas in winter it is farther off, and also in much weaker positions. Hence a cause, as I believe, of the great difference in the amount of variation of declination, and also of its character: in November, December and January, it is from 4′.47 to 4′.65 only, whilst in June it is 11′.52.[1] See the tables, p. 725, and the curves, Pl. XV.

3010. In December or January, being St. Petersburgh winter, the sun-swing east almost disappears. It is over by 1 o'clock,[2] after which the upper end of the needle follows the sun until 9ʰ, having passed its mean position at 5ʰ. It then stops, after which it moves east until 16ʰ or 17ʰ; then again stops, or nearly so, until 21ʰ, and then the sun-swing comes on, carrying it to extreme east. So here there are two very important points to explain, namely, why the needle moves eastward after 9ʰ, and why it does not travel westward from 13ʰ to 20ʰ, but, on the contrary, is travelling eastwards or standing

---

[1] The eastening and westening of a free dipping-needle are not properly represented by the movements of a horizontal needle, inasmuch as at places with different dip the angle is read off on planes differently inclined to the dip itself, and in high latitudes the effect is greatly exaggerated. But though different places may not be compared without a correction, the variations for the same place as St. Petersburgh are comparable and proportionate.

[2] The St. Petersburgh observations are at 21½ minutes after each hour; but I mention the hour without the minutes as sufficient for a general statement.

PLATE   XV(a)

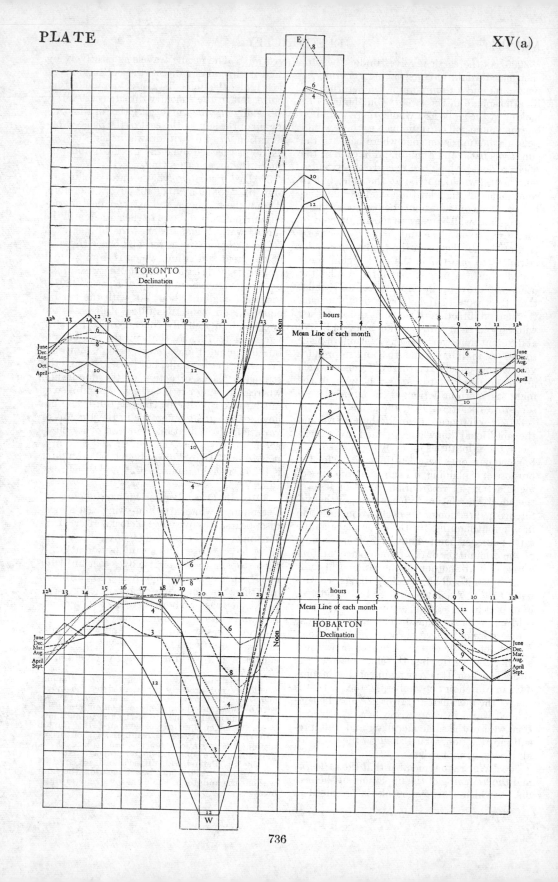

PLATE   XV(b)

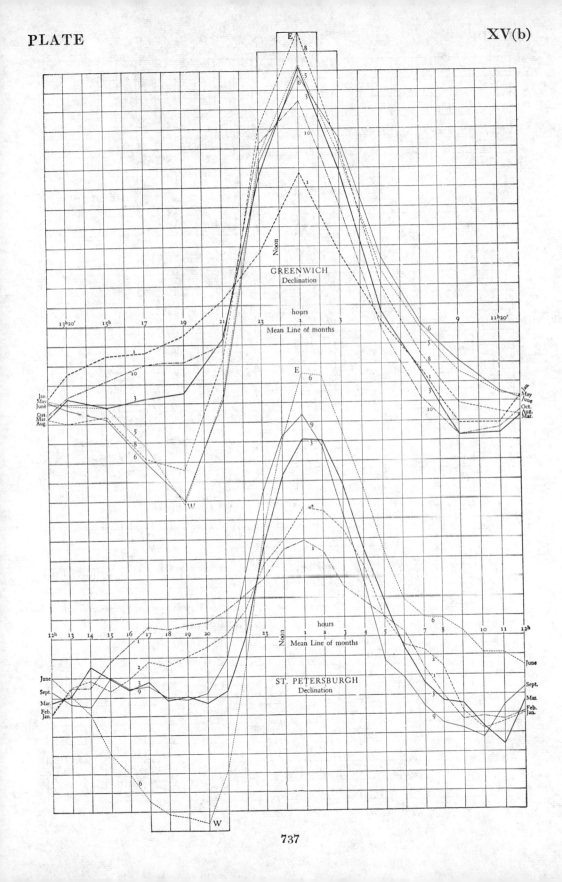

GREENWICH
Declination

hours
Mean Line of months

ST. PETERSBURGH
Declination

hours
Mean Line of months

PLATE XV(c)

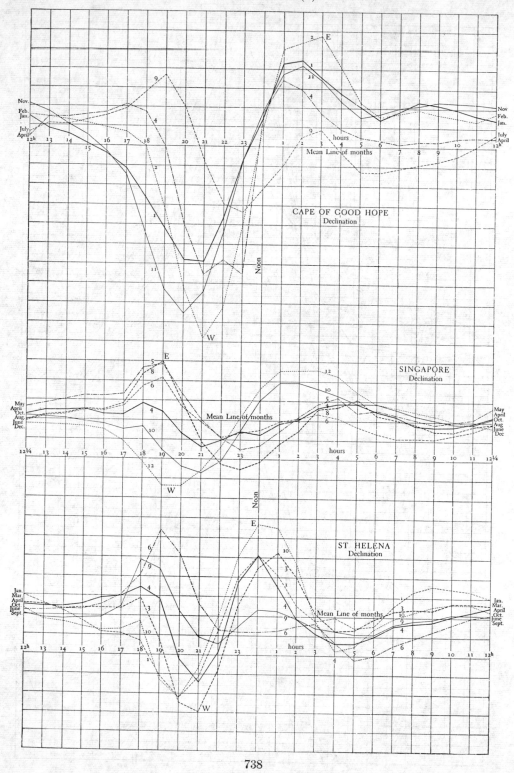

CAPE OF GOOD HOPE
Declination

SINGAPORE
Declination

ST HELENA
Declination

still: the explanation, according to my view, is as follows: St. Petersburgh is a place in which, from its position, the upper cold, consequent upon the daily withdrawal of the sun, would produce a paramagnetic action (2994, 3003). This action, as the sun set, would begin to appear on the east, and I conclude that at 9^h–11^h the cold region coming up from the east, not on the latitude of the sun's path, which is far to the south, but probably near to that of St. Petersburgh itself, is able at 9–11 o'clock, during which the needle is stationary, to counteract any remaining tendency westward, and after that to draw the line of force and the needle end eastward until 17 o'clock, and to hold it there, after which the sun sends it eastward in the great swing. That the cold, considering its probable position, may well direct the needle end eastward till 17^h, and the sun region not send it westward from 17^h to 20^h or 21^h, is seen, I think, to be a very natural consequence of the probable position of the two regions between these hours. For letting the sun (whose place we know) represent the warm region at 17^h, he is then in the eastern quadrant below the horizon, so that if he could affect the needle through or round the earth (2995), it would be to easten it, and it continues in that quadrant until 19^h. Then at 19^h, when he enters the quadrant, in which he begins to exert a westening action on the sun, he is in such a position as respects the needle at St. Petersburgh (as is seen by a line drawn over the surface of the globe [2996] and compared with the magnetic meridian and dip), and in so inefficient a part of the quadrant (2982), and also so far off, that it has no power to send the needle westward, but only in association with the retreating cold region to hold it there, until at 21^h, or thereabout, the sun-swing from west to east occurs as in other cases. After this the needle follows the sun from 1 o'clock, being, as the hours advance, gradually arrested and taken up by the cold region of the next twenty-four hours, as already described.

3011. I have considered the cold eastening as continued until as late as 17^h, which would imply probably that until that hour the cold region was east of St. Petersburgh. It is very difficult to speak, even in a general manner, of the places or times of things so little identified as yet, as the warm and cold regions in the upper atmosphere; but referring to the temperatures on the earth at St. Petersburgh, I may point out, that the extreme cold is, in the month of January, as late as 19 and 20 o'clock, and *five hours* later than it is in the summer months.

I may also point out here, for use in the summer months, that the maximum heat varies three hours in the *opposite direction;* so that whilst from the highest to the lowest temperature in the day is only eleven hours in summer, it is nineteen hours in winter, as may be seen by the temperature table, p. 725. As the day comes on, therefore, in January the highest temperature is only five hours after the lowest, which accords generally with the assumed cause of the effects on the needle.[1]

3012. As I am endeavouring to make St. Petersburgh a general case of night action for the explanation of corresponding effects at other places, so I may notice that the night action must contain a portion of sun effect which combines with that of the cold. The action of the sun is known by observation to be very extended; in the case of St. Petersburgh, the sun, when at the southern tropic and on the meridian, is between 80° and 90° from the station, and yet we see by the observations and curves how large an effect he produces (3009). Wherever the sun may be, he is by his motion causing changes which are felt simultaneously over the whole globe; and at 9 and 10 o'clock he is in an effectual part of that quadrant which would send the needle eastward if the earth were replaced by air, and in the representative experiments with a helix (2995) does so send it eastward when a magnet is interposed. The night action ought therefore to be greatest in winter, as it is, because the cold is then most intense, and also because the action of the distant sun coincides with it. It is very probable that many of the curious contortions of the night action which appear in the curves of Hobarton, Toronto and elsewhere, may depend upon the manner in which, at different hours, these two causes (probably with others) combine together.

3013. Though the declination varies little or nothing between 17^h and 21^h, no westening then appearing (3010), still I should expect a marked action on the inclination at that time, and conclude that it will be on the increase; but I have not been able to obtain a table of the daily variation of inclination.

---

[1] In relation to the cold of the upper atmosphere and the occurrence of its maximum (at certain levels at least), not at midnight but hours after, how often do we in this country see a clear bright night, and then just before the sun rises, the formation of a veil of clouds high up, and, upon his appearing, their dissolution and passing away! In these cases the clouds show the time of greatest cold above by their formation, and by their dissolution its quick reversion and change into increasing warmth.

3014. In the month of February the same remarks apply; but as the sun is now coming
from the southern signs and drawing nearer to
St. Petersburgh its power is increasing, and this
is shown by making the cold eastening for 15^h,
16^h and 17^h less in extent than before by more
than half a minute (of a degree), and by absolutely overcoming it and making a return westwards between 17^h and 18^h, before the swing to
the east comes on. In March the effect is still
more striking; the paramagnetic eastening is
arrested at 14^h, and the following diamagnetic
westening extends to 20^h; then follows the
swing. In April the westening by the warm region is as early as 13^h and continues to 20^h, being very strong. It is interesting to look at the
table of temperatures for these months, even
as they are obtained at the earth's surface. As
the months come on the eastening from the
cold ceases sooner and sooner, being in January and April 17^h and 13^h respectively. The
minimum of temperature also retreats, being
for the same month 20^h and 16^h. On the contrary, the maximum of heat *advances* from the
winter to the summer months, being also greatly increased; and the effect on the sun-swing is
seen both in the *advanced* time of change and
the *increased* amount of variation.

3015. In May and June the night or cold
eastening has disappeared, or is shown only by
a little hesitation; and from midnight, the coming on of the sun region sets the needle end
west. If we look at the globe (2996), we should
be led to expect that it would do this. The sun
is then in the northern tropic nearly, wheeling
round St. Petersburgh and comparatively near
to it; and a free dipping-needle would in twenty-four hours make one revolution in the same
direction as the sun region, but at the opposite
end of the line, joining the two together. If the
needle were at the astronomical pole of the
earth, having great dip, it would describe almost a circle with nearly uniform motion; but
being really much nearer to the warm region in
one part of the uniform daily course of the latter than another, the radius vector joining it
with the region then makes a much greater
angle in a given time than when it is farther
off, and hence the greater rapidity of the motion between 20^h and 1^h, and the production of
what I have familiarly called the *sun-swing* from
west to east.

3016. It will be seen from the table of curves
(Pl. XV), that we have at St. Petersburgh a
fine example of that kind of result which Colonel Sabine called attention to so strongly in

his paper upon the St. Helena phenomena;[1]
and those occurring at Hobarton, Toronto and
elsewhere; namely, a declination variation in
different directions for the same hours in different months. Thus, in the present case, the
needle end goes eastward for the hours 13^h to
20^h in October, November, December, January and February, whilst it goes west for the
same hours in April, May, June, July and August: March and September curves fall midway.
But this difference is now I hope by the hypothesis accounted for (3010, 3015), and I trust
that equally satisfactory reasons will appear
for St. Helena (3045) and other places (3022,
3039, 3065).

3017. The paramagnetic character of the eastening effect by cold in the winter months after
10 o'clock, would probably be illustrated by inclination observations for the same time; for if
the cold region passes to the south of St. Petersburgh the inclination will be decreased by
the paramagnetic action, but increased by the
diamagnetic resultant; and the manner in which
these two elements of direction, i.e., inclination and declination, are combined at any giv-
en moment, is very important to the full elucidation of the magnetic effect of the atmosphere.
I have not been able to give these data for St.
Petersburgh. The total force variations would
also help greatly to clear up the subject. Indeed it is not fair to endeavour to explain the
results of the assigned cause by taking only
one element of three into consideration. What
we require ultimately to know, is all the changes
of a free needle in position and in respect to
power. All are important, and all should be
considered at once. I presume that the theory
of the variations cannot advance very far without their joint consideration.

3018. *Greenwich* presents a fine case of the
night episode, and the different directions of
the magnetic variation for the same hours in
different months. In these respects it is very
much like St. Petersburgh, but has great additional interest, because of the large western declination,[2] and the effect produced by it on the
places of the active quadrants (2979, 3000),
and the times of the variation phenomena. On
setting up its position on the globe (2996), it
will be seen that the equatorial plane is not
likely to be much concerned in the midday action, and that the sun or warm region passes
nearly across the middle of the two chief quadrants in summer; which with its nearness at the

---

[1] *Philosophical Transactions*, 1847, p. 51.
[2] Mean declination 22°51′W. Mean inclination 69°N.

same time ought to make the midday swing to east very great. In winter it is farther off and in much weaker parts of the quadrant, so that the swing ought to be far less, and such is the case. The greatest summer variation is 11'.30, and the least winter variation only 5'.88. In April, May, June, July and August, the great west declination of the south or upper end of the needle is at 19ʰ 20', and the chief east position at 1ʰ 20'. The latter position remains the same all the year round, but the extreme westening is in the other seven (cold) months at 9ʰ 20' and 11ʰ 20',[1] or verging towards midnight; it then surpassing the morning west deflection. Thus the sun's effect in summer, in weakening the cold night effect (3005), is very evident; and so also is the manner in which the night action grows up, until very prominent, in the winter months, through the strengthening of the cold action (3006), when the sun is towards the southern tropic and in the weaker parts of the segments. The assumed principles of this action have been already given in the case of St. Petersburgh (3010, &c.).

3019. The magnetic meridian is much to the east of the astronomical meridian, where the warm region passes it, especially in winter, for then the sun crosses it about 10 o'clock, and in summer about 11 o'clock. Hence the swing ought to be earlier in winter than in summer, though, because of the slower angular motion of the warm region in relation to Greenwich (3015), it ought then to occupy a longer time; and yet, as above said (3018), be, by reason of distance, of smaller amount. All this appears to accord remarkably with the fact. The swing begins at 17ʰ in the winter but not until 19ʰ in the summer, and ending at the same hour at both seasons, namely, 1 o'clock, is much longer in its occurrence in winter than in summer. It begins earlier, because the magnetic meridian is sooner passed than in summer; and the reason also appears why the extension in time is at the beginning rather than at the termination of the swing; for, because of the declination, the warm region is at the same hours much less east of the magnetic meridian in the morning and much farther west of it in the afternoon, in winter than in summer; hence the swing is thrown forward in time in winter; and though prolonged, its termination coincides with the termination in summer, as far at least as these two-hour observations can indicate.

[1] See the curves, Pl. XV. The observations are only for every two hours, so that no degree of nicety can be expected in assigning the time of any given change.

3020. As the region precedes the sun, the degree of mean declination here ought to make the day-swing come on early, i.e., earlier than at Hobarton, and especially earlier than at Toronto, unless other causes of variation interfere. Now the beginning is earlier than at Toronto, but the end the same. Both the beginning and the end are an hour earlier than at Hobarton. The latter difference I believe due to the difference of mean declination: at Toronto, I think we shall find another cause influencing the time (3032).

3021. We are to remember also that in winter the sun or warm region passes the magnetic meridian two hours before he passes the astronomical meridian; and therefore his effect in giving west position to the south or upper end of the needle ceases long before it does in summer, and perhaps even before it ceases to come nearer; and so the eastern after-effect on it ought to be greater, which it is. This eastern effect should be strengthened also, because the action of the warm region on the needle ought to be comparatively great after passing the magnetic meridian; for its path forms an obtuse angle with the meridian before the passage and an acute one afterwards (3000), and therefore is more powerful. To all these causes of action will be added the effect for the time of the cold in the distant west (3005).

3022. The case of difference of direction before 19ʰ (3016) is very marked at Greenwich, as may be seen by looking at the curves for the months (Pl. XV). The south or upper end of the needle goes west in May, June, July and August, from 12ʰ to 19ʰ, i.e., from midnight to five hours before noon; but in October, November, December and January, it is eastening at the same hours. Considering first a summer month, as June, the upper end of the needle is westward as the sun comes onward (as it ought to be) until 19ʰ, when he is almost in the middle of his passage through the east quadrant; and in respect of distance and angular relation to the magnetic meridian, the warm region is then, probably, in the place of greatest power to produce westening of the needle end.[2] In the next six hours the needle passes to extreme east, performing, according to the observations, a fourth of the whole swing in the first two hours, a half in the next two, and a fourth in the remaining two, the journey being no doubt with

[2] It must not be forgotten, that the return from an extreme east or west position is not when the sun or warm region passes by a neutral line, or from one quadrant to another, but when it passes its point of greatest action in a quadrant (2982).

first rapidly increasing and then rapidly diminishing velocity. In this transit of the region, the sun is for about two-thirds of the time in the eastern quadrant, and one-third in the western; and his path in the latter third forms almost the base of an equilateral triangle with Greenwich, having the magnetic meridian for one side, so that all that time it is close to and therefore has strong action on the needle (3000). The sun is at 1^h in such a position as respects this angle that if we assume the region to be somewhat in advance of it, the latter would be in that place where it could exert its maximum eastening effect; and therefore after that, as it recedes westwards, would let the needle return from east to west, as it does, following it. The needle continues to go west, passing its *mean* place for the month about 7^h; in the meantime, before that, at a little after 6 o'clock, the sun has left the western segment by passing the magnetic equator; it has not yet set to Greenwich, and if it have any action, it will, because of the segment it is now in (2979), still be to carry the needle end *westward*. The end in fact continues to go westward, slowly only, after 10 o'clock, gaining a little from 10^h to 15^h; and then, as the sun comes up, passing more rapidly west, as it ought to do, until 19^h, and finally making the great swing to the east as before. The whole progression here is very simple, and apparently a natural result of the assumed cause. Effects of cooling no doubt come in; but the cold region has diminished in intensity and extent (3006), has retreated northward, and its action appears in combining with the former to produce only variations in the velocity of the change.

3023. Then for the winter, let us consider January; and, as the eastening is a maximum in all the months at 1 o'clock, after the sun's passage across the meridian, let us begin the cycle there. At 1^h the upper end of the needle is at extreme east, and the amount of the variation not half what it was in summer, the sun being now far off. The sun and warm region pass the magnetic meridian about 21^h or 22^h; and therefore, in the hours before and after that, should produce the full west to east effect. At 1 o'clock the needle returns west, following the retreating sun, and does so quickly for seven or eight hours, or up to 9^h, during which time the warm region, and also the early morning cold region, are in quadrants and positions, which, if they have any action at all like that referred to in the experiments (2975, 2995), would then set or hold the needle end west of its mean position. Then an action of the follow-

ing kind supervenes; the needle remains stationary until 11^h, after which it goes east at midnight and until 15^h; again remains stationary, or nearly so, for two hours; then eastens again, slowly at first and afterwards more rapidly, until 1^h, when it has attained its maximum eastening and the place from whence it set out.

3024. This night action is another case of the action of a cold region like that considered in respect to St. Petersburgh (3010). It appears to me that at 11^h the immediate sun action and return west after it, were over; that the cold region which was coming round from the east did then act by its paramagnetic condition (combined with the complementary effects of the sun's action on the other side of the globe), and set the needle eastward, as it would be competent to do (2994, 3010) until 14^h or 15^h. In eastening, the needle does not arrive at the mean place, but is still 1′ west of it; and the reason why it hangs there from 15^h to 17^h and then begins to go east again, more and more under the sun's action, is probably that, as the sun rises in the southern tropics, his distance and position bring the resulting distant warm region gradually into action with that of the nearer cold; that at first he stops the action of the latter, and then as he advances combines with and finally replaces it; causing the usual swing to come on, slowly at first and then quickly, from west to east by 1^h. How this would happen is well seen, both as respects the place of the sun in the southern hemisphere, and in the two magnetic segments, by reference to the globe (2996) and the diagram of the curves of variation, Pl. XV.

3025. Considering another and an intermediate month as March; at 1^h the upper end of the needle is at extreme east; then until 9^h it follows the sun as before (3023). From 9^h to 11^h it is stationary; then the paramagnetic action of cold from the east occurs, and the needle moves east until 13^h. It is then stopped, and two hours sooner than before; for the sun now appears to Greenwich as early as 6 o'clock, and in a more favourable position for effect, both as regards the magnetic meridian and the segment in which it has for the time its place; and so the needle is actually sent west for a couple of hours. It is then held almost steady until 19^h, after which the great sun-swing occurs. The holding west and yet the absence of more westening between 15^h and 19^h, is not inconsistent with the southern place of the warm region, and it is probable that at that time the *dip* is increasing; an effect which would accord very harmoniously with the condition of matters at the time.

3026. Other months are on this or that side of March in respect to their effects; the corresponding month on the opposite side of the year (September) is the same as March, except in that portion of effect which is consequent upon a month following one that is warmer or colder than itself (3053). Greenwich therefore satisfactorily illustrates the application of the hypothesis to the case of a difference in direction for the same hour in different months (3016, 3022); and also the occurrence of the night effect, and its transition into the very marked eastening of the early morning.

3027. The cases of *Hobarton* and *Toronto* are so similar, though in opposite hemispheres, that they may be considered together. A very important comparison of the phenomena at both places has been already made by Colonel Sabine in relation to the variations of declination, inclination, and total force.[1] When examined by the globe (2996) the distribution of the quadrants is nearly alike, the sun being in two chief east and west quadrants from about 18 to 6 o'clock, or during the day. The sun is in more influential parts of the quadrants in summer than in winter, and the effect is seen in the difference of the amount of declination variation. At Hobarton it is 12'.05 in summer and only 3'.6 in winter. At Toronto it is 14' in summer and 5'.2 in winter. The night action at both is alike in character, and has been sufficiently explained according to the hypothesis in the former cases (3010, 3024).

3028. Colonel Sabine has given the data by which the variations of the inclination and of the total force at Hobarton and Toronto may be compared with and applied to the hypothesis; but I hesitate to enter upon them in this general view, inasmuch as these and the declination variations should be closely considered and compared together at every hour for each particular place. The inclination variation at Hobarton is greatest in its summer, being then 2'.18, and least in winter, or 1'.28, as was to be expected. The great variation occurs in the day-time, as with the declination; the dip being most as the sun region passes over the meridian. The greatest dip is not at the same hour for all the months; it occurs at 23 o'clock for December, February and March, at 24 o'clock for September, at 1 o'clock for June and July; as it moves on so do the points of

least dip on each side of it, so that the whole curve advances in time in the order of these months. There is also another affection of it, for the *quickest* transition is from *most* to *least* dip in some months, as December, February, and from *least* to *most* dip in other months, as June, July, September. At Toronto the dip variation, though peculiar in some points, may be said to have the same general character.

3029. For the variation of the total force at both places, I will at present only refer to Colonel Sabine's volumes, and the observations he has made thereon.

3030. There is a remarkable difference between the time of the day changes at Hobarton and Toronto, to which Colonel Sabine has called attention. It consists in the occurrence of those at the latter place, about an hour before those of the former. If this had depended upon the declination, then the change should have taken place first at Hobarton, for there the sun arrives at the magnetic meridian before he comes to the astronomical meridian, and for like hours of local time he is in a better position in the quadrant in the afternoon than at Toronto; still it is the later of the two.

3031. If the *time* of the sun-swing from west to east be considered, the middle of it ought to be somewhere near the period when the warm region is passing the magnetic meridian (2982), and in that way supplies an approximative expression of the relative positions of the region and the sun. The swing is at Hobarton from 21 to 2 o'clock, or five hours, and the magnetic meridian is passed by the sun nearly in the middle of the time, or 23h 20' o'clock. But according to the supposition just made, this is also the time at which the warm region ought also to pass, and so the sun and the region in this place appear to arrive at the meridian together. At *Toronto* the sun-swing is about four hours in winter, or from 21 to 1 o'clock, and five hours in summer, or from 20 to 1 o'clock. Of the latter five hours the middle is 22½ o'clock, at which time the region ought to pass over the magnetic meridian, and as that coincides nearly with the astronomical meridian, it appears that the region is about 1½ hour *before* the sun. By a similar comparison for winter, the region would then appear to be about an hour before the sun.[2]

---

[1] *Hobarton Observations*, 1850, Vol. I, p. 68, &c.; also *Philosophical Transactions*, 1847, p. 55; and 1850, pp. 201, 215, &c. See the curves, Pl. XV, and tables for Toronto, pp. 723, 724.

[2] In reference to the position in advance of the sun, of the resultant of those actions which set the needle end westward, we must remember that the preceding cold, being perhaps seven hours only to the west, is by its action on the general system of curves aiding the westening of the needle, whilst the sun is in the east and even over the meridian (3005).

3032. I am inclined to refer much of this precession of the warm region at Toronto to the geographical distribution of land and water there. The Atlantic is on the east and the continent of America on the west of the station, and as Dove's charts and results intimate, the temperature may rise higher and sooner over the land than over the water, and so throw the warm region in respect of Toronto in advance of the time or of the sun. In the case of Hobarton the arrangement is different; and, in fact, what land there is is between the advancing sun and the station, and would tend to hold the warm air region back, and tend to cause its time to coincide with that of the sun. Even the greater difference in summer than in winter at Toronto appears to be explicable in the same manner, by reference to the relative position of the sun at the two seasons to the land and water arrangement.

3033. Though the temperature on the earth's surface is a very uncertain indication of that above (2937), yet as far as it goes it harmonizes with this view. The maximum temperature occurs sooner after midday at Hobarton than at Toronto; in the former place it is at 2 o'clock and very regular, and the minimum at 16–19 o'clock, being earlier in summer and later in winter. At Toronto the maxima are from 2 to 4 o'clock, and the minima at 16–18 o'clock. The maxima are later in summer than in winter; the minima are as at Hobarton, being later in winter than in summer. The mean temperature is lower at Toronto than at Hobarton, being as 44°.48 and 53°.48: the range of variation is also greater, being at Toronto 43° and for Hobarton only 18°.

3034. It is probable that effects of retardation and acceleration, in respect of the passage of the local part of the warm region for a given place, may occur in many parts of the globe, and these will require to be ascertained for every locality and for the different seasons there. A place having the reverse position of Toronto would have a reversed or retarded effect; and hence it might happen that needles in the same latitude might be affected at very different local times, and yet all be regularly affected every twenty-four hours. The region would in that time make its diurnal revolution but vary in the velocity of its different parts at different periods of its journey, and that in a different degree and order for different latitudes, and for different parts of the same parallel of latitude. Even the time during which the effect (as for instance the sun-swing) continued would

probably be altered; one place holding the influence longer and another dismissing it sooner, analogous to two conditions of stable and unstable equilibrium.

3035. *Cape of Good Hope.*[1] This station is in longitude 18° 33′ east and latitude 33° 56′ south. The mean declination is 29° west and the dip 53° 15′ south. The amount of dip, combined with the position of the place, gives a magnetic equator, which passes nearly through the astronomical poles, and so the sun's path in every part of the year intersects it almost at right angles and at the same hour, namely, about 20′ past 7 o'clock in the morning and evening, or at 19^h 20′ and 7^h 20′. But because of the great declination, the sun is in the astronomical meridian two hours before he arrives at the magnetic meridian in Cape winter, and half an hour or more before in Cape summer.

3036. The sun passes obliquely through both the chief quadrants and across their central parts pretty equally; but because of the western character of the mean declination he is much nearer the Cape when in the eastern than when in the western quadrant for all the months, and so the coming up effect, i.e., the westening before the mid-day swing commences, ought to be more powerful than the eastening after it is over, and such is the case. This is in beautiful and striking contrast to Greenwich, which, having the same kind of mean declination and nearly in the same degree, is on the north of the sun's path, and therefore the luminary passes its magnetic meridian before 12 o'clock, and for a time still approaches the station: the result is the reverse effect to what we have at the Cape; for the eastening effect at the end of the mid-day swing is more powerful than the westening effect before it, as is well seen by the curves given in Pl. XV.

3037. Selecting July as the month in which the effect of winter occurs at the Cape we find that the day-swing is very feeble, as it ought to be, the sun being in the northern tropic and far away; and the swing east is at an end by three o'clock when the sun has passed by about one hour over the magnetic meridian. The upper or north end of the needle then westens for two hours, following the sun until 5^h, when the luminary is low to the Cape and at its setting. After that the needle end eastens slowly until 10^h, then a little more quickly until midnight (passing the mean position at 11^h); quicker still until 16^h or 17^h, and still more quickly un-

[1] See tables, pp. 752, 753, and curves of variation, Pl. XV.

til 19^h, when it has attained its maximum east position. This effect I believe to be due to the cold, which in these hours is approaching from the east, and setting by its paramagnetic action (3003) the needle end eastward. On the surface of the earth the maximum cold in this month is at 17^h or 18^h, and as far as it goes this result accords with the effect above described. At 19^h, the sun in rising not only stops the eastening but quickly drives the needle back again, and the latter very rapidly goes westward until about 23^h, at which time the sun-swing from west to east comes on, being over by 2^h or 3^h, completing the daily variation, after which the needle goes west, following the sun as before. In this sun-swing is seen the effect of an inclined magnetic meridian (3000); for though the sun is, at the beginning, only an hour east of the astronomical meridian, he is full three hours to the east of the magnetic meridian. As the swing occupies about four hours, the warm region is probably near the magnetic meridian about half-past 12 or 1 o'clock.

3038. *January* presents a case of Cape summer. The day-swing is then from 21^h to 1^h or 2^h. After 2^h the needle upper end follows the sun westward until 6^h, and then moves a little eastward for two hours; after this it moves slowly westward again, the whole effect being as if a cold region had occurred on the east, had passed over and gone away west, and the temperature below at this time is within 2° of the minimum. This night effect of drawing the needle westward (3004) proceeds slowly until 15^h or 16^h, being assisted by the rising temperature on the east urging the end still more rapidly west until 20^h, when having reached its maximum in that direction, it at 21^h turns back and is driven to extreme east in the sun-swing, through an amount of variation more than twice as great as that produced in July or Cape winter.

3039. I think the above is a true explanation of the reverse motion of the needle in the months of July and January, or Cape winter and summer. In winter the paramagnetic effect of cold air is on between 12^h and 19^h, remaining longer on the east side of the magnetic meridian; as it passes forward, both it and the sun region conspire at 19^h to carry the needle westward, for though they have opposite actions they are then also on opposite sides of the magnetic meridian (3005). In the summer the cold region has much less power, occurs earlier,[1] soon pass-

[1] The minimum temperature below is three hours earlier.

es over, for the summer sun is behind it, and then rather aids the sun in carrying the needle westward.

3040. Some of the other months are still more striking in summer effect. February has a swing through 8′ from west to east between 21^h and 1^h; then from 1^h to 3^h it scarcely changes; from 3^h to 6^h it follows the sun west; from 6^h to 16^h it varies but little, showing the merest trace of east effect about 8^h; and after 16^h it passes west more and more rapidly, so that by 21^h it is at a maximum west, ready to swing back as the sun region passes over. The other and intermediate months are easily traced, and found to be beautifully consistent with the same principle of the hypothesis. As is evident, in almost every case each month partakes of the character of the preceding month in some degree, though not so much in this case of the Cape as in some others (3053). The curves of December and January are more equal.

3041. The time of the sun-swing illustrates exceedingly well the effect of the inclined magnetic meridian (3000). In November, December and January, the swing is from 20^h to between 1^h and 2^h. In these months the sun crosses the astronomical meridian about half an hour before he arrives at the magnetic meridian. In October, February and March, the swing is later, being from 21^h to 2^h or 3^h, for the sun then passes the magnetic meridian an hour or more later than the astronomical or time meridian. In September, April and May, the swing is still later, being from 22^h to 2^h or 3^h, and the sun is still longer than before in reaching the magnetic meridian. In June, July and August, the swing is latest, being from 23^h to 3^h, and the sun is proportionately late in arriving at the magnetic meridian. What I describe as the passage of the sun is of course true of the warm region which precedes it; but I prefer referring to the visible type rather than to the invisible reality, because it ties the considerations of time more simply together.

3042. The inclination at the Cape varies singularly in the twenty-four hours, depending, I think, upon its mean degree. It is such that the warm and cold resultants of action for the Cape will sometimes be above the line of the dip and sometimes below it, not only for different times of the year, but I think in some seasons, even at different times of the day. It would require much attention to unravel the whole effect. In June, July and August, when the sun and its warm region are greatly to the north of the Cape, it appears that the dip is increased as the region passes, which would give a rotation of the upper end of the needle like that at Hobarton (2909); but in November, December, January, February, March and April, the dip diminishes at that time, and the resulting rotation of the pole is of the contrary kind, or like that at St. Helena (3057) and Singapore (3061, 3067).

3043. The daily variations of intensity at the Cape are remarkable. In the months October to April it is at a chief maximum at 19^h or 20^h; by noon it is reduced to a minimum as the sun passes over; gradually rises to a second maximum about 4^h or 5^h, and then, after sinking a little about 8^h or 9^h, reaches the chief maximum about 18^h or 19^h next morning. In the months from May to September the chief maximum is at 21^h or 22^h, which is followed by a minimum at 1^h or 2^h, due to the day effect. Then comes on the 5^h maximum, and after thirteen hours or more the second minimum as low almost as the former, and only three hours before the chief maximum; so that this maximum is placed between minima close on each side of it.

3044. These are exactly the months during which the upper end of the needle moves eastward in early morning up to 19^h, and that is just the hour when the minimum intensity occurs. From 18^h or 19^h to 21^h the intensity rises to a maximum, precisely as the lines of force are moving westward before the sun region, prior to their quick return east; and as they return in their quick journey so the intensity falls to a minimum again, and is at that minimum at 1^h or 2^h, just as the swing is over. Here is a very close connection, and it is curious to see the needle end at east with minimum power at 18^h, and again also at 1^h, remembering that in that time it has swung from east to west and back to east again.

3045. *St. Helena*.[1] This is a station which Colonel Sabine has distinguished as of the highest interest; being near the line of least force, within the tropics, and with little magnetic inclination.[2] It was here also that he called attention to the striking fact that the course of the needle is in some months in one direction, and in other months in the contrary for the same hours of the day.[3] De la Rive attempted to explain this fact,[4] but Sabine has stated that this explanation is not satisfactory.[5]

[1] See tables, pp. 754, 755, and curves of variation, Pl. XV.
[2] *Magnetical Observations, St. Helena*, 1840 to 1843.
[3] *Philosophical Transactions*, 1847, p. 51.
[4] *Annales de Chimie et de Physique*, March 1849, Vol. XXV, p. 310.
[5] *Proceedings of the Royal Society*, May 10, 1849, p. 821.

3046. St. Helena being a small island in the south Atlantic ocean is removed about 1200 miles from the nearest land. The longitude is 5° 40' west, the latitude 15° 56' south; the mean declination 23° 30' west, and the mean dip 22° south. Hence there are three quadrants concerned in the day action of the sun, especially when that luminary is south of the equator. The sun is south of St. Helena itself in the months of November, December, January and February, or for nearly that time; it is north of the island for the rest of the year. At one time the sun passes the astronomical meridian before it arrives at the magnetic meridian, and at another time the contrary is the case. In addition to these peculiar circumstances, St. Helena is a place of great local differences, and also its dip is so low that the sun's day effect is almost constantly to depress and lessen it.

3047. In June and July the sun rises to St. Helena in the south-east quadrant; about an hour after, it passes into the north-east quadrant, and crosses it towards the southern end, being then at mid-distance in the quadrant about one-third of the length, or nearly 60° from the southern termination. It leaves this quadrant about 1^h 20^m, crossing the magnetic meridian at that time (and consequently so long *after* passing the astronomical meridian), and entering the third or north-west quadrant traverses it obliquely towards its northern extremity. In our winter, December and January, the sun also rises to St. Helena in the south-east quadrant, as before; but it now remains in it until 22^h, being for much of the time in strong places of action; it enters the north-east quadrant to the south of St. Helena, and does not remain in it two hours, being then only in the weakest part of it; it leaves it again *before* arriving at the astronomical meridian, then enters the north-west quadrant, gliding along near to its southern side, and is within two-thirds of an hour of leaving it when it sets to St. Helena.

3048. As June presents the aspect of circumstances approaching nearest to that of a station farther south, as Hobarton or the Cape, so I will consider the variations for it first. The north or upper end of the needle is then nearly at its mean place at midnight or 12^h: it advances east (slowly at first) until 16^h, and then more and more rapidly up to 19^h, when it stops and goes as quickly west until about 22^h, after which it changes but little until 3^h, when it moves *west* till 5^h, and then slowly east up to 12^h, and then onwards to 16^h and 19^h, as already said. The eastening from midnight and before, I refer to the paramagnetic action of the cold, which comes up from the east as before (3003, 3025, 3037); the rapid increase of the eastening from 16^h to 19^h is consistent with the increasing cold of the early morning, and also with the circumstance, that the sun and its representative region are then passing from the south-east into the north-east quadrant, and must be not far from the neutral line, for that is the time of quickest transit of the needle. As the sun advances into the north-east quadrant, it first stops the eastening, as at 19^h, and then converts it into westening (3014), which goes on consistently with all former observations until 22^h; the needle is then retained a little west of its mean position until 1^h, at which time it has not yet attained coincidence with the magnetic meridian, and after this hour it is determined east a little until 3^h. This effect, from 22^h to 3^h, I consider as the sun-swing to the east; and I think, examining the globe (2996), its small amount in declination is quite consistent with the relative positions of St. Helena and the warm region, combined with those of the active and neutral parts of the quadrants traversed during the time. From 3^h to 5^h the needle end moves westward, following the sun; and that effect harmonizes with the idea that the previous holding of the needle in an eastern position, from 22^h to 3^h, is the sun effect: then the slow eastening from 5^h to midnight and beyond, is the cold effect coming on.

3049. Colonel Sabine has shown that the months of May, June, July and August, may be classed together, so that I will not speak of each. Whilst they show the analogies they have between themselves, they also indicate the transitions to and from the other months. Let us consider September. From 7^h, through midnight on to 16^h, the needle stands nearly at the mean. From 16^h to 18^h, the upper or north end eastens through the effect of the early morning cold. That the eastening should be fully effected an hour sooner than before (3048) is quite consistent with the principles, for the path of the sun and its diamagnetic region is far nearer to the station than before, being now about the equator. From 18^h to 22^h it sends the end westward in conformity with all former observations, and then comes on the sun-swing from west to east, between 22^h and 24^h, and a hold at extreme east an hour longer. The shortness in time of this transit is, I think, a beautiful point. The sun is still north of St. Helena, but

is now so much nearer that he passes through the *same angle* east and west, in respect to the place of observation, in less than half the time of the former sun effect in June (3041). After this the needle end travels west from 1^h to 6^h, following the sun as on other occasions; and then from 6^h to 9^h it moves a little east by the evening cold in the east, and remains near the mean position until the greater cold before sunrise (3005, 3011) takes it more east between 16^h and 18^h of the coming day.

3050. In looking at the curves of variation (Pl. XV), it will be seen that the curve for the next month, October, is remarkable for being like in general character with, and yet far removed in place from, that of September; and this effect appears due to the circumstance that the sun has now arrived at the latitude of St. Helena, or nearly so. According to my supposition, there has been a feeble night effect (3010); and at midnight the needle is at the mean position and moving slowly westward, when the greater cold which precedes the sunrise coming into action on the east, counterbalances and arrests the western progress, and even draws the needle, as before, east a little for a couple of hours, till 18^h. Even the sun region is at 16^h in that quadrant (the south-east one), so that if it could act on the needle it would combine with the cold in the next or north-east quadrant in setting it eastward. By 18^h both the preceding cold region and the following sun region are so far advanced in their respective quadrants that they combine to carry the needle end west as before, until 20^h, and then comes on the swing from west to east until 24^h. Why this begins sooner, lasts longer, and is above four times the extent of the September swing, appears to be that the sun region comes up upon the latitude of St. Helena, and so acts in respect to the magnetic meridian more powerfully, and also sooner and longer: also that because of the mean declination west it arrives at equidistant points from and passes over the magnetic meridian sooner; and also from the effect of an accumulative action added to it from former months (3053).

3051. At 1 o'clock the needle begins to turn from extreme east, i.e., sooner than in the former months, because the magnetic meridian is sooner passed, and follows the sun until 4^h, when it stops, and then the evening or night action due to cold appearing in the east carries the needle back eastward till 10^h, and then as it advances in the quadrant lets the needle return back again (3004) until between 12^h and

13^h, when the latter is in its mean position. The cold region then appears to draw it westward until 16^h, when its distance increasing, it releases the needle and lets it return east until 18 o'clock, when the latter is still west of its normal position, and then the sun region rising up, helped perhaps by the cold that immediately precedes it, which is probably now over or beyond the magnetic meridian, sets it toward the west prior to the sun-swing.

3052. In December and January the sun is south of the station. This makes no difference in the general character of the curve for these months; nor should it according to the hypothesis, except in this point, that though the sun is very near to St. Helena and has the cumulative effects of the preceding months (3050, 3053) added to its own effect at the time, still it is in weaker parts of the quadrant, and whilst in the chief segment is almost up in the corner and near the place where the two neutral planes cross each other; hence its effect ought to be less, and so it is; for the sun-swing of November and February is larger than that of December and January. The sun-swing happens in December at the same time as for October, though in the latter month it crosses the magnetic meridian after, and in the present before midday: still there is only half an hour's difference from one to the other, and the observations are perhaps not close enough to allow one to separate its peculiar effect out of an interval of four hours. Besides, accumulative causes may interfere. The places of the December curve are altogether a little more west than those for October.

3053. The *cumulative* effect of preceding months is very important and well-shown at St. Helena (3050). Thus, taking the September curve and comparing it with that for October or the following month, we have a great difference of a certain kind; then again comparing September with the month in which the sun is returning from the southern tropic instead of proceeding to it, and has arrived at the same position as it had in October, another striking difference appears. March is the nearest month for the second comparison. Up to 20^h its curve changes like the October curve, but the upper end of the needle is all the time about half a minute east of its place in October. At 20^h the needle in October begins to swing from west, and reaches extreme east at 24^h: in March it westens until 21^h, then returns and reaches extreme east at 1^h; so that the swing is an hour later, and during that time the end

is from half a minute (of space) to a minute more west than in October. This difference I believe to be due to the cumulative effect of the months between October and March, during which time the heat has been diminishing in the northern hemisphere, and increasing in the south. Similar results in other months make it probable that the effect of the atmosphere, though induced by the sun, lags behind the luminary considered as in his astronomical position all the year round; and that therefore in advancing to and receding from a tropic, he seems to do less in the first instance and more in the second than is due to his place for the time.

3054. But where circumstances are apparently equal, a difference also arises. Thus from March to April in one direction, and from September to October in the other, might be expected to be alike, except for a little of the lagging effect (3053), which would appear on both sides: nevertheless March and April are in Sabine's curves *between* September and October, and near together, whilst the other two are far apart. This effect I refer to the different conditions of the two hemispheres as regards heat (Dove). From September to October the sun is passing from a hemisphere having a mean temperature in summer 17°.4 above that of the other hemisphere for its winter; but in March and April it is departing from a hemisphere having a mean summer temperature of only 10°.7 above that of the other hemisphere for its winter (2949); and these respective differences must tend to separate September and October, and bring together March and April, as is seen to be the case by the curve charts, Pl. XV.

3055. I need not go further into the delcination variation of St. Helena: the lines for the other months are subject to the observations already made. Colonel Sabine's important query of the cause of difference in direction for different months (3045) appears to me at present to be answered for this station, as well as for the other stations, in very various latitudes where it makes its appearance (3016, 3022, 3039).

3056. The *dip* at St. Helena is a daily variation very simple in character, being a maximum at 7^h and a minimum at 22^h and 23^h, with only one progression. It proceeds to its minimum therefore in the middle of the sun-swing, i.e. the upper end of the needle proceeds to west, and descends from 16^h to 19^h or 20^h, during which time therefore the dip is decreasing; then it returns east until it reaches the neutral position, the dip decreasing the while still more.

The needle still continues to go east to complete the sun-swing, but now the dip increases; at 24^h or 1^h the needle returns (in declination) after the sun westward, but still with increasing dip; at 5^h or 6^h the westening has almost ceased, and an hour after the dip is at its maximum.

3057. So as the sun and its region pass over they diminish the dip by depressing the upper ends of the lines of force, and as they pass away the lines rise (2926, 2937) and the dip increases. The ellipse or curve, therefore, which represents the motion of the upper end of the needle at St. Helena, as the sun comes up from the east, is above westward and downward, and back below to east; then rising to be repeated in the next twenty-four hours. This is the reverse direction to the representative ellipse for Hobarton, having like south dip in a greater degree. But that is in perfect consistency with the hypothesis; for as the region is located above in the air, it is above the angle which the dip makes with the horizon at St. Helena, and therefore ought to depress the line of force and lessen the dip. At Hobarton, the region being in the tropical parts is within the angle formed by the line of dip with the horizon, and therefore deflects the lines of force upwards and *increases* the dip, and so the portions of ellipse at the two places, which correspond in time and direction as to declination, have contrary variations of inclination.

3058. *Singapore.*[1] This is a very interesting station: being in longitude 103° 53′ E , it has only 1° 16′ N. latitude, and so is close to the equator. Its declination too is only 1° 40′ E., and its inclination 12° S. It is also near the line of weakest force round the earth. The magnetic equator of the needle is almost parallel to the earth's equator, and the quadrants (2929) are distributed with great simplicity, the magnetic and astronomical meridian nearly coinciding. In our summer the sun passes through the east and west northern quadrants during the daytime; in our winter through the east and west southern quadrants; and in certain months through all four quadrants, following nearly the neutral line of the magnetic equator.

3059. Hence if the line of force were free, i.e., if it had no hold in the earth (2919), we should expect from the hypothesis little or no change in the needle, especially in the months when

[1] See tables, pp. 756, 757, and the curves of variation, Pl. XV. The data for Singapore are deduced from the recent very valuable labours of Captain Elliot.

the sun was over the magnetic equator; but because there is dip, and the lines of force which govern the needle are to the south tied up in the earth (2929), whilst they are free to move in the air and space toward the north, so there is variation both of the declination and inclination in a perfectly consistent manner; and keeping this in mind, I think we shall have no difficulty in tracing the monthly results according to the hypothesis.

3060. In the first place, the curves of day variation are so like those of St. Helena, month for month, that the account given of them there will suffice for the present occasion (3048). The sun-swing occurs at the same period, and the effect, dependent, as I suppose, on the character of the two hemispheres, is produced (2949, 3054). There are however striking differences in the latter part of the sun turn, and also in the night hours, from 5^h to 14^h. The amount of variation appears small; but this is chiefly due to the circumstance that the horizontal plane on which we read it, almost coincides with the free needle, and so the correction before referred to (3009, *note*) necessary to give the true value of the variation is here very small.

3061. Considering *June* first, as at St. Helena, the upper needle end moves east as before until 19^h, under the influence of the morning cold, after which it stops and is sun-driven west until 22^h, when it swings downwards and beneath to east by 3^h; then follows the sun west until 7^h; it then stops and returns, creeping more and more east because of the coming cold (3065). In July the needle eastens a little more before 19^h; westens until 23^h, and then eastens until 4^h. The sun-swing is thus thrown an hour later than in June, which I believe to be connected with the accumulation of heat over the land (3054), combined with the lagging effect of the sun (3053). In August the needle end eastens until 19^h; more than in July, and most of all the months: it then westens strongly before the sun until 23^h, after which the sun-swing comes on and continues until 5^h, as if the warm region were behind the sun, perhaps even 2^h. The time of the swing is much prolonged, and not unnaturally, as the place is at the equator and therefore under the sun. In September the eastening is less, the westening is less, and the sun-swing is less. April is like September, except that the latter shows the effect of the previously warmed hemisphere (3053).

3062. Then there are four months in the year, November, December, January and February, when the sun is south of Singapore, and altogether during the day in the southern quadrants (3058). As the sun comes on from 16ʰ or 17ʰ, the upper part of the line of force moves westward (the lower being fixed in the earth) until 19 or 20 o'clock. The sun is at this time in the south-east quadrant, and it might be expected perhaps that the motion of the north or upper end of the needle should be to the east if there were any change at all. But there are two or three reasons, from the hypothesis, why this should not be. For that effect there should first of all be no dip; and in the next place, if there were no dip, the sun is so nearly in the neutral line of the magnetic equator that the deflection, if any, would have been very small. On the other hand, the lines of force have dip to the south, and being therefore held in the earth, that travelling of the sun along the neutral line, which in its coming up would have sent the whole line of force west, and so caused no variation of declination, can now only send the northern parts, as they rise out of the earth and are carried on with the general system of lines, west, and so cause that western travelling of the needle which does occur. Besides this, though the sun be south of that neutral line and also of Singapore, there is reason to suppose that the middle or resultant of the warm region is north even of both (3063), which would aid the westening of the needle just described.

3063. For if we recall to mind Dove's results, they show that the northern hemisphere, as a whole, is warmer than the southern (2949). Again, if we look at the meridian of Singapore, we shall find that there is far more continent on the north of it, to produce a higher temperature, than to the south; and even by the local tables of temperature (p. 757), we shall find that May, June, July and August are the hottest months for Singapore, and November, December, January and February the coldest; all tending to make us suppose that the warm region of the atmosphere is relatively north of the sun's place, and perhaps even of Singapore (3067).

3064. At 20ʰ the sun-swing from west to east comes on, and continues until 2ʰ, after which the needle moves west, following the sun, until 10ʰ or 11ʰ when it is near the mean; it still goes on westening very slowly until 17ʰ, when the morning sun action takes it up and drives it more quickly west, until about 20ʰ, when the sun-swing east occurs. The curve in these months is very simple in its character; the night or cold effect appears to be but small, being indicated rather by a hesitation than by a distinct movement east.

3065. The easterly movement of the needle end in May, June, July and August, and the westerly movement in November, December, January and February, for the same hours, up to 19 o'clock, are in striking contrast; and I have attributed the difference to the effect of a cold region coming on from the east during the former months (3061), which is absent in the latter months. In reference to this point, we have again to consider that the warm region is on the north of the equator (3063), and that as the sun moves north and south it also will move with it, but still keeping north of it. Hence the two cold regions, which come up to the meridian in higher latitudes (3006) before the sun, will not be in the same relation to Singapore, for the one on the south will be nearer to it than the one on the north, or at all events more powerful. So when the sun is near and at the southern tropic, the warm region probably passes *over* Singapore, at which time, therefore, whilst it is the nearest, the most powerful and most direct in position, the cold regions will be *least* in force at the station, and also least favourably disposed by position. But when the sun is at the northern tropic, then the power of the warm region is diminished, both by distance and direction, and the southern cold region grows up into importance by increased strength and closer vicinity, and so produces the eastening before 19ʰ.

3066. A striking difference in the direction of the night curves, from 5ʰ to 14ʰ, at St. Helena and Singapore may be observed. At the former place the needle end tends first east and then west, whilst at the latter it moves first west and then east. The difference is, I believe, due to the appearance of night cold action at St. Helena to a greater extent than at Singapore. Singapore shows that action in June, July and August, as just described (3065), but only in a weak degree and at a late hour. At St. Helena, which is in latitude 16° S., the cold effect should, for the reasons given above (3065), appear in more power, and hence the eastening at 6ʰ and after; and that this is the cause is indicated also in a degree by the tables of temperature; for whilst at Singapore the difference between the maximum and minimum in the twenty-four hours is only from 3° to 4°, at St. Helena it is from 4°.5 to 7°, and four-fifths or even five-sixths of this depression occurs by 9 o'clock: so that four or five hours before that, there was in the east a cold region coming up and producing the eastening effect recorded in the curves.

3067. The *inclination* variation at Singapore is beautifully simple, and such as might be expected from the hypothesis; the sun or warm region, when passing the meridian, always being over the lines to depress them. It is alike in all the months, being greatest at night-time and least at mid-day; it is nearly the same from 8^h to 18^h; then as the sun comes up it decreases quickly until 23^h or 24^h, after which, as the sun passes away, it increases nearly as quickly until 7^h or 8^h. The amount of variation is greatest when the sun is over or to the south of Singapore. It is least in June and July, when he is near the northern tropic. In December and January, when he is near the southern tropic, it is considerably more than in June and July, which again seems to show that the warm region is chiefly north of the sun (3063).

3068. The total force variation is simple, being a maximum from 9^h to 12^h, and a minimum at 22^h or 23^h, near noon. The greatest variation is in April and October, or at the equinoxes, and the least in December and June, when the sun is at the tropics. The force is the least towards noon, when I suppose that the air above is in the worst condition of conduction, and would cause a magnet in it to show more power. But how that may affect the curves beneath on the surface of the earth, where they are compressed together, is doubtful, and the whole matter of intensity is too uncertain and has too many bearings for me to consider it usefully here.

3069. I hope soon to give further experimental data for the purpose of illustrating and testing the view of the physical cause of the magnetic variations which I have put forth, namely, those I expect to obtain by the differential balance, and others concerning the sensible influence of oxygen in causing, under different conditions, deflection of the lines of magnetic force.

Royal Institution, November 16, 1850

CAPE OF GOOD HOPE. Longitude 18° 30' E. Latitude 33° 56' S. Declination 29° 05' W. Inclination 53° 15' S.

Mean Diurnal variation of the Declination in each month of the years 1841 to 1846.
Increasing numbers denote a movement of the north or upper end of the magnet towards the East.

Mean time	Noon 0h	1h	2h	3h	4h	5h	6h	7h	8h	9h	10h	11h	Midn. 12h	13h	14h	15h	16h	17h	18h	19h	20h	21h	22h	23h	Daily means
Jan.	4.11	5.43	5.50	5.04	4.64	4.29	3.96	4.16	4.43	4.36	4.27	4.13	3.98	3.79	3.56	3.32	3.09	2.67	2.01	1.15	0.37	0.36	1.39	2.93	3.28
Feb.	5.51	7.48	8.21	7.86	7.06	6.11	5.74	5.83	5.90	5.82	5.74	5.69	5.78	5.73	5.55	5.50	5.38	5.27	4.90	3.36	1.26	0.00	0.82	2.96	4.93
Mar.	5.34	6.74	7.29	6.93	6.17	5.48	5.32	5.33	5.42	5.39	5.28	5.40	5.34	5.46	5.59	5.54	5.52	5.39	4.95	3.22	1.04	0.02	1.26	3.44	4.66
Apr.	4.07	5.00	4.76	4.21	3.75	3.53	3.42	3.39	3.44	3.45	3.51	3.56	3.53	3.98	3.96	4.07	4.17	4.32	4.15	3.29	1.32	0.00	0.39	0.06	3.30
May	1.83	2.49	2.81	2.92	2.50	2.15	2.17	2.31	2.33	2.30	2.45	2.41	2.64	2.83	2.87	3.10	3.24	3.36	3.80	3.91	2.31	0.68	0.00	0.62	2.42
June	0.74	1.27	1.87	1.54	1.36	1.05	1.11	1.19	1.24	1.34	1.49	1.63	1.74	2.00	2.04	2.25	2.22	2.28	2.59	3.21	2.38	0.86	0.00	0.10	1.58
July	0.60	1.18	1.96	2.09	1.54	1.06	1.06	1.09	1.19	1.31	1.46	1.74	2.03	2.22	2.23	2.32	2.46	2.61	3.08	3.56	2.74	1.35	0.28	0.02	1.71
Aug.	0.62	1.52	2.50	3.23	2.93	2.22	2.27	2.34	2.46	2.56	2.49	2.64	2.77	2.91	3.01	3.32	3.45	3.63	4.35	4.98	3.65	1.74	0.36	0.00	2.71
Sept.	1.58	2.64	3.22	3.27	2.94	2.57	2.64	2.73	2.75	2.76	2.82	2.84	2.91	3.05	3.06	3.19	3.22	3.36	4.33	4.10	2.43	0.84	0.00	0.49	2.65
Oct.	4.90	5.81	5.96	5.23	4.29	3.69	3.84	4.05	4.09	4.17	4.18	4.16	4.16	4.15	3.96	3.79	3.63	3.40	2.78	1.37	0.14	0.00	1.27	3.18	3.59
Nov.	5.19	6.15	6.36	5.98	5.43	4.98	5.08	5.26	5.32	5.39	5.37	5.37	5.34	5.13	4.84	4.55	4.15	3.41	2.05	0.68	0.00	0.57	2.19	3.88	4.28
Dec.	4.64	5.48	5.51	5.08	4.47	4.41	4.24	4.42	4.54	4.60	4.66	4.67	4.62	4.36	4.07	3.74	3.38	2.63	1.42	0.39	0.04	0.55	2.05	3.56	3.62

Mean Diurnal variation of the Inclination in each month of the year, from April 1841 to June 1846.
Increasing numbers denote increasing inclination. Inclination 53° 15' South.

Mean time	Noon 0h	1h	2h	3h	4h	5h	6h	7h	8h	9h	10h	11h	Midn. 12h	13h	14h	15h	16h	17h	18h	19h	20h	21h	22h	23h	Daily means
Jan.	0.03	0.00	0.34	0.56	0.72	1.00	1.25	1.35	1.46	1.51	1.50	1.41	1.37	1.40	1.30	1.22	1.18	1.10	0.94	0.99	0.97	0.92	0.66	0.23	0.98
Feb.	0.13	0.00	0.44	1.05	1.55	1.91	2.01	2.14	2.14	2.09	2.94	1.94	1.70	1.63	1.65	1.56	1.63	1.70	1.66	1.94	2.26	2.08	1.45	0.66	1.56
Mar.	0.11	0.00	0.46	1.05	1.45	1.86	2.09	2.21	2.16	2.02	1.94	1.79	1.79	1.46	1.35	1.46	1.45	1.50	1.51	1.69	1.81	1.66	1.00	0.41	1.38
Apr.	0.00	0.49	1.05	1.55	1.76	1.89	2.16	2.21	2.11	2.06	1.88	1.65	1.45	1.18	1.18	1.07	1.22	1.12	1.10	1.10	1.48	1.53	0.92	0.33	1.35
May	0.00	0.38	0.70	0.86	1.08	1.16	1.27	1.31	1.49	1.59	1.39	1.32	1.16	0.89	0.93	0.89	0.76	0.68	0.30	0.15	0.53	0.66	0.56	0.12	0.84
June	0.41	0.53	0.58	0.64	0.64	0.79	0.96	1.22	1.34	1.40	1.29	1.22	1.04	0.96	0.89	0.81	0.73	0.78	0.36	0.00	0.07	0.36	0.36	0.43	0.75
July	0.62	0.64	0.59	0.64	0.77	0.87	1.18	1.20	1.46	1.43	1.43	1.21	1.07	0.95	0.77	0.87	0.67	0.60	0.28	0.00	0.18	0.51	0.64	0.56	0.80
Aug.	0.12	0.38	0.76	0.99	1.16	1.27	1.34	1.60	1.55	1.52	1.45	1.30	1.16	1.04	0.84	0.83	0.63	0.68	0.27	0.00	0.13	0.33	0.43	0.30	0.84
Sept.	0.00	0.23	0.66	1.09	1.40	1.65	1.78	1.68	1.75	1.75	1.40	1.27	0.91	0.97	0.56	0.81	0.51	0.73	0.18	0.31	0.07	0.35	0.03	0.12	0.84
Oct.	0.00	0.08	0.53	1.17	1.40	1.98	1.98	1.89	1.88	1.75	1.60	1.50	1.28	1.23	1.20	1.10	1.09	1.07	1.07	1.09	1.04	0.77	0.36	0.05	1.14
Nov.	0.14	0.00	0.29	0.64	1.12	1.53	1.41	1.46	1.48	1.33	1.25	1.08	0.99	0.94	0.90	0.87	0.87	0.94	0.80	0.62	0.46	0.26	0.06	0.00	0.81
Dec.	0.13	0.30	0.87	1.22	1.40	1.53	1.78	2.01	2.04	1.81	1.70	1.57	1.50	1.48	1.47	1.50	1.50	1.40	1.05	0.81	0.48	0.15	0.02	0.00	1.15
Means	0.14	0.25	0.61	0.96	1.23	1.45	1.60	1.69	1.74	1.69	1.49	1.44	1.28	1.18	1.09	1.08	1.02	1.02	0.79	0.72	0.79	0.80	0.54	0.27	1.04

CAPE OF GOOD HOPE. Mean Diurnal variation of the Intensity in each month of the year, from April 1841 to June 1846.

Increasing numbers denote increasing intensity.

The numbers express the changes in parts of the whole Force. Approximate Total Intensity 7.5.

Mean time	Noon 0h	1h	2h	3h	4h	5h	6h	7h	8h	9h	10h	11h	Midn. 12h	13h	14h	15h	16h	17h	18h	19h	20h	21h	22h	23h	Daily means
	.00	.00	.00	.00	.00	.00	.00	.00	.00	.00	.00	.00	.00	.00	.00	.00	.00	.00	.00	.00	.00	.00	.00	.00	.00
Jan.	000	003	018	031	041	047	048	039	036	038	040	044	045	047	049	050	052	061	071	079	073	056	028	005	042
Feb.	000	000	020	047	069	083	076	072	068	069	071	071	074	075	078	076	077	080	092	115	127	105	062	026	068
Mar.	000	007	027	052	070	079	074	069	064	064	067	066	070	068	066	068	068	068	081	103	119	094	047	011	063
Apr.	000	017	040	058	070	071	068	065	060	059	059	060	060	059	060	063	061	060	065	083	102	093	059	021	059
May	003	000	000	008	036	038	035	028	025	023	021	021	022	020	020	019	019	018	013	026	056	063	050	020	025
June	008	000	003	019	029	030	026	021	017	014	017	012	010	010	009	007	010	008	004	003	030	041	039	017	015
July	009	004	005	016	032	033	026	023	018	016	013	010	007	007	008	009	009	009	000	005	027	043	041	023	016
Aug.	028	013	003	010	028	035	029	024	019	013	013	016	016	016	017	013	013	009	000	009	044	061	064	044	023
Sept.	007	000	005	015	023	028	021	017	013	012	013	012	019	015	020	014	019	008	005	018	051	057	050	023	019
Oct.	000	009	033	057	070	064	053	047	045	045	047	047	051	055	056	056	056	060	073	088	084	060	025	005	050
Nov.	000	005	021	038	049	057	048	044	043	044	044	047	050	053	056	057	052	074	090	096	082	054	022	007	047
Dec.	000	003	015	029	037	035	034	030	027	026	028	031	035	036	038	042	047	060	074	076	066	042	013	000	034
Means	005	005	017	032	046	050	045	040	036	035	036	036	038	038	040	040	040	043	047	058	072	064	042	017	461

Mean Temperature of the Air from April 1841 to June 1846 inclusive. Fahrenheit's scale.

Mean time	Noon 0h	1h	2h	3h	4h	5h	6h	7h	8h	9h	10h	11h	Midn. 12h	13h	14h	15h	16h	17h	18h	19h	20h	21h	22h	23h	Daily means
	°	°	°	°	°	°	°	°	°	°	°	°	°	°	°	°	°	°	°	°	°	°	°	°	°
Jan.	73.16	73.30	73.03	72.43	71.52	70.30	67.94	66.11	65.45	65.01	64.51	64.10	63.77	63.54	63.32	63.06	62.85	63.18	65.20	67.24	68.78	70.05	71.46	72.59	67.58
Feb.	74.04	74.07	73.63	72.85	71.74	70.36	68.20	66.69	66.13	65.75	65.34	64.93	64.54	64.23	64.00	63.60	63.41	63.12	64.46	66.33	67.94	69.72	71.62	73.10	67.91
Mar.	71.74	72.40	72.19	71.40	69.96	68.07	65.98	64.98	64.38	63.69	63.20	62.85	62.37	62.06	61.69	61.44	61.15	60.97	61.31	63.03	65.39	67.48	69.50	71.00	65.76
Apr.	68.39	68.94	68.90	68.06	66.56	64.22	62.69	62.13	61.54	60.98	60.46	59.87	59.53	59.27	59.00	58.80	58.40	58.28	58.17	59.49	61.82	64.14	65.95	67.35	62.62
May	62.32	62.55	62.43	61.74	60.49	58.99	58.08	57.41	56.81	56.39	55.85	55.48	55.37	55.21	55.05	54.81	54.59	54.32	54.04	54.44	56.42	58.48	60.09	61.29	57.61
June	58.45	58.79	58.78	58.32	57.01	55.58	54.79	54.25	53.71	53.25	52.77	52.32	52.16	51.86	51.69	51.53	51.21	50.95	50.80	50.83	52.20	54.42	56.17	57.42	54.14
July	59.15	59.66	59.65	59.21	57.77	56.13	55.15	54.47	53.83	53.34	52.86	52.37	52.08	51.72	51.42	51.19	50.96	50.83	50.51	50.88	52.67	54.94	56.87	58.28	54.41
Aug.	58.86	59.23	59.07	58.61	57.61	56.13	55.01	54.35	53.91	53.60	53.17	52.91	52.71	52.31	52.07	51.87	51.54	51.19	51.15	51.88	53.19	55.57	57.05	59.30	54.63
Sept.	61.60	61.79	61.68	60.87	59.65	58.02	56.78	56.09	55.62	55.22	54.58	54.47	54.36	53.95	53.64	53.31	53.10	53.20	53.13	54.94	56.90	58.61	59.94	60.94	56.77
Oct.	65.48	65.71	65.46	64.66	63.38	61.56	59.51	58.68	58.05	57.51	57.14	56.74	56.70	56.33	56.11	55.88	55.64	55.63	57.14	59.08	61.00	62.75	64.07	65.04	59.97
Nov.	68.00	68.03	67.63	66.98	66.19	64.82	62.49	61.12	60.38	59.99	59.52	59.12	58.82	58.43	58.00	57.69	58.14	57.48	60.55	62.50	63.96	65.27	66.50	67.50	62.46
Dec.	71.02	71.23	70.84	70.21	69.63	68.23	65.69	63.94	63.19	62.64	62.07	61.59	61.18	60.82	60.49	60.17	59.91	60.83	63.41	65.80	67.17	68.42	69.62	70.42	65.35

St. Helena. Longitude 5° 40′ West. Latitude 15° 56′ South. Declination 23° 36′ West. Inclination 21° 40′ South.

Mean Diurnal variation of the Declination for the years 1841 to 1845 inclusive.

Increasing numbers denote increasing eastening of the north or upper end of the needle. Mean Declination 23° 36′.6 W.

Mean time	Noon 0h.	1h.	2h.	3h.	4h.	5h.	6h.	7h.	8h.	9h.	10h.	11h.	Midn. 12h.	13h.	14h.	15h.	16h.	17h.	18h.	19h.	20h.	21h.	22h.	23h.	Daily means
Jan.	3.72	3.19	2.41	2.03	2.09	1.84	1.92	2.41	2.80	2.90	2.86	2.81	2.63	2.43	2.23	2.01	1.73	1.68	1.50	0.59	0.00	0.57	1.75	3.15	2.13
Feb.	4.53	4.51	4.11	3.39	2.80	2.55	2.61	3.02	3.21	3.35	3.48	3.52	3.42	3.22	3.12	2.98	2.83	2.75	2.64	1.14	0.00	0.31	1.52	3.34	2.85
Mar.	3.76	4.11	3.48	2.57	2.15	2.20	2.48	2.64	2.69	2.68	2.85	2.84	2.80	2.77	2.68	2.70	2.69	2.70	2.96	1.90	0.26	0.00	1.13	2.72	2.49
Apr.	3.28	2.48	1.65	1.27	1.03	1.01	1.23	1.50	1.56	1.60	1.71	1.81	1.96	1.92	1.92	2.00	2.16	2.22	2.47	2.58	0.62	0.00	0.82	2.57	1.70
May	0.71	0.44	0.57	0.71	0.55	0.21	0.25	0.48	0.56	0.72	0.78	0.90	1.02	1.09	1.11	1.18	1.32	1.57	2.04	3.31	1.50	0.32	0.00	0.49	0.88
June	0.71	0.73	0.88	0.94	0.44	0.00	0.10	0.39	0.56	0.73	0.90	1.06	1.17	1.22	1.25	1.29	1.40	1.66	2.16	2.69	2.58	1.31	0.75	0.69	1.10
July	0.82	0.71	0.78	0.84	0.48	0.02	0.00	0.22	0.46	0.64	0.84	0.98	1.08	1.14	1.14	1.24	1.31	1.46	2.02	3.11	2.52	1.19	0.63	0.67	1.02
Aug.	0.11	0.00	0.40	0.86	0.82	0.42	0.25	0.52	0.68	0.78	0.88	1.02	1.02	1.02	1.04	1.18	1.27	1.61	2.37	3.43	2.85	0.54	0.36	0.05	0.99
Sept.	0.89	0.85	0.65	0.44	0.35	0.28	0.28	0.53	0.62	0.67	0.79	0.78	0.75	0.64	0.61	0.65	0.70	0.95	2.12	1.89	0.85	0.17	0.00	0.43	0.70
Oct.	4.41	4.35	3.43	2.06	1.23	1.32	1.80	2.04	2.21	2.34	2.45	2.43	2.23	2.00	1.92	1.81	1.72	1.74	1.99	0.49	0.00	0.72	2.08	3.61	2.10
Nov.	3.97	3.82	3.31	2.52	1.85	1.85	2.29	2.77	2.99	3.13	3.21	3.13	2.96	2.68	2.46	2.22	1.97	1.80	1.53	0.21	0.00	1.03	2.22	3.41	2.39
Dec.	3.65	3.48	2.70	1.94	1.66	1.85	2.15	2.58	2.93	3.12	3.20	3.13	2.89	2.64	2.40	2.17	1.93	1.73	1.38	0.32	0.00	0.86	2.09	3.32	2.25

Mean Diurnal variation of the Inclination in each month, from January 1841 to December 1845.

Increasing numbers denote increasing inclination. Mean Inclination 21° 40′ South.

Mean time	Noon 0h.	1h.	2h.	3h.	4h.	5h.	6h.	7h.	8h.	9h.	10h.	11h.	Midn. 12h.	13h.	14h.	15h.	16h.	17h.	18h.	19h.	20h.	21h.	22h.	23h.	Daily means
Jan.	0.14	0.46	1.07	1.49	2.18	2.53	2.77	2.91	2.87	2.83	2.77	2.63	2.40	2.23	1.99	1.85	1.80	1.77	1.65	1.37	0.88	0.53	0.00	0.02	1.71
Feb.	0.23	0.61	1.33	2.00	2.39	2.78	3.01	3.15	3.12	2.98	2.86	2.73	2.61	2.46	2.44	2.21	2.15	2.00	2.04	1.82	1.40	0.94	0.10	0.00	1.97
Mar.	0.11	0.56	1.33	1.86	2.21	2.47	2.80	2.97	2.99	2.89	2.89	2.67	2.46	2.37	2.26	2.12	1.99	2.01	1.84	1.53	1.06	0.43	0.00	0.10	1.83
Apr.	0.45	0.89	1.54	2.14	2.53	2.83	3.05	3.17	3.26	3.21	2.97	2.63	2.41	2.18	2.15	2.08	1.88	1.77	1.47	1.30	0.94	0.36	0.27	0.03	1.88
May	0.20	0.74	1.16	1.62	1.90	2.10	2.22	2.36	2.28	2.21	2.12	1.99	1.77	1.69	1.56	1.33	1.21	1.16	1.18	1.09	0.81	0.43	0.00	0.03	1.38
June	0.18	0.56	1.04	1.58	1.65	1.91	2.21	2.26	2.24	2.12	2.02	1.98	2.06	1.77	1.68	1.54	1.46	1.36	1.22	0.98	0.80	0.27	0.09	0.03	1.35
July	0.30	0.60	1.06	1.44	1.82	2.01	2.42	2.47	2.40	2.35	2.21	2.04	1.80	1.58	1.52	1.30	1.25	1.08	1.00	0.84	0.53	0.54	0.19	0.00	1.42
Aug.	0.25	0.72	1.21	1.61	1.94	2.16	2.35	2.40	2.39	2.19	2.12	1.98	1.80	1.69	1.58	1.40	1.33	1.25	1.13	1.07	0.79	0.60	0.36	0.00	1.47
Sept.	0.18	0.70	1.29	1.72	2.02	2.19	2.40	2.40	2.32	2.13	2.01	1.99	1.80	1.68	1.47	1.50	1.51	1.44	1.40	1.27	0.92	0.37	0.00	0.00	1.66
Oct.	0.24	0.74	1.36	1.90	2.34	2.56	2.55	2.88	2.65	2.56	2.46	2.28	2.09	2.04	1.89	1.80	1.70	1.69	1.63	1.31	0.88	0.23	0.00	0.00	1.47
Nov.	0.08	0.27	0.74	1.19	1.63	2.00	2.35	2.45	2.38	2.30	2.18	2.07	1.96	1.83	1.71	1.59	1.66	1.48	1.35	0.92	0.55	0.10	0.00	0.10	1.38
Dec.	0.26	0.73	1.06	1.59	2.08	2.41	2.69	2.78	2.61	2.45	2.39	2.15	2.01	1.80	1.72	1.56	1.48	1.38	1.26	0.85	0.40	0.10	0.00	0.07	1.49
Means	0.22	0.63	1.18	1.64	2.06	2.33	2.57	2.68	2.63	2.49	2.42	2.26	2.10	1.94	1.83	1.69	1.62	1.53	1.43	1.20	0.83	0.44	0.08	0.03	1.58

St. Helena. Mean Diurnal variation of the Total Intensity in each month, from January 1841 to December 1845.
Increasing numbers denote increasing intensity.

Mean time	Noon 0h	1h	2h	3h	4h	5h	6h	7h	8h	9h	10h	11h	Midn. 12h	13h	14h	15h	16h	17h	18h	19h	20h	21h	22h	23h	Daily means
	.00	.00	.00	.00	.00	.00	.00	.00	.00	.00	.00	.00	.00	.00	.00	.00	.00	.00	.00	.00	.00	.00	.00	.00	.00
Jan.	130	129	116	098	081	063	046	027	016	004	000	001	001	008	015	015	019	019	024	040	055	080	109	124	051
Feb.	117	109	092	077	063	050	029	014	007	001	002	003	004	002	000	002	002	003	009	023	046	070	095	114	039
Mar.	153	147	124	096	070	055	032	020	010	000	006	004	001	016	014	018	018	021	026	040	068	102	132	149	055
Apr.	162	150	122	088	068	042	021	010	005	001	004	000	007	014	015	016	025	024	024	031	054	090	102	150	051
May	163	142	115	087	065	049	036	023	016	011	004	000	008	008	011	018	019	019	025	034	048	095	132	159	054
June	141	128	101	064	063	047	028	015	006	004	001	010	002	003	004	004	004	009	013	022	042	075	110	137	043
July	126	117	095	073	051	042	027	015	011	002	002	000	003	005	006	011	015	018	019	024	038	068	097	116	041
Aug.	139	126	103	077	053	038	026	013	004	001	000	000	002	005	009	015	015	016	016	018	037	068	103	131	039
Sept.	143	131	105	077	056	037	026	013	004	000	003	007	011	014	018	024	022	024	023	022	038	069	101	134	046
Oct.	135	123	105	088	070	051	030	015	007	001	000	005	011	013	019	020	019	020	017	032	058	093	123	135	050
Nov.	112	111	101	090	076	055	029	018	007	000	002	009	011	011	016	017	017	017	026	048	071	087	105	112	048
Dec.	116	110	105	089	071	051	027	011	004	000	000	003	003	006	008	010	011	012	024	046	064	086	107	117	045
Means	136	127	107	084	066	048	030	016	008	002	002	003	006	009	011	014	015	017	021	032	052	082	110	132	047

Mean Temperature of the Air from 1841 to 1845 inclusive.

Mean time	Noon 0h	1h	2h	3h	4h	5h	6h	7h	8h	9h	10h	11h	Midn. 12h	13h	14h	15h	16h	17h	18h	19h	20h	21h	22h	23h	Daily means
	°	°	°	°	°	°	°	°	°	°	°	°	°	°	°	°	°	°	°	°	°	°	°	°	°
Jan.	67.68	68.05	67.93	67.79	67.30	63.04	64.58	63.39	62.93	62.62	62.42	62.27	62.06	61.88	61.66	61.60	61.49	61.39	61.37	61.84	62.79	64.09	65.38	66.55	63.98
Feb.	69.14	69.61	69.85	69.59	68.95	67.89	66.59	65.43	64.91	64.66	64.46	64.32	64.13	63.96	63.78	63.59	63.51	63.44	63.42	63.62	64.43	65.72	67.08	68.24	65.87
Mar.	69.13	69.57	69.89	69.71	69.10	63.10	66.86	65.84	65.47	65.15	65.00	64.83	64.65	64.50	64.31	64.17	64.15	64.03	64.05	64.29	65.08	66.39	67.35	68.38	66.24
Apr.	68.54	68.89	68.98	68.64	67.99	63.98	65.84	65.15	64.84	64.61	64.45	64.29	64.11	64.02	63.88	63.77	63.66	63.51	63.49	63.69	64.50	65.70	66.74	67.86	65.60
May	65.76	66.01	66.09	65.84	65.17	64.11	63.56	63.32	62.73	62.13	62.03	61.88	61.67	61.57	61.40	61.24	61.19	61.19	61.04	61.06	62.01	63.22	64.11	65.22	63.05
June	62.40	62.76	62.73	62.39	61.83	63.98	60.14	59.68	59.49	59.34	59.20	59.11	59.00	58.86	58.74	58.61	58.56	58.53	58.47	58.52	59.13	60.16	60.98	61.80	60.07
July	60.37	60.83	60.77	60.51	59.87	53.98	58.14	57.70	57.48	57.25	57.13	56.91	56.81	56.72	56.60	56.51	56.43	56.36	56.31	56.38	57.07	58.09	58.90	59.69	57.99
Aug.	59.68	59.99	60.12	59.72	59.11	53.11	57.23	56.83	56.60	56.45	56.32	56.20	56.10	55.98	55.76	55.68	55.53	55.50	55.39	55.56	56.20	57.22	58.07	58.96	57.17
Sept.	59.89	60.26	60.18	59.77	59.11	53.03	57.05	56.56	56.35	56.21	56.04	55.91	55.82	55.67	55.51	55.37	55.29	55.21	55.21	55.44	56.12	57.18	58.31	59.14	57.07
Oct.	61.50	61.98	61.91	61.31	60.46	58.18	58.01	57.57	57.64	57.12	56.99	56.84	56.64	56.48	56.30	56.18	56.11	56.00	56.06	56.50	57.38	58.61	59.71	60.73	58.23
Nov.	63.44	63.88	63.97	63.52	62.63	61.32	59.94	59.11	58.76	58.57	58.41	58.24	58.08	57.90	57.71	57.62	57.55	57.43	57.53	58.03	58.94	60.20	61.35	62.35	59.84
Dec.	65.19	65.81	65.87	65.72	64.88	63.62	62.17	61.10	60.70	60.46	60.27	60.12	59.95	59.75	59.57	59.47	59.34	59.31	59.39	59.77	60.69	61.97	63.03	64.19	61.77

SINGAPORE. Latitude 1° 16' N. Longitude 103° 53' E. Declination 1° 40' E. (Approx.). Inclination 12° S. (Approx.).

Mean Hourly oscillation of the Magnetic Declination for each month of the years 1843, 1844 and 1845.

Increasing numbers denote a movement of the north or upper end of the magnet towards the East.

Mean time	Noon 0¼ʰ	1¼ʰ	2¼ʰ	3¼ʰ	4¼ʰ	5¼ʰ	6¼ʰ	7¼ʰ	8¼ʰ	9¼ʰ	10¼ʰ	11¼ʰ	Midn. 12¼ʰ	13¼ʰ	14¼ʰ	15¼ʰ	16¼ʰ	17¼ʰ	18¼ʰ	19¼ʰ	20¼ʰ	21¼ʰ	22¼ʰ	23¼ʰ	Daily means
Jan.	2.04	2.52	2.79	2.72	2.52	2.24	2.11	2.18	2.04	1.97	1.84	1.70	1.63	1.63	1.50	1.43	1.29	1.02	0.61	0.00	0.00	0.41	0.82	1.22	1.59
Feb.	2.31	2.92	3.13	3.06	2.79	2.52	2.31	2.31	2.18	2.04	1.90	1.90	1.97	1.90	1.90	1.90	1.84	1.70	1.29	0.54	0.00	0.00	0.34	1.43	1.84
Mar.	1.29	1.43	1.63	1.77	1.63	1.43	1.29	1.09	0.95	0.88	0.82	0.82	0.88	0.88	0.88	0.82	0.82	0.82	0.82	0.48	0.00	0.07	0.54	1.02	0.96
Apr.	0.34	0.61	0.75	1.02	1.16	1.16	0.95	0.88	0.61	0.54	0.61	0.68	0.82	0.95	0.95	0.95	0.88	0.82	1.16	0.95	0.34	0.00	0.20	0.41	0.70
May	0.07	0.48	0.82	1.16	1.36	0.95	1.02	0.88	0.75	0.68	0.75	0.82	1.09	1.16	1.29	1.36	1.36	1.43	2.11	2.24	0.34	0.68	0.27	0.00	0.75
June	0.20	0.41	0.54	0.61	0.54	0.34	0.14	0.00	0.00	0.00	0.07	0.20	0.41	0.54	0.61	0.68	0.68	0.82	1.36	1.56	0.82	0.41	0.00	0.14	0.46
July	0.07	0.41	0.61	0.88	1.02	0.88	0.48	0.34	0.27	0.20	0.27	0.34	0.54	0.68	0.82	0.75	0.82	1.16	1.63	1.97	1.29	0.54	0.14	0.00	0.67
Aug.	0.20	0.68	1.02	1.56	1.63	1.84	1.43	1.29	1.09	1.02	1.02	1.16	1.22	1.36	1.29	1.29	1.50	1.70	2.52	2.79	1.77	0.75	0.14	0.00	1.27
Sept.	0.48	0.88	1.36	1.63	1.63	1.56	1.50	1.29	1.16	1.09	1.02	1.09	1.16	1.22	1.29	1.29	1.36	1.43	1.97	1.77	0.75	0.20	0.00	0.20	1.14
Oct.	1.90	2.31	2.31	2.18	1.97	1.77	1.77	1.63	1.50	1.36	1.29	1.29	1.43	1.36	1.36	1.29	1.22	1.09	1.16	0.54	0.14	0.75	0.27	1.02	1.33
Nov.	2.45	2.92	2.99	2.86	2.45	2.11	1.97	1.84	1.70	1.56	1.36	1.36	1.43	1.43	1.36	1.29	1.16	1.02	0.48	0.00	0.00	0.27	0.82	1.63	1.51
Dec.	2.52	2.99	2.99	2.99	2.86	2.45	2.18	2.04	1.97	1.84	1.70	1.63	1.56	1.56	1.56	1.50	1.43	1.16	0.61	0.00	0.00	0.41	1.02	1.77	1.70

Mean Diurnal variation of the Inclination in the several months during the years 1843, 1844 and 1845.

Increasing numbers denote increasing inclination. Approximate inclination 12° South.

Mean time	Noon 0¼ʰ	1¼ʰ	2¼ʰ	3¼ʰ	4¼ʰ	5¼ʰ	6¼ʰ	7¼ʰ	8¼ʰ	9¼ʰ	10¼ʰ	11¼ʰ	Midn. 12¼ʰ	13¼ʰ	14¼ʰ	15¼ʰ	16¼ʰ	17¼ʰ	18¼ʰ	19¼ʰ	20¼ʰ	21¼ʰ	22¼ʰ	23¼ʰ	Daily means
Jan.	0.00	0.43	0.98	1.28	1.90	2.07	2.38	2.57	2.62	2.71	2.76	2.76	2.66	2.71	2.71	2.72	2.72	2.72	2.73	2.52	1.97	1.09	0.32	0.02	1.97
Feb.	0.04	0.64	1.24	1.75	2.00	2.21	2.56	2.82	2.94	3.02	3.10	3.07	3.08	3.03	2.98	2.99	2.97	2.97	3.03	2.88	2.35	1.21	0.40	0.00	2.22
Mar.	0.06	0.29	0.75	1.36	1.75	1.88	2.22	2.55	2.65	2.70	2.74	2.72	2.72	2.67	2.71	2.72	2.72	2.75	2.75	2.54	1.84	0.75	0.11	0.00	1.91
Apr.	0.28	0.82	1.54	2.09	2.47	2.71	3.04	3.00	3.27	3.36	3.41	3.49	3.43	3.40	3.33	3.29	3.29	3.27	3.15	2.92	2.18	1.15	0.28	0.00	2.46
May	0.00	0.32	0.80	1.17	1.62	1.96	2.29	2.34	2.42	2.43	2.42	2.20	2.38	2.40	2.42	2.46	2.52	2.51	2.25	1.87	1.25	0.49	0.03	0.00	1.69
June	0.04	0.20	0.57	0.98	1.44	1.50	2.20	2.25	2.19	2.16	2.10	2.07	2.15	2.21	2.15	2.20	2.21	2.29	2.02	1.71	1.28	0.69	0.22	0.00	1.53
July	0.00	0.15	0.45	0.89	1.34	1.76	2.10	2.16	2.19	2.20	2.20	2.07	2.18	2.19	2.19	2.21	2.21	2.27	2.02	1.74	1.28	0.69	0.27	0.05	1.53
Aug.	0.12	0.34	0.69	1.01	1.35	1.68	1.99	2.32	2.21	2.27	2.26	2.28	2.26	2.20	2.18	2.22	2.21	2.22	1.93	1.68	1.30	0.62	0.14	0.00	1.56
Sept.	0.41	1.00	1.60	1.94	2.11	2.32	2.58	2.69	2.78	2.82	2.85	2.84	2.85	2.79	2.74	2.75	2.75	2.79	2.66	2.39	1.66	0.79	0.15	0.00	2.09
Oct.	0.38	1.17	1.94	2.38	2.48	2.59	2.86	3.07	3.23	3.29	3.34	3.23	3.33	3.23	3.22	3.20	3.24	3.20	3.25	2.96	2.18	1.14	0.21	0.00	2.46
Nov.	0.16	0.63	1.37	1.96	2.32	2.68	2.88	2.87	3.02	3.08	3.07	3.06	3.06	3.03	3.02	2.95	3.01	3.00	3.15	2.80	2.01	1.04	0.17	0.00	2.26
Dec.	0.09	0.54	1.13	1.62	1.92	2.26	2.53	2.66	2.85	2.86	2.85	2.86	2.76	2.76	2.72	2.69	2.65	2.69	2.44	2.38	1.81	1.08	0.34	0.00	2.02
Means	0.13	0.54	1.09	1.54	1.89	2.14	2.47	2.61	2.70	2.74	2.76	2.72	2.74	2.72	2.70	2.70	2.71	2.72	2.62	2.37	1.76	0.89	0.22	0.01	1.98

SINGAPORE. Mean Diurnal variation of the Total Intensity in the several months during the years 1843, 1844, 1845.
Increasing numbers indicate increase of total intensity.
The numbers express the changes in parts of the whole force. Approximate total intensity 8.21.

Mean time	Noon 0¼ʰ	1¼ʰ	2¼ʰ	3¼ʰ	4¼ʰ	5¼ʰ	6¼ʰ	7¼ʰ	8¼ʰ	9¼ʰ	10¼ʰ	11¼ʰ	Midn. 12¼ʰ	13¼ʰ	14¼ʰ	15¼ʰ	16¼ʰ	17¼ʰ	18¼ʰ	19¼ʰ	20¼ʰ	21¼ʰ	22¼ʰ	23¼ʰ	Daily means
	.00	.00	.00	.00	.00	.00	.00	.00	.00	.00	.00	.00	.00	.00	.00	.00	.00	.00	.00	.00	.00	.00	.00	.00	.00
Jan.	086	066	047	030	028	021	015	009	009	003	002	000	007	002	008	007	010	012	022	033	054	074	099	100	031
Feb.	099	080	061	042	027	024	013	008	004	000	000	002	000	001	005	005	009	011	014	025	049	082	103	110	032
Mar.	114	085	055	035	026	020	013	007	005	000	000	002	005	008	007	009	011	012	012	027	057	087	112	122	035
Apr.	122	094	065	040	029	020	016	011	005	003	005	002	000	004	009	011	013	015	020	043	076	110	139	137	041
May	104	081	060	036	020	013	014	011	010	006	006	000	004	001	003	004	008	012	025	044	073	097	114	118	036
June	096	075	051	026	011	012	004	004	001	000	000	000	001	001	006	004	004	008	020	038	062	085	102	105	031
July	100	081	056	033	019	013	007	007	007	004	002	000	002	004	006	004	010	015	026	044	070	091	105	110	034
Aug.	101	081	055	029	016	009	010	005	006	000	002	002	004	010	011	011	016	018	028	046	077	096	115	114	036
Sept.	093	065	037	033	018	009	009	008	002	001	002	002	003	008	014	018	019	017	023	045	079	104	117	115	035
Oct.	102	073	050	029	016	024	013	008	003	000	000	001	006	011	011	016	019	017	020	037	070	101	117	121	037
Nov.	080	063	044	036	021	015	009	003	001	000	001	000	002	006	007	013	012	013	017	034	059	082	098	095	029
Dec.	077	061	044	030	026	021	012	004	000	000	001	002	003	006	009	013	014	014	019	035	056	078	095	091	030
Means	098	075	052	033	022	019	011	007	004	002	002	001	003	006	003	010	012	014	021	038	065	091	110	112	034

Mean Temperature of the Air observed on the Standard Thermometer inside the Observatory, during the years 1841, 1842 and 1843.

Mean time	Noon 0¼ʰ	1¼ʰ	2¼ʰ	3¼ʰ	4¼ʰ	5¼ʰ	6¼ʰ	7¼ʰ	8¼ʰ	9¼ʰ	10¼ʰ	11¼ʰ	Midn. 12¼ʰ	13¼ʰ	14¼ʰ	15¼ʰ	16¼ʰ	17¼ʰ	18¼ʰ	19¼ʰ	20¼ʰ	21¼ʰ	22¼ʰ	23¼ʰ	Daily means
	°	°	°	°	°	°	°	°	°	°	°	°	°	°	°	°	°	°	°	°	°	°	°	°	°
Jan.	79.7	79.5	80.0	79.5	79.7	79.1	79.0	78.4	78.5	78.0	78.1	77.5	77.9	77.3	77.6	76.9	77.4	76.5	77.0	76.3	77.3	77.4	78.6	78.8	78.2
Feb.	80.7	81.6	81.2	82.1	81.2	82.1	80.2	80.6	79.7	80.2	79.2	79.6	78.6	79.0	78.3	78.6	78.2	78.2	77.7	78.2	78.0	79.4	79.6	81.8	79.8
Mar.	81.4	82.1	81.7	82.3	81.6	82.0	80.9	81.5	80.5	81.2	80.1	81.0	79.9	80.6	79.4	79.4	79.1	79.9	78.7	79.8	79.4	80.6	80.6	81.5	80.7
Apr.	81.8	81.8	82.1	81.8	81.9	81.6	81.4	81.2	81.0	80.9	80.7	80.2	80.3	80.3	79.9	79.5	79.6	79.6	79.2	79.8	79.9	80.6	81.1	81.4	80.8
May	82.5		82.7		82.5		82.1		81.8	81.4	81.4	81.4	80.9		80.5	80.3	80.3	80.2	79.9		80.9		81.8		81.4
June	82.4	82.9	82.8	83.1	82.7	82.7	82.2	82.0	81.7	81.9	81.4	81.4	81.2	81.2	80.7	80.7	80.3	80.2	80.1	80.4	81.0	81.7	81.8	82.6	81.6
July	81.7	83.0	81.9	83.1	82.7	82.7	82.4	82.1	81.8	81.9	81.5	81.5	81.1	81.2	80.7	80.9	80.3	80.6	80.1	80.8	80.8	81.9	81.9	82.6	81.7
Aug.	82.1	82.6	82.4	82.3	82.2	81.8	81.4	81.3	81.0	81.2	80.8	80.8	80.4	80.3	80.1	80.1	79.8	79.8	79.5	79.8	80.2	80.8	81.2	81.6	80.9
Sept.	81.5	81.3	81.7	81.4	81.7	82.1	81.7	81.6	81.5	81.2	81.0	80.8	80.5	80.3	80.1	80.0	79.7	79.7	79.4	79.4	80.3	80.9	81.4	80.9	81.0
Oct.	81.1	81.0	81.3	80.8	81.0	80.6	81.2	80.6	80.7	80.1	80.1	79.8	79.3	79.8	79.4	79.3	79.0	79.3	78.7	79.2	79.5	80.0	80.7	80.9	80.3
Nov.	81.1	81.3	81.3	80.8	81.0	80.8	80.4	80.1	80.1	79.7	79.7	79.6	79.3	79.1	78.9	78.7	78.6	78.5	78.4	78.5	79.2	79.6	80.2	80.5	79.8
Dec.	81.0	81.3	81.3	81.3	80.9	80.8	80.2	80.0	79.6	79.4	79.2	79.2	79.0	79.0	78.6	78.4	78.1	78.1	77.9	78.2	78.7	79.5	80.1	80.7	79.6
Means	81.5	81.7	81.8	81.8	81.6	81.5	81.1	80.9	80.7	80.5	80.3	80.1	79.9	79.8	79.5	79.4	79.2	79.1	78.9	79.1	79.6	80.2	80.7	81.3	80.4

TWENTY-EIGHTH SERIES[1]

§ 34. *On Lines of Magnetic Force; their Definite Character; and their Distribution within a Magnet and through Space*

RECEIVED OCTOBER 22, READ NOVEMBER 27 AND DECEMBER 11, 1851

3070. FROM my earliest experiments on the relation of electricity and magnetism (114 *note*), I have had to think and speak of lines of magnetic force as representations of the magnetic power; not merely in the points of quality and direction, but also in quantity. The necessity I was under of a more frequent use of the term in some recent researches (2149, &c.), has led me to believe that the time has arrived, when the idea conveyed by the phrase should be stated very clearly, and should also be carefully examined, that it may be ascertained how far it may be truly applied in representing magnetic conditions and phenomena; how far it may be useful in their elucidation; and, also, how far it may assist in leading the mind correctly on to further conceptions of the physical nature of the force, and the recognition of the possible effects, either new or old, which may be produced by it.

3071. A line of magnetic force may be defined as that line which is described by a very small magnetic needle, when it is so moved in either direction correspondent to its length, that the needle is constantly a tangent to the line of motion; or it is that line along which, if a transverse wire be moved in either direction, there is no tendency to the formation of any current in the wire, whilst if moved in any other direction there is such a tendency; or it is that line which coincides with the direction of the magnecrystallic axis of a crystal of bismuth, which is carried in either direction along it. The direction of these lines about and amongst magnets and electric currents, is easily represented and understood, in a general manner, by the ordinary use of iron filings.

3072. These lines have not merely a determinate direction, recognizable as above (3071), but because they are related to a polar or antithetical power, have opposite qualities or conditions in opposite directions; these qualities, which have to be distinguished and identified, are made manifest to us, either by the position

of the ends of the magnetic needle, or by the direction of the current induced in the moving wire.

3073. A point equally important to the definition of these lines is that they represent a determinate and unchanging amount of force. Though, therefore, their forms, as they exist between two or more centres or sources of magnetic power, may vary very greatly, and also the space through which they may be traced, yet the sum of power contained in any one section of a given portion of the lines is exactly equal to the sum of power in any other section of the same lines, however altered in form, or however convergent or divergent they may be at the second place. The experimental proof of this character of the lines will be given hereafter (3109, &c.).

3074. Now it appears to me that these lines may be employed with great advantage to represent the nature, condition, direction and comparative amount of the magnetic forces; and that in many cases they have, to the physical reasoner at least, a superiority over that method which represents the forces as concentrated in centres of action, such as the poles of magnets or needles; or some other methods, as, for instance, that which considers north or south magnetisms as fluids diffused over the ends or amongst the particles of a bar. No doubt, any of these methods which does not assume too much will, with a faithful application, give true results; and so they all ought to give the same results as far as they can respectively be applied. But some may, by their very nature, be applicable to a far greater extent, and give far more varied results, than others. For just as either geometry or analysis may be employed to solve correctly a particular problem, though one has far more power and capability, generally speaking, than the other; or just as either the idea of the reflection of images, or that of the reverberation of sounds may be used to represent certain physical forces and conditions; so may the idea of the attractions and repulsions

[1] *Philosophical Transactions.* 1852. p. 1.

of centres, or that of the disposition of magnetic fluids, or that of lines of force, be applied in the consideration of magnetic phenomena. It is the occasional and more frequent use of the latter which I at present wish to advocate.

3075. I desire to restrict the meaning of the term *line of force*, so that it shall imply no more than the condition of the force in any given place, as to strength and direction; and not to include (at present) any idea of the nature of the physical cause of the phenomena; or be tied up with, or in any way dependent on, such an idea. Still, there is no impropriety in endeavouring to conceive the method in which the physical forces are either excited, or exist, or are transmitted; nor, when these by experiment and comparison are ascertained in any given degree, in representing them by any method which we adopt to represent the mere forces, provided no error is thereby introduced. On the contrary, when the natural truth and the conventional representation of it most closely agree, then are we most advanced in our knowledge. The emission and the ether theories present such cases in relation to light. The idea of a fluid or of two fluids is the same for electricity; and there the further idea of a current has been raised, which indeed has such hold on the mind as occasionally to embarrass the science as respects the true character of the physical agencies, and may be doing so, even now, to a degree which we at present little suspect. The same is the case with the idea of a magnetic fluid or fluids, or with the assumption of magnetic centres of action of which the resultants are at the poles. How the magnetic force is transferred through bodies or through space we know not:—whether the result is merely action at a distance, as in the case of gravity; or by some intermediate agency, as in the cases of light, heat, the electric current, and (as I believe) static electric action. The idea of magnetic fluids, as applied by some, or of magnetic centres of action, does not include that of the latter kind of transmission, but the idea of lines of force does. Nevertheless, because a particular method of representing the forces does not include such a mode of transmission, the latter is not therefore disproved; and that method of representation which harmonizes with it may be the most true to nature. The general conclusion of philosophers seems to be that such cases are by far the most numerous, and for my own part, considering the relation of a vacuum to the magnetic force and the general character

of magnetic phenomena external to the magnet, I am more inclined to the notion that in the transmission of the force there is such an action, external to the magnet, than that the effects are merely attraction and repulsion at a distance. Such an action may be a function of the ether; for it is not at all unlikely that, if there be an ether, it should have other uses than simply the conveyance of radiations (2591, 2787). Perhaps when we are more clearly instructed in this matter, we shall see the source of the contradictions which are supposed to exist between the results of Coulomb, Harris and other philosophers, and find that they are not contradictions in reality, but mere differences in degree, dependent upon partial or imperfect views of the phenomena and their causes.

3076. Lines of magnetic force may be recognized, either by their action on a magnetic needle, or on a conducting body moving across them. Each of these actions may be employed also to indicate either the direction of the line, or the force exerted at any given point in it, and this they do with advantages for the one method or the other under particular circumstances. The actions are however very different in their nature. The needle shows its results by attractions and repulsions; the moving conductor or wire shows it by the production of a current of electricity. The latter is an effect entirely unlike that produced on the needle, and due to a different action of the forces; so that it gives a view and a result of properties of the lines of force, such as the attractions and repulsions of the needle could never show. For this and other reasons I propose to develop and apply the method by a moving conductor on the present occasion.

3077. The general principles of the development of an electric current in a wire moving under the influence of magnetic forces, were given on a former occasion, in the first and second series of these *Researches* (36, &c); it will therefore be unnecessary to do more than to call attention, at this time, to the special character of its indications as compared to those of a magnetic needle, and to show how it becomes a peculiar and important addition to it, in the illustration of magnetic action.

3078. The moving wire produces its greatest effect and indication, not when passing from stronger to weaker places, or the reverse, but when moving in places of equal action, i.e., transversely across the lines of force (217).

3079. It determines the direction of the polarity by an effect entirely independent of pointing or such like results of attraction or repulsion; i.e., by the direction of the electric current produced in it during the motion.[1]

3080. The principle can be applied to the examination of the forces *within* numerous solid bodies, as the metals, as well as outside in the air. It is not often embarrassed by the difference of the surrounding media, and can be used in fluids, gases or a vacuum with equal facility. Hence it can penetrate and be employed where the needle is forbidden; and in other cases where the needle might be resorted to, though greatly embarrassed by the media around it, the moving wire may be used with an immediate result (3142).

3081. The method can even be applied with equal facility to the interior of a magnet (3116) a place utterly inaccessible to the magnetic needle.

3082. The moving wire can be made to sum up or give the resultant at once of the magnetic action at many different places, i.e., the action due to an area or section of the lines of force, and so supply experimental comparisons which the needle could not give, except with very great labour, and then imperfectly. Whether the wire moves directly or obliquely across the lines of force, in one direction or another, it sums up, with the same accuracy in principle, the amount of the forces represented by the lines it has crossed (3113).

3083. So a moving wire may be accepted as a correct philosophical indication of the presence of magnetic force. Illustrations of the capabilities already referred to will arise and be pointed out in the present paper; and though its sensibility does not as yet approach to that of the magnetic needle, still, there is no doubt that it may be very greatly increased. The diversity of its possible arrangements, and the great advantage of that diversity, is already very manifest to myself. Though both it and the needle depend for their results upon essential characters and qualities of the magnetic force, yet those which are influential, and, therefore indicated, in the one case, are very different from those which are active in the other; I mean, as far as we have been able as yet to refer directly

[1] A natural standard of this polarity may be obtained, by referring to the lines of force of the earth, in the northern hemisphere, thus: if a person with arms extended move forward in these latitudes, then the direction of the electric current, which would tend to be produced in a wire represented by the arms, would be from the right-hand through the arm and body towards the left.

the effects to essential characters: and this difference may, hereafter, enable the wire to give a new insight into the nature of the magnetic force; and so it may, finally, bear upon inquiries, such as whether magnetic polarity is axial or dependent upon transverse lateral conditions; whether the transmission of the force is after the manner of a vibration or current, or simply action at a distance; and the many other questions that arise in the minds of those who are pursuing this branch of knowledge.

3084. I will proceed to take the case of a simple bar magnet, employing it in illustration of what has been said respecting the lines of force and the moving conductor, and also for the pur-

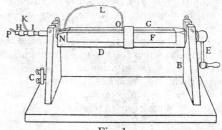

Fig. 1

pose of ascertaining how these lines of force are disposed, both without and within the magnet itself, upon which they are dependent or to which they belong. For this purpose the following apparatus was employed. Let *Fig. 1* represent a wooden stand, of which the base is a board 17.5 inches in length, and 6 inches in breadth, and 0.8 of an inch in thickness: these dimensions will serve as a scale for the other parts. A B are two wooden uprights; D is an axis of wood having two long depressions cut into it, for the purpose of carrying the two bar magnets F and G. The wood is not cut away quite across the axis, but is left in the middle, so that the magnets are about ⅕th of an inch apart. From O towards the support A, it is removed, however, as low down as the axis of revolution, so as to form a notch between the two magnets when they are in their places; and by further removal of the wood, this notch is continued on to the end of the axis at P. This notch, or opening, is intended to receive a wire, which can be carried down the axis of rotation, and then passing out between the two magnets, anywhere between O and N, can be returned towards the end P on the outside. The magnets are so placed, that the central line of their compound system coincides with the axis of rotation; E being a handle by which rotation, when required, is given. H and I are two copper rings, slipping tightly on to the axis, by which communication is to be made between a wire adjusted so as to revolve with the magnets, and the fixed ends of wires proceeding from a galvanometer. Thus, let P L represent a covered wire; which being led along the bottom of the notch in the axis of the apparatus, and passing out at the equatorial parts of the magnets, returns into the notch again near N, and terminates at K. When the form of the wire loop is determined and given to it, then a little piece of soft wood is placed between the wires in the notch at K, of such thickness, that when the ring I is put into its place, it shall press upon the upper wire, the piece of wood, and the lower wire, and keep all tightly fixed together, and at the same time leave the two wires effectually separated. The second ring, H, is then put into its place on the axis, and the introduction of a small wedge of wood, at the end of the axis, serves to press the end P into close and perfect contact with the ring H, and keep all in order. So the wire is free to revolve with the magnets, and the rings H and I are its virtual terminations. Two clips, as at C, hold the ends of the galvanometer wire (also of copper); and the latter are made to press against the rings by their elasticity, and give an effectual contact bearing, which generates no current, either by difference of nature or by friction, during the revolution of the axis.

3085. The two magnets are bars, each 12 inches long, 1 inch broad, and 0.1 of an inch thick. They weigh each 19 ounces, and are of such a strength as to lift each other end to end and no more. When the two are adjusted in their place, it is with the similar poles together, so that they shall act as one magnet, with a division down the middle: they are retained in their place by tying, or, at times, by a ring of copper which slips tightly over them and the axis.

3086. The galvanometer is a very delicate instrument made by Rhumkorff (2651). It was placed about 6 feet from the magnet apparatus, and was not affected by any revolution of the latter. The wires, connecting it with the magnets, were of copper, 0.04 of an inch in diameter, and in their whole length about 25 feet. The length of the wire in the galvanometer I do not know; its diameter was $\frac{1}{135}$th of an inch. The condition of the galvanometer, wires, and magnets, was such, that when the bend of the wires was formed into a loop, and that carried once over the pole of the united magnets, as from *a* to *b*, *Fig. 2*, the galvanometer needle was

deflected two degrees or more. The vibration of the needle was slow, and it was easy therefore to reiterate this action five or six times, or oftener, breaking and making contact with the galvanometer at right intervals, so as to combine the effect of like induced currents; and then a deflection of 10° or 15° on either side of zero could be readily obtained. The arrangement, therefore, was sufficiently sensible for first experiments; and though the resistance opposed by the thin long galvanometer wire to feeble currents was considerable, yet it would always be the same, and would not interfere with results, where the final effect was equal to 0°, nor in those where the consequences were shown, not by absolute measurement, but by comparative differences.

3087. The first practical result produced by the apparatus described, in respect of magneto-electric induction generally, is that a piece of metal or conducting matter which moves across

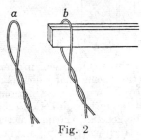

Fig. 2

lines of magnetic force has, or tends to have, a current of electricity produced in it. A more restricted and precise expression of the full effect is the following. If a continuous circuit of conducting matter be traced out, or conceived of, either in a solid or fluid mass of metal or conducting matter, or in wires or bars of metal arranged in non-conducting matter or space; which being moved, crosses lines of magnetic force, or being still, is by the translation of a magnet crossed by such lines of force; and further, if by inequality of angular motion, or by contrary motion of different parts of the circuit, or by inequality of the motion in the same direction, one part crosses either more or fewer lines than the other; then a current will exist round it, due to the differential relation of the two or more intersecting parts during the time of the motion: the direction of which current will be determined (with lines having a given direction of polarity) by the direction of the intersection, combined with the relative amount of the intersection in the two or more efficient and determining (or intersecting) parts of the circuit.

3088. Thus, if *Fig. 3* represent a magnetic pole N, and over it a circuit, formed of metal, which may be of any shape, and which is at first in the position *c*; then if that circuit be moved in one direction into the position 1; or in the contrary direction into position 2; or by a double direction of motion into position 3; or by translation into position 4; or into position 5; or any position between the first and these or any resembling them; or, if the first position *c* being retained, the pole moved to, or towards, the position *n*; then, an electric current will be

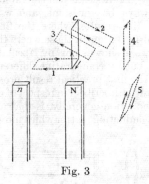

Fig. 3

produced in the circuit, having in every case the same direction, being that which is marked in the figure by arrows. Reverse motions will give currents in the reverse direction (256, &c.).

3089. The general principles of the production of electrical currents by magnetic induction have been formerly given (27, &c.),[1] and the law of the direction of the current in relation to the lines of force, stated (114, 3079 *note*). But the full meaning of the above description can only be appreciated hereafter, when the experimental results, which supply a larger knowledge of the relations of the current to the *lines of force*, have been described.

3090. When *lines of force* are spoken of as crossing a conducting circuit (3087), it must be considered as effected by the *translation* of a magnet. No mere rotation of a bar magnet on its axis, produces any induction effect on circuits exterior to it; for then, the conditions above described (3088) are not fulfilled. The system of power about the magnet must not be considered as necessarily revolving with the magnet, any more than the rays of light which emanate from the sun are supposed to revolve with the sun. The magnet may even, in certain cases (3097), be considered as revolving amongst its own forces, and producing a full electric effect, sensible at the galvanometer.

[1] *Philosophical Transactions*, 1832, p. 131, &c.

3091. In the first instance the wire was carried down the axis of the magnet to the middle distance, then led out at the equatorial part, and returned on the outside; *Fig. 4* will repre-

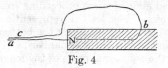

Fig. 4

sent such a disposition. Supposing the magnet and wire to revolve once, it is evident that the wire *a* may be considered as passing in at the axis of the magnet, and returning from *b* across the lines of force external to the magnet, to the axis again at *c*; and that in one revolution, the wire from *b* to *c* has intersected once, all the lines of force emanating from the N end of the magnet. In other words, whatever course the wire may take from *b* to *c*, the whole system of lines belonging to the magnet has been *once* crossed by the wire. In order to have a correct notion of the relation of the result, we will suppose a person standing at the handle E, *Fig. 1* (3084), and looking along the magnets, the magnets being fixed, and the wire loop from *b* to *c* turned over toward the left-hand into a horizontal plane; then, if that loop be moved over towards the right-hand, the magnet remaining stationary, it will be equivalent to a *direct* revolution (according to the hands of a watch or clock) of 180°, and will produce a feeble current in a given direction at the galvanometer. If it be carried back 180° in the reverse direction, it will produce a corresponding current in the reverse direction to the former. If the wire be held in a vertical, or any other plane, so that it may be considered as fixed, and the magnet be rotated through half a revolution, it will also produce a current; and if rotated in the contrary direction, will produce a contrary current; but as to the *direction* of the currents, that produced by the *direct* revolution of the wire is the same as that produced by the *reverse* revolution of the magnet; and that produced by the *reverse* revolution of the wire is the same as that produced by the *direct* revolution of the magnet. A more precise reference to the direction of the current to the particular pole employed, and the direction of the revolution of the wire or magnet, is not at present necessary; but if required is obtained at once by reference to *Fig. 3* (3088), or to the general law (114, 3079 *note*).

3092. The magnet and loop being rotated together in either direction, no trace of an electric current was produced. In this case the effect, if any, could be greatly exalted, because the rotation could be continued for 10, 20, or any number of revolutions without derangement, and it was easy to make thirty revolutions or more within the time of the swing of the galvanometer needle in one direction. It was also easy, if any effect were produced, to accumulate it upon the galvanometer by reversing the rotation at the due time. But no amount of revolution of the magnet and wire together could produce any effect.

3093. The loop was then taken out of the axis of the magnet, but attached to it by a piece of pasteboard, so that all should be fixed together and revolve with the same angular velocity, *Fig. 5*; but whatever the shape or dis-

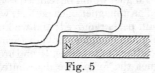

Fig. 5

position of the loop, whether large or small, near or distant, open or shut, in one plane, or contorted into various planes; whatever the shape or condition, or place, provided it moved altogether with the magnet, no current was produced.

3094. Furthermore, when the loop was out of the magnets, and by expedients of arrangement, was retained immoveable, whilst the magnet revolved, no amount of rotation of the magnet (unaccompanied by translation of place) produced any degree of current through the loop.

3095. The loop of wire was then made of two parts; the portion *c*, *Fig. 6*, on the outside of the

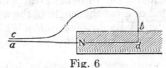

Fig. 6

magnet, was fixed at *b*, and the portion *a*, being a separate piece, was carried along the axis until it came in contact with the former at *d*; the revolution of one part was thus permitted either with or without the other, yet preserving always metallic contact and a complete circuit for the induced current. In this case, when the external wire and the magnet were fixed, no current was produced by any amount of revolution of the wire *a* on its axis. Neither was any current produced when the magnet and wire, *c d*, were revolved together, whether the wire *a* revolved with them or not. When the magnet

was revolved without the external part of *c d*, or the latter revolved without the magnet, then currents were produced as before (3091).

3096. The magnet was now included in the circuit, in the following manner. The wire *a*, *Fig. 7*, was placed in metallic contact on both

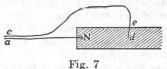

Fig. 7

sides of the interval between the magnets at N (or the pole), and the part *c* was brought into contact with the centre at *d*. The result was in everything the same as when the wire *a* was continued up to *d*, i.e., no amount of revolution of the magnet and part *c* together could produce any electric current. When *c* was made to terminate at *e* or the equatorial part of the magnet, the result was precisely the same. Also, when *c* terminated at *e*, the part *a* of the wire was continued to the centre at *d*, and there the contact perfected, but the result was still the same. No difference, therefore, was produced, by the use between N and *d*, or *d* and *e*, of the parts of the magnet in place of an insulated copper wire, for the completion of the circuit in which the induced current was to travel. No rotation of the part *a* produced any effect, wherever it was made to terminate.

3097. In order to obtain the power of rotating the magnet without the external part of the wire, a copper ring was fixed round, and in contact with it at the equatorial part, and the wire *c*, *Fig. 8*, made to bear by spring pressure against

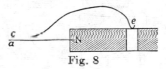

Fig. 8

this ring, and also against the ring H on the axis, *Fig. 1* (3084); the circuit was examined, and found complete. Now when the wire *c e* was fixed and the magnet rotated, a current was produced, and that to the same amount for the same number of revolutions, whether the part of the wire *a* terminated at N, or was continued on to the centre of the magnet, or was insulated from the magnet and continued up to the copper ring *e*. When the wire, by expedients, which though rough were sufficient, was made to revolve whilst the magnet was still, currents in the contrary direction were produced, in accordance with the effect before described (3091);

and the results when the wire and magnet rotated together (3092), show that these are in amount exactly equal to the former. When the inner and the outer wires were both motionless, and the magnet only revolved, a current in the full proportion was produced, and that, whether the axial wire a made contact at the pole of the magnet or in the centre.

3098. Another arrangement of the magnet and wires was of the following kind. A radial insulated wire was fixed in the middle of the magnets, from the centre d, *Fig. 9*, to the circum-

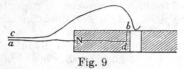

Fig. 9

ference b, being connected there with the equatorial ring (3097); an axial wire touched this radial wire at the centre and passed out at the pole; the external part of the circuit, pressing on the ring at the equator, proceeded on the outside over the pole to form the communication as before. In the case where the magnet was revolved without the axial and the external wire, the full and proper current was produced; the small wire, $d\,b$, being, however, the only part in which this current could be generated by the motion; for it replaced, under these circumstances, the body of the magnet employed on the former occasion (3097).

3099. The external part of the wire instead of being carried back over that pole of the magnet at which the axial wire entered, was con-

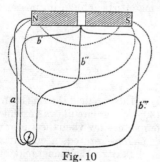

Fig. 10

tinued away over the other pole, and so round by a long circuit to the galvanometer; still the revolution of the magnet, under any of the described circumstances, produced exactly the same results as before. It will be evident by inspection of *Fig. 10*, that, however the wires are carried away, the general result will, according to the assumed principles of action, be the

same; for if a be the axial wire, and b', b'', b''' the equatorial wire, represented in three different positions, whatever magnetic lines of force pass across the latter wire in one position, will also pass across it in the other, or in *any* other position which can be given to it. The distance of the wire at the place of intersection with the lines of force, has been shown, by the experiments (3093), to be unimportant.

3100. Whilst considering the condition of the forces of a magnet, it may be admitted that the two magnets used in the experimental investigations described act truly as one central magnet. We have only to conceive smaller similar magnets to be introduced to fill up the narrow space not occupied by the wire, and then the complete magnet would be realized:—or it may be viewed as a magnet once perfect, which has had certain parts removed; and we know that neither of these changes would disturb the general disposition of the forces. In and around the bar magnet the forces are distributed in the simplest and most regular manner. Supposing the bar removed from other magnetic influences, then its power must be considered as extending to any distance, according to the recognized law; but adopting the representative idea of *lines of force* (3074), any wire or line proceeding from a point in the magnetic equator of the bar, over one of the poles, so as to pass through the magnetic axis, and so on to a point on the opposite side of the magnetic equator, must intersect *all* the lines in the plane through which it passes, whether its course be over the one pole or the other. So also a wire proceeding from the end of the magnet at the magnetic axis, to a point at the magnetic equator, must intersect curves equal to half those of a great plane, however small or great the length of the wire may be; though by its tortuous course it may pass out of one plane into another on its way to the equator.

3101. Further, if such a wire as that last described be revolved once round the end of the magnet to which it is related, a slipping contact at the equator being permitted for the purpose, it will intersect *all* the lines of force during the revolution; and that, whether the polar contact is absolutely coincident with the magnetic axis, or is anywhere else at the end of the bar, provided it remain for the time unchanged. All this is true, though the magnet may be subject, by induction at a distance, to other magnets or bodies, and may be exerting part of its force on them, so as to make the distribution of its power very irregular as compared to the case of the independent bar (3084), or may have an irregular or contorted shape, even up to the horseshoe form. It is evident, indeed, that if a wire have one of its ends applied to *any* point on the surface of a magnet, and the other end to a point in the magnetic equator, and the latter be slipped once round the magnetic equator, and the loop of wire be made to pass over either pole, so as at last to resume its first position, it will in the course of its journey have intersected *once* every line of force belonging to the magnet.

3102. A wire from pole to pole which passes close to the equator, of course intersects half the external lines of force in a great plane, twice, in opposite directions as regards the polarity; and, therefore, when revolved round the magnet, has no electric current induced in it. If it do not touch at the equator, still, whatever lines it intersects are twice intersected, and so the same equilibrium is preserved. If the magnet rotate under the wire, it acts the part of the central rotating wire already referred to (3095); or if any course for the electric current other than a right line is assumed in it, that course is subject to the law of neutrality above stated, as will be seen by reference to the internal condition of the magnet itself (3117). Hence the reason why no currents are produced, under any circumstances of motion, by the application of such conducting circuits to the magnet. I may further observe, in reference to the intersection of the lines of force, that if a wire ring, a little larger in diameter than the magnet, be held edgeways at one of the poles, so that the lines of force there shall be in its plane, and be then turned 90° and carried over the pole to the equator (3088), it will intersect *once* all the lines of the magnet, except the very few which will remain unintersected at the equator.

3103. Whilst endeavouring to establish experimentally the definite amount of the power represented by the *lines of force*, it is necessary to take certain precautions, or the results will be in error. For instance, ten revolutions of the wire about the magnet, or of the magnet within the fixed wire (3097), ought to give a constant deflection at the galvanometer, and yet without any change in the position of the wire the results may at different times differ very much from each other; being at one time 9°, and at another only 4° or 5°. I found this to be due to difference of velocity within certain limits, and to be explained and guarded against as follows.

3104. If a wire move across lines of force slowly, a feeble electric current is produced in it, continuing for the time of the motion; if it move across the same lines quickly, a stronger current is produced for a shorter time. The effect of the current which deflects a galvanometer needle is opposed by the action of the earth, which tends to return the needle to zero. A continuous weak current, therefore, cannot deflect it so far as a continuous stronger current. If the currents be limited in duration, the same effect will occur unless the time of the swing of the needle to one side be not considerably more than the time of either of the currents. If the time of the needle-swing be ten, and the time of ten quick rotations be six, then all the effect of the induced current is exerted in swinging the needle; but if the time of ten slow rotations be twelve or fifteen, then part of the current produced is not recognized by the extent of the vibration, but only by its holding the needle out awhile, at the extremity of a smaller arc of declination. Therefore, when quick and slow velocity were compared, and, indeed, in every case of comparative rotations of the wire and magnet, only that number of rotations was taken which could be well included within the time of the needle's journey to one side; when the needle, therefore, was seen to travel on to its extreme distance after the rotation and the inducing current had ceased. If the needle began to return the instant the motion was over, such an experiment was rejected for purposes of comparison. When these precautions were attended to, and velocities of revolution taken, which occupied times from one-third to three-fourths of that required for the swing of the needle, then the same number of revolutions (ten) gave the same amount of deflection, namely, 9°.5, with my apparatus, though the time of revolution varied as 1 : 2, or even in a higher degree.

3105. Another cause of difference produced by varying velocity, is the diminution of the action of the current on the needle, as the angle which the latter forms with the convolutions of the coil increases. Hence a constant current produces more effect on the deflection of the needle for the first moments of time than afterwards. This effect, however, was scarcely sensible for swinging deflections of 9° or 10°, produced by currents which were over before the needle had moved through 4° or 5°.

3106. It has already been shown, that it is a matter of indifference whether the wire revolve in one direction or the magnet in the other (3091); and this is still further proved by the cases where the magnet and the wire revolve together (3092); for then the currents which tend to form are exactly equal and opposed to each other, whatever the position of the wire may be. As the immobility of the needle is a point more easily ascertained than the extent of an arc, indicated only for a moment, and as the rotations of the magnet and wire conjointly can be made rapid and continuous, the proof in such cases is very satisfactory.

3107. Proceeding to experiment upon the effect of the *distance* of the wire *c*, *Fig. 11*, from the magnet, the wire was made to vary, so that sometimes it was not more than 8 inches long

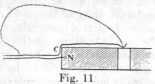

Fig. 11

(being of copper and 0.04 of an inch in diameter), and only half an inch from the magnet, whilst at other times it was 6 or 8 feet long and extended to a great distance. The deflection due to ten revolutions of the magnet was observed, and the average of several observations, for each position of the wire, taken: these were very close (with the precautions before described) for the same position; and the averages for different positions agreed perfectly together, being 9°5. I endeavoured to repeat these experiments on distance by moving the wire and preserving the magnet stationary in the manner before described (3091); they were not so striking because time would only allow of smaller deflections being obtained (3104), but the same number of journeys through an arc of 180° gave the same deflection at the galvanometer, whether the course of the wire was close to the magnet or far off; and the deflection agreed with those obtained when the magnet was rotating and the wire at rest.

3108. As to *velocity* of motion; when the magnet was rotating and the wire placed at *different distances*, then ten revolutions of the magnet produced the same deflection of the needle, whether the motion was *quicker* or *slower*, and whatever the distance of the wire, provided the precautions before described were attended to (3104). That the same would be true if the wire were moving and the magnet still is shown by this; that whatever the velocity with which the wire and magnet revolve together, and whatever their distance apart, they exactly neutralize and equal each other (3096).

3109. From these results the following conclusions may be drawn. The *amount* of magnetic force, as shown by its effect in evolving electric currents, is determinate for the same lines of force, whatever the distance of the point or plane, at which their power is exerted, is from the magnet. Or it is the same in any two, or more, sections of the same lines of force, whatever their form or their distance from the seat of the power may be. This is shown by the results with the magnet and the wire, when both are in the circuit (3108); and also by the wire loop revolving with the magnet (3092); where the tendency of currents to form in the two parts oppose and exactly neutralize or compensate each other.

3110. In the latter case very varying sections outside of the magnet may be compared to each other; thus, the wire may be conceived of as passing (or be actually formed so as to intersect) lines of force near the pole, and then, being continued *along* a line of force until over the equator, may be directed so as to intersect the same lines of force in the contrary direction, and then return along a line of force to its commencement; and so two surface sections may be compared. It is manifest that every loop forming a complete circuit, which is in a great plane passing through the axis of the magnet, must have precisely the same lines of force passing into and passing out of it, though they may, so to say, be expanded in one part and compressed in another; or (speaking in the language of radiation) be more intense in one part and less intense in the other. It is also as manifest that, if the loop be not in one plane, still, on making one complete revolution, either with or without the magnet, it will have intersected in its two opposite parts an exactly equal amount of lines of force. Hence the comparison of any one section of a given amount of lines of force with any other section is rendered, experimentally, very extensive.

3111. Such results prove that, under the circumstances, there is no loss, or destruction, or evanescence, or latent state of the magnetic power by distance.

3112. Also that convergence or divergence of the lines of force causes no difference in their amount.

3113. That obliquity of intersection causes no difference. It is easy so to shape the loop (3110) that it shall intersect the lines of force directly across at both places of intersection, or directly at one and obliquely at the other, or obliquely in any degree at both; and yet the result is always the same (3093).

3114. It is also evident, by the results of the rotation of the wire and magnet (3097, 3106) that when a wire is moving amongst equal lines (or in a field of equal magnetic force), and with a uniform motion, then the current of electricity produced is proportionate to the *time*; and also to the *velocity* of motion.

3115. They also prove, generally, that the quantity of electricity thrown into a current is directly as the amount of curves intersected.

3116. In addition to these results, this method of investigation gives much insight into the internal condition of the magnet, and the manner in which the lines of force (which represent truly all that we are acquainted with of the peculiar action of the magnet) either terminate at its exterior, or at any assumed points, to be called *poles*; or are continued and disposed of within. For this purpose, let us consider the external loop (3093) of *Fig. 5.* When revolving with the magnet no current is produced, because the lines of force which are intersected on the one part, are again intersected in an opposing direction on the other (3110). But if one part of the loop be taken down the axis of the magnet, and the wire then pass out at the equator (3091), still the same absence of effect is produced; and yet it is evident that, external to the magnet, every part of the wire passes through lines of force, which conspire together to produce a current; for all the external lines of force are then intersected by that wire in one revolution (3101). We must therefore look to the part of the wire *within* the magnet for a power equal to that capable of being exerted externally, and we find it in that small portion which represents a radius at the central and equatorial parts. When, in fact, the axial part of the wire was rotated it produced no effect (3095); when the axial, the inner radial, and the external parts were revolved together, they produced no effect; when the external wire alone was revolved, *directly*, it produced a current (3091); and when the internal radius wire alone (being insulated from the magnet) revolved, *directly*, it also produced a current (3095, 3098) in the contrary direction to the former; and the two were exactly equal in power; for when both portions of the wire moved together *directly*, they perfectly compensated each other (3095). This radius wire may be replaced by the magnet itself (3096, 3118).

3117. So, by this test there exist lines of force within the magnet, of the same *nature* as those without. What is more, they are exactly equal in *amount* to those without. They have a relation in *direction* to those without; and in fact

are continuations of them, absolutely unchanged in their nature, so far as the experimental test can be applied to them. Every line of force therefore, at whatever distance it may be taken from the magnet, must be considered as a closed circuit, passing in some part of its course through the magnet, and having an equal amount of force in every part of its course.

3118. When the axial part of the wire is dismissed and the magnet employed in its place, so as to be included in the circuit, it is easy to see how it acts the part of the conductor. For suppose the wire itself to be continued from N to *b*, *Fig. 12*, by any of the three paths indicat-

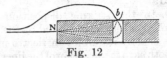

Fig. 12

ed by dotted lines, the effect is the same in all the cases, both by experiment (3093) and by principle (3100). For whatever the form of the path, it will in one revolution intersect the same amount of lines of force within the magnet as are intersected in the contrary direction by the part of the wire outside the magnet; and when the magnet is employed to complete the circuit in place of the internal wire, then its substance produces precisely the same result; for direction and every other circumstance which influences the result remains the same: one conductor has simply been substituted for another. The great mass of the magnet might be supposed able to do something more than the thin wire, but the reason why it only equals it in effect will be seen hereafter (3137). And as the axial wire, in revolving, does nothing but conduct (3095), all the effect being produced by that part which represents a radius between the axis and the equator (3098); so the magnet, revolving as a cylinder, is as to its mass like the revolving wire; with the exception of so much of it as represents a radius connecting together the two points at the pole or axis and at the equator, where communication with the wire is completed. As was shown long ago (220), if a cylinder magnet be revolved, and the ends of the galvanometer wires *a c* be applied to the extremities of its axis, no current is evolved; but if *a* be applied to one end, it matters not which, and *c* be applied at the equator or any other part on the surface of the cylinder, a current always in the same direction for the same rotation will be produced.

3119. Further to prove these points, the magnets were cut in half through the equatorial plane, and then, either a disc of copper placed there, or a wire radius only, or the magnets brought together again: and these three arrangements were used in succession to complete the circuit from the axial wire (3095) to a fixed wire at the surface of the equator. Whichever was employed the current produced was the same, both in direction and amount. If the cylinder magnet above described (3118) be terminated at the ends by attached discs of silver or copper, the wires applied to their surfaces, as they revolve with the magnet, produce precisely the same currents as to direction as if applied to the surface of the magnet itself (218, 219).

3120. In this striking disposition of the forces of a magnet, as exhibited by the moving wire, it exactly resembles an electro-magnetic helix, both as to the direction of the lines of force in closed circuits, and in their equal sum within and without. No doubt, the magnet is the most heterogeneous in its nature, being composed, as we are well-aware, of parts which differ much in the degree of their magnetic development; so much so that some of the internal portions appear frequently to act as keepers or submagnets to the parts which are farther from the centre, and so, for the time, to form complete circuits, or something equivalent to them, within. But these make no part of the resultant of force externally, and it is only that resultant which is sensible to us in any way; either by the action on a needle, or other magnets, or soft iron, or the moving wire. So also the power which is manifest *within* the magnet by its effect on the moving mass is still only that same resultant; being equal to, and by polarity and other qualities, identical with it. No doubt, there are cases, as upon the approach of a keeper to the poles, or the approximation of other magnets, either in favourable or adverse positions, when more external force is developed, or it may be a portion apparently thrown inwards and so the external force diminished. But in these cases, that which remains externally existent, corresponds precisely to that which is the resultant internally; for when either the same, or contrary poles, of a powerful horseshoe magnet were placed within an inch and a half of the poles of the bar-magnets, prepared to rotate with the attached wires (3092), as before described, still, upon their revolution, not the slightest action at the galvanometer was perceived; the forces within the magnet and those without perfectly compensating each other.

3121. The definite character of the forces of an invariable magnet, at whatever distance they are observed from the magnet, has been already insisted upon (3109). How much more strikingly does that point come forth now that, being able to observe within the magnet, we find the same definite character there; every section of the forces, whether within or without the magnet, being exactly of the same amount! The power of a magnet may therefore be easily represented by the effects of *any* section of its lines of force; and as the currents induced by two different magnets may easily be conducted through one wire, or be, in other ways, compared to each other, so facilities may thus arise for the establishment of a standard amongst magnets.

3122. On the other hand, the use of the idea of *lines of force*, which I recommend, to represent the true and real magnetic forces, makes it very desirable that we should find a unit of such force, if it can be attainable, by any experimental arrangement, just as one desires to have a unit for rays of light or heat. It does not seem to me improbable that further research will supply the means of establishing a standard of this kind. In the meantime for the enlargement of the utility of the idea in relation to the magnetic force, and to indicate its conditions graphically, lines may be employed as representing these units in any given case. I have so employed them in former series of these *Researches* (2807, 2821, 2831, 2874, &c.), where the direction of the *line of force* is shown at once, and the relative amount of force, or of lines of force in a given space, indicated by their concentration or separation, i.e., by their number in that space. Such a use of unit lines involves, I believe, no error either in the direction of the polarity or in the amount of force indicated at any given spot included in the diagrams.

3123. The currents produced in wires, when they cross lines of magnetic force, are so feeble in intensity (though abundant enough in quantity, as many results show) that a fine wire galvanometer must of necessity offer great obstruction to their passage. Therefore, before entering upon further experimental inquiries, I had another galvanometer constructed, in which the needles belonging to that made by Rhumkorff were employed, but the coil was replaced by a single convolution of very stout wire. The wire was of copper, 0.2 of an inch in diameter. It passed horizontally under the lower needle, then, as nearly as might be, between that and the upper needle, over the upper, and then again between that and the lower needle, *Fig. 13*, and was afterwards attached to the stand, and continued for 19 or 20 feet outside of the glass cover. Such a wire had abundant conduct-

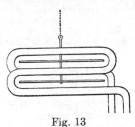

Fig. 13

ing power; and though it passed but once round each needle, gave a deflection many times greater than that belonging to the former galvanometer. Thus when the ends of the nineteen feet of wire were soldered together, so as to form one loop or circuit, the passage of the wire once between the poles of a horseshoe magnet (3124), caused a deflection, or rather swing of the needle of above 90°. I have had a more perfect instrument, of the same kind, constructed, in which the conducting coil was cut out of plates of copper, so as to form a square band 0.2 of an inch in thickness, which passed twice round the vibration plane of each needle, as represented, *Fig. 14*. The length of metal around the needles was 24 inches, and the galvanom-

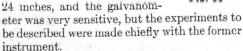

Fig. 14

eter was very sensitive, but the experiments to be described were made chiefly with the former instrument.

3124. It was necessary, first, to ascertain the effect of certain circumstances upon this simple galvanometer, as to their modification of its indications. The magnet to be used was a compound horseshoe instrument, weighing 16 lbs., and able to support 40 lbs. by the keeper or submagnet. It is some years since it was mag-

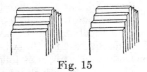

Fig. 15

netized, and it is therefore, probably, in a nearly constant state as to power. The poles have the form delineated, *Fig. 15*. Their distance apart is 1.375 inch, and the distance downwards, from their summit to the bottom or

equator of the magnet, is 8.5 inches. The galvanometer stood in the prolongation of the magnetic axis, i.e. the line from pole to pole, and whether it were 6 or only 3 feet distant, was hardly at all affected in the time of its vibration, being adjusted so nearly astatic as to require about ten seconds to swing to the right or to the left.

3125. On passing the wire across the magnetic field, as just described (3123), but with different velocities, effects different in degree were obtained at the galvanometer, for the reasons formerly given (3104, 3106). The quickest velocity gave the greatest result, equal at times to 140°, whilst a very slow motion gave only 30° or 40°. Still with moderately quick velocities the effects were nearly alike, and by operating with the same velocity, and taking the average of several observations, a very uniform result could be obtained.

3126. On cutting the wire across, and then putting the ends together in various ways it was found that great care was requisite in making contact, in this or in similar cases. Thus, to press the ends lightly together was not sufficient; they required to be well and recently cleaned and pressed closely into contact. Junctions effected by soldering or dipping into cups of mercury were still better, when made with care, and were employed at the galvanometer and elsewhere as often as possible.

3127. To ascertain generally the obstruction caused by the interposition of thin wires, 28 inches of copper wire, 0.045 of an inch in diameter, was introduced into the circuit at a part away from the magnet, with excellent junctions. The oscillation or swing, which before was 140° or more, was now reduced to 40°. On taking out the wire and replacing it by another, also of copper, but only 19.5 inches in length, and 0.0135 in diameter, the deflection was reduced to 7° or 8°.

3128. For a rough comparison of the power of this magnet and the former bar-magnets (3085), by the present galvanometer, the thick wire was bent into a loop (3086), and the two bar-magnets, with like ends together, passed quickly through it up to the equatorial part; the deflection was about 30°. Such a passage intersected nearly all the lines of force of the bar-magnets. A similar motion of the magnets close to, but outside of, the loop, produced no effect at the galvanometer.

3129. In respect to the alteration of the lines of force, either in position or in total amount, by bringing the poles of the horseshoe magnet

(3124) much nearer together, the following experiments were made. The distance between the poles is 1.375 inch; by placing a cube of soft iron, 0.8 of an inch in the side, within this space, it was diminished to 0.575, and thus, virtually, the distance apart much lessened, and, as was afterwards shown experimentally (3130), the external power of the magnet concentrated there. Then, whilst the cube was in place, the thick wire of 0.2 of an inch in diameter was arranged so as to pass across the magnetic axis or place of strongest action, and fixed; after which the iron cube was alternately removed and again restored, and the effects observed. Feeble electric currents were produced at these times; but whether the cube was put into its place from below, or above or the sides, the current produced was always in the same direction; and when it was removed the current produced was in the reverse direction. If the cube were carried up to, by, and away from, the magnetic axis in one motion, then there was no effect at the galvanometer. On the other hand, when the wire was carried across the magnetic field as described (3123), so as to intersect all the lines of force in one movement, and sum up their power at the galvanometer, then there was no difference in the result, whether the iron cube was in its place or not; showing, as far as this apparatus could indicate, that the sum of power in the section of all the lines of force external to the magnet, was the same under both circumstances, though the distribution of it was different.

3130. The very action produced by the cube, when in and out of place (3129), upon the forces which affected the stationary wire, was a proof of the difference of distribution at different times.

3131. A block of bismuth, employed in place of the iron cube, had no sensible effect upon the wire whether it were still or moving.

3132. This galvanometer was first employed for a repetition of all the former experiments with the bar-magnets (3091, &c.). The results were absolutely the same, except that the amount of the deviation produced, when deviation was a result, was larger than in the former cases.

3133. For the comparison of different thicknesses of the same metal, I took copper wires in lengths of 10.5 inches, and different diameters, and bending them into loops of a form and size such as would admit them to pass with facility over a pole of the horseshoe mag-

net, soldered them to the ends of two conducting rods, made of copper wire 0.2 of an inch in diameter and 35 inches in length each, which were fixed on opposite sides of a narrow slip of wood. The whole arrangement is seen in *Fig. 16;* the terminations a b dip into the mercurial

Fig. 16

cups of the galvanometer, the parts at *c* are brought so close together as to touch, except for the intervention of a piece of card, and thus the parts from *c* to *a b* are thrown out of action, except as mere conductors, whilst the loop, being made to descend over one magnetic pole, intersects very nearly the whole of the magnetic curves, and always the same proportion.

3134. The former magnet was too powerful for comparative experiments, therefore a smaller one was employed, consisting of five plates, weighing 8 lbs., and able to carry 21 lbs. easily at the keeper. The poles were 1.2 inch apart and an inch thick each, in the direction of the magnetic axis. If less magnetic power were required, an adjustment was easily made, by applying the keeper to the side upon both limbs, the magnetic communication being effected either nearer to the poles, or nearer to the equator or bend, as less or more power was required. The descent of the loop between the poles is then best regulated by causing the conductor wires to bear ultimately against a stopping-block.

3135. The effect of a quick and a slow motion was found to be the same as before (3104, 3105). Such velocities as the hand could impart were very effectual, and gave results of very considerable uniformity when quick motions were employed.

3136. Three different loops were compared together, consisting of copper wire, the diameters of which were 0.2, 0.1 and 0.5 of an inch, or as 4, 2 and 1; their sectional areas or masses therefore were as 16, 4 and 1. Ten or twelve observations were made with each loop; the results were near together, and the average for each loop, being the extent of the swing declination on one side from zero, is as follows:

Copper wire of $\frac{1}{20}$ of an inch in thickness .... 16.00°

Copper wire of $\frac{1}{10}$th of an inch in thickness .... 44.40°

Copper wire of $\frac{1}{5}$th of an inch in thickness .... 57.37°

Now though the thicker wires produced the largest effect, the results were evidently not at all in proportion to the masses of the wires; the smaller having greatly the advantage in that respect. On the other hand, when four of the smaller wires were placed side by side, so as to form one loop equal in mass to the second loop, they gave the same result as that loop, being of the same power.

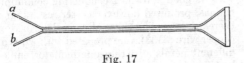

Fig. 17

3137. The disproportion of the *difference* of these three wires is evidently a consequence of the relative difference of the mere conducting part of the circuit. To compare accurately the effect of the lines of force on wires of different diameters moving across them, these diameters should continue to, and through the galvanometer (205), otherwise the thin wire current has an advantage given to it in the conducting part, which the thick wire current has not. Hence the reason why a thin wire galvanometer, such as that before described (3086), gives results which are alike for thick or thin wire loops, or for fasciculi of few or many wires. To enlarge the comparison, I soldered on to two pairs of conductors, the dimensions of those described (3133), two cylinders of copper, each 5.5 inches long, but one was only 0.2 of an inch thick and the other 0.7, or twelve times the mass of the first, *Fig. 17.* They were then passed in succession between the poles of the magnet, and gave results very nearly alike. If there was any difference, the effect was highest with the smaller cylinder; and this may very well be; for as the magnetic field was not equal in force, but most intense in the magnetic axis, so it is evident that whilst one part of the large cylinder, in passing across, was at the axis, other parts were in places of less intense force and action, and so a return current may have existed in them, which could not occur to the same extent in a cylinder little more than a fourth of the diameter of the former, and which, at the same time, had an outlet for the currents equal to its own diameter, through the conducting wires. A similar relation of mass occurs in the case where the body of the magnet itself in revolving, does no more than a small radial wire within it (3118).

3138. The influence of this lateral conduction (3137), in cases of magneto-electric con-

duction, must be well understood; otherwise, in the application of the principles to investigation, errors will frequently creep in. Their effect may be shown in the following instances:—a loop of four wires, 0.048 of an inch in diameter (3136), was passed over the pole of the magnet, and produced a certain result of deflection or swing; when the wires were separated two and two, so as to be half or three-quarters of an inch apart, and when, therefore, in moving across the magnetic field, one pair went before the others, the effect was less, for the reason already given in the case of the copper cylinder (3137). When three wires were allowed to go by together, but one taken aside a couple of inches, the effect fell very much; and when that fourth one was cut across to prevent the return current in it, the effect of the three rose at the galvanometer very greatly, almost equalling the effect of the four when together.

3139. A loop was constructed of seventy-six equal fine copper wires, each 10.5 inches long and 0.0125 of an inch in diameter, and its effect observed when more and more of the wires were cut away. As it is the comparison of the smaller numbers of wires, one with the other, that is of most value, I will give the averages of each number for several observations, in the reverse order in which they were obtained; and I introduce the results with larger numbers of wires only for the general purpose of showing how the effect passes into that with the cylinder of copper (3137), the galvanometer conductors always being of the same length and thickness.

1 wire produced an average swing of	8°.3
2 wires produced an average swing of	15°.3
3 wires produced an average swing of	21°.8
4 wires produced an average swing of	27°.9
5 wires produced an average swing of	34°.4
6 wires produced an average swing of	37°.8
8 wires produced an average swing of	50°.1
12 wires produced an average swing of	65°.1
16 wires produced an average swing of	80°.5
26 wires produced an average swing of	118°.0

36 almost swung the needle round
46 stronger than the last
56 swung the needle quite round
66 a little stronger
76 stronger: swung the needle freely round the circle

Each time that the needle passed 180°, it was returned, that the torsion force might remain the same for every case.

3140. When the loop of four equal wires (3136) was employed, so arranged that, in respect to the part which passed between the poles, they should be close together in one plane, it made no difference in the result, whether that plane was perpendicular to the magnetic axis or parallel to it; i.e., whether the wires in moving formed a band which moved edgeways or flatways; the results were the same as with the four wires close together, so as to represent, as far as they could, a round or square wire.

3141. From all these results it may be concluded that the current or amount of electricity evolved in the wire moving amongst the lines of force is not, simply, as the space occupied by its breadth correspondent to the direction of the line of force, which has relation to the *polarity* of the power, nor by that width or dimension of it which includes the number or *amount* of the lines of force, and which, corresponding to the direction of the motion, has relation to the *equatorial* condition of the lines; but is jointly as the compound ratio of the two, or as the mass of the moving wire. The power acts just as well on the interior portions of the wire as on the exterior or superficial portions, and a central particle, surrounded on all sides by copper, is just in the same relation to the force as those which, being superficial, have air next them on one side.

3142. By immersing the poles of the magnet in different media, and then making comparative experiments with the same copper wire loop (3145), it was found that the amount of the induced current was the same in air, water, alcohol and oil of turpentine. The experiments in air were repeated between those with the liquids, so as to give a very consistent and safe result as to the equality of action in all the cases.

3143. The effect of *variation of substance* was the next subject which seemed to me important to bring under investigation, because it has a direct relation to the amount of force exerted, or ready to be exerted, within solid bodies, at any distance from the magnet, in situations and under circumstances where it was absolutely impossible to apply the vibrations of a magnetic needle, or any other form of the effects of attractive and repulsive forces. The interior of such bodies as iron, copper, bismuth, mercury, &c., including the most paramagnetic and the most diamagnetic, seemed, in this way, open to experimental investigation, both as to the amount of lines of force traversing them under various circumstances, and also as to the direction of the lines or their polarity.

3144. In an early series of these *Researches*,[1] experiments bearing upon this subject are described (205–213). Wires of different metals were moved across the lines of force of a magnet, and the result arrived at was that the currents induced in these different bodies were proportional to their electro-conduction power (202, 213).

3145. The thick wire galvanometer (3123), with its good and short conducting communications, promised however better results, and therefore loops like those already described of copper wire (3133) were prepared with wires of different metals, all of the same diameter, namely, 0.04 of an inch, being only $\frac{1}{25}$th of the substance of the conducting and galvanometer wire. The metals were copper, silver, iron, tin, lead, platinum, zinc. Under these circumstances the substance concerned in the excitement of the current is made to vary, whilst the conducting part of the system is very good and remains the same. The results with these loops were as follows, being the average of from six to ten experiments for each loop:

Copper	63°.0	Iron	18°.0
Silver	61°.9	Platinum	16°.9
Zinc	31°.5	Lead	12°.1
Tin	19°.1		

3146. In order to dismiss, as much as possible, the obstruction caused by bad conducting power, and bring out any difference that might exist between paramagnetic and diamagnetic metals, three metals were selected, namely, tin, iron and lead in wires, as before,

Fig. 18

of 0.04 of an inch diameter; but the length was restricted to 3 inches, instead of extending to 10.5 inches, and the rest of the loop was made up of the conducting copper wire of 0.2 in diameter, as in *Fig. 18*. Of course, the effect of the whole loop is a mixed effect, being partly due to the power represented by the lines intersected by the thick copper portion, and partly by those intersected by the three inches of special wire passing between the poles. But as the great amount of force is concentrated within a space not more than an inch and a half or 2 inches in extent (as is seen on carrying any of the loops across the magnetic axis), and as even that could be made still more concentrated by using

[1] *Philosophical Transactions*, 1832, pp. 179–182.

the iron cube (3129), and so bringing the poles virtually nearer to each other, it was hoped that the chief effect would be there, and so any peculiar difference existing between iron on the one hand and tin and lead on the other, be rendered manifest, especially as the resistance to conduction was greatly diminished by shortening the wires from 10.5 to 3 inches.

3147. The many experiments made with each metal were very close together. The average of the results for the three metals was as follows:

Tin	37°.1
Iron	34°.8
Lead	25°.4

The proportions, and therefore the results, are almost identical with those obtained before (3145).

3148. When lead and copper, arranged at the bar-magnets (3084, 3085), had been compared in former experiments with each other by the fine wire galvanometer, the results for both had been the *same*. But then the two wires used were short, and far thicker than the wires of the galvanometer or of the conducting circuit, and were therefore limited in the production of their peculiar action, by those circumstances of mass already described (3137). To show that that was the case, I now, with the thick wire galvanometer, employed two equal loops of copper and iron wire, 0.2 of an inch in thickness, *Fig. 16* (3133), passing them equably over the pole of the small horseshoe magnet, reduced by the keeper (3134). The results were very consistent, and the mean of them was, for

| Copper | 41°.7 |
| Iron | 33°.7 |

3149. Here, therefore, the difference between copper and iron is not so great as that of 1 to 1.24; whilst when the conductors, not concerned in the excitement, were very good, and able, comparatively, to carry on to the galvanometer nearly all the effect of the excitement, it was as great as 1 to 3.5, the difference being in the latter case above tenfold what it was in the former.

3150. To raise the effect dependent upon the mass in relation to that of the conducting wires to a still higher degree, I had a cylinder of iron, 5.5 inches in length and 0.7 of an inch in diameter, soldered on to the ends of conducting wires, so as to be in all respect like that of copper before described (3137). In this case the iron not only rose up to the copper in effect, but even surpassed it; the results being for copper

35°.66, and for iron 38°.32. Thus, under these circumstances of mass, the difference between iron and copper disappears. The apparent inferiority of copper is probably due to the lateral discharge, which before reduced the effect of a cylinder below that of a thick wire (3137). The iron being a worse conductor in itself, and having equally good conductors in the prolongation of the circuit as when it was employed as wire, would, I think, have proportionately less lateral discharge in it than the copper.

3151. For a comparison, both as regards the particular substance and the mass, I attached a similar cylinder of bismuth to conductors. Its effect, with the same magnet and force, was 23°; a very high proportion in relation to the copper, and no doubt due to its mass. If it could have been compared as a wire, only 0.04 in diameter (3145), it would probably have appeared almost indifferent (3127).[1]

3152. So the current of electricity excited in different substances, moving across lines of magnetic force, appears to be directly as the conducting power of the substance. It appears to have no particular reference to the magnetic character of the body, for iron comes between tin and platinum, presenting no other distinction than that due to conducting power, and differing far less from them, than they do from other metals not magnetic.

3153. The amount of *lines of force* (and of the force represented by them) appears, therefore, to be equal for equal spaces occupied and traversed by tin, iron, and platinum under the circumstances; for the difference in result is in no proportion to the ordinary magnetic difference, and only as the conducting power. This agrees with the conclusion before arrived at, that, for air, water, bismuth, oxygen, nitrogen, or a vacuum, the lines of force are the same in amount, except as they are more or less concentrated in the substance across which they pass (2807), according as it is more or less competent to conduct (2797), or transmit the magnetic force.

3154. Such a conclusion as that just arrived at, brings on the question of what is *magnetic*

---

[1] When bismuth is soldered into the circuit, it requires to be left a long time before it is used for experiments, and should then be covered up, and the loop handled with great care; otherwise thermo-currents are produced. For an hour or two after soldering it generates electrical currents, which appear at the galvanometer very irregularly, being probably due to internal molecular changes, which occur from time to time until the whole has acquired a permanent state of equilibrium.

polarity, and how is it to be defined? For my own part, I should understand the term to mean the opposite and antithetical actions which are manifested at the opposite ends, or the opposite sides, of a limited (or unlimited) portion of a line of force (2835). The line of dip of the earth, or a part of it, may again be referred to as the natural case; and a free needle above or below the part, or a wire moving across it (3076, 3079), will give the direction of the polarity. If we refer to an entirely different and artificial source as the electro-magnetic helix, the same meaning and description will apply.

3155. If the term *polarity* have any meaning, which has reference to experimental facts and not to hypotheses only, beyond that included in the above description, I am not aware that it has ever been distinctly and clearly expressed. It may be so, for I dare not venture to say that I recollect all I have read, or even all the conclusions I myself have at different times come to. But if it neither have, nor should have any other meaning, then the question arises, is it correctly exhibited or indicated in every case by attractions and repulsions, i.e., by such like mutual actions of particular bodies on each other under the magnetic influence? A weak solution of protosulphate of iron, if surrounded by water, will, in the magnetic field, point axially; if in a stronger solution than itself, it will point equatorially (2357, 2366, 2422). The same is true with stronger cases. We cannot doubt it would be true even up to iron, nickel, and cobalt, if we could render these bodies fluid in turn without altering their paramagnetic power, or if we had the command of magnets and of paramagnetic and diamagnetic media, stronger or weaker at pleasure. But in the case of the solutions, we cannot suppose that the weaker has one polarity in the stronger solution and another in the water. The lines of force across the magnetic field have the same general polarity in all the cases, and would be shown experimentally to have it, by the moving wire (3076), though not by the attractions and repulsions.

3156. Here, therefore, we have a *difference* in the two modes of experimental indication; not merely as to the method, but as to the nature of the results, and the very principles which are concerned in their production. Hence the value I think of the moving wire as an investigator; for it leads us into inquiries which touch upon the very nature of the magnetic force. There is no doubt that the needle gives true experimental indications; but it is not so sure that we always interpret them correctly. To assume that pointing is always the direct effect of attractive and repulsive forces acting in couples (as in the cases in question, or as in bismuth crystals), is to shut out ideas, in relation to magnetism, which are already applied in the theories of the nature of light and electricity; and the shutting out of such ideas *may be* an obstruction to the advancement of truth and a defence of wrong assumptions and error.

3157. What is the idea of polarity in a field of *equal force* (whether it be occupied by air or by a mass of soft iron)? A magnetic needle, or an oblong piece of iron, would not show it in the air or elsewhere, except by disturbing the equal arrangement of the force and rendering it unequal; for on that the pointing of the needle or the iron, or the motions of either towards the walls of the magnetic field, if limited (2828), would depend. A crystal of bismuth in showing this polarity by position (2464, 2839), does it without much altering the distribution of the force, and the alteration which does take place is in the contrary direction to that effected by iron (2807), for it expands the lines of force. It seems readily possible that a magnecrystal might exist, which, when in its stable position, should neither cause the convergence nor divergence of the lines of force within it. It need only be neutral in relation to space or any surrounding medium in that direction, and diamagnetic in its relation in the transverse direction, and the conditions would be fulfilled.

3158. But though an ordinary magnetic needle cannot show polarity in a field of equal force,[1] having no reference to it, and in fact ignoring such a condition of things, a moving wire makes it manifest instantly, and also shows the full amount of magnetic power to which such polarity belongs; and this it does without disturbing the distribution of the power, as far as we comprehend or understand distribution, when thinking of magnetic needles. At least such at present appears to me to be the case, from the consideration of the action of thin and thick wires (3141) and wires of different substances (3153).

3159. As an experimentalist, I feel bound to let experiment guide me into any train of thought which it may justify; being satisfied that experiment, like analysis, must lead to strict truth if rightly interpreted; and believing also that it is in its nature far more suggestive of new trains of thought and new conditions

---

[1] One could easily imagine hypothetically a needle that should do so.

of natural power. In order to extend its indications, and vary the form in which the principle of the moving wire may be applied, I had an apparatus constructed, *Fig. 19*, consisting of a wooden axis, one extremity of which was ter-

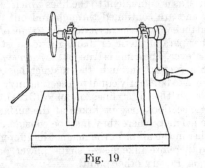

Fig. 19

minated by a copper screw, intended to receive and carry one or more discs of metal that might be screwed on to it. This end projected so far beyond the support that such discs could be partly introduced between the poles of a horseshoe magnet, so as when revolving, to move across the lines of force at their most intense place of action; and, whilst the magnet and the apparatus continued fixed, to revolve continuously across the same lines of force. One of the galvanometer wires was pointed, and so held as to bear into and against the surface of a cup-shaped cavity at the end of the axial screw; and the other was applied by the hand, or so fixed as to bear by a rounded part against the rim of the disc, at that point which was farthest within the poles of the magnet.

3160. Discs of metal were prepared for this apparatus, each 2.5 inches in diameter, and of different thicknesses and material. When a disc of copper was fixed on the axis, and adjusted in association with the large horseshoe magnet (3159), as described above, three, or even two revolutions of it, would deflect the needle of the thick wire galvanometer through a swing of 30°. In this apparatus, the most effectual part of the portion of the disc which is at any moment passing across the magnetic axis is that which is near the circumference; for it has the greatest velocity, consequently moves through more space, and that in a part where the lines of force are most concentrated.

3161. The contact at the end of the axle should always be carefully watched and made good. The degree of pressure on the edge of the disc should not be too slight; otherwise the contact, under the circumstances of the motion, is not sufficient to carry forward the same con-

stant proportion of current generated. Neither should it be made at the angles of the disc edge; if a grating or cutting friction occur, an electric current is generated by it. With a smooth hard friction of copper wire against the copper disc there is very little evolution of current. When the copper wire presses against the edge of an iron disc there is far more. In either case, however, the effect may be eliminated or compensated; for, in whichever direction the disc is revolved *without* the magnet, the deviation of the needle, if any be produced, remains the same; whereas, when the magnet is in place, the deviations produced by it are in the reversed direction for reversed revolutions. Hence, if an equal number of revolutions be made in the two directions, and the unequal deflections in opposite directions be noted, the half of their sum will give nearly the amount of deflection which would have occurred if no current had been exerted by friction at the edge, i.e., provided the deflections have not been through large arcs. These effects of friction are no doubt objections to the principle in this form; still the results are, as it appears to me, valuable in relation to copper and iron, and are as follows.

3162. A copper disc, 0.05 of an inch in thickness, gave a swing deflection for two revolutions, which, being the average of several experiments, = 20°.8. A second copper disc, of 0.1 of an inch in thickness, gave an average deflection of 27°.8. A third copper disc, of 0.2 in thickness, gave a deflection of 26°.5. Here, therefore, not only has the thickness (with the conditions of contact) been attained for the maximum effect, but even surpassed (3137). Then an *iron* disc of 0.05 in thickness, was placed on the axle, and gave, as its mean result, a deflection of 15.4°. Another iron disc of four times the thickness (or 0.2) gave a deflection only of 14°. So here also, as before, the thickness of maximum effect had been surpassed.

3163. The two discs of copper and iron of 0.2 in thickness each, which had produced separately the respective deviations of 26.5° and 14°, were then both fixed on the axle, being separated from mutual contact in respect to their mass, by a disc of paper, though both were of course in contact at the centre of motion with the copper axle, by means of which the electric communication was perfected. In arranging their place between the poles of the magnet, the iron was placed at mid-distance, and therefore the copper a little on one side. When the copper disc was brought into the circuit, it, by two revolutions, gave an average deviation of 23°.4;

and when the iron disc was in the circuit, the deviation produced by it was 11°.91. Here, therefore, the proportions were nearly the same, when the two discs were subject at the same moment to the magnetic power, as when they were examined separately. Both have fallen a little, but not in any manner which seems to indicate that the iron has had any peculiar influence in altering or affecting the lines of force passing across the magnetic field. The effect which has taken place appears to be one due to the action of the collateral mass of conducting matter.

3164. If the direction of the electric current induced by the magnetic force in the moving metal be taken as the true indication of polarity, and, I think, it cannot be denied that it represents that character of the force, which the term polarity is intended to express, and is unchangeably associated with that character; then these results show that the polarity of the lines of force within the iron is the same with that within the copper, when both are submitted in like manner to the magnetic force. In association with the former and new results with *bismuth* (2431, 3151, 3168), and numerous other phenomena, the same conclusion may be drawn as to the lines of force within that substance, for the effects are the same with regard to the production of a current in it; and so further evidence is added to that which I have given, tending to show that bismuth is not polarized in the reverse direction as iron or a magnet (2429, 2640). By reference to the phenomena presented by the relative actions of paramagnetic and diamagnetic substances, the same conclusions may be drawn with respect to all bodies and to space itself (2787, &c.).

3165. That the iron disc affects the disposition of the *lines of force*, is no doubt true, and the extent to which this is done is easily seen, by fixing a small magnetic needle, about 0.1 or 0.05 of an inch in length, across the middle of a piece of stretched thread as an axis, and then bringing it into the magnetic field and near the edges of the stationary disc. The lines of force will be seen (3071, 3076) gathering in upon the iron at and near its edge, but only for a very little distance from it in any direction: the effect is that which I have considered proper to a paramagnetic body (2807). Elsewhere, the lines of force go with the same direction across the magnetic field where the iron is, as where it is not; and it is to me a proved fact, proved by the numerous results given, that a section of the lines of force taken across the magnetic field

through the air, close to the iron, is exactly equal in amount of force to a section taken across parallel to and through the iron disc (3163). All iron under induction must have just as much force, i.e., lines of force in its internal parts, as is equivalent to the lines which fall on to, and are continued through and out of it; and the same is true, as it appears to me, of any other paramagnetic or diamagnetic substance whatever. The same is true *for the magnet itself*; for a section through the magnet has been shown to be exactly equal to a section anywhere through the outer lines of force (3121), and these sections may be taken at the surface of the magnet, where they may be considered as either in the air or in the magnet indifferently; and therefore alike in size, shape, power, polarity, and every other point.

3166. I have used the phrase *conduction polarity* on a former occasion (2818, 2835), but so limited, that it could lead to no mistake of my meaning, either then or now. It requires no words to show how it is included in the higher and general expression of the direction or polarity of the lines of force.

3167. Some other results with the disc apparatus (3159) were obtained, which it may be useful to describe here. *Tin* was formed into a disc of 0.1 in thickness, and 2.5 inches in diameter. The effect of the friction of the copper conductor at its edge was a feeble current, the reverse of that produced in the cases of copper and iron (3161); but the current produced by the revolution, and dependent on the polarity of the lines of force, was the same as before. It produced a swing deflection of 14°.9 for two revolutions of the disc.

3168. A disc of *bismuth* produced far too strong a current by friction against the copper conductor to allow of any useful result in its simple state. A ring of copper foil was therefore formed, and being placed tightly on the bismuth disc, was wedged up by plates of clean copper foil, so as to produce a clean hard contact; imperfect, no doubt, but as general as could be made under the circumstances. When this disc was rotated in the one direction, it gave a deflection in the same direction as if a copper or iron disc had been used; when rotated the other way, the deflection was little or nothing. This difference is due to the united influence of the rotation effect and the friction effect in the one case, and their opposition in the other; but the results show that the lines of force are in the same direction through bismuth, when between the magnetic poles, as they are through copper and iron. The induced current is small, both because of the bad conducting power of the bismuth and the imperfect contact at the edge. When the same copper rim was placed on the copper disc, it reduced the deflection of the needle from 26°.5 to 9°.34.

3169. In illustration of the effect produced by those parts of the disc, which, not being in the place of greatest action, are conducting back those currents formed by the radial parts in the place of maximum effect, I had a wooden disc constructed, 0.2 in thickness and 2.5 inches in diameter, the centre of which was copper, for the purpose of attachment and electrical connexion, and the outer edge a ring of copper not more than ½₀th of an inch in thickness. The two were connected by a single copper wire radius, in thickness 0.056 of an inch, which, as the disc revolved, was of course carried across and through the magnetic field. It gave a deflection of 14°. The copper disc of 0.05 thickness, gave only an average of 28°. Now, though the matter of the copper ring round the wood will cause part of the current, yet the chief portion must be due to the copper radius, which, at the effectual part near the edge (3160), is not more than the ½₄₀th part of the full copper disc; and this indicates how much of the electricity put in motion there by the magnetic force must be returned back in short circuits in the other parts of the disc.

3170. The disc apparatus shows well the dependence of the induced current upon the *intersection* of the lines of force (3082, 3113). If the disc be so arranged as to stand edgeways to the magnetic poles, and in the plane of the magnetic axis, so that it shall be *parallel* to the lines of force which pass by and through it, then no revolution of it, with the most powerful magnet, produces the slightest signs of a current at the galvanometer.

3171. The relation of the induced current to the electro-conducting power of the substance, amongst the metals (3152) leads to the presumption that with other bodies, as water, wax, glass, &c., it is absent, only in consequence of the great deficiency of conducting power. I thought that processes analogous to those employed with the metals, might in such nonconductors as shellac, sulphur, &c., yield some results of static electricity (181, 192); and have made many experiments with this view in the intense magnetic field, but without any distinct result.

3172. All the results described are those obtained with *moving metals*. But mere motion would not generate a relation, which had not a foundation in the existence of some previous state; and therefore the *quiescent* metals must be in some relation to the active centre of force, and that not necessarily dependent on their paramagnetic or diamagnetic condition, because a metal at zero in that respect would have an electric current generated in it as well as the others. The relation is not as the attractions or repulsions of the metals, and therefore not magnetic in the common sense of the word; but according to some other function of the power. Iron, copper, and bismuth are very different in the former sense, but when moving across the lines of force give the same general result, modified only by electro-conducting power.

3173. If such a condition be hereafter verified by experiment and the idea of an electronic state (60, 242, 1114, 1661, 1729) be revived and established, then, such bodies as water, oil, resin, &c., will probably be included in the same state; for the non-conducting condition, which prevents the formation of a current in them, does not militate against the existence of that condition which is prior to the effect of motion. A piece of copper, which cannot have the current, because it is not in a circuit (3087), and a piece of lac, which cannot, because it is a nonconductor of electricity, may have peculiar but analogous states when moving across a field of magnetic power.

3174. On bringing this paper to a close, I cannot refrain from again expressing my conviction of the truthfulness of the representation, which the idea of lines of force affords in regard to magnetic action. All the points which are experimentally established with regard to that action, i.e., all that is not hypothetical, appear to be well and truly represented by it. Whatever idea we employ to represent the power ought ultimately to include electric forces, for the two are so related that one expression ought to serve for both. In this respect, the idea of lines of force appears to me to have advantages over the method of representing magnetic forces by centres of action. In a straight wire, for instance, carrying an electric current, it is apparently impossible to represent the magnetic forces by centres of action, whereas the lines of force simply and truly represent them. The study of these lines have, at different times, been greatly influential in leading me to various results, which I think prove their utility as well as fertility. Thus, the law of magneto-electric induction (114); the earth's inductive action (149, 161, 171); the relation of magnetism and light (2146 and *note*); diamagnetic action and its law (2243), and magnecrystallic action (2454), are cases of this kind: and a similar influence of them, over my mind, will be seen in the further instances of the polarity of diamagnetic bodies (2640); the relation of magnetic curves and the evolved electric currents (243); the explication of Arago's phenomenon (81), and the distinction between that and ordinary magnetism (243, 245); the relation of electric and magnetic forces (1709); the views regarding magnetic conduction (2797) and atmospheric magnetism (2847). I have been so accustomed, indeed, to employ them, and especially in my last *Researches*, that I may, unwittingly, have become prejudiced in their favour, and ceased to be a clear-sighted judge. Still, I have always endeavoured to make experiment the test and controller of theory and opinion; but neither by that nor by close cross examination in principle have I been made aware of any error involved in their use.

3175. Whilst writing this paper I perceive, that, in the late series of these *Researches*, Nos. XXV, XXVI, XXVII, I have sometimes used the term *lines of force* so vaguely as to leave the reader doubtful whether I intended it as a merely representative idea of the forces, or as the description of the path along which the power was continuously exerted. What I have said in the beginning of this paper (3075) will render that matter clear. I have as yet found no reason to wish any part of those papers altered, except these doubtful expressions: but that will be rectified if it be understood that, wherever the expression *line of force* is taken simply to represent the disposition of the forces, it shall have the fullness of that meaning; but that wherever it may seem to represent the idea of the *physical mode* of transmission of the force, it expresses in that respect the opinion to which I incline at present. The opinion may be erroneous, and yet *all* that relates or refers to the disposition of the force will remain the same.

3176. The value of the moving wire or conductor, as an examiner of the magnetic forces, appears to me very great, because it touches the physics of the subject in a manner altogether different to the magnetic needle. It not only gives its indications upon a different principle and in a different manner, but in the mutual action of it and the source of power, it affects the power differently. The wire when quiescent does not sensibly disturb the arrangement of the force in the magnetic field; the needle when present does. When the wire is moving it does not sensibly disturb the forces external to it, unless perhaps in large masses, as in the discs (3163), or when time is concerned (1730), i.e., it does not disturb the disposition of the whole force, or the arrangement of the lines of force; a field of equal magnetic power is still equal to anything but the moving wire, whilst the wire moves across or through it. The moving wire also indicates quantity of force, independent of tension (2870); it shows that the quantity within a magnet and that outside is the same, though the tension be very different. In addition to these advantageous points, the principle is available within magnets, and paramagnetic and diamagnetic bodies, so as to have an application beyond that of the needle, and thus give experimental evidence, of a nature not otherwise attainable.

Royal Institution, October 9, 1851

TWENTY-NINTH SERIES[1]

§ 35. *On the Employment of the Induced Magneto-electric Current as a Test and Measure of Magnetic Forces*

Received December 31, 1851, Read March 25 and April 1, 1852

3177. The proposition which I have made to use the induced magneto-electric current as an experimental indication of the presence, direction and amount of magnetic forces (3074), makes it requisite that I should also clearly demonstrate the principles and develope the prac-

[1] *Philosophical Transactions*, 1852, p. 137.

tice necessary for such a purpose; and especially that I should prove that the amount of current induced is precisely proportionate to the amount of lines of magnetic force intersected by the moving wire, in which the electric current is generated and appears (3082, 3109). The proof already given is, I think, sufficient for those who may repeat the experiments; but in order to accumulate evidence, as is indeed but proper in the first announcement of such a proposition, I proceeded to experiment with the magnetic power of the earth, which presents us with a field of action, not rapidly varying in force with the distance, as in the case of small magnets, but one which for a given place may be considered as uniform in power and direction; for if a room be cleared of all common magnets, then the terrestrial lines of magnetic force which pass through it, have one common direction, being that of the dip, as indicated by a free needle or other means, and are in every part in equal proportion or quantity, i.e., have equal power. Now the force being the same everywhere, the proportion of it to the current evolved in the moving wire is then perhaps more simply and directly determined, than in the case where, a small magnet being employed, the force rapidly changes in amount with the distance.

¶ i. *Galvanometer*

3178. For such experimental results as I now propose to give, I must refer to the galvanometer employed and the precautions requisite for its proper use. The instrument has been already described in principle (3123), and a figure of the conductor which surrounds the needles given. This conductor may be considered as a square copper bar, 0.2 of an inch in thickness, which passes twice round the plane of vibration of each of the needles forming the astatic combination, and then is continued outwards and terminates in two descending portions which are intended to dip into cups of mercury. As both the needles are within the convolutions of this bar, an indicating bristle or fine wire of copper is fixed parallel to, and above

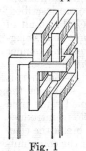

them upon the same axis, and this, in travelling over the usual graduated circle, shows the place and the extent of vibration or swing of the needles below. The suspension is by cocoon silk, and in other respects the instrument is like a good ordinary galvanometer.

3179. It is highly important that the bar of copper about the needles should be perfectly

Fig. 1

clean. The vertical zero plane should, according to the construction, be midway between the two vertical coils of the bar, *Fig. 1*; instead of which the needle at first pointed to the one

side or the other, being evidently attracted by the upright portions of the bar. I at first feared that the copper was magnetic, but on cleaning the surface carefully with fine sandpaper, I was able to remove this effect, due no doubt to iron communicated by handling or the use of tools, and the needle then stood truly in a plane equidistant from the two coils, when that plane corresponded with the magnetic meridian.

3180. The connections for this galvanometer (3123, 3133) were all of copper rod or wire 0.2 of an inch in diameter; but even with wires of this thickness the extent of the conductors should not be made more than is necessary; for the increase from 6 to 8, 10 or 12 feet in length, makes a considerable difference at the galvanometer, when electric currents, low in intensity, are to be measured. It is most beautiful to observe in such cases the application of Ohm's law of currents to the effects produced. When the connections were extended to a distance, straight lengths of wire with dropping ends were provided, and these by dipping into cups of mercury completed the connection and circuit. The cups consisted of cavities turned in flat pieces of wood. The ends of the connecting rods and of the galvanometer bar were first tinned, and then amalgamated; after which their contact with the mercury was both ready and certain. Even where connection had to be made by contact of the solid substances, I found it very convenient and certain to tin and amalgamate the ends of the conductors, wiping off the excess of mercury. The surfaces thus prepared are always ready for a good and perfect contact.

3181. When the needle has taken up its position under the earth's influence, and the copper coil is adjusted to it, the needle ought to stand at true zero, and appears so to do. When that is really the case, equal forces applied in succession on opposite sides of the needle (by two contrary currents through the coil for instance) ought to deflect the needle *equally* on both sides, and they do so. But sometimes, when the needle appears to stand at zero, it may not be truly in the magnetic meridian; for a little torsion in the suspension thread, even though it be only 10° or 15° (for an indifferent needle), and quite insensible to the eye looking at the magnetic needle, does deflect it, and then the force which opposes the swing of the needle, and which stops and returns the needle towards zero (being due both to the torsion and the earth's force), is not equal on the two sides, and the consequence is that the extent of swing in the two directions is not equal for equal powers, but is greater on one side than the other.

3182. I have not yet seen a galvanometer which has an adjustment for the torsion of the suspending filament. Also, there may be other causes, as the presence about a room, in its walls and other places, of unknown masses of iron, which may render the forces on opposite sides of the instrument zero unequal in a slight degree; for these reasons it is better to make *double observations*. All the phenomena we have to deal with, present effects in two contrary directions. If a loop pass over the pole of a magnet (3133), it produces a swing in one direction; if it be taken away, the swing is in the other direction; if the rectangles and rings to be described (3192) be rotated one way, they produce one current; if the contrary way, the other and contrary current is produced. I have therefore, always, in measuring the power of a pole or the effect of a revolving intersecting wire, made many observations in both directions, either alternately or irregularly; have then ascertained the average of those on the one side, and also on the other (which have differed in different cases from $\frac{1}{50}$th to $\frac{1}{300}$th part); and have then taken the mean of these averages as the expression of the power of the induced electric current, or of the magnetic forces inducing it.

3183. Care must be taken as to the position of the instrument and apparatus connected with it, in relation to a fire or sources of different temperatures, that parts which can generate thermocurrents may not become warmed or cooled in different degrees. The instrument is exceedingly sensible to thermo-electric currents; the accidental falling of a sunbeam upon one of two connecting mercury cups for a few moments disturbed the indications and rendered them useless for some time.

3184. In order to ascertain practically, i.e., experimentally, the comparative value of degrees in different parts of the scale or graduation of this instrument and so to render it a measurer, the following trials were made. A loop like that before described (3133), *Fig. 2*,

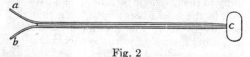

Fig. 2

was connected with the galvanometer by communications which removed the loop 9 feet from the instrument, and it was then fixed. A compound bar-magnet consisting of two plates, each 12 inches long, 1 inch broad, and 0.5 in

thickness, was selected of such strength as to lift a bunch of clean iron filings, averaging 45 grains at either extremity. Blocks were arranged at the loop, so that this magnet, held in a vertical position, could have one end passed downwards through the loop until the latter coincided with the equator of the magnet (3191); after which it could be quickly removed and the same operation be repeated at pleasure. When the magnet was thus moved, the loop being unconnected (at one of the mercury cups) with the galvanometer, there was no sensible change of place in the needles; the direct influence of the magnet at this distance of 9 feet being too small for such an effect.

3185. It must be well understood that, in all the observations made with this instrument, the *swing* is observed as the effect produced, unless otherwise expressed. A constant current in an instrument will give a constant and continued deflection, but such is not the case here. The currents observed are for short periods, and they give, as it were, a blow or push to the needle, the effect of which, in swinging the needle, continues to increase the extent of the deflection long after the current is over. Nevertheless the extent of the swing is dependent on the electricity which passed in that brief current; and, as the experiments seem to indicate, is simply proportional to it, whether the electricity pass in a longer or a shorter time (3104), and notwithstanding the comparative variability of the current in strength during the time of its continuance.

3186. The compound bar being introduced once into the loop and left there, the swing at the galvanometer was observed and found to be 16°; the galvanometer needle was then brought to zero, and the bar removed, which gave a reverse current and swing, and this also was 16°. Many alternations, as before described, gave 16° as the mean result, i.e., the result of one intersection of the lines of force of this magnet (3102). In order to comprehend the manner in which the effect of two or more intersections of these lines of force were added together, it should be remembered that a swing of the needle from right to left occupied some time (13 seconds); so that one is able to introduce the magnet into the loop, then break the electric circuit by raising one end of the communicating wire out of the mercury, remove the magnet, which by this motion does nothing, restore the mercury contact, and reintroduce the magnet into the loop, before a tenth part of the time has passed, during which the needles, urged by the first impulse, would swing. In this way two impulses could be added together, and their joint effect on the needle observed; and, indeed, by practice, three and even four impulses could be given within the needful time, i.e., within one-half or two-thirds of the time of the full swing; but of course the latter impulses would have less power upon the needles, because these would be more or less oblique to the current in the copper coil at the time when the impulses were given. There can be no doubt that, as regarded the currents induced in the loop by the magnet, they would be equal on every introduction of the same magnet.

3187. Proceeding in this way I obtained results for one, two, three, and even four introductions with the same magnet.

One introduction	15°
Two introductions	31°.25
Three introductions	46°.87
Four introductions	58°.50

Here the approximation to 1, 2, 3, 4 cannot escape observation;[1] and I may remark that, whilst observing the place attained at the end of a swing which is retained only for an instant, some degree of error must creep in; and that that error must be greatest, in the first number, where it falls altogether upon the unit of comparison, than in the other observations, where only one-half or one-third of it is added to a half or a third of the whole result. Thus, if we halve the arc for two introductions of the

pole, it gives 15°.625; if we take the third of that for three introductions, it gives 15°.61; numbers which are almost identical, so that if the first number was increased by only 0°.6, the proportion would be as 1, 2 and 3. The reason why the fourth, which is 14°.625, is less may perhaps be referred to the cause already assigned, namely, the declination distance of the needle from the coil when that impulse was given (3186).

3188. In order to avoid in some degree this case, and to compare the degrees at the beginning of the scale, which are most important for the comparison of future experiments with one another, I took only one of the bars of the compound magnet employed above (3184). The results were as follows:

One introduction	8°
Two introductions	15°.75
Three introductions	23°.87
Four introductions	31°.66

which numbers are very closely as 1, 2, 3 and 4. If we divide as before, we have 8°, 7°.87, 7°.95, 7°.91; so that if only 0.09 be subtracted from the first observation, or 8°, it leaves that simple result.[2]

3180. Hence it appears, that in this mode of applying and measuring the magnetic powers, the number of degrees of swing deflection are for small arcs nearly proportional to the magnetic force which has been brought into action on the moving wire.[3]

[1] *See* [also] note to (3189)

$$\sin \frac{15}{2} \qquad\qquad = \sin 7° \ 30' \quad = .130526 \qquad\qquad .130526$$

$$\sin \frac{31.25}{2} = \sin 15.625 = \sin 15° \ 37'.5 = .269200 \qquad \frac{269200}{2} = .134600$$

$$\sin \frac{46.87}{2} = \sin 23.435 = \sin 23° \ 26'.1 = .3976818 \qquad \frac{3976818}{3} = .1328606$$

$$\sin \frac{58.50}{2} = \sin 29.25 = \sin 27° \ 15' \quad = .4886212 \qquad \frac{4886212}{4} = .1221553$$

$$\sin \frac{8}{2} \qquad = \sin 4° \qquad\qquad\qquad = .0697565 \qquad\qquad .0697565$$

$$\sin \frac{15.75}{2} = \sin 7°.875 = \sin 7° \ 52'.5 = .1370123 \qquad \frac{1370123}{2} = .0685061$$

$$\sin \frac{23.87}{2} = \sin 11°.935 = \sin 11° \ 56'.1 = .2068019 \qquad \frac{2068019}{3} = .0689340$$

$$\sin \frac{31.66}{2} = \sin 15°.83 \ = \sin 15° \ 49'.8 = .2727840 \qquad \frac{2727840}{4} = .0681960$$

[3] Mr. Christie has recalled my attention to a paper in the *Philosophical Transactions*, 1833, p. 95, in which he has investigated, at p. 111, &c., the effect of what may be called magneto-electric impulses in deflecting the magnetic needle. He found that the velocity of the projection of the needle, which is a measure of the force acting upon it at the instant of its moving, will be proportional to the sine of half the arc of swing. My statement, therefore, would as a general expression be erroneous; but for small arcs the results as given by it are not far from the truth.

The error does not interfere with the general reasoning and conclusions of the paper; and as the numbers are the results of experiment, which, though made with a first and therefore rough apparatus, were still made with some care, and are expressed simply as deflections, I prefer their appearance as they are rather than in an altered state. Mr. Christie has been so kind as to give me the true expression of force for many of the cases, and I have inserted the results as foot-notes where the cases occur.—*Jan.* 26, 1852.

3190. I have found the needles very constant in their strength for days and weeks together. By care, the constancy of their state for a day is easily secured, and that is all that is required in comparative experiments. Those which I have in use weigh with their axis and indicating wire 9 grains; and when out of the copper coil vibrate to and fro once in 26 seconds.

3191. With this instrument thus examined, I repeated most of the experiments with loops formerly described (3133, &c.), with the same results as before. It was also ascertained that the equator of a regular bar-magnet was the place at which the loop should be arrested, to produce the maximum action; and that if it came short of, or passed beyond that place, the final result was less. Employing a magnet 12 inches long, when the loop passed

2.3 inches over the pole the deflection was 5°.9ℓ
4.1 inches over the pole the deflection was 7°.50
5.1 inches over the pole the deflection was 7°.74
6.1 inches over the pole the deflection was 8°.16
8.0 inches over the pole the deflection was 7°.75
9.0 inches over the pole the deflection was 6°.50

¶ ii. *Revolving Rectangles and Rings*[1]

3192. The form of moving wire which I have adopted for experiments with the magnetic forces of the earth (3177), is either that of a rectangle or a ring. If a wire rectangle (*Fig. 3*) be placed in a plane, perpendicular to the dip and then turned once round the axis *a b*, the two parts *c d* and *e f* will twice inter-

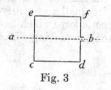

Fig. 3

sect the lines of magnetic force within the area *c e d f*. In the first 180° of revolution the contrary direction in which the two parts *c d* and *e f* intersect those lines, will cause them to conspire in producing one current, tending to run round the rectangle (161) in a given direction; in the following 180° of revolution they will combine in their effect to produce a contrary current; so that if the first current is from *d* by *c e* and *f* to *d* again, the second will be from *d* by *f e* and *c* to *d*. If the rectangle, instead of being closed,

[1] A friend has pointed out to me that in July 1832, Nobili made experiments with rotating rings or spirals subject to the earth's magnetic influence; they were subsequent to and consequent upon my own experiments upon swinging wires (171, 148) and revolving globes (160) of January 1832; but he extended the considerations to the *thickness* of the wire; the *diameter* of the spirals and the *number* of the spirals dependent upon the *length* of the wire. The results (tabulated) will be found in Vol. I, page 244, &c. of the Florence edition of his *Mémoires.—March 1, 1852.*

be open at *b*, and the ends there produced be connected with a commutator, which changes sides when the rectangle comes into the plane perpendicular to the dip, i.e., at every half revolution, then these successive currents can be gathered up and sent on to the galvanometer to be measured. The parts *c e* and *d f* of the rectangle may be looked upon simply as conductors; for as they do not in their motion intersect any of the lines of force, so they do not tend to produce any current.

3193. The apparatus which carries these rectangles, and is also the commutator for changing the induced currents, consists of two uprights, fixed on a wooden stand, and carrying above a wooden horizontal axle, one end of which is furnished with a handle, whilst the other projects, and is shaped as in *Fig. 4.* It

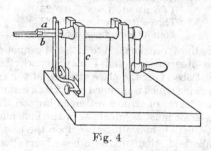

Fig. 4

may there be seen, that two semicylindrical plates of copper *a b* are fixed on the axle, forming a cylinder round it, except that they do not touch each other at their edges, which therefore leave two lines of separation on opposite sides of the axle. Two strong copper rods, 0.2 of an inch in diameter, are fixed to the lower part of the upright *c*, terminating there in sockets with screws for the purpose of receiving the ends of the rods proceeding from the galvanometer cups (3180): in the other direction the rods rise up parallel to each other, and being perfectly straight, press strongly against the curved plates of the commutator on opposite sides; the consequence is that, whenever in the rotation of the axle, the lines of separation between the commutator plates arrive at and pass the horizontal plane, their contact with these bearing rods is changed, and consequently the direction of the current proceeding from these plates to the rods, and so on to the galvanometer, is changed also. The other or outer ends of the commutator plates are tinned, for the purpose of being connected by soldering to the ends of any rectangle or ring which is to be subjected to experiment.

3194. The rectangle itself is tied on a slight wooden cross (*Fig. 5*), which has a socket on one arm that slides on to and over the part of the wooden axle projecting beyond the commutator plates, so that it shall revolve with the axle. A small copper rod forms a continuation of that part of the frame which occupies the place of axle, and the end of this rod enters into a hole in a separate upright, serving to support and steady the rectangle and its frame. The frames are of two or three sizes, so as to receive rectangles of 12 inches in the side, or even larger, up to 36 inches square. The rectangle is adjusted in its place, so that it shall be in the horizontal plane when the division between the commutator plates is in the same plane, and then its extremities are soldered to the two commutator plates, one to each. It is now evident that when dealing with the lines of force of the earth, or any other lines, the axle has only to be turned until the upright copper rods touch on each side at the separation of the commutator plates, and then the instrument adjusted in position, so that the plane of the ring or rectangle is perpendicular to the direction of the lines of force which are to be examined, and then any revolution of the commutator and intersecting wire will produce the maximum current which such wire and such magnetic force can produce. The lines of

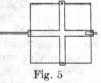

Fig. 5

terrestrial magnetic force are inclined at an angle of 69° to the horizontal plane. As, however, only comparative results were required, the instrument was, in all the ensuing experiments, placed in the horizontal plane, with the axis of rotation perpendicular to the plane of the magnetic meridian; under which circumstances no cause of error or variation was introduced into the results. As no extra magnet was employed, the commutator was placed within 3 feet of the galvanometer, so that two pieces of copper wire 3 feet long and 0.2 of an inch in thickness, sufficed to complete the communication. One end of each of these dipped into the galvanometer mercury cups, the other ends were tinned, amalgamated, introduced into the sockets of the commutator rods (3193), and secured by the pinching screw (*Fig. 4*).

3195. When a given length of wire is to be disposed of in the form best suited to produce the maximum effect, then the circumstances to be considered are contrary for the case of a loop to be employed with a small magnet (39, 3184),

and a rectangle or other formed loop to be employed with the lines of terrestrial force. In the case of the small magnet, *all* the lines of force belonging to it are inclosed by the loop; and if the wire is so long that it can be formed into a loop of two or more convolutions, and yet pass over the pole, then twice or many times the electricity will be evolved than a single loop can produce (36). In the case of the earth's force, the contrary result is true; for as in circles, squares, similar rectangles, &c., the areas inclosed are as the squares of the periphery, and the lines of force intersected are as the areas, it is much better to arrange a given wire in one simple circuit than in two or more convolutions. Twelve feet of wire in one square intersects in one revolution the lines of force passing through an area of nine square feet, whilst if arranged in a triple circuit, about a square of one foot area, it will only intersect the lines due to that area; and it is thrice as advantageous to intersect the lines within nine square feet once, as it is to intersect those of one square foot three times.

3196. A square was prepared, containing 4 feet in length of copper wire 0.05 of an inch in diameter; it inclosed one square foot of area, and was mounted on the commutator and connected in the manner already described (3194). Six revolutions of it produced a swing deflection of 14° or 15°, and twelve quick revolutions were possible within the required time (3104). The results of *quick* and *slow* revolutions were first compared. Six slow revolutions gave as the average of several experiments 15°.5 swing. Six moderate revolutions gave also an average of 15°.5; six quick revolutions gave an average of 15°.66. At another time twelve moderate revolutions gave an average of 28°.75, and twelve quick revolutions gave an average of 31°.33 swing. As before explained (3186), the probable reason why the quick revolutions gave a larger result than the moderate or slow revolutions is, that in slow time the later revolutions are performed at a period when the needle is so far from parallel with the copper coil of the galvanometer that the impulses due to them are less effectually exerted. Hence a small or moderate number of revolutions and a quick motion is best. The difference in the extreme case is less than might have been expected, and shows that there is no practical objection in this respect to the method proposed of experimenting with the lines of magnetic force.

3197. In order to obtain for the present an expression of the power of the earth's magnetic force by this rectangle, observations were made on both sides of zero, as already recommended (3182). Nine moderately quick direct revolutions (i.e., as the hands of the clock) gave as the average of many experiments 23°.87, and nine reverse revolutions gave 23°.37; the mean of these is 23°.62 for the nine revolutions of the rectangle, and therefore 2°.624 per revolution. Now the six quick revolutions (3196) gave 15°.66, which is 2°.61 per revolution, and the twelve quick revolutions gave 31°.33, which is also 2°.61 per revolution; and these results of 2°.624, 2°.61, and 2°.61, are very much in accordance, and give great confidence in this method of investigating magnetic forces.[1]

3198. A rectangle was prepared of the same length (4 feet) of the same wire, but the sides were respectively 8 and 16 inches (*Fig. 6*), so

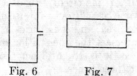

Fig. 6   Fig. 7

that when revolving the intersecting parts should be only 8 inches in length instead of 12. The area of the rectangle was necessarily 128 square inches instead of 144. This rectangle showed the same difference of quick and slow rotations as before (3196). When nine direct revolutions were made, the result was 20°.87 swing. Nine reverse revolutions gave an average of 20°.25 swing; the mean is 20°.56, or 2°.284 per revolution. A third rectangle was prepared of the same length and kind of wire, the sides of which were respectively 8 and 16 inches long (*Fig. 7*), but now so revolved that the intersecting parts were 16 inches, or twice as long as before; the area of the rectangle remained the same, i.e., 128 inches. The like effect of slow and

quick revolutions appeared as in the former cases (3196, 3198). Nine direct revolutions gave as the average effect 20°.75; and nine reverse revolutions produced 21°.375; the mean is 21°.06, or 2°.34 per revolution.

3199. Now 2°.34 is so near to 2°.284, that they may in the present state of the investigation be considered the same. The little difference that is evident was, I suspect, occasioned by centrifugal power throwing out the middle of the longer intersecting parts during the revolution. The coincidence of the numbers shows that the variation in the arrangement of the rectangle and in the length of the parts of the wires intersecting the lines of magnetic force have had no influence in altering the result, which, being dependent alone on the number of lines of force intersected, is the same for both; for the area of the rectangles is the same. This is still further shown by comparing the results with those obtained with the square. The area in that case was 144 square inches, and the effect per revolution 2°.61. With the long rectangles the area is 128 square inches, and the mean of the two results is 2°.312 per revolution. Now 144 square inches is to 128 square inches as 2°.61 is to 2°.32; a result so near to 2°.312 that it may be here considered as the same; proving that the electric current induced is directly as the lines of magnetic force intersected by the moving wire.[2]

3200. It may also be perceived that no difference is produced when the lines of force are chiefly disposed in the direction of the motion of the wire, or else, chiefly in the direction of the length of the wire; i.e., no alterations are occasioned by variations in the *velocity* of the motion, or of the length of the wire, provided the amount of lines of magnetic force intersected remains the same.

$$\sin \frac{15.66}{2} = \sin \ 7°.83 = \sin \ 7° \ 49'.8 = .1362343 \qquad \frac{1362343}{6} = .0227057$$

$$\sin \frac{23.62}{2} = \sin 11°.81 = \sin 11° \ 48'.6 = .2047069 \qquad \frac{2047069}{9} = .0227474$$

$$\sin \frac{31.33}{2} = \sin 15°.665 = \sin 15° \ 40' \quad = .2700403 \qquad \frac{2700403}{12} = .0225034$$

[2] Oblong rectangles of 128 square inches area give a mean of 20°.81 (3198). The rectangle of 144 square inches gave a mean of 23°.62 (3197).

$$\sin \frac{20.81}{2} = \sin 10°.405 = \sin 10° \ 24'.3 = .1806049$$

$$\sin \frac{23.62}{2} = \sin 11°.81 \ = \sin 11° \ 48'.6 = .2047069$$

$$\frac{128}{144} = \frac{8}{9} \qquad \begin{array}{l} .1806049 \times 9 = 1.6254441 \\ .2047069 \times 8 = 1.6376552 \end{array} \qquad \text{Or thus:} \qquad \begin{array}{l} \dfrac{.1806049}{8} = .0225756 \\[2mm] \dfrac{.2047069}{9} = .0227452 \end{array}$$

3201. Having a square on the frame 12 inches in the side but consisting of copper wire 0.1 of an inch in thickness, I obtained the average result of many observations for one, two, three, four and five revolutions of the wire.

One revolution	gave 7°	equal to 7°	per revolution
Two revolutions	gave 13°.875	equal to 6°.937	per revolution
Three revolutions	gave 21°.075	equal to 7°.025	per revolution
Four revolutions	gave 28°.637	equal to 7°.159	per revolution
Five revolutions	gave 37°.637	equal to 7°.527	per revolution

These results are exceedingly close upon each other, especially for the first 30°, and confirm several of the conclusions before drawn (3189, 3199) as to the indications of the instrument, the amount of the curves, &c.[1]

3202. At another time I compared the effect of equable revolutions with other revolutions very irregular in their rates, the motion being sometimes even backwards and continually differing in degree by fits and starts, yet always so that within the proper time a certain number of revolutions should have been completed. The rectangle was of wire 0.2 of an inch thick; the mean of many experiments, which were closely alike in their results, gave for two smooth, equable revolutions, 17°.5, and also for two irregular uncertain revolutions the same amount of 17°.5

3203. The relation of the current produced to the mass of the wire was then examined; a relation, which has been investigated on a former occasion by loops and small magnets (3133).[2] For the present purpose two other equal squares were prepared, each a foot in the side, but the copper wire of which they consisted was respectively 0.1 and 0.2 of an inch in diameter; so that with the former rectangle they formed a series of three, having the same size, shape and area, but the masses of the moving wire increasing in the proportion of one, four and sixteen. When the rectangle of 0.1 wire was employed, six direct revolutions gave an average result of 41°.75, and six to the left gave 46°.25; the mean of the two is 44°, and this divided by six gives 7°.33 as the deflection per revolution. Again, three direct revolutions gave 20°.12, and three reverse revolutions 23°.1; the mean being 21°.61, and the deflection per revolution 7°.20. This is very close to the former result with six revolutions, namely 7°.33, and is a large increase upon the effect of the rectangle of wire 0.05 in diameter, namely 2°.61; nevertheless, it is not as 4 : 1; nor could such a result be expected, inasmuch as the mass of the chief conductor remained the same (3137). When the results are compared with those made with like wires in the form of loops, they are found to be exceedingly close; in that case the results were as 16° to 44°.4 (3136), which would accord with a ratio in the present case of 2°.61 to 7°.26; and it is as 2°.61 to 7°.242, almost identical.

3204. The average of the direct and reverse revolutions is seen above to differ considerably, i.e., up to 4° and 5° in the higher case. This does not indicate any error in principle, but results simply from the circumstance that when the needles were quiescent in the galvanometer they stood a little on one side of zero (3182). I did not wish to adjust the instrument at the time, as I was watching for spontaneous alterations of the zero place, and prefer giving the numbers as they came out in the investigation, to any pen-and-ink correction of the notes.

3205. The third square of 0.2 wire gave such large swings that I employed only a small number of revolutions. Three direct revolutions gave an average of 25°.58; three reverse revolutions gave an average of 25°.58; three reverse revolutions gave 28°.5; the mean is 27°.04 and

Differences.

[1] $\quad \sin \dfrac{7}{2} = \sin \quad 3°.30 \qquad\qquad = .0610485$ $.0597381$ $.0610485$

$\sin \dfrac{13.875}{2} = \sin \quad 6°.9375 = \sin \quad 6° \ 56'.25 = .1207866$ $.0620924$ $\dfrac{.1207866}{2} = .0603933$

$\sin \dfrac{21.075}{2} = \sin 10°.5375 = \sin 10° \ 32'.25 = .1828790$ $.0644329$ $\dfrac{.1828790}{3} = .0609596$

$\sin \dfrac{28.637}{2} = \sin 14°.3185 = \sin 14° \ 19'.11 = .2473119$ $.0752595$ $\dfrac{.2473119}{4} = .0618279$

$\sin \dfrac{37.637}{2} = \sin 18°.8185 = \sin 18° \ 49'.11 = .3225714$ $\dfrac{.3225714}{5} = .0645142$

[2] See a corresponding investigation by Christie, *Philosophical Transactions*, 1833, p. 120.

the amount per revolution 9°.01. Again, two direct revolutions gave 17°.5; two reverse revolutions gave 18°; the mean is 17°.75, and the amount per revolution 8°.87; the mean of the two final results is 8°.94, and is again an increase on the effect produced by the preceding rectangle of wire, only half the diameter of the present. This thickness of wire was also employed formerly as a loop (3136); and if we compare the results then obtained with the present results, it is remarkable how near they approach to each other; a circumstance which leads to great confidence in the principles and practice of both forms of examination. When wires having masses in the proportion of 1, 4, and 16 were employed as loops, the currents indicated by the galvanometer were as 1.00, 2.77, and 3.58; now that they are employed as rectangles subject to the earth's magnetic power, they are as 1.00, 2.78, and 3.45.[1]

3206. I formed a square, 12 inches in the side, of four convolutions of copper wire 0.05 of an inch in diameter; the single wire which formed it was consequently 16 feet long. Such a rectangle will, in revolving, intersect the same number of lines of magnetic force as the former rectangle made with wire 0.1 in diameter (3203): there will also be the same mass of wire intersecting the lines, but, as a conductor, the first wire has in respect of diameter, only one-fourth the conducting power of the second; and then, to increase the obstruction, it is four times as long. Six direct revolutions gave an average result of 20°.6, and six reverse revolutions 19°.7; the mean is 20°.15, and the proportion per revolution 3°.36. With the other rectangle having equal area and mass, but a single wire (3203), the result per revolution was 7°.26; being above, though near upon twice as much as in the present case. Hence for such an excellent conducting galvanometer as that described (3123, 3178), the moving wire had better be as one single thick wire rather than as many convolutions of a thin one. If it be, under all variations of circumstances, the same wire for the same area, then, of course, two or more convolutions are better than one.

[1] $\sin \frac{27.04}{2} = \sin 13°.52 = \sin 13° 31'.2 = .2337848$ $\frac{.2337848}{2} = .0779283$. The square 12 inches side, of wire 0.05 in diameter, gave for six revolutions (3196, 3197) .0227057 as $\sin \frac{1}{2}$ A for one revolution. A like square of wire 0.10 in diameter gave for five revolutions (3021) $\frac{.3225714}{2} = .06451428$ as $\sin \frac{1}{2}$ A for one revolution. A like square of wire 0.20 in diameter gave .0779283 as $\sin \frac{1}{2}$ A for one revolution. $\frac{.06451428}{.0227057} = 2.841$ $\frac{.0779283}{.0227057} = 3.432$

3207. It was to be expected, however, that the thin wire rectangle would produce a current of more *intensity* than that in the thick wire, though less in quantity; and to prove this point experimentally, I connected the two rectangles in succession with Rhumkorff's galvanometer (3086), having wire only 1-135th of an inch in diameter. That of the single thick wire now gave only 1°.66 of swing for twelve revolutions of the rectangle, or 0°.138 per revolution; whilst the other of four convolutions of thin wire gave for twelve revolutions 7°.33, or 0°.61 per revolution. Now the needles of the two instruments were not very different in weight and other circumstances, so that without pretending to an accurate comparison, we may still perceive an immense falling-off in both cases, due to the obstruction of the fine wire in the Rhumkorff's galvanometer: for the thick wire it is from 7°.26 to 0°.138, and for the thin wire from 3°.36 to 0°.610. Still the thin wire rectangle has lost far less proportionately in power than the other; and by this galvanometer is above four times greater in effect than the rectangle of thicker wire. Of the thick wire effect less than a *fiftieth* passes the fine wire galvanometer, all the rest is stopped; of the fine wire effect more than ten times this proportion, or between a fourth and a fifth (because of the higher intensity of the current), surmounts the obstruction presented by the instrument. The quantity of electricity which really passes through the fine wire galvanometer is of course far less than in the proportion indicated above. The thick wire coil makes at the utmost four convolutions about the needles, whereas in the fine wire coil there are probably four hundred or more; so that the electricity which really travels forward as a current, is probably not a hundredth part of that which would be required to give an equal deflection in the thick wire galvanometer. Such a circumstance does not disturb the considerations with respect to the relative intensity of the magneto-electric currents from the two rectangles, which have been stated above.

3208. A large square was now constructed of copper wire 0°.2 of an inch in diameter. The square was 36 inches in the side, and therefore consisted of 12 feet of wire, and inclosed an area of 9 square feet; it was attached to the commutator by expedients, which, though sufficient for the present, were not accurate in the adjustments. It produced a fine effect upon the thick wire galvanometer (3178); for one revolution caused a swing deflection of 80° or more:

and when its rotation was continuous the needles were permanently deflected 40° or 50°. It was very interesting to see how, when this rectangle commenced its motion from the horizontal plane, the current increased in its intensity and then diminished again, the needles showing that whilst the first 10° or 20° of revolution were being passed, there was very little power exerted on them; but that when it was towards, or near the 90°, the power was great; the wires then intersecting the lines of force nearly at right angles, and therefore, with an equal velocity, crossing the greatest number in a given time. It was also very interesting, by the same indications, to see the two chief impulses (3192) given in one revolution of the rectangle. Being large and massive in proportion to the former wires, more time was required for a rotation than before, and the point of *time* or *velocity* of rotation became more essential. One rotation in a second was as much as I could well produce. A speed somewhat less than this was easy, convenient and quick enough; it gave for a single revolution near 80°, whilst a revolution with one-half or one-third the velocity, or less, gave only 60°, 50°, or even smaller amounts of deflection.

3209. Observations were now made on the measurement of one rotation having an easy quick velocity. The average of fifteen observations to the right, which came very near to each other, was 78°.846; the average of seventeen similar observations to the left was 78°.382; and the mean of these results, or 78°.614, I believe to be a good first expression for this rectangle. On measuring the distances across after this result, I found that in one direction, i.e., across between the intersecting portions of wire, it was rather less than 36 inches; having therefore corrected this error, I repeated the observations and obtained the result of 81°.44. The difference of 2°.83, I believe to be a true result of the alteration and increase of the area on making it more accurately 9 square feet; and it is to me an evidence of the sensibility and certainty of the instrument.

3210. As the two impulses upon the needles in one revolution (3208) are here sensibly apart in time, and as the needle has as evidently and necessarily left its first place before the second impulse is impressed upon it, so that second impulse cannot be so effectual as the first. I therefore observed the results with half a revolution, and obtained a mean of 41°.37 for the effect. This number evidently belongs to the first of the two impulses of one revolution; and if we

subtract it from 81°.44, it gives 40°.07 as the value of the second impulse under the changed place of the needle. This difference of the two impulses of one revolution, namely 41°.37 and 40°.07, is in perfect accordance with the results that were to be expected.

3211. The square of this same copper wire, 0.2 in thickness, employed on a former occasion (3205), had an area of one square foot, so that then the lines of force affected or affecting the moving wire were one-ninth part of what they are in the present case: the effect then was 8°.94 per revolution. If, in comparing these cases, we take the ninth part of 81°.44, it gives 9°.04; a number so near the former, that we may consider the two rectangles as proving the same result, and at the same time the truth of the statement that the magneto-electric current evolved is as the amount of lines of force intersected. A ninth part of the result with the large rectangle (78°.614), before its area was corrected, is 8°.734; so that the one is above and the other below the amount of the 12-inch rectangle. As that was not very carefully adjusted, nor indeed any of the arrangements made as yet with extreme accuracy, I have little doubt that with accurately adjusted rectangles the results would be strictly proportional to the areas.[1]

3212. The moving wire, in place of being formed into a rectangle, may be adjusted as a ring; and then the advantage is obtained of the largest area which a given length of wire can inclose, and therefore for a uniform wire, the obstruction to the induced current, as respects its conduction, is the least. Small rings of one or several convolutions will probably be very valuable in the examination of small and local magnets under different circumstances. One consisting of ten spirals of copper wire 0.032 of an inch in diameter, containing 49 inches, in a ring about 1.5 inch in diameter, gave but small results under the earth's influence; but when brought near a horseshoe magnet told in its effects for every difference in distance or in position. A single ring 4 inches in diameter, being made of a convolution of copper wire 0.2 in

---

[1] The 9 square feet rectangle gave 81°.44 sin $\frac{81.44}{2}$=sin 40.72=sin 40° 43′.2=.6523630: or taking 41°.37 for the half revolution for $\frac{1}{2}$ A (3210) sin 41°.37=sin 41° 22′.2=.6609190, which divided by nine give .073435 as the force per square foot. The 1 square foot rectangle of like wire (3205) gave .07714, or .07793 as the force of one revolution; the first of which is .00370 more than $\frac{1}{9}$ of the measure of the effect of the large square; the difference being about $\frac{1}{29}$ of .07714, or the whole force of one revolution.

thickness, was employed with the earth's magnetic force as before; it gave as the average of six revolutions many times repeated 5°.995, or 0°.999 per revolution. For twelve revolutions it gave a mean of 12°.375 or 1°.031 per revolution;[1] the mean of the two results with such different numbers of revolutions being 1°. Another ring, consisting of 26 convolutions of copper wire 0.04 of an inch in diameter, was constructed and had a mean diameter of 3.6 or 3.7 inches; it contained 300 inches in length of wire. So the masses of the metal in the two rings are nearly the same, but the latter wire is singly only 1-25th of the mass of the former. It gave for twelve revolutions a mean of 6°.25, or 0°.52 per revolution. With the earth's power and the thick wire galvanometer, it gave therefore little more than half the result of the single thick wire ring. We know from former considerations (3206), that if the 300 inches had been made into one single ring, it would have given a very high effect compared to the present.

3213. The application of the principle of the moving wire in the form of a revolving rectangle, makes the investigation of *conducting* power, and the results produced by difference in the nature of the *substance*, or in diameter, i.e., *mass*, or in *length*, very easy; and the obstruction offered by those parts, which moving not across but parallel to the lines of force (3071), have no exciting action but perform the part of conductors merely, might be greatly removed by making them massive. They might be made to shift upon the axle so as to bear adjustment for different lengths of wires, and the commutator might in fact be made to a large extent a general instrument.

3214. In looking forward to further applications of the principle of the moving wire, it does not seem at all unlikely that by increased delicacy and perfection of the instrument, by increased velocity, by continued motion for a time in one direction and then reversal of the revolution with the reversal of the direction of the swing, &c., it may be applied with advantage hereafter to the investigation of the earth's magnetic force in different latitudes and places. To obtain the maximum effect, the axis of rotation must be perpendicular to the lines of force, i.e., the dip. It would even be possible to search for the *direction* of the lines of force, or the dip, by making the axis of rotation variable

about the line of dip, adjusting it in two directions until there was no action at the galvanometer, and then observing the position of the axis; a double commutator would be required corresponding to the lines of adjustment, but that is an instrument of very simple construction.

§ 36. *On the Amount and General Disposition of the Forces of a Magnet when Associated with Other Magnets*

3215. Prior to further progress in the experimental development by a moving wire of the disposition of the lines of magnetic force pertaining to a magnet, or of the physical nature of this power and its possible mode of action at a distance, it became quite essential to know what change, if any, took place in the amount of force possessed by a perfect magnet, when subjected to other magnets in favourable or adverse positions; and how the forces combined together, or were disposed of, i.e., generally, and in relation to the principle already asserted and I think proved, that the power is in every case definite under those different conditions. The representation of the magnetic power by *lines of force* (3074), and the employment of the moving wire as a test of the force (3076), will I think assist much in this investigation.

3216. For such a purpose an ordinary magnet is a very irregular and imperfect source of power. It not only, when magnetized to a given degree, is apt by slight circumstances to have its magnetic power diminished or exalted, in a manner which may be considered for the time, permanent; but if placed in adverse or favourable relations to other magnets, frequently admits of a considerable temporary diminution or increase of its power externally, which change disappears as soon as it is removed from the neighborhood of the dominant magnet. These changes produce corresponding effects upon the moving wire, and they render any magnet subject to them unfit for investigation in relation to definite power. Unchangeable magnets are, therefore, required, and these are best obtained, as is well known, by selecting good steel for the bars, and then making them exceedingly hard; I therefore procured some plates of thin steel twelve inches long and one inch broad, and making them as hard as I could,

[1] $\sin \frac{5 \cdot 995}{2} = \sin 2°.9975 = \sin 2° 59'.85 = $ .0522925

$\sin \frac{12 \cdot 375}{2} = \sin 6°.1875 = \sin 6° 11'.25 = .1077825$ $\frac{.1077825}{2} = .0538912$

afterwards magnetized them very carefully and regularly, by two powerful steel bar-magnets, shook them together in different and adverse positions for a little while, and then examined the direction of the forces by iron filings. Small cracks and irregularities were in this way detected in several of them; but two which were very regular in the disposition of their forces were selected for further experiment, and may be distinguished as the subjected magnets D and E.

3217. These two magnets were examined by the moving loop precisely in the manner before described (3133) i.e., by passing the loop over one of the poles, observing the swing, removing it, and again observing the swing and taking an average of many results; the process was performed over both poles at different times. The loop contained 7.25 inches in length of copper wire 0.1 of an inch in diameter, and was of course employed in all the following comparative experiments; the distance of the loop and magnets from the galvanometer was 9 feet. For one passage over the pole either on or off, i.e., for one intersection of the lines of force of the magnet D, the galvanometer deflection was 8°.36. For one intersection of the lines of force of the other bar E, the deflection was 8°.78. The two bars were then placed side by side with like poles together, and afterwards used as one magnet; their conjoined power was 16°.3, being only 0°.84 less than the sum of the powers of the two when estimated separately. This indicates that the component magnets do affect, and in this position reduce, each other somewhat; but it also shows how small the effect is as compared with ordinary magnets (3222).

3218. The compound magnet D E (3217) was now subjected to the close action of another magnet, sometimes under adverse, and at other times under favourable conditions; and was examined by the loop as to the sum of its power (not the direction) under these circumstances. For this purpose it was fixed, and another magnet A brought near, and at times in contact with it, in the positions indicated by the *Figure 8;* the loop in each case being applied many times to D E, that a correct average of its power might be procured. The dominant magnet A was much the stronger of the two, having the power indicated by a swing deflection of 25°.74.

3219. When the relative position of the magnets was as at 1, then the power of D E was 16°.37; when as at 2, the power was 16°.4; when

as at 3, it was 18°.75; and when as at 4, it was 17°.18. All these positions are such as would tend to raise, by induction, the power of the magnet D E, and they do raise it above its first value, which was 16°.3; but it is seen at once

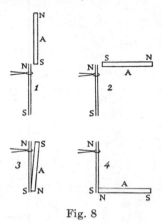

Fig. 8

how little the first and second positions elevate it; and even the third, which presents the most favourable conditions, only increases the power 2°.45, which falls again in the fourth position.

3220. Then the dominant magnet A was placed in the same positions, but with the ends reversed, so as to exert an adverse or depressing influence; and now the results with D E were as follows:

Position 1	15°.37
Position 2	15°.68
Position 3	15°.37
Position 4	16°.06

All these are a little below the original force of D E, or 16°.3, as they ought to be, and show how slightly this hard bar-magnet is affected.

3221. A soft iron bar, now applied in the first, second and third positions instead of the magnet A, raised D E to the following values respectively, 16°.24, 16°.43, and 18°.

3222. When an ordinary bar-magnet was employed instead of the hard magnet D E, great changes took place. Thus a bar B, corresponding to bar A in size and general character, was employed in place of the hard magnet. Alone, B had a power of 14°.83, but when associated adversely with A, as in position 3 (3218), its power fell to 7°.87, being reduced nearly one-half. This loss was chiefly due to a coercion internally, and not to a permanent destruction of the state of magnet B; for when A was

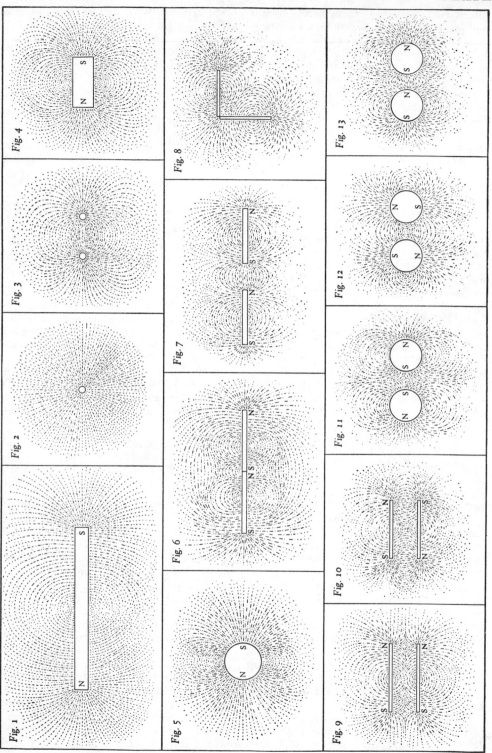

Fig. 4

Fig. 8

Fig. 13

Fig. 3

Fig. 7

Fig. 12

Fig. 2

Fig. 11

Fig. 6

Fig. 1

Fig. 5

Fig. 10

Fig. 9

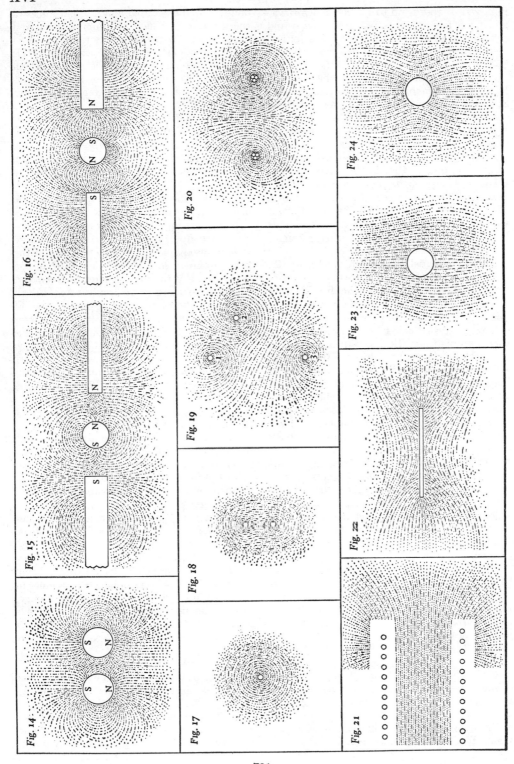

removed, B rose again to 13°.06. When B was laid for a few moments favourably on A and then removed, it was found that the latter had been raised to a permanent external action of 15°.25.

3223. A very hard steel bar 6 inches long, 0.5 broad and 0.1 in thickness, given to me by Dr. Scoresby, was magnetized and then found, by the use of the loop, to have a value at my galvanometer of 6°.88 (3189). It was submitted in position 2 to a compound bar-magnet like D E, having a power of 11°.73, or almost twice its own force, but whether in the adverse or the favourable position, its power was not sensibly altered. When submitted in like manner to a 12-inch bar-magnet having a force of 40°.21, it was raised to 7°.53, or lowered to 5°.87, but here the dominant magnet had nearly six times the power of the one affected.

3224. The variability of soft steel magnets, both in respect to their *absolute* degree of excitation or charge, and also of the disposition of the force externally and internally, when their degree of excitation may for the time be considered as the same, is made very manifest by this mode of examination; and the results agree well with our former knowledge in this respect. It is equally manifest that hard and invariable magnets are requisite for a correct and close investigation of the disposition and characters of the magnetic force. A common soft bar-magnet may be considered as an assemblage of hard and soft parts, disposed in a manner utterly uncertain; of which some parts take a much higher charge than others, and change less under the influence of external magnets; whilst, because of the presence of other parts within, acting as the keeper or submagnet, they may seem to undergo far greater changes than they really do. Hence the value of these hard and comparatively unchangeable magnets which Scoresby describes.

3225. From these and such results, it appears to me, that with perfect, unchangeable magnets, and using the term *line of force* as a mere representant of the force as before defined (3071, 3072), the following useful conclusions may be drawn.

3226. Lines of force of different magnets in favourable positions to each other coalesce.

3227. There is no increase of the total force of the lines by this coalescence; the section between the two associated poles gives the same sum of power as that of the section of the lines of the invariable magnet when it is alone (3217). Under these circumstances there is, I think, no doubt that the external and internal forces of the same magnet have the same relation and are equivalent to each other, as was determined in a former part of these *Researches* (3117); and that therefore the equatorial section, which represents the sum of forces or lines of forces passing through the magnet, remains also unchanged (3232).

3228. In this case the analogy with two or more voltaic batteries associated end to end in one circuit is perfect. Probably some effect, correspondent to *intensity* in the case of the batteries, will be found to exist amongst the magnets.

3229. The increase of power upon a magnetic needle, or piece of soft iron placed between two opposite, favourable poles, is caused by concentration upon it of the lines which before were diffused, and not by the addition of the power represented by the lines of force of one pole to that of the lines of force of the other. There is no more power represented by all the lines of force than before; and a line of force is not more powerful because it coalesces with a line of force of another magnet. In this respect the analogy with the voltaic pile is also perfect.

3230. A line of magnetic force being considered as a closed circuit (3117), passes in its course through *both* the magnets, which are for the time placed so as to act on each other favourably, i.e., whose lines coincide and coalesce. Coalescence is not the addition of one line of force to another *in power*, but their union in one common circuit.

3231. A line of force may pass through many magnets before its circuit is complete; and these many magnets coincide as a case with that of a single magnet. If a thin bar-magnet 12 inches long be examined by filings (3235), it will be found to present the well-known beautiful system of forces, perfectly simple in its arrangement. If it be broken in half, without being separated, and again examined, the manner in which, from the destruction of the continuity, the transmission of the force at the equator is interfered with, and many of the lines, which before were within are made to appear externally there, is at once evident (Pl. XVI, *Fig. 6*). Of those lines, which thus become external, some return back to the pole which is nearest to the new place, at which the lines issue into the air, making their circuit through only one of the halves of the magnet; whilst others proceed onward by paths more or less curved into the second half of the magnet, keeping generally the direction or polarity which they had whilst within the magnet, and complete their circuit through the two. Gradually separating the two halves, and continuing to examine the course of the lines of force, it is beautiful to observe how more and more of the lines which issue from the two new terminations, turn back to the original extremities of the bar (Pl. XVI, *Fig. 7*) and how the portion which makes a common circuit through the two halves diminishes, until the halves are entirely removed from each other's influence, and then become two separate and independent magnets. The same process may be repeated until there are many magnets in place of one.

3232. All this time the amount of lines of force is the same if the fragments of the bar preserve their full state of magnetism; i.e. the sum of lines of force in the equator of *either* of the new magnets is equal to the sum of lines of force in the equator of the original unbroken bar. I took a steel bar 12 inches long, 1 inch broad and 0.05 of an inch thick, made it very hard, and magnetized it to saturation by the use of soft iron cores and a helix; its power was 6°.9. I broke it into two pieces nearly in the middle, and found the power of these respectively 5°.94 and 5°.89, indicating a fall not more than was to be expected considering the saturated state of the original magnet. When these halves were placed side by side, with like poles together as a compound magnet, they had a joint power of 11°.06, which, though it shows a mutual quelling influence, is not much below the sum of their powers ascertained separately. All this is in perfect harmony with the voltaic battery, where lines of dynamic electric force are concerned. If, as is well known, we separate a battery of 20 pair of plates into two batteries of 10 pair, or 4 batteries of 5 pair, each of the smaller batteries can supply as much dynamic electricity as the original battery, provided no sensible obstruction be thrown into the course of the lines, i.e. the path of the current.

3233. When magnets are placed in an adverse position, as neither could add power to the other in the former case, so now each retains its own power; and the lines of magnetic force represent this condition accurately. Two magnets placed end to end with like poles together are in this relation; so also are they if placed with like poles together side by side. In the latter case the two acting as one compound magnet, give a system of lines of force equal to the sum of the two separately (3232), minus the

portion which, as in imperfect magnets, is either directed inwards by the softer parts or ceases to be excited altogether.

§ 37. *Delineation of Lines of Magnetic Force by Iron Filings*

3234. It would be a voluntary and unnecessary abandonment of most valuable aid, if an experimentalist, who chooses to consider magnetic power as represented by lines of magnetic force, were to deny himself the use of iron filings. By their employment he may make many conditions of the power, even in complicated cases, visible to the eye at once; may trace the varying direction of the lines of force and determine the relative polarity; may observe in which direction the power is increasing or diminishing; and in complex systems may determine the neutral points or places where there is neither polarity nor power, even when they occur in the midst of powerful magnets. By their use probable results may be seen at once, and many a valuable suggestion gained for future leading experiments.

3235. Nothing is simpler than to lay a magnet upon a table, place a flat piece of paper over it, and then sprinkling iron filings on the paper, to observe the forms they assume. Nevertheless, to obtain the best and most generally useful results, a few particular instructions may be desirable. The table on which the magnet is laid should be quite horizontal and steady. Means should be taken, by the use of thin boards or laths, or otherwise, to block up round the magnet, so that the paper which is laid over it should be level. The paper should be without any cockle or bend, and perfectly flat, that the filings may be free to assume the position which the magnet tends to give them. I have found well-made cartridge or thin drawing-paper good for the purpose. It should not be too smooth in ordinary cases, or the filings, when slightly agitated, move too freely towards the magnet. With very weak or distant magnets I have found silvered paper sometimes useful. The filings should be clean, i.e. free from much dirt or oxide; the latter forms the lines but does not give good delineations. The filings should be distributed over the paper by means of a sieve more or less fine, their quantity being partly a matter of taste. It is to be remembered, however, that the filings disturb in some degree the conditions of the magnetic power where they are present, and that in the case of small magnets, as needles, a large proportion of them should be avoided. Large and also fine filings are equally useful in turn, when the object is to preserve the forms obtained. For the distribution of the latter it is better to use a fine sieve with the ordinary filings than to separate the filings first: a better distribution on the paper is obtained. The filings being sifted evenly on the paper, the latter should be tapped very lightly by a small piece of wood, as a pen-holder; the taps being applied wherever the particles are not sufficiently arranged. The taps must be perpendicularly downwards, not obliquely, so that the particles, whilst they have the liberty of motion, for an instant are not driven out of their places, and the paper should be held down firmly at one corner, so as not to shift right or left; the lines are instantly formed, especially with fine filings.

3236. The designs thus obtained may be fixed in the following manner, and then form very valuable records of the disposition of the forces in any given case. By turning up two corners of the paper on which the filings rest, they may be used as handles to raise the paper upwards from the magnet, to be deposited on a flat board or other plane surface. A solution of one part of gum in three or four of water having been prepared, a coat of this is to be applied equably by a broad camel-hair pencil, to a piece of cartridge paper, so as to make it fairly wet, but not to float it, and after wafting it through the air once or twice to break the bubbles, it is to be laid carefully over the filings, then covered with ten or twelve folds of equable soft paper, a board placed over the paper, and a half-hundred weight on the board for thirty or forty seconds. Or else, and for large designs it is a better process, whilst the papers are held so that they shall not shift on each other, the hand should be applied so as to rub with moderate pressure over all the surface equably and in one direction. If, after that, the paper be taken up, all the filings will be found to adhere to it with very little injury to the forms of the lines delineated; and when dry they are firmly fixed. If a little solution of the red ferroprussiate of potassa and a small proportion of tartaric acid be added to the gum-water, a yellow tint is given to the paper, which is not unpleasant; but besides that, prussian blue is formed under every particle of iron; and then when the filings are purposely or otherwise displaced, the design still remains recorded. When the designs are to be preserved in blue only, the gum may be dispensed with and the red ferroprussiate solution only be used.

3237. It must be well understood that these forms give no indication by their appearance of the relative strength of the magnetic force at different places, inasmuch as the appearance of the lines depends greatly upon the quantity of filings and the amount of tapping; but the direction and forms of the lines are well given, and these indicate, in a considerable degree, the direction in which the forces increase and diminish.

3238. Pl. XVI, *Fig. 1*, shows the forms assumed about a bar-magnet. On using a little electro-magnet and varying the strength of the current passed through it, I could not find that a variation in the strength of the magnet produced any alteration in the forms of the lines of force external to it. *Fig. 2* shows the lines over a pole, and *Fig. 3* those between contrary poles. The latter accord with the magnetic curves, as determined and described by Dr. Roget and others, with the assumption of the poles as centres of force. The difference between them and those belonging to a continuous magnet, shown in *Fig. 1*, is evident. *Figs. 4, 5* show the lines produced by short magnets. In the latter case the magnet was a steel disc about one inch in diameter and 0.05 in thickness. *Fig. 6* shows the result when a bar-magnet is broken in half, but not separated. *Fig. 7* shows the development of the lines externally at the two new ends as the halves are more and more separated (3231). *Figs. 8, 9* and *10* present the results, with the two halves or new magnets in different positions. *Figs. 11, 12, 13* and *14* show the results with disc magnets. *Fig. 15* shows the condition of a system of magnetic forces when it is inclosed by a larger one, and is contrary to it. *Fig. 16* shows the coalescence of the lines of force (3226) when the magnets are so placed that the polarities are in accordance.

3239. Pl. XVI, *Fig. 17* exhibits the lines of force round a vertical wire carrying a current of electricity. Whether the wire was thick or thin appeared to make no difference as to the intensity of the forces, the current remaining the same. *Fig. 18* represents the lines round two like currents when within mutual influence. *Fig. 19* shows the result when a third current is introduced in the contrary direction. *Fig. 20* presents the transition to a helix of three convolutions. *Fig. 21* indicates the direction of the lines within and outside the end of a cylindrical helix, on a plane through its axis. *Fig. 22* presents the effect when a very small soft iron core is within the helix.

3240. Pl. XVI, *Figs. 23* and *24*, give an experimental illustration of the principles which I have adopted in relation to atmospheric magnetism and the general cause of the daily variations, &c. (2864, 2917). A hemisphere of pure nickel presented to me by Dr. Percy was supported with its flat face uppermost, and a large ring arranged round it to carry paper, which, resting both on the ring and the nickel, could then have iron filings sprinkled and arranged in form on it. The end of a bar-magnet in the same horizontal plane was adjusted about 2 inches from the nickel, and thus the forms of the lines of force associated with this pole could be determined over the place of the nickel hemisphere, under different circumstances, or even when it was removed. When the nickel was away, the forms of the lines of force were as in *Fig. 23*; when the nickel was there, they were as in *Fig. 24*. The application of a spirit-lamp to the nickel when in its place, raised its temperature to such a degree (above 600° Fahr.) that it lost its ordinary magnetic condition; and then the forms of the lines of force, as shown by filings, were the same as if the nickel was away. Removing the lamp, I was able to obtain the disposition of filings on successive pieces of paper, and as many as four results, like *Fig. 23*, could be procured before the temperature had sunk so much as to cause the production of lines of force corresponding to *Fig. 24*.

3241. These are exactly the same results with nickel as those I have assumed for the oxygen of the atmosphere. The change in the forms of the lines about the cooling nickel in this experiment are the same changes as those I have figured in the type globe of cooling air (2865, 2874). Both nickel and oxygen are paramagnetic bodies, and change in the *same direction* by heating and cooling; and as the period of change with oxygen extends through degrees above and below common temperature (2861), so inflections of the lines of force passing through the atmosphere, correspondent to those of the heating and cooling nickel, *must* take place to some extent. It is seen in the nickel results that lines of force entirely outside of it do not for that reason continue an undeviating course, but are curved to and fro in consequence of the disposition of other lines within the nickel; a result which, without reference to either one view or another of the physical action of the magnetic force, must be as true in the oxygen case as in the nickel case, because of the definite character of the magnetic force, whether represented by centres of action or by lines of power.

3242. Whether the amount of the deflection in the case of the atmosphere corresponds with the facts registered by observers, is a question which cannot be answered, I suppose, until we know the effect of very low temperatures upon the magnetic force of the atmosphere. In the nickel experiment the deflection is in places 30° or 40°; in nature the effect to be accounted for is not more than 13 or 14 minutes.

Royal Institution, December 20, 1851

Papers on Electricity from the Quarterly Journal of Science, Philosophical Magazine, *&c.*

On Some New Electro-Magnetical Motions and on the Theory of Magnetism[1]

In making an experiment the beginning of last week, to ascertain the position of the magnetic needle to the connecting wire of a voltaic apparatus, I was led into a series which appear to me to give some new views of electro-magnetic action, and of magnetism altogether; and to render more distinct and clear those already taken. After the great men who have already experimented on the subject, I should have felt doubtful that anything I could do could be new or possess an interest, but that the experiments seem to me to reconcile considerably the

[1] *Quarterly Journal of Science*, XII, 74.

opposite opinions that are entertained on it. I am induced in consequence to publish this account of them, in the hope they will assist in making this important branch of knowledge more nearly perfect.

The apparatus used was that invented by Dr. Hare of Philadelphia, and called by him a calorimotor; it is in fact a single pair of large plates, each having its power heightened by the induction of others, consequently all the positions and motions of the needles, poles, &c., are opposite to those produced by an apparatus of several plates; for, if a current be supposed to exist in the connecting wire of a battery from the zinc to the copper, it will be in each

PLATE XVII

Fig. 1

Fig. 2

Fig. 3

Fig. 4

Fig. 5

Fig. 6

Fig. 7

Fig. 8

Fig. 9

Fig. 10

Fig. 11

Fig. 12

Fig. 13

Fig. 14

Fig. 15

Fig. 16

connected pair of plates from the copper to the zinc; and the wire I have used is that connection between the two plates of one pair. In the diagrams I may have occasion to subjoin, the ends of a connecting wire, marked Z and C, are connected with the zinc and copper-plates respectively; the sections are all horizontal and seen from above, and the arrow-heads have been used sometimes to mark the pole of a needle or magnet which points to the north, and sometimes to mark the direction of motion; no difficulty can occur in ascertaining to which of those uses any particular head is applied.

On placing the wire perpendicularly, and bringing a needle towards it to ascertain the attractive and repulsive positions with regard to the wire; instead of finding these to be four, one attractive and one repulsive for each pole, I found them to be eight, two attractive and two repulsive for each pole; thus allowing the needle to take its natural position across the wire, which is exactly opposite to that pointed out by Oersted for the reason before mentioned, and then drawing the support away from the wire slowly, so as to bring the north pole, for instance, nearer to it, there is attraction, as is to be expected; but on continuing to make the end of the needle come nearer to the wire, repulsion takes place, though the wire still be on the same side of the needle. If the wire be on the other side of the same pole of the needle, it will repel it when opposite to most parts between the centre of motion and the end; but there is a small portion at the end where it attracts it. Pl. XVII, *Fig. 1*, shows the positions of attraction for the north and south poles, *Fig. 2* the positions of repulsion.

If the wire be made to approach perpendicularly towards one pole of the needle, the pole will pass off on one side, in that direction which the attraction and repulsion at the extreme point of the pole would give; but, if the wire be continually made to approach the centre of motion, by either the one or other side of the needle, the tendency to move in the former direction diminishes; it then becomes null, and the needle is quite indifferent to the wire, and ultimately the motion is reversed, and the needle powerfully endeavours to pass the opposite way.

It is evident from this that the centre of the active portion of either limb of the needle, or the true pole, as it may be called, is not at the extremity of the needle, but may be represented by a point generally in the axis of the needle, at some little distance from the end. It was evident, also, that this point had a tendency to revolve round the wire, and necessarily, therefore, the wire round the point; and as the same effects in the opposite direction took place with the other pole, it was evident that each pole had the power of acting on the wire by itself, and not as any part of the needle, or as connected with the opposite pole.

By attending to Pl. XVII, *Fig. 3*, which represents sections of the wire in its different positions to the needle, all this will be plain; the active poles are represented by two dots, and the arrow-heads show the tendency of the wire in its positions to go round these poles.

Several important conclusions flow from these facts; such as that there is no attraction between the wire and either pole of a magnet; that the wire ought to revolve round a magnetic pole and a magnetic pole round the wire; that both attraction and repulsion of connecting wires, and probably magnets, are compound actions; that true magnetic poles are centres of action induced by the whole bar, &c., &c. Such of these as I have been able to confirm by experiment, shall be stated, with their proofs.

The revolution of the wire and the pole round each other being the first important thing required to prove the nature of the force mutually exerted by them, various means were tried to succeed in producing it. The difficulty consisted in making a suspension of part of the wire sufficiently delicate for the motion, and yet affording sufficient mass of matter for contact. This was overcome in the following manner: A piece of brass wire had a small button of silver soldered on to its end, a little cup was hollowed in the silver, and the metal being amalgamated, it would then retain a drop of mercury in it, though placed upside down for an upper centre of motion; for a lower centre, a similar cup was made of copper, into which a little mercury was put; this was placed in a jar of water under the former centre. A piece of copper wire was then bent into the form of a crank, its ends amalgamated, and the distances being arranged, they were placed in the cups. To prevent too much friction from the weight of the wire on the lower cup, it had been passed through a cork duly adjusted in size, and that being pushed down on the wire till immersed in the water, the friction became very little, and the wire very mobile, yet with good contacts. The plates being then connected with the two cups, the apparatus was completed. In this state, a magnetic pole being brought to the centre of motion of the crank, the wire immediately made an effort to revolve until it struck the magnet, and that being rapidly brought round to the other side, the wire again made a revolution, giving evidence that it would have gone round continually but for the extension of the magnet on the outside. To do away with this impediment, the wire and lower metal cup were removed, and a deep basin of mercury placed beneath; at the bottom of this was a piece of wax, and a small round bar magnet was stuck upright in it, so that one pole was about half or three-fourths of an inch above the surface of the mercury, and directly under the silver cup. A straight piece of copper wire, long enough to reach from the cup, and dip about half an inch into the mercury, had its ends amalgamated, and a small round piece of cork fixed on to one of them to make it more buoyant; this being dipped in the mercury close beside the magnet, and the other end placed under the little cup, the wire remained upright, for the adhesion of the cork to the magnet was sufficient for that purpose, and yet at its lower end had freedom of motion round the pole. The connection being now made from the plates to the upper cup, and to the mercury below, the wire immediately began to revolve round the pole of the magnet, and continued to do so as long as the connection was continued.

When it was wished to give a large diameter to the circle described by the wire, the cork was removed from the magnet, and a little loop of platinum passed round the magnet and wire, to prevent them from separating too far. Revolution again took place on making the connection, but more slowly as the distance increased.

The direction in which the wire moved was according to the way in which the connections were made, and to the magnetic pole brought into action. When the upper part of the wire was connected with the zinc, and the lower with the copper plate, the motion round the north and south poles of a magnet were as in Pl. XVII, *Figs. 4* and *5*, looking from above; when the connections were reversed, the motions were in the opposite direction.

On bringing the magnetic pole from the centre of motion to the side of the wire, there was neither attraction nor repulsion; but the wire endeavoured to pass off in a circle, still having the pole for its centre, and that either to the one side or the other, according to the above law.

When the pole was on the outside of the wire, the wire moved in a direction directly contrary to that taken when the pole was in the inside; but it did not move far, the endeavour was still to go round the pole as a centre, and it only moved till that power and the power which retained it in a circle about its own axis were equipoised.

The next object was to make the magnet revolve round the wire. This was done by so loading one pole of the small magnet with platinum that the magnet would float upright in a basin of mercury, with the other pole above its surface; then connecting the mercury with one plate and bringing a wire from the other perpendicularly into it in another part near the floating magnet; the upper pole immediately began to revolve round the wire, whilst the lower pole being removed away caused no interference or counteracting effect.

The motions were again according to the pole and the connections. When the upper part of the wire was in contact with the zinc plate, and the lower with the copper, the direction of the curve described by the north and south poles was as in Pl. XVII, *Figs. 6* and *7*. When the connections were reversed, the motions were in the opposite directions.

Having succeeded thus far, I endeavoured to make a wire and a magnet revolve on their own axis by preventing the rotation in a circle round them, but have not been able to get the slightest indications that such can be the case; nor does it, on consideration, appear probable. The motions evidently belong to the current, or whatever else it be, that is passing through the wire, and not to the wire itself, except as the vehicle of the current. When that current is made a curve by the form of the wire, it is easy to conceive how, in revolving, it should take the wire with it; but when the wire is straight, the current may revolve without any motion being communicated to the wire through which it passes.

M. Ampère has shown that two similar connecting wires, by which is meant, having currents in the same direction through them, attract each other, and that two wires having currents in opposite directions through them, repel each other, the attraction and repulsion taking place in right lines between them. From the attraction of the north pole of a needle on one side the wire, and of the south on the other, and the repulsion of the poles on the opposite sides, Dr. Wollaston called this magnetism *vertiginous*, and conceived that the phenomena might be explained upon the supposition of an electro-magnetic current passing round the axis of the conjunctive wire, its direction depending upon that of the electric current, and exhibiting north and south powers on the opposite sides. It is, indeed, an ascertained fact, that the connecting wire has different powers at its opposite sides; or rather, each power continues all round the wire, the direction being the same, and hence it is evident that the attractions and repulsions of M. Ampère's wires are not simple, but complicated results.

A simple case which may be taken of magnetic motion is the circle described by the wire or the pole round each other. If a wire be made into a helix, as M. Ampère describes, the arrangement is such that all the vertiginous magnetism, as Dr. Wollaston has named it, of the one kind, or one side of the wire, is concentrated in the axis of the helix, whilst the contrary kind is very much diffused, i.e., the power exerted by a great length of wire to make a pole pass one way round it, all tends to carry that pole to a particular spot, whilst the opposite power is diffused and much weakened in its action on any one pole. Hence the power on one side of the wire is very much concentrated, and its particular effects brought out strongly, whilst that on the other is rendered insensible. A means is thus obtained of separating, as it were, the one power from the other; but when this is done, and we examine the end of the helix, it is found very much to resemble a magnetic pole; the power is concentrated at the extremity of the helix; it attracts or repels one pole in all directions; and I find that it causes the revolution of the connecting wire round it, just as a magnetic pole does. Hence it may, for the present, be considered identical with a magnetic pole; and I think that the experimental evidence of the ensuing pages will much strengthen that opinion.

Assuming, then, that the pole of a magnetic needle presents us with the properties of one side of the wire, the phenomena it presents with the wire itself offer us a means of analysis, which, probably, if well pursued, will give us a much more intimate knowledge of the state of the powers active in magnets. When it is placed near the wire, always assuming the latter to be connected with the battery, it is made to revolve round it, passing towards that side by which it is attracted, and from that side by which it is repelled, i.e., the pole is at once attracted and repelled by equal powers,

and therefore neither recedes nor approaches; but the powers being from opposite sides of the wire, the pole in its double effort to recede from one side and approach the other revolves in the circle, that circle being evidently decided by the particular pole and state of the wire, and deducible from the law before mentioned.

The phenomena presented by the approximation of one pole to two or more wires, or two poles to one or more wires, offer many illustrations of this double action, and will lead to more correct views of the magnet. These experiments are easily made by loading a needle with platinum at one pole, that the other may float above mercury, or by almost floating a small magnetic needle by cork in a basin of water, at the bottom of which is some mercury with which to connect the wires. In describing them I shall refrain from entering into all their variations, or pursuing them to such conclusions as are not directly important.

Two similar wires, Ampère has shown, attract each other; and Sir H. Davy has shown that the filings adhering to them attract from one to another on the same side. They are in that position in which the north and south influence of the different wires attract each other. They seem also to neutralize each other in the parts that face, for the magnetic pole is quite inactive between them, but if put close together, it moves round the outside of both, circulating round them as round one wire, and their influences being in the same direction, the greatest effect is found to be at the farther outside surfaces of the wires. If several similar wires be put together, side by side like a ribbon, the result is the same, and the needle revolves round them all; the internal wires appear to lose part of their force, which is carried on towards the extreme wire in opposite directions, so that the floating pole is accelerated in its motion as it passes by the edges that they form. If, in place of a ribbon of parallel wires, a slip of metal be used, the effect is the same, and the edges act as if they contained in a concentrated state the power that belonged to the inner portion of the slip. In this way we procure the means of removing, as it were, in that direction, the two sides of the wire from each other.

If two wires in opposite states be arranged parallel to each other, and the pole be brought near them, it will circulate round either of them in obedience to the law laid down; but as the wires have opposite currents, it moves in opposite directions round the two, so that when equidistant from them, the pole is propelled in a right line perpendicular to the line which joins them, either receding or approaching; and if it approaches, passing between and then receding; hence it exhibits the curious appearance of first being attracted by the two wires, and afterwards repelled (Pl. XVII, *Fig. 8*). If the connection with both wires be inverted, or if the pole be changed, the line it describes is in the opposite direction. If these two opposite currents be made by bending a piece of silked wire parallel to itself, *Fig. 9*, it, when connected with the apparatus, becomes a curious magnet; with the north pole, for instance, it attracts powerfully on one side at the line between the two currents, but repels strongly to the right or left; whilst on the other side the line repels the north pole, but attracts it strongly to the right or left. With the south pole the attractions and repulsions are reversed.

When both poles of the needle were allowed to come into action on the wire or wires, the effects were in accordance with those described. When a magnetic needle was floated on water, and the perpendicular wire brought towards it, the needle turned round more or less, until it took a direction perpendicular to, and across the wire, the poles being in such positions that either of them alone would revolve round the wire in a circle proceeding by the side to which it had gone, according to the law before stated. The needle then approaches to the wire, its centre (not either pole) going in a direct line towards it. If the wire be then lifted up and put down the other side of the needle, the needle passes on in the same line receding from the wire, so that the wire seems here to be both attractive and repulsive of the needle. This effect will be readily understood from Pl. XVII, *Fig. 10*, where the poles and direction of the wire are not marked, because they are the same as before. If either be reversed, the others reverse themselves. The experiment is analogous to the one described above; there the pole passed between two dissimilar wires, here the wire between two dissimilar poles.

If two dissimilar wires be used, and the magnet have both poles active, it is repelled, turned round, or is attracted in various ways, until it settles across between the two wires; all its motions being easily reducible to those impressed on the poles by the wires, both wires and both poles being active in giving that position. Then if it happens not to be midway between the two, or they are not of equal power, it goes slowly towards one of them,

and acts with it just as the single wire of the last paragraph.

Pl. XVII, *Figs. 11* and *12* exhibit more distinctly the direction of the forces which influence the poles in passing between two dissimilar wires: *Fig. 11*, when the pole draws up between the wires; *Fig. 12*, the pole thrown out from between them. The poles and state of the wire are not marked, because the diagrams illustrate the attraction and repulsion of both poles; for any particular pole, the connection of the wires must be accordingly.

If one of the poles be brought purposely near either wire in the position in which it appears to attract most strongly, still if freedom of motion be given by a little tapping, the needle will slip along till it stands midway across the wire.

A beautiful little apparatus has been made by M. de la Rive to whom I am indebted for one of them, consisting of a small voltaic combination floating by a cork; the ends of the little zinc and copper slips come through the cork, and are connected above by a piece of silked wire which has been wrapped four or five times round a cylinder, and the wires tied together with a silk thread so as to form a close helix about one inch in diameter. When placed on acidulated water it is very obedient to the magnet and serves admirably to transform, as it were, the experiments with straight wires that have been mentioned, to the similar ones made with helices. Thus, if a magnet be brought near it and level with its axis, the apparatus will recede or turn round until that side of the curve next to the nearest pole is the side attracted by it. It will then approach the pole, pass it, recede from it until it gains the middle of the magnet, where it will rest like an equator round it, its motions and position being still the same as those before pointed out (Pl. XVII, *Fig. 13*). If brought near either pole it will still return to the centre; and if purposely placed in the opposite direction at the centre of the magnet, it will pass off by either pole to which it happens to be nearest, being apparently first attracted by the pole and afterwards repelled, as is actually the case; will, if any circumstance disturbs its perpendicularity to the magnet, turn half way round; and will then pass on to the magnet again, into the position first described. If, instead of passing the magnet through the curve, it be held over it, it stands in a plane perpendicular to the magnet, but in an opposite direction to the former one. So that a magnet, both within and without this curve, causes it to direct.

When the poles of the magnet are brought over this floating curve, there are some movements and positions which at first appear anomalous, but are by a little attention easily reducible to the circular movement of the wire about the pole. I do not think it necessary to state them particularly.

The attractive and repulsive positions of this curve may be seen by *Fig. 13*, the curve in the two dotted positions is attracted by the poles near them. If the positions be reversed, repulsion takes place.

From the central situation of the magnet in these experiments, it may be concluded that a strong and powerful curve or helix would suspend a powerful needle in its centre. By making a needle almost float on water and putting the helix over a glass tube, this result has in part been obtained.

In all these magnetic movements between wires and poles, those which resemble attraction and repulsion, that is to say those which took place in right lines, required at least either two poles and a wire, or two wires and a pole; for such as appear to exist between the wire and either pole of the battery are deceptive and may be resolved into the circular motion. It has been allowed, I believe, by all who have experimented on these phenomena, that the similar powers repel and the dissimilar powers attract each other; and that, whether there exist in the poles of the magnets or in the opposite sides of conducting wires. This being admitted, the simplest cases of magnetic action will be those exerted by the poles of helices, for, as they offer the magnetic states of the opposite sides of the wire independent, or nearly so, one of the other, we are enabled by them to bring into action two of those powers only, to the exclusion of the rest; and, from experiment it appears that when the powers are similar, repulsion takes place, and when dissimilar, attraction; so that two cases of repulsion and one of attraction are produced by the combination of these magnetic powers.[1]

The next cases of magnetic motion, in the order of simplicity, are those where three powers are concerned, or those produced by a pole and a wire. These are the circular motions described in the early part of this paper. They resolve themselves into two; a north pole and the wire round each other, and a south pole and the wire round each other. The law which governs these motions has been stated.

Then follow the actions between two wires: these when similarly electrified attract as M. Ampère has shown; for then the opposite sides are towards each other, and the four powers all combine to draw the currents together, forming a double attraction; but when the wires are dissimilar they repel, because, then on both sides of the wire the same powers are opposed, and cause a double repulsion.

The motions that result from the action of two dissimilar poles and a wire next follow: the wire endeavours to describe opposite circles round the poles; consequently it is carried in a line passing through the central part of the needle in which they are situated. If the wire is on the side on which the circles close together, it is attracted; if on the opposite side, from whence the circles open, it is repelled (Pl. XVII, *Fig. 10*).

The motions of a pole with two wires are almost the same as the last; when the wires are dissimilar, the pole endeavours to form two opposite circles about the wires; when it is on that side of the wires on which the circles meet, it is attracted; when on the side on which they open, it is repelled (Pl. XVII, *Figs. 8, 11, 12*).

Finally, the motion between two poles and two dissimilar wires, is an instance where several powers combine to produce an effect.

M. Ampère, whilst reasoning on the discovery of M. Oersted, was led to the adoption of a theory, by which he endeavoured to account for the properties of magnets, by the existence of concentric currents of electricity in them, arranged round the axis of the magnet. In support of this theory, he first formed the spiral or helix wire, in which currents could be made to pass nearly perpendicular to, and round the axis of a cylinder. The ends of such helices were found when connected with the voltaic apparatus to be in opposite magnetic states, and to present the appearance of poles. Whilst pursuing the mutual action of poles and wires, and tracing out the circular movements, it seemed to me that much information respecting the competency of this theory might be gained from an attempt to trace the action of the helix, and compare it with that of the magnet more rigorously than had yet been done; and to form artificial electro-magnets, and analyse natural ones. In doing this, I think I have so far succeeded as to trace the action of an electro-magnetic pole, either in attracting or repelling, to the circulating motion before described.

---

[1] This is perhaps not strictly true, because, though the opposite powers are weakened, they still remain in action.

If three inches of connecting wire be taken, and a magnetic pole be allowed to circulate round the middle of it, describing a circle of a little less than one inch in diameter, it will be moved with equal force in all parts of the circle (Pl. XVII, *Fig. 14*); bend then the wire into a circle, leaving that part round which the pole revolves perpendicularly undisturbed, as seen by the dotted lines, and make it a condition that the pole be restrained from moving out of the circle by a radius. It will immediately be evident that the wire now acts very differently on the pole in the different parts of the circle it describes. Every part of it will be active at the same time on the pole, to make it move through the centre of the wire ring, whilst as it passes away from that position the powers diverge from it, and it is either removed from their action or submitted to opposing ones, until on its arriving at the opposite part of the circle it is urged by a very small portion indeed of those which moved it before. As it continues to go round, its motion is accelerated, the forces rapidly gather together on it, until it again reaches the centre of the wire ring where they are at their highest, and afterwards diminish as before. Thus the pole is perpetually urged in a circle, but with powers constantly changing.

If the wire ring be conceived to be occupied by a plane, then the centre of that plane is the spot where the powers are most active on the pole, and move it with most force. Now this spot is actually the pole of this magnetic apparatus. It seems to have powers over the circulating pole, making it approach or attracting it on the one side, and making it recede or repelling it on the other, with powers varying as the distance; but its powers are only apparent, for the force is in the ring, and this spot is merely the place where they are most accumulated; and though it seems to have opposite powers, namely those of attracting and repelling; yet this is merely a consequence of its situation in the circle, the motion being uniform in its direction, and really and truly impressed on the pole by its motor, the wire.

At page 799 it was shown that two or more similar wires put together in a line, acted as one; the power being, as it were, accumulated towards the extreme wires, by a species of induction taking place among them all; and at the same time was noticed the similar case of a plate of metal connecting the ends of the apparatus, its powers being apparently strongest at the edges. If, then, a series of concentric rings be placed one inside the other, they having the electric current sent through them in the same direction; of if, which is the same thing, a flat spiral of silked wire passing from the centre to the circumference be formed, and its ends be in connection with the battery (Pl. XVII, *Fig. 15*), then the circle of revolution would still be as in *Fig.* 14, passing through the centre of the rings or spiral, but the power would be very much increased. Such a spiral, when made, beautifully illustrates this fact; it takes up an enormous quantity of iron filings, which approach to the form of cones, so strong is the action at the centre; and its action on the needle by the different sides, is eminently powerful.

If in place of putting ring within ring, they be placed side by side, so as to form a cylinder, or if a helix be made, then the same kind of neutralization takes place in the intermediate wires, and accumulated effect in the extreme ones, as before. The line which the pole would now travel, supposing the inner end of the radius to move over the inner and outer surface of the cylinder, would be through the axis of the cylinder round the edge to one side, back up that side, and round to the axis, down which it would go, as before. In this case the force would probably be greatest at the two extremes of the axis of the cylinder, and least at the middle distance on the outside.

Now consider the internal space of the cylinder filled up by rings or spirals, all having the currents in the same direction; the direction and kind of force would be the same, but very much strengthened: it would exist in the strongest degree down the axis of the mass, because of the circular form, and it would have the two sides of the point in the centre of the simple ring, which *seemed* to possess attractive and repulsive powers on the pole removed to the ends of the cylinder; giving rise to two points, apparently distinct in their action, one being attractive, and the other repulsive, of the poles of a magnet. Now conceive that the pole is not confined to a motion about the sides of the ring, or the flat spiral, or cylinder; it is evident that if placed in the axis of any of them at a proper distance for action, it, being impelled by two or more powers in equal circles, would move in a right line in the intersection of those circles, and approach directly to or recede from, the points before spoken of, giving the appearance of a direct attraction and repulsion; and if placed out of that axis, it would move towards or from the same spot in a curve line, its direction and force being determined by the curve lines representing the active forces from the portions of wire forming the ends of the cylinder, spiral, or ring, and the strength of those forces.

Thus the phenomena of a helix, or a solid cylinder of spiral silked wire, are reduced to the simple revolution of the magnetic pole round the connecting wire of the battery, and its resemblance, to a magnet is so great, that the strongest presumption arises in the mind that they both owe their powers, as M. Ampère has stated, to the same cause. Filings of iron sprinkled on paper held over this cylinder, arranged themselves in curved lines passing from one end to the other, showing the path the pole would follow, and so they do over a magnet; the ends attract and repel as do those of a magnet; and in almost every point do they agree. The following experiments will illustrate and confirm the truth of these remarks on the action of the ring, helix, or cylinder; and will show in what their actions agree with, and differ (for there are differences) from, the action of a magnet.

A small magnet being nearly floated in water by cork, a ring of silked copper wire (Pl. XVII, Fig. 16), having its ends connected with the battery, was brought near its poles in different positions; sometimes the pole was repelled from, sometimes attracted into, the ring, according to the position of the pole, and the connections with the battery. If the wire happened to be opposite to the pole, the pole passed sideways and outwards when it was repelled, and sideways and inwards when it was attracted; and on entering within the ring and passing through, it moved sideways in the opposite direction, endeavouring to go round the wire. The actions also presented by M. de la Rive's ring are actions of this kind, and indeed are those which best illustrate the relations between the ring and the pole; some of them have been mentioned, and if referred to, will be found to accord with the statement given.

With a flat spiral the magnetic power was very much increased; and when the rings were not continued to the centre, the power of the inner edge over the outer was well shown either by the pole of a needle, or iron filings. With the latter the appearance was extremely beautiful and instructive; when laid flat upon a heap of them, they arranged themselves in lines, passing through the ring parallel to its axis, and then folding up on either side as radii round to the edge, where they met; so that they repre-

sented, exactly, the lines which a pole would have described round the sides of the rings; and those filings which were in the axis of the rings, stood up in perpendicular filaments, half an inch long and so as to form an actual axis to the ring, tending neither one way nor the other, but according in their form and arrangement with what has been described; whilst the intermediate portion also formed long threads, bending this way and that from the centre, more or less, according as they were farther from, or nearer to it.

With a helix the phenomena were interesting, because according to the view given of the attractions and repulsions, that is of the motions toward and from the ends, some conclusions should follow, that if found to be true in fact, and to hold also with magnets, would go far to prove the identity of the two. Thus the end which seems to attract a certain pole on the outside, ought to repel it as if it were on the inside, and that which seems to repel it on the outside, ought to appear to attract it on the inside; i.e., that as the motions on the inside and outside are in different directions for the same pole, it would move in the one case to and in the other case from the same end of the helix. Some phenomena of this kind have been described in explaining Pl. XVII, *Figs. 8, 11, 12,* and *13*; others are as follows.

A helix of silked copper wire was made round a glass tube, the tube being about an inch in diameter; the helix was about three inches long. A magnetic needle nearly as long was floated with cork, so as to move about in water with the slightest impulse. The helix being connected with the apparatus and put into the water in which the needle lay, its ends appeared to attract and repel the poles of the needle according to the laws before mentioned. But, if that end which attracted one of the poles of the needle was brought near that pole, it entered the glass tube, but did not stop just within side in the neighbourhood of this pole (as we may call it for the moment) of the helix, but passed up the tube, drawing the whole needle in, and went to the opposite pole of the helix, or the one which on the outside would have repelled it; on trying the other pole of the magnet with its corresponding end or pole of the helix the same effect took place; the needle pole entered the tube and passed to the other end, taking the whole needle into the same position it was in before.

Thus each end of the helix seemed to attract and repel both poles of the needle; but this is only a natural consequence of the circulating motion before experimentally demonstrated, and each pole would have gone through the helix and round on the outside, but for the counteraction of the opposite pole. It has been stated that the poles circulate in opposite directions round the wires, and they would consequently circulate in opposite directions through and round the helix; when, therefore, one end of the helix was near that pole, which would, according to the law stated, enter it and endeavour to go through, it would enter, and it would continue its course until the other pole, at first at a distance, would be brought within action of the helix; and, when they were both equally within the helix and consequently equally acted on, their tendency to go in different directions would counterbalance each other, and the needle would remain motionless. If it were possible to separate the two poles from each other, they would dart out of each end of the helix, being apparently repelled by those parts that before seemed to attract them, as is evident from the first and many other experiments.

By reversing the needle and placing it purposely in the helix in that position, the poles of the needle and the corresponding poles of the helix as they attract on the outside, are brought together on the inside, but both pairs now seem to repel; and, whichever end of the helix the needle happens to be nearest to, it will be thrown out at. This motion may be seen to exhibit in its passing state, attraction between similar poles, since the inner and active pole is drawn towards that end on the inside, by which it is thrown off on the outside.[1]

These experiments may be made with the single curve of M. de la Rive, in which case it is the wire that moves and not the magnet; but as the motions are reciprocal, they may be readily anticipated.

A plate of copper was bent nearly into a cylinder, and its edges made to dip into two portions of mercury; when placed in a current it acted exactly as a helix.

A solid cylinder of silked wire was made exactly in fashion like a helix, but that one length of the wire served as the axis, and the folds were repeated over and over again. This as well as the former helix, had poles the same in every respect as to kind as the north and south poles

of a magnet; they took up filings, they made the connecting wire revolve, they attracted and repelled in four parallel positions as is described of common magnets in the first pages of this paper, and filings sprinkled on paper over them, formed curves from one to the other as with magnets; these lines indicating the direction in which a north or south pole would move about them.

Now with respect to the accordance which is found between the appearances of a helix or cylinder when in the voltaic circuit, and a cylindrical common magnet, or even a regular square bar magnet; it is so great, as at first to leave little doubt, that whatever it is that causes the properties of the one, also causes the properties of the other, for the one may be substituted for the other in, I believe, every magnetical experiment; and, in the bar magnet, all the effects on a single pole or filings, &c., agree with the notion of a circulation, which if the magnet were not solid would pass through its centre, and back on the outside.

The following, however, are differences between the appearances of a magnet and those of a helix or cylinder: one pole of a magnet attracts the opposite pole of a magnetic needle in all directions and positions; but when the helix is held alongside the needle nearly parallel to it, and with opposite poles together, so that attraction should take place, and then the helix is moved on so that the pole of the needle gradually comes nearer to the middle of the helix, repulsion generally takes place before the pole gets to the middle of the helix, and in a situation where with the magnet it would be attracted. This is probably occasioned by the want of continuity in the sides of the curves or elements of the helix, in consequence of which the unity of action which takes place in the rings into which a magnet may be considered to be divided is interfered with and disturbed.

Another difference is that the poles, or those spots to which the needle points when perpendicular to the ends or sides of a magnet or helix, and where the motive power may be considered perhaps as most concentrated, are in the helix at the extremity of its axis, and not any distance in from the end; whilst in the most regular magnets they are almost always situate in the axis at some distance in from the end; a needle pointing perpendicularly towards the end of a magnet is in a line with its axis, but perpendicularly to the side, it points to a spot some distance from the end, whilst in the helix, or cylinder, it still points to the end. This varia-

[1] The magnetizing power of the helix is so strong that if the experiment be made slowly, the needle will have its magnetism changed and the result will be fallacious.

tion is, probably, to be attributed to the distribution of the exciting cause of magnetism in the magnet and helix. In the latter, it is necessarily uniform everywhere, inasmuch as the current of electricity is uniform. In the magnet it is probably more active in the middle than elsewhere; for as the north pole of a magnet brought near a south one increases its activity, and that the more as it is nearer, it is fair to infer that the similar parts which are actually united in the inner part of the bar have the same power. Thus a piece of soft iron put to one end of a horseshoe magnet, immediately moves the pole towards that end; but if it be then made to touch the other end also, the pole moves in the opposite direction, and is weakened; and it moves the farther, and is made weaker as the contact is more perfect. The presumption is that if it were complete, the two poles of the magnet would be diffused over the whole of its mass, the instrument there exhibiting no attractive or repulsive powers. Hence it is not improbable that, caused by some induction, a greater accumulation of power may take place in the middle of the magnet than at the end, and may cause the poles to be inwards, rather than at the extremities.

A third difference is that the similar poles of magnets, though they repel at most distances, yet when brought very near together, attract each other. This power is not strong, but I do not believe it is occasioned by the superior strength of one pole over the other, since the most equal magnets exert it, and since the poles as to their magnetism remain the same, and are able to take up as much, if not more, iron filings when together, as when separated, whereas opposite poles, when in contact, do not take up so much. With similar helix poles, this attraction does not take place.

The attempts to make magnets resembling the helix and the flat spirals, have been very unsuccessful. A plate of steel was formed into a cylinder and magnetized, one end was north all round, the other south; but the outside and the inside had the same properties, and no pole of a needle would have gone up the axis and down the sides, as with the helix, but would have stopped at the dissimilar pole of the needle. Hence it is certain that the rings of which the cylinder may be supposed to be formed are not in the same state as those of which the helix was composed. All attempts to magnetize a flat circular plate of steel, so as to have one pole in the centre of one side, and the other pole in the centre of the opposite side, for the purpose of imitating the flat spiral (Pl. XVII, *Fig. 15*), failed; nothing but an irregular distribution of the magnetism could be obtained.

M. Ampère is, I believe, undecided with regard to the size of the currents of electricity that are assumed to exist in magnets, perpendicular to their axis. In one part of his memoirs they are said, I think, to be concentric, but this cannot be the case with those of the cylinder magnet, except two be supposed in opposite directions, the one on the inside, the other on the outside surface. In another part, I believe, the opinion is advanced that they may be exceedingly small; and it is, perhaps, possible to explain the cause of the most irregular magnet by theoretically bending such small currents in the direction required.

In the previous attempt to explain some of the electro-magnetic motions, and to show the relation between electro and other magnets, I have not intended to adopt any theory of the cause of magnetism, nor to oppose any. It appears very probable that in the regular bar magnet, the steel, or iron, is in the same state as the copper wire of the helix magnet; and perhaps, as M. Ampère supports in his theory, by the same means, namely, currents of electricity; but still other proofs are wanting of the presence of a power like electricity than the magnetic effects only. With regard to the opposite sides of the connecting wire, and the powers emanating from them, I have merely spoken of them as two, to distinguish the one set of effects from the other. The high authority of Dr. Wollaston is attached to the opinion that a single electro-magnetic current passing round the axis of the wire in a direction determined by the position of the voltaic poles, is sufficient to explain all the phenomena.

M. Ampère, who has been engaged so actively in this branch of natural philosophy, drew from his theory, the conclusion that a circular wire forming part of the connection between the poles of the battery, should be directed by the earth's magnetism, and stand in a plane perpendicular to the magnetic meridian and the dipping needle. This result was said to be actually obtained, but its accuracy has been questioned, both on theoretical and experimental grounds. As the magnet directs the wire when in form of a curve, and the curve a needle, I endeavoured to repeat the experiment, and succeeded in the following manner. A voltaic combination of two plates was formed; these were connected by a copper wire, bent into a

PLATE XVIII

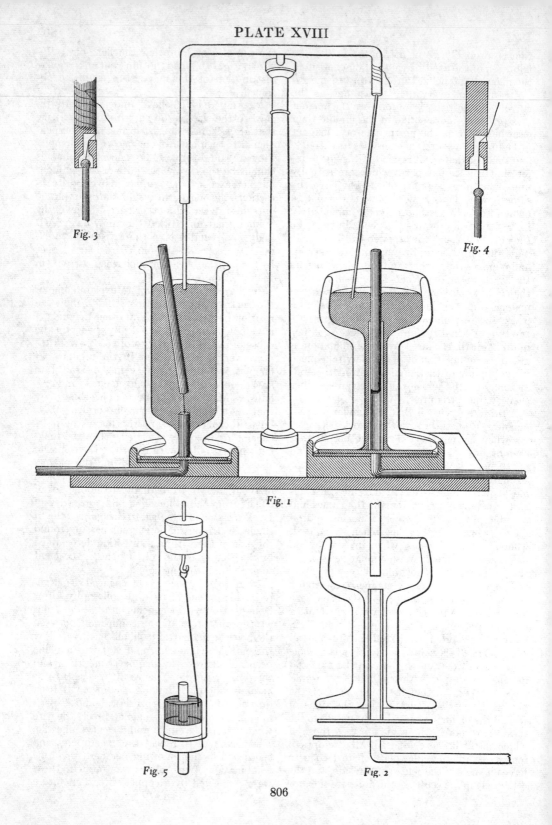

Fig. 3

Fig. 4

Fig. 1

Fig. 5

Fig. 2

circular form; the plates were put into a small glass jar with dilute acid, and the jar floated on the surface of water. Being then left to itself in a quiet atmosphere, the instrument so arranged itself that the curve was in a plane perpendicular to the magnetic meridian; when moved from this position, either one way or the other, it returned again; and on examining the side of the curve towards the north, it was found to be that, which, according to the law already stated, would be attracted by a south pole. A voltaic circle made in a silver capsule, and mounted with a curve, also produced the same effect; as did likewise, very readily, M. de la Rive's small ring apparatus.[1] When placed on acidulated water, the gas liberated from the plates prevented its taking up a steady position; but when put into a little floating cell, made out of the neck of a Florence flask, the whole readily took the position mentioned above, and even vibrated slowly about it.

As the straight connecting wire is directed by a magnet, there is every reason to believe that it will act in the same way with the earth, and take a direction perpendicular to the magnetic meridian. It also should act with the magnetic pole of the earth, as with the pole of a magnet, and endeavour to circulate round it. Theoretically, therefore, a horizontal wire perpendicular to the magnetic meridian, if connected first in one way with a voltaic battery, and then in the opposite way, should have its weight altered; for in the one case it would tend to pass in a circle downwards, and in the other upwards. This alteration should take place differently in different parts of the world. The effect is actually produced by the pole of a magnet, but I have not succeeded in obtaining it, employing only the polarity of the earth.— *September* 11, 1821.

Electro-magnetic Rotation Apparatus[2]

Since the paper in the preceding pages has been printed, I have had an apparatus made by Mr. Newman, of Lisle Street, for the revolutions of the wire round the pole, and a pole round the wire. When Hare's calorimoter was connected with it, the wire revolved so rapidly round the pole that the eye could scarcely follow the motion, and a single galvanic trough, containing ten pair of plates, of Dr. Wollaston's construction, had power enough to move the wire and the pole with considerable rapidity. It consists of a stand, about 3 inches by 6, from

one end of which a brass pillar rises about 6 inches high, and is then continued horizontally by a copper rod over the stand; at the other end of the stand a copper plate is fixed with a wire for communication, brought out to one side; in the middle is a similar plate and a wire; these are both fixed. A small shallow glass cup, supported on a hollow foot of glass has a plate of metal cemented to the bottom, so as to close the aperture and form a connection with the plate on the stand; the hollow foot is a socket, into which a small cylindrical bar magnet can be placed, so that the upper pole shall be a little above the edge of the glass; mercury is then poured in until the glass is nearly full; a rod of metal descends from the horizontal arm perpendicularly over this cup; a little cavity is hollowed at the end and amalgamated, and a piece of stiff copper wire is also amalgamated, and placed in it as described in the paper, except that it is attached by a piece of thread in the manner of a ligament, passing from the end of the wire to the inner surface of the cup; the lower end of the wire is amalgamated, and furnished with a small roller, which dips so as to be under the surface of the mercury in the cup beneath it.

The other plate on the stand has also its cup, which is nearly cylindrical, a metal pin passes through the bottom of it, to connect by contact with the plate below, and to the inner end of the pin a small round bar magnet is attached at one pole by thread, so as to allow the other to be above the surface of the mercury when the cup is filled, and have freedom of motion there; a thick wire descends from the rod above perpendicularly, so as to dip a little way into the mercury of the cup; it forms the connecting wire, and the pole can move in any direction round it. When the connections are made with the pillar, and either of the wires from the stand plates, the revolution of the wire, or pole above, takes place; or if the wires be connected with the two coming from the plates, motion takes place in both cups at once, and in accordance with the law stated in the paper. This apparatus may be much reduced in size, and made very much more delicate and sensible.

Description of an Electro-Magnetical Apparatus for the Exhibition of Rotary Motion[3]

The account given in the Miscellanea of the last *Journal* (p. 147), of the apparatus invented in illustration of the paper in the body of that number, being short and imperfect; a plate

[1] *Quarterly Journal of Science*, XII, 186.
[2] *Ibid.*
[3] *Ibid.* 283.

is given in the present number, presenting a section of that apparatus, and a view of a smaller apparatus, illustrative of the motions of the wire and the pole round each other. The larger apparatus is delineated (*Fig. 1*, Pl. XVIII) on a scale of one half. It consists of two glass vessels, placed side by side with their appendages. In that on the left of the plate the motion of a magnetic pole round the connecting wire of the voltaic battery is produced. That a current of voltaic electricity may be established through this cup, a hole is drilled at the bottom, and into this a copper pin is ground tight, which projects upwards a little way into the cup, and below is riveted to a small round plate of copper, forming part of the foot of the vessel. A similar plate of copper is fixed to the turned wooden base on which the cup is intended to stand, and a piece of strong copper wire, which is attached to it beneath, after proceeding downwards a little way, turns horizontally to the left hand, and forms one of the connections. The surfaces of these two plates intended to come together, are tinned and amalgamated, that they may remain longer clean and bright, and afford better contact. A small cylindrical and powerful magnet has one of its poles fastened to a piece of thread, which, at the other end, is attached to the copper pin at the bottom of the cup; and the height of the magnet and length of the thread are so adjusted that when the cup is nearly filled with clean mercury the free pole shall float almost upright on its surface.

A small brass pillar rises from the stand behind the glass vessels: an arm comes forward from the top of it, supporting at its extremity a cross wire, which at the place on the left hand, where it is perpendicularly over the cup just described, bends downwards, and is continued till it just dips into the centre of the mercurial surface. The wire is diminished in size for a short distance above the surface of the mercury, and its lower extremity amalgamated, for the purpose of ensuring good contact; and so also is the copper pin at the bottom of the cup. When the poles of a voltaic apparatus are connected with the brass pillar, and with the lateral copper wire, the upper pole of the magnet immediately rotates round the wire which dips into the mercury; and in one direction or the other, according as the connections are made.

The other vessel is of the form delineated in the plate. The stem is hollow and tubular; but, instead of being filled by a plug, as is the aperture in the first vessel, a small copper socket is

placed in it, and retained there by being fastened to a circular plate below, which is cemented to the glass foot, so that no mercury shall pass out by it. This plate is tinned and amalgamated on its lower surface, and stands on another plate and wire, just as in the former instance. A small circular bar magnet is placed in the socket, at any convenient height, and then mercury poured in until it rises so high that nothing but the projecting pole of the magnet is left above its surface at the centre. The forms and relative positions of the magnet, socket, plate, &c., are seen in Pl. XVIII, *Fig. 2.*

The cross wire supported by the brass pillar is also prolonged on the right hand, until over the centre of the vessel just described; it then turns downwards and descends about half an inch: it has its lower extremity hollowed out into a cup, the inner surface of which is well amalgamated. A smaller piece of copper wire has a spherical head fixed on to it, of such a size that it may play in the cup in the manner of a ball and socket-joint, and being well amalgamated, it, when in the cup, retains sufficient fluid mercury by capillary attraction to form an excellent contact with freedom of motion. The ball is prevented from falling out of the socket by a piece of fine thread, which, being fastened to it at the top, passes through a small hole at the summit of the cup, and is made fast on the outside of the thick wire. This is more minutely explained by Pl. XVIII, *Figs. 3* and *4.* The small wire is of such a length that it may dip a little way into the mercury, and its lower end is amalgamated. When the connections are so made with the pillar and right-hand wire, that the current of electricity shall pass through this moveable wire, it immediately revolves round the pole of the magnet, in a direction dependent on the pole used, and the manner in which the connections are made.

Pl. XVIII, *Fig. 5* is the delineation of a small apparatus, the wire in which revolves rapidly, with very little voltaic power. It consists of a piece of glass tube, the bottom part of which is closed by a cork, through which a small piece of soft iron wire passes, so as to project above and below the cork. A little mercury is then poured in, to form a channel between the iron wire and the glass tube. The upper orifice is also closed by a cork, through which a piece of platinum wire passes which is terminated within by a loop; another piece of wire hangs from this by a loop, and its lower end, which dips a very little way into the mercury, being amalgamated, it is preserved from adhering either to the iron wire or the glass. When a very minute voltaic combination is connected with the upper and lower ends of this apparatus, and the pole of a magnet is placed in contact with the external end of the iron wire, the moveable wire within rapidly rotates round the magnet thus formed at the moment; and by changing either the connection, or the pole of the magnet in contact with the iron, the direction of the motion itself is changed.

The small apparatus in the plate is not drawn to any scale. It has been made so small as to produce rapid revolutions, by the action of two plates of zinc and copper, containing not more than a square inch of surface each.

In place of the ball and socket-joint (Pl. XVIII, *Figs. 3* and *4*) loops may be used: or the fixed wire may terminate in a small cup containing mercury, with its aperture upwards, and the moveable wire may be bent into the form of a hook, of which the extremity should be sharpened, and rest in the mercury on the bottom of the cup.

Note on New Electro-Magnetical Motions[1]

At page 807 of this volume, I mentioned the expectation I entertained of making a wire through which a current of voltaic electricity was passing, obey the magnetic poles of the earth in the way it does the poles of a bar magnet. In the latter case it rotates, in the former I expected it would vary in weight; but the attempts I then made, to prove the existence of this action, failed. Since then I have been more successful, and the object of the present note is so far to complete that paper, as to show in what manner the rotative force of the wire round the terrestrial magnetic pole is exerted, and what the effects produced by it are.

Considering the magnetic pole as a mere centre of action, the existence and position of which may be determined by well-known means, it was shown by many experiments, in the paper, page 795, that the electro-magnetic wire would rotate round the pole, without any reference to the position of the axis joining it with the opposite pole in the same bar; for sometimes the axis was horizontal, at other times vertical, whilst the rotation continued the same. It was also shown that the wire, when influenced by the pole, moved laterally, its parts describing circles in planes perpendicular nearly to the wire itself. Hence the wire, when straight and confined to one point above, described a cone in its revolution, but when bent

[1] *Quarterly Journal of Science*, XII, 416.

into a crank, it described a cylinder; and the effect was evidently in all cases for each point of the wire to describe a circle round the pole, in a plane perpendicular to the current of electricity through the wire. In dispensing with the magnet, used to give these motions, and operating with the terrestrial magnetic pole, it was easy, by applying the information gained above, to deduce beforehand the direction the motions would probably take; for, assuming that the dipping-needle, if it does not point to the pole of the earth, points at least in the direction in which that pole is active, it is evident that a straight electro-magnetic wire, affected by the terrestrial as by an artificial pole, would move laterally at right angles to the needle; that is to say, it would endeavour to describe a cylinder round the pole, the radius of which may be represented by the line of the needle prolonged to the pole itself. As these cylinders, or circles, would be of immense magnitude, it was evident that only a very minute portion of them could be brought within reach of the experiment; still, however, that portion would be sufficient to indicate their existence, inasmuch as the motions taking place in the part under consideration, must be of the same kind, and in the same direction, as in every other part.

Reasoning thus, I presumed that an electro-magnetic wire should move laterally, or in a line perpendicular to the current of electricity passing through it, in a plane perpendicular to the dipping-needle; and the dip being here 72° 30', that plane would form an angle with the horizon of 17° 30', measured on the magnetic meridian. This is not so far removed from the horizontal plane, but that I expected to get motions in the latter, and succeeded in the following manner: a piece of copper wire, about .045 of an inch thick, and fourteen inches long, had an inch at each extremity bent at right angles, in the same direction, and the ends amalgamated; the wire was then suspended horizontally, by a long silk thread from the ceiling. A basin of clean pure mercury was placed under each extremity of the wire and raised until the ends just dipped into the metal. The mercury in both basins was covered by a stratum of diluted pure nitric acid, which dissolving any film, allowed free motion. Then connecting the mercury in one basin with one pole of Hare's calorimotor, the instrument mentioned page 795, the moment the other pole was connected with the other basin, the suspended wire moved laterally across the basins till it touched the sides: on breaking the connection, the wire resumed its first position; on restoring it, the motion was again produced. On changing the position of the wire, the effect still took place; and the direction of the motion was always the same relative to the wire, or rather to the current passing through it, being at right angles to it. Thus when the wire was east and west, the east end to the zinc, the west end to the copper plate, the motion was towards the north; when the connections were reversed, the motion was towards the south. When the wire hung north and south, the north end to the zinc plate, the south end to the copper plate, the motion was towards the west; when the connexions were reversed, towards the east; and the intermediate positions had their motions in intermediate directions.

The tendency, therefore, of the wire to revolve in a circle round the pole of the earth, is evident, and the direction of the motion is precisely the same as that pointed out in the former experiments. The experiment also points out the power which causes Ampère's curve to traverse, and the way in which that power is exerted. The well-known experiment, made by M. Ampère, proves that a wire ring, made to conduct a current of electricity, if it be allowed to turn on a vertical axis, moves into a plane east and west of the magnetic meridian; if on an east and west horizontal axis, it moves into a plane perpendicular to the dipping-needle. Now if the curve be considered as a polygon of an infinite number of sides, and each of these sides be compared in succession to the straight wire just described, it will be seen that the motions given to them by the terrestrial pole, or poles, are such as would necessarily bring the polygon they form into a plane perpendicular to the dipping-needle; so that the traversing of the ring may be reduced to the simple rotation of the wire round a pole. It is true the whole magnetism of the earth is concerned in producing the effect, and not merely that portion which I have, for the moment, supposed to respect the north pole of the earth as its centre of action; but the effect is the same, and produced in the same manner; and the introduction of the influence of the southern hemisphere, only renders the result analogous to the experiment at page 800, where two poles are concerned, instead of that at page 797, &c., where one pole only is active.

Besides the above proof of rotation round the terrestrial pole, I have made an experiment still more striking. As in the experiment of rotation round the pole of a magnet, the pole is perpendicular to but a small portion of the wire, and more or less oblique to the rest, I considered it probable that a wire, very delicately hung, and connected, might be made to rotate round the dip of the needle by the earth's magnetism alone; the upper part being restrained to a point in the line of the dip, the lower being made to move in a circle surrounding it. This result was obtained in the following manner: a piece of copper wire, about 0.018 of an inch in diameter, and six inches long, was well amalgamated all over, and hung by a loop to another piece of the same wire, as described at page 809, so as to allow very free motion, and its lower end was thrust through a small piece of cork, to make it buoyant on mercury; the upper piece was connected with a thick wire, that went away to one pole of the voltaic apparatus; a glass basin, ten inches in diameter, was filled with pure clear mercury, and a little dilute acid put on its surface as before; the thick wire was then hung over the centre of the glass basin, and depressed so low that the thin moveable wire having its lower end resting on the surface of the mercury, made an angle of about 40° with the horizon. Immediately the circuit through the mercury was completed, this wire began to move and rotate, and continued to describe a cone (whilst the connections were preserved), which though its axis was perpendicular, evidently, from the varying rapidity of its motion, regarded a line parallel to the dipping-needle as that in which the power acted that formed it. The direction of the motion was, as expected, the same as that given by the pole of a magnet pointing to the south. If the centre from which the wire hung was elevated until the inclination of the wire was equal to that of the dip, no motion took place when the wire was parallel to the dip; if the wire was not so much inclined as the dip, the motion in one part of the circle capable of being described by the lower end was reversed; results that necessarily follow from the relation of the dip and the moving wire, and which may easily be extended.

I have described the effects above as produced by the north pole of the earth, assuming that pole as a centre of action, acting in a line represented by the dip of the needle. This has been done that the phenomena might more readily be compared with those produced by the pole of a magnet. M. Biot has shown by calculation that the magnetic poles of the earth may be considered as two points in the magnetic axis very near to each other in the centre of the globe. M. Ampère has in his theory advanced the opinion that the magnetism of the earth is caused by electric currents moving round its axis parallel to the equator. Of the consonance existing among the calculation, the theory and the facts, some idea may perhaps be gained from what was said, page 802, on the rotation of a pole through and round a wire ring. The different sides of the plane which pass through the ring, there described, and which may represent the equator in M. Ampère's theory, accord perfectly with the hemispheres of the globe; and the relative position of the supposed points of attraction and repulsion coincide with those assigned by M. Biot for the poles of the earth itself. Whatever, however, may be the state and arrangement of terrestrial magnetism, the experiments I have described bear me out, I think, in presuming, that in every part of the terrestrial globe an electromagnetic wire, if left to the free action of terrestrial magnetism, will move in a plane (for so the small part we can experiment on may be considered) perpendicular to the dip of the needle, and in a direction perpendicular to the current of electricity passing through it.

Reverting now to the expectation I entertained of altering the apparent weight of a wire, it was founded on the idea that the wire, moving towards the north round the pole, must rise, and moving towards the south, must descend; inasmuch as a plane perpendicular to the dipping-needle, ascends and descends in these directions. In order to ascertain the existence of this effect, I bent a wire twice at right angles, as in the first experiment described in this note, and fastened on to each extremity a short piece of thin wire amalgamated, and made the connection into the basins of mercury by these thin wires. The wire was then suspended, not as before, from the ceiling, but from a small and delicate lever, which would indicate any apparent alteration in the weight of the wire; the connections were then made with a voltaic instrument, but I was surprised to find that the wire seemed to become lighter in both directions, though not so much when its motion was towards the south as towards the north. On further trial it was found to ascend on the contacts being made, whatever its position to the magnetic meridian, and I soon ascertained that it did not depend on the earth's magnetism, nor on any local magnetic action of the conductors, or surrounding bodies on the wire.

After some examination I discovered the cause of this unexpected phenomenon. An amalgamated piece of the thin copper wire was dipped into clean mercury, having a stratum of water or dilute acid over it; this, however, was not necessary, but it preserved the mercury clean and the wire cool. In this position the cohesive attraction of the mercury raised a little elevation of the metal round the wire of a certain magnitude, which tended to depress the wire by adding to its weight. When the mercury and the wire were connected with the poles of the voltaic apparatus, this elevation visibly diminished in magnitude by an apparent alteration in the cohesive attraction of the mercury, and a part of the force which before tended to depress the wire was thus removed. This alteration took place equally, whatever the direction in which the current was passing through the wire and the mercury, and the effect ceased the moment the connections were broken.

Thus the cause which made the wire ascend in the former case was evident, and by knowing it, it was easy to construct an apparatus in which the ascent should be very considerable. A piece of copper bell wire, about two inches long, had portions of the amalgamated fine copper wire soldered on to its ends, and those bent downwards till parallel to each other. This was then hung by a silk thread from the lever, and the fine wire ends dipped into two cups of clean mercury. When the communications were completed from the voltaic instrument through these two cups, the wires would rise nearly an inch out of the mercury, and descend again on breaking the communication.

Thus it appears that, when a fine amalgamated copper wire dips into mercury, and a current of voltaic electricity passes through the combination, a peculiar effect is produced at the place where the wire first touches the mercury, equivalent to a diminution of the cohesive attraction of the mercury. The effect rapidly diminished by increasing the size of the wire, and 20 pair of plates of Dr. Wollaston's construction, and four inches square, would not produce it with the fine wire: on the contrary, two large plates are sufficient. Dr. Hare's calorimotor was the instrument used, and the charge was so weak that it would barely warm two inches of any sized wire. Whether the effect is an actual diminution of the attraction of the particles of the mercury, or depends on some other cause, remains as yet to be determined. But in any case its influence is so powerful that it must always be estimated in experiments made to determine the force and direction of an electro-magnetic wire, acted on by a magnetic pole, if the direction is otherwise than horizontal, and if they are observed in the way described in this note. Thus, at the magnetic equator, for instance, where the apparent alteration of weight in an electro-magnetic wire may be expected to be greatest, the diminution of weight in its attempt to ascend would be increased by this effect, and the apparently increased gravity produced by its attempt to descend would be diminished, or perhaps entirely counteracted.

I have received an account by letter from Paris, of an ingenious apparatus[1] contrived by M. Ampère, to illustrate the rotatory motions described in my former paper. M. Ampère states that, if made of sufficient size, it will rotate by the magnetic action of the earth, and it is evident that will be the case in latitudes at some distance from the equator, if the rotary wires, namely, those by which the ring of zinc is suspended, are in such a position as to form an angle with a vertical line, larger than that formed by the direction of the dip.

It is to be remarked that the motions mentioned in this note were produced by a single pair of plates, and therefore, as well as those described in the paper, page 795, are the reverse of what would be produced by two or more pair of plates. It should be remembered also, that the north pole of the earth is opposite in its powers to what I have called the north poles of needles or magnets, and similar to their south poles.

I may be allowed, in conclusion, to express a hope that the law I have ventured to announce, respecting the directions of the rotatory motions of an electro-magnetic wire, influenced by terrestrial magnetism, will be put to the test in different latitudes; or, what is nearly the same thing, that the law laid down by M. Ampère, as regulating the position taken by his curve, namely, that it moves into a plane perpendicular to the dipping-needle, will be experimentally ascertained by all those having the opportunity.

Effect of Cold on Magnetic Needles[2]

Dr. De Sanctis has lately published some experiments on the effect of cold in destroying the magnetic power of needles,[3] or at least in rendering them insensible to the action of iron and other magnets. Mr. Ellis has claimed the merit of this discovery, and the reasoning upon it, for the late Governor Ellis. Conceiving it important to establish the fact that cold as well as heat injured or destroyed the magnetic power of iron or steel, we wrapped a magnetic needle up in lint, dipped it in sulphuret of carbon, placed it on its pivot under the receiver of an air-pump, and rapidly exhausted: in this way a cold, below the freezing of mercury, is readily obtained. When in this state, the needle was readily affected by iron or a magnet, and the number of vibrations performed in a given time by the influence of the earth upon it were observed. A fire was now placed near the pump, and the whole warmed; and when at about 80° Fahr. the needle was again examined, it appeared to be just in the same state as before as to obedience to iron and a magnet, and the number of oscillations were very nearly the same, though a little greater. The degree of exhaustion remained uniform throughout the experiment.—ED.

Electro-magnetic Current (under the Influence of a Magnet)[4]

As the current of electricity, produced by a voltaic battery when passing through a metallic conductor, powerfully affects a magnet, tending to make its poles pass round the wire, and in this way moving considerable masses of matter, it was supposed that a reaction would be exerted upon the electric current capable of producing some visible effect; and the expectation being, for various reasons, that the approximation of a pole of a powerful magnet would diminish the current of electricity, the following experiment was made. The poles of a battery of from two to thirty 4-inch plates were connected by a metallic wire formed in one part into a helix with numerous convolutions, whilst into the circuit, at another part, was introduced a delicate galvanometer. The magnet was then put, in various positions, and to different extents, into the helix, and the needle of the galvanometer noticed; no effect, however, upon it could be observed. The circuit was made very long, short, of wires of different metals and different diameters down to extreme fineness, but the results were always the same. Magnets more and less powerful were used, some so strong as to bend the wire in its endeavours to pass round it. Hence it appears that however powerful the action of an electric current may be upon a magnet, the latter has no tendency, by reaction, to diminish or increase the intensity

---

[1] See *Quarterly Journal of Science*, XII, 415.
[2] *Quarterly Journal of Science*, XIV, 435.
[3] *Phil. Mag.*, LX, 199.

[4] *Quarterly Journal of Science*, XIX, 338.

of the former; a fact which, though of a negative kind, appears to me to be of some importance.—M. F. [*See* note at end of Series I of *Exp. Res.*, 1843.]

Electric Powers (and Place) of Oxalate of Lime[1]

Some oxalate of lime, obtained by precipitation, when well-washed, was dried in a Wedgewood's basin at a temperature approaching 300°, until so dry as not to render a cold glass plate, placed over it, dim. Being then stirred with a platinum spatula, it, in a few moments, by friction against the metal, became so strongly electrical, that it could not be collected together, but flew about the dish whenever it was moved, and over its sides into the sand-bath. It required some little stirring before the particles of the powder were all of them sufficiently electrical to produce this effect. It was found to take place either in porcelain, glass, or metal basins, and with porcelain, glass, or metal stirrers; and when well excited, the electrified particles were attracted on the approach of all bodies, and when shaken in small quantity on to the cap of a gold-leaf electrometer, would make the leaves diverge two or three inches. The effect was not due to temperature, for when cooled out of the contact of air, it equally took place when stirred; being, however, very hygrometric, the effect soon went off if the powder were exposed to air. Excited in a silver capsule, and then left out of contact of the air, the substance remained electrical a great length of time, proving its very bad conducting power; and in this respect surpassing, perhaps, all other bodies. The effect may be produced any number of times, and after any number of desiccations of the salt.

Platinum rubbed against the powder became negative—the powder positive; all other metals tried, the same as platinum. When rubbed with glass, the glass became strongly negative, the oxalate positive, both being dry and warm; and indeed this body appears to stand at the head of the list of all substances as yet tried, as to its power of becoming positively electrical by friction.

Oxalates of zinc and lead produced none of these effects.—M. F.

On the General Magnetic Relations and Characters of the Metals[2]

GENERAL views have long since led me to an opinion, which is probably also entertained by others, though I do not remember to have met with it, that *all* the metals are magnetic in the same manner as iron, though not at common temperatures or under ordinary circumstances.[3] I do not refer to a feeble magnetism,[4] uncertain in its existence and source, but to a distinct and decided power, such as that possessed by iron and nickel; and my impression has been that there was a certain temperature for each body (well known in the case of iron) beneath which it was magnetic, but above which it lost all power; and that, further, there was some relation between this *point* of temperature, and the *intensity* of magnetic force which the body when reduced beneath it could acquire. In this view iron and nickel were not considered as exceptions from the metals generally with regard to magnetism, any more than mercury could be considered as an exception from this class of bodies as to liquefaction.

I took occasion during the very cold weather of December last, to make some experiments on this point. Pieces of various metals in their pure state were supported at the ends of fine platinum wires, and then cooled to a very low degree by the evaporation of sulphurous acid. They were then brought close to one end of one of the needles of a delicate astatic arrangement, and the magnetic state judged of by the absence or presence of attractive forces. The whole apparatus was in an atmosphere of about 25° Fahr.: the pieces of metal when tried were always far below the freezing-point of mercury, and as judged, generally at from 60° to 70° Fahr. below zero.

The metals tried were,

Antimony	Lead
Arsenic	Mercury
Bismuth	Palladium
Cadmium	Platinum
Cobalt	Silver
Chromium	Tin
Copper	Zinc
Gold	

and also Plumbago; but in none of these cases could I obtain the least indication of magnetism.

Cobalt and chromium are said to be both magnetic metals. I cannot find that either of them is so, in its pure state, at any tempera-

[1] *Quarterly Journal of Science*, XIX, 338.
[2] *Lond. and Edinb. Phil. Mag.*, 1836, Vol. VIII, p. 177.

[3] It may be proper to remark that the observations made in par. 255 of my *Experimental Researches* have reference only to the three classes of bodies there defined as existing at ordinary temperatures.
[4] *Encyclop. Metrop.*, "Mixed Sciences," Vol. I, p. 761.

tures.[1] When the property was present in specimens supposed to be pure, I have traced it to iron or nickel.

The step which we can make downwards in temperature is, however, so small as compared to the changes we can produce in the opposite direction, that negative results of the kind here stated could scarcely be allowed to have much weight in deciding the question under examination, although, unfortunately, they cut off all but two metals from actual comparison. Still, as the only experimental course left open, I proceeded to compare, roughly, iron and nickel with respect to the points of temperature at which they cease to be magnetic. In this respect iron is well known.[2] It loses all magnetic properties at an orange heat, and is then, to a magnet, just like a piece of copper, silver, or any other unmagnetic metal. It does not intercept the magnetic influence between a magnet and a piece of cold iron or a needle. If moved across magnetic curves, a magneto-electric current is produced within it exactly as in other cases. The point at which iron loses and gains its magnetic force appears to be very definite, for the power comes on suddenly and fully in small masses by a small diminution of temperature, and as suddenly disappears upon a small elevation, at that degree.

With nickel I found, as I expected, that the point at which it lost its magnetic relations was very much lower than with iron, but equally defined and distinct. If heated and then cooled, it remained unmagnetic long after it had fallen below a heat visible in the dark: and, in fact, almond oil can bear and communicate that temperature which can render nickel indifferent to a magnet. By a few experiments with the thermometer it appeared that the demagnetizing temperature for nickel is near 630° or 640°. A slight change about this point would either give or take away the full magnetic power of the metal.

Thus the experiments, as far as they go, justify the opinion advanced at the commencement of this paper, that all metals have similar magnetic relations, but that there is a certain temperature for each beneath which it is magnetic in the manner of iron or nickel, and above which it cannot exhibit this property. This magnetic capability, like volatility or fusibility, must depend upon some peculiar relation or condition of the particles of the body; and the striking difference between the necessary temperatures for iron and nickel appears to me to render it far more philosophical to allow that magnetic capability is a general property of all metals, a certain temperature being the essential condition for the development of this state, than to suppose that iron and nickel possess a physical property which is denied to all the other substances of the class.

An opinion has been entertained with regard to iron, that the heat which takes away its magnetic property acts somehow within it and amongst its electrical currents (upon which the magnetism is considered as depending) as flame and heat of a similar intensity act upon conductors charged with ordinary electricity. The difference of temperature necessary for iron and nickel is against this opinion, and the view I take of the whole is still more strongly opposed to it.

The close relation of electric and magnetic phenomena led me to think it probable that the sudden change of condition with respect to the magnetism of iron and nickel at certain temperatures, might also affect, in some degree, their conducting power for electricity in its ordinary form; but I could not, in such trials as I made, discover this to be the case with iron. At the same time, although sufficiently exact to indicate a great change in conduction, they were not delicate enough to render evident any small change; which yet, if it occurred, might be of great importance in illustrating the peculiarity of magnetic action under these circumstances, and might even elucidate its general nature.

Before concluding this short paper, I may describe a few results of magnetic action, which, though not directly concerned in the argument above, are connected generally with the subject.[3] Wishing to know what relation that temperature which could take from a magnet its power over soft iron had to that which could take from soft iron or steel its power relative to a magnet, I gradually raised the temperature of a magnet, and found that when scarcely at the boiling-point of almond oil it lost its polarity rather suddenly, and then acted with a magnet as cold soft iron: it required to be raised to a full orange heat before it lost its power as soft iron. Hence the force of the steel to *retain* that condition of its particles which renders it a permanent magnet, gives way to

[1] Subsequent experiment led Faraday to the conclusion that cobalt shares magnetic properties with iron and nickel. ED.
[2] See Barlow on the "Magnetic Condition of Hot Iron," *Phil. Trans.*, 1822, p. 171, &c.
[3] See on this subject, Christie on "Effects of Temperature," &c., *Phil. Trans.*, 1825, p. 62, &c.

heat at a far lower temperature than that which is necessary to prevent its particles assuming the *same state* by the inductive action of a neighbouring magnet. Hence at one temperature its particles can of themselves retain a permanent state; whilst at a higher temperature, that state, though it can be induced from without, will continue only as long as the inductive action lasts; and at a still higher temperature all capability of assuming this condition is lost.

The temperature at which polarity was destroyed appeared to vary with the hardness and condition of the steel.

Fragments of loadstone of very high power were then experimented with. These preserved their polarity at higher temperatures than the steel magnet; the heat of boiling oil was not sufficient to injure it. Just below visible ignition in the dark they lost their polarity, but from that to a temperature a little higher, being very dull ignition, they acted as soft iron would do, and then suddenly lost that power also. Thus the loadstone retained its polarity longer than the steel magnet, but lost its capability of becoming a magnet by induction much sooner. When magnetic polarity was given to it by contact with a magnet, it retained this power up to the same degree of temperature as that at which it held its first and natural magnetism.

A very ingenious magnetizing process, in which electro-magnets and a high temperature are used, has been proposed lately by M. Aimé.[1] I am not acquainted with the actual results of this process, but it would appear probable that the temperature which decides the existence of the polarity, and above which all seems at liberty in the bar, is that required. Hence probably it will be found that a white heat is not more advantageous in the process than a temperature just above or about that of boiling oil; whilst the latter would be much more convenient in practice. The only theoretical reason for commencing at high temperatures would be to include both the hardening and the polarizing degrees in the same process; but it appears doubtful whether these are so connected as to give any advantage in practice, however advantageous it may be to commence the process above the depolarizing temperature.

Royal Institution, January 27, 1836

[1] *Annales de Chimie et de Physique*, Vol. LVII, p. 442.

On the General Magnetic Relations and Characters of the Metals: Additional Facts[2]

An idea that the metals would be all magnetic if made extremely cold, as they are all non-magnetic if above a certain temperature, was put forth in March 1836,[3] and some experiments were made, in which several were cooled as low as −60 or −70° Fahr., but without acquiring magnetic powers. It was afterwards noticed[4] that Berthier had said, that besides iron, cobalt, and nickel, *manganese also possesses magnetic force beneath a certain degree of temperature, much below zero.* Having had last May the opportunity of working with M. Thilorier's beautiful apparatus for giving both the liquid and the solid state to carbonic acid gas, I was anxious to ascertain what the extremely low temperature procurable by its means would effect with regard to the magnetic powers of metals and other substances, especially with relation to manganese and cobalt; and not having seen any account of similar trials, I send the results to the *Philosophical Magazine* (if it please the Editors to insert them) as an appendix to the two former notices.

The substances were cooled by immersion in the mixture of ether and solid carbonic acid, and moved either by platinum wires attached to them, or by small wooden tongs, also cooled. The temperature, according to Thilorier, would be about 112° below 0° of Fahrenheit. The test of magnetic power was a double astatic needle, each of the two constituent needles being small and powerful, so that the whole system was very sensible to any substance capable of having magnetism induced in it when brought near one of the four poles. Great care was required and was taken to avoid the effect of the downward current of air formed by the cooled body; very thin plates of mica being interposed in the most important cases.

The following metals gave no indications of any magnetic power when thus cooled to −112° Fahr.

Antimony	Lead
Arsenic	Mercury
Bismuth	Palladium
Cadmium	Platinum
Chromium	Rhodium
Cobalt	Silver
Copper	Tin
Gold	Zinc

[2] *Lond. and Edinb. Phil. Mag.*, 1839, Vol. XIV, p. 161.
[3] *Ibid.*, Vol. VIII, p. 177, or p. 217.
[4] *Ibid.*, Vol. IX, p. 65 or above.

A piece of metallic manganese given to me by Mr. Everett was very slightly magnetic and polar at *common* temperatures. It was not more magnetic when cooled to the lowest degree. Hence I believe the statement with regard to its acquiring such powers under such circumstances to be inaccurate. Upon very careful examination a piece of iron was found in the piece of metal, and to that I think the magnetic property which it possessed must be attributed.

I was very careful in ascertaining that pure *cobalt* did not become magnetic at the very low temperature produced.

The native alloy of iridium and osmium, and also crystals of titanium, were found to be slightly magnetic at common temperatures; I believe because of the presence of iron in them.[1] Being cooled to the lowest degree they did not present any additional magnetic force, and therefore it may be concluded that *iridium*, *osmium*, and *titanium* may be added as non-magnetic metals to the list already given.

Carbon and the following metallic combinations were then experimented upon in a similar manner, but all the results were negative: not one of the bodies gave the least sign of the acquirement of magnetic power by the cold applied.

    1. Carbon
    2. Hæmatite

[1] See Dr. Wollaston's paper on this subject, *Phil. Trans.*, 1823, Part II, or *Phil. Mag.*, First Series, Vol. LXIII, p. 15.—Ed.

  3. Protoxide of lead
  4.   antimony
  5.   bismuth
  6. White arsenic
  7. Native oxide of tin
  8.   manganese
  9. Chloride of silver
10.   lead
11. Iodide of mercury
12. Galena
13. Realgar
14. Orpiment
15. Dense native cinnabar
16. Sulphuret of silver
17.   copper
18.   tin
19.   bismuth
20.   antimony
21. Protosul. iron crystallized
22.   anhydrous

The carbon was the dense hard kind obtained from gas retorts; the substances 3, 4, 5, 6, 9, 10, 11, and some of the sulphurets had been first fused and solidified; and all the bodies were taken in the most solid and dense state which they could acquire.

It is perhaps superfluous to add, except in reference to effects which have been supposed by some to occur in northern latitudes, that the iron and nickel did not appear to suffer any abatement of their peculiar power when cooled to the very lowest degree.

Royal Institution, February 7, 1839

On the Physical Lines of Magnetic Force

ROYAL INSTITUTION PROCEEDINGS, JUNE 11, 1852

ON a former occasion certain lines about a bar-magnet were described and defined (being those which are depicted to the eye by the use of iron filings sprinkled in the neighbourhood of the magnet), and were recommended as expressing accurately the nature, condition, direction, and amount of the force in any given region either within or outside of the bar. At that time the lines were considered in the abstract. Without departing from or unsettling anything then said, the inquiry is now entered upon of the possible and probable *physical existence* of such lines. Those who wish to reconsider the different points belonging to these parts of magnetic science may refer to two papers in the first part of the *Phil. Trans.*

for 1852[2] for data concerning the *representative* lines of force, and to a paper in the *Phil. Mag.*, *4th Series*, 1852, Vol. III, p. 401, for the argument respecting the *physical* lines of force.

Many powers act manifestly at a distance; their physical nature is incomprehensible to us: still we may learn much that is real and positive about them, and amongst other things something of the condition of the space between the body acting and that acted upon, or between the two mutually acting bodies. Such powers are presented to us by the phenomena of gravity, light, electricity, magnetism, &c. These when examined will be found to present remarkable differences in relation to their re-

[2] See page 758.

spective lines of forces; and at the same time that they establish the existence of real physical lines in some cases, will facilitate the consideration of the question as applied especially to magnetism.

When two bodies, *a, b,* gravitate towards each other, the line in which they act is a straight line, for such is the line which either would follow if free to move. The attractive force is not altered, either in *direction* or *amount,* if a third body is made to act by gravitation or otherwise upon either or both of the two first. A balanced cylinder of brass gravitates to the earth with a weight exactly the same, whether it is left like a pendulum freely to hang towards it, or whether it is drawn aside by other attractions or by tension, whatever the amount of the latter may be. A new gravitating force may be exerted upon *a,* but that does not in the least affect the amount of power which it exerts towards *b.* We have no evidence that *time* enters in any way into the exercise of this power, whatever the distance between the acting bodies, as that from the sun to the earth, or from star to star. We can hardly conceive of this force in one particle by itself; it is when two or more are present that we comprehend it: yet in gaining this idea we perceive no difference in the character of the power in the different particles; all of the same kind are *equal, mutual,* and *alike.* In the case of gravitation, no effect which sustains the idea of an independent or physical line of force is presented to us; and as far as we at present know, the line of gravitation is merely an ideal line representing the direction in which the power is exerted.

Take the sun in relation to another force which it exerts upon the earth, namely its illuminating or warming power. In this case rays (which are lines of force) pass across the intermediate space; but then we may affect these lines by different media applied to them in their course. We may alter their direction either by reflection or refraction; we may make them pursue curved or angular courses. We may cut them off at their origin and then search for and find them before they have attained their object. They have a relation to *time,* and occupy 8 minutes in coming from the sun to the earth: so that they may exist independently either of their source or their final home, and have in fact a clear distinct physical existence. They are in extreme contrast with the lines of gravitating power in this respect; as they are also in respect to their condition at their terminations. The two bodies terminating a line of gravitat-

ing force are alike in their actions in every respect, and so the line joining them has like relations in both directions. The two bodies at the terminals of a ray are utterly unlike in action; one is a source, the other a destroyer of the line; and the line itself has the relation of a stream flowing in one direction. In these two cases of gravity and radiation, the difference between an abstract and a physical line of force is immediately manifest.

Turning to the case of *static electricity* we find here attractions (and other actions) at a distance as in the former cases; but when we come to compare the attraction with that of gravity, very striking distinctions are presented which immediately affect the question of a physical line of force. In the first place, when we examine the bodies bounding or terminating the lines of attraction, we find them as before, mutually and equally concerned in the action; but they are not alike: on the contrary, though each is endued with a force which speaking generally is of the like nature, still they are in such contrast that their actions on a third body in a state like either of them are precisely the reverse of each other—what the one attracts the other repels; and the force makes itself evident as one of those manifestations of power endued with a dual and antithetical condition. Now with all such dual powers, attraction cannot occur unless the two conditions of force are present and in face of each other through the lines of force. Another essential limitation is that these two conditions must be exactly equal in amount, not merely to produce the effects of attraction, but in every other case; for it is impossible so to arrange things that there shall be present or be evolved more electric power of the one kind than of the other. Another limitation is that they must be in physical relation to each other; and that when a positive and a negative electrified surface are thus associated, we cannot cut off this relation except by transferring the forces of these surfaces to equal amounts of the contrary forces provided elsewhere. Another limitation is that the power is definite in amount. If a ball *a* be charged with 10 of positive electricity, it may be made to act with that amount of power on another ball *b* charged with 10 of negative electricity; but if 5 of its power be taken up by a third ball *c* charged with negative electricity, then it can only act with 5 of power on ball *a,* and that ball must find or evolve 5 of positive power elsewhere: this is quite unlike what occurs with gravity, a power that presents us with nothing dual in its character. Finally, the electric force acts in curved lines. If a ball be electrified positively and insulated in the air, and a round metallic plate be placed about 12 or 15 inches off, facing it and uninsulated, the latter will be found, by the necessity mentioned above, in a negative condition; but it is not negative only on the side facing the ball, but on the other or outer face also, as may be shown by a carrier applied there, or by a strip of gold or silver leaf hung against that outer face. Now the power affecting this face does not pass through the uninsulated plate, for the thinnest gold leaf is able to stop the inductive action, but round the edges of the face, and therefore acts in curved lines. All these points indicate the existence of physical lines of electric force: the absolutely essential relation of positive and negative surfaces to each other, and their dependence on each other contrasted with the known mobility of the forces, admit of no other conclusion. The action also in curved lines must depend upon a physical line of force. And there is a third important character of the force leading to the same result, namely its affection by media having different specific inductive capacities.

When we pass to *dynamic electricity* the evidence of physical lines of force is far more patent. A voltaic battery having its extremities connected by a conducting medium has what has been expressively called a *current of force* running round the circuit, but this current is an axis of power having equal and contrary forces in opposite directions. It consists of lines of force which are compressed or expanded according to the transverse action of the conductor, which changes in direction with the form of the conductor, which are found in every part of the conductor, and can be taken out from any place by channels properly appointed for the purpose; and nobody doubts that they are physical lines of force.

Finally as regards a *magnet*, which is the object of the present discourse. A magnet presents a system of forces perfect in itself, and able, therefore, to exist by its own mutual relations. It has the dual and antithetic character belonging to both static and dynamic electricity; and this is made manifest by what are called its *polarities*, i.e., by the opposite powers of like kind found at and towards its extremities. These powers are found to be absolutely equal to each other; one cannot be changed in any degree as to amount without an equal change of the other; and this is true when the opposite polarities of a magnet are not related to each other, but to

the polarities of other magnets. The polarities, or the *northness* and *southness* of a magnet are not only related to each other, through or within the magnet itself, but they are also related externally to opposite polarities (in the manner of static electric induction) or they cannot exist; and this external relation involves and necessitates an exactly equal amount of the new opposite polarities to which those of the magnet are related. So that if the force of a magnet *a* is related to that of another magnet *b*, it cannot act on a third magnet *c* without being taken off from *b*, to an amount proportional to its action on *c*. The lines of magnetic force are shown by the moving wire to exist both within and outside of the magnet; also they are shown to be closed curves passing in one part of their course through the magnet; and the amount of those within the magnet at its equator is exactly equal in force to the amount in any section including the whole of those on the outside. The lines of force outside a magnet can be affected in their direction by the use of various media placed in their course. A magnet can in no way be procured having only one magnetism, or even the smallest excess of northness or southness one over the other. When the polarities of a magnet are not related externally to the forces of other magnets, then they are related to each other: i.e., the northness and southness of an isolated magnet are externally dependent on and sustained by each other.

Now all these facts, and many more, point to the existence of physical lines of force external to the magnets as well as within. They exist in curved as well as in straight lines; for if we conceive of an isolated straight bar-magnet, or more especially of a round disc of steel magnetized regularly, so that its magnetic axis shall be in one diameter, it is evident that the polarities must be related to each other externally by curved lines of force; for no straight line can at the same time touch two points having northness and southness. Curved lines of force can, as I think, only consist with physical lines of force.

The phenomena exhibited by the moving wire confirm the same conclusion. As the wire moves across the lines of force, a current of electricity passes or tends to pass through it, there being no such current before the wire is moved. The wire when quiescent has no such current, and when it moves it need not pass into places where the magnetic force is greater or less. It may travel in such a course that if a magnetic needle were carried through the same course it would be entirely unaffected magnetically, i.e., it would be a matter of absolute indifference to the needle whether it were moving or still. Matters may be so arranged that the wire when still shall have the same diamagnetic force as the medium surrounding the magnet, and so in no way cause disturbance of the lines of force passing through both; and yet when the wire moves, a current of electricity shall be generated in it. The mere fact of motion cannot have produced this current: there must have been a state or condition around the magnet and sustained by it, within the range of which the wire was placed; and this state shows the physical constitution of the lines of magnetic force.

What this state is, or upon what it depends, cannot as yet be declared. It may depend upon the ether, as a ray of light does, and an association has already been shown between light and magnetism. It may depend upon a state of tension, or a state of vibration, or perhaps some other state analogous to the electric current, to which the magnetic forces are so intimately related. Whether it of necessity requires matter for its sustentation will depend upon what is understood by the term matter. If that is to be confined to ponderable or gravitating substances, then matter is not essential to the physical lines of magnetic force any more than to a ray of light or heat; but if in the assumption of an ether we admit it to be a species of matter, then the lines of force may depend upon some function of it. Experimentally mere space is magnetic; but then the idea of such mere space must include that of the ether, when one is talking on that belief; or if hereafter any other conception of the state or condition of space rise up, it must be admitted into the view of that, which just now in relation to experiment is called mere space. On the other hand it is, I think, an ascertained fact, that ponderable matter is not essential to the existence of physical lines of magnetic force.

Observations on the Magnetic Force[1]

INASMUCH as the general considerations to be brought forward have respect to those great forces of the globe, exerted by it, both as a mass and through its particles, namely magnetism and gravitation, it is necessary briefly to recall certain relations and differences of the two which have been insisted upon on former occasions. Both can act at a distance, and doubtless at any distance; but whilst gravitation may be considered as simple and unpolar in its relations, magnetism is dual and polar. Hence *one* gravitating particle or system cannot be conceived to act by gravitation, as a particle or system, on itself; whereas a magnetic particle or system, because of the dual nature of its force, can have such a self-relation. Again, either polarity of the magnetic force can act either by attraction or repulsion; and not merely so, but the joint or *dual* action of a magnet can act also either by attraction or repulsion, as in the case of paramagnetic and diamagnetic bodies: the action of gravity is always that of attraction. As a further consequence of the difference in character of the powers, little or no doubt was entertained regarding the existence of physical lines of force[2] in the cases of dual powers, as electricity and magnetism; but in respect of gravitation the conclusion did not seem so sure. In reference to the growing magnetic relations of the sun and the earth, it is well to keep in mind Arago's idea, of the relative magnitude of the two; for, supposing that the centres of the two globes were made to coincide, the sun's body would not only extend as far as the moon, but nearly as far again, its bulk being about seven times that of a globe which should be girdled by the moon's orbit.

For the more careful study of the magnetic power, a torsion balance has been constructed of a particular kind. The torsion wire was of hard drawn platinum, 24 inches in length, and of such diameter that 28.5 inches weighed one grain. It was attached as usual to a torsion head and index. The horizontal beam was a small glass tube terminated at the object end by a glass hook. The objects to be submitted to the magnetic force were either cylinders of glass with a filament drawn out from each, so as to make a long stiff hook for suspension from the beam; or cylindrical bulbs of glass, of like shape, but larger size, formed out of glass tube; or other matters. The fine tubular extremities of the bulbs being opened, the way through was free from end to end; the bulbs could then be filled with any fluid or gas, sealed, and be re-

[1] *Proceedings of the Royal Institution*, Jan. 21, 1853.
[2] *Proceedings of the Royal Institution*, June 11, 1852, p. 216 (*see* p. 816); also *Phil. Mag., 4th Series*, 1852, III, p. 401.

submitted many times in succession to the magnetic force. The source of power employed was at first a large electro-magnet; but afterwards, in order to be certain of a constant power, and for the advantage of allowing any length of time for the observations the great magnet, constructed by M. Logeman upon the principles developed by Dr. Elias (and which, weighing above 100 lbs., could support 430 lbs. according to the report of the Great Exhibition Jury), was purchased by the Royal Institution and used in the inquiries. The magnet was so arranged that the axis of power was 5 inches below the level of the glass beam, the interval being traversed by the suspension filament or hook, spoken of above. The form and position of the terminations of soft iron are shown in plan by the diagram upon a scale of $\frac{1}{10}$, and also the place of the object. All this part is en-

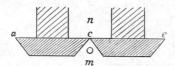

closed in the box which belongs to and carries the torsion-balance, which box is governed by six screws fixed upon the magnet table; and as both the box and the table have lines and scales marked upon them, it is easy to adjust the former on the latter so that the beam shall be over and parallel to the line a, e, with the point of suspension over c; or, by moving the whole box parallel to itself towards m, to give the point of suspension any other distance from the angle c. As already said, the objects were constructed with a suspension filament of such length as to make them coincide in height with the angle in the magnetic field. When suspended on the beam, they were counterpoised by a ring or rings of lead on the farther arm of the beam. These when required were moved along the beam until the latter was horizontal; and that state was ascertained by a double arm support, which sustained the beam when out of use, brought it into a steady state when moving, and delivered it into a condition of freedom when required. The motion of the box to the right or left, so as to place the object in the middle of the magnetic angle, was given by two of the screws before spoken of; the motion to the given distance from c, by the other four.

Supposing the distance from c towards m to be adjusted to 0.6 of an inch, when the beam was loaded above, and no object before the magnet (the beam having been of course pre-

viously adjusted to its normal position and the torsion index placed at zero), it then remained to determine the return of the beam to its place when the object had been suspended on it and repelled: this was done in the following manner. A small plane reflector is fixed on the beam, near its middle part, under the point of suspension; a small telescope associated with a divided scale is placed about 6 feet from the reflector, and in such a position that when the beam is in its right place, a given degree in the scale coincides with the fine wire in the telescope. Of course the scale appears to pass by the wire as the beam itself moves, and with a double angular velocity, because of the reflexion. As it is easy to read to the fiftieth and even to the hundredth of an inch in this way, and as each degree occupies apparently 2.4 inches with the radius of 6 feet, so an angular motion, or difference of $\frac{1}{240}$th of a degree could be observed; and as the radius of the arm of the beam carrying the object was 6 inches, such a quantity there would be less than $\frac{1}{2000}$th of an inch; i.e., the return of the beam to its first or normal position by the torsion force put on to counteract the repulsion, could be ascertained to within that amount. When an object was put on the adjusted beam, if diamagnetic it was repelled; and then, as the observer sat at the telescope, he, by means of a long handle, a wheel and pinion, put on torsion until the place of the beam was restored; and afterwards the amount of torsion read off on the graduated scale became the measure in degrees of the repulsive force exerted. At the time of real observations, the magnet, balance, and telescope were all fixed in a basement room, upon a stone floor. But it is unnecessary to describe here the numerous precautions required in relation to the time of an observation, the set of the suspension wire by a high torsion, the possible electricity of the object or beam by touch, the effect of feeble currents of air within the box, the shape of the object, the precaution against capillary action when fluids were employed as media, and other circumstances; or the use of certain stops, and the mode of procedure in the cases of paramagnetic action; the object being at present to present only an intelligent view of the principles of action.

When a body is submitted to the power of a magnet, it is affected, as to the result, not merely by the magnet, but also by the medium surrounding it; and even if that medium be changed for a vacuum, the vacuum and the body still are in like relation to each other. In fact the result is always differential; any change in the medium changes the action on the object, and there are abundance of substances which when surrounded by air are repelled, and when by water, are attracted, upon the approach of a magnet. When a certain small glass cylinder weighing only 66 grains was submitted on the torsion-balance to the Logeman magnet surrounded by air, at the distance of 0.5 of an inch from the axial line, it required 15° of torsion to overcome the repulsive force and restore the object to its place. When a vessel of water was put into the magnetic field, and the experiment repeated, the cylinder being now in the water was attracted, and 54°.5 of torsion were required to overcome this attraction at the given distance of 0.5. If the vessel had contained a fluid exactly equal in diamagnetic power to the cylinder of glass, neither attraction nor repulsion would have been exerted on the latter, and therefore the torsion would have been 0°. Hence the three bodies, air, glass (the especial specimen), and water, have their relative force measured in relation to each other by the three experimental numbers 15°, 0°, and 54°.5. If other fluids are taken, as oil, ether, &c., and employed as the media surrounding the *same glass cylinder*, then the degrees of torsion obtained with each of them respectively, show its place in the magnetic series. It is the principle of the hydrometer or of Archimedes in respect to gravity applied in the case of the magnetic forces. If a different cylinder be employed of another size or substance, or at a different distance, the torsion numbers will be different, and the zero (given by the cylinder) also different; but the media (with an exception to be made hereafter) will have the same relation to each other as in the former case. Therefore to bring all the experimental results into one common relation, a Centigrade scale has been adopted bounded by air and water at common temperatures, or 60° F. For this purpose every separate series of results made under exactly the same circumstances included air and water; and then all the results of one series were multiplied by such a number as would convert the difference between air and water into 100°: in this way the three results given above become 21°.6, 0°, and 78°.4. By such a process the magnetic intervals between the bodies are obtained on the Centigrade scale, but the true zero is not as yet determined. Either water, or air, or the glass, may be assumed as the zero, the intervals not being in any way dependent upon that point, but the results will then vary in expression thus:—

Air	0°	21°.6	100°
Glass	21°.6	0°	78°.4
Water	100°	78°.4	0°

all above the zero being paramagnetic, and all below diamagnetic, in relation to it. I have adopted a vacuum as the zero in the table of results to be given hereafter.

In this manner it is evident that, upon principle, any solid, whatever its size, shape, or quality, may be included in the list, by its subjection to a magnet in air and water, or in fluids already related to these: also that any fluids may be included, by the use of the *same* immersed solid body for them, air and water; and also that by using the same vessel, as for instance the same glass bulb, and filling it successively with various gases and fluids, including always air and water in each series, these included bodies may then have their results reduced and be entered upon the list. The following is a table of some substances esitmated on the Centigrade scale, and though there are many points both of theory and practice yet to be wrought out, as regards the use of the torsion-balance described, so that the results can only as yet be recorded as approximations, even now, the average of three or four careful experiments gives an expression for any particular substance under the same conditions of distance, power, &c., near upon and often within a degree of the place assigned to it. The powers are expressed for a distance of 0.6 of an inch from the magnetic axis of the magnet as arranged and described, and, of course, for *equal volumes* of the bodies mentioned. The extreme decimal places must not be taken as correct, except as regards the record of the experiments: they are the results of calculation. Hydrogen, nitrogen, and perhaps some other of the bodies near zero, may ultimately turn out to be as a vacuum; it is evident that a very little oxygen would produce a difference, such as that which appears in nitrogen gas. The first solution of copper mentioned was colourless, and the second the same solution oxidized by simple agitation in a bottle with air, the copper, ammonia, and water being in both the same.

Prot-ammo. of copper	134°.23
Per-ammo. of copper	119°.83
Oxygen	17°.5
Air	3°.4
Olefiant gas	0°.6
Nitrogen	0°.3
Vacuum	0°.0

(*Continued on next page.*)

(Continued from preceding page.)

Carbonic acid gas	0°.0
Hydrogen	0°.1
Ammonia gas	0°.5
Cyanogen	0°.9
A glass	18°.2
Pure zinc	74°.6
Ether	75°.3
Alcohol, absolute	78°.7
Oil of lemons	80°
Camphor	82°.59
Camphine	82°.96
Linseed oil	85°.56
Olive oil	85°.6
Wax	86°.73
Nitric acid	87°.96
Water	96°.6
Solution of ammonia	98°.5
Bisulphide of carbon	99°.64
Sat. sol. nitre	100°.08
Sulphuric acid	104°.47
Sulphur	118°
Chloride of arsenic	121°.73
Fused borate of lead	136°.6
Phosphorus	
Bismuth	1967°.6

Plücker in his very valuable paper[1] has dealt with bodies which are amongst the highly paramagnetic substances, and his estimate of power is made for equal weights.

One great object in the construction of an instrument delicate as that described was the investigation of certain points in the philosophy of magnetism; and amongst them especially that of the right application of the law of the inverse square of the distance as the universal law of magnetic action. Ordinary magnetic action may be divided into two kinds, that between magnets permanently magnetized and unchangeable in their condition, and that between bodies of which one is a permanent unchangeable magnet, and the other, having no magnetic state of its own, receives and retains its state only whilst in subjection to the first. The former kind of action appears in the most rigid and pure cases to be subject to that law; but it would be premature to assume beforehand, and without abundant sufficient evidence, that the same law applies in the second set of cases also; for a hasty assumption might be in opposition to the truth of nature, and therefore injurious to the progress of science, by the creation of a preconceived conclusion. We know not whether such bodies as oxygen, copper, water, bismuth, &c., owe their respec-

tive paramagnetic and diamagnetic relation to a greater or less facility of conduction in regard to the lines of magnetic force, or to something like a polarity of their particles or masses, or to some as yet unsuspected state; and there is little hope of our developing the true condition, and therefore the cause of magnetic action, if we assume beforehand the unproved law of action and reject the experiments that already bear upon it; for Plücker has distinctly stated as the fact, that diamagnetic force increases more rapidly than magnetic force, when the power of the dominant magnet is increased; and such a fact is contrary to the law above enunciated. The following are further results in relation to this point.

When a body is submitted to the great unchanging Logeman magnet in air and in water, and the results are reduced to the Centigrade scale, the relation of the three substances remains the same for the same distance, but not for *different* distances. Thus, when a given cylinder of flint-glass was submitted to the magnet surrounded by air and by water, at the distance of 0.3 of an inch, as already described, it proved to be diamagnetic in relation to both; and when the results were corrected to the Centigrade scale, and water made zero, it was 9°.1 below, or on the diamagnetic side of water. At the distance 0.4 of an inch it was 10°.6 below water: at the distance of 0.7 it was 12°.1 below water. When a more diamagnetic body, as heavy glass, was employed, the same result in a higher degree was obtained; for at the distance of 0.3 it was 37°.8 below water, and at that of 0.8 it was 48°.6 beneath it. Bismuth presented a still more striking case, though, as the volume of the substance was necessarily small, equal confidence cannot be placed in the exactitude of the numbers. The results are given below for the three substances, air being always 100° and water 0°; the first column of figures for each substance contains the distance[2] in tenths of an inch from the axial line of the magnetic field, and the second, the place in Centigrade magnetic degrees below water.

---

[1] Taylor's *Scientific Memoirs*, Vol. V, pp. 713, 730.

[2] A given change of distance necessarily implies change in degree of force, and change in the forms of the lines of force; but it does not imply always the same amount of change. The forces are not the same at the same distance of 0.4 of an inch in opposite directions from the axial line towards *m* and *n* in the figure, page 820, nor at any other equal moderate distance; and though by increase and diminution of distance the change is in the same direction, it is not in the same proportion. By fitly arranged terminations, it may be made to alter with extreme rapidity in one direction, and with extreme slowness or not at all in another.

Flint-Glass	Heavy Glass	Bismuth
0.3— 9°.1	0.3—37°.8	0.6—1871°
0.4—10°.6	0.4—38°.6	1.0—2734°
0.5—11°.1	0.6—40°.0	1.5—3626°
0.6—11°.2	0.8—48°.6	
0.7—12°.1	1.0—51°.5	
	1.2—65°.6	

The result here is that the greater the distance of the diamagnetic body from the magnet the more diamagnetic is it in relation to water, taking the interval between water and air as the standard: and it would further appear, if an opinion may be formed from so few experiments, that the more diamagnetic the body compared to air and water, the greater does this difference become. At first it was thought possible that the results might be due to some previous state induced upon the body, by its having been nearer to or farther from the magnet; but it was found that whether the progress of the experiments was from small to large distances, or the reverse; or whether, at any given distance, the object was previous to the measurement held close up to the magnet or brought from a distance, the results were the same; no evidence of a temporary induced state could in any of these ways be found.

It does not follow from the experiments, if they should be sustained by future researches, that it is the glass or the bismuth only that changes in relation to the other two bodies. It may be the oxygen of the air that alters, or the water, or more probably all these bodies; for if the result be a true and natural result in these cases, it is probably common to all substances. The great point is that the three bodies concerned, air, water, and the subject of the experiment, alter in the degree of their magnetic relations to *each other*; at different given distances from the magnet the ratio of their magnetic power does not, according to the experiments, remain the same; and if that result be confirmed, then it cannot be included by a law of action which is inversely as the square of the distance. A hydrometer floating in a fluid and subject to the gravity of the earth alone, would (other things being the same) stand at the same point, whether at the surface of the earth, or removed many diameters of the earth from it, because the action of gravity is inversely as the square of the distance; but if we suppose the substance of the hydrometer and the fluid to differ magnetically, as water and bismuth do, and the earth to act as a magnet instead of by gravity, then the hydrometer would, according to the exper-

iments, stand at a different point for different distances, and if so could not be subject to the former law.

The cause of this variation in the ratio of the substances one to another, if it be finally proved, has still to be searched out. It may depend in some manner upon the *forms* of the lines of magnetic force, which are different at different distances; or not upon the forms of the lines, but the *amount* of power at the different distances; or not upon the mere amount, but on the circumstance that in every case the body submitted to experiment has lines of *different degrees of force* passing through different parts of it (for however different the magnetic or diamagnetic conditions of a body and the fluid surrounding it, they would not move at all in relation to each other in a field of equal force); but whatever be the cause, it will be a concomitant of magnetic actions; and therefore ought to be included in the results of any law by which it is supposed that these actions are governed.

It has not yet been noticed that these general results appear to be in direct opposition to those of Plücker, who finds that diamagnetic power increases more rapidly than magnetic power with increase of force. But such a circumstance, if both conclusions be accordant facts, only shows that we have yet a great deal to learn about the physical nature of this force; and we must not shut our eyes to the first feeble glimpses of these things, because they are inconsistent on both sides with our assumed laws of action; but rather seize them, as hoping that they will give us the key to the truth of nature. Bodies when subject to the power of the magnet appear to acquire a new physical state, which varies with the distance or the power of the magnet. Each body may have its own rate of increase and decrease; and that may be such as to connect the extreme effect of Plücker, amongst paramagnetic bodies on the one hand, and the extreme effects amongst diamagnetic bodies now described, on the other; and when we understand all this rightly, we may see the apparent contradiction become harmony, though it may not conform to the law of the inverse square of the distance as we now try to apply it.

Plücker has already said, because of his observations regarding paramagnetic and diamagnetic force, that no correct list of magnetic substances can be given. The same consequence follows, though in a different direction, from what has now been stated, and hence the reservation before made (p. 821). Still the former table is given as an approximation, and it may be useful for a time. Before leaving this first account of recent experimental researches, it may be as well to state that they are felt to be imperfect and may perhaps even be overturned; but that, as such a result is not greatly anticipated, it was thought well to present them to the Members of the Royal Institution and the scientific world, if peradventure they might excite criticism and experimental examination, and so aid in advancing the cause of physical science.

On a former occasion[1] the existence of *physical* lines of force in relation to magnetism and electricity was inferred from the dual nature of these powers, and the necessity in all cases and at all times of a relation and dependence between the polarities of the magnet, or the positive and negative electrical surfaces. With respect to gravity a more hesitating opinion was expressed, because of the difficulty of observing facts having any relation to *time*, and because two gravitating particles or masses did not seem to have any necessary dependence on each other for the existence or excitement of their mutual power.[2] A passage may now be quoted from Newton which has since been discovered in his works, and which, showing that he was an unhesitating believer in physical lines of gravitating force, must from its nature rank him amongst those who sustain the physical nature of the lines of magnetic and electrical force: it is as follows, in words written to Bentley:[3] "That gravity should be innate, inherent and essential to matter, so that one body may act upon another at a distance through a *vacuum*, without the mediation of anything else, by and through which their action and force may be conveyed from one to another, is to me so great an absurdity, that I believe no man who has in philosophical matters a competent faculty of thinking, can ever fall into it. Gravity must be caused by an agent acting constantly according to certain laws; but whether this agent be material or immaterial, I have left to the consideration of my readers."

On Electric Induction—Associated Cases of Current and Static Effects[4]

CERTAIN phenomena that have presented themselves in the course of the extraordinary

expansion which the works of the Electric Telegraph Company have undergone appeared to me to offer remarkable illustrations of some fundamental principles of electricity, and strong confirmation of the truthfulness of the view which I put forth sixteen years ago, respecting the mutually dependent nature of induction, conduction, and insulation (*Exp. Res.*, 1318, &c.). I am deeply indebted to the Company, to the gutta percha works, and to Mr. Latimer Clarke, for the facts; and also for the opportunity both of seeing and showing them well.

Copper wire is perfectly covered with gutta percha at the Company's works, the metal and the covering being in every part regular and concentric. The covered wire is usually made into half-mile lengths, the necessary junctions being effected by twisting or binding, and ultimately, soldering; after which the place is covered with fine gutta percha, in such a manner as to make the coating as perfect there as elsewhere: the perfection of the whole operation is finally tried in the following striking manner, by Mr. Statham, the manager of the works. The half-mile coils are suspended from the sides of barges floating in a canal, so that the coils are immersed in the water, whilst the two ends of each coil rise into the air: as many as 200 coils are thus immersed at once, and when their ends are connected in series, one great length of 100 miles of submerged wire is produced, the two extremities of which can be brought into a room for experiment. An insulated voltaic battery of many pairs of zinc and copper, with dilute sulphuric acid, has one end connected with the earth, and the other, through a galvanometer, with either end of the submerged wire. Passing by the first effect, and continuing the contact, it is evident that the battery current can take advantage of the whole accumulated conduction or defective insulation in the 100 miles of gutta percha on the wire, and that whatever portion of electricity passes through to the water will be shown by the galvanometer. Now the battery is made one of intensity, in order to raise the character of the proof, and the galvanometer employed is of considerable delicacy; yet so high is the insulation that the deflection is not more than 5°. As another test of the perfect state of the wire, when the two ends of the battery are connected with the two ends of the wire, there is a powerful current of electricity shown by a much coarser instrument; but when any one junction in the course of the 100 miles is separated, the current is stopped, and the leak or deficiency of insula-

[1] *See* p. 816.
[2] *Philosophical Magazine*, 4th Series, 1852, Vol. III, p. 403 (3246).
[3] Newton's *Works*, Horsley's edition, 4to, 1783, Vol. IV, p. 438, or the third letter to Bentley.
[4] *Proceedings of the Royal Institution*, Jan. 20, 1854.

tion rendered as small as before. The perfection and condition of the wire may be judged of by these facts.

The 100 miles, by means of which I saw the phenomena, were thus good as to insulation. The copper wire was ⅟₁₆th of an inch in diameter: the covered wire was ⁵⁄₁₆; some was a little less, being ⁷⁄₃₂ in diameter: the gutta percha on the metal may therefore be considered as 0.1 of an inch in thickness. 100 miles of like covered wire in coils were heaped up on the floor of a dry warehouse and connected in one series, for comparison with that under water.

Consider now an insulated battery of 360 pairs of plates (4×3 inches) having one extremity to the earth; the water wire with both its insulated ends in the room, and a good earth-discharge wire ready for the requisite communications: when the free battery end was placed in contact with the water wire and then removed, and, afterwards, a person touching the earth-discharge touched also the wire, he received a powerful shock. The shock was rather that of a voltaic than of a Leyden battery: it occupied *time*, and by quick tapping touches could be divided into numerous small shocks: I obtained as many as forty sensible shocks from one charge of the wire. If *time* were allowed to intervene between the charge and discharge of the wire, the shock was less; but it was sensible after 2, 3, or 4 minutes, or even a longer period.

When, after the wire had been in contact with the battery, it was placed in contact with a Statham's fuse, it ignited the fuse (or even six fuses in succession) vividly: it could ignite the fuse 3 or 4 seconds after separation from the battery. When, having been in contact with the battery, it was separated and placed in contact with a galvanometer, it affected the instrument very powerfully: it acted on it, though less powerfully, after the lapse of 4 or 5 minutes, and even affected it sensibly 20 or 30 minutes after it had been separated from the battery. When the insulated galvanometer was permanently attached to the end of the water wire, and the battery pole was brought in contact with the free end of the instrument, it was most instructive to see the great rush of electricity into the wire; yet after that was over, though the contact was continued, the deflection was not more than 5°, so high was the insulation. Then separating the battery from the galvanometer, and touching the latter with the earth wire, it was just as striking to see the electricity rush out of the wire, holding for a

time the magnet of the instrument in the reverse direction to that due to the ingress or charge.

These effects were produced equally well with either pole of the battery or with either end of the wire; and whether the electric condition was conferred and withdrawn at the same end, or at the opposite ends of the 100 miles, made no difference in the results. An intensity battery was required, for reasons which will be very evident in the sequel. That employed was able to decompose only a very small quantity of water in a given time. A Grove's battery of eight or ten pair of plates, which would have far surpassed it in this respect, would have had scarcely a sensible power in affecting the wire.

When the 100 miles of wire in the air were experimented with in like manner, not the slightest signs of any of these effects were produced. There is reason, from principle, to believe that an infinitesimal result is obtainable, but as compared to the water wire the action was nothing. Yet the wire was equally well and better insulated, and as regarded a constant current, it was an equally good conductor. This point was ascertained, by attaching the end of the water wire to one galvanometer, and the end of the air wire to another like instrument; the two other ends of the wires were fastened together, and to the earth contact; the two free galvanometer ends were fastened together, and to the free pole of the battery; in this manner the current was divided between the air and water wires, but the galvanometers were affected to precisely the same amount. To make the result more certain, these instruments were changed one for the other, but the deviations were still alike; so that the two wires conducted with equal facility.

The cause of the first results is, upon consideration, evident enough. In consequence of the perfection of the workmanship, a Leyden arrangement is produced upon a large scale; the copper wire becomes charged statically with that electricity which the pole of the battery connected with it can supply;[1] it acts by induction through the gutta percha (without which induction it could not itself become charged, *Exp. Res.*, 1177), producing the opposite state on the surface of the water touching the gutta percha, which forms the outer coating of this curious arrangement. The gutta percha across which the induction occurs, is only 0.1 of an inch thick, and the extent of the coating is enor-

[1] Davy, *Elements of Chemical Philosophy*, p. 154.

mous. The surface of the copper wire is nearly 8300 square feet, and the surface of the outer coating of water is four times that amount, or 33,000 square feet. Hence the striking character of the results. The intensity of the static charge acquired is only equal to the intensity at the pole of the battery whence it is derived; but its quantity is enormous, because of the immense extent of the Leyden arrangement; and hence when the wire is separated from the battery and the charge employed, it has all the powers of a considerable voltaic current, and gives results which the best ordinary electric machines and Leyden arrangements cannot as yet approach.

That the air wire produces none of these effects is simply because there is no outer coating correspondent to the water, or only one so far removed as to allow of no sensible induction, and therefore the inner wire cannot become charged. In the air wire of the warehouse, the floor, walls, and ceiling of the place constituted the outer coating, and this was at a considerable distance; and in any case could only affect the outside portions of the coils of wire. I understand that 100 miles of wire stretched in a line through the air, so as to have its whole extent opposed to earth, is equally inefficient in showing the effects, and there it must be the distance of the inductric and inducteous surfaces (1483), combined with the lower specific inductive capacity of air, as compared with gutta percha, which causes the negative result. The phenomena altogether offer a beautiful case of the identity of static and dynamic electricity. The whole power of a considerable battery may in this way be worked off in separate portions, and measured out in units of static force, and yet be employed afterwards for any or every purpose of voltaic electricity.

I now proceed to further consequences of associated static and dynamic effects. Wires covered with gutta percha, and then enclosed in tubes of lead or of iron, or buried in the earth, or sunk in the sea, exhibit the same phenomena as those described; the like static inductive action being in all these cases permitted by the conditions. Such subterraneous wires exist between London and Manchester, and when they are all connected together so as to make one series, offer above 1500 miles; which, as the duplications return to London, can be observed by one experimenter at intervals of about 400 miles, by the introduction of galvanometers at these returns. This wire, or the half, or fourth of it, presented all the phenomena already described; the only difference was that as the insulation was not so perfect the charged condition fell more rapidly. Consider 750 miles of the wire in one length, a galvanometer *a* being at the beginning of the wire, a second galvanometer *b* in the middle, and a third *c* at the end: these three galvanometers being in the room with the experimenter, and the third *c* perfectly connected with the earth. On bringing the pole of the battery into contact with the wire through the galvanometer *a*, that instrument was instantly affected; after a sensible time *b* was affected, and after a still longer time *c*: when the whole 1500 miles were included, it required two seconds for the electric stream to reach the last instrument. Again; all the instruments being deflected (of course not equally because of the electric leakage along the line), if the battery were cut off at *a*, that instrument instantly fell to zero; but *b* did not fall until a little while after; and *c* only after a still longer interval; a current flowing on to the end of the wire whilst there was none flowing in at the beginning. Again; by a short touch of the battery pole against *a*, it could be deflected and could fall back into its neutral condition, before the electric power had reached *b*; which in its turn would be for an instant affected, and then left neutral before the power had reached *c*; a wave of force having been sent into the wire which gradually travelled along it, and made itself evident at successive intervals of time, in different parts of the wire. It was even possible, by adjusted touches of the battery, to have two simultaneous waves in the wire, following each other, so that at the same moment that *c* was affected by the first wave, *a* or *b* was affected by the second; and there is no doubt that by the multiplication of instruments and close attention, four or five waves might be obtained at once.

If after making and breaking battery contact at *a*, *a* be immediately connected with the earth, then additional interesting effects occur. Part of the electricity which is in the wire will return, and passing through *a* will deflect it in the reverse direction; so that currents will flow out of both extremities of the wire in opposite directions, whilst no current is going into it from any source. Or if *a* be quickly put to the battery and then to the earth, it will show a current first entering into the wire, and then returning out of the wire at the same place; no sensible part of it ever travelling on to *b* or *c*.

When an air wave of equal extent is experimented with in like manner, no such effects as these are perceived: or if, guided by principle, the arrangements are such as to be searching, they are perceived only in a very slight degree, and disappear in comparison with the former gross results. The effect at the end of the very long air wire (or c) is in the smallest degree behind the effect at galvanometer a; and the accumulation of a charge in the wire is not sensible.

All these results as to *time*, &c., evidently depend upon the same condition as that which produced the former effect of static charge, namely *lateral induction;* and are necessary consequences of the principles of conduction, insulation, and induction, three terms which in their meaning are inseparable from each other (*Exp. Res.*, 1320, 1326,[1] 1338, 1561, &c.). If we put a plate of shellac upon a gold-leaf electrometer and a charged carrier (an insulated metal ball of two or three inches diameter) upon it, the electrometer is diverged; removing the carrier, this divergence instantly falls; this is *insulation* and *induction*: if we replace the shellac by metal, the carrier causes the leaves to diverge as before, but when removed, though after the shortest possible contact, the electroscope is left diverged; this is *conduction*. If we employ a plate of spermaceti instead of the metal, and repeat the experiment, we find the divergence partly falls and partly remains, because the spermaceti insulates and also conducts, doing both imperfectly; but the shellac also conducts, as is shown if time be allowed; and the metal also obstructs conduction, and

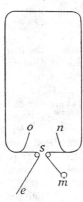

therefore insulates, as is shown by simple arrangements. For if a copper wire, 74 feet in length and 1/12th of an inch in diameter, be insulated in the air, having its end m a metal ball; its end e connected with the earth, and the parts near m and e brought within half an inch of each other, as at s; then an ordinary Leyden jar being charged sufficiently, its outside connected with e and its inside with m, will give a charge to the wire, which instead of travelling wholly through it, though it be so excellent a conductor, will pass in large proportion through the air at s, as a bright spark; for with such a length of wire, the resistance in it is accumulated until it becomes as much, or perhaps even more, than that of the air, for electricity of such high intensity.

Admitting that such and similar experiments show that conduction through a wire is preceded by the act of induction (1338), then all the phenomena presented by the submerged or subterranean wires are explained; and in their explanation confirm, as I think, the principles given. After Mr. Wheatstone had, in 1834, measured the velocity of a wave of electricity through a copper wire, and given it as 288,000 miles in a second, I said, in 1838, upon the strength of these principles (1333), "that the velocity of discharge through the *same wire* may be greatly varied, by attending to the circumstances which cause variations of discharge through spermaceti or sulphur. Thus, for instance, it must vary with the tension or intensity of the first urging force, which tension is charge and induction. So if the two ends of the wire in Professor Wheatstone's experiment were immediately connected with two large insulated metallic surfaces exposed to the air, so that the primary act of induction, after making the contact for discharge, might be in part removed from the internal portion of the wire at the first instant, and disposed for the moment on its surface jointly with the air and surrounding conductors, then I venture to anticipate that the middle spark would be more retarded than before: and if these two plates were the inner and outer coating of a large jar, or a Leyden battery, then the retardation of that spark would be still greater." Now this is precisely the case of the submerged or subterraneous wires, except that instead of carrying their surfaces towards the inducteous coatings (1483), the latter are brought near the former; in both cases the induction consequent upon charge, instead of being exerted almost entirely at the moment within the wire, is to a very large ex-

---

[1] 1326. All these considerations impress my mind strongly with the conviction, that insulation and ordinary conduction cannot be properly separated when we are examining into their nature; that is, into the general law or laws under which their phenomena are produced. They appear to me to consist in an action of contiguous particles, dependent on the forces developed in electrical excitement; these forces bring the particles into a state of tension or polarity, which constitutes both *induction* and *insulation;* and being in this state the contiguous particles have a power or capability of communicating these forces, one to the other, by which they are lowered and discharge occurs. Every body appears to discharge (444, 987); but the possession of this capability in a *greater* or *smaller degree* in different bodies, makes them better or worse conductors, worse or better insulators: and both *induction* and *conduction* appear to be the same in their principle and action (1320), except that in the latter, an effect common to both is raised to the highest degree, whereas in the former, it occurs in the best cases, in only an almost insensible quantity.

tent determined externally; and so the discharge or conduction being caused by a lower tension, therefore requires a longer time. Hence the reason why, with 1500 miles of subterraneous wire, the wave was two seconds in passing from end to end; whilst with the same length of air wire, the time was almost inappreciable.

With these lights it is interesting to look at the measured velocities of electricity in wires of metal, as given by different experimenters.

	Miles per second
[1] Wheatstone in 1834, with copper wire made it	288,000
[1] Walker in America with telegraph iron wire	18,780
[1] O'Mitchell in America with telegraph iron wire	28,524
[1] Fizeau and Gonnelle (copper wire)	112,680
[1] Ditto (iron wire)	62,600
[2] A. B. G. (copper) London and Brussels Telegraph	2,700
[2] A. B. G. (copper) London and Edinburgh Telegraph	7,600

Here, the difference in copper is seen by the first and fifth result to be above a hundredfold. It is further remarked in Liebig's report of Fizeau's and Gonnelle's experiments, that the velocity is not proportional to the conductive capacity, and is independent of the thickness of the wire. All these circumstances and incompatibilities appear rapidly to vanish, as we recognise and take into consideration the lateral induction of the wire carrying the current. If the velocity of a brief electric discharge is to be ascertained in a given length of wire, the simple circumstances of the latter being twined round a frame in small space, or spread through the air through a large space, or adhering to walls, or lying on the ground, will make a difference in the results. And in regard to long circuits such as those described, their conducting power cannot be understood, whilst no reference is made to their lateral static induction, or to the conditions of intensity and quantity which then come into play; especially in the case of short or intermitting currents, for then static and dynamic are continually passing into each other.

It has already been said that the conducting power of the air and water wires is alike for a constant current. This is in perfect accordance with the principles and with the definite character of the electric force, whether in the static or current or transition state. When a voltaic current of a certain intensity is sent into a long

water wire, connected at the farther extremity with the earth, part of the force is in the first instance occupied in raising a lateral induction round the wire, ultimately equal in intensity at the near end to the intensity of the battery stream, and decreasing gradually to the earth end, where it becomes nothing. Whilst this induction is rising, that within the wire amongst its particles is beneath what it would otherwise be; but as soon as the first has attained its maximum state, then that in the wire becomes proportionate to the battery intensity, and therefore equals that in the air wire, in which the same state is (because of the absence of lateral induction) almost instantly attained. Then of course they discharge alike and therefore conduct alike.

A striking proof of the variation of the conduction of a wire by variation of its lateral static induction, is given in the experiment proposed sixteen years ago (1333). If, using a constant charged jar, the interval s, page 827, be adjusted so that the spark shall freely pass there (though it would not if a little wider), whilst the short connecting wires n and o are insulated in the air, the experiment may be repeated twenty times without a single failure; but if after that n and o be connected with the inside and outside of an insulated Leyden jar, as described, the spark will never pass across s, but all the charge will go round the whole of the long wire. Why is this? The quantity of electricity is the same, the wire is the same, its resistance is the same, and that of the air remains unaltered; but because the intensity is lowered, through the lateral induction momentarily allowed, it is never enough to strike across the air at s; and it is finally altogether occupied in the wire, which in a little longer time than before, effects the whole discharge. M. Fizeau has applied the same expedient to the primary voltaic currents of Rhumkorff's beautiful inducting apparatus, with great advantage. He thereby reduces the intensity of these currents at the moment when it would be very disadvantageous, and gives us a striking instance of the advantage of viewing static and dynamic phenomena as the result of the same laws.

Mr. Clarke arranged a Bains' printing telegraph with three pens, so that it gave beautiful illustrations and records of facts like those stated: the pens are iron wires, under which a band of paper imbued with ferro-prussiate of potassa passes at a regular rate by clock-work; and thus regular lines of prussian blue are produced whenever a current is transmitted, and the

[1] *Liebig and Kopp's report*, 1850 (translated), p. 168.
[2] *Athenæum*, 14th January, 1854, p. 54.

time of the current is recorded. In the case to be described, the three lines were side by side, and about 0.1 of an inch apart. The pen *m* belonged to a circuit of only a few feet of wire, and a separate battery; it told whenever the contact key was put down by the finger; the pen *n* was at the earth end of the long air wire, and the pen *o* at the earth end of the long subterraneous wire; and by arrangement, the key could be made to throw the electricity of the chief battery into either of these wires, simultaneously with the passage of the short circuit current through pen *m*. When pens *m* and *n* were in action, the *m* record was a regular line of equal thickness, showing by its length the actual time during which the electricity flowed into the wires; and the *n* record was an equally regular line, parallel to, and of equal length with the former, but the least degree behind it; thus indicating that the long air wire conveyed its electric current almost instantaneously to the farther end. But when pens *m* and *o* were in action, the *o* line did not begin until some time after the *m* line, and it continued after the *m* line had ceased, i.e., after the *o* battery was cut off. Furthermore, it was faint at first, grew up to a maximum of intensity, continued at that as long as battery contact was continued, and then gradually diminished to nothing. Thus the record *o* showed that the wave of power took time in the water wire to reach the farther extremity; by its first faintness, it showed that power was consumed in the exertion of lateral static induction along the wire; by the attainment of a maximum and the after equality, it showed when this induction had become proportionate to the intensity of the battery current; by its beginning to diminish, it showed when the battery current was cut off; and its prolongation and gradual diminution showed the time of the outflow of the static electricity laid up in the wire, and the consequent regular falling of the induction which had been as regularly raised.

With the pens *m* and *o* the conversion of an intermitting into a continuous current could be beautifully shown; the earth wire by the static induction which it permitted, acting in a manner analogous to the fly-wheel of a steam-engine, or the air-spring of a pump. Thus when the contact key was regularly but rapidly depressed and raised, the pen *m* made a series of short lines separated by intervals of equal length. After four or more of these had passed, then pen *o*, belonging to the subterraneous wire, began to make its mark, weak at first,

then rising to a maximum, but always continuous. If the action of the contact key was less rapid, then alternate thickening and attenuations appeared in the *o* record; and if the introductions of the electric current at the one end of the earth wire were at still longer intervals, the records of action at the other end became entirely separated from each other: all showing most beautifully, how the individual current or wave, once introduced into the wire, and never ceasing to go onward in its course, could be affected in its intensity, its time, and other circumstances, by its partial occupation in static induction.

By other arrangements of the pens *n* and *o*, the near end of the subterraneous wire could be connected with the earth immediately after separation from the battery; and then the back flow of the electricity, and the time and manner thereof, were beautifully recorded; but I must refrain from detailing results which have already been described in principle.

Many variations of these experiments have been made and may be devised. Thus the ends of the insulated battery have been attached to the ends of the long subterraneous wire, and then the two halves of the wire have given back opposite return currents when connected with the earth. In such a case the wire is positive and negative at the two extremities, being permanently sustained by its length and the battery, in the same condition which is given to the short wire for a moment by the Leyden discharge, p. 827; or, for an extreme but like case, to a filament of shellac having its extremities charged positive and negative. Coulomb pointed out the difference of long and short as to the insulating or conducting power of such filaments, and the like difference occurs with long and short metal wires.

The character of the phenomena described in this report, induces me to refer to the terms *intensity* and *quantity* as applied to electricity; terms which I have had such frequent occasion to employ. These terms, or equivalents for them, cannot be dispensed with by those who study both the static and the dynamic relations of electricity; every current where there is resistance has the static element and induction involved in it, whilst every case of insulation has more or less of the dynamic element and conduction; and we have seen that with the same voltaic source, the same current in the same length of the same wire, gives a different result as the intensity is made to vary, with variations of the induction around the wire.

The idea of intensity or the power of overcoming resistance is as necessary to that of electricity, either static or current, as the idea of pressure is to steam in a boiler, or to air passing through apertures or tubes; and we must have language competent to express these conditions and these ideas. Furthermore, I have never found either of these terms lead to any mistakes regarding electrical action, or give rise to any false view of the character of electricity or its unity. I cannot find other terms of equally useful significance with these; or any which, conveying the same ideas, are not liable to such misuse as these may be subject to. It would be affectation, therefore, in me to search about for other words; and besides that, the present subject has shown me more than ever their great value and peculiar advantage in electrical language.

The fuse referred to in page 825, is of the following nature. Some copper wire was covered with sulphuretted gutta percha; after some months it was found that a film of sulphuret of copper was formed between the metal and the envelope; and further, that when half the gutta percha was cut away in any place, and then the copper wire removed by about $\frac{1}{4}$ of an inch, so as to remain connected only by the film of sulphuret adhering to the remaining gutta percha, an intensity battery could cause this sulphuret to enter into vivid ignition, and fire gunpowder with the utmost ease. Gunpowder was fired with certainty at the end of eight miles of single wire; and also through 100 miles of covered wire immersed in the canal, by the use of this fuse.

On Some Points of Magnetic Philosophy[1]

3300. WITHIN the last three years I have been bold enough, though only as an experimentalist, to put forth new views of magnetic action in papers having for titles, "On Lines of Magnetic Force,"[2] and "On Physical Lines of Magnetic Force."[3] The first paper was simply an attempt to give, for the use of experimentalists and others, a correct expression of the dual nature, amount, and direction of the magnetic power both within and outside of magnets, apart from any assumption regarding the character of the source of the power; that the mind, in reasoning forward towards new developments and discoveries, might be free from the bondage and deleterious influence of as-

sumptions of such a nature (3075). The second paper was a speculation respecting the possible physical nature of the force, as existing outside of the magnet as well as within it, and within what are called magnetic bodies, and was expressly described as being entirely hypothetical in its character.

3301. There are at present two, or rather three general hypotheses of the physical nature of magnetic action. First, that of ethers, carrying with it the idea of fluxes or currents, and this Euler has set forth in a simple manner to the unmathematical philosopher in his *Letters;*[4] in that hypothesis the magnetic fluid or ether is supposed to move in streams through magnets, and also the space and substances around them. Then there is the hypothesis of two magnetic fluids, which being present in all magnetic bodies, and accumulated at the poles of a magnet, exert attractions and repulsions upon portions of both fluids at a distance, and so cause the attractions and repulsions of the distant bodies containing them. Lastly, there is the hypothesis of Ampère, which assumes the existence of electrical currents round the particles of magnets, which currents, acting at a distance upon other particles having like currents, arranges them in the masses to which they belong, and so renders such masses subject to the magnetic action. Each of these ideas is varied more or less by different philosophers, but the three distinct expressions of them which I have just given will suffice for my present purpose. My physico-hypothetical notion does not go so far in assumption as the second and third of these ideas, for it does not profess to say how the magnetic force is originated or sustained in a magnet; it falls in rather with the first view, yet does not assume so much. Accepting the magnet as a centre of power surrounded by lines of force, which, as representants of the power, are now justified by mathematical analysis (3302), it views these lines as *physical* lines of power, essential both to the existence of the force within the magnet, and to its conveyance to, and exertion upon, magnetic bodies at a distance. Those who entertain in any degree the ether notion might consider these lines as currents, or progressive vibrations, or as stationary undulations, or as a state of tension. For many reasons they should be contemplated round a wire carrying an electric current, as well as when issuing from a magnetic pole.

[1] From the *Philosophical Magazine* for February, 1855.

[2] *Phil. Trans.* 1852, p. 25.

[3] *Phil. Mag.* 1852, June, p. 401.

[4] *Euler's Letters*, translated, 1802, Vol. I, p. 214; Vol. II, pp. 240, 242.

3302. The attention of two very able men and eminent mathematicians has fallen upon my proposition to represent the magnetic power by lines of magnetic force; and it is to me a source of great gratification and much encouragement to find that they affirm the truthfulness and generality of the method of representation. Professor W. Thomson, in referring to a like view of lines of force applied to static electricity (1295, 1304), and to Fourier's law of motion for heat, says that the lines of force give the same mathematical results of Coulomb's theory, and by more simple processes of analysis (if possible) than the latter;[1] and afterwards refers to the "strict foundation for an analogy on which the *conducting power of a magnetic medium for lines of force* may be spoken of."[2] Van Rees has published a mathematical paper on my lines of force in Dutch,[3] which has been transferred into Poggendorff's *Annalen*,[4] and of which I have only a very imperfect knowledge by translated abstracts. He objects, as I understand, to what I may call the physical part of my view as assigning no origin for the lines, and as not presenting the higher principle conveyed by the idea of magnetic fluids or of electric currents: he says it does not displace the old theories, or render them superfluous; but I think I am right in believing that, as far as the lines are taken to be representations of the power, he accepts them as correct representations, even to the full extent of the hypotheses, either of magnetic fluids or electric currents. It was always my intention to *avoid* substituting anything in place of these fluids or currents, that the mind might be delivered from the bondage of preconceived notions; but for those who desire an idea to rest upon, there is the old principle of the ethers.

3303. The encouragement I derive from this appreciation by mathematicians of the mode of figuring to one's self the magnetic forces by lines, emboldens me to dwell a little more upon the further point of the true but unknown natural magnetic action. Indeed, what we really want is not a variety of different methods of representing the forces, but the one true physical signification of that which is rendered apparent to us by the phenomena, and the laws governing them. Of the two assumptions most usually entertained at present, magnetic fluids and electric currents, *one* must be wrong, per-

[1] *Phil. Mag.* 1854, Vol. VIII, p. 53.
[2] *Ibid.*, p. 56.
[3] *Trans. Royal Acad. Sciences of Amsterdam*, 1854, p. 17.
[4] *Poggendorff's Annalen*, 1853, Vol. XC, p. 415.

haps *both* are; and I do not perceive that the mathematician, even though he may think that each contains a higher principle than any I have advanced, can tell the true from the false, or say that either is true. Neither of these views could have led the mind to the phenomena of diamagnetism, and I think not to the magnetic rotation of light; and I suppose that if the question of the possibility of diamagnetic phenomena could have been asked beforehand, a mathematician, guided by either hypothesis, must have denied that possibility. The notion that I have introduced complicates the matter still further, for it is inconsistent with either of the former views, so long as they depend exclusively upon action at a distance without intermediation; and yet in the form of lines of force it represents magnetic actions truly in all that is not hypothetical. So that there are now three fundamental notions, and *two* of them at least must be impossible, i.e., untrue.

3304. It is evident, therefore, that our physical views are very doubtful; and I think good would result from an endeavour to shake ourselves loose from such preconceptions as are contained in them, that we may contemplate for a time the force as much as possible in its purity. At present we cannot think of polarity without feeling ourselves drawn into one or the other of the two hypotheses of the origin of polar powers; and as mathematical considerations cannot give a decision, we feel as if the subject were in that same doubtful condition which hung over the conflicting theories of light prior to the researches of modern time; but as there the use of Wheatstone's reflector, combined with Arago's suggestion of a decisive experiment, and its realization by Leon Foucault, appear to have settled that question, so we may hope by a due exertion of judgement, united with experiment, to obtain a resolution of the magnetic difficulty also.

3305. If we could tell the *disposition* of the force of a magnet, first at the place of its origin and next in the space around, we should then have attained to a very important position in the pursuit of our subject; and if we could do that, assuming little or nothing, then we should be in the very best condition for carrying the pursuit further. Supposing that we imagine the magnet a sort of sun (as there is every reason to believe that the sun is a magnet) polarized, with antithetical powers, ever filling all space around it with its curved beams, as either the sun or a candle fills space with luminous rays; and supposing that such a view takes equal position with either of the two former views in representing truly the disposition of the forces, and that mathematical considerations cannot at present decide which of the three views is either above or inferior to its co-rivals; it surely becomes necessary that physical reasoning should be brought to bear upon the subject as largely as possible. For if there be such physical lines of magnetic force as correspond (in having a real existence) to the rays of light, it does not seem so very impossible for experiment to touch *them;* and it must be very important to obtain an answer to the inquiry respecting their existence, especially as the answer is likely enough to be in the affirmative. I therefore purpose, without asserting anything regarding the physical hypothesis of the magnet more strongly than before (3299), to call the attention of experimenters, in a somewhat desultory manner, to the subject again, both as respects the deficiency of the present physical views and the possible existence of lines of physical force, concentrating the observations I may have to make about a few points—as *polarity, duality,* &c., as occasion may best serve; and I am encouraged to make this endeavour by the following considerations. 1, The confirmation by mathematicians of the truthfulness of the abstract lines of force in representing the direction and amount of the magnetic power; 2, My own personal advantageous use of the lines on numerous occasions (3174); 3, The close analogy of the magnetic force and the other dual powers, either in the static or dynamic state, and especially of the magnet with the voltaic battery or any other sustaining source of an electric current; 4, Euler's idea of magnetic ethers or circulating fluids; 5, The strong conviction expressed by Sir Isaac Newton, that even gravity cannot be carried on to produce a distant effect except by some interposed agent[1] fulfilling the conditions of a physical line of force; 6, The example of the conflict and final experimental settlement of the two theories of light.

3306. I believe that the use by me of the

---

[1] Newton says, "That gravity should be innate, inherent, and essential to matter, so that one body may act upon another at a distance through a *vacuum,* without the mediation of anything else, by and through which their action and force may be conveyed from one to another, is to me so great an absurdity, that I believe no man who has in philosophical matters a competent faculty of thinking can ever fall into it. Gravity must be caused by an agent acting constantly according to certain laws; but whether this agent be material or immaterial I have left to the consideration of my readers." See the third letter to Bentley.

phrase "places of force" has been considered by some as objectionable, inasmuch as it would seem to anticipate the decision that there are physical lines of force. I will endeavour so to use it, if necessary, as not to imply the assertion. Nevertheless I may observe that we use such a phrase in relation to a ray of light, even in those parts of the ray where it is not extinguished, and where therefore we have no better knowledge of it or its existence than in similar magnetic cases; and we also use the phrase when speaking of gravity in respect to places where no second body to gravitate upon is present, and where, when existing, it cannot, according to our present views, cause the gravitating force of the primary body, or even the determination of it, upon that particular place.

Magnetic Polarity

3307. The meaning of this phrase is rapidly becoming more and more uncertain. In the ordinary view, polarity does not necessarily touch much upon the idea of lines of physical force; yet in the one natural truth it must either be essential to, and identified with it, or else absolutely incompatible with, and opposed to it. Coulomb's view makes polarity to depend upon the resultant in direction of the action of two separated and distant portions of two magnetic fluids upon other like separated portions, which are either originally separate, as in a magnet, or are induced to separate, as in soft iron, by the action of the dominant magnet; it is essential to this hypothesis that the polarity force of one name should repel polarity force of the same name and attract that of the other name. Ampère's view of polarity is that there are no magnetic fluids, but that closed currents of electricity can exist round particles of matter (or round masses), and that the known experimental difference on the opposite sides of these currents, shown by attraction and repulsion of other currents, constitutes polarity. Ampère's view is modified (chiefly by addition) in various ways by Weber, De la Rive, Matteucci, and others. My view of polarity is founded upon the character in direction of the force itself, whatever the cause of that force may be, and asserts that when an electro-conducting body moving in a constant direction near or between bodies acting magnetically on themselves or each other, has a current in a constant direction produced in it, the magnetic polarity is the same; if the motion or the current be reversed, the contrary polarity is indicated. The indication is true either for the exterior or the interior of magnetic bodies whenever the electric current is produced, and depends upon the unknown but essential dual or antithetical nature of the force which we call magnetism (3154).

3308. The numerous meanings of the term *polarity*, and various interpretations of *polarity indications* at present current, show the increasing uncertainty of the idea and the word itself. Some consider that the mere set or attraction, or even repulsion, shown by a body when subject to a dominant magnet is sufficient to mark polarity, and I think it is as good a test as any more refined arrangement (2693) when the old notion of polarity only is under consideration. Others require that two bodies under the power of a dominant magnet should by their actions show a mutual relation to each other before they can be considered as polar. Tyndall, without meaning to include any idea of the nature of the magnetic force, takes his type from soft iron, and considers that any body presenting the like or the antithetical phenomena which such iron would present under magnetic action, is in a like or antithetical state of polarity.[1] Thomson does not view two bodies which present these antithetical positions or phenomena as being necessarily the reverse of each other in what may be called their polar states,[2] but, I think, looks more to differential action, and in that approaches towards the views held generally by E. Becquerel and myself. Matteucci considers that the whole mass of the polar body ought to be in dependence by its particles as a mass of iron is, and that a solution of iron and certain salts of iron have not poles, properly speaking, but that at the nearest points to the dominant pole there is the contrary magnetism to that of the pole, surrounded by the same magnetism as of the pole in the farther part, the two ends of a bar of such matter between two dominant poles having no relation to each other.[3] Becquerel considers that polarity may in certain cases occur transverse to the length, and so produce results which others explain by reverse polarity. The views of very many parties always include the idea of the source of the polar action, whether that be supposed to depend on the accumulation of magnetic fluids at the chief poles of the dominant magnet, or the action of electric currents in a determinate position around its molecules; and such views are adhered to even when the polarity induced is of the re-

verse kind, as in bismuth, &c., to that of the inducing magnet. Others, like Weber, add to Ampère's hypothesis an idea of electricity, loose as regards the particles, though inseparably associated with the mass of the body under induction. Some, I think, make the polarity not altogether dependent upon the dominant magnet, but upon the neighbouring or surrounding substances; and I propose, if the physical lines of force should hereafter be justified, to make that which is commonly called polarity, in distinction from the true polarity (3307), dependent upon the curvature of lines of force due to the better or worse magneto-conduction power of the substances presenting the usual polar phenomena (2818).

3309. The views of polar action and of magnetism itself, as formerly entertained, have been powerfully agitated by the discovery of diamagnetism. I was soon driven from my first supposition that the N pole of a magnet induced like or N polarity in the near part of a piece of bismuth or phosphorus; but as that view has been sustained by very eminent men, who tie up with it the existence of magnetic fluids or closed electric currents as the source of magnetic power, it claims continued examination, for it will most likely be a touchstone and developer of real scientific truth, whichever way the arguments may prevail. To me the idea appears to involve, if not magnetic impossibilities, at least great contradiction and much confusion, some of which I proceed to state, but only with the desire of elucidating the general subject.

3310. If an ordinary magnet M, *Fig. 1*, acting upon a piece of iron or other paramagnetic

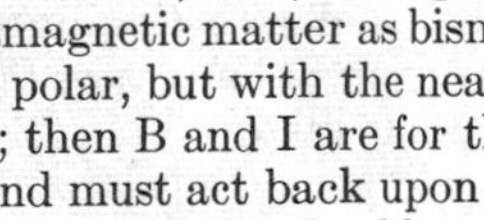

Fig. 1

matter I, renders it polar by throwing its near end into the contrary or S state in the manner usually understood, and, acting upon a like piece of diamagnetic matter as bismuth B, renders it also polar, but with the near end in the same state; then B and I are for the time two magnets, and must act back upon the magnet M; or if they could be made able to retain their states after M is removed (and that is the case with I), would act as magnets upon a third piece of magnetic matter as C. When M acts upon I, it exerts its influence, according to the received theories, upon all the particles of the

[1] *Athenæum*, No. 1406, p. 1203.
[2] *Ibid.*, column 3 at bottom.
[3] *Cours spécial sur l'induction*, &c., p. 201.

latter, bringing them into like polar position with itself, and these, consistently with the simple assumption, act also upon each other as particle magnets, and exalt the polarity of the whole mass in its two extremities. In like manner M should act upon B, polarizing the mass and all its particles; for the particles of the diamagnetic body B, even to the smallest, must be operated upon; and we know experimentally, that a tube filled with powdered bismuth acts as a bar of the metal does. But then, what is the mutual action of these bismuth particles on each other? for though all may be supposed to have a reverse polarity to that of M, they cannot in that case be reverse in respect to each other. All must have like polarity, and the N of one particle must be opposed to the S of the next particle in the polarity direction. That these particles act on each other must be true, and Tyndall's results on the effect of compression have proved that by the right means, namely experiment. If they were supposed to have no such action on each other, it would be in contradiction to the essential nature of magnetic action, and there would remain no reason to think that the magnet itself could act on the particles, or the particles react on it. If they acted on each other as the magnet is supposed to act on them, i.e., to induce contrary poles, then the power of the magnet would be nullified, and the more effectually the nearer the particles were together; whereas Tyndall has shown that the bismuth magnetic condition is exalted by such vicinity of the particles, and hence we have a further right to conclude that they do act on, or influence each other, to the exaltation of the state of the mass. But if the N-ness of one particle corresponds to, and aids in sustaining and exalting, the S-ness of the next particle, the whole mass must have the same kind of force; so that, as a magnet, its polarity must have the same kind of polarity as that of the particles themselves. For whether a particle of bismuth be considered as acting upon a neighbouring particle or upon a distant particle of bismuth, or whether a mass of particles be considered as acting on the distant particle, the action in both cases must be precisely of the same kind.

3311. But why should a polarized particle of bismuth acting upon another particle of bismuth produce in it like polarity, and with a particle of iron produce a contrary polarity? or why should masses of bismuth and iron, when they act as magnets (3310), produce such different effects? If such were the case, then the N pole of a paramagnetic body would induce an S pole on the near end of an iron rod, whilst the N pole of a diamagnetic body would produce a pole contrary to the former, i.e., an N pole at the same end of the iron rod in the same position and place. This would be to assume two kinds of magnetism, i.e., two north fluids (or electric currents) and two south; and the northness of bismuth would differ from the northness of iron as much as pole from pole. Still more, the northness of bismuth and the southness of iron would be found to have exactly like qualities in all points, and to differ in nothing but name; and the southness of bismuth and northness of iron would also prove to be absolutely alike. What is this, in fact, but to say they *are* the same? and why should we not accept the confirmation and unfailing proof that it is so, which is given to us experimentally by the moving wire? (3307, 3356).

3312. If we employ a magnet as the originally inducing body (3310), and entertain the idea of magnetic fluids accumulated at the poles, which act by their power of attracting each other, but repelling their like, then the inconsistency of supposing that the north fluid of a given pole can attract the north fluid of one body and the south fluid of another, or that the north and south fluids of the dominant magnet can attract one and the same fluid in bismuth and in iron, &c., is very manifest. Or if we act by a solenoid or a helix of copper wire carrying an electric current instead of a magnet, and find that analogous effects are produced, are we to admit at once that the electric currents in it, acting upon the assumed electric circuits round the particles of matter, sometimes attract them on the one side and sometimes on the other? or if such bodies as bismuth and platinum are put into such a helix, are we to allow that currents in opposite directions are induced in them by one and the same inducing condition? and that, too, when all the other phenomena, and there are many, point to a uniformity of action as to direction with a variation only in power.

Media.

3313. Let us now consider for a time the action of different *media,* and the evidence they give in respect to polarity. If a weak solution of protosulphate of iron,[1] *m*, be put into a selected thin glass tube about an inch long, and

---

[1] Let *l* contain 4 grains, *m* 8 grains, *n* 16 grains, and *o* 32 grains, of crystallized protosulphate of iron in each cubic inch of water.

one-third or one-fourth of an inch in diameter, and sealed up hermetically (2279), and be then suspended horizontally between the magnetic poles in the air, it will point axially, and behave in other respects as iron; if, instead of air between the poles, a solution of the same kind as *m*, but a little stronger, *n*, be substituted, the solution in the tube will point equatorially, or as bismuth. A like solution somewhat weaker than *m*, to be called *l*, enclosed in a similar tube, will behave like bismuth in air but like iron in water. Now these are precisely the actions which have been attributed to polarity, and by which the assumed reverse polarities of paramagnetic and diamagnetic bodies have been considered as established; but when examined, how will ideas of polarity apply to these cases, or they to it? The solution *l* points and acts like bismuth in air and like iron in water; are we then to conclude that it has reverse polarity in these cases? and if so, what are the reasons and causes for such a singular contrast in that which must be considered as dependent upon its internal or molecular state?

3314. In the first place, no want of magnetic continuity of parts can have anything to do with the inversion of the phenomena; for it has been shown sufficiently by former experiments,[1] that such solutions are as magnetically continuous in character as iron itself.

3315. In the next place, I think it is impossible to say that the medium interposed between the magnet and the suspended cylinder of fluid can cut off, or in any way affect the direct force of the former on the latter, so as to change the direction of its internal polarity. Let the tube be filled with the solution *m*, then if it be surrounded by the solution *l*, it will point as iron; if the stronger solution *n* surround it, it will point as bismuth; and with sufficient care a succession of these fluids may be arranged as indicated in *Figs. 2, 3*, where the outlines between the poles represent the forms of thin glass troughs, and the letters the

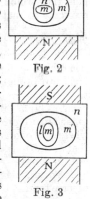

Fig. 2

Fig. 3

solutions in them. In *Fig. 2* we see that the action on *m* is the same as that on *m'*, and the pointing of the two portions is the same, i.e., equatorial; neither has the action on *m* been

[1] *Phil. Mag.* 1846, Vol. XXIX, p. 254.

altered by the power of the poles having to traverse *n*, *m'* and *n'*; and in *Fig.* 3 we see that, under like circumstances of the power, *m'* points as bismuth and *m* as iron, though they are the same solution with each other and with the former *m m'* solutions. No cutting off of power by the media could cause these changes—repetitions of position in the first case, and inversions in the second. All that could be expected from any such interceptions would be perhaps diminutions of action, but not inversions of polarity; and every consideration indicates that all the portions of these solutions in the field at once have *like polarity*, i.e., like direction of force through them, and like internal condition; each solution in its complex arrangement being affected exactly in the same way and degree as if it filled the whole of the magnetic field, although in these particular arrangements it sometimes points like iron, and at other times like bismuth (2362, 2414).

3316. These motions and pointings of the same or of different solutions, contain every action and indication which is supposed to distinguish the contrary polarities of paramagnetic and diamagnetic bodies from each other, and the solutions *l* and *m* in air repeat exactly the phenomena presented in air by phosphorus and platinum, which are respectively diamagnetic and paramagnetic substances. But we know that these actions are due to the differential result of the masses of the moving or setting solution and of that (or the air) surrounding it. No structural or internal polarity, having opposite directions, is necessary to account for them (2361, 2757). If, therefore, it is still said that the solution *m* has one polarity in *l* and the reverse polarity in *n*, that would be to make the polarity depend upon the *mass* of *m* independently of its particles; for it can hardly be supposed that the particles of *m* are more affected by the influence upon them of the surrounding medium (itself under like inductive action only, and almost insensible as a magnet), than they are by the dominant manget.[2] It would be also to make the polarity of *m* as much, or more, dependent upon the surrounding medium than upon the magnet itself; and

[2] If the polarity of the inner mass of solution is dependent upon that of the outer, and cannot be affected but through it, then why are not air and space admitted as being in effective magnetic relation to the bodies surrounded by them? How else could a distant body be acted upon by a magnet, if the inner solution of sulphate of iron is so acted on? Are we to assume one mode of action by contiguous masses or particles in one case, and another through distance in another case?

it would be to make the masses of *m* and *l* and even their *form* the determining cause of the polarity; which would remove polarity altogether from dependence upon internal molecular condition, and, I think, destroy the last remains of the usual idea. For my own part, I cannot conceive that when a little sphere of *m* in the solution *l* is attracted upon the approach of a given magnetic pole, and repelled under the action of the same pole when it is in the solution *n*, its particles are in the two cases polar in two opposite directions; or that if for a north magnetic pole it is the *near* side of the particles of *m* when in *l* that assume the south state, it is the *farther* side which acquires the same state when the solution *l* is changed for *n*. Nor can I think that when the particles of *m* have the same polar state in both solutions, the whole, as a mass, can have the opposite states.

3317. These differential results run on in one uninterrupted course from the extreme of paramagnetic bodies to the extreme of diamagnetic bodies; and there is no substance within the series which, in association with those on each side of it, may not be made to present in itself the appearances and action which are considered as indicating the opposite polarities of iron and bismuth. How then is their case, in the one or the other condition, to be distinguished from the assumed polarity conditions of bismuth or of iron?—only, I think, by assuming other points which beg the whole question. In the first place, it must be, or is assumed, that no magnetic force exists in the space around a magnet when it is in a vacuum, it being denied that the power either crosses or reaches a locality in that space until some material substance, as the bismuth or iron, is there. It is assumed that the space is in a state of magnetic darkness (3305), an assumption so large, considering the knowledge we have of natural powers, and especially of dual forces, that there is none larger in any part of magnetic or electric science, and is the very point which of all others should be held in doubt and pursued by experimental investigation. It is as if one should say there is no light or form of light in the space between the sun and the earth because that space is invisible to the eye. Newton himself durst not make a like assumption even in the case of gravitation (3305), but most carefully guards himself and warns others against it, and Euler[1] seems to follow him in this matter. Such an assumption, however, enables the

[1] *Letters, &c.* translated. Letter LXVIII, or pp. 260–262.

parties who make it to dismiss the consideration of differential effects when bodies are placed in a vacuum, and to divide the bodies into the well-known double series of paramagnetic and diamagnetic substances. But in the second place, even then, those who assume the reverse polarity of diamagnetic bodies, must assume also that the state set up in them by induction is less favourable to either the exercise or the transmission of the magnetic force than the original unpolarized state of the bismuth; an assumption which is, I think, contrary to the natural action and final stable condition into which the physical forces tend to bring all bodies subject to them. That a magnet acting on a piece of iron should so determine and dispose of the forces as to make the magnet and iron mutually accordant in their action, I can conceive; but that it should throw the bismuth into a state which would make it repel the magnet, whereas if unaffected it should be so far favourable as to be at least indifferent, is what I cannot imagine to myself. In the third place, those who rest their ideas on *magnetic fluids*, must assume that in all diamagnetic cases, and in them only, the fundamental idea of their mutual action must not only be set aside but inverted, so that the hypothesis would be at war with itself; and those who assume that *electric currents* are the cause of magnetic effects, would have to give up the law of their inducing action (as far as we know it) in all cases of diamagnetism, at the very same moment when, if they approached the diamagnetic bismuth in the form of a spiral to the pole, they would have a current produced in it *according* to that law.

Time

3318. I will venture another thought or two regarding the condition into which diamagnetic bodies are brought by the act of magnetic induction, in connexion with the point of *time*. It appears, as far as I remember, that all natural forces tend to produce a state of rest, except in cases where vital or organic powers are concerned; and that as in *life* the actions are for ever progressive, and have respect to a future rather than a present state (Paget), so all *inorganic* exertions of force tend to bring about a stable and permanent condition, having as the result a state of rest, i.e., a static condition of the powers.

3319. Applying this consideration to the case of bismuth in the magnetic field, it seems to me more like the truth of nature that the state assumed by the bismuth should be one more favourable to the final and static exercise of the power of the dominant magnet upon it, than that state belonging to the bismuth before it had suffered or undergone the induction; exactly as in soft iron we know that before it has acquired the state which a dominant magnet can induce upon it, it is not so favourable to the final static condition of the powers as it is afterwards. Now it is very manifest, by numerous forms of experiment, that *time* enters as an element into ordinary magnetic and magneto-electric actions, and there is every reason to expect, into diamagnetic actions also; and it is also well known that we can take advantage of this time, and test the state of a piece of iron in the magnetic field before it has attained its finally induced state, and afterwards; as, for instance, by placing it with a helix round it in the magnetic field and quickly connecting the helix *afterwards* with a galvanometer, when a current of electricity in such direction as to prove the truth of the statement will be obtained. In other forms of experiment and with large pieces of iron, the time which can be so separated or snatched up during the act of progressive induction will amount to a minute or more. Supposing this could be done in any sensible degree with diamagnetic bodies, then the following considerations present themselves. A globe or bar of bismuth in the magnetic field may have its states, before and after induction, considered as separated by a moment of time; if the induction raises up a state of polarity the reverse of that of the magnet, then the bismuth ought to be more favourable to the determination of magnetic force upon it *before* the induction than *after;* whereas if, according to my view, the polarity is not reversed, but is the same as that of the magnet, the metal ought to be more favourable to the determination of magnetic force upon or through it *after* induction than *before*. Believing this to be an experiment which would settle the question of reverse polarity, and perhaps the existence or non-existence of physical lines of magnetic force, I have made many attempts in various ways, and especially by alternating motions of cylinders and balls of bismuth between soft iron magnetic poles furnished with helices, to obtain some results due to the *time* of induction, but have been as yet unable to succeed. I cannot doubt that time is concerned; but it seems to be so brief in period as to be inappreciable by the means I have employed.

3320. Professor Thomson has put this matter of time and polarity in another form. If a globe of bismuth be placed without friction in the middle of the magnetic field, it will not point or move because of its shape; but if it have reverse polarity, it will be in a state of unstable equilibrium; and if *time* be an element, then the ball, being once moved on its axis ever so little, would then have its polarity inclined to the magnetic axis, and would go on revolving for ever, producing a perpetual motion. I do not see how this consequence can be avoided, and therefore cannot admit the principles on which it rests. The idea of a perpetual motion produced by static forces is philosophically illogical and impossible, and so I think is the polarly opposed or adverse static condition to which I have already referred.

3321. It is not necessary here that I should refer to the manner in which my view of the lines of magnetic force meet these cases, for it has been done in former papers (2797, &c.); but I will call the attention of those who like to pursue the subject, to a true case of reverse polarity in the magnetic field (*Experimental Researches*, 3238, *Fig. 15*), and there they will easily see and comprehend the beginning of the rotation of Professor Thomson's bismuth globe, and its continuance, if, as supposed, the polar state represented in the figure could be continually renewed.

3322. When the north pole of a magnet repels a piece of bismuth in a vacuum, or makes a bar of it set equatorially, and is found to produce like actions with many paramagnetic bodies when surrounded by media a little more paramagnetic than themselves, and with as many diamagnetic bodies when surrounded by media a little less diamagnetic, it would seem more cautious in the first instance to inquire how these latter motions take place, and how it is that parts, which with the paramagnetics have certainly been brought into a south condition by the north end of the pole, recede from it; and to apply these results in the first instance to those obtained with bismuth in a vacuum, before we assume a total change in principle, and yet an exceptional change as to substances, in the general law of magnetic polarity, without any cause assigned than, or any supporting facts beyond, the effect in question.

Curved Lines of Magnetic Force—Dependence of the Dualities

3323. The representative idea of lines of magnetic force which I entertain, includes in it the thought of the curvature of these lines, not as a merely convenient notion making the idea of the lines more manageable, but as one flowing from and suggested, if not proved, by the phenomena themselves. It is in this point of view that I proceed to consider it; and as the proof of the curvature is, in respect to *principle*, in the essential and necessary dependence of the two qualities or parts of a dual force upon each other (3324, &c.); and in respect to *experiment*, by the numerous results supplied during the mutual actions of magnets and magnetic bodies and the phenomena of moving conductors (3337, &c.), I will consider each in turn.

3324. There is no known case of one form or part of a dual power existing otherwise than with, and in dependence on, the other, which then exists simultaneously to an equivalent, i.e., an equal, degree. In static electricity, where supposed electric fluids are considered as being separated from each other, they are in equal amount (1177), are ever related to each other (1681), often by curved lines of force (1215), and the existence of the one electricity without the other, or in the smallest degree of excess or deficiency, is absolutely impossible (1174). In the voltaic battery, or in the electric current produced in any other way, as by thermo arrangements or inductions, the current in one part of the circuit is absolutely the same in amount and in dual character as in another; and in the insulated, unconnected voltaic battery, where the sustaining power is internal, not the slightest development of the forces, or of either of them, can occur until circuit is completed, or induction allowed at the extremities; for if, when there is no circuit, the induction be prevented, not merely no current, but no stock of electricity at the battery poles ready to produce a current can be evolved in the slightest degree. In like manner I am fully persuaded that the northness and southness of magnetism (in whatever they may be supposed to consist) cannot exist alone; nor without exact proportion to each other; nor without mutual dependence upon each other; but that they are subject to the mutual relation and dependence of all dual force.

3325. Let us consider a hard invariable magnet in space, *Fig. 4*. If a piece of soft iron, I, be brought towards it, the N end of the magnet will cause southness in the near end of the iron and northness in the farther end, and this will continue until the iron is removed, the southness and northness at the two ends or halves of the magnet having remained all the time unchanged in their equality and amount (3221, 3223). Now to say that the force emanating

from N could act on the iron, producing like and the contrary force, and then, by removal of the iron, cease to act there *or elsewhere*; and then again act on the iron if approached, or anything else, and then cease to act, and so on;

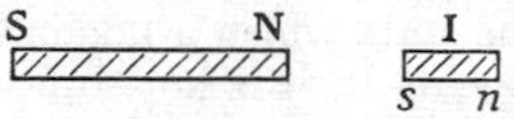

Fig. 4

would in my mind be to deny the *conservation of force:* and we know that there is no equivalent action within the magnet, to explain by any alternate excitement and suppression of the dual parts, any supposed appearance and disappearance of the powers at the different times; for a helix closely applied round the middle part of the magnet during the experiment gives no current, and by that shows that there is no equivalent *internal* derangement of the power, when the outer exercise of it may be supposed to change between active and inert.

3326. Suppose the power of such a magnet to be due to magnetic N and S fluids; can it be thought that the N particles can be sometimes exerting their attraction for S particles, and sometimes not? Would not that be equivalent to the assumption of a suppression, i.e., a destruction of force?—which surely cannot be. Such an assumption could be surpassed only by that which supposes that the N fluid might sometimes attract S and repel N, and at other times repel S and attract N fluids (3311, 3312, 3317).

3327. As to the soft iron under induction (3325), its dual magnetic forces do re-enter into their former mutually dependent and mutually satisfying state: but suppose it to be replaced by steel, and that the magnetisms produced in it do not recombine or disappear on the removal of the dominant magnet, then on what is their power ultimately turned, *if not on each other* (3257, 3324)? Where is the S power of the steel disposed of when it is separated from its relation with the N power of the magnet that evolved it? The case cannot be met except by affirming the independent existence of the two powers (3329); or, admitting the suppression of force, and of either of these forces the one without the other (3330); or allowing the mutual dependence of the two polarities of the magnet (3331).

3328. When the N pole of a magnet (*Fig. 5*) is acting in free space, its force is sensible around to a certain amount (114); when a piece of soft iron, I, is brought near it, much of its force gathers up upon that iron, but the whole amount of force from and about the N pole is the same; when an S pole is brought up, either of another magnet or of itself (for the effect is precisely the same), much of the force exerted upon the iron is removed from it, and falls upon the S

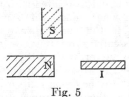

Fig. 5

pole, but the amount of force about the pole N remains the same; all of which can be proved experimentally by a helix on the soft iron and loops carried over the N pole (3218, 3223). Indeed the way in which the power of one pole over either iron or bismuth is affected and diminished by the approximation on the same side of a contrary pole, is perfectly well known, and there are hundreds of cases in which the disposition in direction of the magnetic power can be varied in a great variety of ways, without the slightest change in the *sum* of its amount at the source, each of which gives evidence of the antithetical and inseparable condition of the two forms of force.

3329. As to independent existence of the two powers (3327), how is it then that they cannot be shown separately?—not even up to the degree which is exhibited, so to say, by static electricity. There is nothing like a charge of northness or a charge of southness in any one of the innumerable phenomena presented by magnetism (3341). The two are just as closely connected as the two electricities of a voltaic battery; whether we consider it as giving the current when properly connected, or exhibiting induction at its extremities when unconnected. The difficulty, indeed is to find a fact which gives one the least hold for consideration of the thought that the two magnetic forces can be separated, or considered apart from each other.

3330. As to the suppression of force (3327), I conceive that the creation, annihilation, or suppression of force, and still more emphatically of one form only of a dual force, is as impossible as the like of matter. All that is permitted under the general laws of nature is to displace, remove, and otherwise employ it; and these conditions are as true of the smallest suppression of a force, or part of a force, as of the suppression of the whole. I may further ask,

whether, as it is *physically* impossible to annihilate or suppress force, it is not also *mathematically* impossible to do so, consistently with the law of the conservation of force?

3331. If we say that the forces in the cases of removal (3327) are disposed of, sometimes in one direction and sometimes in another, but with the preservation of their full and equivalent amount, then how are we to consider them disposed of in the case of a cylinder or globular magnet, placed in air or *vacuo*, so as to be entirely self-dependent?—or in the case of a magnetic sphere placed in an inverted position in the magnetic field, so as to be entirely surrounded and enclosed by magnetic forces having a contrary direction to its own (3238, 3321)?

3332. If we say that the dualities of such a magnet are dependent on each other (which is the third case (3327)), then we have to consider how this can be, consistently with the distant mutual action, either of magnetic fluids or electric currents, acting in right lines only. Such action must then be through the body of the magnet (3260). If we confine our attention to magnetic fluids, then the direction of their forces towards each other through the magnet when it is alone must be of the like nature as their direction to approached iron, in which they are supposed to induce collections of the contrary fluids, or towards the fluids at the contrary poles of approached equal or superior magnets; i.e., the two poles of the magnet must be conceived of as centres of force, sometimes exerting their power towards each other in a given direction through the body of the magnet, and at other times exerting them outwardly to external poles in a direction exactly the contrary. But the currents which are evolved by the rotation of the magnet, or of discs of metal combined with it (3119, 3163), show that the direction of the force (which is its polarity) is not thus reverse in the two halves of the case, but is the same within the magnet as in the prolongation of direction through and beyond the pole; and also that whether the magnet be alone, and therefore supposed to have the polar forces exerted on each other through it, or be in relation to outer magnets, so as to have this exertion of force entirely removed from its interior, still it is always the same; having in both cases the same condition, direction, and amount of power within it (3116).

3333. If the charged and polar state of the magnet be supposed to depend upon molecular electric currents, held by some internal condition in a position of parallelism, it is impossible that these can act backwards upon each other through the magnet in straight lines, so as to put the northness and southness of the pole in mutual dependence, as they are supposed to be in relation to external poles, without the currents themselves being *displaced and turned*, until the whole magnet is neutralized; falling back into the undeveloped state, just as a piece of soft iron falls back. When this return of state happens in soft iron or steel in any degree, a helix round these shows the induced currents consequent on such a change; and a loop (3133, 3217) shows the difference when the iron or magnet is polar outwards and when its state has fallen. No such effects happen with a hard magnet, when it is alternately left to itself or put in relation to external poles of other magnets. The body of the magnet, and the forces passing through it, remain unchanged, whether examined by the loop (3223) or by its own motion, or that of discs and wires associated with it (3116, &c.). Its force ever remains the same in quantity and general direction.

3334. The case of the steel ring magnet (3283) is well known, and the manner in which such a magnet, showing no external relation, developes strong poles when it is broken. The phenomena assure us, I think, that when broken the northness and southness then appearing cannot, when the pieces are by themselves, be determined upon each other backward through the magnet; there is no sufficient reason to suppose such a thing. And, again, the mutual destruction of highly-charged linear magnets, such as steel needles, when many of them are made into a thick, short bundle, shows the same thing; for if when alone the polar powers are not external, but are determined upon each other through each individual magnet, they are as free for a like disposal when the elementary magnets are associated as when they are separated: and then there remains no sufficient reason to expect a dominant action over each other superior to that which each has over itself.

3335. It is not to be supposed that the change of force which occurs when the magnet first acting externally is then made to act internally or through itself, would be small and unnoticeable. It should be as great as the whole amount of power which the magnet can show under the most favourable circumstance; and the means are abundantly sufficient, by moving wires and discs, to make that evident in any case which might imply its passing through, or being removed out of, the magnet: so that no difficulty can occur in that respect, and

there remain, therefore, in my mind, but two suppositions; either the N polar force of a magnet when taken off from external compensating S polar force, is not exerted elsewhere as magnetic force at all; or else it is externally thrown upon and associated with the S polar force of the same magnet, and so sustained and disposed of, for the time, in its natural, equivalent, and essential state. If converted into any new form of power, what is that form? where is it disposed of? by what effects is it recognized? what are the proofs of its existence? To these inquiries there are no answers. But if it be directed externally upon the opposite S pole of the magnet, then all the consequences and foundations of my hypotheses of magnetic force and its polarity come forth; and, as I incline to believe, a consistent and satisfactory account of all magnetic phenomena, short of the idea of the nature of the magnetic force itself, is supplied.

3336. For if the dual forces of the poles of a magnet in free space are related to, and dependent upon, each other, and yet not through the magnet (3331), then it must be through the space around. Then space must have a real magnetic relation to the force passing across it, just as it has to the ray of light passing from an illuminating to an illuminated body. Then the directions in which the two forces are exerted upon each other cannot be in right lines, which must, if they existed, pass of necessity through the magnet; but in curved lines, seeing that it is impossible that any but curved lines can hold the poles in relation to each other through the surrounding space (3297): and if they be curved lines, then I cannot imagine them to be anything else than physical lines of force; lines fitted to transfer the power onwards in consistency with its inevitable dual relation, and in conformity with that direction which ought, as I think, to be properly called *polarity*. And it further appears to me, that if we once admit the magnetic relation of a vacuum, then all the phenomena of paramagnetic and diamagnetic bodies; of differential polarity and individual polarity; of solutions, needles, crystals and moving conductors, are presented in a simple mutual relation, without any contradiction of fact or hypothesis, and in perfect harmony with each other.

3337. I wish to avoid prolonging this paper by a repetition of the considerations and reasons already advanced on former occasions, and therefore will very briefly call to mind the idea I have put forth, that there are such lines of force in the space around a magnet; that the mutual dependence of the dualities, which is essential in the isolated magnet, is thus sustained; and that bodies in this space produce paramagnetic or diamagnetic phenomena, according as they favour or oppose the degree of sustaining power which mere space possesses. That these bodies, or *media* as they may be called, have a magnetic relation like that of space, is easily shown by numerous experimental results; but as they have a further relation amongst themselves, dependent upon their relative electro-conducting power, I think a little time may be usefully employed in considering how far the consequent results illustrate the probable condition of space where they are not present. Consider a magnetic pole N, *Fig.* 6,

placed in relation to an equal magnetic pole S, so that their powers are mutually related and sustained, and the space between them, *a, a, a,* occupied by a vacuum, nitrogen, or some other gas at magnetic zero

Fig. 6

(2770, &c.): the force exerted by N on S, or reciprocally, is easily taken cognizance of by spirals, &c., as regards any change in direction or degree. Then consider the medium *a, a, a* to be all copper or all mercury, still the forces are undisturbed: or consider it part mercury or copper, and part vacuum or glass, divided either by a line running from S to N, or along *a, a, a,* or any other way, still the forces are undisturbed; any of these media act exactly like space, or so like it, we can scarcely trace a difference. Then consider the metal moving, either as a finely divided stream at *a, a, a,* or as a solid globe (of copper) C, *Fig.* 7, revolving rapidly round the line from

Fig. 7

N to S; still it is exactly like the vacuum or indifferent gas or glass, and there is no effect as yet by which we might distinguish the material medium from the mere space. But let the stream of metallic particles be converted into a continuous plate, and then we know it becomes filled with abundant currents of electricity; or if we apply the wires of a galvanometer to the revolving copper globe C, at the axial and equatorial parts, we can then cause it to develop (by permission of currents) a new effect, and the currents are sent out most abundantly by the conductors applied. If the copper globe C be rapidly revolved upon an axis perpendicular to the line S N, so strong and influential a medium is it, magnetically considered, that the two poles, N and S, if free to move, do move in the same direction as the near parts of the globe; and are absolutely carried away from each other, in opposition to their mutually attractive force, which tends strongly all the while to draw them together. Now, how is it possible to conceive that the copper or mercury could have this power in the moving state, if it had no relation at all to the magnetic force in the fixed state? or, that it should have like power in the compact state, and yet have no relation to the magnetic force in the divided and moving state? The mere addition of motion could do nothing, unless there were a prior static dependence of the magnet and the metal upon each other. We know very well that the actions in the moving cases involve the evolution, or a tendency to the evolution, of electric currents; but that knowledge is further proof that the metals *are* in prior relation to the magnetic forces; and as bodies, even down to aqueous solution, have these electric currents set up in them under like circumstances, we have full reason to believe that all bodies when in the magnetic field are in like static relation as the copper when not moving: and that when motion is superadded, they would all evolve electric currents, were it not for their bad electro-conducting powers.

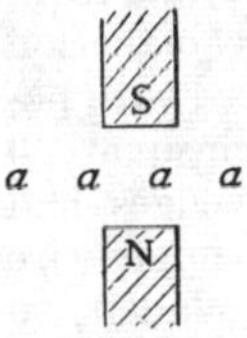

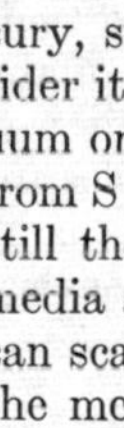

3338. These effects of motion are known to be identical with those of the moving wire (36, 55), or those of voltaic induction (6, &c.); and their intensity and power is very well shown in the force of Elkington's magneto-electric apparatus and Ruhmkorff's induction coil. *Time* is concerned in their production, and Professor Henry has shown us, in some degree, that when the currents are moving in helices, the magnetic action across them is for a time cut off or deflected (1730). These actions are, in every case, simple; i.e., a line of force in a given polar direction produces, or tends to produce, in a body moving across it, whether paramagnetic neutral, or diamagnetic (3146, 3162), a current in the *like* direction; which current must, as I conceive, be dependent upon a previous like *static* state. Nothing in the slightest degree analogous to the supposed oppositely polar states of paramagnetic and diamagnetic bodies has ever been discovered amongst them; and it has never been said, or supposed, as far as I know, that the two actions, i.e., the magnetic and the magneto-electric, are separate in their essential nature, or that they are not the consistent and accordant, and I must add reciprocal, actions of one force.

3339. That the copper, &c., are effectual as magnetic media when in the field, may be stated also thus: Let N, *Fig. 8*, be a magnetic pole, and C a thick disc or short cylinder of copper. If the copper revolve ever so rapidly on its axis, there will be no production of currents in it; and the magnetic action of N on other magnets will be the same, as if the metal were quiescent or even away. If N recede from C there are then currents in C, though it be not moving; and though the effect of N upon other magnets, as far as we know them, is unchanged; yet there is then a slight attraction between C and the N pole. If N be made to approach C, the reverse currents and actions occur. As N approaches or recedes more quickly or slowly, the currents produced, and consequent temporary magnetic state, are higher. A cylinder electro-magnet will show these effects very well. The copper has all the time been still, no motion has been purposely given to it; it has been affected by the approximation and recession of the pole, has passed from one state to another, which states remain stationary as long as the poles are quiescent, and it shows every character of a medium affected by the magnetic force. By expedients the currents in the copper may be allowed or prevented; but whether they be allowed or not, the state the copper medium arrives at is the same. If disallowed as the magnet approaches, but allowed as it recedes, then the current due to the last change occurs, an effect easily shown with a magnet and helix; and this seems to prove very distinctly that the copper within the constant influence of the magnet has a permanent, static, magnetic condition; and is therefore a magnetic medium, having lines of force passing through it. If C be of bismuth instead of copper, the same currents in the same direction occur, though in a far smaller degree; and, as it is believed, only because of deficiency in its conducting power.

Fig. 8

3340. There can be no doubt that very much is involved in these phenomena, of the nature of which we have little of no knowledge; and the results obtained by Matteucci will probably lead to developments and discoveries of great importance. He states[1] that copper, when finely divided, presents very persisting phenomena, proving its right to be considered as a diamagnetic body; but that when aggregated, all, or nearly all, its diamagnetic character disappears. Nothing is known as yet of the man-

[1] *Cours spécial sur l'induction, &c.*, 1854, pp. 165, 269.

ner in which the mere difference of cohesion or division can so affect the diamagnetic character. He finds, too, that in other respects, as in Arago's rotation, particles of matter act in a manner not to be anticipated from what is at present known of them as masses; and it is to be hoped and expected that when these results are enlarged and developed, we shall be able to form a better judgement of the true physical action of magnetism than at present.

Places of No Magnetic Action

3341. The essential relation and dependence of the two magnetic dualities is manifested, I think, in a very striking manner, by the results which occur when we attempt to isolate northness or southness, by concentrating either of them on one space or piece of matter, and looking for their presence by effects, either of tension or any other kind, whether connected with polarity or not. A soft iron bar, an inch square, 3 or 4 inches long and rounded at the edges, had thirty-two convolutions of covered copper wire 0.05 of an inch in diameter put round it, so that covering the middle part of the bar, chiefly, it could be shifted if needful a little nearer to one end than the other; such a bar could be rendered magnetic by an electric current passed through the wire, and a degree of adjustment, in the strength of the N and S extremities, could be effected by this motion of the iron in its helix. Having six of these, it was easy to arrange them with their like poles together, so as to include a cubical space or chamber, *Fig. 9*; and in this space I worked by every means at my disposal. Access to it was easily obtained by a previous removal of a portion of the solid angles of the ends which were to be brought together, or by withdrawing the electro-magnets a little the one from the others, and then a ray of light could be

Fig. 9

passed into or across it; magnetic needles or crystals of bismuth could be suspended in it; a ring helix could be introduced and rotated there; and the motions of anything within could be observed by the eye outside.

3342. A small magnetic needle hung in the middle of this space gave no indication of any magnetic power; near the open edges and angles vibrations occurred, but they were as nothing compared to the powerful indications given outside the chamber; even when the needle was many inches away. A crystal of bismuth was entirely indifferent. A piece of soft iron hung on a jointed copper wire within the chamber showed no trace of magnetic power, whether examined by the little needle or in any other manner. Iron filings on a card across the chamber were not affected in the middle part, but only near the partly open angles. A ring helix of many convolutions, having its terminations passing out at opposite corners, was connected with a very sensitive galvanometer and rotated; it showed no trace of inductive action. Numerous other experiments were made, but with results altogether negative. Attempts (though desperate) were made to ascertain if any electro-chemical conditions were induced there, but in vain. Every kind of trial that I could think of, not merely by tests of a polar character, but of all sorts, were instituted, but with the same negative result.

3343. It was of course not to be expected that any polar, i.e., any dually related polar, action could be exerted in this place; but if the polarities can exist without mutual relation, we might surely expect some condition, some tonic or static state, in a chamber thus prepared and surrounded with a high intensity of magnetic power, acting in great concentration on one particular spot or substance. But it is not so; and the chamber offers a space destitute of magnetic action, and free, under the circumstances, from magnetic influence. It is the complete analogue of the space presented within a deep metallic vessel or globe,[1] when charged with electricity (1174). There is then no electricity within, because that necessary connexion and dependence of the electric duals, which is essential to their nature, cannot be. In like manner, there is no appearance of magnetic force in the cubical chamber, because the duals are not both there at once, and one cannot be present without the other.

3344. There are many ways of examining in a more or less perfect manner these neutral and highly instructive magnetic places. A cavity in the end of an electro-magnetic core or a permanent magnet will present similar phenomena, and in some respects even more perfectly; for though a trace of power will perhaps appear at the bottom of the cavity, the sum or amount, as compared to the sum of power at the end of the magnet, will show how complete the analogy between this space and the interior of a metallic vessel charged with positive or negative electricity is. A cylinder of soft iron, 9

[1] *Phil. Mag.*, Oct. 1846, Vol. XXIX, p. 257, *note.*

inches in length and 1.6 in diameter, had a chamber 0.9 in diameter and 1 inch in depth formed in one extremity concentric with the cylinder; and being placed in a powerful helix of thick copper wire, and associated with a Grove's battery of ten pair of plates, was ready for experiment: a like chambered magnet can be prepared by putting a proper iron ring against the end of any electro- or ordinary magnet, and will show the phenomena I am about to describe. A piece of soft iron, not more than 0.3 of an inch in length or thickness, held at the end of a copper wire and brought near the outer edge of the excited magnet pole, will be very strongly attracted; but if it be applied to the bottom of the chamber it will present no such effect, but be quite indifferent. If applied about the sides of the chamber, it will indicate no effect until it approaches the mouth. If the magnet be placed horizontally, and a piece of cardboard be cut, so that it can enter the chamber and represent a horizontal section of its cavity; and, being sprinkled over with clean iron filings, is then put into its position and the magnet excited for a moment that it may develop its power over the chamber and filings and give them their indicative position; it will be found that only those near the mouth have been driven into a new position (about the outside angles of the pole), and that four-fifths of those upon the surface of the card within the chamber have been left unaffected, unmoved. If the chamber be filled with iron filings, closed with a card, placed in a vertical position with the aperture downward, and the magnet be then excited and the card removed, the filings will fall out; as they come out they will be caught away, and form a fine fringe round the external angles of the pole, but not one will remain at the bottom of the chamber, or even anywhere within the chamber, except near to its external edge. Yet, if a piece of iron long enough to reach out of the chamber, as a nail 2, 3, or 4 inches long, touch the *bottom* of the chamber, it is strongly attracted and held there, and will support a weight of several ounces, though prevented from touching the chamber anywhere else by a card with a hole in it placed over the mouth.

3345. If a small magnetic needle, about 0.1 of an inch long, be brought towards this excited magnet, it is almost unmanageable by reason of the force exerted upon it; but, as soon as it has entered the chamber, the power rapidly diminishes, and at the bottom the needle is scarcely, if at all, affected.

3346. If, instead of the core and chamber described, an iron tube of sufficient thickness of metal (as part of a gun-barrel) be employed, then like effects occur. If the magnetic needle be introduced, it ceases to be acted upon when about 1.5 inch within the tube. If the tube be more or less filled with iron filings, and then be excited and held vertical, they will all pour out and fall away, except those which are retained at the external edges. Yet, if a long nail or iron rod be introduced, so as to be partly out of the cylinder, then it will be strongly attracted at the internal point, where it touches the iron of the tube core.

3347. The realization of like effects by grouping together the poles of ordinary magnets gives most interesting results. I have four very hard steel magnets, each 6 inches in length, 1 inch in breadth, and 0.4 nearly in thickness. When the four like poles are put together, *Fig. 10*, they

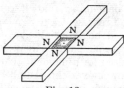

Fig. 10

form a flat square chamber in the same plane as that of the magnets. If a piece of stiff paper, the size of this chamber, be raised on a block 0.2 of an inch high, then sprinkled over with iron filings, and the magnets afterwards approached regularly until the square chamber is formed, a little tapping on the card will then arrange the filings in lines from the sides of the square chamber to the centre. The filings show at once the direction of the lines of force in this medium plane, and their greater abundance at the middle of each pole than at the re-entering angles; and if the filings be then removed and the indication of the course of the lines be followed out by a small magnetic needle, it will be found that the lines rise upwards from this plane above, and descend from it below, and then turn back upon their course in the free space over and beneath the arrangement towards the S poles of the different magnets. The condition will be understood in a moment, by considering the sphondyloids of power belonging to each magnet (3271), and the manner in which they are associated when the four like poles come together.

3348. When the magnets are turned edges upwards, they form a vertical chamber 1 inch high and only 0.4 of an inch in width, and now

phenomena like those just described occur, but only near the entrances to the chamber; as the little needle proceeds into the enclosed space, the power of the magnets becomes less and less, and at the middle of the chamber scarcely a trace remains; that place being, like the closed chamber, formed with six poles (3341), or like the bottom of a chamber formed in the end of a magnetic pole, a neutral place, or place of no magnetic action.

Fig. 11

3349. The transition by degrees, from a pointed conical pole to an enclosed chamber, is, from the results described, very evident; and so also is their connexion with those belonging to the numerous neutral places produced under ordinary circumstances (3234, *Figs. 6, 10, 11, 15*). Not the slightest difficulty or hesitation occurs when these results are read or considered by the principle of representative lines of force: all the variations in the strength of the magnetic force and in the direction appear at once. But the great point is to observe how they all concur in showing the necessity of the complete and equivalent dual relation of the magnetic forces. When that is diminished or interfered with in any degree, in the same proportion does the power as a whole become diminished; until, at last, it absolutely disappears from a given place, though energies of the strongest kind are directing the force on to that spot, supposing that one of the dual elements could exist in any degree without, or independent of, the other.

3350. When formerly working with bismuth and magnets, I described several results (2298, 2487, 2491) due to the principle of neutral magnetic places, more or less developed. If a sphere or cube of bismuth be delicately suspended by a vertical suspension or on a torsion balance, and an N pole be brought towards it, *Fig. 12*, the bismuth will be repelled and the suspension deflected: if a second N′ pole be brought up, as in the figure, the bismuth will be less repelled by N than before, will return towards it, and N′ will also seem to attract it,

Fig. 12

for on approaching the bismuth will tend to go into the angle formed by N and N′. If a third pole, N″, be brought up on the opposite side, the bismuth will then seem to be attracted by it, and by the first pole, and will, in fact, return very nearly into the position it would have if all the magnets were away. I thought at one time that magnetic structure, given by the second north pole N' to the bismuth, might produce the approximation of it to N, and if so, that this would be neutralized by the action of a like pole N'' on the opposite side, and so the approximation of the bismuth (if due to such a cause) be prevented. On the contrary, however, such a pole *increased* it; and a moment's consideration, by showing that the three poles form a chamber of diminished or no action (3341, 3347), shows also that such ought to be the case. All the movements of the bismuth are the result of the tendency which it has to pass from stronger to weaker places of magnetic action (2418); and in the present case they show *that* weakened place, which in a higher degree would be a place of no magnetic force.

The Moving Conductor

3351. I wish to make a few further remarks (3336, 3337) upon the value of the moving conductor, as a means of investigation in magnetical science. It will be sufficient to refer to former papers for a statement of the principles, the power, and the certainty of its indications (3156, 3172, 3176, 3270). At present, I desire to apply it in a direct form of experiment, to the supposed contrary polarities of iron and bismuth (3309).

3352. Four metallic spheres of copper, bismuth, soft iron, and hard steel, 0.8 of an inch in diameter, have been prepared; each has a copper axis carrying a small wooden pulley, so that when in its supporting frame, rotation, more or less rapid, can be given to it by the band of a multiplying wheel; each also has a thin copper ring driven tightly on to it at the equator, which, being grooved, serves to retain a galvanometer wire pressed against that part during the revolution of the globe; the other wire meanwhile being held against the copper axis. These globes, in their frame, could be placed one by one in the magnetic field of a powerful permanent Logeman magnet, so as to be subject to the magnetic force, *Fig. 13;* and then rotated, and the currents of electricity induced in them carried to galvanometers. Two such instruments were employed: one, a Ruhmkorff's, with fine wire (2651), the other with a thick wire of only four revolutions (3178). The latter was the best, but both gave good indications. The position of all things concerned was preserved undisturbed during the experiments, so that it will not be necessary to do more than

to describe a standard effect, and afterwards refer other effects to it. This standard may be taken from the current indicated when the *copper* globe was in the magnetic field; and it was such, when the upper part of the globe moved westward, as to send the south ends of the galvanometer needles to the west also: eight or ten revolutions of the globe would cause the needles to pass through 80° or 90°.

3353. The *soft iron* sphere was placed in the magnetic field; it was so good in character as to retain very slight traces of magnetism when taken out again. Being revolved, it gave a current of electricity, the same in direction as that of the standard or copper ball. It is easy to understand that if the globe be moved parallel to itself, but away from the magnet, in a line perpendicular to the magnetic axis (as into the dotted position, 3352, *Fig. 13*), it will pass

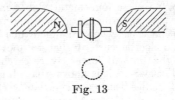

Fig. 13

through places of weaker magnetic action. Under such changes of place, the induced current was weaker or stronger, according to the distance, but always in the same direction. Assuming that the rotating metal supplies a true indication of the polarity or direction of the magnetic force (3077), the results show that the polarity of the force which induces these currents, and which is the magnetic force of the dominant magnet, is the same both in the copper and in the iron. Other cases of the current from revolving iron may be referred to in the *Exp. Res.* (3162).

3354. The *bismuth* globe was placed in the magnetic field. If made to revolve much, with the galvanometer wire pressing against the copper equator (3352), the latter became warm by friction, and a permanent thermo-current was produced: this has been considered on a former occasion (3168). Its effect is easily eliminated by revolving the globe a given number of times in opposite directions, observing the two deflections, adding them together, and taking the half of the sum for the amount of induced current in either one direction or the other; for as the thermo-current is added on the one side and subtracted on the other, such a process gives the real amount of the induced current. When, however, the bismuth sphere is revolved only five or ten times, the thermo-effect is so small as to make the galvanometer deflection very little more in one direction than in the other. When due attention was given, the rotation of the bismuth sphere produced an induced current in precisely the same direction as those obtained with the copper and iron; and so far, therefore, it indicated precisely the same direction of polarity for the magnetic force then acting *upon* and *in* it.

3355. The *hard steel* sphere, having been previously examined by a small needle and found to be unmagnetized, was placed in the magnetic field. It was then revolved, and gave an induced magneto-electric current in the *same* direction as the former currents. Being removed and again examined by the magnetic needle, it was found not to have received any sensible charge of magnetism.

3356. So these four metal globes indicate like polarity of the magnetic force, acting upon and within them, when examined thus by the magneto-electric current due to movement across the lines of force. By researches described elsewhere, it is known that all metals, and all bodies which are sufficiently electro-conductors, down even to aqueous fluids, give the same direction of the magneto-electric current: it is never reversed without reversion of the polarity, and reversion of the polarity *always* reverses the current induced.

3357. The hard steel sphere was now made *a magnet*, and though not of good shape to retain magnetism, yet because of its hardness it was able to sustain being placed in the magnetic field, in a position the reverse of the polarity there, and yet retained its own polarity; for when taken out and examined by a magnetic needle, the polarity was found to be the same as before. Such being the case, it seemed to me that this magnet might be employed to represent, according to the view of those who conceive that iron and bismuth are polarized in opposite directions in the magnetic field, both *iron* and *bismuth*; inasmuch as it could be placed in the field in that condition of polarity, which these are supposed respectively to acquire there. The *globe magnet* was therefore placed in the magnetic field in a position conformable to that of the dominant magnet, i.e., with its N pole towards the S pole of the magnet, &c.; and being rotated, it gave an induced magneto-electric current like that of the standard and of iron (3352, 3353). The dominant magnet was then withdrawn to a distance (3353) and the globe rotated by itself; it gave, as it ought to

do, the same current as before; for it, by its coercive force, retains permanently that state of polarity which the iron could receive only temporarily whilst in the magnetic field: being now turned 180° in a horizontal direction, the globe magnet was reversed as regarded the dominant magnet (the latter being, however, still at a distance), and now the globe magnet gave a current the *reverse* of the former, or of the standard current; and yet a very consistent current in relation to its own polarity.

3358. The dominant magnet was now gradually brought up, and its effect on the reversed globe magnet observed. The current from the latter became less and less, and at last was inverted, becoming like that of the standard current; nor can that be wondered at, when it is considered that the dominant magnet was the largest supplied by Logeman to the Great Exhibition, and able to sustain a weight of 430 pounds, and the sphere magnet only 0.8 of an inch in diameter, and very imperfectly hardened in the interior. But when the dominant magnet was withdrawn a little, a place was soon found for the globe magnet, where its rotation in either direction produced no current at all. Outside of this place, the rotated sphere gave a current, the reverse of that of the standard; whilst the iron and bismuth spheres in the same place, gave currents alike in kind and the same as that of the standard. In this region, therefore (and it is like the whole of the magnetic field of many inferior yet very powerful magnets), if we represent bismuth by a magnet, reversely polar, as bismuth is supposed to be, we obtain induced magneto-electric currents, not like those of bismuth, but the contrary; and if we turn the representative magnet round, so as to give it the position in which it yields currents like those of the bismuth, then its polarity contradicts, or is the reverse of the assumed polarity of the bismuth.

3359. Now until the polarity or direction of the magnetic force which determines the course of the induced magneto-electric currents produced in every moving conductor, is distinguished and separated from the polarity or direction which causes movement amongst bodies subjected to the same force, how can these phenomena be accounted for by the supposition that the bismuth sphere is in the same polar condition as the reversed globe magnet? The reversed magnet is, in fact, the *contrary* to bismuth and to iron; then bismuth and iron must be the same. The direct magnet is the *same* as the bismuth, in that polarity which induces a current; then the magnet and the bismuth are the same. How easily all these effects present themselves in a consistent form, if read by the principle of representative lines of force! The reversed globe magnet at a distance from the dominant, shows, in revolving, the effect of the lines of force within it (3116); as the magnet is approached, its external sphondyloid of power is compressed inwards (3238, *Fig. 15*), and at last the magnet is self-contained; then showing the equalization of its own powers, and as yet the absence from within it of any of the powers of the chief magnet; so that it gives no induced currents, though in a place where bismuth and iron would give them freely. Within that distance the effect of the superior and overpowering force of the great magnet appears (3358), which, though it can take partial possession of the little magnet, still, when removed, suffers the force of the latter to develop itself again, and present the same series of phenomena as before.

3360. Van Rees admits, I believe, that the moving wire shows truly the presence, direction, and nature of the magnetic force or forces; and it is very important to know that the setting of a magnetic needle, or crystal of bismuth and the production of a current of electricity in a moving conductor, are like correlative and consequent effects of the magnetic force; the power of producing one or the other being rigidly the same. Philosophers should either agree or differ distinctly on this point; so that if they differ, they may distinguish clearly the physical separation of the phenomena; which if established, must lead to new and important discoveries. The polarity direction which the moving conductor makes manifest, whether that conductor be one of the paramagnetic or diamagnetic bodies themselves, or whether it be a conductor moving amongst them, either by itself or with them, is *always the same*. The electric current produced never indicates a change in the direction of the polarity, from that belonging to the *first* source or seat of the power; whether it be a magnet, a solenoid, or of any other nature; the only difference being in the strength of the electric current produced, which difference is directly referable to the electro-conducting power (3143, 3152, 3163). If such be the natural truth, how can the two modes of indication ever give opposite results? If opposite results seem to appear, and only occasionally, is it that mode of induction which gives one consistent result that we should doubt, or that which seems to be inconsistent with it-self? especially when similar contrary phenomena in abundance are known to be produced by bodies having *like* polarity (3316), and when excellent physical reasons, founded on differential action, offer themselves for their explication. There is sufficient reason to admit that the magnetic needle cannot be always a true direct indicator of the amount or the direction of magnetic action (2868, 2870, 3156, 3293). Should we not therefore, in respect to the above phenomena, rather conclude, for the time, that the simple and uniform results of the one mode of action, are the true indication; and that where, in the other mode, the phenomena are reversed or doubled, a part of them are *compound* in their nature? I may, in conclusion, remark, that the effects of motion and those produced in the action of magnetism on light, are never reversed in any case, whatever the medium in which they are observed; both point to one direction of polarity only, namely that of the dominant source of magnetism.

3361. I will bring these imperfect observations to an end by a very brief statement of what I suppose to be the condition of a magnet; and by a disclaimer, as to anything like conviction on all points of that which I set forth as a supposition tending to lead to inquiry. Contemplating a bar magnet by itself, I see in it a source of dual power. I believe its dualities are essentially related to each other, and cannot exist but by that relation. I think that though related through the magnet by sustaining power, they are not so related by discharging or inducing power, a power equal in amount to the coercitive or sustaining power. The relation externally appears to me to be through the space around the magnet; in which space a sphondyloid of power is present consisting of closed curves of magnetic force. That the space is not magnetically dark (3305) appears to me by this; that when bodies occupy that space, having like relation by known phenomena to the power as the space has, as copper, mercury, &c., they produce magneto-electric currents when moved. When bodies (media) occupy the space around the magnet, they modify its capability of transmitting and relating the dual forces of the magnet, and as they increase or diminish that capability, are paramagnetic or diamagnetic in their nature; giving rise to the phenomena which come under the term of magnetic conduction (2797). The same magnet can hold different charges, as the medium connecting its poles varies; and so one, fully charged with a good medium as iron between its poles, falls in power when the iron is replaced by air, or space, or bismuth. Corresponding effects occur with longer or shorter magnets (3290), or with magnets made thick by adding many sideways together (3287). The medium about a magnet may be mixed in its nature, and then more dual power is disposed of through the better conductor than the worse, but the whole amount of power remains unchanged. The powers and utility of the media, and of space itself, fail, if the dual force or polar action be interrupted. The magnet could not exist without a surrounding medium or space, and would be extinguished if deprived of it, and is extinguished, if the space be occupied adversely by the dual power of a dominant magnet of sufficient force. The polarity of each line of force is in the same direction throughout the whole of its closed course. Pointing in one direction or another, is a differential action due to the convergence or divergence of the lines of force upon the substance acted on, according as it is a better or a worse conductor of the magnetic force.

3362. But though such is my view, I put it forth with all the reservation made on former occasions (3244, 3299). I do not pretend to explain all points of difficulty. I have no clear idea of the physical condition constituting the charged magnetic state; i.e. the state of the source of magnetic power: or of the coercitivity by which that state is either resisted in its attainment, or sustained in its permanent condition; for the hypotheses as yet put forth give no satisfaction to my mind. I profess rather to point out the difficulties in the way of the views, which are at present somewhat too easily accepted, and to shake men's minds from their habitual trust in them; for, next to developing and expounding, that appears to me the most useful and effectual way of really advancing the subject:—it is better to be aware, or even to suspect, we are wrong, than to be unconsciously or easily led to accept an error as right.

Royal Institution, Dec. 20, 1854

On Static Electrical Inductive Action[1]

To R. Phillips, Esq., F.R.S.

Dear Phillips,

Perhaps you may think the following experiments worth notice; their value consists in their power to give a very precise and decided

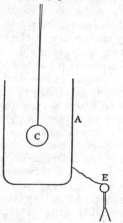

idea to the mind respecting certain principles of inductive electrical action, which I find are by many accepted with a degree of doubt or obscurity that takes away much of their im-

[1] *Lond. and Edinb. Phil. Mag.*, 1843, Vol. XXII.

portance: they are the expression and proof of certain parts of my view of induction. Let A in the diagram represent an insulated pewter ice-pail ten and a half inches high and seven inches diameter, connected by a wire with a delicate gold-leaf electrometer E, and let C be a round brass ball insulated by a dry thread of white silk, three or four feet in length, so as to remove the influence of the hand holding it from the ice-pail below. Let A be perfectly discharged, then let C be charged at a distance by a machine or Leyden jar, and introduced into A as in the figure. If C be positive, E also will diverge positively; if C be taken away, E will collapse perfectly, the apparatus being in good order. As C enters the vessel A the divergence of E will increase until C is about three inches below the edge of the vessel, and will remain quite steady and unchanged for any greater depression. This shows that at that distance the inductive action of C is entirely exerted upon the interior of A, and not in any degree directly upon external objects. If C be made to touch the bottom of A, *all* its charge is communicated to A; there is no longer any inductive action between C and A, and C, upon being withdrawn and examined, is found perfectly discharged.

These are all well-known and recognised actions, but being a little varied, the following conclusions may be drawn from them. If C be merely suspended in A, it acts upon it by induction, evolving electricity of its own kind on the outside of A; but if C touch A its electricity is then communicated to it, and the electricity that is afterwards upon the outside of A may be considered as that which was originally upon the carrier C. As this change, however, produces no effect upon the leaves of the electrometer, it proves that the electricity *induced* by C and the electricity *in* C are accurately equal in amount and power.

Again, if C charged be held equidistant from the bottom and sides of A at one moment, and at another be held as close to the bottom as possible without discharging to A, still the divergence remains absolutely unchanged, showing that whether C acts at a considerable distance or at the very smallest distance, the amount of its force is the same. So also if it be

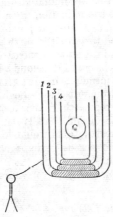

held eccentric and near to the side of the ice-pail in one place, so as to make the inductive action take place in lines expressing almost every degree of force in different directions, still the sum of their forces is the same constant quantity as that obtained before; for the leaves alter not. Nothing like expansion or coercion of the electric force appears under these varying circumstances.

I can now describe experiments with many concentric metallic vessels arranged as in the diagram, where four ice-pails are represented insulated from each other by plates of shellac on which they respectively stand. With this system the charged carrier C acts precisely as

with the single vessel, so that the intervention of many conducting plates causes no difference in the amount of inductive effect. If C touch the inside of vessel 4, still the leaves are unchanged. If 4 be taken out by a silk thread, the leaves perfectly collapse; if it be introduced again, they open out to the same degree as before. If 4 and 3 be connected by a wire let down between them by a silk thread, the leaves remain the same, and so they still remain if 3 and 2 be connected by a similar wire; yet all the electricity originally on the carrier and acting at a considerable distance, is now on the outside of 2, and acting through only a small non-conducting space. If at last it be communicated to the outside of 1, still the leaves remain unchanged.

Again, consider the charged carrier C in the centre of the system, the divergence of the electrometer measures its inductive influence; this divergence remains the same whether 1 be there alone, or whether all four vessels be there; whether these vessels be separate as to insulation, or whether 2, 3 and 4 be connected so as to represent a very thick metallic vessel, or whether all four vessels be connected.

Again, if in place of the metallic vessels 2, 3, 4, a thick vessel of shellac or of sulphur be introduced, or if any other variation in the character of the substance within the vessel 1 be made, still not the slightest change is by that caused upon the divergence of the leaves.

If in place of one carrier many carriers in different positions are within the inner vessel, there is no interference of one with the other; they act with the same amount of force outwardly as if the electricity were spread uniformly over one carrier, however much the distribution on each carrier may be disturbed by its neighbours. If the charge of one carrier be by contact given to vessel 4 and distributed over it, still the others act through and across it with the same final amount of force; and no state of charge given to any of the vessels 1, 2, 3 or 4, prevents a charged carrier introduced within 4 acting with precisely the same amount of force as if they were uncharged. If pieces of shellac, slung by white silk thread and excited, be introduced into the vessel, they act exactly as the metallic carriers, except that their charge cannot be communicated by contact to the metallic vessels.

Thus a certain amount of electricity acting within the centre of the vessel A exerts exactly the same power externally, whether it act by induction through the space between it and A, or whether it be transferred by conduction to A, so as absolutely to destroy the previous induction within. Also, as to the inductive action, whether the space between C and A be filled with air, or with shellac or sulphur, having above twice the specific inductive capacity of air; or contain many concentric shells of conducting matter; or be nine-tenths filled with conducting matter, or be metal on one side and shellac on the other; or whatever other means be taken to vary the forces, either by variation of distance or substance, or actual charge of the matter in this space, still the amount of action is precisely the same.

Hence if a body be charged, whether it be a particle or a mass, there is nothing about its action which can at all consist with the idea of exaltation or extinction; the amount of force is perfectly definite and unchangeable: or to those who in their minds represent the idea of the electric force by a fluid, there ought to be no notion of the compression or condensation of this fluid within itself, or of its coercibility, as some understand that phrase. The only mode of affecting this force is by connecting it with force of the same kind, either in the same or the contrary direction. If we oppose to it force of the contrary kind, we may *by discharge* neutralize the original force, or we may *without discharge* connect them by the simple laws and principles of static induction; but away from induction, which is *always of the same kind*, there is no other state of the power in a charged body; that is, there is no state of static electric force corresponding to the terms of *simulated* or *disguised* or *latent* electricity away from the ordinary principles of inductive action; nor is there any case where the electricity is *more latent* or *more disguised* than when it exists upon the charged conductor of an electrical machine and is ready to give a powerful spark to any body brought near it.

A curious consideration arises from this perfection of inductive action. Suppose a thin uncharged metallic globe two or three feet in diameter, insulated in the middle of a chamber, and then suppose the space within this globe occupied by myriads of little vesicles or particles charged alike with electricity (or differently), but each insulated from its neighbour and the globe; their inductive power would be such that the outside of the globe would be charged with a force equal to the sum of *all* their forces, and any part of this globe (not charged of itself) would give as long and powerful a spark to a body brought near it as if the electricity of all the particles near and distant were on the surface of the globe itself. If we pass from this consideration to the case of a cloud, then, though we cannot altogether compare the external surface of the cloud to the metallic surface of the globe, yet the previous inductive effects upon the *earth* and its buildings are the same; and when a charged cloud is over the earth, although its electricity may be diffused over every one of its particles, and no important part of the *inductric* charge be accumulated upon its under surface, yet the induction upon the earth will be as strong as if all that portion of force which is directed towards the earth *were* upon that surface; and the state of the earth and its tendency to discharge to the cloud will also be as strong in the former as in the latter case. As to whether lightning-discharge begins first at the cloud or at the earth, that is a matter far more difficult to decide than is usually supposed;[1] theoretical notions would lead me to expect that in most cases, perhaps in all, it begins at the earth. I am,

My dear Phillips, ever yours,

M. FARADAY

Royal Institution, February 4, 1843

[1] *Experimental Researches*, Par. 1370, 1410, 1484.

A Speculation Touching Electric Conduction and the Nature of Matter[2]

To RICHARD TAYLOR, ESQ.

DEAR SIR,

Last Friday I opened the weekly evening-meetings here by a subject of which the above was the title, and had no intention of publish-

[2] *Lond. and Edinb. Phil. Mag.*, 1844, Vol. XXIV, p. 136.

ing the matter further, but as it involves the consideration and application of a few of those main elements of natural knowledge, facts, I thought an account of its nature and intention might not be unacceptable to you, and would at the same time serve as the record of my opinion and views, as far as they are at present formed.

The view of the atomic constitution of matter which I think is most prevalent, is that which considers the atom as a something material having a certain volume, upon which those powers were impressed at the creation, which have given it, from that time to the present, the capability of constituting, when many atoms are congregated together into groups, the different substances whose effects and properties we observe. These, though grouped and held together by their powers, do not touch each other, but have intervening space, otherwise pressure or cold could not make a body contract into a smaller bulk, nor heat or tension make it larger; in liquids these atoms or particles are free to move about one another, and in vapours or gases they are also present, but removed very much farther apart, though still related to each other by their powers.

The atomic doctrine is greatly used one way or another in this, our day, for the interpretation of phenomena, especially those of crystallography and chemistry, and is not so carefully distinguished from the facts, but that it often appears to him who stands in the position of student, as a statement of the facts themselves though it is at best but an assumption; of the truth of which we can assert nothing, whatever we may say or think of its probability. The word atom, which can never be used without involving much that is purely hypothetical, is often *intended* to be used to express a simple fact; but good as the intention is, I have not yet found a mind that did habitually separate it from its accompanying temptations; and there can be no doubt that the words definite proportions, equivalents, primes, &c., which did and do express fully all the *facts* of what is usually called the atomic theory in chemistry, were dismissed because they were not expressive enough, and did not say all that was in the mind of him who used the word atom in their stead; they did not express the hypothesis as well as the fact.

But it is always safe and philosophic to distinguish, as much as is in our power, fact from theory; the experience of past ages is sufficient to show us the wisdom of such a course; and considering the constant tendency of the mind to rest on an assumption, and, when it answers every present purpose, to forget that it is an assumption, we ought to remember that it, in such cases, becomes a prejudice, and inevitably interferes, more or less, with a clear-sight-

ed judgment. I cannot doubt but that he who, as a wise philosopher, has most power of penetrating the secrets of nature, and guessing by hypothesis at her mode of working, will also be most careful, for his own safe progress and that of others, to distinguish that knowledge which consists of assumption, by which I mean theory and hypothesis, from that which is the knowledge of facts and laws; never raising the former to the dignity or authority of the latter, nor confusing the latter more than is inevitable with the former.

Light and electricity are two great and searching investigators of the molecular structure of bodies, and it was whilst considering the probable nature of conduction and insulation in bodies not decomposable by the electricity to which they were subject, and the relation of electricity to space contemplated as void of that which by the atomists is called matter, that considerations something like those which follow were presented to my mind.

If the view of the constitution of matter already referred to be assumed to be correct, and I may be allowed to speak of the particles of matter and of the space between them (in water, or in the vapour of water for instance) as two different things, then space must be taken as the only continuous part, for the particles are considered as separated by space from each other. Space will permeate all masses of matter in every direction like a net, except that in place of meshes it will form cells, isolating each atom from its neighbours, and itself only being continuous.

Then take the case of a piece of shellac, a non-conductor, and it would appear at once from such a view of its atomic constitution that space is an insulator, for if it were a conductor the shellac could not insulate, whatever might be the relation as to conducting power of its material atoms; the space would be like a fine metallic web penetrating it in every direction, just as we may imagine of a heap of siliceous sand having all its pores filled with water; or as we may consider of a stick of black wax, which, though it contains an infinity of particles of conducting charcoal diffused through every part of it, cannot conduct, because a non-conducting body (a resin) intervenes and separates them one from another, like the supposed space in the lac.

Next take the case of a metal, platinum or potassium, constituted, according to the atomic theory, in the same manner. The metal is a conductor; but how can this be, except space be a conductor? for it is the only continuous part of the metal, and the atoms not only do not touch (by the theory), but as we shall see presently, must be assumed to be a considerable way apart. Space therefore must be a conductor, or else the metals could not conduct, but would be in the situation of the black sealing-wax referred to a little while ago.

But if space be a conductor, how then can shellac, sulphur, &c. insulate? for space permeates them in every direction. Or if space be an insulator, how can a metal or other similar body conduct?

It would seem, therefore, that in accepting the ordinary atomic theory, space may be proved to be a non-conductor in non-conducting bodies, and a conductor in conducting bodies, but the reasoning ends in this, a subversion of that theory altogether; for if space be an insulator it cannot exist in conducting bodies, and if it be a conductor it cannot exist in insulating bodies. Any ground of reasoning which tends to such conclusions as these must in itself be false.

In connexion with such conclusions we may consider shortly what are the probabilities that present themselves to the mind, if the extension of the atomic theory which chemists have imagined, be applied in conjunction with the conducting powers of metals. If the specific gravity of the metals be divided by the atomic numbers, it gives us the number of atoms, upon the hypothesis, in equal bulks of the metals. In the following table the first column of figures expresses nearly the number of atoms in, and the second column of figures the conducting power of, equal volumes of the metals named.

	Atoms		Conducting power
	1.00	gold	6.00
	1.00	silver	4.66
	1.12	lead	0.52
	1.30	tin	1.00
	2.20	platinum	1.04
	2.27	zinc	1.80
	2.87	copper	6.33
	2.90	iron	1.00

So here iron, which contains the greatest number of atoms in a given bulk, is the worst conductor excepting one; gold, which contains the fewest, is nearly the best conductor. Not that these conditions are in inverse proportions, for copper, which contains nearly as many atoms as iron, conducts better still than gold, and with above six times the power of iron.

Lead, which contains more atoms than gold, has only about one-twelfth of its conducting power; lead, which is much heavier than tin and much lighter than platinum, has only half the conducting power of either of these metals. And all this happens amongst substances which we are bound to consider, at present, as elementary or simple. Whichever way we consider the particles of matter and the space between them, and examine the assumed constitution of matter by this table, the results are full of perplexity.

Now let us take the case of potassium, a compact metallic substance with excellent conducting powers, its oxide or hydrate a non-conductor; it will supply us with some facts having very important bearings on the assumed atomic construction of matter.

When potassium is oxidized an atom of it combines with an atom of oxygen to form an atom of potassa, and an atom of potassa combines with an atom of water, consisting of two atoms of oxygen and hydrogen, to form an atom of hydrate of potassa, so that an atom of hydrate of potassa contains four elementary atoms. The specific gravity of potassium is 0.865, and its atomic weight 40; the specific gravity of cast hydrate of potassa, in such state of purity as I could obtain it, I found to be nearly 2, its atomic weight 57. From these, which may be taken as facts, the following strange conclusions flow. A piece of potassium contains less potassium than an equal piece of the potash formed by it and oxygen. We may cast into potassium oxygen atom for atom, and then again both oxygen and hydrogen in a twofold number of atoms, and yet, with all these additions, the matter shall become less and less, until it is not two-thirds of its original volume. If a given bulk of potassium contains 45 atoms, the same bulk of hydrate of potassa contains 70 atoms nearly *of the metal potassium*, and besides that, 210 atoms more of oxygen and hydrogen. In dealing with assumptions I must assume a little more for the sake of making any kind of statement; let me therefore assume that in the hydrate of potassa the atoms are all of one size and nearly touching each other, and that in a cubic inch of that substance there are 2800 elementary atoms of potassium, oxygen and hydrogen; take away 2100 atoms of oxygen and hydrogen, and the 700 atoms of potassium remaining will swell into more than a cubic inch and a half, and if we diminish the number until only those containable in a cubic inch remain, we shall have 430, or thereabout. So a space which can contain 2800 atoms, and amongst them 700 of potassium itself, is found to be entirely filled by 430 atoms of potassium as they exist in the ordinary state of that metal. Surely then, under the suppositions of the atomic theory, the atoms of potassium must be very far apart in the metal, i.e., there must be much more of space than of matter in that body: yet it is an excellent conductor, and so space must be a conductor; but then what becomes of shellac, sulphur, and all the insulators? for space must also by the theory exist in them.

Again, the volume which will contain 430 atoms of potassium, and nothing else, whilst in the state of metal, will, when that potassium is converted into nitre, contain very nearly the same number of atoms of potassium, i.e., 416, and also then seven times as many, or 2912 atoms of nitrogen and oxygen besides. In carbonate of potassa the space which will contain only the 430 atoms of potassium as metal, being entirely filled by it, will, after the conversion, contain 256 atoms more of potassium, making 686 atoms of that metal, and, in addition 2744 atoms of oxygen and carbon.

These and similar considerations might be extended through compounds of sodium and other bodies with results equally striking, and indeed still more so, when the relations of one substance, as oxygen or sulphur, with different bodies are brought into comparison.

I am not ignorant that the mind is most powerfully drawn by the phenomena of crystallization, chemistry and physics generally, to the acknowledgement of centres of force. I feel myself constrained, for the present hypothetically, to admit them, and cannot do without them, but I feel great difficulty in the conception of atoms of matter which in solids, fluids and vapours are supposed to be more or less apart from each other, with intervening space not occupied by atoms, and perceive great contradictions in the conclusions which flow from such a view.

If we must assume at all, as indeed in a branch of knowledge like the present we can hardly help then the safest course appears to be to assume as little as possible, and in that respect the atoms of Boscovich appear to me to have a great advantage over the more usual notion. His atoms, if I understand aright, are mere centres of forces or powers, not particles of matter, in which the powers themselves reside. If, in the ordinary view of atoms, we call the particle of matter away from the powers a, and

the system of powers or forces in and around it m, then in Boscovich's theory a disappears, or is a mere mathematical point, whilst in the usual notion it is a little unchangeable, impenetrable piece of matter, and m is an atmosphere of force grouped around it.

In many of the hypothetical uses made of atoms, as in crystallography, chemistry, magnetism, &c., this difference in the assumption makes little or no alteration in the results, but in other cases, as of electric conduction, the nature of light, the manner in which bodies combine to produce compounds, the effects of forces, as heat or electricity, upon matter, the difference will be very great.

Thus, referring back to potassium, in which as a metal the atoms must, as we have seen, be, according to the usual view, very far apart from each other, how can we for a moment imagine that its conducting property belongs to it, any otherwise than as a consequence of the properties of the space, or as I have called it above, the m? so also its other properties in regard to light or magnetism, or solidity, or hardness, or specific gravity, must belong to it, in consequence of the properties or forces of the m, not those of the a, which, without the forces, is conceived of as having no powers. But then surely the m is the *matter* of the potassium, for where is there the least ground (except in a gratuitous assumption) for imagining a difference in kind between the nature of that space midway between the centres of two contiguous atoms and any other spot between these centres? a difference in degree, or even in the nature of the power consistent with the law of continuity, I can admit, but the difference between a supposed little hard particle and the powers around it I cannot imagine.

To my mind, therefore, the a or nucleus vanishes, and the substance consists of the powers or m; and indeed what notion can we form of the nucleus independent of its powers? all our perception and knowledge of the atom, and even our fancy, is limited to ideas of its powers: what thought remains on which to hang the imagination of an a independent of the acknowledged forces? A mind just entering on the subject may consider it difficult to think of the powers of matter independent of a separate something to be called *the matter*, but it is certainly far more difficult, and indeed impossible, to think of or imagine that *matter* independent of the powers. Now the powers we know and recognize in every phenomenon of the creation, the abstract matter in none; why then assume the existence of that of which we are ignorant, which we cannot conceive, and for which there is no philosophical necessity?

Before concluding these speculations I will refer to a few of the important differences between the assumption of atoms consisting merely of centres of force, like those of Boscovich, and that other assumption of molecules of something specially material, having powers attached in and around them.

With the latter atoms a mass of matter consists of atoms and intervening space, with the former atoms matter is everywhere present, and there is no intervening space unoccupied by it. In gases the atoms touch each other just as truly as in solids. In this respect the atoms of water touch each other whether that substance be in the form of ice, water or steam; no mere intervening space is present. Doubtless the centres of force vary in their distance one from another, but that which is truly the matter of one atom touches the matter of its neighbours.

Hence matter will be *continuous* throughout, and in considering a mass of it we have not to suppose a distinction between its atoms and any intervening space. The powers around the centres give these centres the properties of atoms of matter; and these powers again, when many centres by their conjoint forces are grouped into a mass, give to every part of that mass the properties of matter. In such a view all the contradiction resulting from the consideration of electric insulation and conduction disappears.

The atoms may be conceived of as highly *elastic*, instead of being supposed excessively hard and unalterable in form; the mere compression of a bladder of air between the hands can alter their size a little; and the experiments of Cagniard de la Tour carry on this change in size until the difference in bulk at one time and another may be made several hundred times. Such is also the case when a solid or a fluid body is converted into vapour.

With regard also to the *shape* of the atoms, and, according to the ordinary assumption, its definite and unalterable character, another view must now be taken of it. An atom by itself might be conceived of as spherical, or spheroidal, or where many were touching in all directions, the form might be thought of as a dodecahedron, for any one would be surrounded by and bear against twelve others, on different sides. But if an atom be conceived to be a centre of power, that which is ordinarily referred to under the term *shape* would now be referred

to the disposition and relative intensity of the forces. The power arranged in and around a centre might be uniform in arrangement and intensity in every direction outwards from that centre, and then a section of equal intensity of force through the radii would be a sphere; or the law of decrease of force from the centre outwards might vary in different directions, and then the section of equal intensity might be an oblate or oblong spheroid, or have other forms; or the forces might be disposed so as to make the atom polar; or they might circulate around it equatorially or otherwise, after the manner of imagined magnetic atoms. In fact nothing can be supposed of the disposition of forces in or about a solid nucleus of matter, which cannot be equally conceived with respect to a centre.

In the view of matter now sustained as the lesser assumption, matter and the atoms of matter would be mutually penetrable. As regards the mutual penetrability of matter, one would think that the facts respecting potassium and its compounds, already described, would be enough to prove that point to a mind which accepts a fact for a fact, and is not obstructed in its judgement by preconceived notions. With respect to the mutual penetrability of the atoms, it seems to me to present in many points of view a more beautiful, yet equally probable and philosophic idea of the constitution of bodies than the other hypotheses, especially in the case of chemical combination. If we suppose an atom of oxygen and an atom of potassium about to combine and produce potash, the hypothesis of solid unchangeable impenetrable atoms places these two particles side by side in a position easily, because mechanically, imagined, and not unfrequently represented; but if these two atoms be centres of power they will mutually penetrate to the very centres, thus forming one atom or molecule with powers, either uniformly around it or arranged as the resultant of the powers of the two constituent atoms; and the manner in which two or many centres of force may in this way combine, and afterwards, under the dominion of stronger forces, separate again, may in some degree be illustrated by the beautiful case of the conjunction of two sea waves of different velocities into one, their perfect union for a time, and final separation into the constituent waves, considered, I think, at the meeting of the British Association at Liverpool. It does not of course follow, from this view, that the centres shall always coincide; that will depend upon the relative disposition of the powers of each atom.

The view now stated of the constitution of matter would seem to involve necessarily the conclusion that matter fills all space, or, at least, all space to which gravitation extends (including the sun and its system); for gravitation is a property of matter dependent on a certain force, and it is this force which constitutes the matter. In that view matter is not merely mutually penetrable, but each atom extends, so to say, throughout the whole of the solar system, yet always retaining its own centre of force. This, at first sight, seems to fall in very harmoniously with Mossotti's mathematical investigations and reference of the phenomena of electricity, cohesion, gravitation, &c., to one force in matter; and also again with the old adage, "matter cannot act where it is not." But it is no part of my intention to enter into such considerations as these, or what the bearings of this hypothesis would be on the theory of light and the supposed ether. My desire has been rather to bring certain facts from electrical conduction and chemical combination to bear strongly upon our views regarding the nature of atoms and matter, and so to assist in distinguishing in natural philosophy our real knowledge, i.e., the knowledge of facts and laws, from that, which, though it has the form of knowledge, may, from its including so much that is mere assumption, be the very reverse.

I am, my dear Sir, yours, &c.,

MICHAEL FARADAY

Royal Institution, January 25, 1844

On the Diamagnetic Conditions of Flame and Gases[1]
TO RICHARD TAYLOR, ESQ.

MY DEAR SIR,

I lately received a paper from Professor Zantedeschi, published by him, and containing an account of the discovery, by P. Bancalari, of the magnetism (diamagnetism) of flame, and of the further experiments of Zantedeschi, by which he confirms the result, and shows that flame is repelled from the axial line joining two magnetic poles. I send you the paper that you may, if you estimate its importance as highly as I do, reprint it in the *Philosophical Magazine;* and I send also with it these further experimental confirmations and extensions of my own. As M. Zantedeschi has published his results, I have felt myself at liberty to work on the subject, which of course interested me very closely. Probably what I may describe will only come in confirmation of that which has been done already in Italy or elsewhere; and if so, I hope to stand excused; for a second witness to an important fact is by no means superfluous, and may in the present case help to induce others to enter actively into the new line of investigation presented by diamagnetic bodies generally.

I soon verified the chief result of the diamagnetic affection of flame, and scarcely know how I could have failed to observe the effect years ago. As I suppose I have obtained much more

striking evidence than that referred to in Zantedeschi's paper, I will describe the shape and arrangement of the essential parts of my apparatus. The electro-magnet used was the powerful one described in the *Experimental Researches* (2247). The two terminal pieces of iron forming the virtual magnetic poles were each 1.7 inch square and six inches long; but the ends were shaped to a form approaching that of a cone, of which the sides have an angle of about 100°, and the axis of which is horizontal and in the upper surface of the pieces of iron. The apex of each end was rounded; nearly a tenth of an inch of the cone being in this way removed. When these terminations are brought near to each other, they give a powerful effect in the magnetic field, and the axial line of magnetic force is of course horizontal, and on a level nearly with the upper surface of the bars. I have found this form exceedingly advantageous in a great variety of experiments.

When the flame of a wax taper was held near the axial line, but on one side or the other, about one-third of the flame rising above the level of the upper surface of the poles, as soon as the magnetic force was on, the flame was affected; and receded from the axial line, moving equatorially, until it took an inclined position, as if a gentle wind was causing its deflection from the upright position; an effect which ceased the instant the magnetism was removed.

[1] *Philosophical Magazine*, S. 3, Vol. XXXI, No. 210, December 1847.

The effect was not instantaneous, but rose gradually to a maximum. It ceased very quickly when the magnetism was removed. The progressive increase is due to the gradual production of currents in the air about the magnetic field, which tend to be, and are, formed on the assumption of the magnetic conditions in the presence of the flame.

When the flame was placed so as to rise truly across the magnetic axis, the effect of the magnetism was to compress the flame between the points of the poles, making it recede in the direction of the axial line from the poles towards the middle transverse plane, and also to shorten the top of the flame. At the same time the top and sides of the compressed part burnt more vividly, because of two streams of air which set in from the poles on each side directly against the flame, and then passed out with it in the equatorial direction. But there was at the same time a repulsion or recession of the parts of the flame from the axial line; for those portions which were below did not ascend so quickly as before, and in ascending they also passed off in an inclined and equatorial direction.

On raising the flame a little more, the effect of the magnetic force was to increase the intensity of the results just described, and the flame actually became of a fish-tail shape, disposed across the magnetic axis.

If the flame was raised until about two-thirds of it were above the level of the axial line, and the poles approached so near to each other (about 0.3 of an inch) that they began to cool and compress the part of the flame at the axial line, yet without interfering with its rising freely between them; then, on rendering the magnet active, the flame became more and more compressed and shortened; and as the effects proceeded to a maximum, the top at last descended, and the flame no more rose between the magnetic poles, but spread out right and left on each side of the axial line, producing a double flame with two long tongues. This flame was very bright along the upper extended forked edge, being there invigorated by a current of air which *descended* from between the poles on to the flame at this part, and in fact drove it away in the equatorial direction.

When the magnet was thrown out of action, the flame resumed its ordinary upright form between the poles, at once; being depressed and redivided again by the renewal of the magnetic action.

When a small flame, only about one-third of an inch high, was placed between the poles, the magnetic force instantly flattened it into an equatorial disc.

If a ball of cotton about the size of a nut be bound up by wire, soaked in ether, and inflamed, it will give a flame six or seven inches high. This large flame rises freely and naturally between the poles; but as soon as the magnet is rendered active, it divides and passes off in two flames, the one on one side, and the other on the other side of the axial line.

Such therefore is the general and very striking effect which may be produced on a flame by magnetic action, the important discovery of which we owe to P. Bancalari.

I verified the results obtained by M. Zantedeschi with different flames, and found that those produced by alcohol, ether, coal-gas, hydrogen, sulphur, phosphorus, and camphor were all affected in the same manner, though not apparently with equal strength. The brightest flames appeared to be most affected.

The chief results may be shown in a manner in some respects still more striking and instructive than those obtained with flame, by using a smoking taper. A taper made of wax, coloured green by verdigris, if suffered to burn upright for a minute and then blown out, will usually leave a wick with a spark of fire on the top. The subdued combustion will however still go on, even for an hour or more, sending up a thin dense stream of smoke, which, in a quiet atmosphere, will rise vertically for six or eight inches; and in a moving atmosphere will show every change of its motion, both as to direction and intensity. When the taper is held beneath the poles, so that the stream of smoke passes a little on one side of the axial line, the stream is scarcely affected by the power of the magnet, the taper being three or four inches below the poles; but if the taper be raised, so that the coal is not more than an inch below the axial line, the stream of smoke is much more affected, being bent outwards; and if it be brought still higher, there is a point at which the smoke leaves the taper-wick even in a horizontal direction, to go equatorially. If the taper be held so that the smoke-stream passes *through* the axial line, and then the distances be varied as before, there is little or no sensible effect when the wick is four inches below: but being raised, as soon as the *warm* part of the stream is between the poles, it tends to divide; and when the ignited wick is about an inch below the axial line, the smoke rises vertically in one column until about two-thirds of that distance is passed over, and then it divides, going right and left, leaving the space between the poles clear. As the taper is slowly raised, the division of the smoke descends, taking place lower down, until it occurs upon the wick, at the distance of 0.4 or 0.5 of an inch below the axial line. If the taper be raised still more, the magnetic effect is so great as not only to divide the stream, but to make it descend on each side of the ignited wick, producing a form resembling that of the letter W; and at the same time the top of the burning wick is greatly brightened by the stream of air that is impelled downwards upon it. In these experiments the magnetic poles should be about 0.25 of an inch apart.

A burning piece of amadou, or the end of a splinter of wood, produced the same effect.

By means of a like small spark and stream of smoke, I have even rendered evident the power of an ordinary magnet. The magnet was a good one, and the poles were close to each other and conical in form.

Before leaving this description of the general phenomenon and proceeding to a consideration of the principles of magnetic action concerned in it, I may say that a single pole of the magnet produces similar effects upon flame and smoke, but that they are much less striking and observable.

Though the effect be so manifest in a flame, it is not, at first sight, evident what is the chief cause or causes of the result. The *heat* of the flame is the most apparent and probable condition; but there are other circumstances which may be equally or more influential. Chemical action is going on at the time: solid matter, which is known to be diamagnetic, exists in several of the flames used: and a great difference exists between the matter of the flame and the surrounding air. Now any or all of these circumstances of temperature, chemical action, solidity of part of the matter, and differential composition in respect to the surrounding air, may concur in producing or influencing the result.

I placed the wires of an electrometer, and also of a galvanometer, in various parts of the affected flame, but could not procure any indications of the evolution of electricity by any action on the instruments.

I examined the neighbourhood of the axial line as to the existence of any current in the air when there was no flame or heat there, using the visible fumes produced when little pellets of paper dipped in strong solutions of ammonia and muriatic acid were held near each

other; and though I found that a stream of such smoke was feebly affected by the magnetic power, yet I was satisfied there was no current or motion in the common air, as such, between the poles. The smoke itself was feebly diamagnetic; due, I believe, to the solid particles in it.

But when flame or a glowing taper is used, strong currents are, under favourable circumstances, produced in the air. If the flame be between the poles, these currents take their course along the surface of the poles, which they leave at the opposite faces connected by the axial line, and passing parallel to the axial line, impinge on the opposite sides of the flame; and feeding the flame, they make part of it, and proceed out equatorially. If the flame be driven asunder by the force of these currents and retreat, the currents follow it; and so, when the flame is forked, the air which is between the poles forms a current which sets from the poles downwards and sideways towards the flame. I do not mean that the air in *every* case travels along the surface of the poles or along the axial lines, or even from between the poles; for in the case of the glowing taper, held half an inch or so beneath the axial line, it is the cool air which is next nearest to the taper, and (generally) between the taper and the axial line, that falls with most force upon it. In fact the movements of the parts of the air and flame are due to a differential action. We shall see presently that the air is diamagnetic as well as flame or hot smoke; i.e. that both tend, according to the general law which I have expressed in the *Experimental Researches* (2267, &c.), to move from stronger to weaker places of magnetic force, but that hot air and flame are more so than cold or cooler air: so, when flame and air, or air at different temperatures, exist at the same time within a space under the influence of magnetic forces, differing in intensity of action, the hotter particles will tend to pass from stronger to weaker places of action, to be replaced by the colder particles; the former therefore will have the effect of being repelled; and the currents that are set up are produced by this action, combined with the mechanical force or current possessed by the flame in its ordinary relation to the atmosphere.

It will be evident to you that I have considered flame only as a particular case of a general law. It is a most important and beautiful one, and it has given us the discovery of diamagnetism in gaseous bodies: but it is a complicated one, as I shall now proceed to show, by analysing some of its conditions and separating their effects.

For the purpose of examining the effect of heat alone in conducing to the diamagnetic condition of flame, a small helix of fine platinum wire was attached to two stronger wires of copper, so that the helix could be placed in any given position as regarded the magnetic poles, and at the same time be ignited at pleasure by a voltaic battery. In this manner it was substituted for the burning taper, and gave a beautiful highly-heated current of air, unchanged in its chemical condition. When the helix was placed directly under the axial line, the hot air rose up between the poles freely, being rendered evident above by a thermometer, or by burning the finger, or even scorching paper; but as soon as the magnet was rendered active, the hot air divided into a double stream, and was found ascending on the two sides of the axial line; but a descending current was formed between the poles, flowing downwards towards the helix and the hot air, which rose and passed off sideways from it.

It is therefore perfectly manifest that hot air is diamagnetic in relation to, or more diamagnetic than, cold air; and, from this fact I concluded, that, by cooling the air below the natural temperature, I should cause it to approach the magnetic axis, or appear to be magnetic in relation to ordinary air. I had a little apparatus made, in which a vertical tube delivering air was passed through a vessel containing a frigorific mixture; the latter being so clothed with flannel that the external air should not be cooled, and so invade the whole of the magnetic field. The central current of cold air was directed downwards a little on one side of the axial line, and falling into a tube containing a delicate air-thermometer, there showed its effect. On rendering the magnet active, this effect however ceased, and the thermometer rose; but on bringing the latter under the axial line it again fell, showing that the cold current of air had been drawn inwards or attracted towards the axial line, i.e., had been rendered magnetic in relation to air at common temperatures, or less diamagnetic than it. The lower temperature was 0° F. The effect was but small; still it was distinct.

The effect of heat upon air, in so greatly increasing its diamagnetic condition, is very remarkable. It is not, I think, at all probable that the mere effect of expanding the air is the cause of the change in its condition, because one would be led to expect that a certain bulk

of expanded air would be less sensible in its diamagnetic effects than an equal bulk of denser air; just as one would anticipate that a vacuum would present no magnetic or diamagnetic effects whatever, but be at the zero point between the two classes of bodies (*Experimental Researches*, 2423, 2424). It is certainly true, that if the air were a body belonging to the magnetic class, then its expansion, being equivalent to dilution, would make it seem diamagnetic in relation to ordinary air (*Experimental Researches*, 2367, 2438); but that, I think, is not likely to be the case, as will be seen by the results described further on in reference to oxygen and nitrogen.

If the power conferred by heat is a direct consequence of, and proportionate to the temperature, then it gives a very remarkable character to gases and vapours, which, as we shall see hereafter, possess it in common. In my former experiments (*Experimental Researches*, 2359, 2397), I heated various diamagnetic bodies, but could not perceive that their degree of magnetic force was at all increased or affected by the temperature given to them. I have again submitted small cylinders of copper and silver to the action of a single pole, at common temperatures and at a red heat, with the same result. If there was any effect of increased temperature, it was that of a very slight increase in the diamagnetic force, but I am not sure of the result. At present, therefore, the gaseous and vaporous bodies seem to be strikingly distinguished by the powerful effect which heat has in increasing their diamagnetic condition.

As all the experiments, whether on flame, smoke, or air, seemed to show that air had a distinct magnetic relation, which, though highly affected by temperature, still belonged to it at all temperatures; so it was a probable conclusion that other gaseous or vaporous bodies would be diamagnetic or magnetic, and that they would differ from each other even at common or equal temperatures. I proceeded therefore to examine them, delivering streams of each into the air, in the first instance, by fit apparatus and arrangements, and examining the course taken by these streams in passing across the magnetic field, the magnetic force being either induced or not at the time.

In delivering the various streams, I sometimes introduced the gases into a globe with a mouth and also a tubular spout, and then poured the gas out of the spout, upwards or downwards, according as it was lighter or heavier than air. At other times, as with muriatic acid or ammonia, I delivered the streams from the mouth of the retort. But as it is very important not to deluge the magnetic field with a quantity of invisible gas, I devised the following arrangement, which answered well for all the gases not soluble in water. A Woulf's bottle was chosen having three apertures at the top, *a*, *b*, and *c*; a wide tube was fixed into aperture *a*, descending within the bottle to the bottom, and being open above and below; by this any water could be poured into the bottle and employed to displace the gas previously within it. Aperture *b* was closed by a stopper. Aperture *c* had an external tube, with a stop-cock fixed in it to conduct the gas to any place desired. To expel the gas and send it forward, a cistern of water was placed above the bottle, and its cock so plugged by a splinter of wood that when full open it delivered only twelve cubic inches of fluid in a minute. This stream of water being directed into aperture *a*, and the cock of tube *c* open, twelve cubic inches of any gas within the Woulf's bottle was delivered in a minute of time; and this I found an excellent proportion for our magnet and apparatus.

With respect to the delivery of this gas at the magnetic poles, a piece of glass tube bent into this shape ⌐ was held by a clamp on the stage of the magnet, so that it could easily be slipped backward and forward, or to one side, and its vertical part be placed anywhere below the axial line. The aperture at this end was about the one-eighth of an inch internal diameter. In the horizontal part near the angle was placed a piece of bibulous paper, moistened with strong solution of muriatic acid (when necessary). The horizontal part of the tube was connected and disconnected in a moment, when necessary, with the tube *c* of the gas-bottle, by a short piece of vulcanized rubber tube. If the gas to be employed as a stream were heavier than the surrounding medium, then the glass tube, instead of having the form delineated above, was so bent as to deliver its stream downwards and over the axial line. In this manner currents of different gases could be delivered, perfectly steady and under perfect command.

The next point was to detect and trace the course of these streams. A little ammonia vapour, delivered near the magnetic field, did this in some degree, but was not satisfactory; for, in the first place, the little cloud of muriate of ammonia particles formed is itself diamagnetic; and further, the tranquil condition of the air in the magnetic field was then too much disturbed. Catch-tubes were therefore arranged,

consisting of tubes of thin glass about the size and length of a finger, open at both ends, and fixed upon little stands so that they could be adjusted either over or under the magnetic poles at pleasure. When they were over the poles, I generally had three at once; one over the axial line and one at each side. When they were under the poles, the lower end was turned up a little for the purpose of facilitating observation there.

The gas delivered at the poles, as already described, contained a little muriatic acid (obtained from the solution in the paper), but not enough to render it visible. To make it manifest up which catch-tube it passed, a little piece of bibulous paper, folded and bound round and suspended by a copper wire, was dipped in the solution of ammonia and hung in each of the tubes. It was then evident at once, by the visible fume formed at the top of one of the tubes, whether the gas delivered below passed up the one or the other tube, and which: and yet the gas was perfectly clear and transparent as it passed by the place of magnetic action.

In addition to these arrangements, I built up a sheltering chamber about the magnetic poles and field, to preserve the air undisturbed. This was about six inches long by four inches in width and height, and was easily made of thin plates of mica, which were put together or taken down in a moment. The chamber was frequently left more or less open at the top or bottom for the escape of gases, or the place of the catch-tubes. Its advantages were very great.

Air. In the first place air was sent in under these arrangements, the stream being directed by the axial line. It made itself visible in the catch-tube above by the smoke produced; but whether the magnet was active or not, its course was the same; showing that, so far, the apparatus worked well, and did not of itself cause any erroneous indications.

Nitrogen. This gas was sent from below upwards, and passed directly by the axial line into the catch-tube above; but when the magnet was made active, the stream was affected, and though not stopped in the middle catch-tube, part appeared in the side tubes. The jet was then arranged a little on one side of the axial line, so that, without the magnetic action, it still ascended and went up the middle catch-tube: then, when the magnetic action was brought on, it was clearly affected, and a great portion of it was sent to the side catch-tube. The nitrogen was, in fact, manifestly diamagnetic in relation to common air, when both were at the same temperature; but as four-fifths of the atmosphere consists of nitrogen, it seemed very evident, from the result, that nitrogen and oxygen must be very different from each other in their magnetic relations.

Oxygen. A stream of oxygen was sent down through air between the poles. When there was no magnetic action it descended vertically, and when the magnetic action was on it appeared to do the same; at all events it did not pass off equatorially. But as there was reason, from the above experiments with nitrogen, to expect that oxygen would appear, not diamagnetic but magnetic in air; so the place of the stream was changed and made to be on one side of the axial line. In this case it fell perfectly well at first into a catch-tube placed beneath; but as soon as the magnet was rendered active, the stream was deflected, being drawn towards the axial line, and fell into another catch-tube placed there to receive it. So oxygen appears to be magnetic in common air. Whether it be really so, or only less diamagnetic than air (a mixture of oxygen and nitrogen), we shall be better able to consider hereafter.

Hydrogen. This gas proved to be clearly and even strongly diamagnetic; for notwithstanding the powerful ascensive force which its stream has in the atmosphere, because of its small specific gravity, still it was well deflected and sent equatorially. Considering the lightness of the gas, one might have expected that it would have been drawn towards the axial line, as a stream of rarefied air (if it could exist) would be. Its diamagnetic state, therefore, shows in a striking point of view that gases, like solids, have peculiar and distinctive degrees of diamagnetic force.

Carbonic acid. This gas made a beautiful experiment. The stream was delivered downwards a little on one side of the axial line; a catch-tube was placed a little farther out, so that the stream should fall clear of it as long as there was no activity in the magnet. But on rendering the magnet efficient, the stream left its vertical direction, passed equatorially, and fell into the catch-tube; and by looking horizontally, it could be seen flowing out at its lower extremity like water, and falling away through the air. Again, the magnet was thrown out of action, and a glass with lime-water placed beneath the lower end of the catch-tube; no carbonic acid appeared there, though the fluid in the glass was continually stirred; but the instant the magnet was excited, the carbonic acid appeared in the catch-tube, fell into the glass and made the lime-water turbid. This gas therefore is diamagnetic in air.

Carbonic oxide. This gas was carefully freed from carbonic acid before it was used. It was employed as a descending stream, and was apparently very diamagnetic: but it is to be remarked, that a substance which is so nearly of the specific gravity of atmospheric air is easily dispersed right and left in it, and therefore that the facility of dispersion is not a correct indication of the diamagnetic force. By introducing a little ammonia into the mica chamber, it was, however, easily seen that carbonic oxide was driven away equatorially with considerable power; and I judge from the appearance, that it is more diamagnetic than carbonic acid.

Nitrous oxide. This gas was moderately, but clearly, diamagnetic in air. Much interest belongs to this and the other compounds of nitrogen and oxygen, both because they contain the same elements as air, and because of the relations of nitrogen and oxygen separately.

Nitric oxide. I tried this gas both as an up and down current, but could not determine its magnetic condition. What with the action of the oxygen of the air, the change of the nature of the substances, and the heat produced, there was so much incidental disturbance and so little effect due to magnetic influence, that I could not be sure of the result. On the whole it was very slightly diamagnetic; but so little that the effect might be due to the smoke particles which served to render it visible.

Nitrous acid gas. Difficult to observe, but I believe it is slightly magnetic in relation to air.

Olefiant gas was diamagnetic, and well so. The little difference in specific gravity of this gas and air even creates a difficulty in following the course of the olefiant gas, unless it be watched for on every side.

Coal-gas. The coal-gas of London is lighter than air, being only about two-thirds in weight of the latter. It is very well diamagnetic, and gives exceedingly good and distinct results.

Sulphurous acid gas is diamagnetic in air. It was generated in a small tube containing liquid sulphurous acid; this being connected, in place of the gas bottle, with the delivery-tube and mouthpiece by the vulcanized rubber tube. The presence or absence of the gas in the catch-tube was well shown by ammonia, and still better by litmus paper.

Muriatic acid. The retort in which it was generated was connected, as just described, with the delivery-tube. The gas was very decidedly diamagnetic in air.

Hydriodic acid was also diamagnetic in air. When there was an abundant stream of gas, its entrance into and passage through the side catch-tube, on rendering the magnet active, was striking. When there was less gas, the stream was dispersed equatorially in all directions, and less entered the tube.

Fluo-silicon. Diamagnetic in air.

Ammonia. This gas was evolved from materials in a retort, and tested in the catch-tube above by muriatic acid in the paper. It was well diamagnetic, corresponding in this respect with the character of its elements. It could also be very well indicated by reddened litmus paper held over the tubes.

Chlorine was sent from the Woulf's bottle apparatus, and proved to be decidedly diamagnetic in air. Either ammonia by its fumes, or litmus paper by its becoming bleached, served to indicate the entrance of the chlorine into the side catch-tube every time the magnet was rendered active.

Iodine. A piece of glass tube was so shaped at its lower extremity as to form a chamber for the reception of iodine, which chamber had a prolonged mouth directed downwards so as to deliver the vapour formed within. On putting a little iodine into the chamber, then heating it, and especially the mouth part, by a spirit-lamp, and afterwards inclining the apparatus, abundance of the vapour of iodine was generated as the substance flowed on to the hotter parts, and passed in a good stream from the mouth downwards. This purple stream was diamagnetic in air, and could be seen flowing right and left from the axial line, when not too dense. If very dense and heavy, its gravity was such as to make it break through the axial line, notwithstanding the action of the magnet; still it was manifest that iodine is diamagnetic to air.

Bromine. A little bromine was put into the horizontal part of the delivery-tube, and then air passed over it by the apparatus already described. So much bromine rose into vapour as to make the air of a yellow colour, and caused it to fall well in a stream by the axial line. A little ammonia delivered near the magnetic field showed that this stream was diamagnetic, and hence it may fairly be presumed that the pure vapour of bromine would be diamagnetic also.

Cyanogen. Strongly diamagnetic in air.

Taking air as the standard of comparison, it is very striking to observe, that much as gases appear to differ one from another in the degree of their diamagnetic condition, there are very few that are not more diamagnetic than it; and when the investigation is carried forward into the relation of the two chief constituents of air, oxygen and nitrogen, it is still more striking to observe the very low condition of oxygen, which, in fact, is the cause of the comparatively low condition of air. Of all the vapours and gases yet tried, oxygen seems to be that which has the least diamagnetic force. It is as yet a question where it stands; for it may be as low as a vacuum, or may even pass to the magnetic side of it, and experiment does not as yet give an answer to the question. I believe it to be diamagnetic; and this belief is strengthened by the action of heat upon it, to be described hereafter; but it is exceedingly low in the scale, and far below chlorine, iodine, and such like bodies.

All the compounds of oxygen and nitrogen seem to show the influence of the presence of the oxygen. Nitrous acid seems to be less diamagnetic than air. Nitric oxide mingled with nitrous acid and warm, is about as air. Nitrous oxide is clearly diamagnetic in air, though it contains more oxygen: but it also contains more nitrogen than air, and is also denser than it, so that there is more matter present; still I think the results are in favour of the idea that oxygen is diamagnetic. By referring to the relation of carbonic oxide to carbonic acid, described further on, it will be seen that the addition of oxygen seems to make a body less diamagnetic. But the truth may be, not that oxygen is really magnetic, but that a compound body possesses a specific diamagnetic force, which is not the sum of the forces of its particles.

It is very difficult to form more than a mere guess at the relative degree of diamagnetic force possessed by different gaseous bodies when they are examined only in air, because of the many circumstances which tend to confuse the results. First, there is the invisibility of the gas which deprives us of the power of adjusting by sight so as to obtain the best effect: then, there is the difference of gravity; for if a gas ascend or descend in a rapid stream, it may seem less deflected than another flowing more slowly, though it be more diamagnetic; and as to gases nearly of the specific gravity of air, whether more or less diamagnetic, they are almost entirely dispersed in different directions, so that little only enters the catch-tube. Another modifying circumstance is the distance of the aperture delivering gas from the axial line, which, to obtain the maximum effect, ought to vary with the gravity of the gases and their diamagnetic force. Again, it is important that the magnetic field be not filled with the gas to be examined, and that generally speaking only a moderate stream be employed; which however must depend again upon the specific gravity.

The only correct way therefore of comparing two gases together is to experiment with them one in the other. For the experiments made with gases, in gases or in air, are differential, and similar in their nature with those made on a former occasion with solutions (*Experimental Researches*, 2362, &c.); I therefore changed the surrounding medium in a few experiments, substituting other gases for air; and first selected carbonic acid as a body easy to experiment with, and one that would, probably, be more powerfully than some other of the gases, diamagnetic (I speak as to the appearances or relative results only) in air.

I constructed a kind of tray or box, by folding up a doubled sheet of waxed paper; thus making a vessel 13 inches long, 5 inches wide, and 5 inches high. This was placed on the ends of the great magnet, and the terminal pieces of iron before described, placed in it. The box was covered over loosely by plates of mica, and formed a long square chamber in which were contained the magnetic poles and field. All the former arrangements in respect of the magnetic field, the delivery-tube, the catch-tubes, &c., were then made; and lastly, the box was filled with carbonic acid by a tube, which entered it at one corner; and was, from time to time, supplied with a fresh portion of gas, as the previous contents became diluted with gases or air. Everything answered perfectly, and the following results were easily obtained.

Air passed axially, being less diamagnetic than carbonic acid gas.

Oxygen passed to the magnetic axis, as was to be expected.

Nitrogen went equatorially, being therefore diamagnetic, even in carbonic acid.

Hydrogen, coal-gas, olefiant gas, muriatic acid and *ammonia* passed equatorially in carbonic acid, and were fairly diamagnetic in relation to it.

Carbonic oxide was very fairly diamagnetic in carbonic acid gas. Here the effect of oxygen seems to be very well illustrated. Equal volumes of carbonic oxide and carbonic acid contain equal quantities of carbon; but the former contains only half as much oxygen as the latter. Yet it is more diamagnetic than the latter; so that, though an additional volume and quantity of oxygen, equal to that in the carbonic oxide, is in the carbonic acid added and com-

pressed into it, it does not add to, but actually takes from, the diamagnetic force.

Nitrous oxide appears to be slightly diamagnetic in relation to carbonic acid; but nitric oxide gas was in the contrary relation and passed towards the axial line.

Hence it seems that carbonic acid, though more diamagnetic than air, is not far removed from it in that respect; and this position it probably holds because of the quantity of oxygen in it. The apparent place of nitrous oxide close to it appears, in a great measure, to depend on the same circumstance of oxygen entering largely into its composition. Still it is manifest that the action is not *directly* as the oxygen, for then common air would be more diamagnetic than either of them. It seems rather that the forces are modified, as in the cases also of iron and oxygen, and that each compound body has its peculiar but constant intensity of action.

In order to make similar experiments in light gases, the two terminal pieces of the magnet were raised, so that they might be covered by a French glass shade, which, with its stand, made a very good chamber about them. The pipe to supply and change the gaseous medium, and also that for bringing the gas under trial as a stream into the magnetic field, passed through holes made in the bottom of the stand. The different gases to be compared with those employed as media, were, except in the cases of ammonia and chlorine, mingled with a trace of muriatic acid, as before described. The gaseous media used were two, coal-gas and hydrogen. Whilst using coal-gas, I observed the direction of the currents of the other gases in it by bringing a little piece of paper, at the end of a wire and dipped in ammonia solution, near the stream. In the case of the hydrogen, I diffused a little ammonia through the whole of the gas in the first instance.

Air passed towards the axial line in coal-gas, but was not much affected.

Oxygen had the appearance of being strongly magnetic in coal-gas, passing with great impetuosity to the magnetic axis, and clinging about it; and if much muriate of ammonia fume were purposely formed at the time, it was carried by the oxygen to the magnetic field with such force as to hide the ends of the magnetic poles. If then the magnetic action were suspended for a moment, this cloud descended by its gravity; but being quite below the poles, if the magnet were again rendered active, the oxygen cloud immediately started up and took its former place. The attraction of iron filings to a magnetic pole is not more striking than the appearance presented by the oxygen under these circumstances.

Nitrogen. Clearly diamagnetic in coal-gas.

Olefiant, carbonic oxide, and *carbonic acid* gases were all slightly, but more or less diamagnetic in the coal-gas.

On substituting hydrogen as the surrounding medium in place of coal-gas, more care was taken in the experiments. Each gas experimented upon was tried in it twice at least; first in the hydrogen of a previous experiment, and then in a new atmosphere of hydrogen.

Air. Air passes axially in hydrogen when there is very little smoke in it: when there is much smoke in the stream the latter is either indifferent or tends to pass equatorially. I believe that air and hydrogen cannot be far from each other.

Nitrogen is strikingly diamagnetic in hydrogen.

Oxygen is as strikingly magnetic in relation to hydrogen. It presented the appearances already described as occurring in coal-gas; but as the jet delivered the descending stream of oxygen a little on one side of the axial line, its centrifugal power, in relation to the axial line, was so balanced by the centripetal power produced by the magnetic action that the stream at first revolved in a regular ring round the axial line, and produced a cloud that continued to spin round it as long as the magnetic force was continued, but fell down to the bottom of the chamber when that force was removed.

Nitrous oxide. This gas was clearly diamagnetic in the hydrogen, and gave rise to a very beautiful result in consequence of its following the oxygen; for at the beginning of the experiment, the little oxygen contained in the conducting tube passed axially; but the instant that was expelled, and the nitrous oxide issued forth, the stream changed its direction, and passed off diamagnetically in the most striking manner.

Nitric oxide. This gas passed axially in hydrogen, and therefore is magnetic in relation to it.

Ammonia. Diamagnetic in hydrogen.

Carbonic oxide, carbonic acid, and *olefiant gases* were diamagnetic in hydrogen; the last most so, and the carbonic acid apparently the least.

Chlorine was slightly diamagnetic in hydrogen. It was clearly so; but the cloudy particles might conduce much to the small effect produced.

Muriatic acid gas. I think it was a little diamagnetic in the hydrogen.

Notwithstanding the many disturbing causes which interfere with first and hasty experiments of this kind, and produce results which occasionally cross and contradict each other, still there are some very striking considerations which arise in comparing the gases with each other at the same temperature. Foremost amongst these is the place of oxygen; for of all the gaseous bodies yet tried it is the least diamagnetic, and seems in this respect to stand far apart from the rest of them. The condition of nitrogen, as being highly diamagnetic, is also important. The place of hydrogen, as being less diamagnetic than nitrogen, and of chlorine, which, instead of approaching to oxygen, is above hydrogen, and also of iodine, which is probably far above chlorine, are marked circumstances.

Air of course owes its place to the proportion and the individual diamagnetic character of the oxygen and nitrogen in it. The great difference existing between these two bodies in respect of magnetic relation, and the striking effect presented by oxygen in coal-gas and hydrogen, bodies not far removed from nitrogen in diamagnetic force, made me think it might not be impossible to separate air into its two chief constituents by magnetic force alone. I made an experiment for this purpose, but did not succeed; but I am not convinced that it cannot be done. For since we can actually distinguish certain gases, and especially these two by their magnetic properties, it does not seem impossible that sufficient power might cause their separation from a state of mixture.

In the course of these experiments I subjected several of the gases to heat, to ascertain whether they generally underwent the same exaltation of their diamagnetic power which occurred with common air (2854). For this purpose a helix of platinum wire was placed in the mouth of the delivering tube, which itself was placed below the magnetic axis between the poles. The helix could be raised to any temperature by a little voltaic battery, and any gas could be sent through it and upwards across the magnetic field by means of the Woulf's bottle apparatus already described. It was easy to ascertain whether the gas went directly up between the poles, or, when the magnet was active, left that direction and formed two equatorial side-streams, either by the sensation on the finger, or by a thermoscope formed of a spiral compound lamina of platinum and silver placed in a tube above. In every case the hot gas was diamagnetic in the air, and I think far more so than if the gas had been at common temperatures. The gases tried were as follows: oxygen, nitrogen, hydrogen, nitrous oxide, carbonic acid, muriatic acid, ammonia, coal-gas, olefiant gas.

But as in these experiments the surrounding air would, of necessity, mingle with the gas first heated, and so form, in fact, a part of the heated stream, I arranged the platinum helix so that I could heat it in a given gas, and thus compare the same gas at different temperatures with itself.

A stream of hot oxygen in cold oxygen was powerfully diamagnetic. The effect and its degree may be judged of by the following circumstances. When the platinum helix below the axial line was ignited, the effect of heat on the indicating compound spiral, placed in a tube over the axial line, was such as to cause its lower extremity to pass through one and a half revolutions, or 540°: when the magnetic force was rendered active, the spiral returned through all these degrees to its first position, as if the ignited helix below had been lowered to the common temperature or taken away; and yet in respect to it, nothing had been changed. On rendering the magnet inactive, the current of hot oxygen instantly resumed its perpendicular course and affected the thermoscope as before.

On experimenting with carbonic acid, it was found that hot carbonic acid was diamagnetic to cold carbonic acid; and the effects were apparently as great in amount as in oxygen.

On making the same arrangement in hydrogen, I failed to obtain any result regarding the relation of the hot and cold gas, for this reason: that I could not, in any case, either with or without the magnetic action, obtain any signs of heat on the thermoscopic spiral above, even when the platinum helix, not more than an inch below it, was nearly white hot. This effect is, I think, greatly dependent upon the rapidity with which hydrogen is heated and cooled in comparison with other gases, and also upon the vicinity of the cold masses of iron forming the magnetic poles, between which the hot gas has to pass in its way upwards: and it is most probably connected with the fact observed by Mr. Grove of the difficulty of igniting a platinum wire in hydrogen.

When the igniting helix was placed in coal-gas, it was found that the hot gas was diamagnetic to that which was cold; as in all the other cases. Here, again, an effect like that which was observed in hydrogen occurred; for when there was no magnetic action, the ascending stream of hot coal-gas could cause the thermoscopic spiral to revolve through only 280° or 300°, in place of above 540°; through which it could pass when the surrounding gas was oxygen, air, or carbonic acid; and that even when the helix was at a higher temperature in the coal-gas than in any of these gases.

The proof is clear then that oxygen, carbonic acid, and coal-gas, are more diamagnetic hot than cold. The same is the case with air; and as air consists of four-fifths nitrogen and only one-fifth oxygen, and yet shows an effect of this kind as strongly as oxygen, it is manifest that nitrogen also has the same relation when hot and cold.

Of the other gases also I have no doubt; though to be quite certain, they ought to be tried in atmospheres of their own substance (2854), or else in gases more diamagnetic at common temperatures than they. The olefiant and coal-gases in air easily bore the elevation of the helix to a full red heat, without inflaming when out of the exit-tube: the hydrogen required that the helix should be at a lower temperature. Muriatic acid and ammonia showed the division of the one stream into two, very beautifully, on holding blue and red litmus paper above.

There is another mode of observing the diamagnetic condition of flame, and experimenting with the various gases, which is sometimes useful, and should always be understood, lest it inadvertently might lead to confusion. I have a pair of terminal magnetic poles which are pierced in a horizontal direction, that a ray of light may pass through them. The opposed faces of these vertical poles are not, as in the former case, the rounded ends of cones; but, though rounded at the edges, may be considered as flat over an extent of surface an inch in diameter. The pierced passages are in the form of cones, the truncation of which in this flat surface is rather more than half an inch in diameter. When these poles were in their place, and from 0.3 to 0.4 of an inch apart, a taper flame, burning freely between them, was for a few moments unaffected by throwing the magnet into action; but then it suddenly changed its form, and extending itself axially, threw off two horizontal tongues, which entered the passages in the poles; and thus it continued as long as the magnetism continued, and no part of it passed equatorially.

On using a large flame made with the cotton ball and ether, two arms could be thrown off from the flame by the force of the magnetism, which passed in an equatorial direction, as before; and other two parts entered the passages in the magnetic poles, and actually issued out occasionally at their farther extremities.

When the poles were about 0.25 of an inch apart, and the smoking taper was placed in the middle between them level with the centres of the passages, the effect was very good; for the smoke passed axially and issued out at the farther ends of the pole passages.

Coal-gas delivered in the same place also passed axially, i.e., into the pole passages and parallel to the line joining them.

A little consideration easily leads to the true cause of these effects, and shows that they are not inconsistent with the former results. The law of all these actions is that if a particle, placed amongst other particles be more diamagnetic (or less magnetic) than they, and free to move, it will go from strong to weaker places of magnetic action; also, that particles less diamagnetic will go from weaker to stronger places of action. Now with the poles just described, the line or lines of maximum force are not coincident with the axis of the holes pierced in the poles, but lie in a circle having a diameter, probably, a little larger than the diameter of the holes; and the lines within that circle will be of lesser power, diminishing in force towards the centre. A hot particle therefore within that circle will be driven inwards, and being urged by successive portions of matter driven also inwards, will find its way out at the other ends of the passages, and therefore seem to go in an axial direction; whilst a hot particle outside of that circle of lines of maximum force will be driven outwards, and so, with others, will form the two tongues of flame which pass off in the equatorial direction. By bringing the glowing taper to different parts, the circle of lines of maximum magnetic intensity can be very beautifully traced; and by placing the taper inside or outside of that circle, the smoke could be made to pass axially or equatorially at pleasure.

I arranged an apparatus on this principle for trying the gases, but did not find it better than, or so good as, the one I have described.

Such are the results I have obtained in verifying and extending the discovery made by P. Bancalari. I would have pursued them much further, but my present state of health will not permit it: I therefore send them to you with, probably, many imperfections. It is now almost proved that many gaseous bodies are diamagnetic in their relations, and probably all will be found to be so. I say almost proved; for it is not, as yet, proved in fact. That many, and most, gaseous bodies are subject to magnetic force is proved; but the zero is not yet distinguished. Now, until it is distinguished, we cannot tell which gaseous bodies will rank as diamagnetic and which as magnetic; and also, whether there may not be some standing at zero. There is evidently no natural impossibility to some gases or vapours being magnetic, or that some should be neither magnetic nor diamagnetic. It is the province of experiment to decide such points; and the affirmative or negative may not be asserted before such proof is given, though it may, very philosophically, be believed.

For myself I have always believed that the zero was represented by a vacuum, and that no body really stood with it. But though I have only guarded myself from asserting more than I knew, Zantedeschi (and I think also De la Rive), with some others, seem to think that I have asserted the gases are *not* subject to magnetic action; whereas I only wished to say that I could not find that they were, and perhaps were not: I will therefore quote a few of my words from the *Experimental Researches.* Speaking of the preparation of a liquid medium at zero, I say, "Thus a *fluid* medium was obtained, which practically, as far as I could perceive, had every magnetic character and effect of a gas, *and even of a vacuum*, &c." *Experimental Researches*, 2423. Again, at 2433 I say, "At one time I looked to air and gases as the bodies which, allowing attenuation of their substance without addition, would permit of the observation of corresponding variations in their magnetic properties, but now all such power by rarefaction *appears* to be taken away." And further down at (2435), "Whether the negative results obtained by the use of gases and vapours depend upon the *smaller quantity of matter* in a given volume, or whether they are the direct consequences of the altered physical condition of the substance, is a point of very great importance to the theory of magnetism. I have imagined in elucidation of the subject an experiment, &c., but expect to find great difficulty in carrying it into execution, &c." Happily P. Bancalari's discovery has now settled this matter for us in a most satisfactory manner. But where the true zero is, or that every body is more or less removed from it on one side or the other, is not, as yet, experimentally shown or proved.

I cannot conclude this letter without expressing a hope that since gases are shown to be magnetically affected, they will also shortly be found, when under magnetic influence, to have the power of affecting light (*Experimental Researches*, 2186, 2212). Neither can I refrain from signalizing the very remarkable and direct relation between the forces of heat and magnetism which is presented in the experiments on flame, and heated air and gases. I did not find on a former occasion (*Experimental Researches*, 2397) that solid diamagnetic bodies were sensibly affected by heat, but shall repeat the experiments and make more extensive ones, if the Italian philosophers have not already done so. In reference to the effect upon the diamagnetic gases, it may be observed, that, speaking generally, it is in the same direction as that of heat upon iron, nickel and cobalt; i.e., heat tends in the two sets of cases, either to the diminution of magnetic force, or the increase of diamagnetic force; but the results are too few to allow of any general conclusion as yet.

As air at different temperatures has different diamagnetic relations, and as the atmosphere is at different temperatures in the upper and lower strata, such conditions may have some general influence and effect upon its final motion and action, subject as it is continually to the magnetic influence of the earth.

I have for the sake of brevity frequently spoken in this letter of bodies as being magnetic or diamagnetic in relation one to another, but I trust that in all the cases no mistake of my meaning could arise from such use of the terms, or any vague notion arise respecting the clear distinction between the two classes, especially as my view of the true zero has been given only a page or two back.

I am, my dear Sir,

Yours, &c.,

M. FARADAY

Richard Taylor, Esq.,

Ed. Phil. Mag., &c., &c.

INDEX

NOTE: Page numbers are preceded by p. or pp.;
all other references are to numbered paragraphs.

PRINTED IN THE U.S.A.